THE MAUGHAM READER

Books by
W. SOMERSET MAUGHAM

Novels
CATALINA
ASHENDEN
THEN AND NOW
THE RAZOR'S EDGE
THE HOUR BEFORE THE DAWN
THE MOON AND SIXPENCE
UP AT THE VILLA
MRS. CRADDOCK
CHRISTMAS HOLIDAY
CAKES AND ALE
THEATRE
THE PAINTED VEIL
THE NARROW CORNER
OF HUMAN BONDAGE
LIZA OF LAMBETH

Short Stories
QUARTET
CREATURES OF CIRCUMSTANCE
THE TREMBLING OF A LEAF
THE MIXTURE AS BEFORE
AH KING
COSMOPOLITANS
THE CASUARINA TREE
FIRST PERSON SINGULAR
EAST AND WEST

Essays
FRANCE AT WAR
STRICTLY PERSONAL

THE SUMMING UP
BOOKS AND YOU
A WRITER'S NOTEBOOK

Travel
ON A CHINESE SCREEN
DON FERNANDO
THE GENTLEMAN IN THE
   PARLOUR
THE LAND OF THE BLESSED
   VIRGIN

Plays
FOR SERVICES RENDERED
A MAN OF HONOUR
THE BREADWINNER
PENELOPE
THE SACRED FLAME
JACK STRAW
SHEPPEY
LADY FREDERICK
THE CONSTANT WIFE
THE TENTH MAN
THE CIRCLE
LANDED GENTRY
THE EXPLORER
THE UNKNOWN MRS. DOT
SMITH
OUR BETTERS
THE LAND OF PROMISE
SIX COMEDIES

W. SOMERSET MAUGHAM
from a portrait by Graham Sutherland

MAUG
READE

William

W. Somerset Maugham

WITH AN INTRODUCTION BY

Glenway Wescott

GARDEN CITY, N.Y.

DOUBLEDAY & COMPANY, INC.

CONTENTS

CONTENTS

STORIES

AN INTRODUCTION
TO MAUGHAM

IN RECENT YEARS I have had the privilege of knowing
Mr. Maugham; and with the stimulus of friendship
added to my old accumulated interest as one of his happy
readers, I have given more thought to his work than to any
other contemporary literature. When asked to write this
prefatory piece I did not even consider declining. The honor
was so appreciable, the challenge so direct: I should have
forfeited a good deal of my self-respect if I had let it pass.
For a while it seemed to go perfectly well, in my head!—
making my plan, entertaining all the ideas that might con-
ceivably be fitted into an essay of the sort, profuse and
variable themes. But a profusion is not ideal when one has
to produce a small prose work; this he himself has taught
me along with other lessons, come to think of it. As I actually sit down to the task now, it is with real uneasiness, in
recognition of my temerity and the difficulty of the matter.

Although Mr. Maugham will not read commentaries on
himself, so he says, once in a while as I weigh my thought
or construct my sentence, I foolishly ask myself how it might
strike him, evoking over my page his remarkable face, in
which the elements of his character and effects of his life are
all as it were inscribed or jotted down, in the most delicate
crisscross wrinkles; his kind though choleric mouth, and his
grand eyes, one almost round and the other sharply focussed
with a slant, as you may see in any good portrait of him. Between fits and starts of my typewriter I seem to hear his soft
but overauthoritative voice making some appropriate, not
quite tactful remark . . .

Henry James said, in I cannot think what connection, that when a work of creative literature is very formally presented, escorted into the reader's mind with too many arguments and considerations, it is like having a dinner guest brought to the house by policemen. (This is not exactly quoted; he put it more volubly and portentously, in his style.) Nevertheless, when he himself came to collect his lifework, he posted prefaces in front of every volume, an entire constabulary of prefaces, armed to the teeth with intellect and imposingly got up with, as one might say, gold braid, and all spit and polish.

I hope these pages are not going to make any such impression. Maugham's own little forewords are models of informality, pertinence, and good grace. It would have been most suitable for him to have introduced this collection; only now he may be tired of helping his readers enjoy his work, or, rather, of putting them at their ease with it.

Young writers especially ought to look for the various editions to which he has contributed his afterthoughts, and read them attentively—likewise his essay, *On Style* (*After Reading Burke*), and the little piece upon his sixty-fifth birthday, and his brief address at the Library of Congress; addenda to the masterpiece, *The Summing Up*. Never having had any conviction that he was a genius, early and late he has used his head about everything having to do with writing, which cannot be said of many writers. With so much consciously learned by him in the first place, it is easier to learn from his remarks, however cursory or circumstantial, than from more expansive, exciting documents of the vocation of letters, such as James's prefaces. Maugham, characteristically, hints more than he expounds; which is just as well, if your interest is personal and serious. You can make what you wish of his helpfulness, to suit your case.

You must not be misled by his rather small and offhand way, in this confidential expository writing. You must allow for a certain manner of the English gentleman, as it were a self-satisfying modesty. Remember also, when in his attitude about anything you may sense a little inflexibility, almost affectation—or when he harps on some of his preferences and theories—sometimes it is his way of criticizing (without unkindly naming) fellow writers whose reputations have appeared to him undeserved or unsound. All his life he has had to share the literary scene with various genius types, forever boasting. This, I think, inclines him to the extreme of unpretentiousness. Others make a glamor of their pure artistry without producing much—all blow and no go. It may be this which has prompted him to set up as a principle, even a duty, that nonstop productivity which comes naturally to him, and which he so greatly enjoys. Now and then he seems to be suggesting that anyone who is not capable of it might as well give up literature; surely an extreme view. Others talk all the time of their inspiration and dedication, message and messianic feeling. Very well, he will speak only of the profession of writing, the career, even the pursuit of fortune.

No insincerity in any of this, mind you! But a man cannot live for half a century in a great constant limelight, sought after and indiscreetly questioned in society, meanwhile subject to the changeable and illogical standards of the literary journalism of the day, without developing some self-consciousness.

*   *   *

He is the dean of novelists writing in English at present. By which advertisement-like statement I mean that he is the one, the only one, who for more than a quarter of a century has had the admiration of an elite of highly cultivated, sophisticated readers and of a sufficient number of good fellow writers, with increasing influence on the younger ones; and at the same time has given great pleasure to, made sense to, and affected the lives of, a million or more ordinary mortals. What else is deanship? It is not a matter of unanimity. Only, in the condition of modern culture, the small superior group in agreement or in coalition with the multitude is very apt to overrule or overwhelm any objection that may start up in medium intellectual circles. Evidently this is what has happened about Maugham, leaving perhaps a vague resentment in the minds of some of those who might be expected to mould (and indeed unmould) contemporary opinion, and are scarcely doing so in his case.

He has become the most controversial literary figure of our time as well as the most successful. As controversies go, this has a certain distinction, in that nothing of miscellaneous thought is at issue, neither politics nor morals nor other ideology. It is all about literary art: whether he is a great artist in any way, or only an ordinary one; whether his career has been a true vocation, or a simple matter of ambition and energetic endeavor crowned with odd success; and whether his fiction is of a high category, or just a present plaything for the mind of a commonplace throng. Unfortunately the arguments pro and con have not been presented at full length or with sufficient clarity and conviction. I cannot think of another important man of letters about whom there is so little to read, of any interest. In both the praise and the blame a few conventional terms keep appearing, as in a kaleidoscope, around and around; and in the last decade or so the blamers have shown more verve and self-assurance than the praisers. Our diligent book reviewers, perhaps having written themselves out upon the theme in general long since, have reacted lassitudinously to the almost annual succession of his books. One or two of our noteworthy serious critics, offended in taste or dissatisfied in intellect, entirely lost their patience with this or that recent book, with a peculiar effect of trying to shame the rest of us out of our enjoyment.

Now surely it would not be proper for me, introducing creative work, to take cognizance of adverse opinion in the daily or the weekly or even the monthly or the quarterly press, for the most part not likely to be perpetuated in book form—or of the group thinking and conversation of intellectuals, which all this may be taken to reflect—were it not for the fact that Maugham himself is to be blamed for some of the confusion and the repetitiousness. In those forewords and other incidental writings which I mentioned just now, all too often he has seemed to be talking his work down, making light of his career. He has presented himself, or, as one might say, typed himself, as having only a limited specific talent; as not knowing or thinking much about anything outside his field of professional dramaturgy and narration—no vision of the state of the world, no psychological science, no profundity—and as not admitting any intention in his writing except to entertain. "The purpose of art is to please." He should have been warned of the riskiness of oversimplification and understatement in an age of advertising.

For his least favorable critics have borrowed a good part of his representation of himself, even parroting certain phrases and epithets, belittlingly, and to the advantage of their preferred school of modern writing, whatever it may be. In their aggressiveness, his defensive position has been turned around, as it were some bit of Maginot Line with forces of the enemy established in it by mischance or by mistake. The confusion is great, *quid pro quo;* and those who disapprove of him come at one so, in the dear uniform of his thought turned inside out, and with his passwords— writing is a livelihood, fiction is a pastime, the mixture as before—that one often feels obliged to fight him too, before one can give him his due praise.

Some people of course are real believers in unpopularity, mistrusters of success; and the recently booming market for whatever bears Maugham's signature, and the adaptations of the motion-picture industry, and all the publicity and the publicizing, have made them disrespectful. His detractors have him on their minds a good deal, and feel romantically about him in their way; they are anti-fans. In ordinary social intercourse one hears far more talk of any sort of relative failure on his part—when a given novel can be said to have fallen short of the standard set by some previous novel, or perhaps has sold a few hundred thousand copies less—than of the successes of other writers. I may seem mocking, but it is not my intention to suggest that the opponents of Maugham are all of a superficial or unreasonable spirit. Certainly they are not. Among my own best friends there are three or four whose opinion of authors as a rule tallies with mine, whose cultivation and judgment I appreciate exceedingly, with whom I cannot have a civil conversation about this one author—so zealous or jealous have they become, in their resolve not to have him overestimated.

All the poor criticism and the captious momentary talk have only increased Maugham's general celebrity, and emphasized his unswerving strength of mind in his own way, and given further advertisement to his tranquil, uninfluenced, unceasing production. The fact is that the anti-Maugham party have not really been able to put up a candidate of their own, for the specific position in contemporary letters—the combined artistic and popular position—which they are so impatient of his continuing to hold, decade after decade. All these years they seem never to have found themselves in agreement with the great public about any contemporary writer, nor succeeded in bringing the collectivity around to the styles of writing they do care for.

*   *   *

Now here let me cast my vote with the majority, for Maugham, in the way of a general statement of admiration —indeed, a statement of faith—before I begin to explain it or to cite particular admirable things. I believe that his best books, perhaps eight or ten volumes, are better than almost anyone's today, and will endure for posterity. Except for the extreme jeopardies facing Western civilization as a whole, I feel no uneasiness whatever about his having his sufficient fame in the outcome of the century; his share of what is called, in rather old-fashioned writers' parlance, immortality.

In the meantime, a really considerable slump of his reputation is to be expected; something more than the restlessness against him in literary society and the carping of professional critics. It is normal, melancholy though it must be for any author who has lived to see it. The present volume may reach the last lot of those who have ignored him until now, or not read enough to form their opinion. Presently a great many of those who for years have delighted in him above all other storytellers will have had their fill; and they will forget to recommend him to the younger generation. Already his imitators have somewhat coarsened and debased the forms and devices of his fiction, so that one looks upon certain of the beauties of it with a dull, dissipated eye; he no longer gets credit for uniqueness.

And meanwhile his successors, it is to be hoped—those who are not too idle or freakish or unfortunate—have been getting ready with some new type or types of literature to suit themselves, with departures from his way of writing, refutations of his way of thinking. In subject matter especially there must always be some frontier opening up: new ruling passions in the ascendant, and strengths of mind and weaknesses ·of character which Maugham in old age could not be expected to understand very well; which his perfected forms and practiced techniques would not suit if he did. Concepts of what is desirable in life, and what is hateful or insufferable, differing radically from those he has exemplified in a hundred various tales, and indeed in his own life story . . .

Do I make him seem older than he is? In point of fact, if he were to live as long as, let us say, George Bernard Shaw or Maréchal Pétain, an infant born today might grow almost to manhood in the remainder of his lifetime. However, he is not one of those stubborn fighters against mortality, not a muscular sanguine egotistical man; and he has felt his age. Since he is still producing books one after the other and manifestly enjoying life, we might scarcely think of it except for his own reminders. When he was only sixty-four he gave it as one of his reasons for writing *The Summing Up* with no further postponement; and again and again he has returned to the solemn theme, the note of farewell. I think this is a trait of literary artists, perhaps of all artists; and as work of art does actually offer the possibility of a kind and degree of survival after death, it must lead to some imagination of the time far ahead. My impression is that Mr. Maugham often wonders how posterity will regard his career and collected works, though I am sure he would never speak of it.

With praise of him by serious critics so insufficient in these last decades of his life (a mountain of clippings, indeed, but more than half of it quibbling, unimpressed or unenlightened), with the word of mouth of the intellectuals so little in unison, likely to make only a weak jangled reverberation in the period to come, with no very remarkable record of official or academic honors—for he has not been greatly indulged in this way either—what is going to lead the good reader of posterity to take the trouble of procuring his books and to try reading them? Curiosity, I suppose, above all. What made this man so beloved by the unliterary, unofficial, unacademic humanity of his time? And, as it has been a crucial historic time, what can his popularity have signified? What good or harm was there in it? So few contemporary men of letters have kept their public for three decades, with a continuous production and increasing sale of books the while; attention will be attracted to him by this. He will be part of a history lesson.

And when it comes to reading for pleasure or for any personal emotion or edification, he will not have, in (let us say) the middle of the twenty-first century, all the competition that appears at present. A quantity of literature, especially fiction, vanishes in thin air. Some of the work of famed contemporaries of his has already been shelved; and in almost all of it we can see the ephemeral and perishable elements. Any little random enumeration and review of them is suggestive of the relative soundness of his narrative art, indicative of its greater staying power. In the various ways in which they have proved weak, he took the trouble to develop particular strength. The mistakes they made, the predilections they indulged in—these were what he most severely forbade himself and guarded against. I gather that in his formative years he studied everything they were doing; then considered, in his reading of all the still-valid fiction of the past, every sort of parallel; and carried the lesson forward in speculation upon the future; and regularly applied it to his day's work—most earnestly desiring not to have written in vain . . .

Wells, for example, so hard-working and serious, so influential for many years, wrote like a newspaper; and since he rashly prophesied things in every volume, what he got right will seem platitudinous, and what he got wrong, absurd. At the other extreme, the truly artistic fiction of the period has been characterized by a certain remoteness of subject matter, elusive and allusive; and obscured by linguistic innovations, a playing with words, like poetry. It is hard to foresee how so luxurious a fabric of writing will endure; there is not much precedent in literary history. Half the work of wonderful Joyce surely will revert to the universities, in the way of recondite crossword puzzles. Not a learned type of reader myself, I feel that the best novels of Ford Madox Ford might be appreciated if they were read at all; but they are likely to be overlooked, his career in his lifetime having gone so modestly. As I remarked just now, there is more than the pecuniary advantage in having sold like hot cakes; readers long afterward wonder why. E. M. Forster will certainly last; only five novels, and (what a mystery it is!) none at all since 1924 . . .

Thus, very naturally, with so little early twentieth-century literature that will still seem readable, the wondering future reader will turn to the wide shelfful of the collected works of Maugham; the one of all his generation the least like a genius, the one most emphatically disavowing any such pretension. Down out of the attic of literary history his narrative art will be brought, as though it were some piece of inherited furniture that had gone out of fashion for a time—comfortably functional, solidly constructed, with not much gilt on it, but finely carved.

And the use and the enjoyment of reading him many years hence, I believe, will not be very different from our own at present—precisely because he has been sagacious and cautious in his handling of themes of the day which grow commonplace or obscure; because he has been content to write a pure prosaic prose without any remarkable invention of new ways of expressing things; because he has written a great amount, so as to constitute a distinct Maugham-world into which his readers can enter, of which they can learn the idiom and the implications, each volume helping them to understand the next, building up their response to the next; and because he has discovered and devised story after story worth telling for the story's sake, the one and only thing he himself has boasted of. The love of narration as such evidently is basic and elemental and permanent in human nature.

* * *

If you have been following Maugham's own line about his work too ingenuously, or reading the current criticism with entire respect, you may have assumed that it is, if not altogether thoughtless, of a very limited intellectual interest. Now I will dispute this, and give you some illustration and analysis of the kind of thought I find in his fiction, or (as I suppose Mr. Maugham would prefer to have me say) the kind of meaning I read into it. Without exaggeration! I maintain only that in all his best stories and novels there is an underlying, somewhat hidden significance, pervasive spiritual sense, important moral counsel, and general view of life and vision of the present world—supplementary to that sole purpose of entertainment continually announced by him— which will repay whatever trouble of intellect you may take in your reading. You will be the wiser for it. Presumably he is not aware of all that he puts in a work of fiction; but I feel sure that he is always conscious of more than he cares to talk about.

In his lifetime he has had an extraordinary range of experience of the world, often in contact with great personages of his generation, sometimes concerned with historic events. Also, year after year, all sorts of persons, struck by the tolerant spirit and sagacity of his writing, have kept bringing him their report or confession of those extreme occurrences of private life in which modern human nature so often strangely manifests itself, unveils itself. He has a reading and speaking knowledge of five languages, and has read everything, including all the classics of religion and metaphysics, studiously. He is the most serious of men, seeking the general truth in all things, holding himself responsible for his every belief or disbelief, never fooling himself or others, thinking hard. It would be odd indeed if his production of books, even unpretentious stories, were as lightweight as the common estimation has it.

To be sure, he has a strict sense of the different literary forms, putting limitations upon his content in each of them accordingly. Not only *The Summing Up* but various other volumes of nonfiction have been somewhat in the vein of autobiography; therefore not appropriate for any display of intellect as an end in itself. In many a story he has made use of the first person singular; and then, quite as modestly as though it were reminiscence or truthful expository writing, he has allowed himself only that extent of thoughtfulness, intelligence rather than intellect, which could be referred to his own character, within plausible radius of himself. In a novel, of course, there is always something or other subject to interpretation in terms of economics and the social sciences, psychology and so on. But he has kept all this somewhat out of evidence, according to his dear tenets of simplicity and clarity; in any case, kept it out of vocabulary.

Now some readers depend a great deal on verbal associations and style in general as indications of seriousness of thought: massive abstruse specialized words, and complicatedness and elaboration in other ways as well, and a mysterious solemnity. There is never anything like that in Maugham. He irately disapproves of it in others' work, even in the writing of technical philosophy and the accounts which scientists give of their research and speculation. Not long ago he took the matter up with certain eminent professors and a biologist or two in person, advocating a less self-indulgent style. In all his mature period his own way of expressing ideas has been direct and plain and pithy, somewhat in emulation of Dryden and Swift and their followers, but with constant observance of the rhythm of informal modern conversation and with some easy colloquialisms.

If you are looking for the deep thoughtfulness in a story or a novel by Maugham, you cannot expect to have it underlined for you as such. You must use your head, in order not to mistake simplicity for insignificance; and you must learn to recognize his idea in that envelope of reality in which ideas do actually generate, in incident and in dialogue and in little sequences of cause and effect. Also, you will need to read fairly slowly, pondering somewhat as you go along, and to bear it all in mind for some time afterward, weighing it against your own experience and ideas and feelings. Otherwise Maugham is not the author for you, and may never be.

If, on the other hand, you are the more natural, easy-minded, unreasoning man, and what you want is the mere spinning of a yarn, now a kind of myth against some exotic background, now a pitiful or exciting bit of low life, now a humorous scene of high life, to pass the time—with perhaps just a little inspiration or revelation incidentally adhering to your mind when this or that feature of the plot chances to correspond to some recollection or present preoccupation of your own—well, you have Maugham's explicit blessing. You are the reader he writes for, by his own account.

For my part, I like works of fiction to have meaning, the deeper and the more consequential the better; and unless I find this to my satisfaction, fiction reading amuses me very little and leaves me discontented. The purest story form can convey a greater and more accurate truth—as to human nature in its various manifestations and secrecies, and general human fate of the day and age—than any abstract or generalized literature, dogma or dialectic or deduction of science. The actual perusal of a book is only a part of the literary experience. By mere mechanism of my mind, the time I pass in recalling and reflecting upon what I have read is greater than the time it takes to read. When, with no difficulty or superfluity or prolixity, I have been given something worth thinking about, I love the writing in question, and the writer; this is my chief reason for admiring Maugham.

The thought in his novels is mostly ethics, religion, or the psychology of creative endeavor. *The Moon and Sixpence,* for example, has to do with the strange compelling destiny of the artist ahead of his time, to whom moral defects, unkindness toward others, even brutality and megalomania, may prove helpful in becoming great; as in the case of Gauguin. *Cakes and Ale*—which I once heard Mr. Maugham himself recommend as his own first choice of his novels—gives a picture of the literary life, with assorted types of men of letters, the celebrity and the young novice, the real creator and the parasitic literary journalist, and others; it also shows the essential goodness of a sexually loose woman, and her benign influence on the men around her. *The Painted Veil* is a portrayal of the unhappiness resulting from irresponsible adultery, the beneficial psychotherapeutic effect of doing good to others, and the appeal of Roman Catholicism when one is unhappy.

To be sure, none of this will greatly impress or entirely satisfy any true intellectual. It is not that absolute learnedness and virtuosity of mind which one has seen exercised in the recent fiction of Thomas Mann, for example, almost as proudly and far-rangingly as in the eclectic philosophy of Santayana or the world history of Toynbee. On the other hand, what Maugham has to offer is not frivolous matter; and the point of thinking, I take it, is not quantity of thought but rightness, relevance, and, indeed, helpfulness.

Christmas Holiday is unique in Maugham's fiction in that its theme is sociological and political—indeed, international. It is the one of his fifteen-odd novels that has meant most to me personally. As you shall see, it is the tale of a happy-natured and fortunate English youngster holidaying in Paris, where he encounters and makes friends with a pathetic Russian-refugee prostitute, who confesses her identity—she is the wife of a notorious murderer—then little by little narrates their love and the circumstances of his evil deed.

Upon its first publication in 1939, so I have been told, the majority of Maugham's readers did not respond with their customary enthusiasm, as though determined to shut their eyes a few more months to what its entire plot and all its characterizations portended. Also, those who wrote the criticisms of it missed its grave implications, not stopping to think. Which is no final matter; books of the greatest importance, even masterpieces, even classics, often have had to wait awhile for their high rating and proper interpretation. For example, take the case of Stendhal. Now the time would appear to be ripe for *Christmas Holiday* particularly; the present omnibus volume puts it to the test again.

Nineteen thirty-nine, the end of the great lull in modern history; the moment of awakening from the sweetest, most heedless sleep humanity ever indulged in . . . As of that date, *Christmas Holiday* has greater significance than any other contemporary novel, I think. Social significance! The phrase is outworn, I know, but here we have exactly what it was meant for.

Maugham in this slight volume, less than a hundred thousand words long, with his air of having nothing on his mind except his little characters—how they came together and what happened and what they said and how they felt—explains more of the human basis of fascism and nazism and communism than anyone else has done: the self-fascinated, intoxicated, insensible character of all that new leadership in Europe; the womanish passivity of the unhappy masses dependent on it and devoted to it; the Anglo-Saxon bewilderment in the matter, which still generally prevails; and the seeds of historic evil yet to come, not at all extirpated in World War II, but rather fortified and multiplied, and flung with greater profusion in no less receptive soil farther afield, even beyond Europe. Europe the starting point, the womb and the cradle, as in fact it has been for millenniums . . .

I remember that when it first appeared, and my friends were reading it and more or less enjoying it, and I spoke of its dread allegory and prophetic sense, a number of them said they had no idea what I was talking about. A year or so later I brought the subject up in conversation with Mr. Maugham. As a rule he dislikes listening to anyone's opinion of his writing. I think this is not just shyness but also a kind of contrariety. If you quibble with him he wants to fight back, even unfairly, haughtily. The least excess of praise, on the other hand, only stimulates in him that deep and painful discontent of the artist with everything he has done to date, which is one of the important nerve centers of art. But upon this occasion he did not shut me up. I outlined all the significance of his book as it appeared to me; I alluded to the various disagreeing or obtuse readers.

Mr. Maugham said, "Certainly I had those things in the back of my mind while I was writing it. But if I had insisted on them, I should have spoiled my story. It is not the business of a novelist to tell his readers what they are to think of his characters and his plot. If you want your work of fiction to be read, and you have some point that you wish to make, you must bring it in discreetly. Your reader may not take your meaning, or it may not interest him. You must let him read for his pleasure."

*   *   *

As to the labor of literature, Mr. Maugham has said that he was greatly influenced by a fact about Darwin which, at an impressionable age, he read in some book or heard someone tell: Darwin never worked more than three hours a day. Reflecting upon which, the ambitious but reasonable youth came to the conclusion that if, at this rate of endeavor, biological science could be revolutionized and much of the ideology and the ethics of the century altered, surely he could earn a sufficient living and make a name for himself as a playwright and storyteller and novelist with as little drudgery.

A willful man, he seems to have persisted in this as well as other plans of those early days. At his present time of life he rouses from sleep at dawn or soon after; but he brings no manuscript or even notebook into his bedroom, and does not go to his writing room until he has read awhile and breakfasted at leisure. Just before one o'clock he steps into the living room, ready for his cocktail and lunch; pleased with himself if the work has gone forward, clear in his conscience anyway. Approximately Darwin's three hours . . .

But in order not to set him up as a dangerous example to any ambitious but lazy literary youngster—and not to give aid and comfort to those of the intelligentsia who maintain that he has had it easy, and all his renown is but good luck— I will give a little more information. Listen to this, and try to imagine yourself working as he does. Week in and week out, year after year, in whatever circumstances—though surrounded by frivolity, though assailed by bothers and anxieties, and touched upon occasion, as all men are, by exceeding affection or pity or self-pity or anger—regularly every morning he goes to his desk and labors at his writing. For months at a time he will not skip a day. One day I did see him in the living room before lunch, grumpily seated by the fireplace; he had a bad toothache, and even then he was engrossed in a heavy laborious tome, preparatory to the composition of something theological or historical.

Indeed, in his middle life he made some voyage every year or so, notably to the Orient and around the South Seas, in what must have seemed a carefree manner. But what a cargo of fiction he brought back upon each return voyage! He was not wasting his time. Today that spirit of travel for travel's sake (and story's sake) has calmed down in him. But I have observed that even in the city, with details of publishing or other commitments of his career to attend to, also when he takes vacations in the summer or week ends with friends, except when actually in transit, in the train or in the plane, regularly, almost every morning, he goes to some desk or substitute table and works awhile.

This is not drudgery, I know; but it is something that for my part I should find harder to endure and sustain: control, inner tension—in fact, faith—faith in oneself. And I dare say it is more to the purpose of literature in the long run than that way of pent-up ambition occasionally overflowing, rushing, making up for lost time, which gives one the feeling of being a genius, or that way of desperate engagement and deadline with stimulants and sedatives and hell to pay, which is the habit of so many contemporary authors.

Furthermore, in Maugham's case, the time he spends at his desk is only a part of the labor. All his stories and novels have been worked out in his mind before he ever takes his ready pen in hand. Someone has told him an incident of real life, perhaps no more than an impressive utterance or gesture at some crucial moment. That is the commencement, as it were the grain of sand in the bivalve. But real life never seems to him as good as imagination, at least not so good to write about. Therefore he ponders, and sometimes years pass before he is able to devise the fulfillment and change, the different ending, the superstructure of moral implication, which will make all the difference between reality and art. Then he begins searching for the bits and pieces of everyone he has ever known which can be moulded into fictitious beings capable of doing or experiencing whatever it is that he has to tell; adding subordinate episodes as they may enhance or clarify the main matter, and drawing all into one unit; regulating whatever faults of implausibility or contradiction may develop; and deciding upon the order of narration most natural to it, most effective for it. All this goes on in his head; not in Darwin's three hours but in the other twenty-one, when he rouses too early in the morning, when he sits by the fire, when he is taking short salubrious walks . . .

There is a touching page in his memoir of the beginning of World War II, *Strictly Personal,* bearing upon this matter of the advance preparation of his fiction. In the disaster of France he was in personal peril, the Germans having learned from his volume of stories entitled *Ashenden* that he had served as a secret agent in World War I, or something on that order. As he was escaping to England on a miserable coal boat, seated with fellow passengers on the deck—as a kindness to them, to pass the deadly tedium and to relieve their collective fear and shock and loss—he told them stories. He began with some which he was in the habit of telling, which he had learned to rely on to amuse people. But he ran through his repertory of these little set pieces; and so he went on and gave his unhappy audience the benefit of certain plots and projects of fiction which he had borne in mind through the years and never been willing to tell, lest the bloom of his own interest in them be worn off before they were ready to be written. The reason he was willing, then and there, on the vessel of refuge, was the shadow of death hanging over them, environing them. They expected to encounter a submarine or perhaps a flight of predatory planes; therefore the aging storyteller felt that he could spare some of his fondly hoarded material. Even in the event of a safe homecoming, he fancied, he would not live to cope with it all.

This must be the most interesting and individual aspect of his vocation of letters and his career: his planning and planning, major matters and minor matters alike; his constant looking ahead and budgeting every faculty and every opportunity, with due strict consideration of the probabilities for and against him; his sense of a significance and a form in the story of his life, beginning and middle and end, as definite as in the construction of any three-act play or short

story or shapely short novel; and his constant thought of
death, the indelible finis on the unfinishable page.

Even in his reading of the works of other men I have
noticed that he keeps to a sort of schedule. Detective stories
are to kill time when he is sleepless or in some pain. Novels
that friends have sent him can be sufficiently perused, in
kindness or out of curiosity, in half-hours of relaxation.
Usually he devotes an hour in the afternoon or evening to
rereading one of the classics of fiction, Goethe, Fielding,
Cervantes, and the rest; and he keeps certain volumes which
mean a great deal to him on his night table, against the difficult hour of daybreak.

As to the great old masters of fiction, remember that it
has always been his hope and intention that the best of his
books should entitle him to some place in their hierarchy of
world fame and centennial duration; though a modest place.
His requirement of himself has never changed in the fifty or
more years: perhaps not to be great, but to be good, according to the standards of their greatness. They are the objects of his devotion, as it were the inspiring and interceding
saints. Also each of them is exemplary to him in some particular of the art; and he still constantly turns to them when
he has come upon any little problem of his own writing, to
consider what solution one or the other may have found in a
parallel case. When anything in his work in progress has
reference to a learned or abstract matter, he researches tire-
lessly. He has been known to study as many as forty volumes
for one short and easily readable chapter.

Naturally, as a fiction writer, his principal research is just
coming to know people, getting them to tell him what they
have experienced, probing their minds, observing their emotions and their morals. In this he has been tireless too; and
also patient, relentless, teasing, and wonderfully kind—
whatever the human instance may call for—and nothing
that does not infringe upon the Darwinian hours seems to
him too much trouble; not a detail of humanity is too small
for his acute and impartial eye. Often as he goes out to dine
he has a question ready to put to someone he expects to meet,
the answer to which will fit into the morrow's page.

He is, as nearly as can be, a single-minded man. Some years ago he confided to a friend that, within his remembrance, he had never gone anywhere or cared to have any new person introduced to him (except for one of his diversions—bridge playing, for example), or pursued a particular acquaintance with anyone, unless he had some idea of a function or utility for his literary art in so doing: some study of the narratable world up to date; or a search for types of humanity, in the way of a painter needing models to pose for him; or a glimpse into strange ways of living; or an experimental discussion of ideas important to him with reference to work coming up.

Naturally the friend, upon hearing this, felt a pang of self-consciousness, a little chill; but later on he remarked that of his observation over a period of years he believed it to be true enough. In appreciation of his friendship in the time he spent in this country during World War II, let me say that I think it is no longer true. Every sort of ulterior motive and craft and documentary sense seems to have waned out of his various human interests. His kindness toward young people has a character of benign, humorous fatherliness, without any very intense urge to understand them. In society he seeks especially those who can tell him of philosophy and religion. For, as the years pass, the shadow of mortality grows no lighter or smaller; no, not in any man's life! Once in a while he recognizes new subject matter as such, when he hears of it or comes upon it, and points out to some young writer its interest and feasibility, and the proper way to handle it. But even more certainly than on the perilous refugee boat he reminds himself that there will not be time for it to rise and swell in his mind, to ripen for his neat final manuscript and printed best-selling page. He makes way for us; he leaves it to us with his blessing, but also with a certain challenging, sardonic, mistrustful sense. He is easy to please but not easy to satisfy.

Let us not have, in praise of a man so realistic and judicious, any mixing of the classifications of men, or any sentimentality. He is not a saint or a sage or a hero; only a true and greatly accomplished literary artist. But neither let us forget that art has its virtues, and they are rewarded in more ways than one. I remember that one day he came in from his writing room, visibly happy—with a light step, the strong downward expression of his mouth softened, his eyes in their silverpoint wrinkles perfectly clear—and remarked, "I will tell you, as it may not have occurred to you, there is a particular drawback in the career of writing."

Upon my inquiring what the drawback was, he answered, "When you have finished the day's work, and you have to take your leisure and wait for your creative gift to be restored next morning, anything you can do in the remaining hours of the day seems a little pale and flat."

To have commenced literature half a century ago, and still, in spite of life—and by life I mean disillusionment and unlucky affections, increase of pain and worldly losses, shames and impertinences of human nature, along with horrible war and civil war, and the ruin of nations, and the failure of a whole structure of delectable usages—still to enjoy writing so much that nothing compares with it, and to write to the end, is a grand and enviable thing, and a spiritual thing. There are a number of good reasons for dedicating oneself to the art of writing; but surely this is as good as any.

GLENWAY WESCOTT

THE MAUGHAM READER

" . . . the painted veil which those who live call Life."

THE PAINTED VEIL

S HE gave a startled cry.
"What's the matter?" he asked.
Notwithstanding the darkness of the shuttered room he saw her face on a sudden distraught with terror.
"Some one just tried the door."
"Well, perhaps it was the amah, or one of the boys."
"They never come at this time. They know I always sleep after tiffin."
"Who else could it be?"
"Walter," she whispered, her lips trembling.
She pointed to his shoes. He tried to put them on, but his nervousness, for her alarm was affecting him, made him clumsy, and besides, they were on the tight side. With a faint gasp of impatience she gave him a shoe-horn. She slipped into a kimono and in her bare feet went over to her dressing-table. Her hair was shingled and with a comb she had repaired its disorder before he had laced his second shoe. She handed him his coat.
"How shall I get out?"
"You'd better wait a bit. I'll look out and see that it's all right."
"It can't possibly be Walter. He doesn't leave the laboratory till five."
"Who is it then?"
They spoke in whispers now. She was quaking. It occurred to him that in an emergency she would lose her head and on a sudden he felt angry with her. If it wasn't safe why the devil had she said it was? She caught her breath and put her hand on his arm. He followed the direction of her glance.

They stood facing the windows that led out on the verandah. They were shuttered and the shutters were bolted. They saw the white china knob of the handle slowly turn. They had heard no one walk along the verandah. It was terrifying to see that silent motion. A minute passed and there was no sound. Then, with the ghastliness of the supernatural, in the same stealthy, noiseless and horrifying manner, they saw the white china knob of the handle at the other window turn also. It was so frightening that Kitty, her nerves failing her, opened her mouth to scream; but, seeing what she was going to do, he swiftly put his hand over it and her cry was smothered in his fingers.

Silence. She leaned against him, her knees shaking, and he was afraid she would faint. Frowning, his jaw set, he carried her to the bed and sat her down upon it. She was as white as the sheet and notwithstanding his tan his cheeks were pale too. He stood by her side looking with fascinated gaze at the china knob. They did not speak. Then he saw that she was crying.

"For God's sake don't do that," he whispered irritably. "If we're in for it we're in for it. We shall just have to brazen it out."

She looked for her handkerchief and knowing what she wanted he gave her her bag.

"Where's your topee?"

"I left it downstairs."

"Oh, my God!"

"I say, you must pull yourself together. It's a hundred to one it wasn't Walter. Why on earth should he come back at this hour? He never does come home in the middle of the day, does he?"

"Never."

"I'll bet you anything you like it was the amah."

She gave him the shadow of a smile. His rich, caressing voice reassured her and she took his hand and affectionately pressed it. He gave her a moment to collect herself.

"Look here, we can't stay here for ever," he said then. "Do you feel up to going out on the verandah and having a look?"

"I don't think I can stand."

"Have you got any brandy in here?"

She shook her head. A frown for an instant darkened his brow, he was growing impatient, he did not quite know what to do. Suddenly she clutched his hand more tightly.

"Suppose he's waiting there?"

He forced his lips to smile and his voice retained the gentle, persuasive tone the effect of which he was so fully conscious of.

"That's not very likely. Have a little pluck, Kitty. How can it possiby be your husband? If he'd come in and seen a strange topee in the hall and come upstairs and found your room locked, surely he would have made some sort of row. It must have been one of the servants. Only a Chinese would turn a handle in that way."

She did feel more herself now.

"It's not very pleasant even if it was only the amah."

"She can be squared and if necessary I'll put the fear of God into her. There are not many advantages in being a government official, but you may as well get what you can out of it."

He must be right. She stood up and turning to him stretched out her arms: he took her in his and kissed her on the lips. It was such rapture that it was pain. She adored him. He released her and she went to the window. She slid back the bolt and opening the shutter a little looked out. There was not a soul. She slipped on to the verandah, looked into her husband's dressing-room and then into her own sitting-room. Both were empty. She went back to the bedroom and beckoned to him.

"Nobody."

"I believe the whole thing was an optical delusion."

"Don't laugh. I was terrified. Go into my sitting-room and sit down. I'll put on my stockings and some shoes."

ii

He did as she bade and in five minutes she joined him. He was smoking a cigarette.

"I say, could I have a brandy and soda?"

"Yes, I'll ring."

"I don't think it would hurt *you* by the look of things."

They waited in silence for the boy to answer. She gave the order.

"Ring up the laboratory and ask if Walter is there," she said then. "They won't know your voice."

He took up the receiver and asked for the number. He inquired whether Dr. Fane was in. He put down the receiver.

"He hasn't been in since tiffin," he told her. "Ask the boy whether he has been here."

"I daren't. It'll look so funny if he has and I didn't see him."

The boy brought the drinks and Townsend helped himself. When he offered her some she shook her head.

"What's to be done if it was Walter?" she asked.

"Perhaps he wouldn't care."

"Walter?"

Her tone was incredulous.

"It's always struck me he was rather shy. Some men can't bear scenes, you know. He's got sense enough to know that there's nothing to be gained by making a scandal. I don't believe for a minute it was Walter, but even if it was my impression is that he'll do nothing. I think he'll ignore it."

She reflected for a moment.

"He's awfully in love with me."

"Well, that's all to the good. You'll get round him."

He gave her that charming smile of his which she had always found so irresistible. It was a slow smile which started in his clear blue eyes and travelled by perceptible degrees to his shapely mouth. He had small white even teeth. It was a very sensual smile and it made her heart melt in her body.

iii

SHE went out on to the verandah and watched him leave the house. He waved his hand to her. It gave her a little thrill as she looked at him; he was forty-one, but he had the lithe figure and the springing step of a boy.

The verandah was in shadow; and lazily, her heart at ease with satisfied love, she lingered. Their house stood in the Happy Valley, on the side of the hill, for they could not afford to live on the more eligible but expensive Peak. But her abstracted gaze scarcely noticed the blue sea and the crowded shipping in the harbour. She could think only of her lover.

Of course it was stupid to behave as they had done that afternoon, but if he wanted her how could she be prudent? He had come two or three times after tiffin, when in the heat of the day no one thought of stirring out, and not even the boys had seen him come and go. It was very difficult at Hong-Kong. She hated the Chinese city and it made her nervous to go into the filthy little house off the Victoria Road in which they were in the habit of meeting. It was a curio dealer's; and the Chinese who were sitting about stared at her un-pleasantly; she hated the ingratiating smile of the old man who took her to the back of the shop and then up a dark flight of stairs. The room into which he led her was frowsy and the large wooden bed against the wall made her shudder.

"This is dreadfully sordid, isn't it?" she said to Charlie the first time she met him there.

"It was till you came in," he answered.

Of course the moment he took her in his arms she forgot everything.

Oh, how hateful it was that she wasn't free, that they both weren't free! She didn't like his wife. Kitty's wandering thoughts dwelt now for a moment on Dorothy Townsend. How unfortunate to be called Dorothy! It dated you. She was thirty-eight at least. But Charlie never spoke of her. Of course he didn't care for her; she bored him to death. But he

"I don't very much care," she said, with a flash of gaie[ty]. "It was worth it."

"It was my fault."

"Why did you come? I was amazed to see you."

"I couldn't resist it."

"You dear."

She leaned a little towards him, her dark and shining [eyes] gazing passionately into his, her mouth a little open [with] desire, and he put his arms round her. She abandoned [her]self with a sigh of ecstasy to their shelter.

"You know you can always count on me," he said.

"I'm so happy with you. I wish I could make you as ha[ppy] as you make me."

"You're not frightened any more?"

"I hate Walter," she answered.

He did not quite know what to say to this, so he kissed [her.] Her face was very soft against his.

But he took her wrist on which was a little gold watch [and] looked at the time.

"Do you know what I must do now?"

"Bolt?" she smiled.

He nodded. For one instant she clung to him more clo[sely,] but she felt his desire to go, and she released him.

"It's shameful the way you neglect your work. Be off [with] you."

He could never resist the temptation to flirt.

"You seem in a devil of a hurry to get rid of me," h[e said] lightly.

"You know that I hate to let you go."

Her answer was low and deep and serious. He g[ave a] flattered laugh.

"Don't worry your pretty little head about our myste[rious] visitor. I'm quite sure it was the amah. And if there['s any] trouble I guarantee to get you out of it."

"Have you had a lot of experience?"

His smile was amused and complacent.

"No, but I flatter myself that I've got a head screw[ed on] my shoulders."

was a gentleman. Kitty smiled with affectionate irony: it was just like him, silly old thing; he might be unfaithful to her, but he would never allow a word in disparagement of her to cross his lips. She was a tallish woman, taller than Kitty, neither stout nor thin, with a good deal of pale brown hair; she could never have been pretty with anything but the prettiness of youth; her features were good enough without being remarkable and her blue eyes were cold. She had a skin that you would never look at twice and no colour in her cheeks. And she dressed like—well, like what she was, the wife of the Assistant Colonial Secretary at Hong-Kong. Kitty smiled and gave her shoulders a faint shrug.

Of course no one could deny that Dorothy Townsend had a pleasant voice. She was a wonderful mother, Charlie always said that of her, and she was what Kitty's mother called a gentlewoman. But Kitty did not like her. She did not like her casual manner; and the politeness with which she treated you when you went there, to tea or dinner, was exasperating because you could not but feel how little interest she took in you. The fact was, Kitty supposed, that she cared for nothing but her children: there were two boys at school in England, and another boy of six whom she was going to take home next year. Her face was a mask. She smiled and in her pleasant, well-mannered way said the things that were expected of her; but for all her cordiality held you at a distance. She had a few intimate friends in the Colony and they greatly admired her. Kitty wondered whether Mrs. Townsend thought her a little common. She flushed. After all there was no reason for her to put on airs. It was true that her father had been a Colonial Governor and of course it was very grand while it lasted—every one stood up when you entered a room and men took off their hats to you as you passed in your car—but what could be more insignificant than a Colonial Governor when he had retired? Dorothy Townsend's father lived on a pension in a small house at Earl's Court. Kitty's mother would think it a dreadful bore if she asked her to call. Kitty's father, Bernard Garstin, was a K.C. and there was no reason why he should not be made a judge one of these days. Anyhow they lived in South Kensington.

iv

KITTY, coming to Hong-Kong on her marriage, had found it hard to reconcile herself to the fact that her social position was determined by her husband's occupation. Of course every one had been very kind and for two or three months they had gone out to parties almost every night; when they dined at Government House the Governor took her in as a bride; but she had understood quickly that as the wife of the Government bacteriologist she was of no particular consequence. It made her angry.

"It's too absurd," she told her husband. "Why, there's hardly any one here that one would bother about for five minutes at home. Mother wouldn't dream of asking any of them to dine at our house."

"You mustn't let it worry you," he answered. "It doesn't really matter, you know."

"Of course it doesn't matter, it only shows how stupid they are, but it is rather funny when you think of all the people who used to come to our house at home that here we should be treated like dirt."

"From a social standpoint the man of science does not exist," he smiled.

She knew that now, but she had not known it when she married him.

"I don't know that it exactly amuses me to be taken in to dinner by the agent of the P. and O.," she said, laughing in order that what she said might not seem snobbish.

Perhaps he saw the reproach behind her lightness of manner, for he took her hand and shyly pressed it.

"I'm awfully sorry, Kitty dear, but don't let it vex you."

"Oh, I'm not going to let it do that."

v

IT COULDN'T have been Walter that afternoon. It must have been one of the servants and after all they didn't matter.

Chinese servants knew everything anyway. But they held their tongues.

Her heart beat a little faster as she remembered the way in which that white china knob slowly turned. They mustn't take risks like that again. It was better to go to the curio shop. No one who saw her go in would think anything of it, and they were absolutely safe there. The owner of the shop knew who Charlie was and he was not such a fool as to put up the back of the Assistant Colonial Secretary. What did anything matter really but that Charlie loved her?

She turned away from the verandah and went back into her sitting-room. She threw herself down on the sofa and stretched out her hand to get a cigarette. Her eye caught sight of a note lying on the top of a book. She opened it. It was written in pencil.

Dear Kitty,

Here is the book you wanted. I was just going to send it when I met Dr. Fane and he said he'd bring it round himself as he was passing the house.

V.H.

She rang the bell and when the boy came asked him who had brought the book and when.

"Master bring it, missy, after tiffin," he answered.

Then it had been Walter. She rang up the Colonial Secretary's Office at once and asked for Charlie. She told him what she had just learned. There was a pause before he answered.

"What shall I do?" she asked.

"I'm in the middle of an important consultation. I'm afraid I can't talk to you now. My advice to you is to sit tight."

She put down the receiver. She understood that he was not alone and she was impatient with his business.

She sat down again, at a desk, and resting her face in her hands sought to think out the situation. Of course Walter might merely have thought she was sleeping: there was no reason why she should not lock herself in. She tried to remember if they had been talking. Certainly they had not been

talking loud. And there was the hat. It was maddening of
Charlie to have left it downstairs. But it was no use blaming
him for that, it was natural enough, and there was nothing
to tell that Walter had noticed it. He was probably in a
hurry and had just left the book and the note on his way to
some appointment connected with his work. The strange
thing was that he should have tried the door and then the
two windows. If he thought she was asleep it was unlike him
to disturb her. What a fool she had been!

She shook herself a little and again she felt that sweet pain
in her heart which she always felt when she thought of
Charlie. It had been worth it. He had said that he would
stand by her, and if the worse came to the worst, well . . .
Let Walter kick up a row if he chose. She had Charlie; what
did she care? Perhaps it would be the best thing for him to
know. She had never cared for Walter and since she had
loved Charlie Townsend it had irked and bored her to
submit to her husband's caresses. She wanted to have nothing
more to do with him. She didn't see how he could prove anything. If he accused her she would deny, and if it came to a
pass that she could deny no longer, well, she would fling the
truth in his teeth, and he could do what he chose.

vi

WITHIN three months of her marriage she knew that she had
made a mistake; but it had been her mother's fault even more
than hers.

There was a photograph of her mother in the room and
Kitty's harassed eyes fell on it. She did not know why she
kept it there, for she was not very fond of her mother; there
was one of her father too, but that was downstairs on the
grand piano. It had been done when he took silk and it represented him in wig and gown. Even they could not make him
imposing; he was a little, wizened man, with tired eyes, a
long upper lip, and a thin mouth: a facetious photographer
had told him to look pleasant, but he had succeeded only in
looking severe. It was on this account, for as a rule the down-

turned corners of his mouth and the dejection of his eyes
gave him an air of mild depression, that Mrs. Garstin, thinking it made him look judicial, had chosen it from among the
proofs. But her own photograph showed her in the dress in
which she had gone to Court when her husband was made a
King's Counsel. She was very grand in the velvet gown, the
long train so disposed as to show to advantage, with feathers
in her hair and flowers in her hand. She held herself erect.
She was a woman of fifty, thin and flat-chested, with prominent cheekbones and a large, well-shaped nose. She had a
great quantity of very smooth black hair and Kitty had always suspected that, if not dyed, it was at least touched up.
Her fine black eyes were never still and this was the most
noticeable thing about her; for when she was talking to you
it was disconcerting to see those restless eyes in that impassive, unlined and yellow face. They moved from one part of
you to another, to other persons in the room, and then back
to you; you felt that she was criticising you, summing you up,
watchful meanwhile of all that went on around her, and that
the words she spoke had no connection with her thoughts.

vii

Mrs. GARSTIN was a hard, cruel, managing, ambitious, par-
simonious and stupid woman. She was the daughter, one of
five, of a solicitor in Liverpool and Bernard Garstin had met
her when he was on the Northern Circuit. He had seemed
then a young man of promise and her father said he would
go far. He hadn't. He was painstaking, industrious and
capable, but he had not the will to advance himself. Mrs.
Garstin despised him. But she recognised, though with bitterness, that she could only achieve success through him, and
she set herself to drive him on the way she desired to go. She
nagged him without mercy. She discovered that if she wanted
him to do something which his sensitiveness revolted against
she had only to give him no peace and eventually, exhausted,
he would yield. On her side she set herself to cultivate the
people who might be useful. She flattered the solicitors who

would send her husband briefs and was familiar with their wives. She was obsequious to the judges and their ladies. She made much of promising politicians.

In twenty-five years Mrs. Garstin never invited any one to dine at her house because she liked him. She gave large dinner parties at regular intervals. But parsimony was as strong in her as ambition. She hated to spend money. She flattered herself that she could make as much show as any one else at half the price. Her dinners were long and elaborate, but thrifty, and she could never persuade herself that people when they were eating and talking knew what they drank. She wrapped sparkling Moselle in a napkin and thought her guests took it for champagne.

Bernard Garstin had a fair, though not a large practice. Men who had been called after him had long outstripped him. Mrs. Garstin made him stand for parliament. The expense of the election was borne by the party, but here again her parsimony balked her ambition, and she could not bring herself to spend enough money to nurse the constituency. The subscriptions Bernard Garstin made to the innumerable funds a candidate is expected to contribute to, were always just a little less than adequate. He was beaten. Though it would have pleased Mrs. Garstin to be a member's wife she bore her disappointment with fortitude. The fact of her husband's standing had brought her in contact with a number of prominent persons and she appreciated the addition to her social consequence. She knew that Bernard would never make his mark in the House. She wanted him to be a member only that he might have a claim on the gratitude of his party and surely to fight two or three losing seats would give him that.

But he was still a junior and many younger men than he had already taken silk. It was necessary that he should too, not only because otherwise he could scarcely hope to be made a judge, but on her account also: it mortified her to go in to dinner after women ten years younger than herself. But here she encountered in her husband an obstinacy which she had not for years been accustomed to. He was afraid that as a K.C. he would get no work. A bird in the hand was worth two in the bush, he told her, to which she retorted that a proverb was the last refuge of the mentally destitute. He suggested to her the possibility that his income would be halved and he knew that there was no argument which could have greater weight with her. She would not listen. She called him pusillanimous. She gave him no peace and at last, as always, he yielded. He applied for silk and it was promptly awarded him.

His misgivings were justified. He made no headway as a leader and his briefs were few. But he concealed any disappointment he may have felt, and if he reproached his wife it was in his heart. He grew perhaps a little more silent, but he had always been silent at home, and no one in his family noticed a change in him. His daughters had never looked upon him as anything but a source of income; it had always seemed perfectly natural that he should lead a dog's life in order to provide them with board and lodging, clothes, holidays and money for odds and ends; and now, understanding that through his fault money was less plentiful, the indifference they had felt for him was tinged with an exasperated contempt. It never occurred to them to ask themselves what were the feelings of the subdued little man who went out early in the morning and came home at night only in time to dress for dinner. He was a stranger to them, but because he was their father they took it for granted that he should love and cherish them.

viii

BUT there was a quality of courage in Mrs. Garstin which in itself was admirable. She let no one in her immediate circle, which to her was the world, see how mortified she was by the frustration of her hopes. She made no change in her style of living. By careful management she was able to give as showy dinners as she had done before, and she met her friends with the same bright gaiety which she had so long cultivated. She had a hard and facile fund of chit-chat which in the society she moved in passed for conversation. She was a useful guest among persons to whom small talk did not come easily, for she was never at a loss with a new topic and could be trusted immediately to break an awkward silence with a suitable observation.

It was unlikely now that Bernard Garstin would ever be made a judge of the High Court, but he might still hope for a County Court judgeship or at the worst an appointment in the Colonies. Meanwhile she had the satisfaction of seeing him appointed Recorder of a Welsh town. But it was on her daughters that she set her hopes. By arranging good marriages for them she expected to make up for all the disappointments of her career. There were two, Kitty and Doris. Doris gave no sign of good looks, her nose was too long and her figure was lumpy; so that Mrs. Garstin could hope no more for her than that she should marry a young man who was well off and in a suitable profession.

But Kitty was a beauty. She gave promise of being so when she was still a child, for she had large, dark eyes, liquid and vivacious, brown, curling hair in which there was a reddish tint, exquisite teeth and a lovely skin. Her features would never be very good, for her chin was too square and her nose, though not so long as Doris's, too big. Her beauty depended a good deal on her youth, and Mrs. Garstin realised that she must marry in the first flush of her maidenhood. When she came out she was dazzling: her skin was still her greatest beauty, but her eyes with their long lashes were so starry and yet so melting that it gave you a catch at the heart to look into them. She had a charming gaiety and the desire to please. Mrs. Garstin bestowed upon her all the affection, a harsh, competent, calculating affection, of which she was capable; she dreamed ambitious dreams; it was not a good marriage she aimed at for her daughter, but a brilliant one.

Kitty had been brought up with the knowledge that she was going to be a beautiful woman and she more than suspected her mother's ambition. It accorded with her own desires. She was launched upon the world and Mrs. Garstin performed prodigies in getting herself invited to dances where her daughter might meet eligible men. Kitty was a success. She was amusing as well as beautiful, and very soon she had a dozen men in love with her. But none was suitable, and Kitty, charming and friendly with all, took care to commit herself with none. The drawing-room in South Kensington was filled on Sunday afternoons with amorous youth, but Mrs. Garstin observed, with a grim smile of approval, that it needed no effort on her part to keep them at a distance from Kitty. Kitty was prepared to flirt with them, and it diverted her to play one off against the other, but when they proposed to her, as none failed to do, she refused them with tact but decision.

Her first season passed without the perfect suitor presenting himself, and the second also; but she was young and could afford to wait. Mrs. Garstin told her friends that she thought it a pity for a girl to marry till she was twenty-one. But a third year passed and then a fourth. Two or three of her old admirers proposed again, but they were still penniless, one or two boys younger than herself proposed; a retired Indian Civilian, a K.C.I.E., did the same: he was fifty-three. Kitty still danced a great deal, she went to Wimbledon and Lord's, to Ascot and Henley; she was thoroughly enjoying herself; but still no one whose position and income were satisfactory asked her to marry him. Mrs. Garstin began to grow uneasy. She noticed that Kitty was beginning to attract men of forty and over. She reminded her that she would not be any longer so pretty in a year or two and that young girls were coming out all the time. Mrs. Garstin did not mince her words in the domestic circle and she warned her daughter tartly that she would miss her market.

Kitty shrugged her shoulders. She thought herself as pretty as ever, prettier perhaps, for she had learnt how to dress in the last four years, and she had plenty of time. If she wanted to marry just to be married there were a dozen boys who would jump at the chance. Surely the right man would come along sooner or later. But Mrs. Garstin judged the situation more shrewdly: with anger in her heart for the beautiful daughter who had missed her chances she set her standard a little lower. She turned back to the professional class at which she had sneered in her pride and looked about for a young lawyer or a business man whose future inspired her with confidence.

Kitty reached the age of twenty-five and was still unmarried. Mrs. Garstin was exasperated and she did not hesitate often to give Kitty a piece of her very unpleasant mind. She asked her how much longer she expected her father to support her. He had spent sums he could ill afford in order to give her a chance and she had not taken it. It never struck Mrs. Garstin that perhaps her own hard affability had frightened the men, sons of wealthy fathers or heirs to a title, whose visits she had too cordially encouraged. She put down Kitty's failure to stupidity. Then Doris came out. She had a long nose still, and a poor figure, and she danced badly. In her first season she became engaged to Geoffrey Dennison. He was the only son of a prosperous surgeon who had been given a baronetcy during the war. Geoffrey would inherit a title—it is not very grand to be a medical baronet, but a title, thank God, is still a title—and a very comfortable fortune.

Kitty in a panic married Walter Fane.

ix

SHE had known him but a little while and had never taken much notice of him. She had no idea when or where they had first met till after their engagement he told her that it was at a dance to which some friends had brought him. She certainly paid no attention to him then and if she danced with him it was because she was good-natured and was glad to dance with any one who asked her. She didn't know him from Adam when a day or two later at another dance he came up and spoke to her. Then she remarked that he was at every dance she went to.

"You know, I've danced with you at least a dozen times now and you must tell me your name," she said to him at last in her laughing way.

He was obviously taken aback.

"Do you mean to say you don't know it? I was introduced to you."

"Oh, but people always mumble. I shouldn't be at all surprised if you hadn't the ghost of an idea what mine was."

He smiled at her. His face was grave and a trifle stern, but his smile was very sweet.

"Of course I know it." He was silent for a moment or two. "Have you no curiosity?" he asked then.

"As much as most women."

"It didn't occur to you to ask somebody or other what my name was?"

She was faintly amused; she wondered why he thought it could in the least interest her; but she liked to please, so she looked at him with that dazzling smile of hers and her beautiful eyes, dewy ponds under forest trees, held an enchanting kindness.

"Well, what is it?"

"Walter Fane."

She did not know why he came to dances, he did not dance very well, and he seemed to know few people. She had a passing thought that he was in love with her; but she dismissed it with a shrug of the shoulders: she had known girls who thought every man they met was in love with them and had always found them absurd. But she gave Walter Fane just a little more of her attention. He certainly did not behave like any of the other youths who had been in love with her. Most of them told her so frankly and wanted to kiss her: a good many did. But Walter Fane never talked of her and very little of himself. He was rather silent; she did not mind that because she had plenty to say and it pleased her to see him laugh when she made a facetious remark; but when he talked it was not stupidly. He was evidently shy. It appeared that he lived in the East and was home on leave.

One Sunday afternoon he appeared at their house in South Kensington. There were a dozen people there, and he sat for some time, somewhat ill at ease, and then went away. Her mother asked her later who he was.

"I haven't a notion. Did you ask him to come here?"

"Yes, I met him at the Baddeleys. He said he'd seen you at various dances. I said I was always at home on Sundays."

"His name is Fane and he's got some sort of job in the East."

"Yes, he's a doctor. Is he in love with you?"

"Upon my word, I don't know."

"I should have thought you knew by now when a young man was in love with you."

"I wouldn't marry him if he were," said Kitty lightly.

Mrs. Garstin did not answer. Her silence was heavy with displeasure. Kitty flushed: she knew that her mother did not care now whom she married so long as somehow she got her off her hands.

x

DURING the next week she met him at three dances and now, his shyness perhaps wearing off a little, he was somewhat more communicative. He was a doctor, certainly, but he did not practise; he was a bacteriologist (Kitty had only a very vague idea what that meant) and he had a job at Hong-Kong. He was going back in the autumn. He talked a good deal about China. She made it a practice to appear interested in whatever people talked to her of, but indeed the life in Hong-Kong sounded quite jolly; there were clubs and tennis and racing and polo and golf.

"Do people dance much there?"

"Oh, yes, I think so."

She wondered whether he told her these things with a motive. He seemed to like her society, but never by a pressure of the hand, by a glance or by a word, did he give the smallest indication that he looked upon her as anything but a girl whom you met and danced with. On the following Sunday he came again to their house. Her father happened to come in, it was raining and he had not been able to play golf, and he and Walter Fane had a long chat. She asked her father afterwards what they had talked of.

"It appears he's stationed in Hong-Kong. The Chief Justice is an old friend of mine at the Bar. He seems an unusually intelligent young man."

She knew that her father was as a rule bored to death by the young people whom for her sake and now her sister's he had been forced for years to entertain.

"It's not often you like any of my young men, father," she said.

His kind, tired eyes rested upon her.

"Are you going to marry him by any chance?"

"Certainly not."

"Is he in love with you?"

"He shows no sign of it."

"Do you like him?"

"I don't think I do very much. He irritates me a little."

He was not her type at all. He was short, but not thick-set, slight rather and thin; dark and clean-shaven, with very regular, clear-cut features. His eyes were almost black, but not large, they were not very mobile and they rested on objects with a singular persistence; they were curious, but not very pleasant eyes. With his straight, delicate nose, his fine brow and well-shaped mouth he ought to have been good-looking. But surprisingly enough he was not. When Kitty began to think of him at all she was surprised that he should have such good features when you took them one by one and yet be so far from handsome. His face was cold. His expression was slightly sarcastic and now that Kitty knew him better she realised that she was not quite at ease with him. He had no gaiety.

By the time the season drew to its end they had seen a good deal of one another, but he had remained as aloof and impenetrable as ever. He was not exactly shy with her, but embarrassed; his conversation remained strangely impersonal. Kitty came to the conclusion that he was not in the least in love with her. He liked her and found her easy to talk to, but when he returned to Hong-Kong in November he would not think of her again. She thought it not impossible that he was engaged all the time to some nurse in a hospital at Hong-Kong, the daughter of a clergyman, dull, plain, flat-footed and strenuous; that was the wife that would exactly suit him.

Then came the announcement of Doris's engagement to Geoffrey Dennison. Doris, at eighteen, was making quite a good marriage, and she was twenty-five and single. Supposing she did not marry at all? That season the only person who had proposed to her was a boy of twenty who was still at Oxford: she couldn't marry a boy five years younger than herself. She had made a hash of things. Last year she had refused a widowed Knight of the Bath with three children. She almost wished she hadn't. Mother would be horrible now, and Doris, Doris who had always been sacrificed because she, Kitty, was expected to make the brilliant match, would not fail to crow over her. Kitty's heart sank.

xi

BUT one afternoon when she was walking home from Harrod's she chanced to meet Walter Fane in the Brompton Road. He stopped and talked to her. Then, casually, he asked her if she would not take a turn with him in the Park. She had no particular wish to go home; it was not just then a very agreeable place. They strolled along, talking as they always talked, of casual things, and he asked her where she was going for the summer.

"Oh, we always bury ourselves in the country. You see, father is exhausted after the term's work and we just go to the quietest place we can find."

Kitty spoke with her tongue in her cheek, for she knew quite well that her father had not nearly enough work to tire him and even if he had his convenience would never have been consulted in the choice of a holiday. But a quiet place was a cheap place.

"Don't you think those chairs look rather inviting?" said Walter suddenly.

She followed his eyes and saw two green chairs by themselves under a tree on the grass.

"Let us sit in them," she said.

But when they were seated he seemed to grow strangely abstracted. He was an odd creature. She chattered on, however, gaily enough and wondered why he had asked her to walk with him in the Park. Perhaps he was going to confide in her his passion for the flat-footed nurse in Hong-Kong. Suddenly he turned to her, interrupting her in the middle of a sentence, so that she could not but see that he had not been listening, and his face was chalk white.

"I want to say something to you."

She looked at him quickly and she saw that his eyes were filled with a painful anxiety. His voice was strained, low and not quite steady. But before she could ask herself what this agitation meant he spoke again.

"I want to ask you if you'll marry me."

"You could knock me down with a feather," she answered so surprised that she looked at him blankly.

"Didn't you know I was awfully in love with you?"

"You never showed it."

"I'm very awkward and clumsy. I always find it more difficult to say the things I mean than the things I don't."

Her heart began to beat a little more quickly. She had been proposed to often before, but gaily or sentimentally, and she had answered in the same fashion. No one had ever asked her to marry him in a manner which was so abrupt and yet strangely tragic.

"It's very kind of you," she said, doubtfully.

"I fell in love with you the first time I saw you. I wanted to ask you before, but I could never bring myself to it."

"I'm not sure if that's very well put," she chuckled.

She was glad to have an opportunity to laugh a little, for on that fine, sunny day the air about them seemed on a sudden heavy with foreboding. He frowned darkly.

"Oh, you know what I mean. I didn't want to lose hope. But now you're going away and in the autumn I have to go back to China."

"I've never thought of you in that way," she said helplessly.

He said nothing more. He looked down on the grass sullenly. He was a very odd creature. But now that he had told her she felt in some mysterious way that his love was something she had never met before. She was a little frightened, but she was elated also. His impassivity was vaguely impressive.

"You must give me time to think."

Still he did not say anything. He did not stir. Did he mean to keep her there till she had decided? That was absurd. She must talk it over with her mother. She ought to have got up when she spoke, she had waited thinking he would answer, and now, she did not know why, she found it difficult to make a movement. She did not look at him, but she was conscious of his appearance; she had never seen herself marrying a man so little taller than herself. When you sat close to him you saw how good his features were, and how cold his face. It was strange when you couldn't help being conscious of the devastating passion which was in his heart.

"I don't know you, I don't know you at all," she said tremulously.

He gave her a look and she felt her eyes drawn to his. They had a tenderness which she had never seen in them before, but there was something beseeching in them, like a dog's that has been whipped, which slightly exasperated her.

"I think I improve on acquaintance," he said.

"Of course you're shy, aren't you?"

It was certainly the oddest proposal she had ever had. And even now it seemed to her that they were saying to one another the last things you would have expected on such an occasion. She was not in the least in love with him. She did not know why she hesitated to refuse him at once.

"I'm awfully stupid," he said, "I want to tell you that I love you more than anything in the world, but I find it so awfully difficult to say."

Now that was odd too, for inexplicably enough it touched her; he wasn't really cold, of course, it was his manner that was unfortunate: she liked him at that moment better than she had ever liked him before. Doris was to be married in November. He would be on his way to China then and if she married him she would be with him. It wouldn't be very nice to be a bridesmaid at Doris's wedding. She would be glad to escape that. And then Doris as a married woman and herself still single! Every one knew how young Doris was and it would make her seem older. It would put her on the shelf. It wouldn't be a very good marriage for her, but it was a marriage, and the fact that she would live in China made it easier. She was afraid of her mother's bitter tongue. Why, all the girls who had come out with her were married long ago and most of them had children; she was tired of going to see them and gushing over their babies. Walter Fane offered her a new life. She turned to him with a smile which she well knew the effect of.

"If I were so rash as to say I'd marry you when would you want to marry me?"

He gave a sudden gasp of delight, and his white cheeks flushed.

"Now. At once. As soon as possible. We'd go to Italy for our honeymoon. August and September."

That would save her from spending the summer in a country vicarage, hired at five guineas a week, with her father and mother. In a flash she saw in her mind's eye the announcement in the *Morning Post* that, the bridegroom having to return to the East, the wedding would take place at once. She knew her mother well enough, she could be counted on to make a splash; for the moment at least Doris would be in the background and when Doris's much grander wedding took place she would be far away.

She stretched out her hand.

"I think I like you very much. You must give me time to get used to you."

"Then it's yes?" he interrupted.

"I suppose so."

xii

SHE knew him very little then, and now, though they had been married for nearly two years, she knew him but little more. At first she had been touched by his kindness and flattered, though surprised, by his passion. He was extremely considerate; he was very attentive to her comfort; she never expressed the slightest wish without his hastening to gratify it. He was constantly giving her little presents. When she happened to feel ill no one could have been kinder or more thoughtful. She seemed to do him a favour when she gave him the opportunity of doing something tiresome for her. And he was always exceedingly polite. He rose to his feet when she entered a room, he gave her his hand to help her out of a car, if he chanced to meet her in the street he took off his hat, he was solicitous to open the door for her when she left a room, he never came into her bedroom or her boudoir without a knock. He treated her not as Kitty had seen most men treat their wives, but as though she were a fellow-guest in a country house. It was pleasing and yet a trifle comic. She would have felt more at home with him if he had been more casual. Nor did their conjugal relations draw her closer to him. He was passionate then, fierce, oddly hysterical too, and sentimental.

It disconcerted her to realise how emotional he really was. His self-control was due to shyness or to long training, she did not know which; it seemed to her faintly contemptible that when she lay in his arms, his desire appeased, he who was so timid of saying absurd things, who so feared to be ridiculous, should use baby talk. She had offended him bitterly once by laughing and telling him that he was talking the most fearful slush. She had felt his arms grow limp about her, he remained quite silent for a little while, and then without a word released her and went into his own room. She didn't want to hurt his feelings and a day or two later she said to him:

"You silly old thing, I don't mind what nonsense you talk to me."

He had laughed in a shamefaced way. She had discovered very soon that he had an unhappy disability to lose himself. He was self-conscious. When there was a party and every one started singing Walter could never bring himself to join in. He sat there smiling to show that he was pleased and amused, but his smile was forced; it was more like a sarcastic smirk, and you could not help feeling that he thought all those people enjoying themselves a pack of fools. He could not bring himself to play the round games which Kitty with her high spirits found such a lark. On their journey out to China he had absolutely refused to put on fancy dress when every one else was wearing it. It disturbed her pleasure that he should so obviously think the whole thing a bore.

Kitty was lively; she was willing to chatter all day long and she laughed easily. His silence disconcerted her. He had a way which exasperated her of returning no answer to some casual remark of hers. It was true that it needed no answer, but an answer all the same would have been pleasant. If it was raining and she said: "It's raining cats and dogs," she would have liked him to say: "Yes, isn't it?" He remained silent. Sometimes she would have liked to shake him.

"I said it was raining cats and dogs," she repeated.

"I heard you," he answered, with his affectionate smile.

It showed that he had not meant to be offensive. He did not speak because he had nothing to say. But if nobody spoke unless he had something to say, Kitty reflected, with a smile, the human race would very soon lose the use of speech.

xiii

THE fact was, of course, that he had no charm. That was why he was not popular, and she had not been long in Hong-Kong before she discovered that he was not. She remained very vague about his work. It was enough for her to realise, and she did this quite distinctly, that to be the government bacteriologist was no great fry. He seemed to have no desire to discuss that part of his life with her. Because she was willing to be interested in anything at first she had asked him about it. He put her off with a jest.

"It's very dull and technical," he said on another occasion. "And it's grossly underpaid."

He was very reserved. All she knew about his antecedents, his birth, his education, and his life before he met her, she had elicited by direct questioning. It was odd, the only thing that seemed to annoy him was a question; and when, in her natural curiosity, she fired a string of them at him, his answers became at every one more abrupt. She had the wit to see that he did not care to reply because he had anything to hide from her, but merely from a natural secretiveness. It bored him to talk about himself. It made him shy and uncomfortable. He did not know how to be open. He was fond of reading, but he read books which seemed to Kitty very dull. If he was not busy with some scientific treatise he would read books about China or historical works. He never relaxed. She did not think he could. He was fond of games: he played tennis and bridge.

She wondered why he had ever fallen in love with her. She could not imagine any one less suited than herself to this restrained, cold and self-possessed man. And yet it was quite certain that he loved her madly. He would do anything in the world to please her. He was like wax in her hands. When she thought of one side he showed her, a side which only she had seen, she a little despised him. She wondered whether his sarcastic manner, with its contemptuous tolerance for so many persons and things she admired, was merely a façade to conceal a profound weakness. She supposed he was clever, every one seemed to think he was, but except very occasionally when he was with two or three people he liked and was in the mood, she had never found him entertaining. He did not precisely bore her, he left her indifferent.

xiv

THOUGH Kitty had met his wife at various tea-parties she had been some weeks in Hong-Kong before she saw Charles Townsend. She was introduced to him only when with her husband she went to dine at his house. Kitty was on the defensive. Charles Townsend was Assistant Colonial Secretary and she had no mind to allow him to use her with the condescension which, notwithstanding her good manners, she discerned in Mrs. Townsend. The room in which they were received was spacious. It was furnished as was every other drawing-room she had been in at Hong-Kong in a comfortable and homely style. It was a large party. They were the last to come and as they entered Chinese servants in uniform

were handing round cocktails and olives. Mrs. Townsend
greeted them in her casual fashion and looking at a list told
Walter whom he was to take in to dinner.

Kitty saw a tall and very handsome man bear down on
them.

"This is my husband."

"I am to have the privilege of sitting next to you," he said.

She immediately felt at ease and the sense of hostility
vanished from her bosom. Though his eyes were smiling she
had seen in them a quick look of surprise. She understood it
perfectly and it made her inclined to laugh.

"I shan't be able to eat any dinner," he said, "and if I
know Dorothy the dinner's damned good."

"Why not?"

"I ought to have been told. Some one really ought to have
warned me."

"What about?"

"No one said a word. How was I to know that I was going to meet a raging beauty?"

"Now what am I to say to that?"

"Nothing. Leave me to do the talking. And I'll say it over
and over again."

Kitty, unmoved, wondered what exactly his wife had told
him about her. He must have asked. And Townsend, looking
down on her with his laughing eyes, suddenly remembered.

"What is she like?" he had inquired when his wife told
him she had met Dr. Fane's bride.

"Oh, quite a nice little thing. Actressy."

"Was she on the stage?"

"Oh, no, I don't think so. Her father's a doctor or a
lawyer or something. I suppose we shall have to ask them to
dinner."

"There's no hurry, is there?"

When they were sitting side by side at table he told her
that he had known Walter Fane ever since he came to the
Colony.

"We play bridge together. He's far and away the best
bridge player at the Club."

She told Walter on the way home.

"That's not saying very much, you know."

"How does he play?"

"Not badly. He plays a winning hand very well, but when he has bad cards he goes all to pieces."

"Does he play as well as you?"

"I have no illusions about my play. I should describe myself as a very good player in the second class. Townsend thinks he's in the first. He isn't."

"Don't you like him?"

"I neither like him nor dislike him. I believe he's not bad at his job and every one says he's a good sportsman. He doesn't very much interest me."

It was not the first time that Walter's moderation had exasperated her. She asked herself why it was necessary to be so prudent: you either liked people or you didn't. She had liked Charles Townsend very much. And she had not expected to. He was probably the most popular man in the Colony. It was supposed that the Colonial Secretary would retire soon and every one hoped that Townsend would succeed him. He played tennis and polo and golf. He kept racing ponies. He was always ready to do any one a good turn. He never let red tape interfere with him. He put on no airs. Kitty did not know why she had resented hearing him so well spoken of, she could not help thinking he must be very conceited: she had been extremely silly; that was the last thing you could accuse him of.

She had enjoyed her evening. They had talked of the theatres in London, and of Ascot and Cowes, all the things she knew about, so that really she might have met him at some nice house in Lennox Gardens; and later, when the men came into the drawing-room after dinner, he had strolled over and sat beside her again. Though he had not said anything very amusing, he had made her laugh; it must have been the way he said it: there was a caressing sound in his deep, rich voice, a delightful expression in his kind, shining blue eyes, which made you feel very much at home with him. Of course he had charm. That was what made him so pleasant.

He was tall, six foot two at least, she thought, and he had

a beautiful figure; he was evidently in very good condition
and he had not a spare ounce of fat on him. He was well-
dressed, the best-dressed man in the room, and he wore his
clothes well. She liked a man to be smart. Her eyes wandered
to Walter: he really should try to be a little better turned
out. She noticed Townsend's cuff-links and waistcoat buttons;
she had seen similar ones at Cartier's. Of course the Townsends had private means. His face was deeply sunburned, but
the sun had not taken the healthy colour from his cheeks.
She liked the little trim curly moustache which did not conceal his full red lips. He had black hair, short and brushed
very sleek. But of course his eyes, under thick, bushy eyebrows, were his best feature: they were so very blue, and
they had a laughing tenderness which persuaded you of the
sweetness of his disposition. No man who had those blue eyes
could bear to hurt any one.

She could not but know that she had made an impression
on him. If he had not said charming things to her his eyes,
warm with admiration, would have betrayed him. His ease
was delightful. He had no self-consciousness. Kitty was at
home in these circumstances and she admired the way in
which amid the banter which was the staple of their conversation he insinuated every now and then a pretty, flattering speech. When she shook hands with him on leaving he
gave her hand a pressure that she could not mistake.

"I hope we shall see you again soon," he said casually, but
his eyes gave his words a meaning which she could not fail
to see.

"Hong-Kong is very small, isn't it?" she said.

xv

WHO would have thought then that within three months
they would be on such terms? He had told her since that he
was crazy about her on that first evening. She was the most
beautiful thing he had ever seen. He remembered the dress
she wore; it was her wedding dress, and he said she looked
like a lily of the valley. She knew that he was in love with

her before he told her, and a little frightened she kept him at a distance. He was impetuous and it was difficult. She was afraid to let him kiss her, for the thought of his arms about her made her heart beat so fast. She had never been in love before. It was wonderful. And now that she knew what love was she felt a sudden sympathy for the love that Walter bore her. She teased him, playfully, and saw that he enjoyed it. She had been perhaps a little afraid of him, but now she had more confidence. She chaffed him and it amused her to see the slow smile with which at first he received her banter. He was surprised and pleased. One of these days, she thought, he would become quite human. Now that she had learnt something of passion it diverted her to play lightly, like a harpist running his fingers across the strings of his harp, on his affections. She laughed when she saw how she bewildered and confused him.

And when Charlie became her lover the situation between herself and Walter seemed exquisitely absurd. She could hardly look at him, so grave and self-controlled, without laughing. She was too happy to feel unkindly towards him. Except for him, after all, she would never have known Charlie. She had hesitated some time before the final step, not because she did not want to yield to Charlie's passion, her own was equal to his, but because her upbringing and all the conventions of her life intimidated her. She was amazed afterwards (and the final act was due to accident; neither of them had seen the opportunity till it was face to face with them) to discover that she felt in no way different from what she had before. She had expected that it would cause some, she hardly knew what, fantastic change in her so that she would feel like somebody else; and when she had a chance to look at herself in the glass she was bewildered to see the same woman she had seen the day before.

"Are you angry with me?" he asked her.

"I adore you," she whispered.

"Don't you think you were very silly to waste so much time?"

"A perfect fool."

xvi

HER happiness, sometimes almost more than she could bear, renewed her beauty. Just before she married, beginning to lose her first freshness, she had looked tired and drawn. The uncharitable said that she was going off. But there is all the difference between a girl of twenty-five and a married woman of that age. She was like a rosebud that is beginning to turn yellow at the edges of the petals, and then suddenly she was a rose in full bloom. Her starry eyes gained a more significant expression; her skin (that feature which had always been her greatest pride and most anxious care) was dazzling: it could not be compared to the peach or to the flower; it was they that demanded comparison with it. She looked eighteen once more. She was at the height of her glowing loveliness. It was impossible not to remark it and her women friends asked her in little friendly asides if she was going to have a baby. The indifferent who had said she was just a very pretty woman with a long nose admitted that they had misjudged her. She was what Charlie had called her the first time he saw her, a raging beauty.

They managed their intrigue with skill. He had a broad back, he told her ("I will not have you swank about your figure," she interrupted lightly), and it did not matter about him; but for her sake they mustn't take the smallest risk. They could not meet often alone, not half often enough for him, but he had to think of her first, sometimes in the curio shop, now and then after luncheon in her house when no one was about; but she saw him a good deal here and there. It amused her then to see the formal way he spoke to her, jovial, for he was always that, with the same manner he used with every one. Who could imagine when they heard him chaff her with that charming humour of his that so lately he had held her in his passionate arms?

She worshipped him. He was splendid, in his smart top boots and his white breeches, when he played polo. In tennis clothes he looked a mere boy. Of course he was proud of his figure: it was the best figure she had ever seen. He took pains to keep it. He never ate bread or potatoes or butter. And he took a great deal of exercise. She liked the care he took of his hands; he was manicured once a week. He was a wonderful athlete and the year before he had won the local tennis championship. Certainly he was the best dancer she had ever danced with; it was a dream to dance with him. No one would think he was forty. She told him she did not believe it.

"I believe it's all bluff and you're really twenty-five."

He laughed. He was well pleased.

"Oh, my dear, I have a boy of fifteen. I'm a middle-aged gent. In another two or three years I shall just be a fat old party."

"You'll be adorable when you're a hundred."

She liked his black, bushy eyebrows. She wondered whether it was they that gave his blue eyes their disturbing expression.

He was full of accomplishments. He could play the piano quite well, rag-time, of course, and he could sing a comic song with a rich voice and good humour. She did not believe there was anything he could not do. He was very clever at his work too and she shared his pleasure when he told her that the Governor had particularly congratulated him on the way he had done some difficult job.

"Although it's I as says it," he laughed, his eyes charming with the love he bore her, "there's not a fellow in the Service who could have done it better."

Oh, how she wished that she were his wife rather than Walter's!

xvii

OF COURSE it was not certain yet that Walter knew the truth, and if he didn't it was better perhaps to leave well alone; but if he did, well, in the end it would be the best thing for all of them. At first she had been, if not satisfied, at least resigned to seeing Charlie only by stealth; but time had increased her passion and for some while now she had been increasingly impatient of the obstacles which prevented them from being always together. He had told her so often that he cursed his position which forced him to be so discreet, the ties which bound him, and the ties which bound her : how marvellous it would have been, he said, if they were both free ! She saw his point of view; no one wanted a scandal, and of course it required a good deal of thinking over before you changed the course of your life; but if freedom were thrust upon them, ah, then, how simple everything would be !

It was not as though any one would suffer very much. She knew exactly what his relations were with his wife. She was a cold woman and there had been no love between them for years. It was habit that held them together, convenience, and of course the children. It was easier for Charlie than for her : Walter loved her; but after all, he was absorbed in his work; and a man always had his club; he might be upset at first, but he would get over it; there was no reason why he should not marry somebody else. Charlie had told her that he could not make out how she came to throw herself away on Walter Fane.

She wondered, half smiling, why a little while before she had been terrified at the thought that Walter had caught them. Of course it was startling to see the handle of the door slowly turn. But after all they knew the worst that Walter could do, and they were ready for it. Charlie would feel as great a relief as she that what they both desired more than anything in the world should be thus forced upon them.

Walter was a gentleman, she would do him the justice to acknowledge that, and he loved her; he would do the right thing and allow her to divorce him. They had made a mistake and the lucky thing was that they had found it out before it was too late. She made up her mind exactly what she was going to say to him and how she would treat him. She would be kind, smiling, and firm. There was no need for them to quarrel. Later on she would always be glad to see him. She hoped honestly that the two years they had spent together would remain with him as a priceless memory.

"I don't suppose Dorothy Townsend will mind divorcing

Charlie a bit," she thought. "Now the youngest boy is going back to England it will be much nicer for her to be in England too. There's absolutely nothing for her to do in Hong-Kong. She'll be able to spend all the holidays with her boys. And then she's got her father and mother in England."

It was all very simple and everything could be managed without scandal or ill-feeling. And then she and Charlie could marry. Kitty drew a long sigh. They would be very happy. It was worth going through a certain amount of bother to achieve that. Confusedly, one picture jostling another, she thought of the life they would lead together, of the fun they would have and the little journeys they would take together, the house they would live in, the positions he would rise to and the help she would be to him. He would be very proud of her and she, she adored him.

But through all these day-dreams ran a current of apprehension. It was funny: it was as though the wood and the strings of an orchestra played Arcadian melodies and in the bass the drums, softly but with foreboding, beat a grim tatoo. Sooner or later Walter must come home and her heart beat fast at the thought of meeting him. It was strange that he had gone away that afternoon without saying a word to her. Of course she was not frightened of him; after all what could he do, she repeated to herself; but she could not quite allay her uneasiness. Once more she repeated what she would say to him. What was the good of making a scene? She was very sorry, Heaven knew she didn't want to cause him pain, but she couldn't help it if she didn't love him. It was no good pretending and it was always better to tell the truth. She hoped he wouldn't be unhappy, but they had made a mistake and the only sensible thing was to acknowledge it. She would always think kindly of him.

But even as she said this to herself a sudden gust of fear made the sweat start out in the palms of her hands. And because she was frightened she grew angry with him. If he wanted to make a scene, that was his lookout; he must not be surprised if he got more than he bargained for. She would tell him that she had never cared two pins for him and that not a day had passed since their marriage without her regretting it. He was dull. Oh, how he'd bored her, bored her, bored her! He thought himself so much better than any one else, it was laughable; he had no sense of humour; she hated his supercilious air, his coldness, and his self-control. It was easy to be self-controlled when you were interested in nothing and nobody but yourself. He was repulsive to her. She hated to let him kiss her. What had he to be so conceited about? He danced rottenly, he was a wet blanket at a party, he couldn't play or sing, he couldn't play polo and his tennis was no better than anybody else's. Bridge? Who cared about bridge?

Kitty worked herself up into a towering passion. Let him dare to reproach her. All that had happened was his own fault. She was thankful that he knew the truth at last. She hated him and wished never to see him again. Yes, she was thankful that it was all over. Why couldn't he leave her alone? He had pestered her into marrying him and now she was fed up.

"Fed up," she repeated aloud, trembling with anger. "Fed up! Fed up!"

She heard the car draw up to the gate of their garden. He was coming up the stairs.

xviii

HE CAME into the room. Her heart was beating wildly and her hands were shaking; it was lucky that she lay on the sofa. She was holding an open book as though she had been reading. He stood for an instant on the threshold and their eyes met. Her heart sank; she felt on a sudden a cold chill pass through her limbs and she shivered. She had that feeling which you describe by saying that some one was walking over your grave. His face was deathly pale; she had seen it like that once before, when they sat together in the Park and he asked her to marry him. His dark eyes, immobile and inscrutable, seemed preternaturally large. He knew everything.

"You're back early," she remarked.

Her lips trembled so that she could hardly frame the words. She was terrified. She was afraid she would faint.

"I think it's about the usual time."

His voice sounded strange to her. It was raised on the last word in order to give his remark a casual air, but it was forced. She wondered if he saw that she was shaking in every limb. It was only by an effort that she did not scream. He dropped his eyes.

"I'm just going to dress."

He left the room. She was shattered. For two or three minutes she could not stir, but at last, raising herself from the sofa with difficulty, as though she had had an illness and were still weak, she found her feet. She did not know if her legs would support her. She felt her way by means of chairs and tables to the verandah and then with one hand on the wall went to her room. She put on a tea-gown and when she went back into her boudoir (they only used the drawing-room when there was a party) he was standing at a table looking at the pictures of the *Sketch*. She had to force herself to enter.

"Shall we go down? Dinner is ready."

"Have I kept you waiting?"

It was dreadful that she could not control the trembling of her lips.

When was he going to speak?

They sat down and for a moment there was silence between them. Then he made a remark and because it was so commonplace it had a sinister air.

"The *Empress* didn't come in to-day," he said. "I wonder if she's been delayed by a storm."

"Was she due to-day?"

"Yes."

She looked at him now and saw that his eyes were fixed on his plate. He made another observation, equally trivial, about a tennis tournament that was about to be played, and he spoke at length. His voice as a rule was agreeable, with a variety of tone, but now he spoke on one note. It was strangely unnatural. It gave Kitty the impression that he was speaking from a long way off. And all the time his eyes were directed to his plate, or the table, or to a picture on the wall. He would not meet hers. She realised that he could not bear to look at her.

"Shall we go upstairs?" he said when dinner was finished.

"If you like."

She rose and he held open the door for her. His eyes were cast down as she passed him. When they reached the sitting-room he took up the illustrated paper once more.

"Is this a new *Sketch?* I don't think I've seen it."

"I don't know. I haven't noticed."

It had been lying about for a fortnight and she knew that he had looked it through and through. He took it and sat down. She lay again on the sofa and took her book. As a rule in the evening, when they were alone, they played coon-can or patience. He was leaning back in an arm-chair, in a comfortable attitude, and his attention seemed absorbed by the illustration he was looking at. He did not turn the page. She tried to read, but she could not see the print before her eyes. The words were blurred. Her head began to ache violently.

When would he speak?

They sat in silence for an hour. She gave up the pretence of reading, and letting her novel fall on her lap, gazed into space. She was afraid to make the smallest gesture or the smallest sound. He sat quite still, in that same easy attitude, and stared with those wide, immobile eyes of his at the picture. His stillness was strangely menacing. It gave Kitty the feeling of a wild beast prepared to spring.

When suddenly he stood up she started. She clenched her hands and she felt herself grow pale. Now!

"I have some work to do," he said in that quiet, toneless voice, his eyes averted. "If you don't mind I'll go into my study. I daresay you'll have gone to bed by the time I've finished."

"I *am* rather tired to-night."

"Well, good-night."

"Good-night."

He left the room.

xix

As SOON as she could next morning she rang Townsend up at his office.

"Yes, what is it?"

"I want to see you."

"My dear, I'm awfully busy. I'm a working man."

"It's very important. Can I come down to the office?"

"Oh, no, I wouldn't do that if I were you."

"Well, come here then."

"I can't possibly get away. What about this afternoon? And don't you think it would be better if I didn't come to your house?"

"I must see you at once."

There was a pause and she was afraid that she had been cut off.

"Are you there?" she asked anxiously.

"Yes, I was thinking. Has anything happened?"

"I can't tell you over the telephone."

There was another silence before he spoke again.

"Well, look here, I can manage to see you for ten minutes at one if that'll do. You'd better go to Ku-Chou's and I'll come along as soon as I can."

"The curio shop?" she asked in dismay.

"Well, we can't meet in the lounge at the Hong-Kong Hotel very well," he answered.

She noticed a trace of irritation in his voice.

"Very well. I'll go to Ku-Chou's."

xx

SHE got out of her rickshaw in the Victoria Road and walked up the steep, narrow lane till she came to the shop. She lingered outside a moment as though her attention were attracted by the bric-a-brac which was displayed. But a boy who was standing there on the watch for customers, recog-

nising her at once, gave her a broad smile of connivance. He
said something in Chinese to some one within and the master,
a little, fat-faced man in a black gown, came out and greeted
her. She walked in quickly.

"Mr. Townsend no come yet. You go top-side, yes?"

She went to the back of the shop and walked up the rickety,
dark stairs. The Chinese followed her and unlocked the door
that led into the bedroom. It was stuffy and there was an
acrid smell of opium. She sat down on a sandalwood chest.

In a moment she heard a heavy step on the creaking stairs.
Townsend came in and shut the door behind him. His face
bore a sullen look, but as he saw her it vanished, and he
smiled in that charming way of his. He took her quickly in
his arms and kissed her lips.

"Now what's the trouble?"

"It makes me feel better just to see you," she smiled.

He sat down on the bed and lit a cigarette.

"You look rather washed out this morning."

"I don't wonder," she answered. "I don't think I closed
my eyes all night."

He gave her a look. He was smiling still, but his smile was
a little set and unnatural. She thought there was a shade of
anxiety in his eyes.

"He knows," she said.

There was an instant's pause before he answered.

"What did he say?"

"He hasn't said anything."

"What!" He looked at her sharply. "What makes you
think he knows then?"

"Everything. His look. The way he talked at dinner."

"Was he disagreeable?"

"No, on the contrary, he was scrupulously polite. For the
first time since we married he didn't kiss me good-night."

She dropped her eyes. She was not sure if Charlie understood. As a rule Walter took her in his arms and pressed his
lips to hers and would not let them go. His whole body grew
tender and passionate with his kiss.

"Why do you imagine he didn't say anything?"

"I don't know."

There was a pause. Kitty sat very still on the sandalwood box and looked with anxious attention at Townsend. His face once more was sullen and there was a frown between his brows. His mouth drooped a little at the corners. But all at once he looked up and a gleam of malicious amusement came into his eyes.

"I wonder if he *is* going to say anything."

She did not answer. She did not know what he meant.

"After all, he wouldn't be the first man who's shut his eyes in a case of this sort. What has he to gain by making a row? If he'd wanted to make a row he would have insisted on coming into your room." His eyes twinkled and his lips broke into a broad smile. "We should have looked a pair of damned fools."

"I wish you could have seen his face last night."

"I expect he was upset. It was naturally a shock. It's a damned humiliating position for any man. He always looks a fool. Walter doesn't give me the impression of a fellow who'd care to wash a lot of dirty linen in public."

"I don't think he would," she answered reflectively. "He's very sensitive, I've discovered that."

"That's all to the good as far as we're concerned. You know, it's a very good plan to put yourself in somebody else's shoes and ask yourself how you would act in his place. There's only one way in which a man can save his face when he's in that sort of position and that is to pretend he knows nothing. I bet you anything you like that that is exactly what he's going to do."

The more Townsend talked the more buoyant he became. His blue eyes sparkled and he was once more his gay and jovial self. He irradiated an encouraging confidence.

"Heaven knows, I don't want to say anything disagreeable about him, but when you come down to brass tacks a bacteriologist is no great shakes. The chances are that I shall be Colonial Secretary when Simmons goes home, and it's to Walter's interest to keep on the right side of me. He's got his bread and butter to think of, like the rest of us: do you think the Colonial Office are going to do much for a fellow who makes a scandal? Believe me, he's got everything to gain by holding his tongue and everything to lose by kicking up a row."

Kitty moved uneasily. She knew how shy Walter was and she could believe that the fear of a scene, and the dread of public attention, might have influence upon him; but she could not believe that he would be affected by the thought of a material advantage. Perhaps she didn't know him very well, but Charlie didn't know him at all.

"Has it occurred to you that he's madly in love with me?"

He did not answer, but he smiled at her with roguish eyes. She knew and loved that charming look of his.

"Well, what is it? I know you're going to say something awful."

"Well, you know, women are often under the impression that men are much more madly in love with them than they really are."

For the first time she laughed. His confidence was catching.

"What a monstrous thing to say!"

"I put it to you that you haven't been bothering much about your husband lately. Perhaps he isn't quite so much in love with you as he was."

"At all events I shall never delude myself that *you* are madly in love with me," she retorted.

"That's where you're wrong."

Ah, how good it was to hear him say that! She knew it and her belief in his passion warmed her heart. As he spoke he rose from the bed and came and sat down beside her on the sandalwood box. He put his arm round her waist.

"Don't worry your silly little head a moment longer," he said. "I promise you there's nothing to fear. I'm as certain as I am of anything that he's going to pretend he knows nothing. You know, this sort of thing is awfully difficult to prove. You say he's in love with you; perhaps he doesn't want to lose you altogether. I swear I'd accept anything rather than that if you were my wife."

She leaned towards him. Her body became limp and yielding against his arm. The love she felt for him was almost torture. His last words had struck her: perhaps Walter loved her so passionately that he was prepared to accept any humiliation if sometimes she would let him love her. She could understand that; for that was how she felt towards Charlie. A thrill of pride passed through her, and at the same time a faint sensation of contempt for a man who could love so slavishly.

She put her arm lovingly round Charlie's neck.

"You're simply wonderful. I was shaking like a leaf when I came here and you've made everything all right."

He took her face in his hand and kissed her lips.

"Darling."

"You're such a comfort to me," she sighed.

"I'm sure you need not be nervous. And you know I'll stand by you. I won't let you down."

She put away her fears, but for an instant unreasonably she regretted that her plans for the future were shattered. Now that all danger was past she almost wished that Walter were going to insist on a divorce.

"I knew I could count on you," she said.

"So I should hope."

"Oughtn't you to go and have your tiffin?"

"Oh, damn my tiffin."

He drew her more closely to him and now she was held tight in his arms. His mouth sought hers.

"Oh, Charlie, you must let me go."

"Never."

She gave a little laugh, a laugh of happy love and of triumph; his eyes were heavy with desire. He lifted her to her feet and not letting her go but holding her close to his breast he locked the door.

xxi

ALL through the afternoon she thought of what Charlie had said about Walter. They were dining out that evening and when he came back from the Club she was dressing. He knocked at her door.

"Come in."

He did not open.

"I'm going straight along to dress. How long will you be?"

"Ten minutes."

He said nothing more, but went to his own room. His voice had that constrained note which she had heard in it the night before. She felt fairly sure of herself now. She was ready before he was and when he came downstairs she was already seated in the car.

"I'm afraid I've kept you waiting," he said.

"I shall survive it," she replied, and she was able to smile as she spoke.

She made an observation or two as they drove down the hill, but he answered curtly. She shrugged her shoulders; she was growing a trifle impatient: if he wanted to sulk, let him, she didn't care. They drove in silence till they reached their destination. It was a large dinner party. There were too many people and too many courses. While Kitty chatted gaily with her neighbours she watched Walter. He was deathly pale and his face was pinched.

"Your husband is looking rather washed out. I thought he didn't mind the heat. Has he been working very hard?"

"He always works hard."

"I suppose you're going away soon?"

"Oh, yes, I think I shall go to Japan as I did last year," she said. "The doctor says I must get out of the heat if I don't want to go all to pieces."

Walter did not as usual when they were dining out give her a little smiling glance now and then. He never looked at her. She had noticed that when he came down to the car he kept his eyes averted, and he did the same when, with his usual politeness, he gave her his hand to alight. Now, talking with the women on either side of him, he did not smile, but looked at them with steady and unblinking eyes; and really his eyes looked enormous and in that pale face coal black. His face was set and stern.

"He must be an agreeable companion," thought Kitty ironically.

The idea of those unfortunate ladies trying to indulge in small talk with that grim mask not a little diverted her.

Of course he knew; there was no doubt about that, and he was furious with her. Why hadn't he said anything? Was it really because, though angry and hurt, he loved her so much that he was afraid she would leave him. The thought made her ever so slightly despise him, but good-naturedly: after all, he was her husband and he provided her with board and lodging; so long as he didn't interfere with her and let her do as she liked she would be quite nice to him. On the other hand perhaps his silence was due merely to a morbid timidity. Charlie was right when he said that no one would hate a scandal more than Walter. He never made a speech if he could help it. He had told her once that when he was sub-pœnaed as a witness on a case where he was to give expert evidence he had hardly slept for a week before. His shyness was a disease.

And there was another thing: men were very vain, and so long as no one knew what had happened it might be that Walter would be content to ignore it. Then she wondered whether by any possibility Charlie was right when he suggested that Walter knew which side his bread was buttered. Charlie was the most popular man in the Colony and soon would be Colonial Secretary. He could be very useful to Walter: on the other hand he could make himself very unpleasant if Walter put his back up. Her heart exulted as she thought of her lover's strength and determination; she felt so defenceless in his virile arms. Men were strange: it would never have occurred to her that Walter was capable of such baseness, and yet you never knew; perhaps his seriousness was merely a mask for a mean and pettifogging nature. The more she considered it the more likely it seemed that Charlie was right; and she turned her glance once more on her husband. There was no indulgence in it.

It happened that just then the women on either side of him were talking with their neighbours and he was left alone. He was staring straight in front of him, forgetful of the party, and his eyes were filled with a mortal sadness. It gave Kitty a shock.

xxii

NEXT day when she was lying down after luncheon, dozing, she was aroused by a knock at her door.

"Who is it?" she cried irritably.

At that hour she was unaccustomed to be disturbed.

"I."

She recognized her husband's voice and she sat up quickly. "Come in."

"Did I wake you?" he asked as he entered.

"In point of fact you did," she answered in the natural tone she had adopted with him for the last two days.

"Will you come into the next room. I want to have a little talk with you."

Her heart gave a sudden beat against her ribs.

"I'll put on a dressing-gown."

He left her. She slipped her bare feet into mules and wrapped herself in a kimono. She looked in the glass; she was very pale and she put on some rouge. She stood at the door for a moment, nerving herself for the interview, and then with a bold face joined him.

"How did you manage to get away from the Laboratory at this hour?" she said. "I don't often see you at this sort of time."

"Won't you sit down?"

He did not look at her. He spoke gravely. She was glad to do as he asked: her knees were a little shaky, and unable to continue in that jocular tone she kept silent. He sat also and lit a cigarette. His eyes wandered restlessly about the room. He seemed to have some difficulty in starting.

Suddenly he looked full at her; and because he had held his eyes so long averted, his direct gaze gave her such a fright that she smothered a cry.

"Have you ever heard of Mei-tan-fu?" he asked. "There's been a good deal about it in the papers lately."

She stared at him in astonishment. She hesitated.

"Is that the place where there's cholera? Mr. Arbuthnot was talking about it last night."

"There's an epidemic. I believe it's the worst they've had for years. There was a medical missionary there. He died of cholera three days ago. There's a French convent there and of course there's the Customs man. Every one else has got out."

His eyes were still fixed on her and she could not lower hers. She tried to read his expression, but she was nervous, and she could only discern a strange watchfulness. How could he look so steadily? He did not even blink.

"The French nuns are doing what they can. They've turned the orphanage into a hospital. But the people are dying like flies. I've offered to go and take charge."

"You?"

She started violently. Her first thought was that if he went she would be free and without let or hindrance could see Charlie. But the thought shocked her. She felt herself go scarlet. Why did he watch her like that? She looked away in embarrassment.

"Is that necessary?" she faltered.

"There's not a foreign doctor in the place."

"But you're not a doctor, you're a bacteriologist."

"I am an M.D., you know, and before I specialised I did a good deal of general work in a hospital. The fact that I'm first and foremost a bacteriologist is all to the good. It will be an admirable chance for research work."

He spoke almost flippantly and when she glanced at him she was surprised to see in his eyes a gleam of mockery. She could not understand.

"But won't it be awfully dangerous?"

"Awfully."

He smiled. It was a derisive grimace. She leaned her forehead on her hand. Suicide. It was nothing short of that. Dreadful! She had not thought he would take it like that. She couldn't let him do that. It was cruel. It was not her fault if she did not love him. She couldn't bear the thought that he should kill himself for her sake. Tears flowed softly down her cheeks.

"What are you crying for?"

His voice was cold.

"You're not obliged to go, are you?"

"No, I go of my own free will."

"Please don't, Walter. It would be too awful if something happened. Supposing you died?"

Though his face remained impassive the shadow of a smile once more crossed his eyes. He did not answer.

"Where is this place?" she asked after a pause.

"Mei-tan-fu? It's on a tributary of the Western River. We should go up the Western River and then by chair."

"Who is we?"

"You and I."

She looked at him quickly. She thought she had heard amiss. But now the smile in his eyes had travelled to his lips. His dark eyes were fixed on her.

"Are you expecting me to come too?"

"I thought you'd like to."

Her breath began to come very fast. A shudder passed through her.

"But surely it's no place for a woman. The missionary sent his wife and children down weeks ago and the A. P. C. man and his wife came down. I met her at a tea-party. I've just remembered that she said they left some place on account of cholera."

"There are five French nuns there."

Panic seized her.

"I don't know what you mean. It would be madness for me to go. You know how delicate I am. Dr. Hayward said I must get out of Hong-Kong on account of the heat. I could never stand the heat up there. And cholera: I should be frightened out of my wits. It's just asking for trouble. There's no reason for me to go. I should die."

He did not answer. She looked at him in her desperation and she could hardly restrain a cry. His face had a sort of black pallor which suddenly terrified her. She saw in it a look of hatred. Was it possible that he wanted her to die? She answered her own outrageous thought.

"It's absurd. If you think you ought to go it's your own

lookout. But really you can't expect me to. I hate illness. A cholera epidemic. I don't pretend to be very brave and I don't mind telling you that I haven't pluck for that. I shall stay here until it's time for me to go to Japan."

"I should have thought that you would want to accompany me when I am about to set out on a dangerous expedition."

He was openly mocking her now. She was confused. She did not quite know whether he meant what he said or was merely trying to frighten her.

"I don't think any one could reasonably blame me for refusing to go to a dangerous place where I had no business or where I could be of no use."

"You could be of the greatest use; you could cheer and comfort me."

She grew even a little paler.

"I don't understand what you're talking about."

"I shouldn't have thought it needed more than average intelligence."

"I'm not going, Walter. It's monstrous to ask me."

"Then I shall not go either. I shall immediately file my petition."

xxiii

SHE looked at him blankly. What he said was so unexpected that at the first moment she could hardly gather its sense.

"What on earth are you talking about?" she faltered.

Even to herself her reply rang false, and she saw the look of disdain which it called forth on Walter's stern face.

"I'm afraid you've thought me a bigger fool than I am."

She did not quite know what to say. She was undecided whether indignantly to assert her innocence or to break out into angry reproaches. He seemed to read her thoughts.

"I've got all the proof necessary."

She began to cry. The tears flowed from her eyes without any particular anguish and she did not dry them: to weep gave her a little time to collect herself. But her mind was blank. He watched her without concern, and his calmness frightened her. He grew impatient.

"You're not going to do much good by crying, you know."

His voice, so cold and hard, had the effect of exciting in her a certain indignation. She was recovering her nerve.

"I don't care. I suppose you have no objection to my divorcing you. It means nothing to a man."

"Will you allow me to ask why I should put myself to the smallest inconvenience on your account?"

"It can't make any difference to you. It's not much to ask you to behave like a gentleman."

"I have much too great a regard for your welfare."

She sat up now and dried her eyes.

"What *do* you mean?" she asked him.

"Townsend will marry you only if he is co-respondent and the case is so shameless that his wife is forced to divorce him."

"You don't know what you're talking about," she cried.

"You stupid fool."

His tone was so contemptuous that she flushed with anger. And perhaps her anger was greater because she had never before heard him say to her any but sweet, flattering and delightful things. She had been accustomed to find him subservient to all her whims.

"If you want the truth you can have it. He's only too anxious to marry me. Dorothy Townsend is perfectly willing to divorce him and we shall be married the moment we're free."

"Did he tell you that in so many words or is that the impression you have gained from his manner?"

Walter's eyes shone with bitter mockery. They made Kitty a trifle uneasy. She was not quite sure that Charlie had ever said exactly that in so many words.

"He's said it over and over again."

"That's a lie and you know it's a lie."

"He loves me with all his heart and soul. He loves me as passionately as I love him. You've found out. I'm not going to deny anything. Why should I? We've been lovers for a year and I'm proud of it. He means everything in the world to me and I'm glad that you know at last. We're sick to death of secrecy and compromise and all the rest of it. It was a mistake that I ever married you, I never should have done it, I was a fool. I never cared for you. We never had anything in common. I don't like the people you like and I'm bored by the things that interest you. I'm thankful it's finished."

He watched her without a gesture and without a movement of his face. He listened attentively and no change in his expression showed that what she said affected him.

"Do you know why I married you?"

"Because you wanted to be married before your sister Doris."

It was true, but it gave her a funny little turn to realise that he knew it. Oddly enough, even in that moment of fear and anger, it excited her compassion. He faintly smiled.

"I had no illusions about you," he said. "I knew you were silly and frivolous and empty-headed. But I loved you. I knew that your aims and ideals were vulgar and commonplace. But I loved you. I knew that you were second-rate. But I loved you. It's comic when I think how hard I tried to be amused by the things that amused you and how anxious I was to hide from you that I wasn't ignorant and vulgar and scandal-mongering and stupid. I knew how frightened you were of intelligence and I did everything I could to make you think me as big a fool as the rest of the men you knew. I knew that you'd only married me for convenience. I loved you so much, I didn't care. Most people, as far as I can see, when they're in love with some one and the love isn't returned feel that they have a grievance. They grow angry and bitter. I wasn't like that. I never expected you to love me, I didn't see any reason that you should, I never thought myself very lovable. I was thankful to be allowed to love you and I was enraptured when now and then I thought you were pleased with me or when I noticed in your eyes a gleam of good-humoured affection. I tried not to bore you with my love; I knew I couldn't afford to do that and I was always on the lookout for the first sign that you were impatient with my affection. What most husbands expect as a right I was prepared to receive as a favor."

Kitty, accustomed to flattery all her life, had never heard

such things said to her before. Blind wrath, driving out fear, arose in her heart: it seemed to choke her, and she felt the blood-vessels in her temples swell and throb. Wounded vanity can make a woman more vindictive than a lioness robbed of her cubs. Kitty's jaw, always a little too square, protruded with an apish hideousness and her beautiful eyes were black with malice. But she kept her temper in check.

"If a man hasn't what's necessary to make a woman love him, it's his fault, not hers."

"Evidently."

His derisive tone increased her irritation. She felt that she could wound him more by maintaining her calm.

"I'm not very well-educated and I'm not very clever. I'm just a perfectly ordinary young woman. I like the things that the people like among whom I've lived all my life. I like dancing and tennis and theatres and I like the men who play games. It's quite true that I've always been bored by you and by the things you like. They mean nothing to me and I don't want them to. You dragged me round those interminable galleries in Venice: I should have enjoyed myself much more playing golf at Sandwich."

"I know."

"I'm sorry if I haven't been all that you expected me to be. Unfortunately I always found you physically repulsive. You can hardly blame me for that."

"I don't."

Kitty could more easily have coped with the situation if he had raved and stormed. She could have met violence with violence. His self-control was inhuman and she hated him now as she had never hated him before.

"I don't think you're a man at all. Why didn't you break into the room when you knew I was there with Charlie? You might at least have tried to thrash him. Were you afraid?"

But the moment she had said this she flushed, for she was ashamed. He did not answer, but in his eyes she read an icy disdain. The shadow of a smile flickered on his lips.

"It may be that, like a historical character, I am too proud to fight."

Kitty, unable to think of anything to answer, shrugged her

shoulders. For a moment longer he held her in his immobile gaze.

"I think I've said all I had to say: if you refuse to come to Mei-tan-fu I shall file my petition."

"Why won't you consent to let me divorce you?"

He took his eyes off her at last. He leaned back in his chair and lit a cigarette. He smoked it to the end without saying a word. Then, throwing away the butt, he gave a little smile. He looked at her once more.

"If Mrs. Townsend will give me her assurance that she will divorce her husband and if he will give me his written promise to marry you within a week of the two decrees being made absolute, I will do that."

There was something in the way he spoke which disconcerted her. But her self-respect obliged her to accept his offer in the grand manner.

"That is very generous of you, Walter."

To her astonishment he burst suddenly into a shout of laughter. She flushed angrily.

"What are you laughing at? I see nothing to laugh at."

"I beg your pardon. I daresay my sense of humour is peculiar."

She looked at him frowning. She would have liked to say something bitter and wounding, but no rejoinder occurred to her. He looked at his watch.

"You had better look sharp if you want to catch Townsend at his office. If you decide to come with me to Mei-tan-fu it would be necessary to start the day after to-morrow."

"Do you want me to tell him to-day?"

"They say there is no time like the present."

Her heart began to beat a little faster. It was not uneasiness that she felt, it was, she didn't quite know what it was. She wished she could have had a little longer; she would have liked to prepare Charlie. But she had the fullest confidence in him, he loved her as much as she loved him, and it was treacherous even to let the thought cross her mind that he would not welcome the necessity that was forced upon them. She turned to Walter gravely.

"I don't think you know what love is. You can have no

conception how desperately in love Charlie and I are with one another. It really is the only thing that matters and every sacrifice that our love calls for will be as easy as falling off a log."

He gave a little bow, but said nothing, and his eyes followed her as she walked with measured step from the room.

xxiv

SHE sent in a little note to Charlie on which she had written: *"Please see me. It is urgent."* A Chinese boy asked her to wait and brought the answer that Mr. Townsend would see her in five minutes. She was unaccountably nervous. When at last she was ushered into his room Charlie came forward to shake hands with her, but the moment the boy, having closed the door, left them alone he dropped the affable formality of his manner.

"I say, my dear, you really mustn't come here in working hours. I've got an awful lot to do and we don't want to give people a chance to gossip."

She gave him a long look with those beautiful eyes of hers and tried to smile, but her lips were stiff and she could not.

"I wouldn't have come unless it was necessary."

He smiled and took her arm.

"Well, since you're here come and sit down."

It was a long bare room, narrow, with a high ceiling; its walls were painted in two shades of terra cotta. The only furniture consisted of a large desk, a revolving chair for Townsend to sit in and a leather arm-chair for visitors. It intimidated Kitty to sit in this. He sat at the desk. She had never seen him in spectacles before; she did not know that he used them. When he noticed that her eyes were on them he took them off.

"I only use them for reading," he said.

Her tears came easily and now, she hardly knew why, she began to cry. She had no deliberate intention of deceiving, but rather an instinctive desire to excite his sympathy. He looked at her blankly.

"Is anything the matter? Oh, my dear, don't cry."

She took out her handkerchief and tried to check her sobs. He rang the bell and when the boy came to the door went to it.

"If any one asks for me say I'm out."

"Very good, sir."

The boy closed the door. Charlie sat on the arm of the chair and put his arm round Kitty's shoulders.

"Now, Kitty dear, tell me all about it."

"Walter wants a divorce," she said.

She felt the pressure of his arm on her shoulder cease. His body stiffened. There was a moment's silence, then Townsend rose from her chair and sat down once more in his.

"What exactly do you mean?" he said.

She looked at him quickly, for his voice was hoarse, and she saw that his face was dully red.

"I've had a talk with him. I've come straight from the house now. He says he has all the proof he wants."

"You didn't commit yourself, did you? You didn't acknowledge anything?"

Her heart sank.

"No," she answered.

"Are you quite sure?" he asked, looking at her sharply.

"Quite sure," she lied again.

He leaned back in his chair and stared vacantly at the map of China which was hanging on the wall in front of him. She watched him anxiously. She was somewhat disconcerted at the manner in which he had received the news. She had expected him to take her in his arms and tell her he was thankful, for now they could be together always; but of course men were funny. She was crying softly, not now to arouse sympathy, but because it seemed the natural thing to do.

"This is a bloody mess we've got into," he said at length. "But it's no good losing our heads. Crying isn't going to do us any good, you know."

She noticed the irritation in his voice and dried her eyes.

"It's not my fault, Charlie. I couldn't help it."

"Of course you couldn't. It was just damned bad luck. I

was just as much to blame as you were. The thing to do now is to see how we're going to get out of it. I don't suppose you want to be divorced any more than I do."

She smothered a gasp. She gave him a searching look. He was not thinking of her at all.

"I wonder what his proofs really are. I don't know how he can actually prove that we were together in that room. On the whole we've been about as careful as any one could be. I'm sure that old fellow at the curio shop wouldn't have given us away. Even if he'd seen us go in there's no reason why we shouldn't hunt curios together."

He was talking to himself rather than to her.

"It's easy enough to bring charges, but it's damned difficult to prove them; any lawyer will tell you that. Our line is to deny everything, and if he threatens to bring an action we'll tell him to go to hell and we'll fight it."

"I couldn't go into court, Charlie."

"Why on earth not? I'm afraid you'll have to. God knows, I don't want a row, but we can't take it lying down."

"Why need we defend it?"

"What a question to ask! After all, it's not only you that are concerned, I'm concerned too. But as a matter of fact I don't think you need be afraid of that. We shall be able to square your husband somehow. The only thing that worries me is the best way to set about it."

It looked as though an idea occurred to him, for he turned towards her with his charming smile and his tone, a moment before abrupt and business-like, became ingratiating.

"I'm afraid you've been awfully upset, poor little woman. It's too bad." He stretched out his hand and took hers. "It's a scrape we've got into, but we shall get out of it. It's not . . ." He stopped and Kitty had a suspicion that he had been about to say that it was not the first he had got out of. "The great thing is to keep our heads. You know I shall never let you down."

"I'm not frightened. I don't care what he does."

He smiled still, but perhaps his smile was a trifle forced.

"If the worst comes to the worst I shall have to tell the Governor. He'll curse me like hell, but he's a good fellow and a man of the world. He'll fix it up somehow. It wouldn't do him any good if there was a scandal."

"What can he do?" asked Kitty.

"He can bring pressure to bear on Walter. If he can't get at him through his ambition he'll get at him through his sense of duty."

Kitty was a little chilled. She did not seem able to make Charlie see how desperately grave the situation was. His airiness made her impatient. She was sorry that she had come to see him in his office. The surroundings intimidated her. It would have been much easier to say what she wanted if she could have been in his arms with hers round his neck.

"You don't know Walter," she said.

"I know that every man has his price."

She loved Charlie with all her heart, but his reply disconcerted her; for such a clever man it was a stupid thing to say.

"I don't think you realise how angry Walter is. You haven't seen his face and the look of his eyes."

He did not reply for a moment, but looked at her with a slight smile. She knew what he was thinking. Walter was the bacteriologist and occupied a subordinate position; he would hardly have the impudence to make himself a nuisance to the upper officials of the Colony.

"It's no good deceiving yourself, Charlie," she said earnestly. "If Walter has made up his mind to bring an action nothing that you or anybody else can say will have the slightest influence."

His face once more grew heavy and sulky.

"Is it his idea to make me co-respondent?"

"At first it was. At last I managed to get him to consent to let me divorce him."

"Oh, well, that's not so terrible." His manner relaxed again and she saw the relief in his eyes. "That seems to me a very good way out. After all, it's the least a man can do, it's the only decent thing."

"But he makes a condition."

He gave her an inquiring glance and he seemed to reflect.

"Of course I'm not a very rich man, but I'll do anything in my power."

Kitty was silent. Charlie was saying things which she would never have expected him to say. And they made it difficult for her to speak. She had expected to blurt it out in one breath, held in his loving arms, with her burning face hid on his breast.

"He agrees to my divorcing him if your wife will give him the assurance that she will divorce you."

"Anything else?"

Kitty could hardly find her voice.

"And—it's awfully hard to say, Charlie, it sounds dreadful—if you'll promise to marry me within a week of the decrees being made absolute."

xxv

FOR a moment he was silent. Then he took her hand again and pressed it gently.

"You know, darling," he said, "whatever happens we must keep Dorothy out of this."

She looked at him blankly.

"But I don't understand. How can we?"

"Well, we can't only think of ourselves in this world. You know, other things being equal, there's nothing in the world I'd love more than to marry you. But it's quite out of the question. I know Dorothy: nothing would induce her to divorce me."

Kitty was becoming horribly frightened. She began to cry again. He got up and sat down beside her with his arm round her waist.

"Try not to upset yourself, darling. We *must* keep our heads."

"I thought you loved me . . ."

"Of course I love you," he said tenderly. "You surely can't have any doubt of that now."

"If she won't divorce you Walter will make you co-respondent."

He took an appreciable time to answer. His tone was dry.

"Of course that would ruin my career, but I'm afraid it

wouldn't do you much good. If the worst came to the worst I should make a clean breast of it to Dorothy; she'd be dreadfully hurt and wretched, but she'd forgive me." He had an idea. "I'm not sure if the best plan wouldn't be to make a clean breast of it anyhow. If she went to your husband I daresay she could persuade him to hold his tongue."

"Does that mean you don't want her to divorce you?"

"Well, I have got my boys to think of, haven't I? And naturally I don't want to make her unhappy. We've always got on very well together. She's been an awfully good wife to me, you know."

"Why did you tell me that she meant nothing to you?"

"I never did. I said I wasn't in love with her. We haven't slept together for years except now and then, on Christmas Day for instance, or the day before she was going home or the day she came back. She isn't a woman who cares for that sort of thing. But we've always been excellent friends. I don't mind telling you that I depend on her more than any one has any idea of."

"Don't you think it would have been better to leave me alone then?"

She found it strange that with terror catching her breath she could speak so calmly.

"You were the loveliest little thing I'd seen for years. I just fell madly in love with you. You can't blame me for that."

"After all, you said you'd never let me down."

"But, good God, I'm not going to let you down. We've got in an awful scrape and I'm going to do everything that's humanly possible to get you out of it."

"Except the one obvious and natural thing."

He stood up and returned to his own chair.

"My dear, you must be reasonable. We'd much better face the situation frankly. I don't want to hurt your feelings, but really I must tell you the truth. I'm very keen on my career. There's no reason why I shouldn't be a Governor one of these days, and it's a damned soft job to be a Colonial Governor. Unless we can hush this up I don't stand a dog's chance. I may not have to leave the service, but there'll always be a black mark against me. If I do have to leave the service then I must go into business in China where I know people. In either case my only chance is for Dorothy to stick to me."

"Was it necessary to tell me that you wanted nothing in the world but me?"

The corners of his mouth drooped peevishly.

"Oh, my dear, it's rather hard to take quite literally the things a man says when he's in love with you."

"Didn't you mean them?"

"At the moment."

"And what's to happen to me if Walter divorces me?"

"If we really haven't a leg to stand on of course we won't defend. There shouldn't be any publicity and people are pretty broad-minded nowadays."

For the first time Kitty thought of her mother. She shivered. She looked again at Townsend. Her pain now was tinged with resentment.

"I'm sure you'd have no difficulty in bearing any inconvenience that I had to suffer," she said.

"We're not going to get much further by saying disagreeable things to one another," he answered.

She gave a cry of despair. It was dreadful that she should love him so devotedly and yet feel such bitterness towards him. It was not possible that he understood how much he meant to her.

"Oh, Charlie, don't you know how I love you?"

"But, my dear, I love you. Only we're not living in a desert island and we've got to make the best we can out of the circumstances that are forced upon us. You really must be reasonable."

"How can I be reasonable? To me our love was everything and you were my whole life. It is not very pleasant to realise that to you it was only an episode."

"Of course it wasn't an episode. But you know, when you ask me to get my wife, to whom I'm very much attached, to divorce me, and ruin my career by marrying you, you're asking a good deal."

"No more than I'm willing to do for you."

"The circumstances are rather different."

"The only difference is that you don't love me."

"One can be very much in love with a woman without wishing to spend the rest of one's life with her."

She gave him a quick look and despair seized her. Heavy tears rolled down her cheeks.

"Oh, how cruel! How can you be so heartless?"

She began to sob hysterically. He gave an anxious glance at the door.

"My dear, do try and control yourself."

"You don't know how I love you," she gasped. "I can't live without you. Have you no pity for me?"

She could not speak any more. She wept without restraint.

"I don't want to be unkind and, Heaven knows, I don't want to hurt your feelings, but I must tell you the truth."

"It's the ruin of my whole life. Why couldn't you leave me alone? What harm had I ever done you?"

"Of course if it does you any good to put all the blame on me you may."

Kitty blazed with sudden anger.

"I suppose I threw myself at your head. I suppose I gave you no peace till you yielded to my entreaties."

"I don't say that. But I certainly should never have thought of making love to you if you hadn't made it perfectly clear that you were ready to be made love to."

Oh, the shame of it! She knew that what he said was true. His face now was sullen and worried and his hands moved uneasily. Every now and then he gave her a little glance of exasperation.

"Won't your husband forgive you?" he said after a while.

"I never asked him."

Instinctively he clenched his hands. She saw him suppress the exclamation of annoyance which came to his lips.

"Why don't you go to him and throw yourself on his mercy? If he's as much in love with you as you say he's bound to forgive you."

"How little you know him!"

xxvi

SHE wiped her eyes. She tried to pull herself together.

"Charlie, if you desert me I shall die."

She was driven now to appeal to his compassion. She ought to have told him at once. When he knew the horrible alternative that was placed before her his generosity, his sense of justice, his manliness, would be so vehemently aroused that he would think of nothing but her danger. Oh, how passionately she desired to feel his dear, protecting arms around her!

"Walter wants me to go to Mei-tan-fu."

"Oh, but that's the place where the cholera is. They've got the worst epidemic that they've had for fifty years. It's no place for a woman. You can't possibly go there."

"If you let me down I shall have to."

"What do you mean? I don't understand."

"Walter is taking the place of the missionary doctor who died. He wants me to go with him."

"When?"

"Now. At once."

Townsend pushed back his chair and looked at her with puzzled eyes.

"I may be very stupid, but I can't make head or tail out of what you're saying. If he wants you to go to this place with him what about a divorce?"

"He's given me my choice. I must either go to Mei-tan-fu or else he'll bring an action."

"Oh, I see." Townsend's tone changed ever so slightly. "I think that's rather decent of him, don't you?"

"Decent?"

"Well, it's a damned sporting thing of him to go there. It's not a thing I'd fancy. Of course he'll get a C.M.G. for it when he comes back."

"But me, Charlie?" she cried, with anguish in her voice.

"Well, I think if he wants you to go, under the circumstances I don't see how you can very well refuse."

"It means death. Absolutely certain death."

"Oh, damn it all, that's rather an exaggeration. He would hardly take you if he thought that. It's no more risk for you than for him. In point of fact there's no great risk if you're careful. I've been here when there's been cholera and I haven't turned a hair. The great thing is not to eat anything uncooked, no raw fruit or salads, or anything like that, and see that your drinking water is boiled." He was gaining confidence as he proceeded, and his speech was fluent; he was even becoming less sullen and more alert; he was almost breezy. "After all, it's his job, isn't it? He's interested in bugs. It's rather a chance for him if you come to think of it."

"But me, Charlie?" she repeated, not with anguish now, but with consternation.

"Well, the best way to understand a man is to put yourself in his shoes. From his point of view you've been rather a naughty little thing and he wants to get you out of harm's way. I always thought he never wanted to divorce you, he doesn't strike me as that sort of chap; but he made what he thought was a very generous offer and you put his back up by turning it down. I don't want to blame you, but really for all our sakes I think you ought to have given it a little consideration."

"But don't you see it'll kill me? Don't you know that he's taking me there because he *knows* it'll kill me."

"Oh, my dear, don't talk like that. We're in a damned awkward position and really it's no time to be melodramatic."

"You've made up your mind not to understand." Oh, the pain in her heart, and the fear! She could have screamed. "You can't send me to certain death. If you have no love or pity for me you must have just ordinary human feeling."

"I think it's rather hard on me to put it like that. As far as I can make out your husband is behaving very generously. He's willing to forgive you if you'll let him. He wants to get you away and this opportunity has presented itself to take you to some place where for a few months you'll be out of harm's way. I don't pretend that Mei-tan-fu is a health resort, I never knew a Chinese city that was, but there's no reason to get the wind up about it. In fact that's the worst thing you can do. I believe as many people die from sheer fright in an epidemic as because they get infected."

"But I'm frightened now. When Walter spoke of it I almost fainted."

"At the first moment I can quite believe it was a shock, but when you come to look at it calmly you'll be all right. It'll be the sort of experience that not every one has had."

"I thought, I thought . . ."

She rocked to and fro in an agony. He did not speak, and once more his face wore that sullen look which till lately she had never known. Kitty was not crying now. She was dry-eyed, calm, and though her voice was low it was steady.

"Do you want me to go?"

"It's Hobson's choice, isn't it?"

"Is it?"

"It's only fair to you to tell you that if your husband brought an action for divorce and won it I should not be in a position to marry you."

It must have seemed an age to him before she answered. She rose slowly to her feet.

"I don't think that my husband ever thought of bringing an action."

"Then why in God's name have you been frightening me out of my wits?" he asked.

She looked at him coolly.

"He knew that you'd let me down."

She was silent. Vaguely, as when you are studying a foreign language and read a page which at first you can make nothing of, till a word or a sentence gives you a clue; and on a sudden a suspicion, as it were, of the sense flashes across your troubled wits, vaguely she gained an inkling into the workings of Walter's mind. It was like a dark and ominous landscape seen by a flash of lightning and in a moment hidden again by the night. She shuddered at what she saw.

"He made that threat only because he knew that you'd crumple up at it, Charlie. It's strange that he should have judged you so accurately. It was just like him to expose me to such a cruel disillusion."

Charlie looked down at the sheet of blotting paper in front of him. He was frowning a little and his mouth was sulky. But he did not reply.

"He knew that you were vain, cowardly and self-seeking. He wanted me to see it with my own eyes. He knew that you'd run like a hare at the approach of danger. He knew how grossly deceived I was in thinking that you were in love with me, because he knew that you were incapable of loving any one but yourself. He knew you'd sacrifice me without a pang to save your own skin."

"If it really gives you any satisfaction to say beastly things to me I suppose I've got no right to complain. Women always are unfair and they generally manage to put a man in the wrong. But there is something to be said on the other side."

She took no notice of his interruption.

"And now I know all that he knew. I know that you're callous and heartless, I know that you're selfish, selfish beyond words, and I know that you haven't the nerve of a rabbit, I know you're a liar and a humbug, I know that you're utterly contemptible. And the tragic part is"—her face was on a sudden distraught with pain—"the tragic part is that notwithstanding I love you with all my heart."

"Kitty."

She gave a bitter laugh. He had spoken her name in that melting, rich tone of his which came to him so naturally and meant so little.

"You fool," she said.

He drew back quickly, flushing and offended; he could not make her out. She gave him a look in which there was a glint of amusement.

"You're beginning to dislike me, aren't you? Well, dislike me. It doesn't make any difference to me now."

She began to put on her gloves.

"What are you going to do?" he asked.

"Oh, don't be afraid, you'll come to no harm. You'll be quite safe."

"For God's sake, don't talk like that, Kitty," he answered and his deep voice rang with anxiety. "You must know that

everything that concerns you concerns me. I shall be frightfully anxious to know what happens. What are you going to
say to your husband?"

"I'm going to tell him that I'm prepared to go to Mei-
tan-fu with him."

"Perhaps when you consent he won't insist."

He could not have known why, when he said this, she
looked at him so strangely.

"You're not really frightened?" he asked her.

"No," she said. "You've inspired me with courage. To go
into the midst of a cholera epidemic will be a unique experience and if I die it—well, I die."

"I was trying to be as kind to you as I could."

She looked at him again. Tears sprang into her eyes once
more and her heart was very full. The impulse was almost
irresistible to fling herself on his breast and crush her lips
against his. It was no use.

"If you want to know," she said, trying to keep her voice
steady, "I go with death in my heart and fear. I do not know
what Walter has in that dark, twisted mind of his, but I'm
shaking with terror. I think it may be that death will be
really a release."

She felt that she could not hold on to her self-control for
another moment. She walked swiftly to the door and let herself out before he had time to move from his chair. Townsend gave a long sigh of relief. He badly wanted a brandy
and soda.

xxvii

WALTER was in when she got home. She would have liked
to go straight to her room, but he was downstairs, in the
hall, giving instructions to one of the boys. She was so
wretched that she welcomed the humiliation to which she
must expose herself. She stopped and faced him.

"I'm coming with you to that place," she said.

"Oh, good."

"When do you want me to be ready?"

"To-morrow night."

She did not know what spirit of bravado entered into her. His indifference was like the prick of a spear. She said a thing that surprised herself.

"I suppose I needn't take more than a few summer things and a shroud, need I?"

She was watching his face and knew that her flippancy angered him.

"I've already told your amah what you'll want."

She nodded and went up to her room. She was very pale.

xxviii

THEY were reaching their destination at last.

They were borne in chairs, day after day, along a narrow causeway between interminable ricefields. They set out at dawn and travelled till the heat of the day forced them to take shelter in a wayside inn and then went on again till they reached the town where they had arranged to spend the night. Kitty's chair headed the procession and Walter followed her; then in a straggling line came the coolies that bore their bedding, stores and equipment. Kitty passed through the country with unseeing eyes. All through the long hours, the silence broken only by an occasional remark from one of the bearers or a snatch of uncouth song, she turned over in her tortured mind the details of that heart-rending scene in Charlie's office. Recalling what he had said to her and what she had said to him, she was dismayed to see what an arid and business-like turn their conversation had taken. She had not said what she wanted to say and she had not spoken in the tone she intended. Had she been able to make him see her boundless love, the passion in her heart, and her helplessness, he could never have been so inhuman as to leave her to her fate. She had been taken unawares. She could hardly believe her ears when he told her, more clearly than with words, that he cared nothing for her. That was why she had not even cried very much, she had been so dazed. She had wept since, wept miserably.

At night in the inns, sharing the principal guest chamber with her husband and conscious that Walter, lying on his camp bed, a few feet away from her, lay awake, she dug her teeth in the pillow so that no sound might escape her. But in the daytime, protected by the curtains of her chair, she allowed herself to give way. Her pain was so great that she could have screamed at the top of her voice; she had never known that one could suffer so much; and she asked herself desperately what she had done to deserve it. She could not make out why Charlie did not love her: it was her fault, she supposed, but she had done everything she knew to make him fond of her. They had always got on so well, they laughed all the time they were together, they were not only lovers but good friends. She could not understand; she was broken. She told herself that she hated and despised him; but she had no idea how she was going to live if she was never to see him again. If Walter was taking her to Mei-tan-fu as a punishment he was making a fool of himself, for what did she care now what became of her? She had nothing to live for any more. It was rather hard to be finished with life at twenty-seven.

xxix

ON THE steamer that took them up the Western River Walter read incessantly, but at mealtimes he endeavoured to make some kind of conversation. He talked to her as though she were a stranger with whom he happened to be making the journey, of indifferent things, from politeness, Kitty imagined, or because so he could render more marked the gulf that separated them.

In a flash of insight she had told Charlie that Walter had sent her to him with the threat of divorce as the alternative to her accompanying him to the stricken city in order that she might see for herself how indifferent, cowardly and selfish he was. It was true. It was a trick which accorded very well with his sardonic humour. He knew exactly what would happen and he had given her amah necessary instructions before her return. She had caught in his eyes a disdain which seemed to include her lover as well as herself. He said to himself, perhaps, that if he had been in Townsend's place nothing in the world would have hindered him from making any sacrifice to gratify her smallest whim. She knew that was true also. But then, when her eyes were opened, how could he make her do something which was so dangerous, and which he must know frightened her so terribly? At first she thought he was only playing with her and till they actually started, no, later, till they left the river and took to the chairs for the journey across country, she thought he would give that little laugh of his and tell her that she need not come. She had no inkling what was in his mind. He could not really desire her death. He had loved her so desperately. She knew what love was now and she remembered a thousand signs of his adoration. For him really, in the French phrase, she did make fine weather and foul. It was impossible that he did not love her still. Did you cease to love a person because you had been treated cruelly? She had not made him suffer as Charlie had made her suffer and yet, if Charlie made a sign, notwithstanding everything, even though she knew him now, she would abandon all the world had to offer and fly to his arms. Even though he had sacrificed her and cared nothing for her, even though he was callous and unkind, she loved him.

At first she thought that she had only to bide her time, and sooner or later Walter would forgive her. She had been too confident of her power over him to believe that it was gone for ever. Many waters could not quench love. He was weak if he loved her, and she felt that love her he must. But now she was not quite sure. When in the evening he sat reading in the straight-backed blackwood chair of the inn with the light of a hurricane lamp on his face she was able to watch him at her ease. She lay on the pallet on which her bed presently would be set and she was in shadow. Those straight, regular features of his made his face look very severe. You could hardly believe that it was possible for them on occasion to be changed by so sweet a smile. He was able to read as calmly as though she were a thousand

miles away; she saw him turn the pages and she saw his
eyes move regularly as they travelled from line to line. He
was not thinking of her. And when, the table being set and
dinner brought in, he put aside his book and gave her a
glance (not knowing how the light on his face threw into
distinctness his expression), she was startled to see in his
eyes a look of physical distaste. Yes, it startled her. Was it
possible that his love had left him entirely? Was it possible
that he really designed her death? It was absurd. That
would be the act of a madman. It was odd, the little shiver
that ran through her as the thought occurred to her that
perhaps Walter was not quite sane.

xxx

SUDDENLY her bearers, long silent, began to speak and one
of them, turning round, with words she could not understand
and with a gesture, sought to attract her attention. She
looked in the direction he pointed and there, on the top of
a hill, saw an archway; she knew by now that it was a memorial in compliment of a fortunate scholar or a virtuous
widow, she had passed many of them since they left the river;
but this one, silhouetted against the westering sun, was more
fantastic and beautiful than any she had seen. Yet, she knew
not why, it made her uneasy; it had a significance which she
felt but could not put into words: Was it a menace that she
vaguely discerned or was it derision? She was passing a
grove of bamboos and they leaned over the causeway
strangely as if they would detain her; though the summer
evening was windless their narrow green leaves shivered a
little. It gave her the sensation that some one hidden among
them was watching her as she passed. Now they came to the
foot of the hill and the rice-fields ceased. The bearers took
it with a swinging stride. The hill was covered close with
little green mounds, close, close to one another, so that the
ground was ribbed like the sea-sand when the tide has gone
out; and this she knew too, for she had passed just such a
spot as they approached each populous city and left it. It

was the graveyard. Now she knew why the bearers had called her attention to the archway that stood on the crest of the hill: they had reached the end of their journey.

They passed through the archway and the chairbearers paused to change the pole from shoulder to shoulder. One of them wiped his sweating face with a dirty rag. The causeway wound down. There were bedraggled houses on each side. Now the night was falling. But the bearers on a sudden broke into excited talk and with a jump that shook her ranged themselves as near as they could to the wall. In a moment she knew what had startled them, for as they stood there, chattering to one another, four peasants passed, quick and silent, bearing a new coffin, unpainted, and its fresh wood gleamed white in the approaching darkness. Kitty felt her heart beat in terror against her ribs. The coffin passed, but the bearers stood still; it seemed as though they could not summon up the will to go on. But there was a shout from behind and they started. They did not speak now.

They walked for a few minutes longer and then turned sharply into an open gateway. The chair was set down. She had arrived.

xxxi

IT WAS a bungalow and she entered the sitting-room. She sat down while the coolies, straggling in one by one, brought in their loads. Walter in the courtyard gave directions where this or that was to be placed. She was very tired. She was startled to hear an unknown voice.

"May I come in?"

She flushed and grew pale. She was overwrought and it made her nervous to meet a stranger. A man came out of the darkness, for the long low room was lit only by a shaded lamp, and held out his hand.

"My name is Waddington. I am the Deputy Commissioner."

"Oh, the Customs. I know. I heard that you were here."

In that dim light she could see only that he was a little thin man, no taller than she, with a bald head and a small, bare face.

"I live just at the bottom of the hill, but coming in this way you wouldn't have seen my house. I thought you'd be too fagged to come and dine with me, so I've ordered your dinner here and I've invited myself."

"I'm delighted to hear it."

"You'll find the cook's not bad. I kept on Watson's boys for you."

"Watson was the missionary who was here?"

"Yes. Very nice fellow. I'll show you his grave to-morrow if you like."

"How kind you are," said Kitty, with a smile.

At that moment Walter came in. Waddington had introduced himself to him before coming in to see Kitty and now he said:

"I've just been breaking it to your missus that I'm dining with you. Since Watson died I haven't had anybody much to talk to but the nuns, and I can never do myself justice in French. Besides, there is only a limited number of subjects you can talk to them about."

"I've just told the boy to bring in some drinks," said Walter.

The servant brought whisky and soda and Kitty noticed that Waddington helped himself generously. His manner of speaking and his easy chuckle had suggested to her when he came in that he was not quite sober.

"Here's luck," he said. Then, turning to Walter: "You've got your work cut out for you here. They're dying like flies. The magistrate's lost his head and Colonel Yü, the officer commanding the troops, is having a devil of a job to prevent them from looting. If something doesn't happen soon we shall all be murdered in our beds. I tried to get the nuns to go, but of course they wouldn't. They all want to be martyrs, damn them."

He spoke lightly and there was in his voice a sort of ghostly laughter so that you could not listen to him without smiling.

"Why haven't you gone?" asked Walter.

"Well, I've lost half my staff and the others are ready to lie down and die at any minute. Somebody's got to stay and keep things together."

"Have you been inoculated?"

"Yes. Watson did me. But he did himself too, and it didn't do him much good, poor blighter." He turned to Kitty and his funny little face was gaily puckered. "I don't think there's any great risk if you take proper precautions. Have your milk and water boiled and don't eat fresh fruit or uncooked vegetables. Have you brought any gramophone records with you?"

"No, I don't think so," said Kitty.

"I'm sorry for that. I was hoping you would. I haven't had any for a long time and I'm sick of my old ones."

The boy came in to ask if they would have dinner.

"You won't dress to-night, will you?" asked Waddington. "My boy died last week and the boy I have now is a fool, so I haven't been dressing in the evening."

"I'll go and take off my hat," said Kitty.

Her room was next door to that in which they sat. It was barely furnished. An amah was kneeling on the floor, the lamp beside her, unpacking Kitty's things.

xxxii

THE dining-room was small and the greater part of it was filled by an immense table. On the walls were engravings of scenes from the Bible and illuminated texts.

"Missionaries always have large dining-tables," Waddington explained. "They get so much a year more for every child they have and they buy their tables when they marry so that there shall be plenty of room for little strangers."

From the ceiling hung a large paraffin lamp, so that Kitty was able to see better what sort of a man Waddington was. His baldness had deceived her into thinking him no longer young, but she saw now that he must be well under forty. His face, small under a high, rounded forehead, was unlined and fresh-coloured; it was ugly like a monkey's, but with an ugliness that was not without charm; it was an amusing face. His features, his nose and his mouth, were hardly larger than a child's, and he had small, very bright blue eyes. His eyebrows were fair and scanty. He looked like a funny little old boy. He helped himself constantly to liquor and as dinner proceeded it became evident that he was far from sober. But if he was drunk it was without offensiveness, gaily, as a satyr might be who had stolen a wine-skin from a sleeping shepherd.

He talked of Hong-Kong; he had many friends there and he wanted to know about them. He had been down for the races a year before and he talked of ponies and their owners.

"By the way, what about Townsend?" he asked suddenly. "Is he going to become Colonial Secretary?"

Kitty felt herself flush, but her husband did not look at her.

"I shouldn't wonder," he answered.

"He's the sort that gets on."

"Do you know him?" asked Walter.

"Yes, I know him pretty well. We travelled out from home together once."

From the other side of the river they heard the beating of gongs and the clatter of fire-crackers. There, so short a way from them, the great city lay in terror; and death, sudden and ruthless, hurried through its tortuous streets. But Waddington began to speak of London. He talked of the theatres. He knew everything that was being played at the moment and he told them what pieces he had seen when he was last home on leave. He laughed as he recollected the humour of this low comedian and sighed as he reflected on the beauty of that star of musical comedy. He was pleased to be able to boast that a cousin of his had married one of the most celebrated. He had lunched with her and she had given him her photograph. He would show it to them when they came and dined with him at the Customs.

Walter looked at his guest with a cold and ironic gaze, but he was evidently not a little amused by him, and he made an effort to show a civil interest in topics of which Kitty was well aware he knew nothing. A faint smile lingered on his lips. But Kitty, she knew not why, was filled with awe. In the house of that dead missionary, over against the stricken city, they seemed immeasurably apart from all the world. Three solitary creatures and strangers to each other.

Dinner was finished and she rose from the table.

"Do you mind if I say good-night to you? I'm going to bed."

"I'll take myself off, I expect the doctor wants to go to bed too," answered Waddington. "We must be out early tomorrow."

He shook hands with Kitty. He was quite steady on his feet, but his eyes were shining more than ever.

"I'll come and fetch you," he told Walter, "and take you to see the Magistrate and Colonel Yü, and then we'll go along to the Convent. You've got your work cut out, I can tell you."

xxxiii

HER night was tortured with strange dreams. She seemed to be carried in her chair and she felt the swaying motion as the bearers marched with their long, uneven stride. She entered cities, vast and dim, where the multitude thronged about her with curious eyes. The streets were narrow and tortuous and in the open shops, with their strange wares, all traffic stopped as she went by and those who bought and those who sold, paused. Then she came to the memorial arch and its fantastic outline seemed on a sudden to gain a monstrous life; its capricious contours were like the waving arms of a Hindu god, and, as she passed under it, she heard the echo of mocking laughter. But then Charlie Townsend came towards her and took her in his arms, lifting her out of the chair, and said it was all a mistake, he had never meant to treat her as he had, for he loved her and he couldn't live without her. She felt his kisses on her mouth and she wept with joy, asking him why he had been so cruel, but though she asked she knew it did not matter. And then there was a hoarse, abrupt cry and they were separated, and between, hurrying silently, coolies passed in their ragged blue and they bore a coffin.

She awoke with a start.

The bungalow stood half way down a steep hill and from her window she saw the narrow river below her and opposite, the city. The dawn had just broken and from the river rose a white mist shrouding the junks that lay moored close to one another like peas in a pod. There were hundreds of them, and they were silent, mysterious in that ghostly light, and you had a feeling that their crews lay under an enchantment, for it seemed that it was not sleep, but something strange and terrible, that held them so still and mute.

The morning drew on and the sun touched the mist so that it shone whitely like the ghost of snow on a dying star. Though on the river it was light so that you could discern palely the lines of the crowded junks and the thick forest of their masts, in front it was a shining wall the eye could not pierce. But suddenly from that white cloud a tall, grim and massive bastion emerged. It seemed not merely to be made visible by the all-discovering sun but rather to rise out of nothing at the touch of a magic wand. It towered, the stronghold of a cruel and barbaric race, over the river. But the magician who built worked swiftly and now a fragment of coloured wall crowned the bastion; in a moment, out of the mist, looming vastly and touched here and there by a yellow ray of sun, there was seen a cluster of green and yellow roofs. Huge they seemed and you could make out no pattern; the order, if order there was, escaped you; wayward and extravagant, but of an unimaginable richness. This was no fortress, nor a temple, but the magic palace of some emperor of the gods where no man might enter. It was too airy, fantastic and unsubstantial to be the work of human hands; it was the fabric of a dream.

The tears ran down Kitty's face and she gazed, her hands clasped to her breast and her mouth, for she was breathless, open a little. She had never felt so light of heart and it seemed to her as though her body were a shell that lay at her feet and she pure spirit. Here was Beauty. She took it as the believer takes in his mouth the wafer which is God.

xxxiv

Since Walter went out early in the morning, came back at tiffin only for half an hour, and did not then return till dinner was just ready, Kitty found herself much alone. For some days she did not stir from the bungalow. It was very hot and for the most part she lay in a long chair by the open window, trying to read. The hard light of midday had robbed the magic palace of its mystery and now it was no more than a temple on the city wall, garish and shabby, but because she had seen it once in such an ecstasy it was never again quite commonplace; and often at dawn or at dusk, and again at night, she found herself able to recapture something of that beauty. What had seemed to her a mighty bastion was but the city wall and on this, massive and dark, her eyes rested continually. Behind its crenellations lay the city in the dread grip of the pestilence.

Vaguely she knew that terrible things were happening there, not from Walter who when she questioned him (for otherwise he rarely spoke to her) answered with a humorous nonchalance which sent a shiver down her spine; but from Waddington and from the amah. The people were dying at the rate of a hundred a day, and hardly any of those who were attacked by the disease recovered from it; the gods had been brought out from the abandoned temples and placed in the streets; offerings were laid before them and sacrifices made, but they did not stay the plague. The people died so fast that it was hardly possible to bury them. In some houses the whole family had been swept away and there was none to perform the funeral rights. The officer commanding the troops was a masterful man and if the city was not given over to riot and arson it was due to his determination. He forced his soldiers to bury such as there was no one else to bury and he had shot with his own hand an officer who demurred at entering a stricken house.

Kitty sometimes was so frightened that her heart sank within her and she would tremble in every limb. It was all

very well to say that the risk was small if you took
reasonable precautions: she was panic-stricken. She turned
over in her mind crazy plans of escape. To get away, just to
get away, she was prepared to set out as she was and make
her way alone, without anything but what she stood up in,
to some place of safety. She thought of throwing herself on
the mercy of Waddington, telling him everything and
beseeching him to help her to get back to Hong-Kong. If
she flung herself on her knees before her husband, and admitted that she was frightened, frightened, even though he
hated her now he must have enough human feeling in him to
pity her.

It was out of the question. If she went, where could she
go? Not to her mother; her mother would make her see very
plainly that, having married her off, she counted on being
rid of her; and besides she did not want to go to her mother.
She wanted to go to Charlie, and he did not want her. She
knew what he would say if she suddenly appeared before
him. She saw the sullen look of his face and the shrewd
hardness behind his charming eyes. It would be difficult for
him to find words that sounded well. She clenched her hands.
She would have given anything to humiliate him as he had
humiliated her. Sometimes she was seized with such a fenzy
that she wished she had let Walter divorce her, ruining herself if only she could have ruined him too. Certain things he
had said to her made her blush with shame when she recalled
them.

xxxv

THE first time she was alone with Waddington she brought
the conversation round to Charlie. Waddington had spoken
of him on the evening of their arrival. She pretended that
he was no more than an acquaintance of her husband.

"I never much cared for him," said Waddington. "I've
always thought him a bore."

"You must be very hard to please," returned Kitty, in
the bright, chaffing way she could assume so easily. "I

suppose he's far and away the most popular man in Hong-Kong."

"I know. That is his stock in trade. He's made a science of popularity. He has the gift of making every one he meets feel that he is the one person in the world he wants to see. He's always ready to do a service that isn't any trouble to himself, and even if he doesn't do what you want he manages to give you the impression that it's only because it's not humanly possible."

"That is surely an attractive trait."

"Charm and nothing but charm at last grows a little tiresome, I think. It's a relief then to deal with a man who isn't quite so delightful but a little more sincere. I've known Charlie Townsend for a good many years and once or twice I've caught him with the mask off—you see, I never mattered, just a subordinate official in the Customs—and I know that he doesn't in his heart give a damn for any one in the world but himself."

Kitty, lounging easily in her chair, looked at him with smiling eyes. She turned her wedding-ring round and round her finger.

"Of course he'll get on. He knows all the official ropes. Before I die I have every belief that I shall address him as Your Excellency and stand up when he enters the room."

"Most people think he deserves to get on. He's generally supposed to have a great deal of ability."

"Ability? What nonsense! He's a very stupid man. He gives you the impression that he dashes off his work and gets it through from sheer brilliancy. Nothing of the kind. He's as industrious as a Eurasian clerk."

"How has he got the reputation of being so clever?"

"There are many foolish people in the world and when a man in a rather high position puts on no frills, slaps them on the back, and tells them he'll do anything in the world for them, they are very likely to think him clever. And then of course, there's his wife. There's an able woman if you like. She has a good sound head and her advice is always worth taking. As long as Charlie Townsend's got her to depend on he's pretty safe never to do a foolish thing, and that's the first thing necessary for a man to get on in Government service. They don't want clever men; clever men have ideas, and ideas cause trouble; they want men who have charm and tact and who can be counted on never to make a blunder. Oh, yes, Charlie Townsend will get to the top of the tree all right."

"I wonder why you dislike him?"

"I don't dislike him."

"But you like his wife better?" smiled Kitty.

"I'm an old-fashioned little man and I like a well-bred woman."

"I wish she were well-dressed as well as well-bred."

"Doesn't she dress well? I never noticed."

"I've always heard that they were a devoted couple," said Kitty, watching him through her eyelashes.

"He's very fond of her: I will give him that credit. I think that is the most decent thing about him."

"Cold praise."

"He has his little flirtations, but they're not serious. He's much too cunning to let them go to such lengths as might cause him inconvenience. And of course he isn't a passionate man; he's only a vain one. He likes admiration. He's fat and forty now, he does himself too well, but he was very good-looking when he first came to the Colony. I've often heard his wife chaff him about his conquests."

"She doesn't take his flirtations very seriously?"

"Oh, no, she knows they don't go very far. She says she'd like to be able to make friends of the poor little things who fall to Charlie; but they're always so common. She says it's really not very flattering to her that the women who fall in love with her husband are so uncommonly second-rate."

xxxvi

WHEN Waddington left her Kitty thought over what he had so carelessly said. It hadn't been very pleasant to hear and she had had to make something of an effort not to show how much it touched her. It was bitter to think that all he said was true. She knew that Charlie was stupid and vain, hungry for flattery, and she remembered the complacency with which he had told her little stories to prove his cleverness. He was proud of a low cunning. How worthless must she be if she had given her heart so passionately to such a man because—because he had nice eyes and a good figure! She wished to despise him, because so long as she only hated him she knew that she was very near loving him. The way he had treated her should have opened her eyes. Walter had always held him in contempt. Oh, if she could only get him out of her mind altogether! And had his wife chaffed him about her obvious infatuation for him? Dorothy would have liked to make a friend of her, but that she found her second-rate. Kitty smiled a little: how indignant her mother would be to know that her daughter was considered that!

But at night she dreamt of him again. She felt his arms pressing her close and the hot passion of his kisses on her lips. What did it matter if he was fat and forty? She laughed with soft affection because he minded so much; she loved him all the more for his childlike vanity and she could be sorry for him and comfort him. When she awoke tears were streaming from her eyes.

She did not know why it seemed to her so tragic to cry in her sleep.

xxxvii

SHE saw Waddington every day, for he strolled up the hill to the Fanes' bungalow when his day's work was done; and so after a week had arrived at an intimacy which under other circumstances they could scarcely have achieved in a year. Once when Kitty told him she didn't know what she would do there without him he answered, laughing:

"You see, you and I are the only people here who walk quite quietly and peaceably on solid ground. The nuns walk in heaven and your husband—in darkness."

Though she gave a careless laugh she wondered what he

meant. She felt that his merry little blue eyes were scanning
her face with an amiable, but disconcerting attention. She
had discovered already that he was shrewd and she had a
feeling that the relations between herself and Walter excited his cynical curiosity. She found a certain amusement in
baffling him. She liked him and she knew that he was kindly
disposed towards her. He was not witty nor brilliant, but
he had a dry and incisive way of putting things which was
diverting, and his funny, boyish face under that bald skull,
all screwed up with laughter, made his remarks sometimes
extremely droll. He had lived for many years in outports,
often with no man of his own colour to talk to, and his
personality had developed in eccentric freedom. He was full
of fads and oddities. His frankness was refreshing. He
seemed to look upon life in a spirit of banter, and his ridicule
of the Colony at Hong-Kong was acid; but he laughed also
at the Chinese officials in Mei-tan-fu and at the cholera
which decimated the city. He could not tell a tragic story
or one of heroism without making it faintly absurd. He had
many anecdotes of his adventures during twenty years in
China, and you concluded from them that the earth was a
very grotesque, bizarre and ludicrous place.

Though he denied that he was a Chinese scholar (he
swore that the Sinologues were as mad as march hares) he
spoke the language with ease. He read little and what he
knew he had learned from conversation. But he often told
Kitty stories from the Chinese novels and from Chinese
history and though he told them with that airy badinage
which was natural to him it was good-humoured and even
tender. It seemed to her that, perhaps unconsciously, he
had adopted the Chinese view that the Europeans were
barbarians and their life a folly: in China alone was it so
led that a sensible man might discern in it a sort of reality.
Here was food for reflection: Kitty had never heard the
Chinese spoken of as anything but decadent, dirty and unspeakable. It was as though the corner of a curtain were
lifted for a moment, and she caught a glimpse of a world
rich with a colour and significance she had not dreamt of.

He sat there, talking, laughing and drinking.

"Don't you think you drink too much?" said Kitty to him boldly.

"It's my great pleasure in life," he answered. "Besides, it keeps the cholera out."

When he left her he was generally drunk, but he carried his liquor well. It made him hilarious, but not disagreeable.

One evening Walter, coming back earlier than usual, asked him to stay to dinner. A curious incident happened. They had their soup and their fish and then with the chicken a fresh green salad was handed to Kitty by the boy.

"Good God, you're not going to eat that," cried Waddington, as he saw Kitty take some.

"Yes, we have it every night."

"My wife likes it," said Walter.

The dish was handed to Waddington, but he shook his head.

"Thank you very much, but I'm not thinking of committing suicide just yet."

Walter smiled grimly and helped himself. Waddington said nothing more, in fact he became strangely taciturn, and soon after dinner he left them.

It was true that they ate salad every night. Two days after their arrival the cook, with the unconcern of the Chinese, had sent it in and Kitty, without thinking, took some. Walter leaned forward quickly.

"You oughtn't to eat that. The boy's crazy to serve it."

"Why not?" asked Kitty, looking at him full in the face.

"It's always dangerous, it's madness now. You'll kill yourself."

"I thought that was the idea," said Kitty.

She began to eat it coolly. She was seized with she knew not what spirit of bravado. She watched Walter with mocking eyes. She thought that he grew a trifle pale, but when the salad was handed to him he helped himself. The cook, finding they did not refuse it, sent them some in every day and every day, courting death, they ate it. It was grotesque to take such a risk. Kitty, in terror of the disease, took it with the feeling not only that she was thus maliciously avenging herself on Walter, but that she was flouting her own desperate fears.

xxxviii

IT WAS the day after this that Waddington, coming to the bungalow in the afternoon, when he had sat a little asked Kitty if she would not go for a stroll with him. She had not been out of the compound since her arrival. She was glad enough.

"There are not many walks, I'm afraid," he said. "But we'll go to the top of the hill."

"Oh, yes, where the archway is. I've seen it often from the terrace."

One of the boys opened the heavy doorway for them and they stepped out into the dusty lane. They walked a few yards and then Kitty, seizing Waddington's arm in fright, gave a startled cry.

"Look!"

"What's the matter?"

At the foot of the wall that surrounded the compound a man lay on his back with his legs stretched out and his arms thrown over his head. He wore the patched blue rags and the wild mop of hair of the Chinese beggar.

"He looks as if he were dead," Kitty gasped.

"He is dead. Come along; you'd better look the other way. I'll have him moved when we come back."

But Kitty was trembling so violently that she could not stir.

"I've never seen any one dead before."

"You'd better hurry up and get used to it then, because you'll see a good many before you've done with this cheerful spot."

He took her hand and drew it in his arm. They walked for a little in silence.

"Did he die of cholera?" she said at last.

"I suppose so."

They walked up the hill till they came to the archway. It

was richly carved. Fantastic and ironical it stood like a landmark in the surrounding country. They sat down on the pedestal and faced the wide plain. The hill was sown close with the little green mounds of the dead, not in lines but disorderly, so that you felt that beneath the surface they must strangely jostle one another. The narrow causeway meandered sinuously among the green rice fields. A small boy seated on the neck of a water-buffalo drove it slowly home, and three peasants in wide straw hats lolloped with sidelong gait under their heavy loads. After the heat of the day it was pleasant in that spot to catch the faint breeze of the evening and the wide expanse of country brought a sense of restful melancholy to the tortured heart. But Kitty could not rid her mind of the dead beggar.

"How can you talk and laugh and drink whisky when people are dying all around you?" she asked suddenly.

Waddington did not answer. He turned round and looked at her, then he put his hand on her arm.

"You know, this is no place for a woman," he said gravely. "Why don't you go?"

She gave him a sidelong glance from beneath her long lashes and there was the shadow of a smile on her lips.

"I should have thought under the circumstances a wife's place was by her husband's side."

"When they telegraphed to me that you were coming with Fane I was astonished. But then it occurred to me that perhaps you'd been a nurse and all this sort of thing was in the day's work. I expected you to be one of those grim-visaged females who lead you a dog's life when you're ill in hospital. You could have knocked me down with a feather when I came into the bungalow and saw you sitting down and resting. You looked very frail and white and tired."

"You couldn't expect me to look my best after nine days on the road."

"You look frail and white and tired now, and if you'll allow me to say so, desperately unhappy."

Kitty flushed because she could not help it, but she was able to give a laugh that sounded merry enough.

"I'm sorry you don't like my expression. The only reason

I have for looking unhappy is that since I was twelve I've known that my nose was a little too long. But to cherish a secret sorrow is a most effective pose: you can't think how many sweet young men have wanted to console me."

Waddington's blue and shining eyes rested on her and she knew that he did not believe a word she said. She did not care so long as he pretended to.

"I knew that you hadn't been married very long and I came to the conclusion that you and your husband were madly in love with each other. I couldn't believe that he had wished you to come, but perhaps you had absolutely refused to stay behind."

"That's a very reasonable explanation," she said lightly.

"Yes, but it isn't the right one."

She waited for him to go on, fearful of what he was about to say, for she had a pretty good idea of his shrewdness and was aware that he never hesitated to speak his mind, but unable to resist the desire to hear him talk about herself.

"I don't think for a moment that you're in love with your husband. I think you dislike him, I shouldn't be surprised if you hated him. But I'm quite sure you're afraid of him."

For a moment she looked away. She did not mean to let Waddington see that anything he said affected her.

"I have a suspicion that you don't very much like my husband," she said with cool irony.

"I respect him. He has brains and character; and that, I may tell you, is a very unusual combination. I don't suppose you know what he is doing here, because I don't think he's very expansive with you. If any man single-handed can put a stop to this frightful epidemic he's going to do it. He's doctoring the sick, cleaning the city up, trying to get the drinking water pure. He doesn't mind where he goes nor what he does. He's risking his life twenty times a day. He's got Colonel Yü in his pocket and he's induced him to put the troops at his disposal. He's even put a little pluck into the magistrate and the old man is really trying to do something. And the nuns at the convent swear by him. They think he's a hero."

"Don't you?"

"After all this isn't his job, is it? He's a bacteriologist. There was no call for him to come here. He doesn't give me the impression that he's moved by compassion for all these dying Chinamen. Watson was different. He loved the human race. Though he was a missionary it didn't make any difference to him if they were Christian, Buddhist or Confucian; they were just human beings. Your husband isn't here because he cares a damn if a hundred thousand Chinese die of cholera; he isn't here either in the interests of science. Why is he here?"

"You'd better ask him."

"It interests me to see you together. I sometimes wonder how you behave when you're alone. When I'm there you're acting, both of you, and acting damned badly, by George. You'd neither of you get thirty bob a week in a touring company if that's the best you can do."

"I don't know what you mean," smiled Kitty, keeping up a pretence of frivolity which she knew did not deceive.

"You're a very pretty woman. It's funny that your husband should never look at you. When he speaks to you it sounds as though it were not his voice but somebody else's."

"Do you think he doesn't love me?" asked Kitty in a low voice, hoarsely, putting aside suddenly her lightness.

"I don't know. I don't know if you fill him with such a repulsion that it gives him goose-flesh to be near you or if he's burning with a love that for some reason he will not allow himself to show. I've asked myself if you're both here to commit suicide."

Kitty had seen the startled glance and then the scrutinising look Waddington gave them when the incident of the salad took place.

"I think you're attaching too much importance to a few lettuce leaves," she said flippantly. She rose. "Shall we go home? I'm sure you want a whisky and soda."

"You're not a heroine at all events. You're frightened to death. Are you sure you don't want to go away?"

"What has it got to do with you?"

"I'll help you."

"Are *you* going to fall to my look of secret sorrow? Look

at my profile and tell me if my nose isn't a trifle too long."

He gazed at her reflectively, that malicious, ironical look in his bright eyes, but mingled with it, a shadow, like a tree standing at a river's edge and its reflection in the water, was an expression of singular kindliness. It brought sudden tears to Kitty's eyes.

"Must you stay?"

"Yes."

They passed under the flamboyant archway and walked down the hill. When they came to the compound they saw the body of the dead beggar. He took her arm, but she released herself. She stood still.

"It's dreadful, isn't it?"

"What? Death."

"Yes. It makes everything else seem so horribly trivial. He doesn't look human. When you look at him you can hardly persuade yourself that he's ever been alive. It's hard to think that not so very many years ago he was just a little boy tearing down the hill and flying a kite."

She could not hold back the sob that choked her.

xxxix

A FEW days later Waddington, sitting with Kitty, a long glass of whisky and soda in his hand, began to speak to her of the convent.

"The Mother Superior is a very remarkable woman," he said. "The Sisters tell me that she belongs to one of the greatest families in France, but they won't tell me which; the Mother Superior, they say, doesn't wish it to be talked of."

"Why don't you ask her if it interests you?" smiled Kitty.

"If you knew her you'd know it was impossible to ask her an indiscreet question."

"She must certainly be very remarkable if she can impress you with awe."

"I am the bearer of a message from her to you. She has asked me to say that, though of course you may not wish to adventure into the very centre of the epidemic, if you do not mind that it will give her great pleasure to show you the convent."

"It's very kind of her. I shouldn't have thought she was aware of my existence."

"I've spoken about you; I go there two or three times a week just now to see if there's anything I can do; and I daresay your husband has told them about you. You must be prepared to find that they have an unbounded admiration for him."

"Are you a Catholic?"

His malicious eyes twinkled and his funny little face was puckered with laughter.

"Why are you grinning at me?" asked Kitty.

"Can any good come out of Galilee? No, I'm not a Catholic. I describe myself as a member of the Church of England, which I suppose is an inoffensive way of saying that you don't believe in anything very much. . . . When the Mother Superior came here ten years ago she brought seven nuns with her and of those all but three are dead. You see, at the best of times, Mei-tan-fu is not a health resort. They live in the very middle of the city, in the poorest district, they work very hard and they never have a holiday."

"But are there only three and the Mother Superior now?"

"Oh, no, more have taken their places. There are six of them now. When one of them died of cholera at the beginning of the epidemic two others came up from Canton."

Kitty shivered a little.

"Are you cold?"

"No, it was only some one walking over my grave."

"When they leave France they leave it for ever. They're not like the Protestant missionaries who have a year's leave every now and then. I always think that must be the hardest thing of all. We English have no very strong attachment to the soil, we can make ourselves at home in any part of the world, but the French, I think, have an attachment to their country which is almost a physical bond. They're never really at ease when they're out of it. It always seems to me very moving that these women should make just that sacrifice. I suppose if I *were* a Catholic it would seem very natural to me."

Kitty looked at him coolly. She could not quite understand the emotion with which the little man spoke and she asked herself whether it was a pose. He had drunk a good deal of whisky and perhaps he was not quite sober.

"Come and see for yourself," he said, with his bantering smile, quickly reading her thought. "It's not nearly so risky as eating a tomato."

"If you're not frightened there's no reason why I should be."

"I think it'll amuse you. It's like a little bit of France."

xl

THEY crossed the river in a sampan. A chair was waiting for Kitty at the landing-stage and she was carried up the hill to the water-gate. It was through this that the coolies came to fetch water from the river and they hurried to and fro with huge buckets hanging from the yoke on their shoulder, splashing the causeway so that it was as wet as though it had heavily rained. Kitty's bearers gave short, sharp cries to urge them to make way.

"Of course all business is at a standstill," said Waddington, walking by her side. "Under normal circumstances you have to fight your way through the coolies carrying loads up and down to the junks."

The street was narrow and winding so that Kitty lost all sense of the direction in which she was going. Many of the shops were closed. She had grown used on the journey up to the untidiness of a Chinese street, but here was the litter of weeks, garbage and refuse; and the stench was so horrible that she had to put her handkerchief to her face. Passing through Chinese cities she had been incommoded by the staring of the crowd, but now she noticed that no more than an indifferent glance was thrown at her. The passers-by, scattered rather than as usual thronging, seemed intent on their own affairs. They were cowed and listless. Now and then as they went by a house they heard the beating of gongs and the shrill, sustained lament of unknown instruments. Behind those closed doors one was lying dead.

"Here we are," said Waddington at last.

The chair was set down at a small doorway, surmounted by a cross, in a long white wall, and Kitty stepped out. He rang the bell.

"You mustn't expect anything very grand, you know. They're miserably poor."

The door was opened by a Chinese girl, and after a word or two from Waddington she led them into a little room on the side of the corridor. It contained a large table covered with a chequered oilcloth and round the walls was a set of stiff chairs. At one end of the room was a statue, in plaster, of the Blessed Virgin. In a moment a nun came in, short and plump, with a homely face, red cheeks and merry eyes. Waddington, introducing Kitty to her, called her Sœur St. Joseph.

"C'est la dame du docteur?" she asked, beaming, and then added that the Mother Superior would join them directly.

Sister St. Joseph could speak no English and Kitty's French was halting; but Waddington, fluent, voluble and inaccurate, maintained a stream of facetious comment which convulsed the good-humoured nun. Her cheerful, easy laughter not a little astonished Kitty. She had an idea that the religious were always grave and this sweet and childlike merriment touched her.

xli

THE door opened, to Kitty's fancy not quite naturally but as though it swung back of itself on its hinges, and the Mother Superior entered the little room. She stood for an instant on the threshold and a grave smile hovered upon her lips as she looked at the laughing Sister and Waddington's puckered, clownish face. Then she came forward and held out her hand to Kitty.

"Mrs. Fane?" She spoke in English with a good deal of accent, but with a correct pronunciation, and she gave the shadow of a bow. "It is a great pleasure to me to make the acquaintance of the wife of our good and brave doctor."

Kitty felt that the Superior's eyes held her in a long and unembarrassed look of appraisal. It was so frank that it was not uncivil; you felt that here was a woman whose business it was to form an opinion of others and to whom it never occurred that subterfuge was necessary. With a dignified affability she motioned to her visitors to take chairs and herself sat down. Sister St. Joseph, smiling still but silent, stood at the side but a little behind the Superior.

"I know you English like tea," said the Mother Superior, "and I have ordered some. But I must make my excuses if it is served in the Chinese fashion. I know that Mr. Waddington prefers whisky, but that I am afraid I cannot offer him."

She smiled and there was a hint of malice in her grave eyes.

"Oh, come, *ma mère,* you speak as if I were a confirmed drunkard."

"I wish you could say that you never drink, Mr. Waddington."

"I can at all events say that I never drink except to excess."

The Mother Superior laughed and translated into French for Sister St. Joseph the flippant remark. She looked at him with lingering, friendly eyes.

"We must make allowances for Mr. Waddington because two or three times when we had no money at all and did not know how we were to feed our orphans Mr. Waddington came to our rescue."

The convert who had opened the door for them now came in with a tray on which were Chinese cups, a tea-pot, and a little plate of the French cakes called *Madeleines.*

"You must eat the *Madeleines,*" said the Mother Superior, "because Sister St. Joseph made them for you herself this morning."

They talked of commonplace things. The Mother Superior asked Kitty how long she had been in China and if the journey from Hong-Kong had greatly tired her. She asked her if she had been in France and if she did not find the climate of Hong-Kong trying. It was a conversation, trivial but friendly, which gained a peculiar savour from the circumstances. The parlour was very quiet, so that you could hardly believe that you were in the midst of a populous city. Peace dwelt there. And yet all round about the epidemic was raging and the people, terrified and restless, were kept in check but by the strong will of a soldier who was more than half a brigand. Within the convent walls the infirmary was crowded with sick and dying soldiers, and of the orphans in the nuns' charge a quarter were dead.

Kitty, impressed she hardly knew why, observed the grave lady who asked her these amiable questions. She was dressed in white and the only colour on her habit was the red heart that burned on her breast. She was a woman of middle age, she might have been forty or fifty, it was impossible to say, for there were few wrinkles on her smooth, pale face, and you received the impression that she was far from young chiefly from the dignity of her bearing, her assurance, and the emaciation of her strong and beautiful hands. The face was long, with a large mouth and large, even teeth; the nose, though not small, was delicate and sensitive; but it was the eyes, under their thin black brows, which gave her face its intense and tragic character. They were very large, black, and though not exactly cold, by their calm steadiness strangely compelling. Your first thought when you looked at the Mother Superior was that as a girl she must have been beautiful, but in a moment you realised that this was a woman whose beauty, depending on character, had grown with advancing years. Her voice was deep, low and controlled, and whether she spoke in English or in French she spoke slowly. But the most striking thing about her was the air she had of authority tempered by Christian charity; you felt in her the habit of command. To be obeyed was natural to her, but she accepted obedience with humility. You could not fail to see that she was deeply conscious of the authority of the church which upheld her. But Kitty had a surmise that notwithstanding her austere demeanour she had for human frailty a human tolerance; and it was impossible to look at her grave smile when she listened to Waddington, unabashed, talking nonsense, without being sure that she had a lively sense of the ridiculous.

But there was some other quality in her which Kitty vaguely felt, but could not put a name to. It was something that notwithstanding the Mother Superior's cordiality and the exquisite manners which made Kitty feel like an awkward school-girl, held her at a distance.

xlii

"MONSIEUR NE MANGE RIEN," said Sister St. Joseph.

"Monsieur's palate is ruined by Manchu cooking," replied the Mother Superior.

The smile left Sister St. Joseph's face and she assumed an expression of some primness. Waddington, a roguish glance in his eyes, took another cake. Kitty did not understand the incident.

"To prove to you how unjust you are, *ma mère,* I will ruin the excellent dinner that awaits me."

"If Mrs. Fane would like to see over the convent I shall be glad to show her." The Mother Superior turned to Kitty with a deprecating smile. "I am sorry you should see it just now when everything is in disorder. We have so much work and not enough Sisters to do it. Colonel Yü has insisted on our putting our infirmary at the disposal of sick soldiers and we have had to make the *réfectoire* into an infirmary for our orphans."

She stood at the door to allow Kitty to pass and together, followed by Sister St. Joseph and Waddington, they walked along cool white corridors. They went first into a large, bare room where a number of Chinese girls were working at elaborate embroideries. They stood up when the visitors entered and the Mother Superior showed Kitty specimens of the work.

"We go on with it notwithstanding the epidemic because it takes their minds off the danger."

They went to a second room in which younger girls were doing plain sewing, hemming and stitching, and then into a third where there were only tiny children under the charge of a Chinese convert. They were playing noisily and when the Mother Superior came in they crowded round her, mites of two and three, with their black Chinese eyes and their black hair; and they seized her hands and hid themselves in her great skirts. An enchanting smile lit up her grave face, and she fondled them; she spoke little chaffing words which Kitty, ignorant though she was of Chinese, could tell were like caresses. She shuddered a little, for in their uniform dress, sallow-skinned, stunted, with their flat noses, they looked to her hardly human. They were repulsive. But the Mother Superior stood among them like Charity itself. When she wished to leave the room they would not let her go, but clung to her, so that, with smiling expostulations, she had to use a gentle force to free herself. They at all events found nothing terrifying in this great lady.

"You know of course," she said, as they walked along another corridor, "that they are only orphans in the sense that their parents have wished to be rid of them. We give them a few cash for every child that is brought in, otherwise they will not take the trouble, but do away with them." She turned to the Sister. "Have any come to-day?" she asked.

"Four."

"Now, with the cholera, they are more than ever anxious not to be burdened with useless girls."

She showed Kitty the dormitories and then they passed a door on which was painted the word *infirmerie*. Kitty heard groans and loud cries and sounds as though beings not human were in pain.

"I will not show you the infirmary," said the Mother Superior in her placid tones. "It is not a sight that one would wish to see." A thought struck her. "I wonder if Dr. Fane is there?"

She looked interrogatively at the Sister and she, with her merry smile, opened the door and slipped in. Kitty shrank back as the open door allowed her to hear more horribly the tumult within. Sister St. Joseph came back.

"No, he has been and will not be back again till later."

"What about number six?"

"*Pauvre garçon,* he's dead."

The Mother Superior crossed herself and her lips moved in a short and silent prayer.

They passed by a courtyard and Kitty's eyes fell upon two long shapes that lay side by side on the ground covered with a piece of blue cotton. The Superior turned to Waddington.

"We are so short of beds that we have to put two patients in one and the moment a sick man dies he must be bundled out in order to make room for another." But she gave Kitty a smile. "Now we will show you our chapel. We are very proud of it. One of our friends in France sent us a little while ago a life-size statue of the Blessed Virgin."

xliii

THE chapel was no more than a long low room with whitewashed walls and rows of deal benches; at the end was the altar on which stood the image; it was in plaster of Paris painted in crude colours; it was very bright and new and garish. Behind it was a picture in oils of the Crucifixion with the two Maries at the foot of the Cross in extravagant attitudes of grief. The drawing was bad and the dark pigments were put on with an eye that knew nothing of the beauty of colour. Around the walls were the Stations of the Cross painted by the same unfortunate hand. The chapel was hideous and vulgar.

The two nuns on entering knelt down to say a prayer and then, rising, the Mother Superior began once more to chat with Kitty.

"Everything that can be broken is broken when it comes here, but the statue presented to us by our benefactor came from Paris without so much as the smallest chip. There is no doubt that it was a miracle."

Waddington's malicious eyes gleamed, but he held his tongue.

"The altarpiece and the Stations of the Cross were painted by one of our Sisters, Sœur St. Anselme." The Mother Superior crossed herself. "She was a real artist. Unfortunately, she fell a victim to the epidemic. Do you not think that they are very beautiful?"

Kitty faltered an affirmative. On the altar were bunches of paper flowers and the candlesticks were distractingly ornate.

"We have the privilege of keeping here the Blessed Sacrament."

"Yes?" said Kitty, not understanding.

"It has been a great comfort to us during this time of so terrible trouble."

They left the chapel and retraced their steps to the parlour in which they had first sat.

"Would you like to see the babies that came in this morning before you go?"

"Very much," said Kitty.

The Mother Superior led them into a tiny room on the other side of the passage. On a table, under a cloth, there was a singular wriggling. The Sister drew back the cloth and displayed four tiny, naked infants. They were very red and they made funny restless movements with their arms and legs; their quaint little Chinese faces were screwed up into strange grimaces. They looked hardly human; queer animals of an unknown species, and yet there was something singularly moving in the sight. The Mother Superior looked at them with an amused smile.

"They seem very lively. Sometimes they are brought in only to die. Of course we baptise them the moment they come."

"The lady's husband will be pleased with them," said Sister St. Joseph. "I think he could play by the hour with the babies. When they cry he has only to take them up, and he makes them comfortable in the crook of his arm, so that they laugh with delight."

Then Kitty and Waddington found themselves at the door. Kitty gravely thanked the Mother Superior for the trouble she had taken. The nun bowed with a condescension that was at once dignified and affable.

"It has been a great pleasure. You do not know how kind and helpful your husband has been to us. He has been sent

to us by Heaven. I am glad that you came with him. When
he goes home it must be a great comfort to him to have you
there with your love and your—your sweet face. You must
take care of him and not let him work too hard. You must
look after him for all our sakes."

Kitty flushed. She did not know what to say. The Mother
Superior held out her hand and while she held it Kitty was
conscious of those cool, thoughtful eyes which rested on her
with detachment and yet with something that looked like a
profound understanding.

Sister St. Joseph closed the door behind them and Kitty
got into her chair. They went back through the narrow,
winding streets. Waddington made a casual remark; Kitty
did not answer. He looked round, but the side curtains of
the chair were drawn and he could not see her. He walked
on in silence. But when they reached the river and she
stepped out to his surprise he saw that her eyes were streaming with tears.

"What is the matter?" he asked, his face puckered into
an expression of dismay.

"Nothing." She tried to smile. "Only foolishness."

xliv

ALONE once more in the sordid parlour of the dead missionary, lying on the long chair that faced the window, her abstracted eyes on the temple across the river (now again at
the approach of evening aerial and lovely), Kitty tried to set
in order the feelings in her heart. She would never have believed that this visit to the convent could so have moved her.
She had gone from curiosity. She had nothing else to do and
after looking for so many days at the walled city across the
water she was not unwilling to have at least a glimpse of its
mysterious streets.

But once within the convent it had seemed to her that she
was transported into another world situated strangely
neither in space nor time. Those bare rooms and the white
corridors, austere and simple, seemed to possess the spirit

of something remote and mystical. The little chapel, so ugly and vulgar, in its very crudeness was pathetic; it had something which was wanting in the greatness of a cathedral, with its stained glass and its pictures: it was very humble; and the faith which had adorned it, the affection which cherished it, had endued it with a delicate beauty of the soul. The methodical way in which the convent's work was carried on in the midst of the pestilence showed a coolness in the face of danger and a practical sense, almost ironical it was so matter of fact, which were deeply impressive. In Kitty's ears rang still the ghastly sounds she heard when for a moment Sister St. Joseph opened the infirmary door.

It was unexpected the way they had spoken of Walter. First the Sister and then the Mother Superior herself, and the tone of her voice had been very gentle when she praised him. Oddly enough it gave her a little thrill of pride to know that they thought so well of him. Waddington also had told something of what Walter was doing; but it was not only his competence that the nuns praised (in Hong-Kong she had known that he was thought clever), they spoke of his thoughtfulness and his tenderness. Of course he could be very tender. He was at his best when you were ill; he was too intelligent to exasperate, and his touch was pleasant, cool and soothing. By some magic he seemed able by his mere presence to relieve your suffering. She knew that she would never see again in his eyes the look of affection which she had once been so used to that she found it merely exasperating. She knew now how immense was his capacity for loving; in some odd way he was pouring it out on these wretched sick who had only him to look to. She did not feel jealousy, but a sense of emptiness; it was as though a support that she had grown so accustomed to as not to realise its presence were suddenly withdrawn from her so that she swayed this way and that like a thing that was top-heavy.

She had only contempt for herself because once she had felt contempt for Walter. He must have known how she regarded him and he had accepted her estimate without bitterness. She was a fool and he knew it and because he loved her it had made no difference to him. She did not hate him now, nor feel resentment of him, but fear rather and perplexity. She could not but admit that he had remarkable qualities, sometimes she thought that there was even in him a strange and unattractive greatness; it was curious then that she could not love him, but loved still a man whose worthlessness was now so clear to her. After thinking, thinking, all through those long days she rated accurately Charles Townsend's value; he was a common fellow and his qualities were second-rate. If she could only tear from her heart the love that still lingered there! She tried not to think of him.

Waddington too thought highly of Walter. She alone had been blind to his merit. Why? Because he loved her and she did not love him. What was it in the human heart that made you despise a man because he loved you? But Waddington had confessed that he did not like Walter. Men didn't. It was easy to see that those two nuns had for him a feeling which was very like affection. He was different with women; notwithstanding his shyness you felt in him an exquisite kindliness.

xlv

BUT after all it was the nuns that had most deeply touched her. Sister St. Joseph, with her merry face and apple red cheeks; she had been one of the little band that came out to China with the Mother Superior ten years before and she had seen one after another of her companions die of disease, privation and homesickness; and yet she remained cheerful and happy. What was it that gave her that naïve and charming humour? And the Mother Superior. Kitty in fancy stood again in her presence and once more she felt humble and ashamed. Though she was so simple and unaffected she had a native dignity which inspired awe, and you could not imagine that any one could treat her without respect. Sister St. Joseph by the way she stood, by every small gesture and the intonation of her answers, had shown the deep submission in which she held herself; and Waddington, frivolous and impertinent, had shown by his tone that he was not quite at his ease. Kitty thought it unnecessary to have told her that the

Mother Superior belonged to one of the great families of France; there was that in her bearing which suggested ancient race; and she had the authority of one who has never known that it is possible to be disobeyed. She had the condescension of a great lady and the humility of a saint. There was in her strong, handsome and ravaged face an austerity that was passionate; and at the same time she had a solicitude and a gentleness which permitted those little children to cluster, noisy and unafraid, in the assurance of her deep affection. When she had looked at the four new-born babies she had worn a smile that was sweet and yet profound: it was like a ray of sunshine on a wild and desolate heath. What Sister St. Joseph had said so carelessly of Walter moved Kitty strangely; she knew that he had desperately wanted her to bear a child, but she had never suspected from his reticence that he was capable with a baby of showing without embarrassment a charming and playful tenderness. Most men were silly and awkward with babies. How strange he was!

But to all that moving experience there had been a shadow (a dark lining to the silver cloud), insistent and plain, which disconcerted her. In the sober gaiety of Sister St. Joseph, and much more in the beautiful courtesy of the Mother Superior, she had felt an aloofness which oppressed her. They were friendly and even cordial, but at the same time they held something back, she knew not what, so that she was conscious that she was nothing but a casual stranger. There was a barrier between her and them. They spoke a different language not only of the tongue but of the heart. And when the door was closed upon her she felt that they had put her out of their minds so completely, going about their neglected work again without delay, that for them she might never have existed. She felt shut out not only from that poor little convent, but from some mysterious garden of the spirit after which with all her soul she hankered. She felt on a sudden alone as she had never felt alone before. That was why she had wept.

And now, throwing back her head wearily, she sighed: "Oh, I'm so worthless."

xlvi

THAT evening Walter came back to the bungalow a little earlier than usual. Kitty was lying on the long chair by the open window. It was nearly dark.

"Don't you want a lamp?" he asked.

"They'll bring it when dinner is ready."

He talked to her always quite casually, of trifling things, as though they were friendly acquaintances, and there was never anything in his manner to suggest that he harboured malice in his heart. He never met her eyes and he never smiled. He was scrupulously polite.

"Walter, what do you propose we should do if we get through the epidemic?" she asked.

He waited for a moment before answering. She could not see his face.

"I haven't thought."

In the old days she said carelessly whatever came into her head; it never occurred to her to think before she spoke; but now she was afraid of him; she felt her lips tremble and her heart beat painfully.

"I went to the convent this afternoon."

"So I heard."

She forced herself to speak though she could hardly frame the words.

"Did you really want me to die when you brought me here?"

"If I were you I'd leave well alone, Kitty. I don't think any good will come of talking about what we should do much better to forget."

"But you don't forget; neither do I. I've been thinking a great deal since I came here. Won't you listen to what I have to say?"

"Certainly."

"I treated you very badly. I was unfaithful to you."

He stood stock still. His immobility was strangely terrifying.

"I don't know whether you'll understand what I mean. That sort of thing doesn't mean very much to a woman when it's over. I think women have never quite understood the attitude that men take up." She spoke abruptly, in a voice she would hardly have recognised as her own. "You know what Charlie was and you knew what he'd do. Well, you were quite right. He's a worthless creature. I suppose I shouldn't have been taken in by him if I hadn't been as worthless as he. I don't ask you to forgive me. I don't ask you to love me as you used to love me. But couldn't we be friends? With all these people dying in thousands round us, and with those nuns in their convent . . ."

"What have they got to do with it?" he interrupted.

"I can't quite explain. I had such a singular feeling when I went there to-day. It all seems to mean so much. It's all so terrible and their self-sacrifice is so wonderful; I can't help feeling it's absurd and disproportionate, if you understand what I mean, to distress yourself because a foolish woman has been unfaithful to you. I'm much too worthless and insignificant for you to give me a thought."

He did not answer, but he did not move away; he seemed to be waiting for her to continue.

"Mr. Waddington and the nuns have told me such wonderful things about you. I'm very proud of you, Walter."

"You used not to be; you used to feel contempt for me. Don't you still?"

"Don't you know that I'm afraid of you?"

Again he was silent.

"I don't understand you," he said at last. "I don't know what it is you want."

"Nothing for myself. I only want you to be a little less unhappy."

She felt him stiffen and his voice was very cold when he answered.

"You're mistaken in thinking I'm unhappy. I have a great deal too much to do to think of you very often."

"I have wondered if the nuns would allow me to go and work at the convent. They are very shorthanded and if I could be of any help I should be grateful to them."

"It is not easy work or pleasant work. I doubt if it would amuse you long."

"Do you absolutely despise me, Walter?"

"No." He hesitated and his voice was strange. "I despise myself."

xlvii

IT WAS after dinner. As usual Walter sat by the lamp and read. He read every evening till Kitty went to bed and then went into a laboratory which he had fitted up in one of the bungalow's empty rooms. Here he worked late into the night. He slept little. He was occupied with she knew not what experiments. He told her nothing of his work; but even in the old days he had been reticent on this: he was not by nature expansive. She thought deeply of what he had just said to her: the conversation had led to nothing. She knew him so little that she could not be sure if he was speaking the truth or not. Was it possible that, whereas he now existed so ominously for her, she had entirely ceased to exist for him? Her conversation which had entertained him once because he loved her, now that he loved her no longer might be merely tedious to him. It mortified her.

She looked at him. The light of the lamp displayed his profile as though it were a cameo. With his regular and finely-cut features it was very distinguished, but it was more than severe, it was grim: that immobility of his, only his eyes moving as he perused each page, was vaguely terrifying. Who would have thought that this hard face could be melted by passion to such a tenderness of expression? She knew and it excited in her a little shiver of distaste. It was strange that though he was good-looking as well as honest, reliable and talented, it had been so impossible for her to love him. It was a relief that she need never again submit to his caresses.

He would not answer when she had asked him whether in forcing her to come here he had really wished to kill her. The mystery of this fascinated and horrified her. He was so extraordinarily kind; it was incredible that he could have had such a devilish intention. He must have suggested it only to frighten her and to get back on Charlie (that would be like his sardonic humour) and then from obstinacy or from fear of looking foolish insisted on her going through with it.

Yes, he said he despised himself. What did he mean by that? Once again Kitty looked at his calm cool face. She might not even be in the room, he was so unconscious of her.

"Why do you despise yourself?" she asked, hardly knowing that she spoke, as though she were continuing without a break the earlier conversation.

He put down his book and observed her reflectively. He seemed to gather his thoughts from a remote distance.

"Because I loved you."

She flushed and looked away. She could not bear his cold, steady and appraising gaze. She understood what he meant. It was a little while before she answered.

"I think you do me an injustice," she said. "It's not fair to blame me because I was silly and frivolous and vulgar. I was brought up like that. All the girls I know are like that. . . . It's like reproaching some one who has no ear for music because he's bored at a symphony concert. Is it fair to blame me because you ascribed to me qualities I hadn't got? I never tried to deceive you by pretending I was anything I wasn't. I was just pretty and gay. You don't ask for a pearl necklace or a sable coat at a booth in a fair; you ask for a tin trumpet and a toy balloon."

"I don't blame you."

His voice was weary. She was beginning to feel a trifle impatient with him. Why could he not realise, what suddenly had become so clear to her, that beside all the terror of death under whose shadow they lay and beside the awe of the beauty which she had caught a glimpse of that day, their own affairs were trivial? What did it really matter if a silly woman had committed adultery and why should her husband, face to face with the sublime, give it a thought? It was strange that Walter with all his cleverness should have so little sense of proportion. Because he had dressed a doll in gorgeous robes and set her in a sanctuary to worship her, and then discovered that the doll was filled with sawdust he could neither forgive himself nor her. His soul was lacerated. It was all make-believe that he had lived on, and when the truth shattered it he thought reality itself was shattered. It was true enough, he would not forgive her because he could not forgive himself.

She thought that she heard him give a faint sigh and she shot a rapid glance at him. A sudden thought struck her and it took her breath away. She only just refrained from giving a cry.

Was it what they called—a broken heart—that he suffered from?

xlviii

ALL the next day Kitty thought of the convent; and the morning after, early, soon after Walter had gone, taking the amah with her to get chairs, she crossed the river. It was barely day and the Chinese crowding the ferry boat, some in the blue cotton of the peasant, others in the black robes of respectability, had a strange look of the dead being borne over the water to the land of shadow. And when they stepped ashore they stood for a little at the landing-place uncertainly as though they did not quite know where to go, before desultorily, in twos and threes, they wandered up the hill.

At that hour the streets of the city were very empty so that more than ever it seemed a city of the dead. The passers-by had an abstracted air so that you might almost have thought them ghosts. The sky was unclouded and the early sun shed a heavenly mildness on the scene; it was difficult to imagine, on that blithe, fresh and smiling morn, that the city lay gasping, like a man whose life is being throttled out of him by a maniac's hands, in the dark clutch of the pestilence. It was incredible that nature (the blue of the sky was clear like a child's heart) should be so indifferent when men were writhing in agony and going to their death in fear. When the chairs were set down at the convent door a beggar arose from the ground and asked Kitty for alms. He was clad in faded and shapeless rags that looked as though he had raked them out of a muck-heap, and through their rents you saw his skin hard and rough and tanned like the hide of a goat; his bare legs were emaciated, and his head, with its shock of coarse grey hair (the cheeks hollow, the eyes wild), was the head of a madman. Kitty turned from him in frightened horror, and the chair-bearers in gruff tones bade him begone, but he was importunate, and to be rid of him, shuddering, Kitty gave him a few cash.

The door was opened and the amah explained that Kitty wished to see the Mother Superior. She was taken once more into the stiff parlour in which it seemed a window had never been opened, and here she sat so long that she began to think her message had not been delivered. At last the Mother Superior came in.

"I must ask you to excuse me for keeping you waiting," she said. "I did not expect you and I was occupied."

"Forgive me for troubling you. I am afraid I have come at an inconvenient moment."

The Mother Superior gave her a smile, austere but sweet, and begged her to sit down. But Kitty saw that her eyes were swollen. She had been weeping. Kitty was startled, for she had received from the Mother Superior the impression that she was a woman whom earthly troubles could not greatly move.

"I am afraid something has happened," she faltered. "Would you like me to go away? I can come another time."

"No, no. Tell me what I can do for you. It is only—only that one of our Sisters died last night." Her voice lost its even tone and her eyes filled with tears. "It is wicked of me to grieve, for I know that her good and simple soul has flown straight to heaven; she was a saint; but it is difficult always to control one's weakness. I am afraid I am not always very reasonable."

"I'm so sorry, I'm so dreadfully sorry," said Kitty.

Her ready sympathy brought a sob into her voice.

"She was one of the Sisters who came out from France with me ten years ago. There are only three of us left now. I remember, we stood in a little group at the end of the boat (what do you call it, the bow?) and as we steamed out of the harbour at Marseilles and we saw the golden figure of Saint-Marie la Grace, we said a prayer together. It had been my greatest wish since I entered religion to be allowed to come to China, but when I saw the land grow distant I could not prevent myself from weeping. I was their Superior; it was not a very good example I was giving my daughters. And then Sister St. Francis Xavier—that is the name of the Sister who died last night—took my hand and told me not to grieve; for wherever we were, she said, there was France and there was God."

That severe and handsome face was distorted by the grief which human nature wrung from her and by the effort to restrain the tears which her reason and her faith refused. Kitty looked away. She felt that it was indecent to peer into that struggle.

"I have been writing to her father. She, like me, was her mother's only daughter. They were fisher folk in Brittany, and it will be hard for them. Oh, when will this terrible epidemic cease? Two of our girls have been attacked this morning and nothing but a miracle can save them. These Chinese have no resistance. The loss of Sister St. Francis is very severe. There is so much to do and now fewer than ever to do it. We have Sisters at our other houses in China who are eager to come, all our Order, I think, would give anything in the world (only they have nothing) to come here; but it is almost certain death; and so long as we can manage with the Sisters we have I am unwilling that others should be sacrificed."

"That encourages me, *ma mère*," said Kitty. "I have been feeling that I had come at a very unfortunate moment. You said the other day that there was more work than the Sisters could do, and I was wondering if you would allow me to come and help them. I do not mind what I do if I can only be useful. I should be thankful if you just set me to scrub the floors."

The Mother Superior gave an amused smile and Kitty was astonished at the mobile temperament which could so easily pass from mood to mood.

"There is no need to scrub the floors. That is done after a fashion by the orphans." She paused and looked kindly at Kitty. "My dear child, do you not think that you have done enough in coming with your husband here? That is more than many wives would have had the courage to do, and for the rest how can you be better occupied than in giving him peace and comfort when he comes home to you after the day's work? Believe me, he needs then all your love and all your consideration."

Kitty could not easily meet the eyes which rested on her with a detached scrutiny and with an ironical kindliness.

"I have nothing whatever to do from morning till night," said Kitty. "I feel that there is so much to be done that I cannot bear to think that I am idle. I don't want to make a nuisance of myself, and I know that I have no claim either on your kindness or on your time, but I mean what I say and it would be a charity that you were doing me if you would let me be of some help to you."

"You do not look very strong. When you did us the pleasure of coming to see us the day before yesterday it seemed to me that you were very pale. Sister St. Joseph thought that perhaps you were going to have a baby."

"No, no," cried Kitty, flushing to the roots of her hair.

The Mother Superior gave a little, silvery laugh.

"It is nothing to be ashamed of, my dear child, nor is there anything improbable in the supposition. How long have you been married?"

"I am pale because I am naturally pale, but I am very strong, and I promise you I am not afraid of work."

Now the Superior was complete mistress of herself. She assumed unconsciously the air of authority which was habitual to her and she held Kitty in an appraising scrutiny. Kitty felt unaccountably nervous.

"Can you speak Chinese?"

"I'm afraid not," answered Kitty.

"Ah, that is a pity. I could have put you in charge of the elder girls. It is very difficult just now, and I am afraid they will get—what do you call? Out of hand?" she concluded with a tentative sound.

"Could I not be of help to the Sisters in nursing? I am not at all afraid of the cholera. I could nurse the girls or the soldiers."

The Mother Superior, unsmiling now, a reflective look on her face, shook her head.

"You do not know what the cholera is. It is a dreadful thing to see. The work in the infirmary is done by soldiers and we need a Sister only to supervise. And so far as the girls are concerned . . . no, no, I am sure your husband would not wish it; it is a terrible and frightening sight."

"I should grow used to it."

"No, it is out of the question. It is our business and our privilege to do such things, but there is no call for you to do so."

"You make me feel very useless and very helpless. It seems incredible that there should be nothing that I can do."

"Have you spoken to your husband of your wish?"

"Yes."

The Mother Superior looked at her as though she were delving into the secrets of her heart, but when she saw Kitty's anxious and appealing look she gave a smile.

"Of course you are a Protestant?" she asked.

"Yes."

"It doesn't matter. Dr. Watson, the missionary who died, was a Protestant and it made no difference. He was all that was most charming to us. We owe him a deep debt of gratitude."

Now the flicker of a smile passed over Kitty's face, but she did not say anything. The Mother Superior seemed to reflect. She rose to her feet.

"It is very good of you. I think I can find something for you to do. It is true that now Sister St. Francis has been taken from us, it is impossible for us to cope with the work. When will you be ready to start?"

"Now."

"*A la bonne heure.* I am content to hear you say that."

"I promise you I will do my best. I am very grateful to you for the opportunity that you are giving me."

The Mother Superior opened the parlour door, but as she

was going out she hesitated. Once more she gave Kitty a long, searching and sagacious look. Then she laid her hand gently on her arm.

"You know, my dear child, that one cannot find peace in work or in pleasure, in the world or in a convent, but only in one's soul."

Kitty gave a little start, but the Mother Superior passed swiftly out.

xlix

KITTY found the work a refreshment to her spirit. She went to the convent every morning soon after sunrise and did not return to the bungalow till the westering sun flooded the narrow river and its crowded junks with gold. The Mother Superior gave into her care the smaller children. Kitty's mother had brought to London from her native Liverpool a practical sense of housewifery and Kitty, notwithstanding her air of frivolity, had always had certain gifts to which she referred only in bantering tones. Thus she could cook quite well and she sewed beautifully. When she disclosed this talent she was set to supervise the stitching and hemming of the younger girls. They knew a little French and every day she picked up a few words of Chinese so that it was not difficult for her to manage. At other times she had to see that the smallest children did not get into mischief; she had to dress and undress them and take care that they rested when rest was needed. There were a good many babies and these were in charge of amahs, but she was bidden to keep an eye on them. None of the work was very important and she would have liked to do something which was more arduous; but the Mother Superior paid no attention to her entreaties and Kitty stood sufficiently in awe of her not to be importunate.

For the first few days she had to make something of an effort to overcome the faint distaste she felt for these little girls, in their ugly uniforms, with their stiff black hair, their round yellow faces, and their staring, sloe-black eyes. But she remembered the soft look which had transfigured so beautifully the countenance of the Mother Superior when on Kitty's first visit to the convent she had stood surrounded by those ugly little things, and she would not allow herself to surrender to her instinct. And presently, taking in her arms one or other of the tiny creatures, crying because of a fall or a cutting tooth, when Kitty found that a few soft words, though in a language the child could not understand, the pressure of her arms and the softness of her cheek against the weeping yellow face, could comfort and console, she began to lose all her feeling of strangeness. The small children, without any fear of her, came to her in their childish troubles and it gave her a peculiar happiness to discern their confidence. It was the same with the older girls, those to whom she taught sewing; their bright, clever smiles and the pleasure she could give them by a word of praise, touched her. She felt that they liked her and, flattered and proud, she liked them in return.

But there was one child that she could not grow used to. It was a little girl of six, an idiot with a huge hydrocephalic head that swayed top-heavily on a small, squat body, large vacant eyes and a drooling mouth; the creature spoke hoarsely a few mumbled words; it was revolting and horrible; and for some reason it conceived an idiot attachment for Kitty so that it followed her about as she changed her place from one part of the large room to another. It clung to her skirt and rubbed its face against her knees. It sought to fondle her hands. She shivered with disgust. She knew it yearned for caresses and she could not bring herself to touch it.

Once, speaking of it to Sister St. Joseph, she said that it was a pity it lived. Sister St. Joseph smiled and stretched out her hand to the misformed thing. It came and rubbed its bulging forehead against it.

"Poor little mite," said the nun. "She was brought here positively dying. By the mercy of Providence I was at the door just as she came. I thought there was not a moment to lose so I baptised her at once. You would not believe what trouble we have had to keep her with us. Three or four times we thought that her little soul would escape to heaven."

Kitty was silent. Sister St. Joseph in her loquacious way began to gossip of other things. And next day when the idiot child came to her and touched her hand Kitty nerved herself to place it in a caress on the great bare skull. She forced her lips into a smile. But suddenly the child, with an idiot perversity, left her; it seemed to lose interest in her, and that day and the following days paid her no attention. Kitty did not know what she had done and tried to lure it to her with smiles and gestures, but it turned away and pretended not to see her.

l

SINCE the nuns were busy from morning till night with a hundred duties Kitty saw little of them but at the services in the bare, humble chapel. On her first day the Mother Superior, catching sight of her seated at the back behind the girls on the benches according to their ages, stopped and spoke to her.

"You must not think it necessary for you to come to the chapel when we do," she said. "You are a Protestant and you have your own convictions."

"But I like to come, Mother. I find that it rests me."

The Mother Superior gave her a moment's glance and slightly inclined her grave head.

"Of course you will do exactly as you choose. I merely wanted you to understand that you are under no obligation."

But with Sister St. Joseph Kitty soon became on terms not of intimacy perhaps but of familiarity. The economy of the convent was in her charge and to look after the material well-being of that big family kept the Sister on her feet all day. She said that the only time she had to rest was that which she devoted to prayer. But it pleased her towards evening when Kitty was with the girls at their work to come in and, vowing that she was tired out and had not a moment to spare, sit down for a few minutes and gossip. When she was not in the presence of the Mother Superior she was a talkative, merry creature, fond of a joke, and she did not dislike a bit of scandal. Kitty stood in no fear of her, her habit did not prevent Sister St. Joseph from being a good-natured, homely woman, and she chattered with her gaily. She did not mind with her showing how badly she talked French and they laughed with one another over Kitty's mistakes. The Sister taught her every day a few useful words of Chinese. She was a farmer's daughter and at heart she was still a peasant.

"I used to keep the cows when I was little," she said, "like St. Joan of Arc. But I was too wicked to have visions. It was fortunate, I think, for my father would certainly have whipped me if I had. He used often to whip me, the good old man, for I was a very naughty little girl. I am ashamed sometimes when I think now of the pranks I used to play."

Kitty laughed at the thought that this corpulent, middle-aged nun could ever have been a wayward child. And yet there was something childlike in her still so that your heart went out to her: she seemed to have about her an aroma of the countryside in autumn when the apple trees are laden with fruit and the crops are in and safely housed. She had not the tragic and austere saintliness of the Mother Superior, but a gaiety that was simple and happy.

"Do you never wish to go home again, *ma sœur?*" asked Kitty.

"Oh, no. It would be too hard to come back. I love to be here and I am never so happy as when I am among the orphans. They're so good, they're so grateful. But it is all very well to be a nun (*on a beau être religieuse*) still one has a mother and one cannot forget that one drank the milk of her breasts. She is old, my mother, and it is hard never to see her again; but then she is fond of her daughter-in-law, and my brother is good to her. His son is growing up now, I should think they will be glad of an extra pair of strong arms on the farm; he was only a child when I left France, but he promised to have a fist that you could fell an ox with."

It was almost impossible in that quiet room, listening to the nun, to realise that on the other side of these four walls cholera was raging. Sister St. Joseph had an unconcern which conveyed itself to Kitty.

She had a naïve curiosity about the world and its inhabitants. She asked Kitty all kinds of questions about London and England, a country, she thought, where so thick was the fog that you could not see your hand at midday, and she wanted to know if Kitty went to balls and whether she lived in a grand house and how many brothers and sisters she had. She spoke often of Walter. The Mother Superior said he was wonderful and every day they prayed for him. How lucky Kitty was to have a husband who was so good and so brave and so clever.

li

BUT sooner or later Sister St. Joseph returned to the subject of the Mother Superior. Kitty had been conscious from the beginning that the personality of this woman dominated the convent. She was regarded by all that dwelt there with love certainly and with admiration, but also with awe and not a little dread. Notwithstanding her kindliness Kitty herself felt like a schoolgirl in her presence. She was never quite at her ease with her, for she was filled with a sentiment which was so strange that it embarrassed her: reverence. Sister St. Joseph with an ingenuous desire to impress, told Kitty how great the family was to which the Mother Superior belonged; she had among her ancestors persons of historic importance and she was *un peu cousine* with half the kings in Europe: Alphonso of Spain had hunted at her father's, and they had châteaux all over France. It must have been hard to leave so much grandeur. Kitty listened smilingly, but not a little impressed.

"*Du reste,* you have only to look at her," said the Sister, "to see that, *comme famille, c'est le dessus du panier.*"

"She has the most beautiful hands that I have ever seen," said Kitty.

"Ah, but if you only knew how she had used them. She is not afraid of work, *notre bonne mère.*"

When they had come to this city there had been nothing. They had built the convent. The Mother Superior had made

the plans and supervised the work. The moment they arrived
they began to save the poor little unwanted girls from the
baby-tower and the cruel hands of the midwife. At first they
had had no beds to sleep in and no glass to keep out the
night air ("and there is nothing," said Sister St. Joseph,
"which is more unwholesome"); and often they had no
money left, not only to pay the builders, but even to buy
their simple fare; they lived like peasants, what was she
saying? the peasants in France, *tenez,* the men who worked
for her father, would have thrown to the pigs the food they
ate. And then the Mother Superior would collect her daughters round her and they would kneel and pray; and the
Blessed Virgin would send money. A thousand francs would
arrive by post next day, or a stranger, an Englishman (a
Protestant, if you please) or even a Chinaman would knock
at the door while they were actually on their knees and bring
them a present. Once they were in such straits that they all
made a vow to the Blessed Virgin that they would recite a
neuvaine in her honour if she succoured them, and, would
you believe it? that funny Mr. Waddington came to see us
next day and saying that we looked as though we all wanted
a good plate of roast beef gave us a hundred dollars.

What a comic little man he was, with his bald head and
his little shrewd eyes (*ses petits yeux malins*) and his jokes.
Mon Dieu, how he murdered the French language, and yet
you could not help laughing at him. He was always in a good
humour. All through this terrible epidemic he carried himself as if he were enjoying a holiday. He had a heart quite
French and a wit so that you would hardly believe he was
English. Except for his accent. But sometimes Sister St.
Joseph thought he spoke badly on purpose to make you
laugh. Of course his morals were not all one could wish; but
still that was his business (with a sigh, a shrug and a shake
of the head) and he was a bachelor and a young man.

"What is wrong with his morals, *ma sœur?*" asked Kitty
smiling.

"Is it possible that you do not know? It is a sin for me to
tell you. I have no business to say such things. He lives with
a Chinese woman, that is to say, not a Chinese woman, but

a Manchu. A princess, it appears, and she loves him to distraction."

"That sounds quite impossible," cried Kitty.

"No, no, I promise you, it is everything that is most true. It is very wicked of him. Those things are not done. Did you not hear, when you first came to the convent and he would not eat the *madeleines* that I had made expressly, that *notre bonne mère* said his stomach was deranged by Manchu cooking? That was what she meant and you should have seen the head that he made. It is a story altogether curious. It appears that he was stationed at Hankow during the revolution when they were massacring the Manchus and this good little Waddington saved the lives of one of their great families. They are related to the Imperial Family. The girl fell violently in love with him and—well, the rest you can imagine. And then when he left Hankow she ran away and followed him and now she follows him everywhere, and he has had to resign himself to keep her, poor fellow, and I daresay he is very fond of her; they are quite charming sometimes, these Manchu women. But what am I thinking of? I have a thousand things to do and I sit here. I am a bad religious. I am ashamed of myself."

lii

KITTY had a queer feeling that she was growing. The constant occupation distracted her mind and the glimpses she had of other lives and other outlooks awakened her imagination. She began to regain her spirits; she felt better and stronger. It had seemed to her that she could do nothing now but weep; but to her surprise, and not a little to her confusion, she caught herself laughing at this and that. It began to seem quite natural to live in the midst of a terrible epidemic. She knew that people were dying to the right and left of her, but she ceased very much to think of it. The Mother Superior had forbidden her to go into the infirmaries and the closed doors excited her curiosity. She would have liked to peep in, but could not do so without being seen, and she did not know what punishment the Mother Superior would inflict upon her. It would be dreadful to be sent away. She was devoted to the children now and they would miss her if she went; in fact she did not know what they would do without her.

And one day it occurred to her that she had neither thought of Charles Townsend nor dreamt of him for a week. Her heart gave a sudden thud against her ribs: she was cured. She could think of him now with indifference. She loved him no longer. Oh, the relief and the sense of liberation! It was strange to look back and remember how passionately she had yearned for him; she thought she would die when he failed her; she thought life thenceforward had nothing to offer but misery. And now already she was laughing. A worthless creature. What a fool she had made of herself! And now, considering him calmly, she wondered what on earth she had seen in him. It was lucky that Waddington knew nothing, she could never have endured his malicious eyeing and his ironical innuendos. She was free, free at last, free! She could hardly prevent herself from laughing aloud.

The children were playing some romping game and it was her habit to look on with an indulgent smile, restraining them when they made too much noise and taking care that in their boisterousness none was hurt; but now in her high spirits, feeling as young as any of them, she joined in the game. The little girls received her with delight. They chased up and down the room, shouting at the top of their shrill voices, with fantastic and almost barbarous glee. They grew so excited that they leaped into the air with joy. The noise was terrific.

Suddenly the door opened and the Mother Superior stood on the threshold. Kitty, abashed, extricated herself from the clutches of a dozen little girls who with wild shrieks had seized her.

"Is this how you keep these children good and quiet?" asked the Mother Superior, a smile on her lips.

"We were having a game, Mother. They got excited. It is my fault, I led them on."

The Mother Superior came forward and as usual the children clustered about her. She put her hands round their narrow shoulders and playfully pulled their little yellow ears. She looked at Kitty with a long, soft look. Kitty was flushed and she was breathing quickly. Her liquid eyes were shining and her lovely hair, disarranged in all the struggling and the laughter, was in adorable confusion.

"Que vous êtes belle, ma chère enfant," said the Mother Superior. "It does the heart good to look at you. No wonder these children adore you."

Kitty blushed deeply and, she knew not why, tears suddenly filled her eyes. She covered her face with her hands.

"Oh, Mother, you make me ashamed."

"Come, do not be silly. Beauty is also a gift of God, one of the most rare and precious, and we should be thankful if we are happy enough to possess it and thankful, if we are not, that others possess it for our pleasure."

She smiled again and as though Kitty were a child too gently patted her soft cheek.

liii

SINCE she had been working at the convent Kitty had seen less of Waddington. Two or three times he had come down to the river bank to meet her and they had walked up the hill together. He came in to drink a whisky and soda, but he would seldom stay to dinner. One Sunday, however, he suggested that they should take their luncheon with them and go in chairs to a Buddhist monastery. It was situated ten miles from the city and had some reputation as a place of pilgrimage. The Mother Superior, insisting that Kitty must have a day's rest, would not let her work on Sundays and Walter of course was as busy then as usual.

They started early in order to arrive before the heat of the day and were carried along a narrow causeway between the rice fields. Now and then they passed comfortable farmhouses nestling with friendly intimacy in a grove of bamboos. Kitty enjoyed the idleness; it was pleasant after being cooped

up in the city to see about her the wide country. They came
to the monastery, straggling low buildings by the side of the
river, agreeably shaded by trees, and were led by smiling
monks through courtyards, empty with a solemn emptiness,
and shown temples with grimacing gods. In the sanctuary
sat the Buddha, remote and sad, wistful, abstracted and
faintly smiling. There was about everything a sense of dejection; the magnificence was shoddy and ruined; the gods
were dusty and the faith that had made them was dying.
The monks seemed to stay on sufferance, as though they
awaited a notice to quit; and in the smile of the abbot, with
his beautiful politeness, was the irony of resignation. One
of these days the monks would wander away from the shady,
pleasant wood, and the buildings, crumbling and neglected,
would be battered by fierce storms and besieged by the surrounding nature. Wild creepers would twine themselves
about the dead images and trees would grow in the courtyards. Then the gods would dwell there no longer, but evil
spirits of darkness.

liv

THEY sat on the steps of a little building (four lacquered
columns and a high, tiled roof under which stood a great
bronze bell) and watched the river flow sluggish and with
many a bend towards the stricken city. They could see its
crenellated walls. The heat hung over it like a pall. But the
river, though it flowed so slowly, had still a sense of movement and it gave one a melancholy feeling of the transitoriness of things. Everything passed, and what trace of its
passage remained? It seemed to Kitty that they were all,
the human race, like the drops of water in that river and
they flowed on, each so close to the other and yet so far
apart, a nameless flood, to the sea. When all things lasted
so short a time and nothing mattered very much, it seemed
pitiful that men, attaching an absurd importance to trivial
objects, should make themselves and one another so unhappy.

"Do you know Harrington Gardens?" she asked Waddington, with a smile in her beautiful eyes.

"No. Why?"

"Nothing; only it's a long way from here. It's where my people live."

"Are you thinking of going home?"

"No."

"I suppose you'll be leaving here in a couple of months. The epidemic seems to be abating and the cool weather should see the end of it."

"I almost think I shall be sorry to go."

For a moment she thought of the future. She did not know what plans Walter had in mind. He told her nothing. He was cool, polite, silent and inscrutable. Two little drops in that river that flowed silently towards the unknown; two little drops that to themselves had so much individuality and to the onlooker were but an undistinguishable part of the water.

"Take care the nuns don't start converting you," said Waddington, with his malicious little smile.

"They're much too busy. Nor do they care. They're wonderful and so kind; and yet—I hardly know how to explain it—there is a wall between them and me. I don't know what it is. It is as though they possessed a secret which made all the difference in their lives and which I was unworthy to share. It is not faith; it is something deeper and more—more significant: they walk in a different world from ours and we shall always be strangers to them. Each day when the convent door closes behind me I feel that for them I have ceased to exist."

"I can understand that it is something of a blow to your vanity," he returned mockingly.

"My vanity."

Kitty shrugged her shoulders. Then, smiling once more, she turned to him lazily.

"Why did you never tell me that you lived with a Manchu princess?"

"What have those gossiping old women been telling you?

I am sure that it is a sin for nuns to discuss the private affairs of the Customs officials."

"Why should you be so sensitive?"

Waddington glanced down, sideways, so that it gave him an air of slyness. He faintly shrugged his shoulders.

"It's not a thing to advertise. I do not know that it would greatly add to my chances of promotion in the service."

"Are you very fond of her?"

He looked up now and his ugly little face had the look of a naughty schoolboy's.

"She's abandoned everything for my sake, home, family, security and self-respect. It's a good many years now since she threw everything to the winds to be with me. I've sent her away two or three times, but she's always come back; I've run away from her myself, but she's always followed me. And now I've given it up as a bad job; I think I've got to put up with her for the rest of my life."

"She must really love you to distraction."

"It's a rather funny sensation, you know," he answered, wrinkling a perplexed forehead. "I haven't the smallest doubt that if I really left her, definitely, she would commit suicide. Not with any ill-feeling towards me, but quite naturally, because she was unwilling to live without me. It is a curious feeling it gives one to know that. It can't help meaning something to you."

"But it's loving that's the important thing, not being loved. One's not even grateful to the people who love one; if one doesn't love them, they only bore one."

"I have no experience of the plural," he replied. "Mine is only in the singular."

"Is she really an Imperial Princess?"

"No," that is a romantic exaggeration of the nuns. She belongs to one of the great families of the Manchus, but they have, of course, been ruined by the revolution. She is all the same a very great lady."

He said it in a tone of pride, so that a smile flickered in Kitty's eyes.

"Are you going to stay here for the rest of your life then?"

"In China? Yes. What would she do elsewhere? When I

retire I shall take a little Chinese house in Peking and spend the rest of my days there."

"Have you any children?"

"No."

She looked at him curiously. It was strange that this little bald-headed man with his monkey face should have aroused in the alien woman so devastating a passion. She could not tell why the way he spoke of her, notwithstanding his casual manner and his flippant phrases, gave her the impression so strongly of the woman's intense and unique devotion. It troubled her a little.

"It does seem a long way to Harrington Gardens," she smiled.

"Why do you say that?"

"I don't understand anything. Life is so strange. I feel like some one who's lived all his life by a duck-pond and suddenly is shown the sea. It makes me a little breathless, and yet it fills me with elation. I don't want to die, I want to live. I'm beginning to feel a new courage. I feel like one of those old sailors who set sail for undiscovered seas and I think my soul hankers for the unknown."

Waddington looked at her reflectively. Her abstracted gaze rested on the smoothness of the river. Two little drops that flowed silently, silently towards the dark, eternal sea.

"May I come and see the Manchu lady?" asked Kitty, suddenly raising her head.

"She can't speak a word of English."

"You've been very kind to me, you've done a great deal for me, perhaps I could show her by my manner that I had a friendly feeling towards her."

Waddington gave a thin, mocking little smile, but he answered with good-humour.

"I will come and fetch you one day and she shall give you a cup of jasmine tea."

She would not tell him that this story of an alien love had from the first moment strangely intrigued her fancy, and the Manchu Princess stood now as the symbol of something that vaguely, but insistently, beckoned to her. She pointed enigmatically to a mystic land of the spirit.

lv

BUT a day or two later Kitty made an unforeseen discovery.

She went to the convent as usual and set about her first
work of seeing that the children were washed and dressed.
Since the nuns held firmly that the night air was harmful,
the atmosphere in the dormitory was close and fetid. After
the freshness of the morning it always made Kitty a little
uncomfortable and she hastened to open such windows as
would. But to-day she felt on a sudden desperately sick and
with her head swimming she stood at a window trying to
compose herself. It had never been as bad as this before.
Then nausea overwhelmed her and she vomited. She gave
a cry so that the children were frightened, and the older
girl who was helping her ran up and, seeing Kitty white
and trembling, stopped short with an exclamation. Cholera!
The thought flashed through Kitty's mind and then a death-
like feeling came over her; she was seized with terror, she
struggled for a moment against the night that seemed ago-
nisingly to run through her, veins; she felt horribly ill; and
then darkness.

When she opened her eyes she did not at first know where
she was. She seemed to be lying on the floor and, moving
her head slightly, she thought that there was a pillow under
it. She could not remember. The Mother Superior was
kneeling by her side, holding smelling salts to her nose, and
Sister St. Joseph stood looking at her. Then it came back.
Cholera! She saw the consternation on the nuns' faces. Sister
St. Joseph looked huge and her outline was blurred. Once
more terror overwhelmed her.

"Oh, Mother, Mother," she sobbed. "Am I going to die?
I don't want to die."

"Of course you're not going to die," said the Mother
Superior.

She was quite composed and there was even amusement
in her eyes.

"But it's cholera. Where's Walter? Has he been sent for? Oh, Mother, Mother."

She burst into a flood of tears. The Mother Superior gave her hand and Kitty seized it as though it were a hold upon the life she feared to lose.

"Come, come, my dear child, you mustn't be so silly. It's not cholera or anything of the kind."

"Where's Walter?"

"Your husband is much too busy to be troubled. In five minutes you'll be perfectly well."

Kitty looked at her with staring, harassed eyes. Why did she take it so calmly? It was cruel.

"Keep perfectly quiet for a minute," said the Mother Superior. "There is nothing to alarm yourself about."

Kitty felt her heart beat madly. She had grown so used to the thought of cholera that it had ceased to seem possible that she could catch it. Oh, the fool she had been! She knew she was going to die. She was frightened. The girls brought in a long rattan chair and placed it by the window.

"Come, let us lift you," said the Mother Superior. "You will be more comfortable on the *chaise longue*. Do you think you can stand?"

She put her hands under Kitty's arms and Sister St. Joseph helped her to her feet. She sank exhausted into the chair.

"I had better shut the window," said Sister St. Joseph. "The early morning air cannot be good for her."

"No, no," said Kitty. "Please leave it open."

It gave her confidence to see the blue sky. She was shaken, but certainly she began to feel better. The two nuns looked at her for a moment in silence, and Sister St. Joseph said something to the Mother Superior which she could not understand. Then the Mother Superior sat on the side of the chair and took her hand.

"Listen, *ma chère enfant* . . ."

She asked her one or two questions. Kitty answered them without knowing what they meant. Her lips were trembling so that she could hardly frame the words.

"There is no doubt about it," said Sister St. Joseph. "I am not one to be deceived in such a matter."

She gave a little laugh in which Kitty seemed to discern a certain excitement and not a little affection. The Mother Superior, still holding Kitty's hand, smiled with soft tenderness.

"Sister St. Joseph has more experience of these things than I have, dear child, and she said at once what was the matter with you. She was evidently quite right."

"What do you mean?" asked Kitty anxiously.

"It is quite evident. Did the possibility of such a thing never occur to you? You are with child, my dear."

The start that Kitty gave shook her from head to foot, and she put her feet to the ground as though to spring up.

"Lie still, lie still," said the Mother Superior.

Kitty felt herself blush furiously and she put her hands to her breasts.

"It's impossible. It isn't true."

"*Qu'est ce qu'elle dit?*" asked Sister St. Joseph.

The Mother Superior translated. Sister St. Joseph's broad simple face, with its red cheeks, was beaming.

"No mistake is possible. I give you my word of honour."

"How long have you been married, my child?" asked the Mother Superior. "Why, when my sister-in-law had been married as long as you she had already two babies."

Kitty sank back into the chair. There was death in her heart.

"I'm so ashamed," she whispered.

"Because you are going to have a baby? Why, what can be more natural?"

"*Quelle joie pour le docteur,*" said Sister St. Joseph.

"Yes, think what a happiness for your husband. He will be overwhelmed with joy. You have only to see him with babies, and the look on his face when he plays with them, to see how enchanted he will be to have one of his own."

For a little while Kitty was silent. The two nuns looked at her with tender interest and the Mother Superior stroked her hand.

"It was silly of me not to have suspected it before," said Kitty. "At all events I'm glad it's not cholera. I feel very much better. I will get back to my work."

"Not to-day, my dear child. You have had a shock, you had much better go home and rest yourself."

"No, no, I would much rather stay and work."

"I insist. What would our good doctor say if I let you be imprudent? Come to-morrow, if you like, or the day after, but to-day you must be quiet. I will send for a chair. Would you like me to let one of our young girls go with you?"

"Oh, no, I shall be all right alone."

lvi

KITTY was lying on her bed and the shutters were closed. It was after luncheon and the servants slept. What she had learnt that morning (and now she was certain that it was true) filled her with consternation. Ever since she came home she had been trying to think; but her mind was a blank, and she could not collect her thoughts. Suddenly she heard a step, the feet were booted so that it could not be one of the boys; with a gasp of apprehension she realised that it could only be her husband. He was in the sitting-room and she heard herself called. She did not reply. There was a moment's silence and then a knock on her door.

"Yes?"

"May I come in?"

Kitty rose from her bed and slipped into a dressing-gown.
"Yes."

He entered. She was glad that the closed shutters shadowed her face.

"I hope I didn't wake you. I knocked very, very gently."

"I haven't been asleep."

He went to one of the windows and threw open the shutter. A flood of warm light streamed into the room.

"What is it?" she asked. "Why are you back so early?"

"The Sisters said that you weren't very well. I thought I had better come and see what was the matter."

A flash of anger passed through her.

"What would you have said if it had been cholera?"

"If it had been you certainly couldn't have made your way home this morning."

She went to the dressing-table and passed the comb through her shingled hair. She wanted to gain time. Then, sitting down, she lit a cigarette.

"I wasn't very well this morning and the Mother Superior thought I'd better come back here. But I'm perfectly all right again. I shall go to the convent as usual to-morrow."

"What was the matter with you?"

"Didn't they tell you?"

"No. The Mother Superior said that you must tell me yourself."

He did now what he did seldom; he looked her full in the face; his professional instincts were stronger than his personal. She hesitated. Then she forced herself to meet his eyes.

"I'm going to have a baby," she said.

She was accustomed to his habit of meeting with silence a statement which you would naturally expect to evoke an exclamation, but never had it seemed to her more devastating. He said nothing; he made no gesture; no movement on his face nor change of expression in his dark eyes indicated that he had heard. She felt suddenly inclined to cry. If a man loved his wife and his wife loved him, at such a moment they were drawn together by a poignant emotion. The silence was intolerable and she broke it.

"I don't know why it never occurred to me before. It was stupid of me, but . . . what with one thing and another . . ."

"How long have you . . . when do you expect to be confined?"

The words seemed to issue from his lips with difficulty. She felt that his throat was as dry as hers. It was a nuisance that her lips trembled so when she spoke; if he was not of stone it must excite his pity.

"I suppose I've been like this between two and three months."

"Am I the father?"

She gave a little gasp. There was just a shadow of a tremor in his voice; it was dreadful that cold self-control of his which made the smallest token of emotion so shattering. She did not know why she thought suddenly of an instrument she had been shown in Hong-Kong upon which a needle oscillated a little and she had been told that this represented an earthquake a thousand miles away in which perhaps a thousand persons had lost their lives. She looked at him. He was ghastly pale. She had seen that pallor on him once, twice before. He was looking down, a little sideways.

"Well?"

She clasped her hands. She knew that if she could say yes it would mean everything in the world to him. He would believe her, of course he would believe her, because he wanted to; and then he would forgive. She knew how deep was his tenderness and how ready he was, for all his shyness, to expend it. She knew that he was not vindictive; he would forgive her if she could but give him an excuse to, an excuse that touched his heart, and he would forgive completely. She could count on him never to throw the past in her teeth. Cruel he might be, cold and morbid, but he was neither mean nor petty. It would alter everything if she said yes.

And she had an urgent need for sympathy. The unexpected knowledge that she was with child had overwhelmed her with strange hopes and unforeseen desires. She felt weak, frightened a little, alone and very far from any friends. That morning, though she cared little for her mother, she had had a sudden craving to be with her. She needed help and consolation. She did not love Walter, she knew that she never could, but at this moment she longed with all her heart for him to take her in his arms so that she could lay her head on his breast; clinging to him she could have cried happily; she wanted him to kiss her and she wanted to twine her arms around his neck.

She began to weep. She had lied so much and she could lie so easily. What could a lie matter when it could only do good? A lie, a lie, what was a lie? It was so easy to say yes. She saw Walter's eyes melt and his arms outstretched towards her. She couldn't say it; she didn't know why, she just couldn't. All she had gone through during these bitter weeks, Charlie and his unkindness, the cholera and all these people dying, the nuns, oddly enough even that funny, drunken little Waddington, it all seemed to have changed her so that she did not know herself; though she was so deeply moved, some bystander in her soul seemed to watch her with terror and surprise. She *had* to tell the truth. It did not seem worth while to lie. Her thoughts wandered strangely: on a sudden she saw that dead beggar at the foot of the compound wall. Why should she think of him? She did not sob; the tears streamed down her face, quite easily, from wide eyes. At last she answered the question. He had asked her if he was the child's father.

"I don't know," she said.

He gave the ghost of a chuckle. It made Kitty shudder.

"It's a bit awkward, isn't it?"

His answer was characteristic, it was exactly what she would have expected him to say, but it made her heart sink. She wondered if he realised how hard it had been for her to tell the truth (at the same moment she recognised that it had not been in the least hard, but inevitable) and if he gave her credit for it. Her answer, *I don't know, I don't know,* hammered away in her head. It was impossible now to take it back. She got her handkerchief from her bag and dried her eyes. They did not speak. There was a syphon on the table by her bed and he got her a glass of water. He brought it to her and held the glass while she drank. She noticed how thin his hand was, it was a fine hand, slender, with long fingers, but now it was nothing but skin and bone; it trembled a little : he could control his face, but his hand betrayed him.

"Don't mind my crying," she said. "It's nothing really; it's only that I can't help the water running out of my eyes."

She drank the water and he put the glass back. He sat down on a chair and lit a cigarette. He gave a little sigh. Once or twice before she had heard him sigh like that and it always gave her a catch at the heart. Looking at him now, for he was staring with abstracted gaze out of the window, she was surprised that she had not noticed before how terribly thin he had grown during the last weeks. His temples were sunken and the bones of his face showed through the skin. His clothes hung on him loosely as though they had been made for a larger man. Through his sunburn his face had a greenish pallor. He looked exhausted. He was working too hard, sleeping little and eating nothing. In her own grief and perturbation she found room to pity him. It was cruel to think that she could do nothing for him.

He put his hand over his forehead, as though his head were aching, and she had a feeling that in his brain too those words hammered madly: *I don't know, I don't know.* It was strange that this moody, cold and shy man should have such a natural affection for very little babies; most men didn't care much even for their own, but the nuns, touched and a little amused, had more than once spoken of it. If he felt like that about those funny little Chinese babies what would he have felt about his own? Kitty bit her lips in order to prevent herself from crying again.

He looked at his watch.

"I'm afraid I must go back to the city. I have a great deal to do to-day . . . . Shall you be all right?"

"Oh, yes. Don't bother about me."

"I think you'd better not wait for me this evening. I may be very late and I'll get something to eat from Colonel Yü."

"Very well."

He rose.

"If I were you, I wouldn't try to do anything to-day. You'd better take it easy. Is there anything you want before I go?"

"No, thanks. I shall be quite all right."

He paused for an instant, as though he were undecided, and then, abruptly and without looking at her, took his hat and walked out of the room. She heard him go through the compound. She felt terribly alone. There was no need for self-restraint now and she gave herself up to a passion of tears.

lvii

THE night was sultry and Kitty sat at the window looking at the fantastic roofs, dark against the starlight, of the Chinese temple, when at last Walter came in. Her eyes were heavy with weeping, but she was composed. Notwithstanding all there was to harass her she felt, perhaps only from exhaustion, strangely at peace.

"I thought you'd be already in bed," said Walter as he came in.

"I wasn't sleepy. I thought it cooler to sit up. Have you had any dinner?"

"All I want."

He walked up and down the long room and she saw that he had something to say to her. She knew that he was embarrassed. Without concern she waited for him to summon up his resolution. He began abruptly.

"I've been thinking about what you told me this afternoon. It seems to me that it would be better if you went away. I have spoken to Colonel Yü and he will give you an escort. You could take the amah with you. You will be quite safe."

"Where is there for me to go?"

"You can go to your mother's."

"Do you think she would be pleased to see me?"

He paused for a moment, hesitating, as though for reflection.

"Then you can go to Hong-Kong."

"What should I do there?"

"You will need a good deal of care and attention. I don't think it's fair to ask you to stay here."

She could not prevent the smile, not only of bitterness but of frank amusement, that crossed her face. She gave him a glance and very nearly laughed.

"I don't know why you should be so anxious about my health."

He came over to the window and stood looking out at the night. There had never been so many stars in the unclouded sky.

"This isn't the place for a woman in your condition."

She looked at him, white in his thin clothes against the darkness; there was something sinister in his fine profile, and yet oddly enough at this moment it excited in her no fear.

"When you insisted on my coming here did you want it to kill me?" she asked suddenly.

He was so long answering that she thought he had refused to hear.

"At first."

She gave a little shudder, for it was the first time he had admitted his intention. But she bore him no ill will for it. Her feeling surprised herself; there was a certain admiration in it and a faint amusement. She did not quite know why, but suddenly thinking of Charlie Townsend he seemed to her an abject fool.

"It was a terrible risk you were taking," she answered. "With your sensitive conscience I wonder if you could ever have forgiven yourself if I had died."

"Well, you haven't. You've thrived on it."

"I've never felt better in my life."

She had an instinct to throw herself on the mercy of his humour. After all they had gone through, when they were living amid these scenes of horror and desolation, it seemed inept to attach importance to the ridiculous act of fornication. When death stood round the corner, taking lives like a gardener digging up potatoes, it was foolishness to care what dirty things this person or that did with his body. If she could only make him realise how little Charlie meant to her, so that now already she had difficulty in calling up his features to her imagination, and how entirely the love of him had passed out of her heart! Because she had no feeling for Townsend the various acts she had committed with him had lost their significance. She had regained her heart and what she had given of her body seemed not to matter a rap. She was inclined to say to Walter: "Look here, don't you think we've been silly long enough? We've sulked with one another like children. Why can't we kiss and be friends. There's no reason why we shouldn't be friends just because we're not lovers."

He stood very still and the lamplight made the pallor of his impassive face startling. She did not trust him; if she said the wrong thing he would turn upon her with such an icy sternness. She knew by now his extreme sensitiveness, for which his acid irony was a protection, and how quickly he could close his heart if his feelings were hurt. She had a moment's irritation at his stupidity. Surely what troubled him most was the wound to his vanity: she vaguely realised that this is the hardest of all wounds to heal. It was singular that men attached so much importance to their wives' faithfulness; when first she had gone with Charlie she had expected to feel quite different, a changed woman; but she had seemed to herself exactly the same, she had experienced only well-being and a greater vitality. She wished now that she had been able to tell Walter that the child was his; the lie would have meant so little to her, and the assurance would have been so great a comfort to him. And after all it might not be a lie: it was funny, that something in her heart which had prevented her from giving herself the benefit of the doubt. How silly men were! Their part in procreation was so unimportant; it was the woman who carried the child through long months of uneasiness and bore it with pain, and yet a man because of his momentary connection made such preposterous claims. Why should that make any difference to him in his feeling towards the child? Then Kitty's thoughts wandered to the child which she herself would bear; she thought of it not with emotion nor with a passion of maternity, but with an idle curiosity.

"I daresay you'd like to think it over a little," said Walter, breaking the long silence.

"Think what?"

He turned a little as if he were surprised.

"About when you want to go?"

"But I don't want to go."

"Why not?"

"I like my work at the convent. I think I'm making myself useful. I should prefer to stay as long as you do."

"I think I should tell you that in your present condition you are probably more liable to catch any infection that happens to be about."

"I like the discreet way you put it," she smiled ironically.

"You're not staying for my sake?"

She hesitated. He little knew that now the strongest emotion he excited in her, and the most unexpected, was pity.

"No. You don't love me. I often think I rather bore you."

"I shouldn't have thought you were the sort of person to put yourself out for a few stuffy nuns and a parcel of Chinese brats."

Her lips outlined a smile.

"I think it's rather unfair to despise me so much because you made such a mistake in your judgment of me. It's not my fault that you were such an ass."

"If you're determined to stay you are of course at liberty to do so."

"I'm sorry I can't give you the opportunity of being magnanimous." She found it strangely hard to be quite serious with him. "As a matter of fact you're quite right, it's not only for the orphans that I'm staying: you see, I'm in the peculiar position that I haven't got a soul in the world that I can go to. I know no one who wouldn't think me a nuisance. I know no one who cares a row of pins if I'm alive or dead."

He frowned. But he did not frown in anger.

"We have made a dreadful hash of things, haven't we?" he said.

"Do you still want to divorce me? I don't think I care any more."

"You must know that by bringing you here I've condoned the offence."

"I didn't know. You see, I haven't made a study of infidelity. What are we going to do then when we leave here? Are we going on living together?"

"Oh, don't you think we can let the future take care of itself?"

There was the weariness of death in his voice.

lviii

Two or three days later Waddington fetched Kitty from the convent (for her restlessness had induced her immediately to resume her work) and took her to drink the promised cup of tea with his mistress. Kitty had on more than one occasion dined at Waddington's house. It was a square, white and pretentious building, such as the Customs build for their officials all over China; and the dining-room in which they ate, the drawing-room in which they sat, were furnished with prim and solid furniture. They had the appearance of being partly offices and partly hotel; there was nothing homelike in them and you understood that these houses were merely places of haphazard sojourn to their successive occupants. It would never have occurred to you that on an upper floor mystery and perhaps, romance dwelt shrouded. They ascended a flight of stairs and Waddington opened a door. Kitty went into a large, bare room with white-washed walls on which hung scrolls in various calligraphies. At a square table, on a stiff arm-chair, both of blackwood and heavily carved, sat the Manchu. She rose as Kitty and Waddington entered, but made no step forward.

"Here she is," said Waddington, and added something in Chinese.

Kitty shook hands with her. She was slim in her long embroidered gown and somewhat taller than Kitty, used to the Southern people, had expected. She wore a jacket of pale green silk with tight sleeves that came over her wrists and on her black hair, elaborately dressed, was the head-dress of the Manchu women. Her face was coated with powder and her cheeks from the eyes to the mouth heavily rouged; her plucked eyebrows were a thin dark line and her mouth was scarlet. From this mask her black, slightly slanting, large eyes burned like lakes of liquid jet. She seemed more like an idol than a woman. Her movements were slow and assured. Kitty had the impression that she was slightly shy but very curious. She nodded her head two or three times, looking at Kitty, while Waddington spoke of her. Kitty noticed her hands; they were preternaturally long, very slender, of the colour of ivory; and the exquisite nails were painted. Kitty thought she had never seen anything so lovely as those languid and elegant hands. They suggested the breeding of uncounted centuries.

She spoke a little, in a high voice, like the twittering of birds in an orchard, and Waddington, translating, told Kitty that she was glad to see her; how old was she and how many children had she got? They sat down on three straight chairs at the square table and a boy brought in bowls of tea, pale and scented with jasmine. The Manchu lady handed Kitty a green tin of Three Castles cigarettes. Beside the table and the chairs the room contained little furniture; there was a wide pallet bed on which was an embroidered head rest and two sandalwood chests.

"What does she do with herself all day long?" asked Kitty.

"She paints a little and sometimes she writes a poem. But she mostly sits. She smokes, but only in moderation, which is fortunate, since one of my duties is to prevent the traffic in opium."

"Do you smoke?" asked Kitty.

"Seldom. To tell you the truth I much prefer whisky."

There was in the room a faintly acrid smell; it was not unpleasant, but peculiar and exotic.

"Tell her that I am sorry I cannot talk to her. I am sure we have many things to say to one another."

When this was translated to the Manchu she gave Kitty a quick glance in which there was the hint of a smile. She was impressive as she sat, without embarrassment, in her beautiful clothes; and from the painted face the eyes looked out wary, self-possessed and unfathomable. She was unreal, like a picture, and yet had an elegance which made Kitty feel all thumbs. Kitty had never paid anything but passing and somewhat contemptuous attention to the China in which fate had thrown her. It was not done in her set. Now she seemed on a sudden to have an inkling of something remote and mysterious. Here was the East, immemorial, dark and inscrutable. The beliefs and the ideals of the West seemed crude beside ideals and beliefs of which in this exquisite creature she seemed to catch a fugitive glimpse. Here was a different life, lived on a different plane. Kitty felt strangely that the sight of this idol, with her painted face and slanting, wary eyes, made the efforts and the pains of the everyday world she knew slightly absurd. That coloured mask seemed to hide the secret of an abundant, profound and significant experience: those long, delicate hands with their tapering fingers held the key of riddles undivined.

"What does she think about all day long?" asked Kitty.

"Nothing," smiled Waddington.

"She's wonderful. Tell her I've never seen such beautiful hands. I wonder what she sees in *you*."

Waddington, smiling, translated the question.

"She says I'm good."

"As if a woman ever loved a man for his virtue," Kitty mocked.

The Manchu laughed but once. This was when Kitty, for something to say, expressed admiration of a jade bracelet she wore. She took it off and Kitty, trying to put it on, found, though her hands were small enough, that it would not pass over her knuckles. Then the Manchu burst into childlike laughter. She said something to Waddington and called for an amah. She gave her an instruction and the amah in a moment brought in a pair of very beautiful Manchu shoes.

"She wants to give you these if you can wear them," said Waddington. "You'll find they make quite good bedroom slippers."

"They fit me perfectly," said Kitty, not without satisfaction.

But she noticed a roguish smile on Waddington's face.

"Are they too big for her?" she asked quickly.

"Miles."

Kitty laughed and when Waddington translated, the Manchu and the amah laughed also.

When Kitty and Waddington, a little later, were walking up the hill together, she turned to him with a friendly smile.

"You did not tell me that you had a great affection for her."

"What makes you think I have?"

"I saw it in your eyes. It's strange, it must be like loving a phantom or a dream. Men are incalculable; I thought you were like everybody else and now I feel that I don't know the first thing about you."

As they reached the bungalow he asked her abruptly:

"Why did you want to see her?"

Kitty hesitated for a moment before answering.

"I'm looking for something and I don't quite know what

it is. But I know that it's very important for me to know it, and if I did it would make all the difference. Perhaps the nuns know it; when I'm with them I feel that they hold a secret which they will not share with me. I don't know why it came into my head that if I saw this Manchu woman I should have an inkling of what I am looking for. Perhaps she would tell me if she could."

"What makes you think she knows it?"

Kitty gave him a sidelong glance, but did not answer. Instead she asked him a question.

"Do you know it?"

He smiled and shrugged his shoulders.

"Tao. Some of us look for the Way in opium and some in God, some of us in whisky and some in love. It is all the same Way and it leads nowhither."

lix

KITTY fell again into the comfortable routine of her work and though in the early morning feeling far from well she had spirit enough not to let it discompose her. She was astonished at the interest the nuns took in her: sisters who, when she saw them in a corridor, had done no more than bid her good morning now on a flimsy pretext came into the room in which she was occupied and looked at her, chatting a little, with a sweet and childlike excitement. Sister St. Joseph told her with a repetition which was sometimes tedious how she had been saying to herself for days past: "Now, I wonder," or: "I shouldn't be surprised"; and then, when Kitty fainted: "There can be no doubt, it jumps to the eyes." She told Kitty long stories of her sister-in-law's confinements, which but for Kitty's quick sense of humour would have been not a little alarming. Sister St. Joseph combined in a pleasant fashion the realistic outlook of her upbringing (a river wound through the meadows of her father's farm and the poplars that stood on its bank trembled in the faintest breeze) with a charming intimacy with religious things. One day, firmly convinced that a heretic could know

nothing of such matters, she told Kitty of the Annunciation.
"I can never read those lines in the Holy Writ without
weeping," she said. "I do not know why, but it gives me
such a funny feeling."

And then in French, in words that to Kitty sounded unfamiliar and in their precision a trifle cold, she quoted:

*"And the angel came in unto her, and said, Hail full of
grace, the Lord is with thee: blessed art thou among
women."*

The mystery of birth blew through the convent like a little
fitful wind playing among the white blossoms of an orchard.
The thought that Kitty was with child disturbed and excited
those sterile women. She frightened them a little now and
fascinated them. They looked upon the physical side of her
condition with robust common sense, for they were the
daughters of peasants and fishermen; but in their childlike
hearts was awe. They were troubled by the thought of her
burden and yet happy and strangely exalted. Sister St.
Joseph told her that they all prayed for her, and Sister St.
Martin had said what a pity it was she was not a Catholic;
but the Mother Superior had reproved her; she said that
it was possible to be a good woman—*une brave femme,* she
put it—even though one was Protestant and *le Bon Dieu*
would in some way or other arrange all that.

Kitty was both touched and diverted by the interest she
aroused, but surprised beyond measure when she found that
even the Mother Superior, so austere in her saintliness,
treated her with a new complaisance. She had always been
kind to Kitty, but in a remote fashion; now she used her with
a tenderness in which there was something maternal. Her
voice had in it a new and gentle note and in her eyes was a
sudden playfulness as though Kitty were a child who had
done a clever and amusing thing. It was oddly moving. Her
soul was like a calm, grey sea rolling majestically, awe-
inspiring in its sombre greatness, and then suddenly a ray
of sunshine made it alert, friendly and gay. Often now in
the evening she would come and sit with Kitty.

"I must take care that you do not tire yourself, *mon enfant,*" she said, making a transparent excuse to herself, "or

Dr. Fane will never forgive me. Oh, this British self-control! There he is delighted beyond measure and when you speak to him of it he becomes quite pale."

She took Kitty's hand and patted it affectionately.

"Dr. Fane told me that he wished you to go away, but you would not because you could not bear to leave us. That was kind of you, my dear child, and I want you to know that we appreciate the help you have been to us. But I think that you did not want to leave him either, and that is better, for your place is by his side, and he needs you. Ah, I do not know what we should have done without that admirable man."

"I am glad to think that he has been able to do something for you," said Kitty.

"You must love him with all your heart, my dear. He is a saint."

Kitty smiled and in her heart sighed. There was only one thing she could do for Walter now and that she could not think how to. She wanted him to forgive her, not for her sake any more, but for his own; for she felt that this alone could give him peace of mind. It was useless to ask him for his forgiveness, and if he had a suspicion that she desired it for his good rather than hers his stubborn vanity would make him refuse at all costs (it was curious that his vanity now did not irritate her, it seemed natural and only made her sorrier for him); and the only chance was that some unexpected occurrence might throw him off his guard. She had an idea that he would welcome an uprush of emotion which would liberate him from this nightmare of resentment, but that, in his pathetic folly, he would fight when it came with all his might against it.

Was it not pitiful that men, tarrying so short a space in a world where there was so much pain, should thus torture themselves?

lx

THOUGH the Mother Superior talked with Kitty not more than three or four times and once or twice for but ten

minutes the impression she made upon Kitty was profound.
Her character was like a country which on first acquaintance
seems grand, but inhospitable; but in which presently you
discover smiling little villages among fruit trees in the folds
of the majestic mountains, and pleasant ambling rivers that
flow kindly through lush meadows. But these comfortable
scenes, though they surprise and even reassure you, are not
enough to make you feel at home in the land of tawny
heights and windswept spaces. It would have been impossible
to become intimate with the Mother Superior; she had that
something impersonal about her which Kitty had felt with
the other nuns, even with the good-humoured, chatty Sister
St. Joseph, but with her it was a barrier which was almost
palpable. It gave you quite a curious sensation, chilling but
awe-inspiring, that she could walk on the same earth as you,
attend to mundane affairs, and yet live so obviously upon a
plane you could not reach. She once said to Kitty:

"It is not enough that a religious should be continually
in prayer with Jesus; she should be herself a prayer."

Though her conversation was interwoven with her religion, Kitty felt that this was natural to her and that no
effort was made to influence the heretic. It seemed strange
to her that the Mother Superior, with her deep sense of
charity, should be content to leave Kitty in a condition of
what must seem to her sinful ignorance.

One evening the two of them were sitting together. The
days were shortening now and the mellow light of the evening was agreeable and a little melancholy. The Mother
Superior looked very tired. Her tragic face was drawn and
white; her fine dark eyes had lost their fire. Her fatigue perhaps urged her to a rare mood of confidence.

"This is a memorable day for me, my child," she said,
breaking from a long reverie, "for this is the anniversary of
the day on which I finally determined to enter religion. For
two years I had been thinking of it, but I had suffered as it
were a fear of this calling, for I dreaded that I might be re-
captured by the spirit of the world. But that morning when
I communicated I made the vow that I would before night-
fall announce my wish to my dear mother. After I had re-

ceived the Holy Communion I asked Our Lord to give me peace of mind: Thou shalt have it only, the answer seemed to come to me, when thou hast ceased to desire it.''

The Mother Superior seemed to lose herself in thoughts of the past.

"That day, one of our friends, Madame de Viernot, had left for the Carmel without telling any of her relatives. She knew that they were opposed to her step, but she was a widow and thought that as such she had the right to do as she chose. One of my cousins had gone to bid farewell to the dear fugitive and did not come back till the evening. She was much moved. I had not spoken to my mother, I trembled at the thought of telling her what I had in mind, and yet I wished to keep the resolution I had made at Holy Communion. I asked my cousin all manner of questions. My mother, who appeared to be absorbed in her tapestry, lost no word. While I talked I said to myself: If I want to speak to-day I have not a minute to lose.

"It is strange how vividly I remember the scene. We were sitting round the table, a round table covered with a red cloth, and we worked by the light of a lamp with a green shade. My two cousins were staying with us and we were all working at tapestries to re-cover the chairs in the drawing-room. Imagine, they had not been re-covered since the days of Louis XIV, when they were bought, and they were so shabby and faded, my mother said it was a disgrace.

"I tried to form the words, but my lips would not move; and then, suddenly, after a few minutes of silence my mother said to me: 'I really cannot understand the conduct of your friend. I do not like this leaving without a word all those to whom she is so dear. The gesture is theatrical and offends my taste. A well-bred woman does nothing which shall make people talk of her. I hope that if ever you caused us the great sorrow of leaving us you would not take flight as though you were committing a crime.'

"It was the moment to speak, but such was my weakness that I could only say: 'Ah, set your mind at rest, *maman,* I should not have the strength.'

"My mother made no answer and I repented because I

had not dared to explain myself. I seemed to hear the word of Our Lord to St. Peter: 'Peter, lovest thou me?' Oh, what weakness, what ingratitude was mine! I loved my comfort, the manner of my life, my family and my diversions. I was lost in these bitter thoughts when a little later, as though the conversation had not been interrupted, my mother said to me: 'Still, my Odette, I do not think that you will die without having done something that will endure.'

"I was still lost in my anxiety and my reflections, while my cousins, never knowing the beating of my heart, worked quietly, when suddenly my mother, letting her tapestry fall and looking at me attentively, said: 'Ah, my dear child, I am very sure that you will end by becoming a religious.'

" 'Are you speaking seriously, my good mother,' I answered. 'You are laying bare the innermost thought and desire of my heart.'

" '*Mais oui*,' cried my cousins without giving me time to finish, 'For two years Odette has thought of nothing else. But you will not give your permission, *ma tante,* you must not give your permission.'

" 'By what right, my dear children, should we refuse it,' said my mother, 'if it is the Will of God?'

"My cousins then, wishing to make a jest of the conversation, asked me what I intended to do with the trifles that belonged to me and quarrelled gaily about which should take possession of this and which of that. But these first moments of gaiety lasted a very little while and we began to weep. Then we heard my father come up the stairs."

The Mother Superior paused for a moment and sighed.

"It was very hard for my father. I was his only daughter and men often have a deeper feeling for their daughters than they ever have for their sons."

"It is a great misfortune to have a heart," said Kitty, with a smile.

"It is a great good fortune to consecrate that heart to the love of Jesus Christ."

At that moment a little girl came up to the Mother Superior and confident in her interest showed her a fantastic toy that she had somehow got hold of. The Mother Superior put her beautiful, delicate hand round the child's shoulder and the child nestled up to her. It intrigued Kitty to observe how sweet her smile was and yet how impersonal.

"It is wonderful to see the adoration that all your orphans have for you, Mother," she said. "I think I should be very proud if I could excite so great a devotion."

The Mother Superior gave once more her aloof and yet beautiful smile.

"There is only one way to win hearts and that is to make oneself like unto those of whom one would be loved."

lxi

WALTER did not come back to dinner that evening. Kitty waited for him a little, for when he was detained in the city he always managed to send her word, but at last she sat down. She made no more than a pretence of eating the many courses which the Chinese cook, with his regard for propriety notwithstanding pestilence and the difficulty of provisioning, invariably set before her; and then, sinking into the long rattan chair by the open window, surrendered herself to the beauty of the starry night. The silence rested her.

She did not try to read. Her thoughts floated upon the surface of her mind like little white clouds reflected on a still lake. She was too tired to seize upon one, follow it up and absorb herself in its attendant train. She wondered vaguely what there was for her in the various impressions which her conversations with the nuns had left upon her. It was singular that, though their way of life so profoundly moved her, the faith which occasioned it left her untouched. She could not envisage the possibility that she might at any time be captured by the ardor of belief. She gave a little sigh: perhaps it would make everything easier if that great white light should illuminate her soul. Once or twice she had had the desire to tell the Mother Superior of her unhappiness and its cause; but she dared not: she could not bear that this austere woman should think ill of her. To her what she had done would naturally seem a grievous sin. The odd thing was that she herself could not regard it as wicked so much as stupid and ugly.

Perhaps it was due to an obtuseness in herself that she looked upon her connection with Townsend as regrettable and shocking even, but to be forgotten rather than to be repented of. It was like making a blunder at a party; there was nothing to do about it, it was dreadfully mortifying, but it showed a lack of sense to ascribe too much importance to it. She shuddered as she thought of Charlie with his large frame too well covered, the vagueness of his jaw and the way he had of standing with his chest thrown out so that he might not seem to have a paunch. His sanguine temperament showed itself in the little red veins which soon would form a network on his ruddy cheeks. She had liked his bushy eyebrows: there was to her in them now something animal and repulsive.

And the future? It was curious how indifferent it left her; she could not see into it at all. Perhaps she would die when her baby was born. Her sister Doris had always been much stronger than she, and Doris had nearly died. (She had done her duty and produced an heir to the new baronetry; Kitty smiled as she thought of her mother's satisfaction.) If the future was so vague it meant perhaps that she was destined never to see it. Walter would probably ask her mother to take care of the child—if the child survived; and she knew him well enough to be sure that, however uncertain of his paternity, he would treat it with kindness. Walter could be trusted under any circumstances to behave admirably. It was a pity that with his great qualities, his unselfishness and honour, his intelligence and sensibility, he should be so un-lovable. She was not in the least frightened of him now, but sorry for him, and at the same time she could not help thinking him slightly absurd. The depth of his emotion made him vulnerable and she had a feeling that somehow and at some time she so could work upon it as to induce him to forgive her. The thought haunted her now that in thus giving him peace of mind she would make the only possible amends for the anguish she had caused him. It was a pity he had so little sense of humour: she could see them both, some day,

laughing together at the way they had tormented themselves.

She was tired. She took the lamp into her room and undressed. She went to bed and presently fell asleep.

lxii

BUT she was awakened by a loud knocking. At first, since
it was interwoven with the dream from which she was roused,
she could not attach the sound to reality. The knocking went
on and she was conscious that it must be at the gateway of
the compound. It was quite dark. She had a watch with
phosphorised hands and saw that it was half past two. It
must be Walter coming back—how late he was—and he
could not awake the boy. The knocking went on, louder
and louder, and in the silence of the night it was really not
a little alarming. The knocking stopped and she heard the
withdrawing of the heavy bolt. Walter had never come back
so late. Poor thing, he must be tired out! She hoped he
would have the sense to go straight to bed instead of working as usual in that laboratory of his.

There was a sound of voices, and people came into the
compound. That was strange, for Walter coming home late,
in order not to disturb her, took pains to be quiet. Two or
three persons ran swiftly up the wooden steps and came into
the room next door. Kitty was a little frightened. At the
back of her mind was always the fear of an anti-foreign
riot. Had something happened? Her heart began to beat
quickly. But before she had time to put her vague apprehension into shape some one walked across the room and
knocked at her door.

"Mrs. Fane."

She recognised Waddington's voice.

"Yes. What is it?"

"Will you get up at once. I have something to say to you."

She rose and put on a dressing-gown. She unlocked the
door and opened it. Her glance took in Waddington in a
pair of Chinese trousers and a pongee coat, the house-boy

holding a hurricane lamp, and a little further back three Chinese solders in khaki. She started as she saw the consternation on Waddington's face; his head was tousled as though he had just jumped out of bed.

"What is the matter?" she gasped.

"You must keep calm. There's not a moment to lose. Put on your clothes at once and come with me."

"But what is it? Has something happened in the city?"

The sight of the soldiers suggested to her at once that there had been an outbreak and they were come to protect her.

"Your husband's been taken ill. We want you to come at once."

"Walter?" she cried.

"You mustn't be upset. I don't exactly know what's the matter. Colonel Yü sent this officer to me and asked me to bring you to the Yamen at once."

Kitty stared at him for a moment, she felt a sudden cold in her heart, and then she turned.

"I shall be ready in two minutes."

"I came just as I was," he answered. "I was asleep, I just put on a coat and some shoes."

She did not hear what he said. She dressed by the light of the stars, taking the first things that came to hand; her fingers on a sudden were so clumsy that it seemed to take her an age to find the little clasps that closed her dress. She put round her shoulders the Cantonese shawl she had worn in the evening.

"I haven't put a hat on. There's no need, is there?"

"No."

The boy held the lantern in front of them and they hurried down the steps and out of the compound gate.

"Take care you don't fall," said Waddington. "You'd better hang on to my arm."

The soldiers followed immediately behind them.

"Colonel Yü has sent chairs. They're waiting on the other side of the river."

They walked quickly down the hill. Kitty could not bring herself to utter the question that trembled so horribly on her lips. She was mortally afraid of the answer. They came to the bank and there, with a thread of light at the bow, a sampan was waiting for them.

"Is it cholera?" she said then.

"I'm afraid so."

She gave a little cry and stopped short.

"I think you ought to come as quickly as you can."

He gave her his hand to help her into the boat. The passage was short and the river almost stagnant; they stood in a bunch at the bow, while a woman with a child tied on her hip with one oar impelled the sampan across.

"He was taken ill this afternoon, the afternoon of yesterday that is," said Waddington.

"Why wasn't I sent for at once?"

Although there was no reason for it they spoke in whispers. In the darkness Kitty could only feel how intense was her companion's anxiety.

"Colonel Yü wanted to, but he wouldn't let him. Colonel Yü has been with him all the time."

"He ought to have sent for me all the same. It's heartless."

"Your husband knew that you had never seen any one with cholera. It's a terrible and revolting sight. He didn't want you to see it."

"After all he is my husband," she said in a choking voice.

Waddington made no reply.

"Why am I allowed to come now?"

Waddington put his hand on her arm.

"My dear, you must be very brave. You must be prepared for the worst."

She gave a wail of anguish and turned away a little, for she saw that the three Chinese soldiers were looking at her. She had a sudden strange glimpse of the whites of their eyes.

"Is he dying?"

"I only know the message Colonel Yü gave to this officer who came and fetched me. As far as I can judge collapse has set in."

"Is there no hope at all?"

"I'm dreadfully sorry, I'm afraid that if we don't get there quickly we shan't find him alive."

She shuddered. The tears began to stream down her cheeks.

"You see, he's been overworking, he has no powers of resistance."

She withdrew from the pressure of his arm with a gesture of irritation. It exasperated her that he should talk in that low, anguished voice.

They reached the side and two men, Chinese coolies, standing on the bank helped her to step on shore. The chairs were waiting. As she got into hers Waddington said to her:

"Try and keep a tight hold on your nerves. You'll want all your self-control."

"Tell the bearers to make haste."

"They have orders to go as fast as they can."

The officer, already in his chair, passed by and as he passed called out to Kitty's bearers. They raised the chair smartly, arranged the poles on their shoulders, and at a swift pace set off. Waddington followed close behind. They took the hill at a run, a man with a lantern going before each chair, and at the water-gate the gate-keeper was standing with a torch. The officer shouted to him as they approached and he flung open one side of the gate to let them through. He uttered some sort of interjection as they passed and the bearers called back. In the dead of the night those guttural sounds in a strange language were mysterious and alarming. They slithered up the wet and slippery cobbles of the alley and one of the officer's bearers stumbled. Kitty heard the officer's voice raised in anger, the shrill retort of the bearer, and then the chair in front hurried on again. The streets were narrow and tortuous. Here in the city was deep night. It was a city of the dead. They hastened along a narrow lane, turned a corner, and then at a run took a flight of steps; the bearers were beginning to blow hard; they walked with long, rapid strides, in silence; one took out a ragged handkerchief and as he walked wiped from his forehead the sweat that ran down into his eyes; they wound this way and that so that it might have been a maze through which they sped; in the shadow of the shuttered shops sometimes a form seemed to be lying, but you did not know whether it was a man who slept to awake at dawn or a man who slept to awake never; the narrow streets were ghostly in their silent emptiness and when on a sudden a dog barked loudly it sent a shock of terror through Kitty's tortured nerves. She did not know where they went. The way seemed endless. Could they not go faster? Faster. Faster. The time was going and any moment it might be too late.

lxiii

SUDDENLY, walking along a blank long wall they came to a gateway flanked by sentry boxes, and the bearers set down the chairs. Waddington hurried up to Kitty. She had already jumped out. The officer knocked loudly on the door and shouted. A postern was opened and they passed into a court-yard. It was large and square. Huddled against the walls, under the eaves of the overhanging roofs, soldiers wrapped in their blankets were lying in huddled groups. They stopped for a moment while the officer spoke to a man who might have been a sergeant on guard. He turned and said something to Waddington.

"He's still alive," said Waddington in a low voice. "Take care how you walk."

Still preceded by the men with lanterns they made their way across the yard, up some steps, through a great doorway and then down into another wide court. On one side of this was a long chamber with lights in it; the lights within shining through the rice paper silhouetted the elaborate pattern of the lattice. The lantern-bearers led them across the yard towards this room and at the door the officer knocked. It was opened immediately and the officer with a glance at Kitty stepped back.

"Will you walk in," said Waddington.

It was a long, low room and the smoky lamps that lit it made the gloom ominous. Three or four orderlies stood about. On a pallet against the wall opposite the door a man was lying huddled under a blanket. An officer was standing motionless at the foot.

Kitty hurried up and leaned over the pallet. Walter lay with his eyes closed and in that sombre light his face had the greyness of death. He was horribly still.

"Walter, Walter," she gasped, in a low, terrified tone.

There was a slight movement in the body, or the shadow of a movement; it was so slight it was like a breath of air which you cannot feel and yet for an instant ruffles the surface of still water.

"Walter, Walter, speak to me."

The eyes were opened slowly, as though it were an infinite effort to raise those heavy lids, but he did not look, he stared at the wall a few inches from his face. He spoke; his voice, low and weak, had the hint of a smile in it.

"This is a pretty kettle of fish," he said.

Kitty dared not breathe. He made no further sound, no beginning of a gesture, but his eyes, those dark, cold eyes of his (seeing now what mysteries?) stared at the white-washed wall. Kitty raised herself to her feet. With haggard gaze she faced the man who stood there.

"Surely something can be done. You're not going to stand there and do nothing?"

She clasped her hands. Waddington spoke to the officer who stood at the end of the bed.

"I'm afraid they've done everything that was possible. The regimental surgeon has been treating him. Your husband has trained him and he's done all that your husband could do himself."

"Is that the surgeon?"

"No, that is Colonel Yü. He's never left your husband's side."

Distracted, Kitty gave him a glance. He was a tallish man, but stockily built, and he seemed ill at ease in his khaki uniform. He was looking at Walter and she saw that his eyes were wet with tears. It gave her a pang. Why should that man with his yellow, flat face have tears in his eyes? It exasperated her.

"It's awful to be able to do nothing."

"At least he's not in pain any more," said Waddington.

She leaned once more over her husband. Those ghastly eyes of his still stared vacantly in front of him. She could not tell if he saw with them. She did not know whether he had heard what was said. She put her lips close to his ears.

"Walter, isn't there something we can do?"

She thought that there must be some drug they could give him which would stay the dreadful ebbing of his life. Now that her eyes were more accustomed to the dimness she saw with horror that his face had fallen. She would hardly have recognised him. It was unthinkable that in a few short hours he should look like another man; he hardly looked like a man at all; he looked like death.

She thought that he was making an effort to speak. She put her ear close.

"Don't fuss. I've had a rough passage, but I'm all right now."

Kitty waited for a moment, but he was silent. His immobility rent her heart with anguish; it was terrifying that he should lie so still. He seemed prepared already for the stillness of the grave. Some one, the surgeon or a dresser, came forward and with a gesture motioned her aside; he leaned over the dying man and with a dirty rag wet his lips. Kitty stood up once more and turned to Waddington despairingly.

"Is there no hope at all?" she whispered.

He shook his head.

"How much longer can he live?"

"No one can tell. An hour perhaps."

Kitty looked round the bare chamber and her eyes rested for an instant on the substantial form of Colonel Yü.

"Can I be left alone with him for a little while?" she asked. "Only for a minute."

"Certainly, if you wish it."

Waddington stepped over to the Colonel and spoke to him. The Colonel gave a little bow and then in a low tone an order.

"We shall wait on the steps," said Waddington as they trooped out. "You have only to call."

Now that the incredible had overwhelmed her consciousness, like a drug coursing through her veins, and she realised
that Walter was going to die she had but one thought, and
that was to make his end easier for him by dragging from
his soul the rancour which poisoned it. If he could die at
peace with her it seemed to her that he would die at peace
with himself. She thought now not of herself at all but only
of him.

"Walter, I beseech you to forgive me," she said, leaning
over him. For fear that he could not bear the pressure she
took care not to touch him. "I'm so desperately sorry for
the wrong I did you. I so bitterly regret it."

He said nothing. He did not seem to hear. She was obliged
to insist. It seemed to her strangely that his soul was a
fluttering moth and its wings were heavy with hatred.

"Darling."

A shadow passed over his wan and sunken face. It was
less than a movement, and yet it gave all the effect of a
terrifying convulsion. She had never used that word to him
before. Perhaps in his dying brain there passed the thought,
confused and difficultly grasped, that he had only heard her
use it, a commonplace of her vocabulary, to dogs and babies
and motor-cars. Then something horrible occurred. She
clenched her hands, trying with all her might to control herself, for she saw two tears run slowly down his wasted
cheeks.

"Oh, my precious, my dear, if you ever loved me—I know
you loved me and I was hateful—I beg you to forgive me.
I've no chance now to show my repentance. Have mercy on
me. I beseech you to forgive."

She stopped. She looked at him, all breathless, waiting
passionately for a reply. She saw that he tried to speak. Her
heart gave a great bound. It seemed to her that it would be
in a manner a reparation for the suffering she had caused
him if at this last moment she could effect his deliverance
from that load of bitterness. His lips moved. He did not look
at her. His eyes stared unseeing at the white-washed wall.
She leaned over him so that she might hear. But he spoke
quite clearly.

"The dog it was that died."

She stayed as still as though she were turned to stone. She could not understand and gazed at him in terrified perplexity. It was meaningless. Delirium. He had not understood a word she said.

It was impossible to be so still and yet to live. She stared and stared. His eyes were open. She could not tell if he breathed. She began to grow frightened.

"Walter," she whispered. "Walter."

At last, suddenly, she raised herself. A sudden fear seized her. She turned and went to the door.

"Will you come, please. He doesn't seem to . . ."

They stepped in. The little Chinese surgeon went up to the bed. He had an electric torch in his hand and he lit it and looked at Walter's eyes. Then he closed them. He said something in Chinese. Waddington put his arm round Kitty.

"I'm afraid he's dead."

Kitty gave a deep sigh. A few tears fell from her eyes. She felt dazed rather than overcome. The Chinese stood about, round the bed, helplessly, as though they did not quite know what to do next. Waddington was silent. In a minute the Chinese began to speak in a low tone among themselves.

"You'd better let me take you back to the bungalow," said Waddington. "He'll be brought there."

Kitty passed her hand wearily across her forehead. She went up to the pallet bed and leaned over it. She kissed Walter gently on the lips. She was not crying now.

"I'm sorry to give you so much trouble."

The officers saluted as she passed and she gravely bowed. They walked back across the courtyard and got into their chairs. She saw Waddington light a cigarette. A little smoke lost in the air, that was the life of man.

lxiv

DAWN was breaking now, and here and there a Chinaman was taking down the shutters of his shop. In its dark recesses, by the light of a taper, a woman was washing her hands and face. In a teahouse at a corner a group of men were eating an early meal. The grey, cold light of the rising day sidled along the narrow lanes like a thief. There was a pale mist on the river and the masts of the crowded junks loomed through it like the lances of a phantom army. It was chilly as they crossed and Kitty huddled herself up in her gay and coloured shawl. They walked up the hill and they were above the mist. The sun shone from an unclouded sky. It shone as though this were a day like another and nothing had happened to distinguish it from its fellows.

"Wouldn't you like to lie down?" said Waddington when they entered the bungalow.

"No. I'll sit at the window."

She had sat at the window so often and so long during the weeks that had passed and her eyes now were so familiar with the fantastic, garish, beautiful and mysterious temple on its great bastion that it rested her spirit. It was so unreal, even in the crude light of midday, that it withdrew her from the reality of life.

"I'll get the boy to make you some tea. I'm afraid it will be necessary to bury him this morning. I'll make all arrangements."

"Thank you."

lxv

THEY buried him three hours later. It seemed horrible to Kitty that he must be put into a Chinese coffin, as though in so strange a bed he must rest uneasily, but there was no help for it. The nuns, learning of Walter's death as they learned everything that happened in the city, sent by a messenger a cross of dahlias, stiff and formal, but made as though by the accustomed hands of a florist; and the cross, alone on the Chinese coffin, looked grotesque and out of place. When all was ready they had to wait for Colonel Yü who had sent to Waddington to say that he desired to attend the funeral. He came accompanied by an A.D.C. They walked up the hill, the coffin borne by half a dozen coolies, to a little plot of land where lay buried the missionary whose place Walter had taken. Waddington had found among the missionary's effects an English prayer-book and in a low voice, with an embarrassment that was unusual to him, read the burial service. Perhaps, reciting those solemn but terrible words, the thought hovered in his mind that if he in his turn fell a victim to the pestilence there would be no one now to say them over him. The coffin was lowered into the grave and the grave-diggers began to throw in the earth.

Colonel Yü, who had stood with bared head by the grave-side, put on his hat, saluted Kitty gravely, said a word or two to Waddington and followed by his A.D.C. walked away. The coolies, curious to watch a Christian burial, had lingered and now in a straggling group, their yokes trailing in their hands, sauntered off. Kitty and Waddington waited till the grave was filled and then placed on the mound, smelling of fresh earth, the nuns' prim dahlias. She had not wept, but when the first shovelful of earth rattled on the coffin she felt a dreadful pang at her heart.

She saw that Waddington was waiting for her to come away.

"Are you in a hurry?" she asked. "I don't want to go back to the bungalow just yet."

"I have nothing to do. I am entirely in your hands."

lxvi

THEY sauntered along the causeway till they came to the top of the hill on which stood that archway, the memorial to a virtuous widow, which had occupied so large a part of Kitty's impression of the place. It was a symbol, but of what she scarcely knew; she could not tell why it bore a note of so sardonic irony.

"Shall we sit down a little? We haven't sat here for ages." The plain was spread before her widely; it was tranquil and serene in the morning light. "It's only a few weeks that I've been here and it seems a lifetime."

He did not answer and for a while she allowed her thoughts to wander. She gave a sigh.

"Do you think that the soul is immortal?" she asked.

He did not seem surprised at the question.

"How should I know?"

"Just now, when they'd washed Walter, before they put him into the coffin I looked at him. He looked very young. Too young to die. Do you remember that beggar that we saw the first time you took me for a walk? I was frightened not because he was dead, but because he looked as though he'd never been a human being. He was just a dead animal. And now again, with Walter, it looked so like a machine that has run down. That's what is so frightening. And if it is only a machine how futile is all this suffering and the heart pains and the misery."

He did not answer, but his eyes travelled over the landscape at their feet. The wide expanse on that gay and sunny morning filled the heart with exultation. The trim little rice fields stretched as far as the eye could see and in many of them the blue-clad peasants with their buffaloes were working industriously. It was a peaceful and a happy scene. Kitty broke the silence.

"I can't tell you how deeply moved I've been by all I've seen at the convent. They're wonderful, those nuns, they make me feel utterly worthless. They give up everything, their home, their country, love, children, freedom; and all the little things which I sometimes think must be harder still to give up, flowers and green fields, going for a walk on an autumn day, books and music, comfort, everything they give up, everything. And they do it so that they may devote themselves to a life of sacrifice and poverty, obedience, killing work and prayer. To all of them this world is really and truly a place of exile. Life is a cross which they willingly bear, but in their hearts all the time is the desire— oh, it's so much stronger than desire, it's a longing, an eager, passionate longing for the death which shall lead them to life everlasting."

Kitty clasped her hands and looked at him with anguish.

"Well?"

"Supposing there is no life everlasting? Think what it means if death is really the end of all things. They've given up all for nothing. They've been cheated. They're dupes."

Waddington reflected for a little while.

"I wonder. I wonder if it matters that what they have aimed at is illusion. Their lives are in themselves beautiful. I have an idea that the only thing which makes it possible to regard this world we live in without disgust is the beauty which now and then men create out of the chaos. The pictures they paint, the music they compose, the books they write, and the lives they lead. Of all these the richest in beauty is the beautiful life. That is the perfect work of art."

Kitty sighed. What he said seemed hard. She wanted more.

"Have you ever been to a symphony concert?" he continued.

"Yes," she smiled. "I know nothing of music, but I'm rather fond of it."

"Each member of the orchestra plays his own little instrument, and what do you think he knows of the complicated harmonies which unroll themselves on the indifferent air? He is concerned only with his own small share. But he knows that the symphony is lovely, and though there's none to hear it, it is lovely still, and he is content to play his part."

"You spoke of Tao the other day," said Kitty, after a pause. "Tell me what it is."

Waddington gave her a little look, hesitated an instant, and then with a faint smile on his comic face answered:

"It is the Way and the Waygoer. It is the eternal road along which walk all beings, but no being made it, for itself is being. It is everything and nothing. From it all things spring, all things conform to it, and to it at last all things return. It is a square without angles, a sound which ears cannot hear, and an image without form. It is a vast net and though its meshes are as wide as the sea it lets nothing through. It is the sanctuary where all things find refuge. It is nowhere, but without looking out of the window you may see it. Desire not to desire, it teaches, and leave all things to take their course. He that humbles himself shall be preserved entire. He that bends shall be made straight. Failure is the foundation of success and success is the lurking-place of failure; but who can tell when the turning point will come? He who strives after tenderness can become even as a little child. Gentleness brings victory to him who attacks and safety to him who defends. Mighty is he who conquers himself."

"Does it mean anything?"

"Sometimes, when I've had half a dozen whiskies and look at the stars, I think perhaps it does."

Silence fell upon them and when it was broken it was again by Kitty.

"Tell me, is: the dog it was that died, a quotation?"

Waddington's lips outlined a smile and he was ready with his answer. But perhaps at that moment his sensibilities were abnormally acute. Kitty was not looking at him, but there was something about her expression which made him change his mind.

"If it is I don't know it," he answered warily. "Why?"

"Nothing. It crossed my mind. It had a familiar ring."

There was another silence.

"When you were alone with your husband," said Waddington presently, "I had a talk with the regimental surgeon. I thought we ought to have some details."

"Well?"

"He was in a very hysterical state. I couldn't really quite understand what he meant. So far as I can make out your husband got infected during the course of experiments he was making."

"He was always experimenting. He wasn't really a doctor, he was a bacteriologist; that is why he was so anxious to come here."

"But I can't quite make out from the surgeon's statements whether he was infected accidentally or whether he was actually experimenting on himself."

Kitty grew very pale. The suggestion made her shudder. Waddington took her hand.

"Forgive me for talking about this again," he said gently, "but I thought it might comfort you—I know how frightfully difficult it is on these occasions to say anything that is of the least use—I thought it might mean something to you that Walter died a martyr to science and to his duty."

Kitty shrugged her shoulders with a suspicion of impatience.

"Walter died of a broken heart," she said.

Waddington did not answer. She turned and looked at him slowly. Her face was white and set.

"What did he mean by saying: the dog it was that died? What is it?"

"It's the last line of Goldsmith's *Elegy.*"

lxvii

NEXT morning Kitty went to the convent. The girl who opened the door seemed surprised to see her and when Kitty had been for a few minutes about her work the Mother Superior came in. She went up to Kitty and took her hand.

"I am glad to see you, my dear child. You show a fine courage in coming back here so soon after your great sorrow; and wisdom, for I am sure that a little work will keep you from brooding."

Kitty cast down her eyes, reddening a little; she did not want the Mother Superior to see into her heart.

"I need not tell you how sincerely all of us here sympathise with you."

"You are very kind," whispered Kitty.

"We all pray for you constantly and for the soul of him you have lost."

Kitty made no reply. The Mother Superior released her hand and in her cool, authoritative tone imposed various tasks upon her. She patted two or three children on the head, gave them her aloof, but winning smile, and went about her more pressing affairs.

lxviii

A WEEK went by. Kitty was sewing. The Mother Superior entered the room and sat down beside her. She gave Kitty's work a shrewd glance.

"You sew very well, my dear. It is a rare accomplishment for young women of your world nowadays."

"I owe it to my mother."

"I am sure that your mother will be very glad to see you again."

Kitty looked up. There was that in the Mother Superior's manner which prevented the remark from being taken as a casual politeness. She went on.

"I allowed you to come here after the death of your dear husband because I thought occupation would distract your mind. I did not think you were fit at that moment to take the long journey to Hong-Kong by yourself, nor did I wish you to sit alone in your house with nothing to do but to remember your loss. But now eight days have passed. It is time for you to go."

"I don't want to go, Mother. I want to stay here."

"There is nothing for you to stay for. You came to be with your husband. Your husband is dead. You are in a condition in which you will shortly need a care and attention which it is impossible for you to get here. It is your duty, my dear child, to do everything in your power for the welfare of the being that God has entrusted to your care."

Kitty was silent for a moment. She looked down.

"I was under the impression that I was of some use here. It has been a great pleasure to me to think that I was. I hoped that you would allow me to go on with my work till the epidemic had come to an end."

"We are all very grateful for what you have done for us," answered the Superior, with a slight smile, "but now that the epidemic is waning the risk of coming here is not so great and I am expecting two sisters from Canton. They should be here very shortly and when they arrive I do not think that I shall be able to make any use of your services."

Kitty's heart sank. The Mother Superior's tone admitted of no reply; she knew her well enough to know that she would be insensible to entreaty. That she found it necessary to reason with Kitty had brought into her voice a note, if hardly of irritation, at least of the peremptoriness which might lead to it.

"Mr. Waddington was good enough to ask my advice."

"I wish he could have minded his own business," interrupted Kitty.

"If he hadn't I should all the same have felt obliged to give it him," said the Mother Superior gently. "At the present moment your place is not here, but with your mother. Mr. Waddington has arranged with Colonel Yü to give you a strong escort so that you will be perfectly safe on the journey, and he has arranged for bearers and coolies. The amah will go with you and arrangements will be made at the cities you pass through. In fact, everything possible for your comfort has been done."

Kitty's lips tightened. She thought that they might at least have consulted her in a matter which only concerned herself. She had to exercise some self-control in order not to answer sharply.

"And when am I to start?"

The Mother Superior remained quite placid.

"The sooner you can get back to Hong-Kong and then sail to England the better, my dear child. We thought you would like to start at dawn the day after to-morrow."

"So soon."

Kitty felt a little inclined to cry. But it was true enough; she had no place there.

"You all seem in a great hurry to be rid of me," she said ruefully.

Kitty was conscious of a relaxation in the Superior's demeanour. She saw that Kitty was prepared to yield and unconsciously she assumed a more gracious tone. Kitty's sense of humour was acute and her eyes twinkled as she reflected that even the saints liked to have their own way.

"Don't think that I fail to appreciate the goodness of your heart, my dear child, and the admirable charity which makes you unwilling to abandon your self-imposed duties."

Kitty stared straight in front of her. She faintly shrugged her shoulders. She knew that she could ascribe to herself no such exalted virtues. She wanted to stay because she had nowhere else to go. It was a curious sensation this, that nobody in the world cared two straws whether she was alive or dead.

"I cannot understand that you should be reluctant to go home," pursued the Superior amiably. "There are many foreigners in this country who would give a great deal to have your chance!"

"But not you, Mother?"

"Oh, with us it is different, my dear child. When we come here we know that we have left our homes for ever."

Out of her own wounded feelings emerged the desire in Kitty's mind, malicious perhaps, to seek the joint in the armour of faith which rendered the nuns so aloofly immune to all the natural feelings. She wanted to see whether there was left in the Superior any of the weakness of humanity.

"I should have thought that sometimes it was hard never to see again those that are dear to you and the scenes amid which you were brought up."

The Mother Superior hesitated for a moment, but Kitty watching her could see no change in the serenity of her beautiful and austere face.

"It is hard for my mother who is old now, for I am her only daughter and she would dearly like to see me once more before she dies. I wish I could give her that joy. But it cannot be and we shall wait till we can meet in paradise."

"All the same, when one thinks of those to whom one is so dear, it must be difficult not to ask oneself if one was right in cutting oneself off from them."

"Are you asking me if I have ever regretted the step I took?" On a sudden the Mother Superior's face grew radiant. "Never, never. I have exchanged a life that was trivial and worthless for one of sacrifice and prayer."

There was a brief silence and then the Mother Superior, assuming a lighter manner, smiled.

"I am going to ask you to take a little parcel and post it for me when you get to Marseilles. I do not wish to entrust it to the Chinese post-office. I will fetch it at once."

"You can give it to me to-morrow," said Kitty.

"You will be too busy to come here to-morrow, my dear. It will be more convenient for you to bid us farewell to-night."

She rose and with the easy dignity which her voluminous

habit could not conceal left the room. In a moment Sister St. Joseph came in. She was come to say good-bye. She hoped that Kitty would have a pleasant journey; she would be quite safe, for Colonel Yü was sending a strong escort with her; and the sisters constantly did the journey alone and no harm came to them. And did she like the sea? *Mon Dieu,* how ill she was when there was a storm in the Indian ocean, *Madame* her mother would be pleased to see her daughter, and she must take care of herself; after all she had another little soul in her care now, and they would all pray for her; she would pray constantly for her and the dear little baby and for the soul of the poor, brave doctor. She was voluble, kindly, and affectionate; and yet Kitty was deeply conscious that for Sister St. Joseph (her gaze intent on eternity) she was but a wraith without body or substance. She had a wild impulse to seize the stout, good-natured nun by the shoulders and shake her, crying: "Don't you know that I'm a human being, unhappy and alone, and I want comfort and sympathy and encouragement; oh, can't you turn a minute away from God and give me a little compassion; not the Christian compassion that you have for all suffering things, but just human compassion for me?" The thought brought a smile to Kitty's lips: how very surprised Sister St. Joseph would be! She would certainly be convinced of what now she only suspected, that all English people were mad.

"Fortunately I am a very good sailor," Kitty answered. "I've never been sea-sick yet."

The Mother Superior returned with a small, neat parcel.

"They're handkerchiefs that I've had made for the nameday of my mother," she said. "The initials have been embroidered by our young girls."

Sister St. Joseph suggested that Kitty would like to see how beautifully the work was done and the Mother Superior with an indulgent, deprecating smile untied the parcel. The handkerchiefs were of very fine lawn and the initials embroidered in a complicated cypher were surmounted by a crown of strawberry leaves. When Kitty had properly admired the workmanship the handkerchiefs were wrapped up again and the parcel handed to her. Sister St. Joseph, with an *"eh bien, Madame, je vous quitte"* and a repetition of her polite and impersonal salutations, went away. Kitty realised that this was the moment to take her leave of the Superior. She thanked her for her kindness to her. They walked together along the bare, white-washed corridors.

"Would it be asking too much of you to register the parcel when you arrive at Marseilles?" said the Superior.

"Of course I'll do that," said Kitty.

She glanced at the address. The name seemed very grand, but the place mentioned attracted her attention.

"But that is one of the *châteaux* I've seen. I was motoring with friends in France."

"It is very possible," said the Mother Superior. "Strangers are permitted to view it on two days a week."

"I think if I had ever lived in such a beautiful place I should never have had the courage to leave it."

"It is of course a historical monument. It is scarcely intimate. If I regretted anything it would not be that, but the little *château* that we lived in when I was a child. It was in the Pyrenees. I was born within sound of the sea. I do not deny that sometimes I should like to hear the waves beating against the rocks."

Kitty had an idea that the Mother Superior, divining her thought and the reason for her remarks, was slyly making fun of her. But they reached the little, unpretentious door of the convent. To Kitty's surprise the Mother Superior took her in her arms and kissed her. The pressure of her pale lips on Kitty's cheeks, she kissed her first on one side and then on the other, was so unexpected that it made her flush and inclined to cry.

"Good-bye, God bless you, my dear child." She held her for a moment in her arms. "Remember that it is nothing to do your duty, that is demanded of you and is no more meritorious than to wash your hands when they are dirty; the only thing that counts is the love of duty; when love and duty are one, then grace is in you and you will enjoy a happiness which passes all understanding."

The convent door closed for the last time behind her.

lxix

WADDINGTON walked with Kitty up the hill and they turned aside for a moment to look at Walter's grave; at the memorial arch he said good-bye to her, and looking at it for the last time she felt that she could reply to the enigmatic irony of its appearance with an equal irony of her own. She stepped into her chair.

One day passed after the other. The sights of the wayside served as a background to her thoughts. She saw them as it were in duplicate, rounded as though in a stereoscope, with an added significance because to everything she saw was added the recollection of what she had seen when but a few short weeks before she had taken the same journey in the contrary direction. The coolies with their loads straggled disorderly, two or three together, and then a hundred yards behind one by himself, and then two or three more; the soldiers of the escort shuffled along with a clumsy walk that covered five and twenty miles a day; the amah was carried by two bearers and Kitty, not because she was heavier, but for face' sake, by four. Now and then they met a string of coolies lolloping by in line with their heavy burdens, now and then a Chinese official in a sedan who looked at the white woman with inquisitive eyes; now they came across peasants in faded blue and huge hats on their way to market and now a woman, old or young, tottering along on her bound feet. They passed up and down little hills laid out with trim rice fields and farmhouses nestling cosily in a grove of bamboos; they passed through ragged villages and populous cities walled like the cities in a missal. The sun of the early autumn was pleasant, and if at daybreak, when the shimmering dawn lent the neat fields the enchantment of a fairy tale, it was cold, the warmth later was very grateful. Kitty was filled by it with a sense of beatitude which she made no effort to resist.

The vivid scenes with their elegant colour, their unexpected distinction, and their strangeness, were like an arras before which, like mysterious, shadowy shapes, played the phantoms of Kitty's fancy. They seemed wholly unreal. Mei-tan-fu with its crenellated walls was like the painted canvas placed on the stage in an old play to represent a city. The nuns, Waddington, and the Manchu woman who loved him, were fantastic characters in a masque; and the rest, the people sidling along the tortuous streets and those who died, were nameless supers. Of course it had, they all had, a significance of some sort, but what was it? It was as though they performed a ritual dance, elaborate and ancient, and you knew that those complicated measures had a meaning which it was important for you to know; and yet you could see no clue, no clue.

It seemed incredible to Kitty (an old woman was passing along the causeway, in blue, and the blue in the sunshine was like lapis lazuli; her face with its thousand little wrinkles was like a mask of old ivory; and she leaned, as she walked on her tiny feet, on a long black staff) it seemed incredible to Kitty that she and Walter had taken part in that strange and unreal dance. They had played important parts too. She might easily have lost her life: he had. Was it a joke? Perhaps it was nothing but a dream from which she would suddenly awake with a sigh of relief. It seemed to have taken place a long time ago and in a far-off place. It was singular how shadowy the persons of that play seemed against the sunny background of real life. And now it seemed to Kitty like a story that she was reading; it was a little startling that it seemed to concern her so little. She found already that she could not recall with distinctness Waddington's face which had been so familiar to her.

This evening they should reach the city on the Western River from which she was to take the steamer to Canton. Thence it was but a night's run to Hong-Kong.

lxx

AT FIRST because she had not wept when Walter died she was ashamed. It seemed dreadfully callous. Why, the eyes of the Chinese officer, Colonel Yü, had been wet with tears. She was dazed by her husband's death. It was difficult to understand that he would not come into the bungalow again and that when he got up in the morning she would not hear him take his bath in the Suchow tub. He was alive and now he was dead. The sisters wondered at her Christian resignation and admired the courage with which she bore her loss. But Waddington was shrewd; for all his grave sympathy she had a feeling that—how should she put it?—that he had his tongue in his cheek. Of course, Walter's death had been a shock to her. She didn't want him to die. But after all she didn't love him, she had never loved him; it was decent to bear herself with becoming sorrow; it would be ugly and vulgar even to let any one see into her heart; but she had gone through too much to make pretences to herself. It seemed to her that this at least the last few weeks had taught her, that if it is necessary sometimes to lie to others it is always despicable to lie to oneself. She was sorry that Walter had died in that tragic manner, but she was sorry with a purely human sorrow such as she might have felt if it had been an acquaintance. She would acknowledge that Walter had admirable qualities; it just happened that she did not like him; he had always bored her. She would not admit that his death was a relief to her, she could say honestly that if by a word of hers she could bring him back to life she would say it, but she could not resist the feeling that his death made her way to some extent a trifle easier. They would never have been happy together and yet to part would have been terribly difficult. She was startled at herself for feeling as she did; she supposed that people would think her heartless and cruel if they knew. Well, they shouldn't know. She wondered if all her fellows had in their hearts shameful secrets which they spent their time guarding from curious glances.

She looked very little into the future and she made no plans. The only thing she knew was that she wanted to stay in Hong-Kong as short a while as might be. She looked forward to arriving there with horror. It seemed to her that she would like to wander for ever through that smiling and friendly country in her rattan chair, and, an indifferent spectator for ever of the phantasmagoria of life, pass each night under a different roof. But of course the immediate future must be faced: she would go to the hotel when she reached Hong-Kong, she would arrange about getting rid of the house and selling the furniture; there would be no need to see Townsend. He would have the grace to keep out of her way. She would like, all the same, to see him once more in order to tell him what a despicable creature she thought him.

But what did Charles Townsend matter?

Like a rich melody on a harp that rang in exultant arpeggios through the complicated harmonies of a symphony, one thought beat in her heart insistently. It was this thought which gave their exotic beauty to the rice-fields, which made a little smile break on her pale lips as a smooth-faced lad swung past her on his way to the market town with exultation in his carriage and audacity in his eyes, and which gave the magic of a tumultuous life to the cities she passed through. The city of the pestilence was a prison from which she was escaped, and she had never known before how exquisite was the blueness of the sky and what a joy there was in the bamboo copses that leaned with such an adorable grace across the causeway. Freedom! That was the thought that sung in her heart so that even though the future was so dim, it was iridescent like the mist over the river where the morning sun fell upon it. Freedom! Not only freedom from a bond that irked, and a companionship which depressed her; freedom, not only from the death which had threatened, but freedom from the love that had degraded her; freedom from all spiritual ties, the freedom of a disembodied spirit; and with freedom, courage and a valiant unconcern for whatever was to come.

lxxi

WHEN the boat docked at Hong-Kong Kitty, who had been standing on deck to look at the coloured, gay and vivacious traffic of the river, went into her cabin to see that the amah had left nothing behind. She gave herself a look in the glass.

She wore black, the nuns had dyed a dress for her, but not mourning; and the thought crossed her mind that the first thing she must do was to see to this. The habiliments of woe could not but serve as an effective disguise to her unexpected feelings. There was a knock on her cabin door. The amah opened it.

"Mrs. Fane."

Kitty turned round and saw a face which at the first moment she did not recognise. Then her heart gave a sudden quick beat and she flushed. It was Dorothy Townsend. Kitty so little expected to see her that she knew neither what to do nor what to say. But Mrs. Townsend came into the cabin and with an impulsive gesture took Kitty in her arms.

"Oh, my dear, my dear, I'm so dreadfully sorry for you."

Kitty allowed herself to be kissed. She was a little surprised at this effusiveness in a woman whom she had always thought cold and distant.

"It's very kind of you," murmured Kitty.

"Come on deck. The amah will look after your things and my boys are here."

She took Kitty's hand and Kitty, allowing herself to be led, noticed that her good-natured, weather-beaten face bore an expression of real concern.

"Your boat's early, I very nearly didn't get down in time," said Mrs. Townsend. "I couldn't have borne it if I'd missed you."

"But you didn't come to meet me?" exclaimed Kitty.

"Of course I did."

"But how did you know I was coming?"

"Mr. Waddington sent me a telegram."

Kitty turned away. She had a lump in her throat. It was funny that a little unexpected kindness should so affect her. She did not want to cry; she wished Dorothy Townsend would go away. But Dorothy took the hand that was hanging by Kitty's side and pressed it. It embarrassed Kitty that this shy woman should be so demonstrative.

"I want you to do me a great favour. Charlie and I want you to come and stay with us while you're in Hong-Kong."

Kitty snatched her hand away.

"It's awfully kind of you. I couldn't possibly."

"But you must. You can't go and live all by yourself in your own house. It would be dreadful for you. I've prepared everything. You shall have your own sitting-room. You can have your meals there if you don't care to have them with us. We both want you to come."

"I wasn't thinking of going to the house. I was going to get myself a room at the Hong-Kong Hotel. I couldn't possibly put you to so much trouble."

The suggestion had taken her by surprise. She was confused and vexed. If Charlie had had any sense of decency he would never have allowed his wife to make the invitation. She did not wish to be under an obligation to either of them.

"Oh, but I couldn't bear the idea of your living at a hotel. And you'd hate the Hong-Kong Hotel just now. With all those people about and the band playing jazz all the time. Please say you'll come to us. I promise you that Charlie and I won't bother you."

"I don't know why you should be so kind to me." Kitty was getting a little short of excuses; she could not bring herself to utter a blunt and definite no. "I'm afraid I'm not very good company among strangers just now."

"But need we be strangers to you? Oh, I do so want not to be, I so want you to allow me to be your friend." Dorothy clasped her hands and her voice, her cool, deliberate and distinguished voice, was tremulous with tears. "I so awfully want you to come. You see, I want to make amends to you."

Kitty did not understand. She did not know what amends Charlie's wife owed her.

"I'm afraid I didn't very much like you at first. I thought you rather fast. You see, I'm old-fashioned and I suppose I'm intolerant."

Kitty gave her a passing glance. What she meant was that at first she had thought Kitty vulgar. Though Kitty allowed no shadow of it to show on her face in her heart she laughed. Much she cared for what any one thought of her now!

"And when I heard that you'd gone with your husband into the jaws of death, without a moment's hesitation, I felt such a frightful cad. I felt so humiliated. You've been so wonderful, you've been so brave, you make all the rest of us look so dreadfully cheap and second-rate." Now the tears were pouring down her kind, homely face. "I can't tell you how much I admire you and what a respect I have for you. I know I can do nothing to make up for your terrible loss, but I want you to know how deeply, how sincerely I feel for you. And if you'll only allow me to do a little something for you it will be a privilege. Don't bear me a grudge because I misjudged you. You're heroic and I'm just a silly fool of a woman."

Kitty looked down at the deck. She was very pale. She wished that Dorothy would not show such uncontrollable emotion. She was touched, it was true, but she could not help a slight feeling of impatience that this simple creature should believe such lies.

"If you really mean that you'd like to have me, of course I shall be glad to come," she sighed.

lxxii

THE Townsends lived on the Peak in a house with a wide view over the sea, and Charlie did not as a rule come up to luncheon, but on the day of Kitty's arrival Dorothy (they were Kitty and Dorothy to one another by now) told her that if she felt up to seeing him he would like to come and bid her welcome. Kitty reflected that since she must see him she might just as well see him at once and she looked forward with grim amusement to the embarrassment she must cause him. She saw very well that the invitation to stay had arisen in his wife's fancy and notwithstanding his own feelings he had immediately approved. Kitty knew how great his desire was always to do the right thing and to offer her a gracious hospitality was obviously very much the right thing. But he could hardly remember that last interview of theirs without mortification: to a man so vain as Townsend it must be galling like an ulcer that would not heal. She hoped that she had hurt him as much as he had hurt her. He must hate her now. She was glad to think that she did not hate, but only despised him. It gave her a sardonic satisfaction to reflect that whatever his feelings he would be obliged to make much of her. When she left his office that afternoon he must have hoped with all his heart that he would never set eyes on her again.

And now, sitting with Dorothy, she waited for him to come in. She was conscious of her delight in the sober luxury of the drawing room. She sat in an arm-chair, there were lovely flowers here and there, on the walls were pleasing pictures; the room was shaded and cool, it was friendly and homelike. She remembered with a faint shudder the bare and empty parlour of the missionary's bungalow; the rattan chairs and the kitchen table with its cotton cloth, the stained shelves with all those cheap editions of novels, and the little skimpy red curtains that had such a dusty look. Oh, it had been so uncomfortable! She supposed that Dorothy had never thought of that.

They heard a motor drive up, and Charlie strode into the room.

"Am I late? I hope I haven't kept you waiting. I had to see the Governor and I simply couldn't get away."

He went up to Kitty, and took both her hands.

"I'm so very, very glad you've come here. I know Dorothy has told you that we want you to stay as long as ever you like and that we want you to look upon our house as your home. But I want to tell you so myself as well. If there's anything in the world I can do for you I shall only be too happy." His eyes wore a charming expression of sincerity; she wondered if he saw the irony in hers. "I'm awfully stupid at saying some things and I don't want to seem a clumsy fool, but I do want you to know how deeply I sympathise with you in your husband's death. He was a thundering good chap, and he'll be missed here more than I can say."

"Don't, Charlie," said his wife. "I'm sure Kitty understands. . . . Here are the cocktails."

Following the luxurious custom of the foreigners in China two boys in uniform came into the room with savouries and cocktails. Kitty refused.

"Oh, you must have one," insisted Townsend in his

breezy, cordial way. "It'll do you good and I'm sure you haven't had such a thing as a cocktail since you left Hong-Kong. Unless I'm very much mistaken you couldn't get ice at Mei-tan-fu."

"You're not mistaken," said Kitty.

For a moment she had a picture before her mind's eye of that beggar with the tousled head in the blue rags through which you saw the emaciated limbs, who had lain dead against the compound wall.

lxxiii

THEY went in to luncheon. Charlie, sitting at the head of his table, easily took charge of the conversation. After those first few words of sympathy he treated Kitty, not as though she had just suffered a devastating experience, but rather as though she had come in from Shanghai for a change after an operation for appendicitis. She needed cheering and he was prepared to cheer her. The best way of making her feel at home was to treat her as one of the family. He was a tactful man. He began talking of the autumn race meeting, and the polo—by Jove, he would have to give up playing polo if he couldn't get his weight down—and a chat he had had that morning with the Governor. He spoke of a party they had been to on the Admiral's flag-ship, the state of affairs in Canton, and of the links at Kowloon. In a few minutes Kitty felt that she might have been away for no longer than a week-end. It was incredible that over there, up country, six hundred miles away only (the distance from London to Edinburgh, wasn't it?) men, women and children had been dying like flies. Soon she found herself asking about so and so who had broken a collar bone at polo and if Mrs. This had gone home or Mrs. That was playing in the tennis tournament. Charlie made his little jokes and she smiled at them. Dorothy with her faint air of superiority (which now included Kitty and so was no longer slightly offensive, but a bond of union rather) was gently ironic about various persons in the colony. Kitty began to feel more alert.

"Why, she's looking better already," said Charlie to his wife. "She was so pale before tiffin that I was quite startled; she's really got some colour in her cheeks now."

But while she took her part in the conversation, if not with gaiety (for she felt that neither Dorothy nor Charlie with his admirable sense of decorum would approve of that) at least with cheerfulness, Kitty observed her host. In all those weeks during which her fancy had been revengefully occupied with him she had built up in her mind a very vivid impression of him. His thick curling hair was a little too long and too carefully brushed, in order to hide the fact that it was greying there was too much oil on it; his face was too red, with its network of mauve veins on the cheeks, and his jowl was too massive: when he did not hold his head up to hide it you saw that he had a double chin; and there was something apelike in those bushy, grizzled eyebrows of his that vaguely disgusted her. He was heavy in his movements, and all the care he took in his diet and all his exercise did not prevent him from being fat; his bones were much too well covered and his joints had a middle-aged stiffness. His smart clothes were a little tight for him and a little too young.

But when he came into the drawing-room before luncheon Kitty received quite a shock (this perhaps was why her pallor had been so marked), for she discovered that her imagination had played an odd trick on her: he did not in the least look as she had pictured him. She could hardly help laughing at herself. His hair was not grey at all, oh, there were a few white hairs on the temple, but they were becoming; and his face was not red, but sunburned; his head was very well placed on his neck; and he wasn't stout and he wasn't old: in fact he was almost slim and his figure was admirable—could you blame him if he was a trifle vain of it?—he might have been a young man. And of course he did know how to wear his clothes; it was absurd to deny that: he looked neat and clean and trim. Whatever could have possessed her to think him this and that? He was a very handsome man. It was lucky that she knew how worthless he was. Of course she had always admitted that his voice had a winning quality, and his voice was exactly as she remembered it: it made the falseness of every word he said more exasperating; its richness of tone and its warmth rang now in her ears with insincerity and she wondered how she could ever have been taken in by it. His eyes were beautiful: that was where his charm lay, they had such a soft, blue brilliance and even when he was talking balderdash an expression which was so delightful; it was almost impossible not to be moved by them.

At last the coffee was brought in and Charlie lit his cheroot. He looked at his watch and rose from the table.

"Well, I must leave you two young women to your own devices. It's time for me to get back to the office." He paused and then with his friendly, charming eyes on Kitty said to her: "I'm not going to bother you for a day or two till you're rested, but then I want to have a little business talk with you."

"With me?"

"We must make arrangements about your house, you know, and then there's the furniture."

"Oh, but I can go to a lawyer. There's no reason why I should bother you about that."

"Don't think for a moment I'm going to let you waste your money on legal expenses. I'm going to see to everything. You know you're entitled to a pension: I'm going to talk to H.E. about it and see if by making representations in the proper quarter we can't get something extra for you. You put yourself in my hands. But don't bother about anything just yet. All we want you to do now is to get fit and well: isn't that right, Dorothy?"

"Of course."

He gave Kitty a little nod and then passing by his wife's chair took her hand and kissed it. Most Englishmen look a little foolish when they kiss a woman's hand; he did it with a graceful ease.

lxxiv

IT WAS not till Kitty was fairly settled at the Townsends that she discovered that she was weary. The comfort and the unaccustomed amenity of this life broke up the strain under which she had been living. She had forgotten how pleasant it was to take one's ease, how lulling to be surrounded by pretty things, and how agreeable it was to receive attention. She sank back with a sigh of relief into the facile existence of the luxurious East. It was not displeasing to feel that in a discreet and well-bred fashion she was an object of sympathetic interest. Her bereavement was so recent that it was impossible for entertainments to be given for her, but ladies of consequence in the Colony (His Excellency's wife, the wives of the Admiral and of the Chief Justice) came to drink a quiet cup of tea with her. His Excellency's wife said that His Excellency was most anxious to see her and if she would come very quietly to luncheon at Government House ("not a party, of course, only ourselves and the A.D.C.'s!"), it would be very nice. These ladies used Kitty as though she were a piece of porcelain which was as fragile as it was precious. She could not fail to see that they looked upon her as a little heroine, and she had sufficient humour to play the part with modesty and discretion. She wished sometimes that Waddington were there; with his malicious shrewdness he would have seen the fun of the situation; and when alone they might have had a good laugh over it together. Dorothy had had a letter from him, and he had said all manner of things about her devoted work at the convent, about her courage and her self-control. Of course he was skilfully pulling their legs: the dirty dog.

lxxv

KITTY did not know whether it was by chance or by design that she never found herself for a moment alone with Charlie. His tact was exquisite. He remained kindly, sympathetic, pleasant and amiable. No one could have guessed that they had ever been more than acquaintances. But one afternoon when she was lying on a sofa outside her room reading he passed along the verandah and stopped.

"What is that you're reading?" he asked.

"A book."

She looked at him with irony. He smiled.

"Dorothy's gone to a garden-party at Government House."

"I know. Why haven't you gone too?"

"I didn't feel I could face it and I thought I'd come back and keep you company. The car's outside, would you like to come for a drive round the island?"

"No, thank you."

He sat down on the foot of the sofa on which she lay.

"We haven't had the chance of a talk by ourselves since you got here."

She looked straight into his eyes with cool insolence.

"Do you think we have anything to say to one another?"

"Volumes."

She shifted her feet a little so that she should not touch him.

"Are you still angry with me?" he asked, the shadow of a smile on his lips and his eyes melting.

"Not a bit," she laughed.

"I don't think you'd laugh if you weren't."

"You're mistaken; I despise you much too much to be angry with you."

He was unruffled.

"I think you're rather hard on me. Looking back calmly, don't you honestly think I was right?"

"From your standpoint."

"Now that you know Dorothy, you must admit she's rather nice?"

"Of course. I shall always be grateful for her great kindness to me."

"She's one in a thousand. I should never have had a moment's peace if we'd bolted. It would have been a rotten trick to play on her. And after all I had to think of my children; it would have been an awful handicap for them."

For a minute she held him in her reflective gaze. She felt completely mistress of the situation.

"I've watched you very carefully during the week I've been here. I've come to the conclusion that you really are fond of Dorothy. I should never have thought you capable of it."

"I told you I was fond of her. I wouldn't do anything to cause her a moment's uneasiness. She's the best wife a man ever had."

"Have you never thought that you owed her any loyalty?"

"What the eye doesn't see the heart doesn't grieve for," he smiled.

She shrugged her shoulders.

"You're despicable."

"I'm human. I don't know why you should think me such a cad because I fell head over ears in love with you. I didn't particularly want to, you know."

It gave her a little twist of the heart-strings to hear him say that.

"I was fair game," she answered bitterly.

"Naturally I couldn't foresee that we were going to get into such a devil of a scrape."

"And in any case you had a pretty shrewd idea that if any one suffered it wouldn't be you."

"I think that's a bit thick. After all, now it's all over, you must see I acted for the best for both of us. You lost your head and you ought to be jolly glad that I kept mine. Do you think it would have been a success if I'd done what you wanted me to? We were dashed uncomfortable in the frying-pan, but we should have been a damned sight worse off in the fire. And you haven't come to any harm. Why can't we kiss and make friends?"

She almost laughed.

"You can hardly expect me to forget that you sent me to almost certain death without a shadow of compunction?"

"Oh, what nonsense! I told you there was no risk if you took reasonable precautions. Do you think I'd have let you go for a moment if I hadn't been perfectly convinced of that?"

"You were convinced because you wanted to be. You're one of those cowards who only think what it's profitable for them to think."

"Well, the proof of the pudding is in the eating. You have

come back, and if you don't mind my saying anything so objectionable you've come back prettier than ever."

"And Walter?"

He could not resist the facetious answer which came to his mind. Charlie smiled.

"Nothing suits you so well as black."

She stared at him for a moment. Tears filled her eyes and she began to cry. Her beautiful face was distorted with grief. She did not seek to hide it, but lay on her back with her hands along her sides.

"For God's sake don't cry like that. I didn't mean to say anything unkind. It was only a joke. You know how sincerely I feel for you in your bereavement."

"Oh, hold your stupid tongue."

"I'd give anything to have Walter back again."

"He died because of you and me."

He took her hand, but she snatched it away from him.

"Please go away," she sobbed. "That's the only thing you can do for me now. I hate and despise you. Walter was worth ten of you and I was too big a fool to see it. Go away. Go away."

She saw he was going to speak again and she sprang to her feet and went into her room. He followed her, and as he entered, with instinctive prudence, drew the shutter so that they were almost in darkness.

"I can't leave you like this," he said, putting his arms round her. "You know I didn't mean to hurt you."

"Don't touch me. For God's sake go. Go away."

She tried to tear herself from him, but he would not let her. She was crying hysterically now.

"Darling, don't you know that I've always loved you," he said in his deep, charming voice. "I love you more than ever."

"How can you tell such lies! Let me go. Damn you, let me go."

"Don't be unkind to me, Kitty. I know I've been a brute to you, but forgive me."

She was shaking and sobbing, struggling to get away from him, but the pressure of his arms was strangely comforting.

She had so longed to feel them round her once more, just once, and all her body trembled. She felt dreadfully weak. It seemed as though her bones were melting, and the sorrow she felt for Walter shifted into pity for herself.

"Oh, how could you be so unkind to me?" she sobbed. "Don't you know that I loved you with all my heart. No one has ever loved you as I loved you."

"Darling."

He began to kiss her.

"No, no," she cried.

He sought her face, but she turned it away; he sought her lips; she did not know what he was saying, broken, passion-ate words of love; and his arms held her so firmly that she felt like a child that has been lost and now at last is safe at home. She moaned faintly. Her eyes were closed and her face was wet with tears. And then he found her lips and the pressure of his upon them shot through her body like the flame of God. It was an ecstasy and she was burnt to a cinder and she glowed as though she were transfigured. In her dreams, in her dreams she had known this rapture. What was he doing with her now? She did not know. She was not a woman, her personality was dissolved, she was nothing but desire. He lifted her off her feet, she was very light in his arms, he carried her and she clung to him, desperate and adoring; her head sank on the pillow and his lips clung to hers.

lxxvi

SHE sat on the edge of the bed hiding her face with her hands.

"Would you like a drop of water?"

She shook her head. He went over to the washing-stand, filled the tooth-glass and brought it to her.

"Come along, have a little drink and you'll feel better."

He put the glass to her lips and she sipped the water. Then, with horrified eyes, she stared at him. He was stand-ing over her, looking down, and in his eyes was a twinkle of self-satisfaction.

"Well, do you think I'm such a dirty dog as you did?" he asked.

She looked down.

"Yes. But I know that I'm not a bit better than you. Oh, I'm so ashamed."

"Well, I think you're very ungrateful."

"Will you go now?"

"To tell you the truth I think it's about time. I'll just go and tidy myself up before Dorothy comes in."

He went out of the room with a jaunty step.

Kitty sat for a while, still on the edge of the bed, hunched up like an imbecile. Her mind was vacant. A shudder passed through her. She staggered to her feet and, going to the dressing-table, sank into a chair. She stared at herself in the glass. Her eyes were swollen with tears; her face was stained and there was a red mark on one cheek where his had rested. She looked at herself with horror. It was the same face. She had expected in it she knew not what change of degradation.

"Swine," she flung at her reflection. "Swine."

Then, letting her face fall on her arms, she wept bitterly. Shame, shame! She did not know what had come over her. It was horrible. She hated him and she hated herself. It had been ecstasy. Oh, hateful! She could never look him in the face again. He was so justified. He had been right not to marry her, for she was worthless; she was no better than a harlot. Oh, worse, for those poor women gave themselves for bread. And in this house too into which Dorothy had taken her in her sorrow and cruel desolation! Her shoulders shook with her sobs. Everything was gone now. She had thought herself changed, she had thought herself strong, she thought she had returned to Hong-Kong a woman who possessed herself; new ideas flitted about her heart like little yellow butterflies in the sunshine and she had hoped to be so much better in the future; freedom like a spirit of light had beckoned her on, and the world was like a spacious plain through which she could walk light of foot and with head erect. She had thought herself free from lust and vile passions, free to live the clean and healthy life of the spirit; she had likened herself to the white egrets that fly with leisurely flight across the rice fields at dusk and they are like the soaring thoughts of a mind at rest with itself; and she was a slave. Weak, weak! It was hopeless, it was no good to try, she was a slut.

She would not go in to dinner. She sent the boy to tell Dorothy that she had a headache and preferred to remain in her room. Dorothy came in and, seeing her red, swollen eyes, talked for a little in her gentle, commiserating way of trivial things. Kitty knew that Dorothy thought she had been crying on account of Walter and, sympathising like the good and loving wife she was, respected the natural sorrow.

"I know it's very hard, dear," she said as she left Kitty. "But you must try to have courage. I'm sure your dear husband wouldn't wish you to grieve for him."

lxxvii

BUT next morning Kitty rose early and leaving a note for Dorothy to say that she was gone out on business took a tram down the hill. She made her way through the crowded streets with their motor cars, rickshaws and chairs, and the motley throng of Europeans and Chinese, to the offices of the P. & O. Company. A ship was sailing in two days, the first ship out of the port, and she had made up her mind that at all costs she must go on it. When the clerk told her that every berth was booked she asked to see the chief agent. She sent in her name and the agent, whom she had met before, came out to fetch her into his office. He knew her circumstances and when she told him what she wished he sent for the passenger list. He looked at it with perplexity.

"I beseech you to do what you can for me," she urged him.

"I don't think there's any one in the Colony who wouldn't do anything in the world for you, Mrs. Fane," he answered.

He sent for a clerk and made enquiries. Then he nodded.

"I'm going to shift one or two people. I know you want to get home and I think we ought to do our best for you. I can give you a little cabin to yourself. I expect you'd prefer that."

She thanked him. She left him with an elated heart. Flight: that was her only thought. Flight! She sent a cable to her father to announce her immediate return; she had already cabled to him to say that Walter was dead; and then went back again to the Townsends to tell Dorothy what she had done.

"We shall be dreadfully sorry to lose you," the kind creature said, "but of course I understand that you want to be with your mother and father."

Since her return to Hong-Kong Kitty had hesitated from day to day to go to her house. She dreaded entering it again and meeting face to face the recollections with which it was peopled. But now she had no alternative. Townsend had arranged for the sale of the furniture and he had found some one eager to take on the lease, but there were all her clothes and Walter's, for they had taken next to nothing to Mei-tan-fu, and there were books, photographs, and various odds and ends. Kitty, indifferent to everything and anxious to cut herself off completely from the past, realised that it would outrage the susceptibilities of the Colony if she allowed these things to go with the rest to an auction-room. They must be packed and sent to her. So after tiffin she prepared to go to the house. Dorothy, eager to give her help, offered to accompany her, but Kitty begged to be allowed to go alone. She agreed that two of Dorothy's boys should come and assist in the packing.

The house had been left in charge of the head boy and he opened the door for Kitty. It was curious to go into her own house as though she were a stranger. It was neat and clean. Everything was in its place, ready for her use, but although the day was warm and sunny there was about the silent rooms a chill and desolate air. The furniture was stiffly arranged, exactly where it should be, and the vases which should have held flowers were in their places; the book which Kitty had laid face downwards she did not remember when still lay face downwards. It was as though the house had been left empty but a minute before and yet that minute was fraught with eternity so that you could not imagine that ever again that house would echo with talk and resound with laughter. On the piano the open music of a foxtrot seemed to wait to be played, but you had a feeling that if you struck the keys no sound would come. Walter's room was as tidy as when he was there. On the chest of drawers were two large photographs of Kitty, one in her presentation dress and one in her wedding-gown.

But the boys fetched up the trunks from the box-room and she stood over them watching them pack. They packed neatly and quickly. Kitty reflected that in the two days she had it would be easy to get everything done. She must not let herself think; she had no time for that. Suddenly she heard a step behind her and turning round saw Charles Townsend. She felt a sudden chill at her heart.

"What do you want?" she said.

"Will you come into your sitting-room? I have something to say to you."

"I'm very busy."

"I shall only keep you five minutes."

She said no more, but with a word to the boys to go on with what they were doing, preceded Charles into the next room. She did not sit down, in order to show him that she expected him not to detain her. She knew that she was very pale and her heart was beating fast, but she faced him coolly, with hostile eyes.

"What is it you want?"

"I've just heard from Dorothy that you're going the day after to-morrow. She told me that you'd come here to do your packing and she asked me to ring up and find out if there was anything I could do for you."

"I'm grateful to you, but I can manage quite well by myself."

"So I imagined. I didn't come here to ask you that. I came to ask if your sudden departure is due to what happened yesterday."

"You and Dorothy have been very good to me. I didn't wish you to think I was taking advantage of your good nature."

"That's not a very straight answer."

"What does it matter to you?"

"It matters a great deal. I shouldn't like to think that anything I'd done had driven you away."

She was standing at the table. She looked down. Her eyes fell on the *Sketch*. It was months old now. It was that paper which Walter had stared at all through the terrible evening when—and Walter now was . . . She raised her eyes.

"I feel absolutely degraded. You can't possibly despise me as much as I despise myself."

"But I don't despise you. I meant every word that I said yesterday. What's the good of running away like this? I don't know why we can't be good friends. I hate the idea of your thinking I've treated you badly."

"Why couldn't you leave me alone?"

"Hang it all, I'm not a stick or a stone. It's so unreasonable, the way you look at it; it's so morbid. I thought after yesterday you'd feel a little more kindly to me. After all, we're only human."

"I don't feel human. I feel like an animal. A pig or a rabbit or a dog. Oh, I don't blame you, I was just as bad. I yielded to you because I wanted you. But it wasn't me, it wasn't the real me. I'm not that hateful, beastly, lustful woman. I disown her. It wasn't me that lay on that bed panting for you when my husband was hardly cold in his grave and your wife had been so kind to me, so indescribably kind. It was only the animal in me, dark and fearful like an evil spirit, and I disown, and hate, and despise it. And ever since, when I've thought of it, my gorge rises and I feel that I must vomit."

He frowned a little and gave a short, uneasy snigger.

"Well, I'm fairly broadminded, but sometimes you say things that positively shock me."

"I should be sorry to do that. You'd better go now. You're a very unimportant little man and I'm silly to talk to you seriously."

He did not answer for a while and she saw by the shadow in his blue eyes that he was angry with her. He would heave a sigh of relief when, tactful and courteous as ever, he had finally seen her off. It amused her to think of the politeness with which, while they shook hands and he wished her a pleasant journey, she would thank him for his hospitality. But she saw his expression change.

"Dorothy tells me you're going to have a baby," he said.

She felt herself colour, but she allowed no gesture to escape her.

"I am."

"Am I by any chance the father?"

"No, no. It's Walter's child."

She spoke with an emphasis which she could not prevent, but even as she spoke she knew that it was not the tone with which to carry conviction.

"Are you quite sure?" He was now roguishly smiling. "After all, you were married to Walter a couple of years and nothing happened. The dates seem to fit all right. I think it's much more likely to be mine than Walter's."

"I would rather kill myself than have a child of yours."

"Oh, come now, that's nonsense. I should be awfully pleased and proud. I'd like it to be a girl, you know. I've only had boys with Dorothy. You won't be able to be in doubt very long, you know: my three kiddies are absolutely the living image of me."

He had regained his good humour and she knew why. If the child was his, though she might never see him again, she could never entirely escape him. His power over her would reach out and he would still, obscurely but definitely, influence every day of her life.

"You really are the most vain and fatuous ass that it's ever been my bad luck to run across," she said.

lxxviii

As THE ship steamed into Marseilles Kitty, looking at the rugged and beautiful outline of the coast glowing in the sunlight, on a sudden caught sight of the golden statue of the Blessed Virgin which stands upon the church of Sainte Marie de la Grace as a symbol of safety to the mariner at sea. She remembered how the Sisters of the convent at Mei-tan-fu, leaving their own land for ever, had knelt as the figure faded in the distance so that it was no more than a little golden flame in the blue sky and sought in prayer to allay the pang of separation. She clasped her hands in supplication to what power she knew not.

During the long, quiet journey she had thought incessantly of the horrible thing that had happened to her. She could not understand herself. It was so unexpected. What was it that had seized her, so that, despising him, despising him with all her heart, she had yielded passionately to Charlie's foul embrace? Rage filled her and disgust of herself obsessed her. She felt that she could never forget her humiliation. She wept. But as the distance from Hong-Kong increased she found that she was insensibly losing the vividness of her resentment. What had happened seemed to have happened in another world. She was like a person who has been stricken with sudden madness and recovering is distressed and ashamed at the grotesque things he vaguely remembers to have done when he was not himself. But because he knows he was not himself he feels that in his own eyes at least he can claim indulgence. Kitty thought that perhaps a generous heart might pity rather than condemn her. But she sighed as she thought how woefully her self-confidence had been shattered. The way had seemed to stretch before her straight and easy and now she saw that it was a tortuous way and that pitfalls awaited her. The vast spaces and the tragic and beautiful sunsets of the Indian Ocean rested her. She seemed borne then to some country where she might in freedom possess her soul. If she could only regain her self-respect at the cost of a bitter conflict, well, she must find the courage to affront it.

The future was lonely and difficult. At Port Saïd she had received a letter from her mother in answer to her cable. It was a long letter written in the large and fanciful writing which was taught to young ladies in her mother's youth. Its ornateness was so neat that it gave you an impression of insincerity. Mrs. Garstin expressed her regret at Walter's death and sympathised properly with her daughter's grief. She feared that Kitty was left inadequately provided for, but naturally the Colonial Office would give her a pension. She was glad to know that Kitty was coming back to England and of course she must come and stay with her father and mother till her child was born. Then followed certain instructions that Kitty must be sure to follow and various details of her sister Doris's confinement. The little boy weighed so and so much and his paternal grandfather said he had never seen a finer child. Doris was expecting again and they hoped for another boy in order to make the succession to the baronetcy quite sure.

Kitty saw that the point of the letter lay in the definite date set for the invitation. Mrs. Garstin had no intention of being saddled with a widowed daughter in modest circumstances. It was singular, when she reflected how her mother had idolised her, that now, disappointed in her, she found her merely a nuisance. How strange was the relation between parents and children! When they were small the parents doted on them, passed through agonies of apprehension at each childish ailment, and the children clung to their parents with love and adoration; a few years passed, the children grew up, and persons not of their kin were more important to their happiness than father or mother. Indifference displaced the blind and instinctive love of the past. Their meetings were a source of boredom and irritation. Distracted once at the thought of a month's separation they were able now to look forward with equanimity to being parted for years. Her mother need not worry: as soon as she could she would make herself a home of her own. But she must have a little time; at present everything was vague and she could not form any picture of the future: perhaps she would die at childbirth; that would be a solution of many difficulties.

But when they docked two letters were handed to her. She was surprised to recognise her father's writing: she did not remember that he had ever written to her. He was not effusive, and began: dear Kitty. He told her that he was writing instead of her mother who had not been well and was obliged to go into a nursing home to have an operation. Kitty was not to be frightened and was to keep to her intention of going round by sea; it was much more expensive to come across by land and with her mother away it would be inconvenient for Kitty to stay at the house in Harrington Gardens. The other was from Doris and it started: Kitty darling, not because Doris had any particular affection for her, but because it was her way thus to address every one she knew.

Kitty darling

I expect Father has written to you. Mother has got to have an operation. It appears that she has been rotten for the last year, but you know she hates doctors and she's been taking all sorts of patent medicines. I don't quite know what's the matter with her as she insists on making a secret of the whole thing and flies into a passion if you ask her questions. She has been looking simply awful and if I were you I think I'd get off at Marseilles and come back as quick as you can. But don't let on that I told you to come as she pretends there's nothing much the matter with her and she doesn't want you to get here till she's back at home. She's made the doctors promise that she shall be moved in a week. Best love.

Doris.

I'm awfully sorry about Walter. You must have had a hell of a time, poor darling. I'm simply dying to see you. It's rather funny our both having babies together. We shall be able to hold one another's hands.

Kitty, lost in reflection, stood for a little while on the deck. She could not imagine her mother ill. She never remembered to have seen her other than active and resolute; she had always been impatient of other people's ailments. Then a steward came up to her with a telegram.

Deeply regret to inform you that your mother died this morning. Father.

lxxix

Kitty rang the bell at the house in Harrington Gardens. She was told that her father was in his study and going to the door she opened it softly: he was sitting by the fire reading the last edition of the evening paper. He looked up as she entered, put down the paper, and sprang nervously to his feet.

"Oh, Kitty, I didn't expect you till the later train."

"I thought you wouldn't want the bother of coming to meet me so I didn't wire the time I expected to arrive."

He gave her his cheek to kiss in the manner she so well remembered.

"I was just having a look at the paper," he said. "I haven't read the paper for the last two days."

She saw that he thought it needed some explanation if he occupied himself with the ordinary affairs of life.

"Of course," she said. "You must be tired out. I'm afraid mother's death has been a great shock to you."

He was older and thinner than when she had last seen him. A little, lined, dried-up man, with a precise manner.

"The surgeon said there had never been any hope. She hadn't been herself for more than a year, but she refused to see a doctor. The surgeon told me that she must have been in constant pain, he said it was a miracle that she had been able to endure it."

"Did she never complain?"

"She said she wasn't very well. But she never complained of pain." He paused and looked at Kitty. "Are you very tired after your journey?"

"Not very."

"Would you like to go up and see her?"

"Is she here?"

"Yes, she was brought here from the nursing home."

"Yes, I'll go now."

"Would you like me to come with you?"

There was something in her father's tone that made her look at him quickly. His face was slightly turned from her; he did not want her to catch his eye. Kitty had acquired of late a singular proficiency at reading the thoughts of others. After all, day after day she had applied all her sensibilities to divine from a casual word or an unguarded gesture the hidden thoughts of her husband. She guessed at once what her father was trying to hide from her. It was relief he felt, an infinite relief, and he was frightened of himself. For hard on thirty years he had been a good and faithful husband, he had never uttered a single word in dispraise of his wife, and now he should grieve for her. He had always done the things that were expected of him. It would have been shocking to him by the flicker of an eyelid or by the smallest hint to betray that he did not feel what under the circumstances a bereaved husband should feel.

"No, I would rather go by myself," said Kitty.

She went upstairs and into the large, cold and pretentious bedroom in which her mother for so many years had slept. She remembered so well those massive pieces of mahogany and the engravings after Marcus Stone which adorned the walls. The things on the dressing-table were arranged with the stiff precision which Mrs. Garstin had all her life insisted upon. The flowers looked out of place; Mrs. Garstin would have thought it silly, affected and unhealthy to have flowers in her bedroom. Their perfume did not cover that acrid, musty smell, as of freshly washed linen, which Kitty remembered as characteristic of her mother's room.

Mrs. Garstin lay on the bed, her hands folded across her breast with a meekness which in life she would have had no patience with. With her strong sharp features, the cheeks hollow with suffering and the temples sunken, she looked handsome and even imposing. Death had robbed her face of its meanness and left only an impression of character. She might have been a Roman empress. It was strange to Kitty that of the dead persons she had seen this was the only one who in death seemed to preserve a look as though that clay had been once a habitation of the spirit. Grief she could not feel, for there had been too much bitterness between her mother and herself to leave in her heart any deep feeling of affection; and looking back on the girl she had been she knew that it was her mother who had made her what she was. But when she looked at that hard, domineering and ambitious woman who lay there so still and silent with all her petty aims frustrated by death, she was aware of a vague pathos. She had schemed and intrigued all her life and never had she desired anything but what was base and unworthy. Kitty wondered whether perhaps in some other sphere she looked upon her earthly course with consternation.

Doris came in.

"I thought you'd come by this train. I felt I must look in for a moment. Isn't it dreadful? Poor darling mother."

Bursting into tears, she flung herself into Kitty's arms. Kitty kissed her. She knew how her mother had neglected Doris in favour of her and how harsh she had been with her because she was plain and dull. She wondered whether Doris really felt the extravagant grief she showed. But Doris had always been emotional. She wished she could cry: Doris would think her dreadfully hard. Kitty felt that she had been through too much to feign a distress she did not feel.

"Would you like to come and see father?" she asked her when the strength of the outburst had somewhat subsided.

Doris wiped her eyes. Kitty noticed that her sister's pregnancy had blunted her features and in her black dress she looked gross and blousy.

"No, I don't think I will. I shall only cry again. Poor old thing, he's bearing it wonderfully."

Kitty showed her sister out of the house and then went back to her father. He was standing in front of the fire and the newspaper was neatly folded. He wanted her to see that he had not been reading it again.

"I haven't dressed for dinner," he said. "I didn't think it was necessary."

lxxx

THEY dined. Mr. Garstin gave Kitty the details of his wife's illness and death, and he told her the kindness of the friends who had written (there were piles of sympathetic letters on his table and he sighed when he considered the burden of answering them) and the arrangements he had made for the funeral. Then they went back into his study. This was the only room in the house which had a fire. He mechanically took from the chimney-piece his pipe and began to fill it, but he gave his daughter a doubtful look and put it down.

"Aren't you going to smoke?" she asked.

"Your mother didn't very much like the smell of a pipe after dinner and since the war I've given up cigars."

His answer gave Kitty a little pang. It seemed dreadful that a man of sixty should hesitate to smoke what he wanted in his own study.

"I like the smell of a pipe," she smiled.

A faint look of relief crossed his face and taking his pipe once more he lit it. They sat opposite one another on each side of the fire. He felt that he must talk to Kitty of her own troubles.

"You received the letter your mother wrote to you to Port Saïd, I suppose. The news of poor Walter's death was a great shock to both of us. I thought him a very nice fellow."

Kitty did not know what to say.

"Your mother told me that you were going to have a baby."

"Yes."

"When do you expect it?"

"In about four months."

"It will be a great consolation to you. You must go and see Doris's boy. He's a fine little fellow."

They were talking more distantly than if they were strangers who had just met, for if they had been he would have been interested in her just because of that, and curious, but their common past was a wall of indifference between them. Kitty knew too well that she had done nothing to beget her father's affection, he had never counted in the house and had been taken for granted, the bread-winner who was a little despised because he could provide no more luxuriously for his family; but she had taken for granted that he loved her just because he was her father, and it was a shock to discover that his heart was empty of feeling for her. She had known that they were all bored by him, but it had never occurred to her that he was equally bored by them. He was as ever kind and subdued, but the sad perspicacity which she had learnt in suffering suggested to her that, though he had probably never acknowledged it to himself and never would, in his heart he disliked her.

His pipe was not drawing and he rose to find something to poke it with. Perhaps it was an excuse to hide his nervousness.

"Your mother wished you to stay here till your baby was born and she was going to have your old room got ready for you."

"I know. I promise you I won't be a bother."

"Oh, it's not that. Under the circumstances it was evident that the only place for you to come to was your father's house. But the fact is that I've just been offered the post of Chief Justice of the Bahamas and I have accepted it."

"Oh, father, I'm so glad. I congratulate you with all my heart."

"The offer arrived too late for me to tell your poor mother. It would have given her a great satisfaction."

The bitter irony of fate! After all her efforts, intrigues and humiliations, Mrs. Garstin had died without knowing that her ambition, however modified by past disappointments, was at last achieved.

"I am sailing early next month. Of course this house will be put in the agent's hands and my intention was to sell the furniture. I'm sorry that I shan't be able to have you to stay here, but if you'd like any of the furniture to furnish a flat I shall be extremely pleased to give it you."

Kitty looked into the fire. Her heart beat quickly; it was curious that on a sudden she should be so nervous. But at last she forced herself to speak. In her voice was a little tremor.

"Couldn't I come with you, father?"

"You? Oh, my dear Kitty." His face fell. She had often heard the expression, but thought it only a phrase, and now for the first time in her life she saw the movement that it described. It was so marked that it startled her. "But all your friends are here and Doris is here. I should have thought you'd be much happier if you took a flat in London. I don't exactly know what your circumstances are, but I shall be very glad to pay the rent of it."

"I have enough money to live on."

"I'm going to a strange place. I know nothing of the conditions."

"I'm used to strange places. London means nothing to me any more. I couldn't breathe here."

He closed his eyes for a moment and she thought he was going to cry. His face bore an expression of utter misery. It wrung her heart. She had been right; the death of his wife had filled him with relief and now this chance to break entirely with the past had offered him freedom. He had seen a new life spread before him and at last after all these years rest and the mirage of happiness. She saw dimly all the suffering that had preyed on his heart for thirty years. At last he opened his eyes. He could not prevent the sigh that escaped him.

"Of course if you wish to come I shall be very pleased."

It was pitiful. The struggle had been short and he had surrendered to his sense of duty. With those few words he abandoned all his hopes. She rose from her chair and going over to him knelt down and seized his hands.

"No, father, I won't come unless you want me. You've sacrificed yourself enough. If you want to go alone, go. Don't think of me for a minute."

He released one of his hands and stroked her pretty hair.

"Of course I want you, my dear. After all I'm your father and you're a widow and alone. If you want to be with me it would be very unkind of me not to want you."

"But that's just it, I make no claims on you because I'm your daughter, you owe me nothing."

"Oh, my dear child."

"Nothing," she repeated vehemently. "My heart sinks when I think how we've battened on you all our lives and have given you nothing in return. Not even a little affection. I'm afraid you've not had a very happy life. Won't you let me try to make up a little for all I've failed to do in the past?"

He frowned a little. Her emotion embarrassed him.

"I don't know what you mean. I've never had any complaint to make of you."

"Oh, father, I've been through so much, I've been so unhappy. I'm not the Kitty I was when I went away. I'm terribly weak, but I don't think I'm the filthy cad I was then.

Won't you give me a chance? I have nobody but you in the world now. Won't you let me try to make you love me? Oh, father, I'm so lonely and so miserable; I want your love so badly."

She buried her face in his lap and cried as though her heart were breaking.

"Oh, my Kitty, my little Kitty," he murmured.

She looked up and put her arms round his neck.

"Oh, father, be kind to me. Let us be kind to one another."

He kissed her, on the lips as a lover might, and his cheeks were wet with her tears.

"Of course you shall come with me."

"Do you want me to? Do you really want me to?"

"Yes."

"I'm so grateful to you."

"Oh, my dear, don't say things like that to me. It makes me feel quite awkward."

He took out his handkerchief and dried her eyes. He smiled in a way that she had never seen him smile before. Once more she threw her arms round his neck.

"We'll have such a lark, father dear. You don't know what fun we're going to have together."

"You haven't forgotten that you're going to have a baby."

"I'm glad she'll be born out there within sound of the sea and under a wide blue sky."

"Have you already made up your mind about the sex?" he murmured, with his thin, dry smile.

"I want a girl because I want to bring her up so that she shan't make the mistakes I've made. When I look back upon the girl I was I hate myself. But I never had a chance. I'm going to bring up my daughter so that she's free and can stand on her own feet. I'm not going to bring a child into the world, and love her, and bring her up, just so that some man may want to sleep with her so much that he's willing to provide her with board and lodging for the rest of her life."

She felt her father stiffen. He had never spoken of such things and it shocked him to hear these words in his daughter's mouth.

"Let me be frank just this once, father. I've been foolish

and wicked and hateful. I've been terribly punished. I'm determined to save my daughter from all that. I want her to be fearless and frank. I want her to be a person, independent of others because she is possessed of herself, and I want her to take life like a free man and make a better job of it than I have."

"Why, my love, you talk as though you were fifty. You've got all your life before you. You mustn't be down-hearted."

Kitty shook her head and slowly smiled.

"I'm not. I have hope and courage."

The past was finished; let the dead bury their dead. Was that dreadfully callous? She hoped with all her heart that she had learnt compassion and charity. She could not know what the future had in store for her, but she felt in herself the strength to accept whatever was to come with a light and buoyant spirit. Then, on a sudden, for no reason that she knew of, from the depths of her unconscious arose a reminiscence of the journey they had taken, she and poor Walter, to the plague-ridden city where he had met his death: one morning they set out in their chairs while it was still dark, and as the day broke she divined rather than saw a scene of such breath-taking loveliness that for a brief period the anguish of her heart was assuaged. It reduced to insignificance all human tribulation. The sun rose, dispelling the mist, and she saw winding onwards as far as the eye could reach, among the rice-fields, across a little river and through undulating country the path they were to follow: perhaps her faults and follies, the unhappiness she had suffered, were not entirely vain if she could follow the path that now she dimly discerned before her, not the path that kind funny old Waddington had spoken of that led nowhither, but the path those dear nuns at the convent followed so humbly, the path that led to peace.

JANE

I REMEMBER very well the occasion on which I first saw
Jane Fowler. It is indeed only because the details of
the glimpse I had of her then are so clear that I trust
my recollection at all, for, looking back, I must confess that
I find it hard to believe that it has not played me a fantastic
trick. I had lately returned to London from China and was
drinking a dish of tea with Mrs. Tower. Mrs. Tower had
been seized with the prevailing passion for decoration; and
with the ruthlessness of her sex had sacrificed chairs in which
she had comfortably sat for years, tables, cabinets, ornaments, on which her eyes had dwelt in peace since she was
married, pictures that had been familiar to her for a generation; and delivered herself into the hands of an expert.
Nothing remained in her drawing-room with which she
had any association, or to which any sentiment was attached;
and she had invited me that day to see the fashionable glory
in which she now lived. Everything that could be pickled
was pickled and what couldn't be pickled was painted. Nothing matched, but everything harmonized.

"Do you remember that ridiculous drawing-room suite
that I used to have?" asked Mrs. Tower.

The curtains were sumptuous yet severe; the sofa was
covered with Italian brocade; the chair on which I sat was in
petit point. The room was beautiful, opulent without garish-
ness and original without affectation; yet to me it lacked
something; and while I praised with my lips I asked myself
why I so much preferred the rather shabby chintz of the
despised suite, the Victorian water-colours that I had known
so long, and the ridiculous Dresden china that had adorned

the chimney-piece. I wondered what it was that I missed in all these rooms that the decorators were turning out with a profitable industry. Was it heart? But Mrs. Tower looked about her happily.

"Don't you like my alabaster lamps?" she said. "They give such a soft light."

"Personally I have a weakness for a light that you can see by," I smiled.

"It's so difficult to combine that with a light that you can't be too much seen by," laughed Mrs. Tower.

I had no notion what her age was. When I was quite a young man she was a married woman a good deal older than I, but now she treated me as her contemporary. She constantly said that she made no secret of her age, which was forty, and then added with a smile that all women took five years off. She never sought to conceal the fact that she dyed her hair (it was a very pretty brown with reddish tints), and she said she did this because hair was hideous while it was going grey; as soon as hers was white she would cease to dye it.

"Then they'll say what a young face I have."

Meanwhile it was painted, though with discretion, and her eyes owed not a little of their vivacity to art. She was a handsome woman, exquisitely gowned, and in the sombre glow of the alabaster lamps did not look a day more than the forty she gave herself.

"It is only at my dressing-table that I can suffer the naked brightness of a thirty-two-candle electric bulb," she added with smiling cynicism. "There I need it to tell me first the hideous truth and then to enable me to take the necessary steps to correct it."

We gossiped pleasantly about our common friends and Mrs. Tower brought me up to date in the scandal of the day. After roughing it here and there it was very agreeable to sit in a comfortable chair, the fire burning brightly on the hearth, charming tea-things set out on a charming table, and talk with this amusing, attractive woman. She treated me as a prodigal returned from his husks and was disposed to make much of me. She prided herself on her dinner-parties; she took no less trouble to have her guests suitably assorted than to give them excellent food; and there were few persons who did not look upon it as a treat to be bidden to one of them. Now she fixed a date and asked me whom I would like to meet.

"There's only one thing I must tell you. If Jane Fowler is still here I shall have to put it off."

"Who is Jane Fowler?" I asked.

Mrs. Tower gave a rueful smile.

"Jane Fowler is my cross."

"Oh!"

"Do you remember a photograph that I used to have on the piano before I had my room done of a woman in a tight dress with tight sleeves and a gold locket, with her hair drawn back from a broad forehead and her ears showing and spectacles on a rather blunt nose? Well, that was Jane Fowler."

"You had so many photographs about the room in your unregenerate days," I said, vaguely.

"It makes me shudder to think of them. I've made them into a huge brown-paper parcel and hidden them in an attic."

"Well, who is Jane Fowler?" I asked again, smiling.

"She's my sister-in-law. She was my husband's sister and she married a manufacturer in the north. She's been a widow for many years, and she's very well-to-do."

"And why is she your cross?"

"She's worthy, she's dowdy, she's provincial. She looks twenty years older than I do and she's quite capable of telling anyone she meets that we were at school together. She has an overwhelming sense of family affection, and because I am her only living connection she's devoted to me. When she comes to London it never occurs to her that she should stay anywhere but here—she thinks it would hurt my feelings—and she'll pay me visits of three or four weeks. We sit here and she knits and reads. And sometimes she insists on taking me to dine at Claridge's and she looks like a funny old charwoman and everyone I particularly don't want to be seen by is sitting at the next table. When we are driving home she says she loves giving me a little treat. With her own hands she makes me tea-cozies that I am forced to use when she is here and doilies and centrepieces for the dining-room table."

Mrs. Tower paused to take breath.

"I should have thought a woman of your tact would find a way to deal with a situation like that."

"Ah, but don't you see, I haven't a chance. She's so immeasurably kind. She has a heart of gold. She bores me to death, but I wouldn't for anything let her suspect it."

"And when does she arrive?"

"To-morrow."

But the answer was hardly out of Mrs. Tower's mouth when the bell rang. There were sounds in the hall of a slight commotion and in a minute or two the butler ushered in an elderly lady.

"Mrs. Fowler," he announced.

"Jane!" cried Mrs. Tower, springing to her feet. "I wasn't expecting you to-day."

"So your butler has just told me. I certainly said to-day in my letter."

Mrs. Tower recovered her wits.

"Well, it doesn't matter. I'm very glad to see you whenever you come. Fortunately I'm doing nothing this evening."

"You mustn't let me give you any trouble. If I can have a boiled egg for my dinner that's all I shall want."

A faint grimace for a moment distorted Mrs. Tower's handsome features. A boiled egg!

"Oh, I think we can do a little better than that."

I chuckled inwardly when I recollected that the two ladies were contemporaries. Mrs. Fowler looked a good fifty-five. She was a rather big woman; she wore a black straw hat with a wide brim, and from it a black lace veil hung over her shoulders, a cloak that oddly combined severity with fussiness, a long black dress, voluminous as though she wore several petticoats under it, and stout boots. She was evidently short-sighted, for she looked at you through large gold-rimmed spectacles.

"Won't you have a cup of tea?" asked Mrs. Tower.

"If it wouldn't be too much trouble. I'll take off my mantle."

She began by stripping her hands of the black gloves she wore, and then took off her cloak. Round her neck was a solid gold chain from which hung a large gold locket in which I felt certain was a photograph of her deceased husband. Then she took off her hat and placed it neatly with her gloves and cloak on the sofa corner. Mrs. Tower pursed her lips. Certainly those garments did not go very well with the austere but sumptuous beauty of Mrs. Tower's redecorated drawing-room. I wondered where on earth Mrs. Fowler had found the extraordinary clothes she wore. They were not old, and the materials were expensive. It was astounding to think that dressmakers still made things that had not been worn for a quarter of a century. Mrs. Fowler's grey hair was very plainly done, showing all her forehead and her ears, with a parting in the middle. It had evidently never known the tongs of Monsieur Marcel. Now her eyes fell on the tea-table with its teapot of Georgian silver and its cups in old Worcester.

"What have you done with the tea-cozy I gave you last time I came up, Marion?" she asked. "Don't you use it?"

"Yes, I use it every day, Jane," answered Mrs. Tower glibly. "Unfortunately we had an accident with it a little while ago. It got burnt."

"But the last one I gave you got burnt."

"I'm afraid you'll think us very careless."

"It doesn't really matter," smiled Mrs. Fowler. "I shall enjoy making you another. I'll go to Liberty's to-morrow and buy some silks."

Mrs. Tower kept her face bravely.

"I don't deserve it, you know. Doesn't your vicar's wife need one?"

"Oh, I've just made her one," said Mrs. Fowler brightly.

I noticed that when she smiled she showed white, small and regular teeth. They were a real beauty. Her smile was certainly very sweet.

But I felt it high time for me to leave the two ladies to themselves, so I took my leave.

Early next morning Mrs. Tower rang me up, and I heard at once from her voice that she was in high spirits.

"I've got the most wonderful news for you," she said. "Jane is going to be married."

"Nonsense."

"Her fiancé is coming to dine here to-night to be introduced to me, and I want you to come too."

"Oh, but I shall be in the way."

"No, you won't. Jane suggested herself that I should ask you. Do come."

She was bubbling over with laughter.

"Who is he?"

"I don't know. She tells me he's an architect. Can you imagine the sort of man Jane would marry?"

I had nothing to do and I could trust Mrs. Tower to give me a good dinner.

When I arrived Mrs. Tower, very splendid in a teagown a little too young for her, was alone.

"Jane is putting the finishing touches to her appearance. I'm longing for you to see her. She's all in a flutter. She says he adores her. His name is Gilbert and when she speaks of him her voice gets all funny and tremulous. It makes me want to laugh."

"I wonder what he's like."

"Oh, I'm sure I know. Very big and massive, with a bald head and an immense gold chain across an immense tummy. A large, fat, clean-shaven, red face and a booming voice."

Mrs. Fowler came in. She wore a very stiff black silk dress with a wide skirt and a train. At the neck it was cut into a timid V and the sleeves came down to the elbows. She wore a necklace of diamonds set in silver. She carried in her hands a long pair of black gloves and a fan of black ostrich feathers. She managed (as so few people do) to look exactly what she was. You could never have thought her anything in the world but the respectable relict of a north-country manufacturer of ample means.

"You've really got quite a pretty neck, Jane," said Mrs. Tower with a kindly smile.

It was indeed astonishingly young when you compared it

with her weather-beaten face. It was smooth and unlined
and the skin was white. And I noticed then that her head
was very well placed on her shoulders.

"Has Marion told you my news?" she said, turning to
me with that really charming smile of hers as if we were
already old friends.

"I must congratulate you," I said.

"Wait to do that till you've seen my young man."

"I think it's too sweet to hear you talk of your young
man," smiled Mrs. Tower.

Mrs. Fowler's eyes certainly twinkled behind her preposterous spectacles.

"Don't expect anyone too old. You wouldn't like me to
marry a decrepit old gentleman with one foot in the grave,
would you?"

This was the only warning she gave us. Indeed there was
no time for any further discussion, for the butler flung open
the door and in a loud voice announced:

"Mr. Gilbert Napier."

There entered a youth in a very well-cut dinner jacket.
He was slight, not very tall, with fair hair in which there
was a hint of a natural wave, clean-shaven and blue-eyed.
He was not particularly good-looking, but he had a pleasant,
amiable face. In ten years he would probably be wizened
and sallow; but now, in extreme youth, he was fresh, and
clean and blooming. For he was certainly not more than
twenty-four. My first thought was that this was the son of
Jane Fowler's fiancé (I had not known he was a widower)
come to say that his father was prevented from dining by a
sudden attack of gout. But his eyes fell immediately on Mrs.
Fowler, his face lit up, and he went towards her with both
hands outstretched. Mrs. Fowler gave him hers, a demure
smile on her lips, and turned to her sister-in-law.

"This is my young man, Marion," she said.

He held out his hand.

"I hope you'll like me, Mrs. Tower," he said. "Jane tells
me you're the only relation she has in the world."

Mrs. Tower's face was wonderful to behold. I saw then
to admiration how bravely good breeding and social usage

could combat the instincts of the natural woman. For the astonishment and then the dismay that for an instant she could not conceal were quickly driven away, and her face assumed an expression of affable welcome. But she was evidently at a loss for words. It was not unnatural if Gilbert felt a certain embarrassment, and I was too busy preventing myself from laughing to think of anything to say. Mrs. Fowler alone kept perfectly calm.

"I know you'll like him, Marion. There's no one enjoys good food more than he does." She turned to the young man. "Marion's dinners are famous."

"I know," he beamed.

Mrs. Tower made some quick rejoinder and we went downstairs. I shall not soon forget the exquisite comedy of that meal. Mrs. Tower could not make up her mind whether the pair of them were playing a practical joke on her or whether Jane by wilfully concealing her fiancé's age had hoped to make her look foolish. But then Jane never jested and she was incapable of doing a malicious thing. Mrs. Tower was amazed, exasperated and perplexed. But she had recovered her self-control, and for nothing would she have forgotten that she was a perfect hostess whose duty it was to make her party go. She talked vivaciously; but I wondered if Gilbert Napier saw how hard and vindictive was the expression of her eyes behind the mask of friendliness that she turned to him. She was measuring him. She was seeking to delve into the secret of his soul. I could see that she was in a passion, for under her rouge her cheeks glowed with an angry red.

"You've got a very high colour, Marion," said Jane, looking at her amiably through her great round spectacles.

"I dressed in a hurry. I daresay I put on too much rouge."

"Oh, is it rouge? I thought it was natural. Otherwise I shouldn't have mentioned it." She gave Gilbert a shy little smile. "You know, Marion and I were at school together. You would never think it to look at us now, would you? But of course I've lived a very quiet life."

I do not know what she meant by these remarks; it was almost incredible that she made them in complete simplicity;

but anyhow they goaded Mrs. Tower to such a fury that she flung her own vanity to the winds. She smiled brightly.

"We shall neither of us see fifty again, Jane," she said.

If the observation was meant to discomfit the widow it failed.

"Gilbert says I mustn't acknowledge to more than forty-nine for his sake," she answered blandly.

Mrs. Tower's hands trembled slightly, but she found a retort.

"There is of course a certain disparity of age between you," she smiled.

"Twenty-seven years," said Jane. "Do you think it's too much? Gilbert says I'm very young for my age. I told you I shouldn't like to marry a man with one foot in the grave."

I was really obliged to laugh, and Gilbert laughed too. His laughter was frank and boyish. It looked as though he were amused at everything Jane said. But Mrs. Tower was almost at the end of her tether, and I was afraid that unless relief came she would for once forget that she was a woman of the world. I came to the rescue as best I could.

"I suppose you're very busy buying your trousseau," I said.

"No. I wanted to get my things from the dressmaker in Liverpool I've been to ever since I was first married. But Gilbert won't let me. He's very masterful, and of course he has wonderful taste."

She looked at him with a little affectionate smile, demurely, as though she were a girl of seventeen.

Mrs. Tower went quite pale under her make-up.

"We're going to Italy for our honeymoon. Gilbert has never had a chance of studying Renaissance architecture, and of course it's important for an architect to see things for himself. And we shall stop in Paris on the way and get my clothes there."

"Do you expect to be away long?"

"Gilbert has arranged with his office to stay away for six months. It will be such a treat for him, won't it? You see, he's never had more than a fortnight's holiday before."

"Why not?" asked Mrs. Tower in a tone that no effort of will could prevent from being icy.

"He's never been able to afford it, poor dear."

"Ah!" said Mrs. Tower, and into the exclamation put volumes.

Coffee was served and the ladies went upstairs. Gilbert and I began to talk in the desultory way in which men talk who have nothing whatever to say to one another; but in two minutes a note was brought in to me by the butler. It was from Mrs. Tower and ran as follows:

Come upstairs quickly and then go as soon as you can. Take him with you. Unless I have it out with Jane at once I shall have a fit.

I told a facile lie.

"Mrs. Tower has a headache and wants to go to bed. I think if you don't mind we'd better clear out."

"Certainly," he answered.

We went upstairs and five minutes later were on the doorstep. I called a taxi and offered the young man a lift.

"No, thanks," he answered. "I'll just walk to the corner and jump on a bus."

Mrs. Tower sprang to the fray as soon as she heard the front door close behind us.

"Are you crazy, Jane?" she cried.

"Not more than most people who don't habitually live in a lunatic asylum, I trust," Jane answered blandly.

"May I ask why you're going to marry this young man?" asked Mrs. Tower with formidable politeness.

"Partly because he won't take no for an answer. He's asked me five times. I grew positively tired of refusing him."

"And why do you think he's so anxious to marry you?"

"I amuse him."

Mrs. Tower gave an exclamation of annoyance.

"He's an unscrupulous rascal. I very nearly told him so to his face."

"You would have been wrong, and it wouldn't have been very polite."

"He's penniless and you're rich. You can't be such a besotted fool as not to see that he's marrying you for your money."

Jane remained perfectly composed. She observed her sister-in-law's agitation with detachment.

"I don't think he is, you know," she replied. "I think he's very fond of me."

"You're an old woman, Jane."

"I'm the same age as you are, Marion," she smiled.

"I've never let myself go. I'm very young for my age. No one would think I was more than forty. But even I wouldn't dream of marrying a boy twenty years younger than myself."

"Twenty-seven," corrected Jane.

"Do you mean to tell me that you can bring yourself to believe that it's possible for a young man to care for a woman old enough to be his mother?"

"I've lived very much in the country for many years. I daresay there's a great deal about human nature that I don't know. They tell me there's a man called Freud, an Austrian, I believe——"

But Mrs. Tower interrupted her without any politeness at all.

"Don't be ridiculous, Jane. It's so undignified. It's so ungraceful. I always thought you were a sensible woman. Really you're the last person I should ever have thought likely to fall in love with a boy."

"But I'm not in love with him. I've told him that. Of course I like him very much or I wouldn't think of marrying him. I thought it only fair to tell him quite plainly what my feelings were towards him."

Mrs. Tower gasped. The blood rushed to her head and her breathing oppressed her. She had no fan, but she seized the evening paper and vigorously fanned herself with it.

"If you're not in love with him why do you want to marry him?"

"I've been a widow a very long time and I've led a very quiet life. I thought I'd like a change."

"If you want to marry just to be married why don't you marry a man of your own age?"

"No man of my own age has asked me five times. In fact no man of my own age has asked me at all."

Jane chuckled as she answered. It drove Mrs. Tower to the final pitch of frenzy.

"Don't laugh, Jane. I won't have it. I don't think you can be right in your mind. It's dreadful."

It was altogether too much for her and she burst into tears. She knew that at her age it was fatal to cry; her eyes would be swollen for twenty-four hours and she would look a sight. But there was no help for it. She wept. Jane remained perfectly calm. She looked at Marion through her large spectacles and reflectively smoothed the lap of her black silk dress.

"You're going to be so dreadfully unhappy," Mrs. Tower sobbed, dabbing her eyes cautiously in the hope that the black on her lashes would not smudge.

"I don't think so, you know," Jane answered in those equable, mild tones of hers, as if there were a little smile behind the words. "We've talked it over very thoroughly. I always think I'm a very easy person to live with. I think I shall make Gilbert very happy and comfortable. He's never had anyone to look after him properly. We're only marrying after mature consideration. And we've decided that if either of us wants his liberty the other will place no obstacles in the way of his getting it."

Mrs. Tower had by now recovered herself sufficiently to make a cutting remark.

"How much has he persuaded you to settle on him?"

"I wanted to settle a thousand a year on him, but he wouldn't hear of it. He was quite upset when I made the suggestion. He says he can earn quite enough for his own needs."

"He's more cunning than I thought," said Mrs. Tower acidly.

Jane paused a little and looked at her sister-in-law with kindly but resolute eyes.

"You see, my dear, it's different for you," she said. "You've never been so very much a widow, have you?"

Mrs. Tower looked at her. She blushed a little. She even

felt slightly uncomfortable. But of course Jane was much too simple to intend an innuendo. Mrs. Tower gathered herself together with dignity.

"I'm so upset that I really must go to bed," she said. "We'll resume the conversation to-morrow morning."

"I'm afraid that won't be very convenient, dear. Gilbert and I are going to get the license to-morrow morning."

Mrs. Tower threw up her hands in a gesture of dismay, but she found nothing more to say.

The marriage took place at a registrar's office. Mrs. Tower and I were the witnesses. Gilbert in a smart blue suit looked absurdly young, and he was obviously nervous. It is a trying moment for any man. But Jane kept her admirable composure. She might have been in the habit of marrying as frequently as a woman of fashion. Only a slight colour on her cheeks suggested that beneath her calm was some faint excitement. It is a thrilling moment for any woman. She wore a very full dress of silver grey velvet, in the cut of which I recognized the hand of the dressmaker in Liverpool (evidently a widow of unimpeachable character), who had made her gowns for so many years; but she had so far succumbed to the frivolity of the occasion as to wear a large picture hat covered with blue ostrich feathers. Her gold-rimmed spectacles made it extraordinarily grotesque. When the ceremony was over the registrar (somewhat taken aback, I thought, by the difference of age between the pair he was marrying) shook hands with her, tendering his strictly official congratulations; and the bridegroom, blushing slightly, kissed her. Mrs. Tower, resigned but implacable, kissed her; and then the bride looked at me expectantly. It was evidently fitting that I should kiss her too. I did. I confess that I felt a little shy as we walked out of the registrar's office past loungers who waited cynically to see the bridal pairs, and it was with relief that I stepped into Mrs. Tower's car. We drove to Victoria Station, for the happy couple were to go over to Paris by the two o'clock train, and Jane had insisted that the wedding-breakfast should be eaten at the station restaurant. She said it always made her nervous not to be on the platform in good time. Mrs. Tower, present only from a strong sense of family duty, was able to do little to make the party go off well; she ate nothing (for which I could not blame her, since the food was execrable, and anyway I hate champagne at luncheon) and talked in a strained voice. But Jane went through the menu conscientiously.

"I always think one should make a hearty meal before starting out on a journey," she said.

We saw them off, and I drove Mrs. Tower back to her house.

"How long do you give it?" she said. "Six months?"

"Let's hope for the best," I smiled.

"Don't be so absurd. There can be no best. You don't think he's marrying her for anything but her money, do you? Of course it can't last. My only hope is that she won't have to go through as much suffering as she deserves."

I laughed. The charitable words were spoken in such a tone as to leave me in small doubt of Mrs. Tower's meaning.

"Well, if it doesn't last you'll have the consolation of saying 'I told you so,' " I said.

"I promise you I'll never do that."

"Then you'll have the satisfaction of congratulating yourself on your self-control in not saying 'I told you so.' "

"She's old and dowdy and dull."

"Are you sure she's dull?" I said. "It's true she doesn't say very much, but when she says anything it's very much to the point."

"I've never heard her make a joke in my life."

I was once more in the Far East when Gilbert and Jane returned from their honeymoon, and this time I remained away for nearly two years. Mrs. Tower was a bad correspondent and though I sent her an occasional picture-postcard I received no news from her. But I met her within a week of my return to London; I was dining out and found that I was seated next to her. It was an immense party—I think we were four-and-twenty like the blackbirds in the pie—and, arriving somewhat late, I was too confused by the crowd in which I found myself to notice who was there. But when we sat down, looking round the long table I saw that a good many of my fellow-guests were well known to the public from their photographs in the illustrated papers. Our hostess had a weakness for the persons technically known as celebrities, and this was an unusually brilliant gathering. When Mrs. Tower and I had exchanged the conventional remarks that two people make when they have not seen one another for a couple of years I asked about Jane.

"She's very well," said Mrs. Tower with a certain dryness.

"How has the marriage turned out?"

Mrs. Tower paused a little and took a salted almond from the dish in front of her.

"It appears to be quite a success."

"You were wrong, then?"

"I said it wouldn't last and I still say it won't last. It's contrary to human nature."

"Is she happy?"

"They're both happy."

"I suppose you don't see very much of them."

"At first I saw quite a lot of them. But now . . . ." Mrs. Tower pursed her lips a little. "Jane is becoming very grand."

"What *do* you mean?" I laughed.

"I think I should tell you that she's here to-night."

"Here?"

I was startled. I looked round the table again. Our hostess was a delightful and an entertaining woman, but I could not imagine that she would be likely to invite to a dinner such as this the elderly and dowdy wife of an obscure architect. Mrs. Tower saw my perplexity and was shrewd enough to see what was in my mind. She smiled thinly.

"Look on the left of our host."

I looked. Oddly enough the woman who sat there had by her fantastic appearance attracted my attention the moment I was ushered into the crowded drawing-room. I thought I noticed a gleam of recognition in her eye, but to the best of my belief I had never seen her before. She was not a young woman, for her hair was iron-grey; it was cut very short and clustered thickly round her well-shaped head in tight curls. She made no attempt at youth, for she was conspicuous in that gathering by using neither lipstick, rouge nor powder. Her face, not a particularly handsome one, was red and weather-beaten; but because it owed nothing to artifice had a naturalness that was very pleasing. It contrasted oddly with the whiteness of her shoulders. They were really magnificent. A woman of thirty might have been proud of them. But her dress was extraordinary. I had not seen often anything more audacious. It was cut very low, with short skirts, which were then the fashion, in black and yellow; it had almost the effect of fancy-dress and yet so became her that though on anyone else it would have been outrageous, on her it had the inevitable simplicity of nature. And to complete the impression of an eccentricity in which there was no pose and of an extravagance in which there was no ostentation she wore, attached by a broad black ribbon, a single eyeglass.

"You're not going to tell me *that* is your sister-in-law," I gasped.

"That is Jane Napier," said Mrs. Tower icily.

At that moment she was speaking. Her host was turned towards her with an anticipatory smile. A baldish white-haired man, with a sharp, intelligent face, who sat on her left, was leaning forward eagerly, and the couple who sat opposite, ceasing to talk with one another, listened intently. She said her say and they all, with a sudden movement, threw themselves back in their chairs and burst into vociferous laughter. From the other side of the table a man addressed Mrs. Tower: I recognized a famous statesman.

"Your sister-in-law has made another joke, Mrs. Tower," he said.

Mrs. Tower smiled.

"She's priceless, isn't she?"

"Let me have a long drink of champagne and then for heaven's sake tell me all about it," I said.

Well, this is how I gathered it had all happened. At the

beginning of their honeymoon Gilbert took Jane to various
dressmakers in Paris and he made no objection to her choosing a number of "gowns" after her own heart; but he persuaded her to have a "frock" or two made according to his
own design. It appeared that he had a knack for that kind
of work. He engaged a smart French maid. Jane had never
had such a thing before. She did her own mending and
when she wanted "doing up" was in the habit of ringing for
the housemaid. The dresses Gilbert had devised were very
different from anything she had worn before; but he had
been careful not to go too far too quickly, and because it
pleased him she persuaded herself, though not without
misgivings, to wear them in preference to those she had
chosen herself. Of course she could not wear them with the
voluminous petticoats she had been in the habit of using,
and these, though it cost her an anxious moment, she discarded.

"Now, if you please," said Mrs. Tower, with something
very like a sniff of disapproval, "she wears nothing but thin
silk tights. It's a wonder to me she doesn't catch her death
of cold at her age."

Gilbert and the French maid taught her how to wear her
clothes, and, unexpectedly enough, she was very quick at
learning. The French maid was in raptures over Madame's
arms and shoulders. It was a scandal not to show anything
so fine.

"Wait a little, Alphonsine," said Gilbert. "The next lot
of clothes I design for Madame we'll make the most of her."

The spectacles of course were dreadful. No one could
look really well in gold-rimmed spectacles. Gilbert tried some
with tortoise-shell rims. He shook his head.

"They'd look all right on a girl," he said. "You're too
old to wear spectacles, Jane." Suddenly he had an inspiration. "By George, I've got it. You must wear an eyeglass."

"Oh, Gilbert, I couldn't."

She looked at him, and his excitement, the excitement of
the artist, made her smile. He was so sweet to her she
wanted to do what she could to please him.

"I'll try," she said.

When they went to an optician and, suited with the right size, she placed an eyeglass jauntily in her eye Gilbert clapped his hands. There and then, before the astonished shopman, he kissed her on both cheeks.

"You look wonderful," he cried.

So they went down to Italy and spent happy months studying Renaissance and Baroque architecture. Jane not only grew accustomed to her changed appearance but found she liked it. At first she was a little shy when she went into the dining-room of a hotel and people turned round to stare at her——no one had ever raised an eyelid to look at her before ——but presently she found that the sensation was not disagreeable. Ladies came up to her and asked her where she got her dress.

"Do you like it?" she answered demurely. "My husband designed it for me."

"I should like to copy it if you don't mind."

Jane had certainly for many years lived a very quiet life, but she was by no means lacking in the normal instincts of her sex. She had her answer ready.

"I'm so sorry, but my husband's very particular and he won't hear of anyone copying my frocks. He wants me to be unique."

She had an idea that people would laugh when she said this, but they didn't; they merely answered:

"Oh, of course I quite understand. You *are* unique."

But she saw them making mental notes of what she wore, and for some reason this quite "put her about." For once in her life when she wasn't wearing what everybody else did, she reflected, she didn't see why everybody else should want to wear what she did.

"Gilbert," she said, quite sharply for her, "next time you're designing dresses for me I wish you'd design things that people *can't* copy."

"The only way to do that is to design things that only you can wear."

"Can't you do that?"

"Yes, if you'll do something for me."

"What is it?"

"Cut off your hair."

I think this was the first time that Jane jibbed. Her hair
was long and thick, and as a girl she had been quite vain of
it; to cut it off was a very drastic proceeding. This really
was burning her boats behind her. In her case it was not the
first step that cost so much, it was the last; but she took it
("I know Marion will think me a perfect fool, and I shall
never be able to go to Liverpool again," she said), and
when they passed through Paris on their way home Gilbert
led her (she felt quite sick, her heart was beating so fast)
to the best hairdresser in the world. She came out of his
shop with a jaunty, saucy, impudent head of crisp grey curls.
Pygmalion had finished his fantastic masterpiece: Galatea
was come to life.

"Yes," I said, "but that isn't enough to explain why Jane
is here to-night amid this crowd of duchesses, cabinet ministers and such like; nor why she is sitting on one side of her
host with an admiral of the Fleet on the other."

"Jane is a humorist," said Mrs. Tower. "Didn't you see
them all laughing at what she said?"

There was no doubt now of the bitterness in Mrs. Tower's
heart.

"When Jane wrote and told me they were back from their
honeymoon I thought I must ask them both to dinner. I
didn't much like the idea, but I felt it had to be done. I knew
the party would be deadly and I wasn't going to sacrifice
any of the people who really mattered. On the other hand
I didn't want Jane to think I hadn't any nice friends. You
know I never have more than eight, but on this occasion I
thought it would make things go better if I had twelve. I'd
been too busy to see Jane until the evening of the party.
She kept us all waiting a little—that was Gilbert's cleverness—and at last she sailed in. You could have knocked me
down with a feather. She made the rest of the women look
dowdy and provincial. She made me feel like a painted old
trollop."

Mrs. Tower drank a little champagne.

"I wish I could describe the frock to you. It would have
been quite impossible on anyone else; on her it was perfect.

And the eyeglass! I'd known her for thirty-five years and I'd never seen her without spectacles."

"But you knew she had a good figure."

"How should I? I'd never seen her except in the clothes you first saw her in. Did *you* think she had a good figure? She seemed not to be unconscious of the sensation she made but to take it as a matter of course. I thought of my dinner and I heaved a sigh of relief. Even if she was a little heavy in hand, with that appearance it didn't so very much matter. She was sitting at the other end of the table and I heard a good deal of laughter; I was glad to think that the other people were playing up well; but after dinner I was a good deal taken aback when no less than three men came up to me and told me that my sister-in-law was priceless, and did I think she would allow them to call on her. I didn't quite know whether I was standing on my head or my heels. Twenty-four hours later our hostess of to-night rang me up and said she had heard my sister-in-law was in London and she was priceless and would I ask her to luncheon to meet her. She has an infallible instinct, that woman: in a month everyone was talking about Jane. I am here to-night, not because I've known our hostess for twenty years and have asked her to dinner a hundred times, but because I'm Jane's sister-in-law."

Poor Mrs. Tower. The position was galling, and though I could not help being amused, for the tables were turned on her with a vengeance, I felt that she deserved my sympathy.

"People never can resist those who make them laugh," I said, trying to console her.

"She never makes *me* laugh."

Once more from the top of the table I heard a guffaw and guessed that Jane had said another amusing thing.

"Do you mean to say that you are the only person who doesn't think her funny?" I asked, smiling.

"Had it struck *you* that she was a humorist?"

"I'm bound to say it hadn't."

"She says just the same things as she's said for the last thirty-five years. I laugh when I see everyone else does because I don't want to seem a perfect fool, but I am not amused."

"Like Queen Victoria," I said.

It was a foolish jest and Mrs. Tower was quite right sharply to tell me so. I tried another tack.

"Is Gilbert here?" I asked, looking down the table.

"Gilbert was asked because she won't go out without him, but to-night he's at a dinner of the Architects' Institute or whatever it's called."

"I'm dying to renew my acquaintance with her."

"Go and talk to her after dinner. She'll ask you to her Tuesdays."

"Her Tuesdays?"

"She's at home every Tuesday evening. You'll meet there everyone you ever heard of. They're the best parties in London. She's done in one year what I've failed to do in twenty."

"But what you tell me is really miraculous. How has it been done?"

Mrs. Tower shrugged her handsome but adipose shoulders.

"I shall be glad if you'll tell me," she replied.

After dinner I tried to make my way to the sofa on which Jane was sitting, but I was intercepted and it was not till a little later that my hostess came up to me and said:

"I must introduce you to the star of my party. Do you know Jane Napier? She's priceless. She's much more amusing than your comedies."

I was taken up to the sofa. The admiral who had been sitting beside her at dinner was with her still. He showed no sign of moving, and Jane, shaking hands with me, introduced me to him.

"Do you know Sir Reginald Frobisher?"

We began to chat. It was the same Jane as I had known before, perfectly simple, homely and unaffected, but her fantastic appearance certainly gave a peculiar savour to what she said. Suddenly I found myself shaking with laughter. She had made a remark, sensible and to the point, but not in the least witty, which her manner of saying and the bland look she gave me through her eyeglass made perfectly irresistible. I felt light-hearted and buoyant. When I left her she said to me:

"If you've got nothing better to do, come and see us on Tuesday evening. Gilbert will be so glad to see you."

"When he's been a month in London he'll know that he *can* have nothing better to do," said the admiral.

So, on Tuesday but rather late, I went to Jane's. I confess I was a little surprised at the company. It was quite a remarkable collection of writers, painters and politicians, actors, great ladies and great beauties: Mrs. Tower was right, it was a grand party; I had seen nothing like it in London since Stafford House was sold. No particular entertainment was provided. The refreshments were adequate without being luxurious. Jane in her quiet way seemed to be enjoying herself; I could not see that she took a great deal of trouble with her guests, but they seemed to like being there, and the gay, pleasant party did not break up till two in the morning. After that I saw much of her. I not only went often to her house, but seldom went out to luncheon or to dinner without meeting her. I am an amateur of humour and I sought to discover in what lay her peculiar gift. It was impossible to repeat anything she said, for the fun, like certain wines, would not travel. She had no gift for epigram. She never made a brilliant repartee. There was no malice in her remarks nor sting in her rejoinders. There are those who think that impropriety, rather than brevity, is the soul of wit; but she never said a thing that could have brought a blush to a Victorian cheek. I think her humour was unconscious and I am sure it was unpremeditated. It flew like a butterfly from flower to flower, obedient only to its own caprice and pursuivant of neither method nor intention. It depended on the way she spoke and on the way she looked. Its subtlety gained by the flaunting and extravagant appearance that Gilbert had achieved for her; but her appearance was only an element in it. Now of course she was the fashion and people laughed if she but opened her mouth. They no longer wondered that Gilbert had married a wife so much older than himself. They saw that Jane was a woman with whom age did not count. They thought him a devilish lucky young fellow. The admiral quoted Shakespeare to me: "Age cannot wither her, nor custom stale her infinite variety." Gilbert was delighted with her success. As I came to know him better I grew to like him. It was quite evident that he was neither a rascal nor a fortune-hunter. He was not only immensely proud of Jane but genuinely devoted to her. His kindness to her was touching. He was a very unselfish and sweet-tempered young man.

"Well, what do you think of Jane now?" he said to me once, with boyish triumph.

"I don't know which of you is more wonderful," I said. "You or she."

"Oh, I'm nothing."

"Nonsense. You don't think I'm such a fool as not to see that it's you, and you only, who've made Jane what she is."

"My only merit is that I saw what was there when it wasn't obvious to the naked eye," he answered.

"I can understand your seeing that she had in her the possibility of that remarkable appearance, but how in the world have you made her into a humorist?"

"But I always thought the things she said a perfect scream. She was always a humorist."

"You're the only person who ever thought so."

Mrs. Tower, not without magnanimity, acknowledged that she had been mistaken in Gilbert. She grew quite attached to him. But notwithstanding appearances she never faltered in her opinion that the marriage could not last. I was obliged to laugh at her.

"Why, I've never seen such a devoted couple," I said.

"Gilbert is twenty-seven now. It's just the time for a pretty girl to come along. Did you notice the other evening at Jane's that pretty little niece of Sir Reginald's? I thought Jane was looking at them both with a good deal of attention, and I wondered to myself."

"I don't believe Jane fears the rivalry of any girl under the sun."

"Wait and see," said Mrs. Tower.

"You gave it six months."

"Well, now I give it three years."

When anyone is very positive in an opinion it is only human nature to wish him proved wrong. Mrs. Tower was really too cocksure. But such a satisfaction was not mine, for the end that she had always and confidently predicted to the ill-assorted match did in point of fact come. Still, the fates seldom give us what we want in the way we want it, and though Mrs. Tower could flatter herself that she had been right, I think after all she would sooner have been wrong. For things did not happen at all in the way she expected.

One day I received an urgent message from her and fortunately went to see her at once. When I was shown into the room Mrs. Tower rose from her chair and came towards me with the stealthy swiftness of a leopard stalking his prey. I saw that she was excited.

"Jane and Gilbert have separated," she said.

"Not really? Well, you were right after all."

Mrs. Tower looked at me with an expression I could not understand.

"Poor Jane," I muttered.

"Poor Jane!" she repeated, but in tones of such derision that I was dumbfounded.

She found some difficulty in telling me exactly what had occurred.

Gilbert had left her a moment before she leaped to the telephone to summon me. When he entered the room, pale and distraught, she saw at once that something terrible had happened. She knew what he was going to say before he said it.

"Marion, Jane has left me."

She gave him a little smile and took his hand.

"I knew you'd behave like a gentleman. It would have been dreadful for her for people to think that *you* had left her."

"I've come to you because I knew I could count on your sympathy."

"Oh, I don't blame you, Gilbert," said Mrs. Tower, very kindly. "It was bound to happen."

He sighed.

"I suppose so. I couldn't hope to keep her always. She was too wonderful and I'm a perfectly commonplace fellow."

Mrs. Tower patted his hand. He was really behaving beautifully.

"And what is going to happen now?"

"Well, she's going to divorce me."

"Jane always said she'd put no obstacle in your way if ever you wanted to marry a girl."

"You don't think it's likely I should ever be willing to marry anyone else after being Jane's husband," he answered.

Mrs. Tower was puzzled.

"Of course you mean that *you've* left Jane."

"I? That's the last thing I should ever do."

"Then why is she divorcing you?"

"She's going to marry Sir Reginald Frobisher as soon as the decree is made absolute."

Mrs. Tower positively screamed. Then she felt so faint that she had to get her smelling salts.

"After all you've done for her?"

"I've done nothing for her."

"Do you mean to say you're going to allow yourself to be made use of like that?"

"We arranged before we married that if either of us wanted his liberty the other should put no hindrance in the way."

"But that was done on your account. Because you were twenty-seven years younger than she was."

"Well, it's come in very useful for her," he answered bitterly.

Mrs. Tower expostulated, argued, and reasoned; but Gilbert insisted that no rules applied to Jane, and he must do exactly what she wanted. He left Mrs. Tower prostrate. It relieved her a good deal to give me a full account of this interview. It pleased her to see that I was as surprised as herself, and if I was not so indignant with Jane as she was she ascribed that to the criminal lack of morality incident to my sex. She was still in a state of extreme agitation when the door was opened and the butler showed in—Jane herself.

She was dressed in black and white as no doubt befitted her slightly ambiguous position, but in a dress so original and fantastic, in a hat so striking, that I positively gasped at the sight of her. But she was as ever bland and collected. She came forward to kiss Mrs. Tower, but Mrs. Tower withdrew herself with icy dignity.

"Gilbert has been here," she said.

"Yes, I know," smiled Jane. "I told him to come and see you. I'm going to Paris to-night and I want you to be very kind to him while I am away. I'm afraid just at first he'll be rather lonely and I shall feel more comfortable if I can count on your keeping an eye on him."

Mrs. Tower clasped her hands.

"Gilbert has just told me something that I can hardly bring myself to believe. He tells me that you're going to divorce him to marry Reginald Frobisher."

"Don't you remember, before I married Gilbert you advised me to marry a man of my own age. The admiral is fifty-three."

"But, Jane, you owe everything to Gilbert," said Mrs. Tower indignantly. "You wouldn't exist without him. Without him to design your clothes, you'll be nothing."

"Oh, he's promised to go on designing my clothes," Jane answered blandly.

"No woman could want a better husband. He's always been kindness itself to you."

"Oh, I know he's been sweet."

"How *can* you be so heartless?"

"But I was never in love with Gilbert," said Jane. "I always told him that. I'm beginning to feel the need of the companionship of a man of my own age. I think I've probably been married to Gilbert long enough. The young have no conversation." She paused a little and gave us both a charming smile. "Of course I shan't lose sight of Gilbert. I've arranged that with Reginald. The admiral has a niece that would just suit him. As soon as we're married we'll ask them to stay with us at Malta—you know that the admiral is to have the Mediterranean Command—and I shouldn't be at all surprised if they fell in love with one another."

Mrs. Tower gave a little sniff.

"And have you arranged with the admiral that if you want your liberty neither should put any hindrance in the way of the other?"

"I suggested it," Jane answered with composure. "But the admiral says he knows a good thing when he sees it and he won't want to marry anyone else, and if anyone wants to marry me—he has eight twelve-inch guns on his flagship and he'll discuss the matter at short range." She gave us a look through her eyeglass which even the fear of Mrs. Tower's wrath could not prevent me from laughing at. "I think the admiral's a very passionate man."

Mrs. Tower indeed gave me an angry frown.

"I never thought you funny, Jane," she said, "I never understood why people laughed at the things you said."

"I never thought I was funny myself, Marion," smiled Jane, showing her bright, regular teeth. "I am glad to leave London before too many people come round to our opinion."

"I wish you'd tell me the secret of your astonishing success," I said.

She turned to me with that bland, homely look I knew so well.

"You know, when I married Gilbert and settled in London and people began to laugh at what I said no one was more surprised than I was. I'd said the same things for thirty years and no one ever saw anything to laugh at. I thought it must be my clothes or my bobbed hair or my eyeglass. Then I discovered it was because I spoke the truth. It was so unusual that people thought it humorous. One of these days someone else will discover the secret, and when people habitually tell the truth of course there'll be nothing funny in it."

"And why am I the only person not to think it funny?" asked Mrs. Tower.

Jane hesitated a little as though she were honestly searching for a satisfactory explanation.

"Perhaps you don't know the truth when you see it, Marion dear," she answered in her mild good-natured way.

It certainly gave her the last word. I felt that Jane would always have the last word. She *was* priceless.

THE OPIUM ADDICT

I FOUND nothing much to interest me at Hanoi. It is the capital of Tonkin, and the French tell you it is the most attractive town in the East, but when you ask them why, answer that it is exactly like a town, Montpellier or Grenoble, in France. And Haiphong to which I went in order to get a ship to Hong Kong is a commercial town and dull. It is true that from it you can visit the Bay of Along, which is one of the *sehenswürdigkeiten* of Indo-China, but I was tired of sights. I contented myself with sitting in the café (for here it was none too warm, and I was glad to get out of tropical clothes) and reading back numbers of *L'Illustration* or, for the sake of exercise, taking a brisk walk along straight, wide streets. Haiphong is traversed by canals, and sometimes I caught a glimpse of a scene which in its varied life, with all the native craft on the water, was multicoloured and charming. There was one canal, with tall Chinese houses on each side of it, that had a pleasant curve. The houses were whitewashed, but the whitewash was discoloured and stained; with their gray roofs they made an agreeable composition against the pale sky. The picture had the faded elegance of an old water colour. There was nowhere an emphatic note. It was soft and a little weary and inspired one with a faint melancholy. I was reminded, I scarcely know why, of an old maid I knew in my youth, a relic of the Victorian age, who wore black silk mittens and made crochet shawls for the poor, black for widows and white for married women. She had suffered in her youth, but whether from ill health or unrequited love, no one exactly knew.

But there was a local paper at Haiphong, a small dingy

sheet with stubby type the ink of which came off on your
fingers, and it gave you a political article, the wireless news,
advertisements, and local intelligence. The editor, doubtless
hard pressed for matter, printed the names of the persons,
Europeans, natives of the country, or Chinese, who had arrived each day at Haiphong or left it, and mine was put in
with the rest. On the morning of the day before that on
which my boat was to sail for Hong Kong I was sitting in
the café of the hotel drinking a Dubonnet before luncheon
when the boy came in and said that a gentleman wished to
see me. I did not know a soul in Haiphong and asked who
it was. The boy said he was an Englishman and lived there,
but he could not tell me his name. The boy spoke very little
French, and it was hard for me to understand what he said.
I was mystified, but told him to show the visitor in. A moment later he came back followed by a white man and pointed
me out to him. The man gave me a look and walked towards
me. He was a very tall fellow, well over six feet high, rather
fat and bloated, with a red, clean-shaven face and extremely
pale blue eyes. He wore very shabby khaki shorts, and a
stengah-shifter unbuttoned at the neck, and a battered
helmet. I concluded at once that he was a stranded beach
comber who was going to touch me for a loan and wondered
how little I could hope to get off for.

He came up to me and held out a large red hand with
broken, dirty nails.

"I don't suppose you remember me," he said. "My name's
Grosely. I was at St. Thomas's Hospital with you. I recognized your name as soon as I saw it in the papers, and I
thought I'd look you up."

I had not the smallest recollection of him, but I asked him
to sit down and offered him a drink. By his appearance I had
first thought he would ask me for ten piastres, and I might
have given him five, but now it looked more likely that he
would ask for a hundred, and I should have to think myself
lucky if I could content him with fifty. The habitual bor-
rower always asks twice what he expects to get, and it only
dissatisfies him to give him what he has asked, since then he

is vexed with himself for not having asked more. He feels you have cheated him.

"Are you a doctor?" I asked.

"No, but I was only at the bloody place a year."

He took off his sun helmet and showed me a mop of gray hair which needed a brush. His face was curiously mottled, and he did not look healthy. His teeth were badly decayed, and at the corners of his mouth were empty spaces. When the boy came to take the orders he asked for brandy.

"Bring the bottle," he said. *"La bouteille.* Savvy?" He turned to me. "I've been living here for the last five years, but I can't get along with French somehow. I talk Tonkinese." He leaned his chair back and looked at me. "I remember you, you know. You used to go about with those twins. What was their name? I expect I've changed more than you have. I've spent the best part of my life in China. Rotten climate, you know. It plays hell with a man."

I still had not the smallest recollection of him. I thought it best to say so.

"Were you the same year as I was?" I asked.

"Yes, '92."

"It's a devil of a long time ago."

About sixty boys and young men entered the hospital every year; they were most of them shy and confused by the new life they were entering upon; many had never been in London before; and to me at least they were shadows that passed without any particular rhyme or reason across a white sheet. During the first year a certain number for one reason or another dropped out, and in the second year those that remained gained by degrees the beginnings of a personality. They were not only themselves, but the lectures one had attended with them, the scone and coffee one had eaten at the same table for luncheon, the dissection one had done at the same board in the same dissecting room, and *The Belle of New York* one had seen together from the pit of the Shaftesbury Theatre.

The boy brought the bottle of brandy, and Grosely, if that was really his name, pouring himself out a generous helping, drank it down at a gulp without water or soda.

"I couldn't stand doctoring," he said. "I chucked it. My people got fed up with me, and I went out to China. They gave me a hundred pounds and told me to shift for myself. I was damned glad to get out, I can tell you. I guess I was just about as much fed up with them as they were with me. I haven't troubled them much since."

Then from somewhere in the depths of my memory a faint hint crept into the rim, as it were, of consciousness, as on a rising tide the water slides up the sand and then withdraws, to advance with the next wave in a fuller volume. I had first an inkling of some shabby little scandal that had got into the papers. Then I saw a boy's face, and so gradually the facts recurred to me; I remembered him now. I didn't believe he was called Grosely then, I think he had a one syllabled name, but that I was uncertain of. He was a very tall lad (I began to see him quite well), thin, with a slight stoop, he was only eighteen and had grown too fast for his strength; he had curly, shining brown hair, rather large features (they did not look so large now, perhaps because his face was fat and puffy) and a peculiarly fresh complexion, very pink and white, like a girl's. I imagine people, women especially, would have thought him a very handsome boy, but to us he was only a clumsy, shuffling lout. Then I remembered that he did not often come to lectures—no, it wasn't that I remembered; there were too many students in the theatre to recollect who was there and who wasn't. I remembered the dissecting room. He had a leg at the next table to the one I was working at, and he hardly ever touched it. I forget why the men who had other parts of the body complained of his neglecting the work; I suppose somehow it interfered with them. In those days a good deal of gossip went on over the dissection of a "part," and out of the distance of thirty years some of it came back to me. Someone started the story that Grosely was a very gay dog. He drank like a fish and was an awful womanizer. Most of those boys were very simple, and they had brought to the hospital the notions they had acquired at home and at school. Some were prudish and they were shocked; others, those who worked hard, sneered at him and asked how he could hope to pass his exams; but a good many were excited and impressed, he was doing what they would have liked to do if they had had the courage. Grosely had his admirers, and you could often see him surrounded by a little band listening open-mouthed to stories of his adventures. Recollections now were crowding upon me. In a very little while he lost his shyness and assumed the airs of a man of the world. They must have looked absurd on this smooth-cheeked boy with his pink and white skin. Men (so they called themselves) used to tell one another of his escapades. He became quite a hero. He would make caustic remarks as he passed the museum and saw a pair of earnest students going over their anatomy together. He was at home in the public houses of the neighbourhood and was on familiar terms with the bar-maids. Looking back, I imagine that, newly arrived from the country and the tutelage of parents and schoolmasters, he was captivated by his freedom and the thrill of London. His dissipations were harmless enough. They were due only to the urge of youth. He lost his head.

But we were all very poor, and we did not know how Grosely managed to pay for his garish amusements. We knew his father was a country doctor, and I think we knew exactly how much he gave his son a month. It was not enough to pay for the harlots he picked up on the promenade at the Pavilion and for the drinks he stood his friends in the Criterion Bar. We told one another in awestruck tones that he must be getting fearfully into debt. Of course, he could pawn things, but we knew by experience that you could not get more than three pounds for a microscope and thirty shillings for a skeleton. We said he must be spending at least ten pounds a week. Our ideas were not very grand, and this seemed to us the wildest pitch of extravagance. At last one of his friends disclosed the mystery: Grosely had discovered a wonderful system for making money. It amused and impressed us. None of us would have thought of anything so ingenious or have had the nerve to attempt it if he had. Grosely went to auctions, not Christie's, of course, but auctions in the Strand and Oxford Street and in private houses, and bought anything portable that was going cheap.

Then he took his purchase to a pawnbroker's and pawned it for ten shillings or a pound more than he had paid. He was making money, four or five pounds a week, and he said he was going to give up medicine and make a regular business of it. Not one of us had ever made a penny in his life, and we regarded Grosely with admiration.

"By Jove, he's clever," we said.

"He's just about as sharp as they make them."

"That's the sort that ends up as a millionaire."

We were all very worldly wise, and what we didn't know about life at eighteen we were pretty sure wasn't worth knowing. It was a pity that when an examiner asked us a question we were so nervous that the answer often flew straight out of our head and when a nurse asked us to post a letter we blushed scarlet. It became known that the dean had sent for Grosely and hauled him over the coals. He had threatened him with sundry penalties if he continued systematically to neglect his work. Grosely was indignant. He'd had enough of that sort of thing at school, he said, he wasn't going to let a horse-faced eunuch treat him like a boy. Damn it all, he was getting on for nineteen, and there wasn't much you could teach him. The dean had said he heard he was drinking more than was good for him. Damned cheek. He could carry his liquor as well as any man of his age; he'd been blind last Saturday, and he meant to get blind next Saturday, and if anyone didn't like it he could do the other thing. Grosely's friends quite agreed with him that a man couldn't let himself be insulted like that.

But the blow fell at last, and now I remembered quite well the shock it gave us all. I suppose we had not seen Grosely for two or three days, but he had been in the habit of coming to the hospital more and more irregularly, so if we thought anything about it, I imagine we merely said that he was off on one of his bats. He would turn up again in a day or so, rather pale, but with a wonderful story of some girl he had picked up and the time he had had with her. The anatomy lecture was at nine in the morning, and it was a rush to get there in time. On this particular day little attention was paid to the lecturer who, with a visible pleasure in his limpid English and admirable elocution, was describing I know not what part of the human skeleton, for there was much excited whispering along the benches and a newspaper was surreptitiously passed from hand to hand. Suddenly the lecturer stopped. He had a pedagogic sarcasm. He affected not to know the names of his students.

"I am afraid I am disturbing the gentleman who is reading the paper. Anatomy is a very tedious science, and I regret that the regulations of the Royal College of Surgeons oblige me to ask you to give it enough of your attention to pass an examination in it. Any gentleman, however, who finds this impossible is at liberty to continue his perusal of the paper outside."

The wretched boy to whom this reproof was addressed reddened to the roots of his hair and in his embarrassment tried to stuff the newspaper in his pocket. The professor of anatomy observed him coldly.

"I am afraid, sir, that the paper is a little too large to go into your pocket," he remarked. "Perhaps you would be good enough to hand it down to me."

The newspaper was passed from row to row to the well of the theatre, and, not content with the confusion to which he had put the poor lad, the eminent surgeon, taking it, asked:

"May I inquire what it is in the paper that the gentleman in question found of such absorbing interest?"

The student who gave it to him without a word pointed out the paragraph that we had all been reading. The professor read it, and we watched him in silence. He put the paper down and went on with his lecture. The headline ran: "ARREST OF A MEDICAL STUDENT." Grosely had been brought before the police court magistrate for getting goods on credit and pawning them. It appears that this is an indictable offence, and the magistrate had remanded him for a week. Bail was refused. It looked as though his method of making money by buying things at auctions and pawning them had not in the long run proved as steady a source of income as he expected, and he had found it more profitable to pawn things that he was not at the expense of paying for.

We talked the matter over excitedly as soon as the lecture was over, and I am bound to say that, having no property ourselves, so deficient was our sense of its sanctity we could none of us look upon his crime as a very serious one; but with the natural love of the young for the terrible there were few who did not think he would get anything from two years hard labour to seven years penal servitude.

I do not know why, but I did not seem to have any recollection of what happened to Grosely. I think he may have been arrested towards the end of a session, and his case may have come on again when we had all separated for holidays. I did not know if it was disposed of by the police court magistrate or whether it went up for trial. I had a sort of feeling that he was sentenced to a short term of imprisonment, six weeks perhaps, for his operations had been pretty extensive; but I knew that he had vanished from our midst and in a little while was thought of no more. It was strange to me that after all these years I should recollect so much of the incident so clearly. It was as though, turning over an album of old snapshots, I saw all at once the photographs of a scene I had quite forgotten.

But of course in that gross elderly man with gray hair and mottled red face I should never have recognized the lanky pink-cheeked boy. He looked sixty, but I knew he must be much less than that. I wondered what he had done with himself in the intervening time. It did not look as though he had excessively prospered.

"What were you doing in China?" I asked him.

"I was a tide waiter."

"Oh, were you?"

It is not a position of great importance, and I took care to keep out of my tone any note of surprise. The tide waiters are employees of the Chinese customs whose duty it is to board the ships and junks at the various treaty ports, and I think their chief business is to prevent opium smuggling. They are mostly retired A. B.'s from the Royal Navy and noncommissioned officers who have finished their time. I have seen them come on board at various places up the Yangtze. They hobnob with the pilot and the engineer, but

the skipper is a trifle curt with them. They learn to speak
Chinese more fluently than most Europeans and often marry
Chinese women.

"When I left England I swore I wouldn't go back till I'd
made my pile. And I never did. They were glad enough to
get anyone to be a tide waiter in those days, any white man,
I mean, and they didn't ask questions. They didn't care who
you were. I was damned glad to get the job, I can tell you;
I was about broke to the wide when they took me on. I only
took it till I could get something better, but I stayed on; it
suited me. I wanted to make money, and I found out that a
tide waiter could make a packet if he knew the right way to
go about. I was with the Chinese customs for the best part
of twenty-five years, and when I came away I wouldn't mind
betting that lots of commissioners would have been glad to
have the money I had."

He gave me a sly, mean look. I had an inkling of what
he meant. But there was a point on which I was willing to be
reassured; if he was going to ask me for a hundred piastres
(I was resigned to that sum now) I thought I might just as
well take the blow at once.

"I hope you kept it," I said.

"You bet I did. I invested all my money in Shanghai, and
when I left China I put it all in American railway bonds.
Safety first is my motto. I know too much about crooks to
take any risks myself."

I liked that remark, so I asked him if he wouldn't stay
and have luncheon with me.

"No, I don't think I will. I don't each much tiffin, and,
anyway, my chow's waiting for me at home. I think I'll be
getting along." He got up and he towered over me. "But
look here, why don't you come along this evening and see
my place? I've married a Haiphong girl. Got a baby too. It's
not often I get a chance of talking to anyone about London.
You'd better not come to dinner. We only eat native food,
and I don't suppose you'd care for that. Come along about
nine, will you?"

"All right," I said.

I had already told him that I was leaving Haiphong next

day. He asked the boy to bring him a piece of paper so that he might write down his address. He wrote laboriously in the hand of a boy of fourteen.

"Tell the porter to explain to your rickshaw boy where it is. I'm on the second floor. There's no bell. Just knock. Well, see you later."

He walked out, and I went in to luncheon.

After dinner I called a rickshaw and with the porter's help made the boy understand where I wanted to go. I found presently that he was taking me along the curved canal the houses of which had looked to me so like a faded Victorian water colour. He stopped at one of them and pointed to the door. It looked so shabby and the neighbourhood was so squalid that I hesitated, thinking he had made a mistake. It seemed unlikely that Grosely could live so far in the native quarter and in a house so bedraggled. I told the rickshaw boy to wait and pushing open the door saw a dark staircase in front of me. There was no one about, and the street was empty. It might have been the small hours of the morning. I struck a match and fumbled my way upstairs. On the second floor I struck another match and saw a large brown door in front of me. I knocked, and in a moment it was opened by a little Tonkinese woman holding a candle. She was dressed in the earth brown of the poorer classes, with a tight little black turban on her head; her lips and the skin round them were stained red with betel, and when she opened her mouth to speak I saw that she had the black teeth and black gums that so disfigure these people. She said something in her native language, and then I heard Grosely's voice.

"Come along in. I was beginning to think you weren't going to turn up."

I passed through a little dark antechamber and entered a large room that evidently looked on the canal. Grosely was lying on a long chair, and he raised his length from it as I came in. He was reading the Hong Kong papers by the light of a paraffin lamp that stood on a table by his side.

"Sit down," he said, "and put your feet up."

"There's no reason I should take your chair."

"Go on. I'll sit on this."

He took a kitchen chair and, sitting on it, put his feet on the end of mine.

"That's my wife," he said, pointing with his thumb at the Tonkinese woman who had followed me into the room. "And over there in the corner's the kid."

I followed his eyes, and against the wall, lying on bamboo mats and covered with a blanket, I saw a child sleeping.

"Lively little beggar when he's awake. I wish you could have seen him. She's going to have another soon."

I glanced at her, and the truth of what he said was apparent. She was very small, with tiny hands and feet, but her face was flat and the skin muddy. She looked sullen but may only have been shy. She went out of the room and presently came back with a bottle of whisky, two glasses, and a siphon. I looked round. There was a partition at the back of dark unpainted wood which I suppose shut off another room, and pinned against the middle of this was a portrait cut out of an illustrated paper of John Galsworthy. He looked austere, mild, and gentlemanly, and I wondered what he did there. The other walls were whitewashed, but the whitewash was dingy and stained. Pinned onto them were pages of pictures from *The Graphic* or *The Illustrated London News*.

"I put them up," said Grosely, "I thought they made the place look homelike."

"What made you put up Galsworthy? Do you read his books?"

"No, I didn't know he wrote books. I liked his face."

There were one or two torn and shabby rattan mats on the floor and in a corner a great pile of *The Hong Kong Times*. The only furniture consisted of a washstand, two or three kitchen chairs, a table or two, and a large teak native bed. It was cheerless and sordid.

"Not a bad little place, is it?" said Grosely. "Suits me all right. Sometimes I've thought of moving, but I don't suppose I ever shall now." He gave a little chuckle. "I came to Haiphong for forty-eight hours and I've been here five years. I was on my way to Shanghai really."

He was silent. Having nothing to say I said nothing. Then

the little Tonkinese woman made a remark to him, which I could not of course understand, and he answered her. He was silent again for a minute or two, but I thought he looked at me as though he wanted to ask me something. I did not know why he hesitated.

"Have you ever tried smoking opium on your travels in the East?" he inquired at last casually.

"Yes, I did once, at Singapore. I thought I'd like to see what it was like."

"What happened?"

"Nothing very thrilling to tell you the truth. I thought I was going to have the most exquisite emotions. I expected visions, like De Quincey's, you know. The only thing I felt was a kind of physical well-being, the same sort of feeling that you get when you've had a Turkish bath and are lying in the cooling room, and then a peculiar activity of mind so that everything I thought of seemed extremely clear."

"I know."

"I really felt that two and two are four and there could not be the smallest doubt about it. But next morning—oh, God! My head reeled. I was as sick as a dog, I was sick all day, I vomited my soul out, and as I vomited I said to myself miserably: 'And there are people who call this fun.' "

Grosely leaned back in his chair and gave a low, mirthless laugh.

"I expect it was bad stuff. Or you went at it too hard. They saw you were a mug and gave you dregs that had been smoked already. They're enough to turn anybody up. Would you like to have another try now? I've got some stuff here that I know's good."

"No, I think once was enough for me."

"D'you mind if I have a pipe or two? You want it in a climate like this. It keeps you from getting dysentery. And I generally have a bit of a smoke about this time."

"Go ahead," I said.

He spoke again to the woman, and she, raising her voice, called out something in a raucous tone. An answer came from the room behind the wooden partition, and after a minute or two an old woman came out carrying a little round tray. She was shrivelled and old and when she entered gave me an ingratiating smile of her stained mouth. Grosely got up and crossed over to the bed and lay on it. The old woman set the tray down on the bed; on it was a spirit lamp, a pipe, a long needle, and a little round box of opium. She squatted on the bed, and Grosely's wife got on it too and sat, her feet tucked up under her with her back against the wall. Grosely watched the old woman while she put a little pellet of the drug on the needle, held it over the flame till it sizzled, and then plugged it into the pipe. She handed it to him, and with a great breath he inhaled it. He held the smoke for a little while and then blew it out in a thick gray cloud. He handed her back the pipe, and she started to make another. Nobody spoke. He smoked three pipes in succession and then sank back.

"By George, I feel better now. I was feeling all in. She makes a wonderful pipe, this old hag. Are you sure you won't have one?"

"Quite."

"Please yourself. Have some tea, then."

He spoke to his wife, who scrambled off the bed and went out of the room. Presently she came back with a little china pot of tea and a couple of Chinese bowls.

"A lot of people smoke here, you know. It does you no harm if you don't do it to excess. I never smoke more than twenty to twenty-five pipes a day. You can go on for years if you limit yourself to that. Some of the Frenchmen smoke as many as forty or fifty a day. That's too much. I never do that, except now and then when I feel I want a binge. I'm bound to say it's never done me any harm."

We drank our tea, pale and vaguely scented and clean on the palate. Then the old woman made him another pipe and then another. His wife had got back onto the bed and soon, curling herself up at his feet, went to sleep. Grosely smoked two or three pipes at a time and while he was smoking seemed intent upon nothing else, but in the intervals he was loquacious. Several times I suggested going, but he would not let me. The hours wore on. Once or twice while he smoked I dozed. He told me all about himself. He went on and on. I spoke only to give him a cue. I cannot relate what he told me in his own words. He repeated himself. He was very long-winded, and he told me his story confusedly, first a late bit, then an early bit, so that I had to arrange the sequence for myself; sometimes I saw that, afraid he had said too much, he held something back; sometimes he lied and I had to make a guess at the truth from the smile he gave me or the look in his eyes. He had not the words to describe what he had felt, and I had to conjecture his meaning from slangy metaphors and hackneyed, vulgar phrases. I kept on asking myself what his real name was: it was on the tip of my tongue, and it irritated me not to be able to recall it, though why it should in the least matter to me I did not know. He was somewhat suspicious of me at first, and I saw that this escapade of his in London and his imprisonment had been all these years a tormenting secret. He had always been haunted by the fear that sooner or later someone would find out.

"It's funny that even now you shouldn't remember me at the hospital," he said, looking at me shrewdly. "You must have a rotten memory."

"Hang it all, it's nearly thirty years ago. Think of the thousands of people I've met since then. There's no reason why I should remember you any more than you remember me."

"That's right. I don't suppose there is."

It seemed to reassure him. At last he had smoked enough, and the old woman made herself a pipe and smoked it. Then she went over to the mat on which the child was lying and huddled down beside it. She lay so still that I supposed she had fallen directly asleep. When at last I went I found my boy curled up on the footboard of the rickshaw in so deep slumber that I had to shake him. I knew where I was, and I wanted air and exercise, so I gave him a couple of piastres and told him I would walk.

It was a strange story I carried away with me.

It was with a sort of horror that I had listened to Grosely telling me of those twenty years he had spent in China. He had made money, I do not know how much, but from the way he talked I should think something between fifteen and twenty thousand pounds, and for a tide waiter it was a fortune. He could not have come by it honestly, and little as I knew of the details of his trade, by his sudden reticences, by his leers and hints I guessed that there was no base transaction that, if it was made worth his while, he jibbed at. I suppose that nothing paid him better than smuggling opium, and his position gave him the opportunity to do this with safety and profit. I understood that his superior officers had often had their suspicions of him, but had never been able to get such proof of his malpractices as to justify them in taking any steps. They contented themselves with moving him from one port to another, but that did not disturb him; they watched him, but he was too clever for them. I saw that he was divided between the fear of telling me too much to his discredit and the desire to boast of his own astuteness. He prided himself on the confidence the Chinese had placed in him.

"They knew they could trust me," he said, "and it gave me a pull. I never double-crossed a Chinaman once."

The thought filled him with the complacency of the honest man. The Chinese discovered that he was keen on curios, and they got in the habit of giving him bits or bringing him things to buy; he never made inquiries how they had come by them, and he bought them cheap. When he had got a good lot he sent them to Peking and sold them at a handsome profit. I remembered how he had started his commercial career by buying things at auctions and pawning them. For twenty years, by shabby shift and petty dishonesty he added pound to pound, and everything he made he invested in Shanghai. He lived penuriously, saving half his pay; he never went on leave because he did not want to waste his money; he would not have anything to do with the Chinese women, he wanted to keep himself free from any entanglement; he did not drink. He was consumed by one ambition, to save enough to be able to go back to England and live the life from which he had been snatched as a boy. That was the only thing he wanted. He lived in China as though in a dream; he paid no attention to the life around him; its colour and strangeness, its possibilities of pleasure, meant nothing to him. There was always before him the mirage of London, the Criterion Bar, himself standing with his foot on the rail, the promenade at the Empire and the Pavilion, the picked-up harlot, the serio-comic at the music hall, and the musical comedy at the Gaiety. This was life and love and adventure. This was romance. This was what he yearned for with all his heart. There was surely something impressive in the way in which during all those years he had lived like an anchorite with that one end in view of leading again a life that was so vulgar. It showed character.

"You see," he said to me, "even if I'd been able to get back to England on leave I wouldn't have gone. I didn't want to go till I could go for good. And then I wanted to do the thing in style."

He saw himself putting on evening clothes every night and going out with a gardenia in his buttonhole, and he saw himself going to the Derby in a long coat and a brown hat and a pair of opera glasses slung over his shoulder. He saw himself giving the girls a look-over and picking out the one he fancied. He made up his mind that on the night he arrived in London he would get blind, he hadn't been drunk for twenty years; he couldn't afford to in his job, you had to keep your wits about you. He'd take care not to get drunk on the ship on the way home. He'd wait till he got to London. What a night he'd have! He thought of it for twenty years.

I do not know why Grosely left the Chinese customs, whether the place was getting too hot for him, whether he had reached the end of his service, or whether he had amassed the sum he had fixed. But at last he sailed. He went second class; he did not intend to start spending money till he reached London. He took rooms in Jermyn Street, he had always wanted to live there, and he went straight to a tailor's and ordered himself an outfit. Slap up. Then he had a look round the town. It was different from how he remembered it, there was much more traffic, and he felt confused and a little at sea. He went to the Criterion and found there was no longer a bar where he had been used to lounge and drink. There was a restaurant in Leicester Square where he had been in the habit of dining when he was in funds, but he could not find it; he supposed it had been torn down. He went to the Pavilion, but there were no women there. He was rather disgusted and went on to the Empire: he found they had done away with the Promenade. It was rather a blow. He could not quite make it out. Well, anyhow, he must be prepared for changes in twenty years, and if he couldn't do anything else he could get drunk. He had had fever several times in China, and the change of climate had brought it on again. He wasn't feeling any too well, and after four or five drinks he was glad to go to bed.

That first day was only a sample of many that followed it. Everything went wrong. Grosely's voice grew peevish and bitter as he told me how one thing and another had failed him. The old places were gone, the people were different, he found it hard to make friends, he was strangely lonely; he had never expected that in a great city like London. That's what was wrong with it, London had become too big; it wasn't the jolly, intimate place it had been in the early 'Nineties. It had gone to pieces. He picked up a few girls, but they weren't as nice as the girls he had known before; they weren't the fun they used to be, and he grew dimly conscious that they thought him a rum sort of cove. He was only just over forty, and they looked upon him as an old man. When he tried to cotton on to a lot of young fellows standing round a bar they gave him the cold shoulder. Anyway, these young fellows didn't know how to drink. He'd show them. He got soused every night, it was the only thing to do in that damned place, but, by jove, it made him feel rotten next day. He supposed it was the climate of China. When he was a medical student he could drink a bottle of whisky every night and be as fresh as a daisy in the morning. He began to think more about China. All sorts of things that he never knew he had noticed came back to him. It wasn't a bad life he'd led there. Perhaps he'd been a fool to keep away from those Chinese girls: they were pretty little things, some of them, and they didn't put on the airs these English girls did. One could have a damned good time in China if one had the money he had. One could keep a Chinese girl and get into the club, and there'd be a lot of nice fellows to drink with and play bridge with and billiards. He remembered the Chinese shops and all the row in the streets and the coolies carrying loads and the ports with the junks in them and the rivers with pagodas on the banks. It was funny, he never thought much of China while he was there, and now— well, he couldn't get it out of his mind. It obsessed him. He began to think that London was no place for a white man. It had just gone to the dogs, that was the long and short of it, and one day the thought came to him that perhaps it would be a good thing if he went back to China. Of course it was silly, he'd worked like a slave for twenty years to be able to have a good time in London, and it was absurd to go and live in China. With his money he ought to be able to have a good time anywhere. But somehow he couldn't think of any- thing else but China. One day he went to the pictures and saw a scene at Shanghai. That settled it. He was fed up with London. He hated it. He was going to get out, and this time he'd get out for good. He had been home a year and a half, and it seemed longer to him than all his twenty years in the East. He took a passage on a French boat sailing from Marseilles, and when he saw the coast of Europe sink into the sea he heaved a great sigh of relief. When they got to Suez and he felt the first touch of the East he knew he had done the right thing. Europe was finished. The East was the only place.

He went ashore at Djibouti and again at Colombo and Singapore, but though the ship stopped for two days at Saigon he remained on board there. He'd been drinking a good deal and he was feeling a bit under the weather. But when they reached Haiphong where they were staying for forty-eight hours he thought he might just as well have a look at it. That was the last stopping place before they got to China. He was bound for Shanghai. When he got there he meant to go to a hotel and look around a bit and then get hold of a girl and a place of his own. He would buy a pony or two and race. He'd soon make friends. In the East they weren't so stiff and stand-offish as they were in London. Going ashore, he dined at the hotel, and after dinner he got into a rickshaw and told the boy he wanted a woman. The boy took him to the shabby tenement in which I had sat for so many hours, and there were the old woman and the girl who was now the mother of his child. After a while the old woman asked him if he wouldn't like to smoke. He had never tried opium, he had always been frightened of it, but now he didn't see why he shouldn't have a go. He was feeling good that night and the girl was a jolly, cuddlesome little thing; she was rather like a Chinese girl, small and pretty, like an idol. Well, he had a pipe or two, and he began to feel very happy and comfortable. He stayed all night. He didn't sleep. He just lay, feeling very restful, and thought about things.

"I stopped there till my ship went on to Hong Kong," he said. "And when she left I just stopped on."

"How about your luggage?" I asked.

For I am perhaps unworthily interested in the manner people combine practical details with the ideal aspects of life. When in a novel penniless lovers drive away in a long swift racing car over the distant hills I have always a desire to know how they managed to pay for it; and I have often asked myself how the characters of Henry James in the intervals of subtly examining their situation coped with the physiological necessities of their bodies.

"I only had a trunk full of clothes, I was never one to want much more than I stood up in, and I went down with the girl in a rickshaw to fetch it. I only meant to stay on till the next boat came through. You see, I was so near China here I thought I'd wait a bit and get used to things, if you understand what I mean, before I went on."

I did. Those last words of his revealed him to me. I knew that on the threshold of China his courage had failed him. England had been such a terrible disappointment that now he was afraid to put China to the test too. If that failed him he had nothing. For years England had been like a mirage in the desert. But when he had yielded to the attraction, those shining pools and the palm trees and the green grass were nothing but the rolling sandy dunes. He had China, and so long as he never saw it again he kept it.

"Somehow I stayed on. You know, you'd be surprised how quickly the days pass. I don't seem to have time to do half the things I want to. After all, I'm comfortable here. The old woman makes a damned good pipe, and she's a jolly little girl, my girl, and then there's the kid. A lively young beggar. If you're happy somewhere what's the good of going somewhere else?"

"And are you happy here?" I asked him.

I looked round that large, bare, sordid room. There was no comfort in it, and not one of the little personal things that one would have thought might have given him the feeling of home. Grosely had taken on this equivocal little apartment which served as a house of assignation and as a place for Europeans to smoke opium in, with the old woman who kept it, just as it was, and he camped, rather than lived, there still as though next day he would pack his traps and go. After a little while he answered my question.

"I've never been so happy in my life. I often think I'll go on to Shanghai some day, but I don't suppose I ever shall. And God knows I never want to see England again."

"Aren't you awfully lonely sometimes for people to talk to?"

"No. Sometimes a Chinese tramp comes in with an English skipper or a Scotch engineer and then I go on board and we have a talk about old times. There's an old fellow here, a Frenchman who was in the customs, and he speaks English; I go and see him sometimes. But the fact is I don't want anybody very much. I think a lot. It gets on my nerves when people come between me and my thoughts. I'm not a big smoker, you know, I just have a pipe or two in the morning to settle my stomach, but I don't really smoke till night. Then I think."

"What d'you think about?"

"Oh, all sorts of things. Sometimes about London and what it was like when I was a boy. But mostly about China. I think of the good times I had and the way I made my money, and I remember the fellows I used to know, and the Chinese. I had some narrow squeaks now and then, but I always came through all right. And I wonder what the girls would have been like that I might have had. Pretty little things. I'm sorry now I didn't keep one or two. It's a great country, China; I love those shops with an old fellow sitting on his heels smoking a water pipe, and all the shop signs. And the temples. By George, that's the place for a man to live in. There's life."

The mirage shone before his eyes. The illusion held him. He was happy. I wondered what would be his end. Well, that was not yet. For the first time in his life perhaps he held the present in his hand.

THE FACTS OF LIFE

IT WAS Henry Garnet's habit on leaving the city of an afternoon to drop in at his club and play bridge before going home to dinner. He was a pleasant man to play with. He knew the game well, and you could be sure that he would make the best of his cards. He was a good loser; and when he won was more inclined to ascribe his success to his luck than to his skill. He was indulgent, and if his partner made a mistake, could be trusted to find an excuse for him. It was surprising then on this occasion to hear him telling his partner with unnecessary sharpness that he had never seen a hand worse played; and it was more surprising still to see him not only make a grave error himself, an error of which you would never have thought him capable, but when his partner, not unwilling to get a little of his own back, pointed it out, insist against all reason and with considerable heat that he was perfectly right. But they were all old friends, the men he was playing with, and none of them took his ill humour very seriously. Henry Garnet was a broker, a partner in a firm of repute, and it occurred to one of them that something had gone wrong with some stock he was interested in.

"How's the market today?" he asked.

"Booming. Even the suckers are making money."

It was evident that stocks and shares had nothing to do with Henry Garnet's vexation; but something was the matter; that was evident, too. He was a hearty fellow who enjoyed excellent health; he had plenty of money; he was fond of his wife and devoted to his children. As a rule he had high spirits, and he laughed easily at the nonsense they were apt to talk while they played; but today he sat glum and silent. His brows were crossly puckered, and there was a sulky look about his mouth. Presently, to ease the tension, one of the others mentioned a subject upon which they all knew Henry Garnet was glad to speak.

"How's your boy, Henry? I see he's done pretty well in the tournament."

Henry Garnet's frown grew darker.

"He's done no better than I expected him to."

"When does he come back from Monte?"

"He got back last night."

"Did he enjoy himself?"

"I suppose so; all I know is that he made a damned fool of himself."

"Oh. How?"

"I'd rather not talk about it if you don't mind."

The three men looked at him with curiosity. Henry Garnet scowled at the green baize.

"Sorry, old boy. Your call."

The game proceeded in a strained silence. Garnet got his bid, and when he played his cards so badly that he went three down not a word was said. Another rubber was begun, and in the second game Garnet denied a suit.

"Having none?" his partner asked him.

Garnet's irritability was such that he did not even reply, and when at the end of the hand it appeared that he had re-voked, and that his revoke cost the rubber, it was not to be expected that his partner should let his carelessness go without remark.

"What the devil's the matter with you, Henry?" he said. "You're playing like a fool."

Garnet was disconcerted. He did not so much mind losing a big rubber himself, but he was sore that his inattention should have made his partner lose too. He pulled himself together.

"I'd better not play any more. I thought a few rubbers would calm me, but the fact is I can't give my mind to the game. To tell you the truth I'm in a hell of a temper."

They all burst out laughing.

"You don't have to tell us that, old boy. It's obvious."

Garnet gave them a rueful smile.

"Well, I bet you'd be in a temper if what's happened to me had happened to you. As a matter of fact I'm in a damned awkward situation, and if any of you fellows can give me any advice how to deal with it I'd be grateful."

"Let's have a drink and you tell us all about it. With a K.C., a Home Office official and an eminent surgeon—if we can't tell you how to deal with a situation, nobody can."

The K.C. got up and rang the bell for a waiter.

"It's about that damned boy of mine," said Henry Garnet.

Drinks were ordered and brought. And this is the story that Henry Garnet told them.

The boy of whom he spoke was his only son. His name was Nicholas, and of course he was called Nicky. He was eighteen. The Garnets had two daughters besides, one of sixteen and the other of twelve, but however unreasonable it seemed, for a father is generally supposed to like his daughters best, and though he did all he could not to show his preference, there was no doubt that the greater share of Henry Garnet's affection was given to his son. He was kind, in a chaffing, casual way, to his daughters, and gave them handsome presents on their birthdays and at Christmas; but he doted on Nicky. Nothing was too good for him. He thought the world of him. He could hardly take his eyes off him. You could not blame him, for Nicky was a son that any parent might have been proud of. He was six foot two, lithe but muscular, with broad shoulders and a slim waist, and he held himself gallantly erect; he had a charming head, well placed on the shoulders, with pale brown hair that waved slightly, blue eyes with long dark lashes under well-marked eyebrows, a full red mouth and a tanned, clean skin. When he smiled he showed very regular and very white teeth. He was not shy, but there was a modesty in his demeanour that was attractive. In social intercourse he was easy, polite and quietly gay. He was the offspring of nice, healthy, decent parents, he had been well brought up in a good home, he had been sent to a good school, and the general result was as engaging a specimen of young manhood as you were likely to find in a long time. You felt that he was as honest, open and virtuous as he looked.

He had never given his parents a moment's uneasiness. As a child he was seldom ill and never naughty. As a boy he did everything that was expected of him. His school reports were excellent. He was wonderfully popular, and he ended his career, with a creditable number of prizes, as head of the school and captain of the football team. But this was not all. At the age of fourteen Nicky had developed an unexpected gift for lawn tennis. This was a game that his father not only was fond of, but played very well, and when he discerned in the boy the promise of a tennis player he fostered it. During the holidays he had him taught by the best professionals, and by the time he was sixteen he had won a number of tournaments for boys of his age. He could beat his father so badly that only parental affection reconciled the older player to the poor show he put up. At eighteen Nicky went to Cambridge and Henry Garnet conceived the ambition that before he was through with the university he should play for it. Nicky had all the qualifications for becoming a great tennis player. He was tall, he had a long reach, he was quick on his feet and his timing was perfect. He realized instinctively where the ball was coming and, seemingly without hurry, was there to take it. He had a powerful serve, with a nasty break that made it difficult to return, and his forehand drive, low, long and accurate, was deadly. He was not so good on the backhand and his volleying was wild, but all through the summer before he went to Cambridge Henry Garnet made him work on these points under the best teacher in England. At the back of his mind, though he did not even mention it to Nicky, he cherished a further ambition, to see his son play at Wimbledon, and who could tell, perhaps be chosen to represent his country in the Davis Cup. A great lump came into Henry Garnet's throat as he saw in fancy his son leap over the net to shake hands with the American champion whom he had just defeated, and walk off the court to the deafening plaudits of the multitude.

As an assiduous frequenter of Wimbledon, Henry Garnet had a good many friends in the tennis world, and one evening he found himself at a city dinner sitting next to one of them, a Colonel Brabazon, and in due course began talking to him

of Nicky and what chance there might be of his being chosen
to play for his university during the following season.

"Why don't you let him go down to Monte Carlo and play
in the spring tournament there?" said the Colonel suddenly.

"Oh, I don't think he's good enough for that. He's not
nineteen yet, he only went up to Cambridge last October; he
wouldn't stand a chance against all those cracks."

"Of course, Austin and Von Cramm and so on would
knock spots off him, but he might snatch a game or two; and
if he got up against some of the smaller fry there's no reason
why he shouldn't win two or three matches. He's never been
up against any of the first-rate players, and it would be wonderful practice for him. He'd learn a lot more than he'll ever
learn in the seaside tournaments you enter him for."

"I wouldn't dream of it. I'm not going to let him leave
Cambridge in the middle of a term. I've always impressed
upon him that tennis is only a game and it mustn't interfere
with work."

Colonel Brabazon asked Garnet when the term ended.

"That's all right. He'd only have to cut about three days.
Surely that could be arranged. You see, two of the men we
were depending on have let us down, and we're in a hole. We
want to send as good a team as we can. The Germans are
sending their best players, and so are the Americans."

"Nothing doing, old boy. In the first place Nicky's not
good enough, and secondly, I don't fancy the idea of sending
a kid like that to Monte Carlo without anyone to look after
him. If I could get away myself I might think of it, but that's
out of the question."

"I shall be there. I'm going as the nonplaying captain of
the English team. I'll keep an eye on him."

"You'll be busy, and besides, it's not a responsibility I'd
like to ask you to take. He's never been abroad in his life, and
to tell you the truth, I shouldn't have a moment's peace all
the time he was there."

They left it at that, and presently Henry Garnet went
home. He was so flattered by Colonel Brabazon's suggestion
that he could not help telling his wife.

"Fancy his thinking Nicky's as good as that. He told me

he'd seen him play and his style was fine. He only wants more practice to get into the first flight. We shall see the kid playing in the semifinals at Wimbledon yet, old girl."

To his surprise Mrs. Garnet was not so much opposed to the notion as he would have expected.

"After all the boy's eighteen. Nicky's never got into mischief yet, and there's no reason to suppose he will now."

"There's his work to be considered; don't forget that. I think it would be a very bad precedent to let him cut the end of term."

"But what can three days matter? It seems a shame to rob him of a chance like that. I'm sure he'd jump at it if you asked him."

"Well, I'm not going to. I haven't sent him to Cambridge just to play tennis. I know he's steady, but it's silly to put temptation in his way. He's much too young to go to Monte Carlo by himself."

"You say he won't have a chance against these crack players, but you can't tell."

Henry Garnet sighed a little. On the way home in the car it had struck him that Austin's health was uncertain and that Von Cramm had his off days. Supposing, just for the sake of argument, that Nicky had a bit of luck like that—then there would be no doubt that he would be chosen to play for Cambridge. But of course that was all nonsense.

"Nothing doing, my dear. I've made up my mind, and I'm not going to change it."

Mrs. Garnet held her peace. But next day she wrote to Nicky, telling him what had happened, and suggested to him what she would do in his place if, wanting to go, he wished to get his father's consent. A day or two later Henry Garnet received a letter from his son. He was bubbling over with excitement. He had seen his tutor, who was a tennis player himself, and the Provost of his college, who happened to know Colonel Brabazon, and no objection would be made to his leaving before the end of term; they both thought it an opportunity that shouldn't be missed. He didn't see what harm he could come to, and if only, just this once, his father would stretch a point, well, next term, he promised faithfully, he'd work like blazes. It was a very pretty letter. Mrs. Garnet watched her husband read it at the breakfast table; she was undisturbed by the frown on his face. He threw it over to her.

"I don't know why you thought it necessary to tell Nicky something I told you in confidence. It's too bad of you. Now you've thoroughly unsettled him."

"I'm so sorry. I thought it would please him to know that Colonel Brabazon had such a high opinion of him. I don't see why one should only tell people the disagreeable things that are said about them. Of course I made it quite clear that there could be no question of his going."

"You've put me in an odious position. If there's anything I hate it's for the boy to look upon me as a spoilsport and a tyrant."

"Oh, he'll never do that. He may think you rather silly and unreasonable, but I'm sure he'll understand that it's only for his own good that you're being so unkind."

"Christ," said Henry Garnet.

His wife had a great inclination to laugh. She knew the battle was won. Dear, oh dear, how easy it was to get men to do what you wanted. For appearance' sake Henry Garnet held out for forty-eight hours, but then he yielded, and a fortnight later Nicky came to London. He was to start for Monte Carlo next morning, and after dinner, when Mrs. Garnet and her elder daughter had left them, Henry took the opportunity to give his son some good advice.

"I don't feel quite comfortable about letting you go off to a place like Monte Carlo at your age practically by yourself," he finished, "but there it is, and I can only hope you'll be sensible. I don't want to play the heavy father, but there are three things especially that I want to warn you against: one is gambling, don't gamble; the second is money, don't lend anyone money; and the third is women, don't have anything to do with women. If you don't do any of those three things you can't come to much harm, so remember them well."

"All right, Father," Nicky smiled.

"That's my last word to you. I know the world pretty well, and believe me, my advice is sound."

"I won't forget it. I promise you."

"That's a good chap. Now let's go up and join the ladies."

Nicky beat neither Austin nor Von Cramm in the Monte Carlo tournament, but he did not disgrace himself. He snatched an unexpected victory over a Spanish player and gave one of the Austrians a closer match than anyone had thought possible. In the mixed doubles he got into the semifinals. His charm conquered everyone, and he vastly enjoyed himself. It was generally allowed that he showed promise, and Colonel Brabazon told him that when he was a little older and had had more practice with first-class players he would be a credit to his father. The tournament came to an end, and the day following he was to fly back to London. Anxious to play his best, he had lived very carefully, smoking little and drinking nothing, and going to bed early; but on his last evening he thought he would like to see something of the life in Monte Carlo of which he had heard so much. An official dinner was given to the tennis players, and after dinner with the rest of them he went into the Sporting Club. It was the first time he had been there. Monte Carlo was very full, and the rooms were crowded. Nicky had never before seen roulette played except in the pictures; in a maze he stopped at the first table he came to; chips of different sizes were scattered over the green cloth in what looked like a hopeless muddle; the croupier gave the wheel a sharp turn and with a flick threw in the little white ball. After what seemed an endless time the ball stopped and another croupier with a broad, indifferent gesture raked in the chips of those who had lost.

Presently Nicky wandered over to where they were playing *trente et quarante,* but he couldn't understand what it was all about, and he thought it dull. He saw a crowd in another room and sauntered in. A big game of baccara was in progress, and he was immediately conscious of the tension. The players were protected from the thronging bystanders by a brass rail; they sat round the table, nine on each side, with the dealer in the middle and the croupier facing him. Big money was changing hands. The dealer was a member of the Greek Syndicate. Nicky looked at his impassive face. His eyes were watchful, but his expression never changed whether he won or lost. It was a terrifying, strangely impressive sight. It gave Nicky, who had been thriftily brought up, a peculiar thrill to see someone risk a thousand pounds on the turn of a card and when he lost make a little joke and laugh. It was all terribly exciting. An acquaintance came up to him.

"Been doing any good?" he asked.

"I haven't been playing."

"Wise of you. Rotten game. Come and have a drink."

"All right."

While they were having it Nicky told his friend that this was the first time he had ever been in the rooms.

"Oh, but you must have one little flutter before you go. It's idiotic to leave Monte without having tried your luck. After all it won't hurt you to lose a hundred francs or so."

"I don't suppose it will, but my father wasn't any too keen on my coming at all, and one of the three things he particularly advised me not to do was to gamble."

But when Nicky left his companion he strolled back to one of the tables where they were playing roulette. He stood for a while looking at the losers' money being raked in by the croupier and the money that was won paid out to the winners. It was impossible to deny that it was thrilling. His friend was right, it did seem silly to leave Monte without putting something on the table just once. It would be an experience, and at his age you had to have all the experience you could get. He reflected that he hadn't promised his father not to gamble, he'd promised him not to forget his advice. It wasn't quite the same, was it? He took a hundred-franc note out of his pocket and rather shyly put it on number eighteen. He chose it because that was his age. With a wildly beating heart he watched the wheel turn; the little white ball whizzed about like a small demon of mischief; the wheel went round more slowly, the little white ball hesitated, it seemed about to stop, it went on again; Nicky could hardly believe his eyes when it fell into number eighteen. A lot of chips were passed over to him, and his hands trembled as he took them. It seemed to amount to a lot of money. He was so confused that he never thought of putting anything on the following round; in fact he had no intention of playing any more, once was enough; and he was surprised when eighteen again came up. There was only one chip on it.

"By George, you've won again," said a man who was standing near to him.

"Me? I hadn't got anything on."

"Yes, you had. Your original stake. They always leave it on unless you ask for it back. Didn't you know?"

Another packet of chips was handed over to him. Nicky's head reeled. He counted his gains: seven thousand francs. A queer sense of power seized him; he felt wonderfully clever. This was the easiest way of making money that he had ever heard of. His frank, charming face was wreathed in smiles. His bright eyes met those of a woman standing by his side. She smiled.

"You're in luck," she said.

She spoke English, but with a foreign accent.

"I can hardly believe it. It's the first time I've ever played."

"That explains it. Lend me a thousand francs, will you? I've lost everything I've got. I'll give it you back in half an hour."

"All right."

She took a large red chip from his pile and with a word of thanks disappeared. The man who had spoken to him before grunted.

"You'll never see that again."

Nicky was dashed. His father had particularly advised him not to lend anyone money. What a silly thing to do! And to somebody he'd never seen in his life. But the fact was, he felt at that moment such a love for the human race that it had never occurred to him to refuse. And that big red chip, it was almost impossible to realize that it had any value. Oh, well, it didn't matter, he still had six thousand francs, he'd just try his luck once or twice more, and if he didn't win he'd go home. He put a chip on sixteen, which was his elder sister's age, but it didn't come up; then on twelve, which was his younger sister's, and that didn't come up either; he tried various numbers at random, but without success. It was funny, he seemed to have lost his knack. He thought he would try just once more and then stop; he won. He had made up all his losses and had something over. At the end of an hour, after various ups and downs, having experienced such thrills as he had never known in his life, he found himself with so many chips that they would hardly go in his pockets. He decided to go. He went to the changers' office, and he gasped when twenty thousand-franc notes were spread out before him. He had never had so much money in his life. He put it in his pocket and was turning away when the woman to whom he had lent the thousand francs came up to him.

"I've been looking for you everywhere," she said. "I was afraid you'd gone. I was in a fever, I didn't know what you'd think of me. Here's your thousand francs and thank you so much for the loan."

Nicky, blushing scarlet, stared at her with amazement. How he had misjudged her! His father had said, don't gamble; well, he had, and he'd made twenty thousand francs; and his father had said, don't lend anyone money; well, he had, he'd lent quite a lot to a total stranger, and she'd returned it. The fact was that he wasn't nearly such a fool as his father thought: he'd had an instinct that he could lend her the money with safety, and you see, his instinct was right. But he was so obviously taken aback that the little lady was forced to laugh.

"What is the matter with you?" she asked.

"To tell you the truth I never expected to see the money back."

"What did you take me for? Did you think I was a—cocotte?"

Nicky reddened to the roots of his wavy hair.

"No, of course not."

"Do I look like one?"

"Not a bit."

She was dressed very quietly, in black, with a string of gold beads round her neck; her simple frock showed off a neat, slight figure; she had a pretty little face and a trim head. She was made up, but not excessively, and Nicky supposed that she was not more than three or four years older than himself. She gave him a friendly smile.

"My husband is in the administration in Morocco, and I've come to Monte Carlo for a few weeks because he thought I wanted a change."

"I was just going," said Nicky because he couldn't think of anything else to say.

"Already!"

"Well, I've got to get up early tomorrow. I'm going back to London by air."

"Of course. The tournament ended today, didn't it? I saw you play, you know, two or three times."

"Did you? I don't know why you should have noticed me."

"You've got a beautiful style. And you looked very sweet in your shorts."

Nicky was not an immodest youth, but it did cross his mind that perhaps she had borrowed that thousand francs in order to scrape acquaintance with him.

"Do you ever go to the Knickerbocker?" she asked.

"No. I never have."

"Oh, but you mustn't leave Monte without having been there. Why don't you come and dance a little? To tell you the truth, I'm starving with hunger, and I should adore some bacon and eggs."

Nicky remembered his father's advice not to have anything to do with women, but this was different; you had only to look at the pretty little thing to know at once that she was perfectly respectable. Her husband was in what corresponded, he supposed, to the civil service. His father and mother had friends who were civil servants, and they and their wives sometimes came to dinner. It was true that the wives were neither so young nor so pretty as this one, but she was just as ladylike as they were. And after winning twenty thousand francs he thought it wouldn't be a bad idea to have a little fun.

"I'd love to go with you," he said. "But you won't mind if I don't stay very long. I've left instructions at my hotel that I'm to be called at seven."

"We'll leave as soon as ever you like."

Nicky found it very pleasant at the Knickerbocker. He ate his bacon and eggs with appetite. They shared a bottle of champagne. They danced, and the little lady told him he danced beautifully. He knew he danced pretty well, and of course she was easy to dance with. As light as a feather. She laid her cheek against his and when their eyes met there was in hers a smile that made his heart go pit-a-pat. A coloured woman sang in a throaty, sensual voice. The floor was crowded.

"Have you ever been told that you're very good-looking?" she asked.

"I don't think so," he laughed. "Gosh," he thought, "I believe she's fallen for me."

Nicky was not such a fool as to be unaware that women often liked him, and when she made that remark he pressed her to him a little more closely. She closed her eyes, and a faint sigh escaped her lips.

"I suppose it wouldn't be quite nice if I kissed you before all these people," he said.

"What do you think they would take me for?"

It began to grow late, and Nicky said that really he thought he ought to be going.

"I shall go too," she said. "Will you drop me at my hotel on your way?"

Nicky paid the bill. He was rather surprised at its amount, but with all that money he had in his pocket he could afford not to care, and they got into a taxi. She snuggled up to him, and he kissed her. She seemed to like it.

"By Jove," he thought, "I wonder if there's anything doing."

It was true that she was a married woman, but her husband was in Morocco, and it certainly did look as if she'd fallen for him. Good and proper. It was true also that his father had warned him to have nothing to do with women, but, he reflected again, he hadn't actually promised he wouldn't, he'd only promised not to forget his advice. Well, he hadn't; he was bearing it in mind that very minute. But circumstances alter cases. She was a sweet little thing; it seemed silly to miss the chance of an adventure when it was handed to you like that on a tray. When they reached the hotel he paid off the taxi.

"I'll walk home," he said. "The air will do me good after the stuffy atmosphere of that place."

"Come up a moment," she said. "I'd like to show you the photo of my little boy."

"Oh, have you got a little boy?" he exclaimed, a trifle dashed.

"Yes, a sweet little boy."

He walked upstairs after her. He didn't in the least want to see the photograph of her little boy, but he thought it only civil to pretend he did. He was afraid he'd made a fool of himself; it occurred to him that she was taking him up to look at the photograph in order to show him in a nice way that he'd made a mistake. He'd told her he was eighteen.

"I suppose she thinks I'm just a kid."

He began to wish he hadn't spent all that money on champagne at the night club.

But she didn't show him the photograph of her little boy after all. They had no sooner got into her room than she turned to him, flung her arms round his neck, and kissed him full on the lips. He had never in all his life been kissed so passionately.

"Darling," she said.

For a brief moment his father's advice once more crossed Nicky's mind, and then he forgot it.

Nicky was a light sleeper, and the least sound was apt to wake him. Two or three hours later he awoke and for a moment could not imagine where he was. The room was not quite dark, for the door of the bathroom was ajar, and the light in it had been left on. Suddenly he was conscious that someone was moving about the room. Then he remembered. He saw that it was his little friend, and he was on the point of speaking when something in the way she was behaving stopped him. She was walking very cautiously, as though she were afraid of waking him; she stopped once or twice and looked over at the bed. He wondered what she was after. He soon saw. She went over to the chair on which he had placed his clothes and once more looked in his direction. She waited for what seemed to him an interminable time. The silence was so intense that Nicky thought he could hear his own heart beating. Then, very slowly, very quietly, she took up his coat, slipped her hand into the inside pocket and drew out all those beautiful thousand-franc notes that Nicky had been so proud to win. She put the coat back and placed some other clothes on it so that it should look as though it had not been disturbed, then, with the bundle of notes in her hand, for an appreciable time stood once more stock-still. Nicky had repressed an instinctive impulse to jump up and grab her; it was partly surprise that had kept him quiet, partly the notion that he was in a strange hotel, in a foreign country, and if he made a row he didn't know what might happen. She looked at him. His eyes were partly closed, and he was sure that she thought he was asleep. In the silence she could hardly fail to hear his regular breathing. When she had reassured herself that her movements had not disturbed him, she stepped, with infinite caution, across the room. On a small table in the window a cineraria was growing in a pot. Nicky watched her now with his eyes wide open. The plant was evidently placed quite loosely in the pot, for, taking it by the stalks, she lifted it out; she put the bank notes in the bottom of the pot and replaced the plant. It was an excellent hiding place. No one could have guessed that anything was concealed under that richly flowering plant. She pressed the earth down with her fingers and then, very slowly, taking care not to make the smallest noise, crept across the room and slipped back into bed.

"Chéri," she said, in a caressing voice.

Nicky breathed steadily, like a man immersed in deep sleep. The little lady turned over on her side and disposed herself to slumber. But though Nicky lay so still, his thoughts worked busily. He was extremely indignant at the scene he had just witnessed, and to himself he spoke his thoughts with vigour.

"She's nothing but a damned tart. She and her dear little boy and her husband in Morocco. My eye! She's a rotten thief, that's what she is. Took me for a mug. If she thinks she's going to get away with anything like that, she's mistaken."

He had already made up his mind what he was going to do with the money he had so cleverly won. He had long wanted a car of his own and had thought it rather mean of his father not to have given him one. After all, a feller doesn't always went to drive about in the family bus. Well, he'd just teach the old man a lesson and buy one himself. For twenty thousand francs, two hundred pounds roughly, he could get a very decent second-hand car. He meant to get the money back, but just then he didn't quite know how. He didn't like the idea of kicking up a row, he was a stranger, in a hotel he knew nothing of; it might very well be that the beastly woman had friends there; he didn't mind facing anyone in a fair fight, but he'd look pretty foolish if someone pulled a gun on him. He reflected besides, very sensibly, that he had no proof the money was his. If it came to a showdown and she swore it was hers, he might very easily find himself hauled off to a police station. He really didn't know what to do. Presently by her regular breathing he knew that the little lady was asleep. She must have fallen asleep with an easy mind, for she had done her job without a hitch. It infuriated Nicky that she should rest so peacefully while he lay awake, worried to death. Suddenly an idea occurred to him. It was such a good one that it was only by the exercise of all his self-control that he prevented himself from jumping out of bed and carrying it out at once. Two could play at her game. She'd stolen his money; well, he'd steal it back again, and they'd be all square. He made up his mind to wait quite quietly until he was sure that deceitful woman was sound asleep. He waited for what seemed to him a very long time. She did not stir. Her breathing was as regular as a child's.

"Darling," he said at last.

No answer. No movement. She was dead to the world. Very slowly, pausing after every movement, very silently, he slipped out of bed. He stood still for a while, looking at her to see whether he had disturbed her. Her breathing was as

regular as before. During the time he was waiting he had
taken note carefully of the furniture in the room so that in
crossing it he should not knock against a chair or a table and
make a noise. He took a couple of steps and waited; he took
a couple of steps more; he was very light on his feet and
made no sound as he walked; he took fully five minutes to
get to the window, and here he waited again. He started, for
the bed slightly creaked, but it was only because the sleeper
turned in her sleep. He forced himself to wait till he had
counted one hundred. She was sleeping like a log. With infinite care he seized the cineraria by the stalks and gently
pulled it out of the pot; he put his other hand in, his heart
beat nineteen to the dozen as his fingers touched the notes, his
hand closed on them and he slowly drew them out. He replaced the plant and in his turn carefully pressed down the
earth. While he was doing all this he had kept one eye on the
form lying in the bed. It remained still. After another pause
he crept softly to the chair on which his clothes were lying.
He first put the bundle of notes in his coat pocket and then
proceeded to dress. It took him a good quarter of an hour,
because he could afford to make no sound. He had been
wearing a soft shirt with his dinner jacket, and he congratulated himself on this because it was easier to put on silently
than a stiff one. He had some difficulty in tying his tie without a looking glass, but he very wisely reflected that it didn't
really matter if it wasn't tied very well. His spirits were rising. The whole thing now began to seem rather a lark. At
length he was completely dressed except for his shoes, which
he took in his hand; he thought he would put them on when
he got into the passage. Now he had to cross the room to get
to the door. He reached it so quietly that he could not have
disturbed the lightest sleeper. But the door had to be unlocked. He turned the key very slowly; it creaked.

"Who's that?"

The little woman suddenly sat up in bed. Nicky's heart
jumped to his mouth. He made a great effort to keep his
head.

"It's only me. It's six o'clock and I've got to go. I was
trying not to wake you."

"Oh, I forgot."

She sank back onto the pillow.

"Now that you're awake I'll put on my shoes."

He sat down on the edge of the bed and did this.

"Don't make a noise when you go out. The hotel people don't like it. Oh, I'm so sleepy."

"You go right off to sleep again."

"Kiss me before you go." He bent down and kissed her. "You're a sweet boy and a wonderful lover. *Bon voyage.*"

Nicky did not feel quite safe till he got out of the hotel. The dawn had broken. The sky was unclouded, and in the harbour the yachts and the fishing boats lay motionless on the still water. On the quay fishermen were getting ready to start on their day's work. The streets were deserted. Nicky took a long breath of the sweet morning air. He felt alert and well. He also felt as pleased as Punch. With a swinging stride, his shoulders well thrown back, he walked up the hill and along the gardens in front of the Casino—the flowers in that clear light had a dewy brilliance that was delicious—till he came to his hotel. Here the day had already begun. In the hall porters with mufflers round their necks and berets on their heads were busy sweeping. Nicky went up to his room and had a hot bath. He lay in it and thought with satisfaction that he was not such a mug as some people might think. After his bath he did his exercises, dressed, packed and went down to breakfast. He had a grand appetite. No continental breakfast for him! He had grapefruit, porridge, bacon and eggs, rolls fresh from the oven, so crisp and delicious they melted in your mouth, marmalade and three cups of coffee. Though feeling perfectly well before, he felt better after that. He lit the pipe he had recently learnt to smoke, paid his bill and stepped into the car that was waiting to take him to the aerodrome on the other side of Cannes. The road as far as Nice ran over the hills, and below him was the blue sea and the coast line. He couldn't help thinking it damned pretty. They passed through Nice, so gay and friendly in the early morning, and presently they came to a long stretch of straight road that ran by the sea. Nicky had paid his bill, not with the money he had won the night before, but with the money his father had given him; he had changed a thousand francs to pay for supper at the Knickerbocker, but that deceitful little woman had returned him the thousand francs he had lent her, so that he still had twenty thousand-franc notes in his pocket. He thought he would like to have a look at them. He had so nearly lost them that they had a double value for him. He took them out of his hip pocket into which for safety's sake he had stuffed them when he put on the suit he was travelling in, and counted them one by one. Something very strange had happened to them. Instead of there being twenty notes, as there should have been, there were twenty-six. He couldn't understand it at all. He counted them twice more. There was no doubt about it; somehow or other he had twenty-six thousand francs instead of the twenty he should have had. He couldn't make it out. He asked himself if it was possible that he had won more at the Sporting Club than he had realized. But no, that was out of the question; he distinctly remembered the man at the desk laying the notes out in four rows of five, and he had counted them himself. Suddenly the explanation occurred to him; when he had put his hand into the flower pot, after taking out the cineraria, he had grabbed everything he felt there. The flower pot was the little hussy's money box, and he had taken out not only his own money, but her savings as well. Nicky leant back in the car and burst into a roar of laughter. It was the funniest thing he had ever heard in his life. And when he thought of her going to the flower pot sometime later in the morning when she awoke, expecting to find the money she had so cleverly got away with, and finding, not only that it wasn't there, but that her own had gone too, he laughed more than ever. And so far as he was concerned there was nothing to do about it, he knew neither her name nor the name of the hotel to which she had taken him. He couldn't return her money even if he wanted to.

"It serves her damned well right," he said.

This then was the story that Henry Garnet told his friends over the bridge table, for the night before, after dinner when his wife and daughter had left them to their port, Nicky had narrated it in full.

"And you know what infuriated me is that he's so damned pleased with himself. Talk of a cat swallowing a canary. And d'you know what he said to me when he'd finished? He looked at me with those innocent eyes of his and said: 'You know, Father, I can't help thinking there was something wrong about the advice you gave me. You said, don't gamble; well, I did, and I made a packet; you said, don't lend money; well, I did, and I got it back; and you said, don't have anything to do with women; well, I did, and I made six thousand francs on the deal.' "

It didn't make it any better for Henry Garnet that his three companions burst out laughing.

"It's all very well for you fellows to laugh, but you know, I'm in a damned awkward position. The boy looked up to me, he respected me, he took whatever I said as gospel truth, and now, I saw it in his eyes, he just looks upon me as a drivelling old fool. It's no good my saying one swallow doesn't make a summer; he doesn't see that it was just a fluke, he thinks the whole thing was due to his own cleverness. It may ruin him."

"You do look a bit of a damned fool, old man," said one of the others. "There's no denying that, is there?"

"I know I do, and I don't like it. It's so dashed unfair. Fate has no right to play one tricks like that. After all, you must admit that my advice was good."

"Very good."

"And the wretched boy ought to have burnt his fingers. Well, he hasn't. You're all men of the world, you tell me how I'm to deal with the situation now."

But they none of them could.

"Well, Henry, if I were you I wouldn't worry," said the lawyer. "My belief is that your boy's born lucky, and in the long run that's better than to be born clever or rich."

RAIN

IT WAS nearly bed-time and when they awoke next morning
land would be in sight. Dr. Macphail lit his pipe and,
leaning over the rail, searched the heavens for the Southern Cross. After two years at the front and a wound that
had taken longer to heal than it should, he was glad to settle
down quietly at Apia for twelve months at least, and he felt
already better for the journey. Since some of the passengers
were leaving the ship next day at Pago-Pago they had had a
little dance that evening and in his ears hammered still the
harsh notes of the mechanical piano. But the deck was quiet
at last. A little way off he saw his wife in a long chair talking
with the Davidsons, and he strolled over to her. When he sat
down under the light and took off his hat you saw that he had
very red hair, with a bald patch on the crown, and the red,
freckled skin which accompanies red hair; he was a man of
forty, thin, with a pinched face, precise and rather pedantic;
and he spoke with a Scots accent in a very low, quiet voice.

Between the Macphails and the Davidsons, who were
missionaries, there had arisen the intimacy of shipboard,
which is due to propinquity rather than to any community of
taste. Their chief tie was the disapproval they shared of the
men who spent their days and nights in the smoking-room
playing poker or bridge and drinking. Mrs. Macphail was
not a little flattered to think that she and her husband were
the only people on board with whom the Davidsons were
willing to associate, and even the doctor, shy but no fool, half
unconsciously acknowledged the compliment. It was only because he was of an argumentative mind that in their cabin at
night he permitted himself to carp.

"Mrs. Davidson was saying she didn't know how they'd have got through the journey if it hadn't been for us," said Mrs. Macphail, as she neatly brushed out her transformation. "She said we were really the only people on the ship they cared to know."

"I shouldn't have thought a missionary was such a big bug that he could afford to put on frills."

"It's not frills. I quite understand what she means. It wouldn't have been very nice for the Davidsons to have to mix with all that rough lot in the smoking-room."

"The founder of their religion wasn't so exclusive," said Dr. Macphail with a chuckle.

"I've asked you over and over again not to joke about religion," answered his wife. "I shouldn't like to have a nature like yours, Alec. You never look for the best in people."

He gave her a sidelong glance with his pale, blue eyes, but did not reply. After many years of married life he had learned that it was more conducive to peace to leave his wife with the last word. He was undressed before she was, and climbing into the upper bunk he settled down to read himself to sleep.

When he came on deck next morning they were close to land. He looked at it with greedy eyes. There was a thin strip of silver beach rising quickly to hills covered to the top with luxuriant vegetation. The coconut trees, thick and green, came nearly to the water's edge, and among them you saw the grass houses of the Samoans; and here and there, gleaming white, a little church. Mrs. Davidson came and stood beside him. She was dressed in black and wore round her neck a gold chain, from which dangled a small cross. She was a little woman, with brown, dull hair very elaborately arranged, and she had prominent blue eyes behind invisible *pince-nez*. Her face was long, like a sheep's, but she gave no impression of foolishness, rather of extreme alertness; she had the quick movements of a bird. The most remarkable thing about her was her voice, high, metallic, and without inflection; it fell on the ear with a hard monotony, irritating to the nerves like the pitiless clamour of the pneumatic drill.

"This must seem like home to you," said Dr. Macphail, with his thin, difficult smile.

"Ours are low islands, you know, not like these. Coral. These are volcanic. We've got another ten days' journey to reach them."

"In these parts that's almost like being in the next street at home," said Dr. Macphail facetiously.

"Well, that's rather an exaggerated way of putting it, but one does look at distances differently in the South Seas. So far you're right."

Dr. Macphail sighed faintly.

"I'm glad we're not stationed here," she went on. "They say this is a terribly difficult place to work in. The steamers' touching makes the people unsettled; and then there's the naval station; that's bad for the natives. In our district we don't have difficulties like that to contend with. There are one or two traders, of course, but we take care to make them behave, and if they don't we make the place so hot for them they're glad to go."

Fixing the glasses on her nose she looked at the green island with a ruthless stare.

"It's almost a hopeless task for the missionaries here. I can never be sufficiently thankful to God that we are at least spared that."

Davidson's district consisted of a group of islands to the North of Samoa; they were widely separated and he had frequently to go long distances by canoe. At these times his wife remained at their headquarters and managed the mission. Dr. Macphail felt his heart sink when he considered the efficiency with which she certainly managed it. She spoke of the depravity of the natives in a voice which nothing could hush, but with a vehemently unctuous horror. Her sense of delicacy was singular. Early in their acquaintance she had said to him:

"You know, their marriage customs when we first settled in the islands were so shocking that I couldn't possibly describe them to you. But I'll tell Mrs. Macphail and she'll tell you."

Then he had seen his wife and Mrs. Davidson, their deck-chairs close together, in earnest conversation for about two hours. As he walked past them backwards and forwards for the sake of exercise, he had heard Mrs. Davidson's agitated whisper, like the distant flow of a mountain torrent, and he saw by his wife's open mouth and pale face that she was enjoying an alarming experience. At night in their cabin she repeated to him with bated breath all she had heard.

"Well, what did I say to you?" cried Mrs. Davidson, exultant, next morning. "Did you ever hear anything more dreadful? You don't wonder that I couldn't tell you myself, do you? Even though you are a doctor."

Mrs. Davidson scanned his face. She had a dramatic eagerness to see that she had achieved the desired effect.

"Can you wonder that when we first went there our hearts sank? You'll hardly believe me when I tell you it was impossible to find a single good girl in any of the villages."

She used the word *good* in a severely technical manner.

"Mr. Davidson and I talked it over, and we made up our minds the first thing to do was to put down the dancing. The natives were crazy about dancing."

"I was not averse to it myself when I was a young man," said Dr. Macphail.

"I guessed as much when I heard you ask Mrs. Macphail to have a turn with you last night. I don't think there's any real harm if a man dances with his wife, but I was relieved that she wouldn't. Under the circumstances I thought it better that we should keep ourselves to ourselves."

"Under what circumstances?"

Mrs. Davidson gave him a quick look through her *pince-nez,* but did not answer his question.

"But among white people it's not quite the same," she went on, "though I must say I agree with Mr. Davidson, who says he can't understand how a husband can stand by and see his wife in another man's arms, and as far as I'm concerned I've never danced a step since I married. But the native dancing is quite another matter. It's not only immoral in itself, but it distinctly leads to immorality. However, I'm thankful to God that we stamped it out, and I don't think

I'm wrong in saying that no one has danced in our district for eight years."

But now they came to the mouth of the harbour and Mrs. Macphail joined them. The ship turned sharply and steamed slowly in. It was a great landlocked harbour big enough to hold a fleet of battleships; and all around it rose, high and steep, the green hills. Near the entrance, getting such breeze as blew from the sea, stood the governor's house in a garden. The Stars and Stripes dangled languidly from a flagstaff. They passed two or three trim bungalows, and a tennis court, and then they came to the quay with its warehouses. Mrs. Davidson pointed out the schooner, moored two or three hundred yards from the side, which was to take them to Apia. There was a crowd of eager, noisy, and good-humoured natives come from all parts of the island, some from curiosity, others to barter with the travellers on their way to Sydney; and they brought pineapples and huge bunches of bananas, *tapa* cloths, necklaces of shells or sharks' teeth, *kava*-bowls, and models of war canoes. American sailors, neat and trim, clean-shaven and frank of face, sauntered among them, and there was a little group of officials. While their luggage was being landed the Macphails and Mrs. Davidson watched the crowd. Dr. Macphail looked at the yaws from which most of the children and the young boys seemed to suffer, disfiguring sores like torpid ulcers, and his professional eyes glistened when he saw for the first time in his experience cases of elephantiasis, men going about with a huge, heavy arm or dragging along a grossly disfigured leg. Men and women wore the *lava-lava*.

"It's a very indecent costume," said Mrs. Davidson. "Mr. Davidson thinks it should be prohibited by law. How can you expect people to be moral when they wear nothing but a strip of red cotton round their loins?"

"It's suitable enough to the climate," said the doctor, wiping the sweat off his head.

Now that they were on land the heat, though it was so early in the morning, was already oppressive. Closed in by its hills, not a breath of air came in to Pago-Pago.

"In our islands," Mrs. Davidson went on in her high-pitched tones, "we've practically eradicated the *lava-lava*. A few old men still continue to wear it, but that's all. The women have all taken to the Mother Hubbard, and the men wear trousers and singlets. At the very beginning of our stay Mr. Davidson said in one of his reports: the inhabitants of these islands will never be thoroughly Christianised till every boy of more than ten years is made to wear a pair of trousers."

But Mrs. Davidson had given two or three of her birdlike glances at heavy grey clouds that came floating over the mouth of the harbour. A few drops began to fall.

"We'd better take shelter," she said.

They made their way with all the crowd to a great shed of corrugated iron, and the rain began to fall in torrents. They stood there for some time and then were joined by Mr. Davidson. He had been polite enough to the Macphails during the journey, but he had not his wife's sociability, and had spent much of his time reading. He was a silent, rather sullen man, and you felt that his affability was a duty that he imposed upon himself Christianly; he was by nature reserved and even morose. His appearance was singular. He was very tall and thin, with long limbs loosely jointed; hollow cheeks and curiously high cheek-bones; he had so cadaverous an air that it surprised you to notice how full and sensual were his lips. He wore his hair very long. His dark eyes, set deep in their sockets, were large and tragic; and his hands with their big, long fingers, were finely shaped; they gave him a look of great strength. But the most striking thing about him was the feeling he gave you of suppressed fire. It was impressive and vaguely troubling. He was not a man with whom any intimacy was possible.

He brought now unwelcome news. There was an epidemic of measles, a serious and often fatal disease among the Kanakas, on the island, and a case had developed among the crew of the schooner which was to take them on their journey. The sick man had been brought ashore and put in hospital on the quarantine station, but telegraphic instructions had been sent from Apia to say that the schooner would not be allowed to enter the harbour till it was certain no other member of the crew was affected.

"It means we shall have to stay here for ten days at least."

"But I'm urgently needed at Apia," said Dr. Macphail.

"That can't be helped. If no more cases develop on board, the schooner will be allowed to sail with white passengers, but all native traffic is prohibited for three months."

"Is there a hotel here?" asked Mrs. Macphail.

Davidson gave a low chuckle.

"There's not."

"What shall we do then?"

"I've been talking to the governor. There's a trader along the front who has rooms that he rents, and my proposition is that as soon as the rain lets up we should go along there and see what we can do. Don't expect comfort. You've just got to be thankful if we get a bed to sleep on and a roof over our heads."

But the rain showed no sign of stopping, and at length with umbrellas and waterproofs they set out. There was no town, but merely a group of official buildings, a store or two, and at the back, among the coconut trees and plantains, a few native dwellings. The house they sought was about five minutes' walk from the wharf. It was a frame house of two storeys, with broad verandahs on both floors and a roof of corrugated iron. The owner was a half-caste named Horn, with a native wife surrounded by little brown children, and on the ground-floor he had a store where he sold canned goods and cottons. The rooms he showed them were almost bare of furniture. In the Macphails' there was nothing but a poor, worn bed with a ragged mosquito net, a rickety chair, and a washstand. They looked round with dismay. The rain poured down without ceasing.

"I'm not going to unpack more than we actually need," said Mrs. Macphail.

Mrs. Davidson came into the room as she was unlocking a portmanteau. She was very brisk and alert. The cheerless surroundings had no effect on her.

"If you'll take my advice you'll get a needle and cotton

and start right in to mend the mosquito net," she said, "or you'll not be able to get a wink of sleep to-night."

"Will they be very bad?" asked Dr. Macphail.

"This is the season for them. When you're asked to a party at Government House at Apia you'll notice that all the ladies are given a pillow-slip to put their—their lower extremities in."

"I wish the rain would stop for a moment," said Mrs. Macphail. "I could try to make the place comfortable with more heart if the sun were shining."

"Oh, if you wait for that, you'll wait a long time. Pago-Pago is about the rainiest place in the Pacific. You see, the hills, and that bay, they attract the water, and one expects rain at this time of year anyway."

She looked from Macphail to his wife, standing helplessly in different parts of the room, like lost souls, and she pursed her lips. She saw that she must take them in hand. Feckless people like that made her impatient, but her hands itched to put everything in the order which came so naturally to her.

"Here, you give me a needle and cotton and I'll mend that net of yours, while you go on with your unpacking. Dinner's at one. Dr. Macphail, you'd better go down to the wharf and see that your heavy luggage has been put in a dry place. You know what these natives are, they're quite capable of storing it where the rain will beat in on it all the time."

The doctor put on his waterproof again and went downstairs. At the door Mr. Horn was standing in conversation with the quartermaster of the ship they had just arrived in and a second-class passenger whom Dr. Macphail had seen several times on board. The quartermaster, a little, shrivelled man, extremely dirty, nodded to him as he passed.

"This is a bad job about the measles, doc," he said. "I see you've fixed yourself up already."

Dr. Macphail thought he was rather familiar, but he was a timid man and he did not take offence easily.

"Yes, we've got a room upstairs."

"Miss Thompson was sailing with you to Apia, so I've brought her along here."

The quartermaster pointed with his thumb to the woman standing by his side. She was twenty-seven perhaps, plump, and in a coarse fashion pretty. She wore a white dress and a large white hat. Her fat calves in white cotton stockings bulged over the tops of long white boots in glacé kid. She gave Macphail an ingratiating smile.

"The feller's tryin' to soak me a dollar and a half a day for the meanest sized room," she said in a hoarse voice.

"I tell you she's a friend of mine, Jo," said the quartermaster. "She can't pay more than a dollar, and you've sure got to take her for that."

The trader was fat and smooth and quietly smiling.

"Well, if you put it like that, Mr. Swan, I'll see what I can do about it. I'll talk to Mrs. Horn and if we think we can make a reduction we will."

"Don't try to pull that stuff with me," said Miss Thompson. "We'll settle this right now. You get a dollar a day for the room and not one bean more."

Dr. Macphail smiled. He admired the effrontery with which she bargained. He was the sort of man who always paid what he was asked. He preferred to be over-charged than to haggle. The trader sighed.

"Well, to oblige Mr. Swan I'll take it."

"That's the goods," said Miss Thompson. "Come right in and have a shot of hooch. I've got some real good rye in that grip if you'll bring it along, Mr. Swan. You come along too, doctor."

"Oh, I don't think I will, thank you," he answered. "I'm just going down to see that our luggage is all right."

He stepped out into the rain. It swept in from the opening of the harbour in sheets and the opposite shore was all blurred. He passed two or three natives clad in nothing but the *lava-lava*, with huge umbrellas over them. They walked finely, with leisurely movements, very upright; and they smiled and greeted him in a strange tongue as they went by.

It was nearly dinner-time when he got back, and their meal was laid in the trader's parlour. It was a room designed not to live in but for purposes of prestige, and it had a musty, melancholy air. A suite of stamped plush was arranged neatly round the walls, and from the middle of the ceiling, protected from the flies by yellow tissue paper, hung a gilt chandelier. Davidson did not come.

"I know he went to call on the governor," said Mrs. Davidson, "and I guess he's kept him to dinner."

A little native girl brought them a dish of Hamburger steak, and after a while the trader came up to see that they had everything they wanted.

"I see we have a fellow lodger, Mr. Horn," said Dr. Macphail.

"She's taken a room, that's all," answered the trader. "She's getting her own board."

He looked at the two ladies with an obsequious air.

"I put her downstairs so she shouldn't be in the way. She won't be any trouble to you."

"Is it someone who was on the boat?" asked Mrs. Macphail.

"Yes, ma'am, she was in the second cabin. She was going to Apia. She has a position as cashier waiting for her."

"Oh!"

When the trader was gone Macphail said:

"I shouldn't think she'd find it exactly cheerful having her meals in her room."

"If she was in the second cabin I guess she'd rather," answered Mrs. Davidson. "I don't exactly know who it can be."

"I happened to be there when the quartermaster brought her along. Her name's Thompson."

"It's not the woman who was dancing with the quartermaster last night?" asked Mrs. Davidson.

"That's who it must be," said Mrs. Macphail. "I wondered at the time what she was. She looked rather fast to me."

"Not good style at all," said Mrs. Davidson.

They began to talk of other things, and after dinner, tired with their early rise, they separated and slept. When they awoke, though the sky was still grey and the clouds hung low, it was not raining and they went for a walk on the high road which the Americans had built along the bay.

On their return they found that Davidson had just come in.

"We may be here for a fortnight," he said irritably. "I've argued it out with the governor, but he says there is nothing to be done."

"Mr. Davidson's just longing to get back to his work," said his wife, with an anxious glance at him.

"We've been away for a year," he said, walking up and down the verandah. "The mission has been in charge of native missionaries and I'm terribly nervous that they've let things slide. They're good men, I'm not saying a word against them, God-fearing, devout, and truly Christian men —their Christianity would put many so-called Christians at home to the blush—but they're pitifully lacking in energy. They can make a stand once, they can make a stand twice, but they can't make a stand all the time. If you leave a mission in charge of a native missionary, no matter how trust-worthy he seems, in course of time you'll find he's let abuses creep in."

Mr. Davidson stood still. With his tall, spare form, and his great eyes flashing out of his pale face, he was an impressive figure. His sincerity was obvious in the fire of his gestures and in his deep, ringing voice.

"I expect to have my work cut out for me. I shall act and I shall act promptly. If the tree is rotten it shall be cut down and cast into the flames."

And in the evening after the high tea which was their last meal, while they sat in the stiff parlour, the ladies working and Dr. Macphail smoking his pipe, the missionary told them of his work in the islands.

"When we went there they had no sense of sin at all," he said. "They broke the commandments one after the other and never knew they were doing wrong. And I think that was the most difficult part of my work, to instil into the natives the sense of sin."

The Macphails knew already that Davidson had worked in the Solomons for five years before he met his wife. She had been a missionary in China, and they had become acquainted in Boston, where they were both spending part of their leave to attend a missionary congress. On their marriage they had been appointed to the islands in which they had laboured ever since.

In the course of all the conversations they had had with Mr. Davidson one thing had shone out clearly and that was the man's unflinching courage. He was a medical missionary, and he was liable to be called at any time to one or other of the islands in the group. Even the whaleboat is not so very safe a conveyance in the stormy Pacific of the wet season, but often he would be sent for in a canoe, and then the danger was great. In cases of illness or accident he never hesitated. A dozen times he had spent the whole night baling for his life, and more than once Mrs. Davidson had given him up for lost.

"I'd beg him not to go sometimes," she said, "or at least to wait till the weather was more settled, but he'd never listen. He's obstinate, and when he's once made up his mind, nothing can move him."

"How can I ask the natives to put their trust in the Lord if I am afraid to do so myself?" cried Davidson. "And I'm not, I'm not. They know that if they send for me in their trouble I'll come if it's humanly possible. And do you think the Lord is going to abandon me when I am on his business? The wind blows at his bidding and the waves toss and rage at his word."

Dr. Macphail was a timid man. He had never been able to get used to the hurtling of the shells over the trenches, and when he was operating in an advanced dressing-station the sweat poured from his brow and dimmed his spectacles in the effort he made to control his unsteady hand. He shuddered a little as he looked at the missionary.

"I wish I could say that I've never been afraid," he said.

"I wish you could say that you believed in God," retorted the other.

But for some reason, that evening the missionary's thoughts travelled back to the early days he and his wife had spent on the islands.

"Sometimes Mrs. Davidson and I would look at one another and the tears would stream down our cheeks. We worked without ceasing, day and night, and we seemed to make no progress. I don't know what I should have done without her then. When I felt my heart sink, when I was very near despair, she gave me courage and hope."

Mrs. Davidson looked down at her work, and a slight colour rose to her thin cheeks. Her hands trembled a little. She did not trust herself to speak.

"We had no one to help us. We were alone, thousands of miles from any of our own people, surrounded by darkness. When I was broken and weary she would put her work aside and take the Bible and read to me till peace came and settled upon me like sleep upon the eyelids of a child, and when at last she closed the book she'd say: 'We'll save them in spite of themselves.' And I felt strong again in the Lord, and I answered: 'Yes, with God's help I'll save them. I must save them.' "

He came over to the table and stood in front of it as though it were a lectern.

"You see, they were so naturally depraved that they couldn't be brought to see their wickedness. We had to make sins out of what they thought were natural actions. We had to make it a sin, not only to commit adultery and to lie and thieve, but to expose their bodies, and to dance and not to come to church. I made it a sin for a girl to show her bosom and a sin for a man not to wear trousers."

"How?" asked Dr. Macphail, not without surprise.

"I instituted fines. Obviously the only way to make people realise that an action is sinful is to punish them if they commit it. I fined them if they didn't come to church, and I fined them if they danced. I fined them if they were improperly dressed. I had a tariff, and every sin had to be paid for either in money or work. And at last I made them understand."

"But did they never refuse to pay?"

"How could they?" asked the missionary.

"It would be a brave man who tried to stand up against Mr. Davidson," said his wife, tightening her lips.

Dr. Macphail looked at Davidson with troubled eyes.

What he heard shocked him, but he hesitated to express his disapproval.

"You must remember that in the last resort I could expel them from their church membership."

"Did they mind that?"

Davidson smiled a little and gently rubbed his hands.

"They couldn't sell their copra. When the men fished they got no share of the catch. It meant something very like starvation. Yes, they minded quite a lot."

"Tell him about Fred Ohlson," said Mrs. Davidson.

The missionary fixed his fiery eyes on Dr. Macphail.

"Fred Ohlson was a Danish trader who had been in the islands a good many years. He was a pretty rich man as traders go and he wasn't very pleased when we came. You see, he'd had things very much his own way. He paid the natives what he liked for their copra, and he paid in goods and whiskey. He had a native wife, but he was flagrantly unfaithful to her. He was a drunkard. I gave him a chance to mend his ways, but he wouldn't take it. He laughed at me."

Davidson's voice fell to a deep bass as he said the last words, and he was silent for a minute or two. The silence was heavy with menace.

"In two years he was a ruined man. He'd lost everything he'd saved in a quarter of a century. I broke him, and at last he was forced to come to me like a beggar and beseech me to give him a passage back to Sydney."

"I wish you could have seen him when he came to see Mr. Davidson," said the missionary's wife. "He had been a fine, powerful man, with a lot of fat on him, and he had a great big voice, but now he was half the size, and he was shaking all over. He'd suddenly become an old man."

With abstracted gaze Davidson looked out into the night. The rain was falling again.

Suddenly from below came a sound, and Davidson turned and looked questioningly at his wife. It was the sound of a gramophone, harsh and loud, wheezing out a syncopated tune.

"What's that?" he asked.

Mrs. Davidson fixed her *pince-nez* more firmly on her nose.

"One of the second-class passengers has a room in the house. I guess it comes from there."

They listened in silence, and presently they heard the sound of dancing. Then the music stopped, and they heard the popping of corks and voices raised in animated conversation.

"I daresay she's giving a farewell party to her friends on board," said Dr. Macphail. "The ship sails at twelve, doesn't it?"

Davidson made no remark, but he looked at his watch.

"Are you ready?" he asked his wife.

She got up and folded her work.

"Yes, I guess I am," she answered.

"It's early to go to bed yet, isn't it?" said the doctor.

"We have a good deal of reading to do," explained Mrs. Davidson. "Wherever we are, we read a chapter of the Bible before retiring for the night and we study it with the commentaries, you know, and discuss it thoroughly. It's a wonderful training for the mind."

The two couples bade one another good night. Dr. and Mrs. Macphail were left alone. For two or three minutes they did not speak.

"I think I'll go and fetch the cards," the doctor said at last.

Mrs. Macphail looked at him doubtfully. Her conversation with the Davidsons had left her a little uneasy, but she did not like to say that she thought they had better not play cards when the Davidsons might come in at any moment. Dr. Macphail brought them and she watched him, though with a vague sense of guilt, while he laid out his patience. Below the sound of revelry continued.

It was fine enough next day, and the Macphails, condemned to spend a fortnight of idleness at Pago-Pago, set about making the best of things. They went down to the quay and got out of their boxes a number of books. The doctor called on the chief surgeon of the naval hospital and went round the beds with him. They left cards on the governor.

They passed Miss Thompson on the road. The doctor took off his hat, and she gave him a "Good morning, doc," in a loud, cheerful voice. She was dressed as on the day before, in a white frock, and her shiny white boots with their high heels, her fat legs bulging over the tops of them, were strange things on that exotic scene.

"I don't think she's very suitably dressed, I must say," said Mrs. Macphail. "She looks extremely common to me."

When they got back to their house, she was on the verandah playing with one of the trader's dark children.

"Say a word to her," Dr. Macphail whispered to his wife. "She's all alone here, and it seems rather unkind to ignore her."

Mrs. Macphail was shy, but she was in the habit of doing what her husband bade her.

"I think we're fellow lodgers here," she said, rather foolishly.

"Terrible, ain't it, bein' cooped up in a one-horse burg like this?" answered Miss Thompson. "And they tell me I'm lucky to have gotten a room. I don't see myself livin' in a native house, and that's what some have to do. I don't know why they don't have a hotel."

They exchanged a few more words. Miss Thompson, loud-voiced and garrulous, was evidently quite willing to gossip, but Mrs. Macphail had a poor stock of small talk and presently she said:

"Well, I think we must go upstairs."

In the evening when they sat down to their high-tea Davidson on coming in said:

"I see that woman downstairs has a couple of sailors sitting there. I wonder how she's gotten acquainted with them."

"She can't be very particular," said Mrs. Davidson.

They were all rather tired after the idle, aimless day.

"If there's going to be a fortnight of this I don't know what we shall feel like at the end of it," said Dr. Macphail.

"The only thing to do is to portion out the day to different activities," answered the missionary. "I shall set aside a certain number of hours to study and a certain number to exercise, rain or fine—in the wet season you can't afford to pay any attention to the rain—and a certain number to recreation."

Dr. Macphail looked at his companion with misgiving. Davidson's programme oppressed him. They were eating Hamburger steak again. It seemed the only dish the cook knew how to make. Then below the gramophone began. Davidson started nervously when he heard it, but said nothing. Men's voices floated up. Miss Thompson's guests were joining in a well-known song and presently they heard her voice too, hoarse and loud. There was a good deal of shouting and laughing. The four people upstairs, trying to make conversation, listened despite themselves to the clink of glasses and the scrape of chairs. More people had evidently come. Miss Thompson was giving a party.

"I wonder how she gets them all in," said Mrs. Macphail, suddenly breaking into a medical conversation between the missionary and her husband.

It showed whither her thoughts were wandering. The twitch of Davidson's face proved that, though he spoke of scientific things, his mind was busy in the same direction. Suddenly, while the doctor was giving some experience of practice on the Flanders front, rather prosily, he sprang to his feet with a cry.

"What's the matter, Alfred?" asked Mrs. Davidson.

"Of course! It never occurred to me. She's out of Iwelei."

"She can't be."

"She came on board at Honolulu. It's obvious. And she's carrying on her trade here. Here."

He uttered the last word with a passion of indignation.

"What's Iwelei?" asked Mrs. Macphail.

He turned his gloomy eyes on her and his voice trembled with horror.

"The plague spot of Honolulu. The Red Light district. It was a blot on our civilisation."

Iwelei was on the edge of the city. You went down side streets by the harbour, in the darkness, across a rickety bridge, till you came to a deserted road, all ruts and holes, and then suddenly you came out into the light. There was parking room for motors on each side of the road, and there were saloons, tawdry and bright, each one noisy with its mechanical piano, and there were barbers' shops and tobacconists. There was a stir in the air and a sense of expectant gaiety. You turned down a narrow alley, either to the right or to the left, for the road divided Iwelei into two parts, and you found yourself in the district. There were rows of little bungalows, trim and neatly painted in green, and the pathway between them was broad and straight. It was laid out like a garden-city. In its respectable regularity, its order and spruceness, it gave an impression of sardonic horror; for never can the search for love have been so systematised and ordered. The pathways were lit by a rare lamp, but they would have been dark except for the lights that came from the open windows of the bungalows. Men wandered about, looking at the women who sat at their windows, reading or sewing, for the most part taking no notice of the passers-by; and like the women they were of all nationalities. There were Americans, sailors from the ships in port, enlisted men off the gunboats, sombrely drunk, and soldiers from the regiments, white and black, quartered on the island; there were Japanese, walking in twos and threes; Hawaiians, Chinese in long robes, and Filipinos in preposterous hats. They were silent and as it were oppressed. Desire is sad.

"It was the most crying scandal of the Pacific," exclaimed Davidson vehemently. "The missionaries had been agitating against it for years, and at last the local press took it up. The police refused to stir. You know their argument. They say that vice is inevitable and consequently the best thing is to localise and control it. The truth is, they were paid. Paid. They were paid by the saloon-keepers, paid by the bullies, paid by the women themselves. At last they were forced to move."

"I read about it in the papers that came on board in Honolulu," said Dr. Macphail.

"Iwelei, with its sin and shame, ceased to exist on the very day we arrived. The whole population was brought before the justices. I don't know why I didn't understand at once what that woman was."

"Now you come to speak of it," said Mrs. Macphail, "I remember seeing her come on board only a few minutes before the boat sailed. I remember thinking at the time she was cutting it rather fine."

"How dare she come here!" cried Davidson indignantly. "I'm not going to allow it."

He strode towards the door.

"What are you going to do?" asked Macphail.

"What do you expect me to do? I'm going to stop it. I'm not going to have this house turned into—into . . ."

He sought for a word that should not offend the ladies' ears. His eyes were flashing and his pale face was paler still in his emotion.

"It sounds as though there were three or four men down there," said the doctor. "Don't you think it's rather rash to go in just now?"

The missionary gave him a contemptuous look and without a word flung out of the room.

"You know Mr. Davidson very little if you think the fear of personal danger can stop him in the performance of his duty," said his wife.

She sat with her hands nervously clasped, a spot of colour on her high cheek bones, listening to what was about to happen below. They all listened. They heard him clatter down the wooden stairs and throw open the door. The singing stopped suddenly, but the gramophone continued to bray out its vulgar tune. They heard Davidson's voice and then the noise of something heavy falling. The music stopped. He had hurled the gramophone on the floor. Then again they heard Davidson's voice, they could not make out the words, then Miss Thompson's, loud and shrill, then a confused clamour as though several people were shouting together at the top of their lungs. Mrs. Davidson gave a little gasp, and she clenched her hands more tightly. Dr. Macphail looked uncertainly from her to his wife. He did not want to go down, but he wondered if they expected him to. Then there was something that sounded like a scuffle. The noise now was more distinct. It might be that Davidson was being thrown out of the room. The door was slammed. There was a moment's silence and they heard Davidson come up the stairs again. He went to his room.

"I think I'll go to him," said Mrs. Davidson.

She got up and went out.

"If you want me, just call," said Mrs. Macphail, and then when the other was gone: "I hope he isn't hurt."

"Why couldn't he mind his own business?" said Dr. Macphail.

They sat in silence for a minute or two and then they both started, for the gramophone began to play once more, defiantly, and mocking voices shouted hoarsely the words of an obscene song.

Next day Mrs. Davidson was pale and tired. She complained of headache, and she looked old and wizened. She told Mrs. Macphail that the missionary had not slept at all; he had passed the night in a state of frightful agitation and at five had got up and gone out. A glass of beer had been thrown over him and his clothes were stained and stinking. But a sombre fire glowed in Mrs. Davidson's eyes when she spoke of Miss Thompson.

"She'll bitterly rue the day when she flouted Mr. Davidson," she said. "Mr. Davidson has a wonderful heart and no one who is in trouble has ever gone to him without being comforted, but he has no mercy for sin, and when his righteous wrath is excited he's terrible."

"Why, what will he do?" asked Mrs. Macphail.

"I don't know, but I wouldn't stand in that creature's shoes for anything in the world."

Mrs. Macphail shuddered. There was something positively alarming in the triumphant assurance of the little woman's manner. They were going out together that morning, and they went down the stairs side by side. Miss Thompson's door was open, and they saw her in a bedraggled dressing-gown, cooking something in a chafing-dish.

"Good morning," she called. "Is Mr. Davidson better this morning?"

They passed her in silence, with their noses in the air, as

if she did not exist. They flushed, however, when she burst
into a shout of derisive laughter. Mrs. Davidson turned on
her suddenly.

"Don't you dare speak to me," she screamed. "If you
insult me I shall have you turned out of here."

"Say, did I ask Mr. Davidson to visit with me?"

"Don't answer her," whispered Mrs. Macphail hurriedly.

They walked on till they were out of earshot.

"She's brazen, brazen," burst from Mrs. Davidson.
Her anger almost suffocated her.

And on their way home they met her strolling towards
the quay. She had all her finery on. Her great white hat
with its vulgar, showy flowers was an affront. She called out
cheerily to them as she went by, and a couple of American
sailors who were standing there grinned as the ladies set
their faces to an icy stare. They got in just before the rain
began to fall again.

"I guess she'll get her fine clothes spoilt," said Mrs.
Davidson with a bitter sneer.

Davidson did not come in till they were half way through
dinner. He was wet through, but he would not change. He
sat, morose and silent, refusing to eat more than a mouthful,
and he stared at the slanting rain. When Mrs. Davidson told
him of their two encounters with Miss Thompson he did
not answer. His deepening frown alone showed that he had
heard.

"Don't you think we ought to make Mr. Horn turn her
out of here?" asked Mrs. Davidson. "We can't allow her
to insult us."

"There doesn't seem to be any other place for her to go,"
said Macphail.

"She can live with one of the natives."

"In weather like this a native hut must be a rather uncomfortable place to live in."

"I lived in one for years," said the missionary.

When the little native girl brought in the fried bananas
which formed the sweet they had every day, Davidson turned
to her.

"Ask Miss Thompson when it would be convenient for me to see her," he said.

The girl nodded shyly and went out.

"What do you want to see her for, Alfred?" asked his wife.

"It's my duty to see her. I won't act till I've given her every chance."

"You don't know what she is. She'll insult you."

"Let her insult me. Let her spit on me. She has an immortal soul, and I must do all that is in my power to save it."

Mrs. Davidson's ears rang still with the harlot's mocking laughter.

"She's gone too far."

"Too far for the mercy of God?" His eyes lit up suddenly and his voice grew mellow and soft. "Never. The sinner may be deeper in sin than the depth of hell itself, but the love of the Lord Jesus can reach him still."

The girl came back with the message.

"Miss Thompson's compliments and as long as Rev. Davidson don't come in business hours she'll be glad to see him any time."

The party received it in stony silence, and Dr. Macphail quickly effaced from his lips the smile which had come upon them. He knew his wife would be vexed with him if he found Miss Thompson's effrontery amusing.

They finished the meal in silence. When it was over the two ladies got up and took their work, Mrs. Macphail was making another of the innumerable comforters which she had turned out since the beginning of the war, and the doctor lit his pipe. But Davidson remained in his chair and with abstracted eyes stared at the table. At last he got up and without a word went out of the room. They heard him go down and they heard Miss Thompson's defiant "Come in" when he knocked at the door. He remained with her for an hour. And Dr. Macphail watched the rain. It was beginning to get on his nerves. It was not like our soft English rain that drops gently on the earth; it was unmerciful and somehow terrible; you felt in it the malignancy of the primitive powers of nature. It did not pour, it flowed. It was like a deluge from heaven, and it rattled on the roof of corrugated iron with a steady persistence that was maddening. It seemed to have a fury of its own. And sometimes you felt that you must scream if it did not stop, and then suddenly you felt powerless, as though your bones had suddenly become soft; and you were miserable and hopeless.

Macphail turned his head when the missionary came back. The two women looked up.

"I've given her every chance. I have exhorted her to repent. She is an evil woman."

He paused, and Dr. Macphail saw his eyes darken and his pale face grow hard and stern.

"Now I shall take the whips with which the Lord Jesus drove the usurers and the money changers out of the Temple of the Most High."

He walked up and down the room. His mouth was close set, and his black brows were frowning.

"If she fled to the uttermost parts of the earth I should pursue her."

With a sudden movement he turned round and strode out of the room. They heard him go downstairs again.

"What is he going to do?" asked Mrs. Macphail.

"I don't know." Mrs. Davidson took off her *pince-nez* and wiped them. "When he is on the Lord's work I never ask him questions."

She sighed a little.

"What is the matter?"

"He'll wear himself out. He doesn't know what it is to spare himself."

Dr. Macphail learnt the first results of the missionary's activity from the half-caste trader in whose house they lodged. He stopped the doctor when he passed the store and came out to speak to him on the stoop. His fat face was worried.

"The Rev. Davidson has been at me for letting Miss Thompson have a room here," he said, "but I didn't know what she was when I rented it to her. When people come and ask if I can rent them a room all I want to know is if they've the money to pay for it. And she paid me for hers a week in advance."

Dr. Macphail did not want to commit himself.

"When all's said and done it's your house. We're very much obliged to you for taking us in at all."

Horn looked at him doubtfully. He was not certain yet how definitely Macphail stood on the missionary's side.

"The missionaries are in with one another," he said, hesitatingly. "If they get it in for a trader he may just as well shut up his store and quit."

"Did he want you to turn her out?"

"No, he said so long as she behaved herself he couldn't ask me to do that. He said he wanted to be just to me. I promised she shouldn't have no more visitors. I've just been and told her."

"How did she take it?"

"She gave me Hell."

The trader squirmed in his old ducks. He had found Miss Thompson a rough customer.

"Oh, well, I daresay she'll get out. I don't suppose she wants to stay here if she can't have anyone in."

"There's nowhere she can go, only a native house, and no native'll take her now, not now that the missionaries have got their knife in her."

Dr. Macphail looked at the falling rain.

"Well, I don't suppose it's any good waiting for it to clear up."

In the evening when they sat in the parlour Davidson talked to them of his early days at college. He had had no means and had worked his way through by doing odd jobs during the vacations. There was silence downstairs. Miss Thompson was sitting in her little room alone. But suddenly the gramophone began to play. She had set it on in defiance, to cheat her loneliness, but there was no one to sing, and it had a melancholy note. It was like a cry for help. Davidson took no notice. He was in the middle of a long anecdote and without change of expression went on. The gramophone continued. Miss Thompson put on one reel after another. It looked as though the silence of the night were getting on her nerves. It was breathless and sultry. When the Macphails went to bed they could not sleep. They lay side by side with their eyes wide open, listening to the cruel singing of the mosquitoes outside their curtain.

"What's that?" whispered Mrs. Macphail at last.

They heard a voice, Davidson's voice, through the wooden partition. It went on with a monotonous, earnest insistence. He was praying aloud. He was praying for the soul of Miss Thompson.

Two or three days went by. Now when they passed Miss Thompson on the road she did not greet them with ironic cordiality or smile; she passed with her nose in the air, a sulky look on her painted face, frowning, as though she did not see them. The trader told Macphail that she had tried to get lodging elsewhere, but had failed. In the evening she played through the various reels of her gramophone, but the pretence of mirth was obvious now. The ragtime had a cracked, heart-broken rhythm as though it were a one-step of despair. When she began to play on Sunday Davidson sent Horn to beg her to stop at once since it was the Lord's day. The reel was taken off and the house was silent except for the steady pattering of the rain on the iron roof.

"I think she's getting a bit worked up," said the trader next day to Macphail. "She don't know what Mr. Davidson's up to and it makes her scared."

Macphail had caught a glimpse of her that morning and it struck him that her arrogant expression had changed. There was in her face a hunted look. The half-caste gave him a sidelong glance.

"I suppose you don't know what Mr. Davidson is doing about it?" he hazarded.

"No, I don't."

It was singular that Horn should ask him that question, for he also had the idea that the missionary was mysteriously at work. He had an impression that he was weaving a net around the woman, carefully, systematically, and suddenly, when everything was ready would pull the strings tight.

"He told me to tell her," said the trader, "that if at any time she wanted him she only had to send and he'd come."

"What did she say when you told her that?"

"She didn't say nothing. I didn't stop. I just said what he said I was to and then I beat it. I thought she might be going to start weepin'."

"I have no doubt the loneliness is getting on her nerves," said the doctor. "And the rain—that's enough to make anyone jumpy," he continued irritably. "Doesn't it ever stop in this confounded place?"

"It goes on pretty steady in the rainy season. We have three hundred inches in the year. You see, it's the shape of the bay. It seems to attract the rain from all over the Pacific."

"Damn the shape of the bay," said the doctor.

He scratched his mosquito bites. He felt very short-tempered. When the rain stopped and the sun shone, it was like a hothouse, seething, humid, sultry, breathless, and you had a strange feeling that everything was growing with a savage violence. The natives, blithe and childlike by reputation, seemed then, with their tattooing and their dyed hair, to have something sinister in their appearance; and when they pattered along at your heels with their naked feet you looked back instinctively. You felt they might at any moment come behind you swiftly and thrust a long knife between your shoulder blades. You could not tell what dark thoughts lurked behind their wide-set eyes. They had a little the look of ancient Egyptians painted on a temple wall, and there was about them the terror of what is immeasurably old.

The missionary came and went. He was busy, but the Macphails did not know what he was doing. Horn told the doctor that he saw the governor every day, and once Davidson mentioned him.

"He looks as if he had plenty of determination," he said, "but when you come down to brass tacks he has no backbone."

"I suppose that means he won't do exactly what you want," suggested the doctor facetiously.

The missionary did not smile.

"I want him to do what's right. It shouldn't be necessary to persuade a man to do that."

"But there may be differences of opinion about what is right."

"If a man had a gangrenous foot would you have patience with anyone who hesitated to amputate it?"

"Gangrene is a matter of fact."

"And Evil?"

What Davidson had done soon appeared. The four of them had just finished their midday meal, and they had not yet separated for the siesta which the heat imposed on the ladies and on the doctor. Davidson had little patience with the slothful habit. The door was suddenly flung open and Miss Thompson came in. She looked round the room and then went up to Davidson.

"You low-down skunk, what have you been saying about me to the governor?"

She was sputtering with rage. There was a moment's pause. Then the missionary drew forward a chair.

"Won't you be seated, Miss Thompson? I've been hoping to have another talk with you."

"You poor low-life bastard."

She burst into a torrent of insult, foul and insolent. Davidson kept his grave eyes on her.

"I'm indifferent to the abuse you think fit to heap on me, Miss Thompson," he said, "but I must beg you to remember that ladies are present."

Tears by now were struggling with her anger. Her face was red and swollen as though she were choking.

"What has happened?" asked Dr. Macphail.

"A feller's just been in here and he says I gotter beat it on the next boat."

Was there a gleam in the missionary's eyes? His face remained impassive.

"You could hardly expect the governor to let you stay here under the circumstances."

"You done it," she shrieked. "You can't kid me. You done it."

"I don't want to deceive you. I urged the governor to take the only possible step consistent with his obligations."

"Why couldn't you leave me be? I wasn't doin' you no harm."

"You may be sure that if you had I should be the last man to resent it."

"Do you think I want to stay on in this poor imitation of a burg? I don't look no busher, do I?"

"In that case I don't see what cause of complaint you have," he answered.

She gave an inarticulate cry of rage and flung out of the room. There was a short silence.

"It's a relief to know that the governor has acted at last," said Davidson finally. "He's a weak man and he shilly-shallied. He said she was only here for a fortnight anyway, and if she went on to Apia that was under British jurisdiction and had nothing to do with him."

The missionary sprang to his feet and strode across the room.

"It's terrible the way the men who are in authority seek to evade their responsibility. They speak as though evil that was out of sight ceased to be evil. The very existence of that woman is a scandal and it does not help matters to shift it to another of the islands. In the end I had to speak straight from the shoulder."

Davidson's brow lowered, and he protruded his firm chin. He looked fierce and determined.

"What do you mean by that?"

"Our mission is not entirely without influence at Washington. I pointed out to the governor that it wouldn't do him any good if there was a complaint about the way he managed things here."

"When has she got to go?" asked the doctor, after a pause.

"The San Francisco boat is due here from Sydney next Tuesday. She's to sail on that."

That was in five days' time. It was next day, when he was coming back from the hospital where for want of something better to do Macphail spent most of his mornings, that the half-caste stopped him as he was going upstairs.

"Excuse me, Dr. Macphail. Miss Thompson's sick. Will you have a look at her."

"Certainly."

Horn led him to her room. She was sitting in a chair idly, neither reading nor sewing, staring in front of her. She wore her white dress and the large hat with the flowers on it. Macphail noticed that her skin was yellow and muddy under her powder, and her eyes were heavy.

"I'm sorry to hear you're not well," he said.

"Oh, I ain't sick really. I just said that, because I just had to see you. I've got to clear on a boat that's going to 'Frisco."

She looked at him and he saw that her eyes were suddenly startled. She opened and clenched her hands spasmodically. The trader stood at the door, listening.

"So I understand," said the doctor.

She gave a little gulp.

"I guess it ain't very convenient for me to go to 'Frisco just now. I went to see the governor yesterday afternoon, but I couldn't get to him. I saw the secretary, and he told me I'd got to take that boat and that was all there was to it. I just had to see the governor, so I waited outside his house this morning, and when he come out I spoke to him. He didn't want to speak to me, I'll say, but I wouldn't let him shake me off, and at last he said he hadn't no objection to my staying here till the next boat to Sydney if the Rev. Davidson will stand for it."

She stopped and looked at Dr. Macphail anxiously.

"I don't know exactly what I can do," he said.

"Well, I thought maybe you wouldn't mind asking him. I swear to God I won't start anything here if he'll just only let me stay. I won't go out of the house if that'll suit him. It's no more'n a fortnight."

"I'll ask him."

"He won't stand for it," said Horn. "He'll have you out on Tuesday, so you may as well make up your mind to it."

"Tell him I can get work in Sydney, straight stuff, I mean. 'Tain't asking very much."

"I'll do what I can."

"And come and tell me right away, will you? I can't set down to a thing till I get the dope one way or the other."

It was not an errand that much pleased the doctor, and, characteristically perhaps, he went about it indirectly. He told his wife what Miss Thompson had said to him and asked her to speak to Mrs. Davidson. The missionary's attitude seemed rather arbitrary and it could do no harm if the girl were allowed to stay in Pago-Pago another fortnight. But he was not prepared for the result of his diplomacy. The missionary came to him straightway.

"Mrs. Davidson tells me that Thompson has been speaking to you."

Dr. Macphail, thus directly tackled, had the shy man's resentment at being forced out into the open. He felt his temper rising, and he flushed.

"I don't see that it can make any difference if she goes to Sydney rather than to San Francisco, and so long as she promises to behave while she's here it's dashed hard to persecute her."

The missionary fixed him with his stern eyes.

"Why is she unwilling to go back to San Francisco?"

"I didn't enquire," answered the doctor with some asperity. "And I think one does better to mind one's own business."

Perhaps it was not a very tactful answer.

"The governor has ordered her to be deported by the first boat that leaves the island. He's only done his duty and I will not interfere. Her presence is a peril here."

"I think you're very harsh and tyrannical."

The two ladies looked up at the doctor with some alarm, but they need not have feared a quarrel, for the missionary smiled gently.

"I'm terribly sorry you should think that of me, Dr. Macphail. Believe me, my heart bleeds for that unfortunate woman, but I'm only trying to do my duty."

The doctor made no answer. He looked out of the window sullenly. For once it was not raining and across the bay you saw nestling among the trees the huts of a native village.

"I think I'll take advantage of the rain stopping to go out," he said.

"Please don't bear me malice because I can't accede to your wish," said Davidson, with a melancholy smile. "I respect you very much, doctor, and I should be sorry if you thought ill of me."

"I have no doubt you have a sufficiently good opinion of yourself to bear mine with equanimity," he retorted.

"That's one on me," chuckled Davidson.

When Dr. Macphail, vexed with himself because he had been uncivil to no purpose, went downstairs, Miss Thompson was waiting for him with her door ajar.

"Well," she said, "have you spoken to him?"

"Yes, I'm sorry, he won't do anything," he answered, not looking at her in his embarrassment.

But then he gave her a quick glance, for a sob broke from her. He saw that her face was white with fear. It gave him a shock of dismay. And suddenly he had an idea.

"But don't give up hope yet. I think it's a shame the way they're treating you and I'm going to see the governor myself."

"Now?"

He nodded. Her face brightened.

"Say, that's real good of you. I'm sure he'll let me stay if you speak for me. I just won't do a thing I didn't ought all the time I'm here."

Dr. Macphail hardly knew why he had made up his mind to appeal to the governor. He was perfectly indifferent to Miss Thompson's affairs, but the missionary had irritated him, and with him temper was a smouldering thing. He found the governor at home. He was a large, handsome man, a sailor, with a grey toothbrush moustache; and he wore a spotless uniform of white drill.

"I've come to see you about a woman who's lodging in the same house as we are," he said. "Her name's Thompson."

"I guess I've heard nearly enough about her, Dr. Macphail," said the governor, smiling. "I've given her the order to get out next Tuesday and that's all I can do."

"I wanted to ask you if you couldn't stretch a point and let her stay here till the boat comes in from San Francisco so that she can go to Sydney. I will guarantee her good behaviour."

The governor continued to smile, but his eyes grew small and serious.

"I'd be very glad to oblige you, Dr. Macphail, but I've given the order and it must stand."

The doctor put the case as reasonably as he could, but now the governor ceased to smile at all. He listened sullenly, with averted gaze. Macphail saw that he was making no impression.

"I'm sorry to cause any lady inconvenience, but she'll have to sail on Tuesday and that's all there is to it."

"But what difference can it make?"

"Pardon me, doctor, but I don't feel called upon to explain my official actions except to the proper authorities."

Macphail looked at him shrewdly. He remembered Davidson's hint that he had used threats, and in the governor's attitude he read a singular embarrassment.

"Davidson's a damned busybody," he said hotly.

"Between ourselves, Dr. Macphail, I don't say that I have formed a very favourable opinion of Mr. Davidson, but I am bound to confess that he was within his rights in pointing out to me the danger that the presence of a woman of Miss Thompson's character was to a place like this where a number of enlisted men are stationed among a native population."

He got up and Dr. Macphail was obliged to do so too.

"I must ask you to excuse me. I have an engagement. Please give my respects to Mrs. Macphail."

The doctor left him crest-fallen. He knew that Miss Thompson would be waiting for him, and unwilling to tell her himself that he had failed, he went into the house by the back door and sneaked up the stairs as though he had something to hide.

At supper he was silent and ill-at-ease, but the missionary

was jovial and animated. Dr. Macphail thought his eyes rested on him now and then with triumphant good-humour. It struck him suddenly that Davidson knew of his visit to the governor and of its ill success. But how on earth could he have heard of it? There was something sinister about the power of that man. After supper he saw Horn on the verandah and, as though to have a casual word with him, went out.

"She wants to know if you've seen the governor," the trader whispered.

"Yes. He wouldn't do anything. I'm awfully sorry, I can't do anything more."

"I knew he wouldn't. They daren't go against the missionaries."

"What are you talking about?" said Davidson affably, coming out to join them.

"I was just saying there was no chance of your getting over to Apia for at least another week," said the trader glibly.

He left them, and the two men returned into the parlour. Mr. Davidson devoted one hour after each meal to recreation. Presently a timid knock was heard at the door.

"Come in," said Mrs. Davidson, in her sharp voice.

The door was not opened. She got up and opened it. They saw Miss Thompson standing at the threshold. But the change in her appearance was extraordinary. This was no longer the flaunting hussy who had jeered at them in the road, but a broken, frightened woman. Her hair, as a rule so elaborately arranged, was tumbling untidily over her neck. She wore bedroom slippers and a skirt and blouse. They were unfresh and bedraggled. She stood at the door with the tears streaming down her face and did not dare to enter.

"What do you want?" said Mrs. Davidson harshly.

"May I speak to Mr. Davidson?" she said in a choking voice.

The missionary rose and went towards her.

"Come right in, Miss Thompson," he said in cordial tones. "What can I do for you?"

She entered the room.

"Say, I'm sorry for what I said to you the other day an' for—for everythin' else. I guess I was a bit lit up. I beg pardon."

"Oh, it was nothing. I guess my back's broad enough to bear a few hard words."

She stepped towards him with a movement that was horribly cringing.

"You've got me beat. I'm all in. You won't make me go back to 'Frisco?"

His genial manner vanished and his voice grew on a sudden hard and stern.

"Why don't you want to go back there?"

She cowered before him.

"I guess my people live there. I don't want them to see me like this. I'll go anywhere else you say."

"Why don't you want to go back to San Francisco?"

"I've told you."

He leaned forward, staring at her, and his great, shining eyes seemed to try to bore into her soul. He gave a sudden gasp.

"The penitentiary."

She screamed, and then she fell at his feet, clasping his legs.

"Don't send me back there. I swear to you before God I'll be a good woman. I'll give all this up."

She burst into a torrent of confused supplication and the tears coursed down her painted cheeks. He leaned over her and, lifting her face, forced her to look at him.

"Is that it, the penitentiary?"

"I beat it before they could get me," she gasped. "If the bulls grab me it's three years for mine."

He let go his hold of her and she fell in a heap on the floor, sobbing bitterly. Dr. Macphail stood up.

"This alters the whole thing," he said. "You can't make her go back when you know this. Give her another chance. She wants to turn over a new leaf."

"I'm going to give her the finest chance she's ever had. If she repents let her accept her punishment."

She misunderstood the words and looked up. There was a gleam of hope in her heavy eyes.

"You'll let me go?"

"No. You shall sail for San Francisco on Tuesday."

She gave a groan of horror and then burst into low, hoarse shrieks which sounded hardly human, and she beat her head passionately on the ground. Dr. Macphail sprang to her and lifted her up.

"Come on, you mustn't do that. You'd better go to your room and lie down. I'll get you something."

He raised her to her feet and partly dragging her, partly carrying her, got her downstairs. He was furious with Mrs. Davidson and with his wife because they made no effort to help. The half-caste was standing on the landing and with his assistance he managed to get her on the bed. She was moaning and crying. She was almost insensible. He gave her a hypodermic injection. He was hot and exhausted when he went upstairs again.

"I've got her to lie down."

The two women and Davidson were in the same positions as when he had left them. They could not have moved or spoken since he went.

"I was waiting for you," said Davidson, in a strange, distant voice. "I want you all to pray with me for the soul of our erring sister."

He took the Bible off a shelf, and sat down at the table at which they had supped. It had not been cleared, and he pushed the tea-pot out of the way. In a powerful voice, resonant and deep, he read to them the chapter in which is narrated the meeting of Jesus Christ with the woman taken in adultery.

"Now kneel with me and let us pray for the soul of our dear sister, Sadie Thompson."

He burst into a long, passionate prayer in which he implored God to have mercy on the sinful woman. Mrs. Macphail and Mrs. Davidson knelt with covered eyes. The doctor, taken by surprise, awkward and sheepish, knelt too. The missionary's prayer had a savage eloquence. He was extraordinarily moved, and as he spoke the tears ran down his cheeks. Outside, the pitiless rain fell, fell steadily, with a fierce malignity that was all too human.

At last he stopped. He paused for a moment and said: "We will now repeat the Lord's prayer."

They said it and then, following him, they rose from their knees. Mrs. Davidson's face was pale and restful. She was comforted and at peace, but the Macphails felt suddenly bashful. They did not know which way to look.

"I'll just go down and see how she is now," said Dr. Macphail.

When he knocked at her door it was opened for him by Horn. Miss Thompson was in a rocking-chair, sobbing quietly.

"What are you doing there?" exclaimed Macphail. "I told you to lie down."

"I can't lie down. I want to see Mr. Davidson."

"My poor child, what do you think is the good of it? You'll never move him."

"He said he'd come if I sent for him."

Macphail motioned to the trader.

"Go and fetch him."

He waited with her in silence while the trader went upstairs. Davidson came in.

"Excuse me for asking you to come here," she said, looking at him sombrely.

"I was expecting you to send for me. I knew the Lord would answer my prayer."

They stared at one another for a moment and then she looked away. She kept her eyes averted when she spoke.

"I've been a bad woman. I want to repent."

"Thank God! thank God! He has heard our prayers."

He turned to the two men.

"Leave me alone with her. Tell Mrs. Davidson that our prayers have been answered."

They went out and closed the door behind them.

"Gee whizz," said the trader.

That night Dr. Macphail could not get to sleep till late, and when he heard the missionary come upstairs he looked at his watch. It was two o'clock. But even then he did not go to bed at once, for through the wooden partition that separated their rooms he heard him praying aloud, till he himself, exhausted, fell asleep.

When he saw him next morning he was surprised at his appearance. He was paler than ever, tired, but his eyes shone with an inhuman fire. It looked as though he were filled with an overwhelming joy.

"I want you to go down presently and see Sadie," he said. "I can't hope that her body is better, but her soul—her soul is transformed."

The doctor was feeling wan and nervous.

"You were with her very late last night," he said.

"Yes, she couldn't bear to have me leave her."

"You look as pleased as Punch," the doctor said irritably.

Davidson's eyes shone with ecstasy.

"A great mercy has been vouchsafed me. Last night I was privileged to bring a lost soul to the loving arms of Jesus."

Miss Thompson was again in the rocking-chair. The bed had not been made. The room was in disorder. She had not troubled to dress herself, but wore a dirty dressing-gown, and her hair was tied in a sluttish knot. She had given her face a dab with a wet towel, but it was all swollen and creased with crying. She looked a drab.

She raised her eyes dully when the doctor came in. She was cowed and broken.

"Where's Mr. Davidson?" she asked.

"He'll come presently if you want him," answered Macphail acidly. "I came here to see how you were."

"Oh, I guess I'm O. K. You needn't worry about that."

"Have you had anything to eat?"

"Horn brought me some coffee."

She looked anxiously at the door.

"D'you think he'll come down soon? I feel as if it wasn't so terrible when he's with me."

"Are you still going on Tuesday?"

"Yes, he says I've got to go. Please tell him to come right along. You can't do me any good. He's the only one as can help me now."

"Very well," said Dr. Macphail.

During the next three days the missionary spent almost all his time with Sadie Thompson. He joined the others only to have his meals. Dr. Macphail noticed that he hardly ate.

"He's wearing himself out," said Mrs. Davidson pitifully. "He'll have a breakdown if he doesn't take care, but he won't spare himself."

She herself was white and pale. She told Mrs. Macphail that she had no sleep. When the missionary came upstairs from Miss Thompson he prayed till he was exhausted, but even then he did not sleep for long. After an hour or two he got up and dressed himself, and went for a tramp along the bay. He had strange dreams.

"This morning he told me that he'd been dreaming about the mountains of Nebraska," said Mrs. Davidson.

"That's curious," said Dr. Macphail.

He remembered seeing them from the windows of the train when he crossed America. They were like huge mole-hills, rounded and smooth, and they rose from the plain abruptly. Dr. Macphail remembered how it struck him that they were like a woman's breasts.

Davidson's restlessness was intolerable even to himself. But he was buoyed up by a wonderful exhilaration. He was tearing out by the roots the last vestiges of sin that lurked in the hidden corners of that poor woman's heart. He read with her and prayed with her.

"It's wonderful," he said to them one day at supper. "It's a true rebirth. Her soul, which was black as night, is now pure and white like the new-fallen snow. I am humble and afraid. Her remorse for all her sins is beautiful. I am not worthy to touch the hem of her garment."

"Have you the heart to send her back to San Francisco?" said the doctor. "Three years in an American prison. I should have thought you might have saved her from that."

"Ah, but don't you see? It's necessary. Do you think my heart doesn't bleed for her? I love her as I love my wife and my sister. All the time that she is in prison I shall suffer all the pain that she suffers."

"Bunkum," cried the doctor impatiently.

"You don't understand because you're blind. She's sinned,

and she must suffer. I know what she'll endure. She'll be starved and tortured and humiliated. I want her to accept the punishment of man as a sacrifice to God. I want her to accept it joyfully. She has an opportunity which is offered to very few of us. God is very good and very merciful."

Davidson's voice trembled with excitement. He could hardly articulate the words that tumbled passionately from his lips.

"All day I pray with her and when I leave her I pray again, I pray with all my might and main, so that Jesus may grant her this great mercy. I want to put in her heart the passionate desire to be punished so that at the end, even if I offered to let her go, she would refuse. I want her to feel that the bitter punishment of prison is the thank-offering that she places at the feet of our Blessed Lord, who gave his life for her."

The days passed slowly. The whole household, intent on the wretched, tortured woman downstairs, lived in a state of unnatural excitement. She was like a victim that was being prepared for the savage rites of a bloody idolatry. Her terror numbed her. She could not bear to let Davidson out of her sight; it was only when he was with her that she had courage, and she hung upon him with a slavish dependence. She cried a great deal, and she read the Bible, and prayed. Sometimes she was exhausted and apathetic. Then she did indeed look forward to her ordeal, for it seemed to offer an escape, direct and concrete, from the anguish she was enduring. She could not bear much longer the vague terrors which now assailed her. With her sins she had put aside all personal vanity, and she slopped about her room, unkempt and dishevelled, in her tawdry dressing-gown. She had not taken off her night-dress for four days, nor put on stockings. Her room was littered and untidy. Meanwhile the rain fell with a cruel persistence. You felt that the heavens must at last be empty of water, but still it poured down, straight and heavy, with a maddening iteration, on the iron roof. Everything was damp and clammy. There was mildew on the walls and on the boots that stood on the floor. Through the sleepless nights the mosquitoes droned their angry chant.

"If it would only stop raining for a single day it wouldn't be so bad," said Dr. Macphail.

They all looked forward to the Tuesday when the boat for San Francisco was to arrive from Sydney. The strain was intolerable. So far as Dr. Macphail was concerned, his pity and his resentment were alike extinguished by his desire to be rid of the unfortunate woman. The inevitable must be accepted. He felt he would breathe more freely when the ship had sailed. Sadie Thompson was to be escorted on board by a clerk in the governor's office. This person called on the Monday evening and told Miss Thompson to be prepared at eleven in the morning. Davidson was with her.

"I'll see that everything is ready. I mean to come on board with her myself."

Miss Thompson did not speak.

When Dr. Macphail blew out his candle and crawled cautiously under his mosquito curtains, he gave a sigh of relief.

"Well, thank God that's over. By this time tomorrow she'll be gone."

"Mrs. Davidson will be glad too. She says he's wearing himself to a shadow," said Mrs. Macphail. "She's a different woman."

"Who?"

"Sadie. I should never have thought it possible. It makes one humble."

Dr. Macphail did not answer, and presently he fell asleep. He was tired out, and he slept more soundly than usual.

He was awakened in the morning by a hand placed on his arm, and, starting up, saw Horn by the side of his bed. The trader put his finger on his mouth to prevent any exclamation from Dr. Macphail and beckoned to him to come. As a rule he wore shabby ducks, but now he was barefoot and wore only the *lava-lava* of the natives. He looked suddenly savage, and Dr. Macphail, getting out of bed, saw that he was heavily tattooed. Horn made him a sign to come on to the verandah. Dr. Macphail got out of bed and followed the trader out.

"Don't make a noise," he whispered. "You're wanted. Put on a coat and some shoes. Quick."

Dr. Macphail's first thought was that something had happened to Miss Thompson.

"What is it? Shall I bring my instruments?"

"Hurry, please, hurry."

Dr. Macphail crept back into the bedroom, put on a waterproof over his pyjamas, and a pair of rubber-soled shoes. He rejoined the trader, and together they tiptoed down the stairs. The door leading out to the road was open and at it were standing half a dozen natives.

"What is it?" repeated the doctor.

"Come along with me," said Horn.

He walked out and the doctor followed him. The natives came after them in a little bunch. They crossed the road and came on to the beach. The doctor saw a group of natives standing round some object at the water's edge. They hurried along, a couple of dozen yards perhaps, and the natives opened out as the doctor came up. The trader pushed him forwards. Then he saw, lying half in the water and half out, a dreadful object, the body of Davidson. Dr. Macphail bent down—he was not a man to lose his head in an emergency— and turned the body over. The throat was cut from ear to ear, and in the right hand was still the razor with which the deed was done.

"He's quite cold," said the doctor. "He must have been dead some time."

"One of the boys saw him lying there on his way to work just now and came and told me. Do you think he did it himself?"

"Yes. Someone ought to go for the police."

Horn said something in the native tongue, and two youths started off.

"We must leave him here till they come," said the doctor.

"They mustn't take him into my house. I won't have him in my house."

"You'll do what the authorities say," replied the doctor sharply. "In point of fact I expect they'll take him to the mortuary."

They stood waiting where they were. The trader took a cigarette from a fold in his *lava-lava* and gave one to Dr. Macphail. They smoked while they stared at the corpse. Dr. Macphail could not understand.

"Why do you think he did it?" asked Horn.

The doctor shrugged his shoulders. In a little while native police came along, under the charge of a marine, with a stretcher, and immediately afterwards a couple of naval officers and a naval doctor. They managed everything in a businesslike manner.

"What about the wife?" said one of the officers.

"Now that you've come I'll go back to the house and get some things on. I'll see that it's broken to her. She'd better not see him till he's been fixed up a little."

"I guess that's right," said the naval doctor.

When Dr. Macphail went back he found his wife nearly dressed.

"Mrs. Davidson's in a dreadful state about her husband," she said to him as soon as he appeared. "He hasn't been to bed all night. She heard him leave Miss Thompson's room at two, but he went out. If he's been walking about since then he'll be absolutely dead."

Dr. Macphail told her what had happened and asked her to break the news to Mrs. Davidson.

"But why did he do it?" she asked, horror-stricken.

"I don't know."

"But I can't. I can't."

"You must."

She gave him a frightened look and went out. He heard her go into Mrs. Davidson's room. He waited a minute to gather himself together and then began to shave and wash. When he was dressed he sat down on the bed and waited for his wife. At last she came.

"She wants to see him," she said.

"They've taken him to the mortuary. We'd better go down with her. How did she take it?"

"I think she's stunned. She didn't cry. But she's trembling like a leaf."

"We'd better go at once."

When they knocked at her door Mrs. Davidson came out. She was very pale, but dry-eyed. To the doctor she seemed unnaturally composed. No word was exchanged, and they set out in silence down the road. When they arrived at the mortuary Mrs. Davidson spoke.

"Let me go in and see him alone."

They stood aside. A native opened a door for her and closed it behind her. They sat down and waited. One or two white men came and talked to them in undertones. Dr. Macphail told them again what he knew of the tragedy. At last the door was quietly opened and Mrs. Davidson came out. Silence fell upon them.

"I'm ready to go back now," she said.

Her voice was hard and steady. Dr. Macphail could not understand the look in her eyes. Her pale face was very stern. They walked back slowly, never saying a word, and at last they came round the bend on the other side of which stood their house. Mrs. Davidson gave a gasp, and for a moment they stopped still. An incredible sound assaulted their ears. The gramophone which had been silent for so long was playing, playing ragtime loud and harsh.

"What's that?" cried Mrs. Macphail with horror.

"Let's go on," said Mrs. Davidson.

They walked up the steps and entered the hall. Miss Thompson was standing at her door, chatting with a sailor. A sudden change had taken place in her. She was no longer the cowed drudge of the last days. She was dressed in all her finery, in her white dress, with the high shiny boots over which her fat legs bulged in their cotton stockings; her hair was elaborately arranged; and she wore that enormous hat covered with gaudy flowers. Her face was painted, her eyebrows were boldly black, and her lips were scarlet. She held herself erect. She was the flaunting quean that they had known at first. As they came in she broke into a loud, jeering laugh; and then, when Mrs. Davidson involuntarily stopped, she collected the spittle in her mouth and spat. Mrs. Davidson cowered back, and two red spots rose suddenly to her cheeks. Then, covering her face with her hands, she broke

away and ran quickly up the stairs. Dr. Macphail was outraged. He pushed past the woman into her room.

"What the devil are you doing?" he cried. "Stop that
damned machine."

He went up to it and tore the record off. She turned on
him.

"Say, doc, you can that stuff with me. What the hell are
you doin' in my room?"

"What do you mean?" he cried. "What d'you mean?"

She gathered herself together. No one could describe
the scorn of her expression or the contemptuous hatred she
put into her answer.

"You men! You filthy, dirty pigs! You're all the same, all
of you. Pigs! Pigs!"

Dr. Macphail gasped. He understood.

THE TREASURE

RICHARD HARENGER was a happy man. Notwithstanding
what the pessimists, from Ecclesiastes onwards, have
said, this is not so rare a thing to find in this unhappy
world, but Richard Harenger knew it, and that is a very
rare thing indeed. The golden mean which the ancients so
highly prized is out of fashion, and those who follow it
must put up with polite derision from those who see no
merit in self-restraint and no virtue in common sense.
Richard Harenger shrugged a polite and amused shoulder.
Let others live dangerously, let others burn with a hard
gemlike flame, let others stake their fortunes on the turn of
a card, walk the tightrope that leads to glory or the grave,
or hazard their lives for a cause, a passion or an adventure.
He neither envied the fame their exploits brought them nor
wasted his pity on them when their efforts ended in disaster.

But it must not be inferred from this that Richard
Harenger was a selfish or a callous man. He was neither. He
was considerate and of a generous disposition. He was always ready to oblige a friend, and he was sufficiently well
off to be able to indulge himself in the pleasure of helping
others. He had some money of his own, and he occupied in
the Home Office a position that brought him an adequate
stipend. The work suited him. It was regular, responsible
and pleasant. Every day when he left the office he went to
his club to play bridge for a couple of hours, and on Saturdays and Sundays he played golf. He went abroad for his
holidays, staying at good hotels, and visited churches,
galleries and museums. He was a regular first-nighter. He
dined out a good deal. His friends liked him. He was easy

to talk to. He was well read, knowledgeable and amusing. He was besides of a personable exterior, not remarkably handsome, but tall, slim and erect of carriage, with a lean, intelligent face; his hair was growing thin, for he was now approaching the age of fifty, but his brown eyes retained their smile and his teeth were all his own. He had from nature a good constitution, and he had always taken care of himself. There was no reason in the world why he should not be a happy man, and if there had been in him a trace of self-complacency he might have claimed that he deserved to be.

He had the good fortune even to sail safely through those perilous, unquiet straits of marriage in which so many wise and good men have made shipwreck. Married for love in the early twenties, his wife and he, after some years of almost perfect felicity, had drifted gradually apart. Neither of them wished to marry anyone else, so there was no question of divorce (which indeed Richard Harenger's situation in the government service made undesirable), but for convenience' sake, with the help of the family lawyer, they arranged a separation which left them free to lead their lives as each one wished without interference from the other. They parted with mutual expressions of respect and good will.

Richard Harenger sold his house in St. John's Wood and took a flat within convenient walking distance of Whitehall. It had a sitting room which he lined with his books, a dining room into which his Chippendale furniture just fitted, a nice-sized bedroom for himself, and beyond the kitchen a couple of maids' rooms. He brought his cook, whom he had had for many years, from St. John's Wood, but needing no longer so large a staff dismissed the rest of the servants and applied at a registry office for a house-parlourmaid. He knew exactly what he wanted, and he explained his needs to the superintendent of the agency with precision. He wanted a maid who was not too young, first because young women are flighty and secondly because, though he was of mature age and a man of principle, people would talk, the porter and the tradesmen if nobody else, and both for the sake of his own reputation and that of the young person he considered that the applicant should have reached years of discretion. Besides that he wanted a maid who could clean silver well. He had always had a fancy for old silver, and it was reasonable to demand that the forks and spoons that had been used by a woman of quality under the reign of Queen Anne should be treated with tenderness and respect. He was of a hospitable nature and liked to give at least once a week little dinners of not less than four people and not more than eight. He could trust his cook to send in a meal that his guests would take pleasure in eating and he desired his parlourmaid to wait with neatness and dispatch. Then he needed a perfect valet. He dressed well, in a manner that suited his age and condition, and he liked his clothes to be properly looked after. The parlourmaid he was looking for must be able to press trousers and iron a tie, and he was very particular that his shoes should be well shone. He had small feet, and he took a good deal of trouble to have well-cut shoes. He had a large supply, and he insisted that they should be treed up the moment he took them off. Finally the flat must be kept clean and tidy. It was of course understood that any applicant for the post must be of irreproachable character, sober, honest, reliable and of a pleasing exterior. In return for this he was prepared to offer good wages, reasonable liberty and ample holidays. The superintendent listened without batting an eyelash, and telling him that she was quite sure she could suit him, sent him a string of candidates which proved that she had not paid the smallest attention to a word he said. He saw them all personally. Some were obviously inefficient, some looked fast, some were too old, others too young, some lacked the presence he thought essential; there was not one to whom he was inclined even to give a trial. He was a kindly, polite man, and he declined their services with a smile and a pleasant expression of regret. He did not lose patience. He was prepared to interview house-parlourmaids till he found one who was suitable.

Now it is a funny thing about life, if you refuse to accept anything but the best you very often get it: if you utterly decline to make do with what you can get, then somehow or other you are very likely to get what you want. It is as though Fate said, "This man's a perfect fool, he's asking for perfection," and then just out of her feminine wilfulness flung it in his lap. One day the porter of the flats said to Richard Harenger out of a blue sky:

"I hear you're lookin' for a house-parlourmaid, sir. There's someone I know lookin' for a situation as might do."

"Can you recommend her personally?"

Richard Harenger had the sound opinion that one servant's recommendation of another was worth much more than that of an employer.

"I can vouch for her respectability. She's been in some very good situations."

"I shall be coming in to dress about seven. If that's convenient to her I could see her then."

"Very good, sir. I'll see that she's told."

He had not been in more than five minutes when the cook, having answered a ring at the front door, came in and told him that the person the porter had spoken to him about had called.

"Show her in," he said.

He turned on some more light so that he could see what the applicant looked like, and getting up, stood with his back to the fireplace. A woman came in and stood just inside the door in a respectful attitude.

"Good evening," he said. "What is your name?"

"Pritchard, sir."

"How old are you?"

"Thirty-five, sir."

"Well, that's a reasonable age."

He gave his cigarette a puff and looked at her reflectively. She was on the tall side, nearly as tall as he, but he guessed that she wore high heels. Her black dress fitted her station. She held herself well. She had good features and a rather high colour.

"Will you take off your hat?" he asked.

She did so, and he saw that she had pale brown hair. It was neatly and becomingly dressed. She looked strong and healthy. She was neither fat nor thin. In a proper uniform she would look very presentable. She was not inconveniently handsome, but she was certainly a comely, in another class of life you might almost have said a handsome, woman. He proceeded to ask her a number of questions. Her answers were satisfactory. She had left her last place for an adequate reason. She had been trained under a butler and appeared to be well acquainted with her duties. In her last place she had been head parlourmaid of three, but she did not mind undertaking the work of the flat single-handed. She had valeted a gentleman before who had sent her to a tailor's to learn how to press clothes. She was a little shy, but neither timid nor ill at ease. Richard asked her his questions in his amiable, leisurely way, and she answered them with modest composure. He was considerably impressed. He asked her what references she could give. They seemed extremely satisfactory.

"Now look here," he said, "I'm very much inclined to engage you. But I hate changes, I've had my cook for twelve years: if you suit me and the place suits you I hope you'll stay. I mean, I don't want you to come to me in three or four months and say that you're leaving to get married."

"There's not much fear of that, sir. I'm a widow. I don't believe marriage is much catch for anyone in my position, sir. My husband never did a stroke of work from the day I married him to the day he died, and I had to keep him. What I want now is a good home."

"I'm inclined to agree with you," he smiled. "Marriage is a very good thing, but I think it's a mistake to make a habit of it."

She very properly made no reply to this, but waited for him to announce his decision. She did not seem anxious about it. He reflected that if she was as competent as she appeared she must be well aware that she would have no difficulty in finding a place. He told her what wages he was offering, and these seemed to be satisfactory to her. He gave her the necessary information about the place, but she gave him to understand that she was already apprised of this, and he received the impression, which amused rather than disconcerted him, that she had made certain enquiries about him before applying for the situation. It showed prudence on her part and good sense.

"When would you be able to come in if I engaged you? I haven't got anybody at the moment. The cook's managing as best she can with a char, but I should like to get settled as soon as possible."

"Well, sir, I was going to give myself a week's holiday, but if it's a matter of obliging a gentleman I don't mind giving that up. I could come in tomorrow if it was convenient."

Richard Harenger gave her his attractive smile.

"I shouldn't like you to do without a holiday that I daresay you've been looking forward to. I can very well go on like this for another week. Go and have your holiday and come to me when it's over."

"Thank you very much, sir. Would it do if I came in tomorrow week?"

"Quite well."

When she left, Richard Harenger felt he had done a good day's work. It looked as though he had found exactly what he was after. He rang for the cook and told her he had engaged a house-parlourmaid at last.

"I think you'll like her, sir," she said. "She came in and 'ad a talk with me this afternoon. I could see at once she knew her duties. And she's not one of them flighty ones."

"We can but try, Mrs. Jeddy. I hope you gave me a good character."

"Well, I said you was particular, sir. I said you was a gentleman as liked things just so."

"I admit that."

"She said she didn't mind that. She said she liked a gentleman as knew what was what. She said there's no satisfaction in doing things proper if nobody notices. I expect you'll find she'll take a rare lot of pride in her work."

"That's what I want her to do. I think we might go farther and fare worse."

"Well, sir, there is that to it, of course. And the proof of the pudding's the eating. But if you ask my opinion I think she's going to be a real treasure."

And that is precisely what Pritchard turned out. No man was ever better served. The way she shone shoes was marvellous, and he set out of a fine morning for his walk to the office with a more jaunty step because you could almost see yourself reflected in them. She looked after his clothes with such attention that his colleagues began to chaff him about being the best-dressed man in the Civil Service. One day, coming·home unexpectedly, he found a line of socks and handkerchiefs hung up to dry in the bathroom. He called Pritchard.

"D'you wash my socks and handkerchiefs yourself, Pritchard? I should have thought you had enough to do without that."

"They do ruin them so at the laundry, sir. I prefer to do them at home if you have no objection."

She knew exactly what he should wear on every occasion, and without asking him was aware whether she should put out a dinner jacket and a black tie in the evening or a dress coat and a white one. When he was going to a party where decorations were to be worn he found his neat little row of medals automatically affixed to the lapel of his coat. He soon ceased to choose every morning from his wardrobe the tie he wanted, for he found that she put out for him without fail the one he would have himself selected. Her taste was perfect. He supposed she read his letters, for she always knew what his movements were, and if he had forgotten at what hour he had an engagement he had no need to look in his book, for Pritchard could tell him. She knew exactly what tone to use with persons with whom she conversed on the telephone. Except with tradesmen, with whom she was apt to be peremptory, she was always polite, but there was a distinct difference in her manner if she was addressing one of Mr. Harenger's literary friends or the wife of a Cabinet Minister. She knew by instinct with whom he wished to speak and with whom he didn't. From his sitting room he sometimes heard her with placid sincerity assuring a caller that he was out, and then she would come in and tell him that So-and-so had rung up, but she thought he wouldn't wish to be disturbed.

"Quite right, Pritchard," he smiled.

"I knew she only wanted to bother you about that concert," said Pritchard.

His friends made appointments with him through her, and she would tell him what she had done on his return in the evening.

"Mrs. Soames rang up, sir, and asked if you would lunch with her on Thursday, the eighth, but I said you were very sorry but you were lunching with Lady Versinder. Mr. Oakley rang up and asked if you'd go to a cocktail party at the Savoy next Tuesday at six. I said you would if you possibly could, but you might have to go to the dentist's."

"Quite right."

"I thought you could see when the time came, sir."

She kept the flat like a new pin. On one occasion soon after she entered his service, Richard, coming back from a holiday, took out a book from his shelves and at once noticed that it had been dusted. He rang the bell.

"I forgot to tell you, when I went away, under no circumstances ever to touch my books. When books are taken out to be dusted they're never put back in the right place. I don't mind my books being dirty, but I hate not being able to find them."

"I'm very sorry, sir," said Pritchard. "I know some gentlemen are very particular and I took care to put back every book exactly where I took it from."

Richard Harenger gave his books a glance. So far as he could see, every one was in its accustomed place. He smiled.

"I apologize, Pritchard."

"They were in a muck, sir. I mean, you couldn't open one without getting your hands black with dust."

She certainly kept his silver as he had never had it kept before. He felt called upon to give her a special word of praise.

"Most of it's Queen Anne and George I, you know," he explained.

"Yes, I know, sir. When you've got something good like that to look after, it's a pleasure to keep it like it should be."

"You certainly have a knack for it. I never knew a butler who kept his silver as well as you do."

"Men haven't the patience women have," she replied modestly.

As soon as he thought Pritchard had settled down in the place, he resumed the little dinners he was fond of giving once a week. He had already discovered that she knew how to wait at table, but it was with a warm sense of complacency that he realized then how competently she could manage a party. She was quick, silent and watchful. A guest had hardly felt the need of something before Pritchard was at his elbow offering him what he wanted. She soon learned the tastes of his more intimate friends and remembered that one liked water instead of soda with his whisky and that another particularly fancied the knuckle end of a leg of lamb. She knew exactly how cold a hock should be not to ruin its taste and how long claret should have stood in the room to bring out its bouquet. It was a pleasure to see her pour out a bottle of burgundy in such a fashion as not to disturb the grounds. On one occasion she did not serve the wine Richard had ordered. He somewhat sharply pointed this out to her.

"I opened the bottle, sir, and it was slightly corked. So I got the Chambertin, as I thought it was safer."

"Quite right, Pritchard."

Presently he left this matter entirely in her hands, for he discovered that she knew perfectly what wines his guests would like. Without orders from him she would provide the best in his cellar and his oldest brandy if she thought they were the sort of people who knew what they were drinking. She had no belief in the palate of women, and when they were of the party was apt to serve the champagne which had to be drunk before it went off. She had the English servant's instinctive knowledge of social differences, and neither rank nor money blinded her to the fact that someone was not a gentleman, but she had favourites among his friends, and when someone she particularly liked was dining, with the air of a cat that has swallowed a canary she would pour out for him a bottle of a wine that Harenger kept for very special occasions. It amused him.

"You've got on the right side of Pritchard, old boy," he exclaimed. "There aren't many people she gives this wine to."

Pritchard became an institution. She was known very soon to be the perfect parlourmaid. People envied Harenger the possession of her as they envied nothing else that he had. She was worth her weight in gold. Her price was above rubies. Richard Harenger beamed with self-complacency when they praised her.

"Good masters make good servants," he said gaily.

One evening, when they were sitting over their port and she had left the room, they were talking about her.

"It'll be an awful blow when she leaves you."

"Why should she leave me? One or two people have tried to get her away from me, but she turned them down. She knows where she's well off."

"She'll get married one of these days."

"I don't think she's that sort."

"She's a good-looking woman."

"Yes, she has quite a decent presence."

"What are you talking about? She's a very handsome creature. In another class of life she'd be a well-known society beauty with her photograph in all the papers."

At that moment Pritchard came in with the coffee. Richard Harenger looked at her. After seeing her every day, off and on, for four years it was now, my word, how time flies, he had really forgotten what she looked like. She did not seem to have changed much since he had first seen her. She was no stouter than then, she still had the high colour, and her regular features bore the same expression which was at once intent and vacuous. The black uniform suited her. She left the room.

"She's a paragon, and there's no doubt about it."

"I know she is," answered Harenger. "She's perfection. I should be lost without her. And the strange thing is that I don't very much like her."

"Why not?"

"I think she bores me a little. You see, she has no conversation. I've often tried to talk to her. She answers when I speak to her, but that's all. In four years she's never volunteered a remark of her own. I know absolutely nothing about her. I don't know if she likes me or if she's completely indifferent to me. She's an automaton. I respect her, I appreciate her, I trust her. She has every quality in the world, and I've often wondered why it is that with all that I'm so completely indifferent to her. I think it must be that she is entirely devoid of charm."

They left it at that.

Two or three days after this, since it was Pritchard's night out and he had no engagement, Richard Harenger dined by himself at his club. A page boy came to him and told him that they had just rung up from his flat to say that he had gone out without his keys and should they be brought along to him in a taxi? He put his hand to his pocket. It was a fact. By a singular chance he had forgotten to replace them when he had changed into a blue serge suit before coming out to dinner. His intention had been to play bridge, but it was an off night at the club, and there seemed little chance of a decent game; it occurred to him that it would be a good opportunity to see a picture that he had heard talked about, so he sent back the message by the page that he would call for the keys himself in half an hour.

He rang at the door of his flat, and it was opened by Pritchard. She had the keys in her hand.

"What are you doing here, Pritchard?" he asked. "It's your night out, isn't it?"

"Yes, sir. But I didn't care about going, so I told Mrs. Jeddy she could go instead."

"You ought to get out when you have the chance," he said, with his usual thoughtfulness. "It's not good for you to be cooped up here all the time."

"I get out now and then on an errand, but I haven't been out in the evening for the last month."

"Why on earth not?"

"Well, it's not very cheerful going out by yourself, and somehow I don't know anyone just now that I'm particularly keen on going out with."

"You ought to have a bit of fun now and then. It's good for you."

"I've got out of the habit of it somehow."

"Look here, I'm just going to the cinema. Would you like to come along with me?"

He spoke in kindliness, on the spur of the moment, and the moment he had said the words half regretted them.

"Yes, sir, I'd like to," said Pritchard.

"Run along then and put on a hat."

"I shan't be a minute."

She disappeared, and he went into the sitting room and lit a cigarette. He was a little amused at what he was doing, and pleased, too; it was nice to be able to make someone happy with so little trouble to himself. It was characteristic of Pritchard that she had shown neither surprise nor hesitation. She kept him waiting about five minutes, and when she came back he noticed that she had changed her dress. She wore a blue frock in what he supposed was artificial silk, a small black hat with a blue brooch on it, and a silver fox round her neck. He was a trifle relieved to see that she looked neither shabby nor showy. It would never occur to anyone who happened to see them that this was a distinguished official in the Home Office taking his housemaid to the pictures.

"I'm sorry to have kept you waiting, sir."

"It doesn't matter at all," he said graciously.

He opened the front door for her, and she went out before him. He remembered the familiar anecdote of Louis XIV and the courtier and appreciated the fact that she had not hesitated to precede him. The cinema for which they were bound was at no great distance from Mr. Harenger's flat, and they walked there. He talked about the weather and the state of the roads and Adolf Hitler. Pritchard made suitable replies. They arrived just as Mickey the Mouse was starting, and this put them in a good humour. During the four years she had been in his service Richard Harenger had hardly ever seen Pritchard even smile, and now it diverted him vastly to hear her peal upon peal of joyous laughter. He enjoyed her pleasure. Then the principal attraction was thrown on the screen. It was a good picture, and they both watched it with breathless excitement. Taking his cigarette case out to help himself, he automatically offered it to Pritchard.

"Thank you, sir," she said, taking one.

He lit it for her. Her eyes were on the screen and she was almost unconscious of his action. When the picture was finished they streamed out with the crowd into the street. They walked back towards the flat. It was a fine starry night.

"Did you like it?" he said.

"Like anything, sir. It was a real treat."

A thought occurred to him.

"By the way, did you have any supper tonight?"

"No, sir, I didn't have time."

"Aren't you starving?"

"I'll have a bit of bread and cheese when I get in and I'll make myself a cup of cocoa."

"That sounds rather grim." There was a feeling of gaiety in the air, and the people who poured past them, one way and another, seemed filled with a pleasant elation. In for a penny, in for a pound, he said to himself. "Look here, would you like to come and have a bit of supper with me somewhere?"

"If you'd like to, sir."

"Come on."

He hailed a cab. He was feeling very philanthropic and it was not a feeling that he disliked at all. He told the driver to go to a restaurant in Oxford Street which was gay, but at which he was confident there was no chance of meeting anyone he knew. There was an orchestra, and people danced. It would amuse Pritchard to see them. When they sat down a waiter came up to them.

"They've got a set supper here," he said, thinking that was what she would like. "I suggest we have that. What would you like to drink? A little white wine?"

"What I really fancy is a glass of ginger beer," she said.

Richard Harenger ordered himself a whisky and soda. She ate the supper with hearty appetite, and though Harenger was not hungry, to put her at her ease he ate too. The picture they had just seen gave them something to talk about.

It was quite true what they had said the other night, Pritchard was not a bad-looking woman, and even if someone had seen them together he would not have minded. It would make rather a good story for his friends when he told them how he had taken the incomparable Pritchard to the cinema and then afterwards to supper. Pritchard was looking at the dancers with a faint smile on her lips.

"Do you like dancing?" he said.

"I used to be a rare one for it when I was a girl. I never danced much after I was married. My husband was a bit shorter than me, and somehow I never think it looks well unless the gentleman's taller, if you know what I mean. I suppose I shall be getting too old for it soon."

Richard was certainly taller than his parlourmaid. They would look all right. He was fond of dancing and he danced well. But he hesitated. He did not want to embarrass Pritchard by asking her to dance with him. It was better not to go too far perhaps. And yet what did it matter? It was a drab life she led. She was so sensible, if she thought it a mistake he was pretty sure she would find a decent excuse.

"Would you like to take a turn, Pritchard?" he said, as the band struck up again.

"I'm terribly out of practice, sir."

"What does that matter?"

"If you don't mind, sir," she answered coolly, rising from her seat.

She was not in the least shy. She was only afraid that she would not be able to follow his step. They moved on to the floor. He found she danced very well.

"Why, you dance perfectly, Pritchard," he said.

"It's coming back to me."

Although she was a big woman, she was light on her feet, and she had a natural sense of rhythm. She was very pleasant to dance with. He gave a glance at the mirrors that lined the walls, and he could not help reflecting that they looked very well together. Their eyes met in the mirror; he wondered whether she was thinking that, too. They had two more dances, and then Richard Harenger suggested that they should go. He paid the bill and they walked out. He noticed that she threaded her way through the crowd without a trace of self-consciousness. They got into a taxi and in ten minutes were at home.

"I'll go up the back way, sir," said Pritchard.

"There's no need to do that. Come up in the lift with me."

He took her up, giving the night porter an icy glance, so that he should not think it strange that he came back at that somewhat late hour with his parlourmaid, and with his latchkey let her into the flat.

"Well, good night, sir," she said. "Thank you very much. It's been a real treat for me."

"Thank *you*, Pritchard. I should have had a very dull evening by myself. I hope you've enjoyed your outing."

"That I have, sir, more than I can say."

It had been a success. Richard Harenger was satisfied with himself. It was a kindly thing for him to have done. It was a very agreeable sensation to give anyone so much real pleasure. His benevolence warmed him and for a moment he felt a great love in his heart for the whole human race.

"Good night, Pritchard," he said, and because he felt happy and good he put his arm round her waist and kissed her on the lips.

Her lips were very soft. They lingered on his, and she returned his kiss. It was the warm, hearty embrace of a healthy woman in the prime of life. He found it very pleasant, and he held her to him a little more closely. She put her arms round his neck.

As a general rule he did not wake till Pritchard came in with his letters, but next morning he woke at half past seven. He had a curious sensation that he did not recognize. He was accustomed to sleep with two pillows under his head, and he suddenly grew aware of the fact that he had only one. Then he remembered and with a start looked round. The other pillow was beside his own. Thank God, no sleeping head rested there, but it was plain that one had. His heart sank. He broke out into a cold sweat.

"My God, what a fool I've been!" he cried out loud.

How could he have done anything so stupid? What on

earth had come over him? He was the last man to play about with servant girls. What a disgraceful thing to do! At his age and in his position. He had not heard Pritchard slip away. He must have been asleep. It wasn't even as if he'd liked her very much. She wasn't his type. And as he had said the other night, she rather bored him. Even now he only knew her as Pritchard. He had no notion what her first name was. What madness! And what was to happen now? The position was impossible. It was obvious he couldn't keep her, and yet to send her away for what was his fault as much as hers seemed shockingly unfair. How idiotic to lose the best parlourmaid a man ever had just for an hour's folly!

"It's that damned kindness of heart of mine," he groaned.

He would never find anyone else to look after his clothes so admirably or clean the silver so well. She knew all his friends' telephone numbers, and she understood wine. But of course she must go. She must see for herself that after what had happened things could never be the same. He would make her a handsome present and give her an excellent reference. At any minute she would be coming in now. Would she be arch, would she be familiar? Or would she put on airs? Perhaps even she wouldn't trouble to come in with his letters. It would be awful if he had to ring the bell and Mrs. Jeddy came in and said: "Pritchard's not up yet, sir, she's having a lie in after last night."

"What a fool I've been! What a contemptible cad!"

There was a knock at the door. He was sick with anxiety. "Come in."

Richard Harenger was a very unhappy man.

Pritchard came in as the clock struck. She wore the print dress she was in the habit of wearing during the early part of the day.

"Good morning, sir," she said.

"Good morning."

She drew the curtains and handed him his letters and the papers. Her face was impassive. She looked exactly as she always looked. Her movements had the same competent deliberation that they always had. She neither avoided Richard's glance nor sought it.

"Will you wear your grey, sir? It came back from the tailor's yesterday."

"Yes."

He pretended to read his letters, but he watched her from under his eyelashes. Her back was turned to him. She took his vest and drawers and folded them over a chair. She took the studs out of the shirt he had worn the day before and studded a clean one. She put out some clean socks for him and placed them on the seat of a chair with the suspenders to match by the side. Then she put out his grey suit and attached the braces to the back buttons of the trousers. She opened his wardrobe and after a moment's reflection chose a tie to go with the suit. She collected on her arm the suit of the day before and picked up the shoes.

"Will you have breakfast now, sir, or will you have your bath first?"

"I'll have breakfast now," he said.

"Very good, sir."

With her slow quiet movements, unruffled, she left the room. Her face bore that rather serious, deferential, vacuous look it always bore. What had happened might have been a dream. Nothing in Pritchard's demeanour suggested that she had the smallest recollection of the night before. He gave a sigh of relief. It was going to be all right. She need not go, she need not go. Pritchard was the perfect parlourmaid. He knew that never by word nor gesture would she ever refer to the fact that for a moment their relations had been other than those of master and servant. Richard Harenger was a very happy man.

THE OUTSTATION

THE new assistant arrived in the afternoon. When the Resident, Mr. Warburton, was told that the prahu was in sight he put on his solar topee and went down to the landing-stage. The guard, eight little Dyak soldiers, stood to attention as he passed. He noted with satisfaction that their bearing was martial, their uniforms neat and clean, and their guns shining. They were a credit to him. From the landing-stage he watched the bend of the river round which in a moment the boat would sweep. He looked very smart in his spotless ducks and white shoes. He held under his arm a gold-headed Malacca cane which had been given him by the Sultan of Perak. He awaited the newcomer with mingled feelings. There was more work in the district than one man could properly do, and during his periodical tours of the country under his charge it had been inconvenient to leave the station in the hands of a native clerk, but he had been so long the only white man there that he could not face the arrival of another without misgiving. He was accustomed to loneliness. During the war he had not seen an English face for three years; and once when he was instructed to put up an afforestation officer he was seized with panic, so that when the stranger was due to arrive, having arranged everything for his reception, he wrote a note telling him he was obliged to go up-river, and fled; he remained away till he was informed by a messenger that his guest had left.

Now the prahu appeared in the broad reach. It was manned by prisoners, Dyaks under various sentences, and a couple of warders were waiting on the landing-stage to take them back to jail. They were sturdy fellows, used to the river, and they rowed with a powerful stroke. As the boat reached the side a man got out from under the attap awning and stepped on shore. The guard presented arms.

"Here we are at last. By God, I'm as cramped as the devil. I've brought you your mail."

He spoke with exuberant joviality. Mr. Warburton politely held out his hand.

"Mr. Cooper, I presume?"

"That's right. Were you expecting any one else?"

The question had a facetious intent, but the Resident did not smile.

"My name is Warburton. I'll show you your quarters. They'll bring your kit along."

He preceded Cooper along the narrow pathway and they entered a compound in which stood a small bungalow.

"I've had it made as habitable as I could, but of course no one has lived in it for a good many years."

It was built on piles. It consisted of a long living-room which opened on to a broad verandah, and behind, on each side of a passage, were two bedrooms.

"This'll do me all right," said Cooper.

"I daresay you want to have a bath and a change. I shall be very much pleased if you'll dine with me to-night. Will eight o'clock suit you?"

"Any old time will do for me."

The Resident gave a polite, but slightly disconcerted, smile and withdrew. He returned to the Fort where his own residence was. The impression which Allen Cooper had given him was not very favourable, but he was a fair man, and he knew that it was unjust to form an opinion on so brief a glimpse. Cooper seemed to be about thirty. He was a tall, thin fellow, with a sallow face in which there was not a spot of colour. It was a face all in one tone. He had a large, hooked nose and blue eyes. When, entering the bungalow, he had taken off his topee and flung it to a waiting boy, Mr. Warburton noticed that his large skull, covered with short, brown hair, contrasted somewhat oddly with a weak, small chin. He was dressed in khaki shorts and a khaki shirt, but they were shabby and soiled; and his battered topee had not been cleaned for days. Mr. Warburton reflected that the young man had spent a week on a coasting steamer and had passed the last forty-eight hours lying in the bottom of a prahu.

"We'll see what he looks like when he comes in to dinner."

He went into his room where his things were as neatly laid out as if he had an English valet, undressed, and, walking down the stairs to the bath-house, sluiced himself with cool water. The only concession he made to the climate was to wear a white dinner-jacket; but otherwise, in a boiled shirt and a high collar, silk socks and patent-leather shoes, he dressed as formally as though he were dining at his club in Pall Mall. A careful host, he went into the dining-room to see that the table was properly laid. It was gay with orchids and the silver shone brightly. The napkins were folded into elaborate shapes. Shaded candles in silver candlesticks shed a soft light. Mr. Warburton smiled his approval and returned to the sitting-room to await his guest. Presently he appeared. Cooper was wearing the khaki shorts, the khaki shirt, and the ragged jacket in which he had landed. Mr. Warburton's smile of greeting froze on his face.

"Hulloa, you're all dressed up," said Cooper. "I didn't know you were going to do that. I very nearly put on a sarong."

"It doesn't matter at all. I daresay your boys were busy."

"You needn't have bothered to dress on my account, you know."

"I didn't. I always dress for dinner."

"Even when you're alone?"

"Especially when I'm alone," replied Mr. Warburton, with a frigid stare.

He saw a twinkle of amusement in Cooper's eyes, and he flushed an angry red. Mr. Warburton was a hot-tempered man; you might have guessed that from his red face with its pugnacious features and from his red hair, now growing white; his blue eyes, cold as a rule and observing, could flush with sudden wrath; but he was a man of the world and he hoped a just one. He must do his best to get on with this fellow.

"When I lived in London I moved in circles in which it would have been just as eccentric not to dress for dinner every night as not to have a bath every morning. When I came to Borneo I saw no reason to discontinue so good a habit. For three years, during the war, I never saw a white man. I never omitted to dress on a single occasion on which I was well enough to come in to dinner. You have not been very long in this country; believe me, there is no better way to maintain the proper pride which you should have in yourself. When a white man surrenders in the slightest degree to the influences that surround him he very soon loses his self-respect, and when he loses his self-respect you may be quite sure that the natives will soon cease to respect him."

"Well, if you expect me to put on a boiled shirt and a stiff collar in this heat I'm afraid you'll be disappointed."

"When you are dining in your own bungalow you will, of course, dress as you think fit, but when you do me the pleasure of dining with me, perhaps you will come to the conclusion that it is only polite to wear the costume usual in civilized society."

Two Malay boys, in sarongs and songkoks, with smart white coats and brass buttons, came in, one bearing gin pahits, and the other a tray on which were olives and anchovies. Then they went in to dinner. Mr. Warburton flattered himself that he had the best cook, a Chinese, in Borneo, and he took great trouble to have as good food as in the difficult circumstances was possible. He exercised much ingenuity in making the best of his materials.

"Would you care to look at the menu?" he said, handing it to Cooper.

It was written in French and the dishes had resounding names. They were waited on by the two boys. In opposite corners of the room two more waved immense fans, and so gave movement to the sultry air. The fare was sumptuous and the champagne excellent.

"Do you do yourself like this every day?" said Cooper.

Mr. Warburton gave the menu a careless glance.

"I have not noticed that the dinner is any different from usual," he said. "I eat very little myself, but I make a point

of having a proper dinner served to me every night. It keeps
the cook in practice and it's good discipline for the boys."

The conversation proceeded with effort. Mr. Warburton
was elaborately courteous, and it may be that he found a
slightly malicious amusement in the embarrassment which he
thereby occasioned in his companion. Cooper had not been
more than a few months in Sembulu, and Mr. Warburton's
enquiries about friends of his in Kuala Solor were soon exhausted.

"By the way," he said presently, "did you meet a lad
called Hennerley? He's come out recently, I believe."

"Oh, yes, he's in the police. A rotten bounder."

"I should hardly have expected him to be that. His uncle
is my friend Lord Barraclough. I had a letter from Lady
Barraclough only the other day asking me to look out for
him."

"I heard he was related to somebody or other. I suppose
that's how he got the job. He's been to Eton and Oxford
and he doesn't forget to let you know it."

"You surprise me," said Mr. Warburton. "All his family
have been at Eton and Oxford for a couple of hundred years.
I should have expected him to take it as a matter of course."

"I thought him a damned prig."

"To what school did you go?"

"I was born in Barbadoes. I was educated there."

"Oh, I see."

Mr. Warburton managed to put so much offensiveness
into his brief reply that Cooper flushed. For a moment he
was silent.

"I've had two or three letters from Kuala Solor," continued Mr. Warburton, "and my impression was that young
Hennerley was a great success. They say he's a first-rate
sportsman."

"Oh, yes, he's very popular. He's just the sort of fellow
they would like in K.S. I haven't got much use for the first-
rate sportsman myself. What does it amount to in the long
run that a man can play golf and tennis better than other
people? And who cares if he can make a break of seventy-

five at billiards? They attach a damned sight too much importance to that sort of thing in England."

"Do you think so? I was under the impression that the
first-rate sportsman had come out of the war certainly no
worse than any one else."

"Oh, if you're going to talk of the war then I do know
what I'm talking about. I was in the same regiment as Hennerley and I can tell you that the men couldn't stick him at
any price."

"How do you know?"

"Because I was one of the men."

"Oh, you hadn't got a commission."

"A fat chance I had of getting a commission. I was what
was called a Colonial. I hadn't been to a public school and
I had no influence. I was in the ranks the whole damned
time."

Cooper frowned. He seemed to have difficulty in preventing himself from breaking into violent invective. Mr. Warburton watched him, his little blue eyes narrowed, watched
him and formed his opinion. Changing the conversation, he
began to speak to Cooper about the work that would be required of him, and as the clock struck ten he rose.

"Well, I won't keep you any more. I daresay you're tired
by your journey."

They shook hands.

"Oh, I say, look here," said Cooper, "I wonder if you can
find me a boy. The boy I had before never turned up when
I was starting from K.S. He took my kit on board and all
that and then disappeared. I didn't know he wasn't there
till we were out of the river."

"I'll ask my head-boy. I have no doubt he can find you
some one."

"All right. Just tell him to send the boy along and if I like
the look of him I'll take him."

There was a moon, so that no lantern was needed. Cooper
walked across from the Fort to his bungalow.

"I wonder why on earth they've sent me a fellow like
that?" reflected Mr. Warburton. "If that's the kind of man
they're going to get out now I don't think much of it."

He strolled down his garden. The Fort was built on the top of a little hill and the garden ran down to the river's edge; on the bank was an arbour, and hither it was his habit to come after dinner to smoke a cheroot. And often from the river that flowed below him a voice was heard, the voice of some Malay too timorous to venture into the light of day, and a complaint or an accusation was softly wafted to his ears, a piece of information was whispered to him or a useful hint, which otherwise would never have come into his official ken. He threw himself heavily into a long rattan chair. Cooper! An envious, ill-bred fellow, bumptious, self-assertive and vain. But Mr. Warburton's irritation could not withstand the silent beauty of the night. The air was scented with the sweet-smelling flowers of a tree that grew at the entrance to the arbour, and the fireflies, sparkling dimly, flew with their slow and silvery flight. The moon made a pathway on the broad river for the light feet of Siva's bride, and on the further bank a row of palm trees was delicately silhouetted against the sky. Peace stole into the soul of Mr. Warburton.

He was a queer creature and he had had a singular career. At the age of twenty-one he had inherited a considerable fortune, a hundred thousand pounds, and when he left Oxford he threw himself into the gay life which in those days (now Mr. Warburton was a man of four and fifty) offered itself to the young man of good family. He had his flat in Mount Street, his private hansom, and his hunting-box in Warwickshire. He went to all the places where the fashionable congregate. He was handsome, amusing and generous. He was a figure in the society of London in the early nineties, and society then had not lost its exclusiveness nor its brilliance. The Boer War which shook it was unthought of; the Great War which destroyed it was prophesied only by the pessimists. It was no unpleasant thing to be a rich young man in those days, and Mr. Warburton's chimney-piece during the season was packed with cards for one great function after another. Mr. Warburton displayed them with complacency. For Mr. Warburton was a snob. He was not a timid snob, a little ashamed of being impressed by his betters, nor a snob who sought the intimacy of persons who had acquired celebrity in politics or notoriety in the arts, nor the snob who was dazzled by riches; he was the naked, unadulterated common snob who dearly loved a lord. He was touchy and quick-tempered, but he would much rather have been snubbed by a person of quality than flattered by a commoner. His name figured insignificantly in Burke's Peerage, and it was marvellous to watch the ingenuity he used to mention his distant relationship to the noble family he belonged to; but never a word did he say of the honest Liverpool manufacturer from whom, through his mother, a Miss Gubbins, he had come by his fortune. It was the terror of his fashionable life that at Cowes, maybe, or at Ascot, when he was with a duchess or even with a prince of the blood, one of these relatives would claim acquaintance with him.

His failing was too obvious not soon to become notorious, but its extravagance saved it from being merely despicable. The great whom he adored laughed at him, but in their hearts felt his adoration not unnatural. Poor Warburton was a dreadful snob, of course, but after all he was a good fellow. He was always ready to back a bill for an impecunious nobleman, and if you were in a tight corner you could safely count on him for a hundred pounds. He gave good dinners. He played whist badly, but never minded how much he lost if the company was select. He happened to be a gambler, an unlucky one, but he was a good loser, and it was impossible not to admire the coolness with which he lost five hundred pounds at a sitting. His passion for cards, almost as strong as his passion for titles, was the cause of his undoing. The life he led was expensive and his gambling losses were formidable. He began to plunge more heavily, first on horses· and then on the Stock Exchange. He had a certain simplicity of character and the unscrupulous found him an ingenuous prey. I do not know if he ever realized that his smart friends laughed at him behind his back, but I think he had an obscure instinct that he could not afford to appear other than careless of his money. He got into the hands of money-lenders. At the age of thirty-four he was ruined.

He was too much imbued with the spirit of his class to

hesitate in the choice of his next step. When a man in his set
had run through his money he went out to the colonies. No
one heard Mr. Warburton repine. He made no complaint because a noble friend had advised a disastrous speculation, he
pressed nobody to whom he had lent money to repay it, he
paid his debts (if he had only known it, the despised blood of
the Liverpool manufacturer came out in him there), sought
help from no one, and, never having done a stroke of work
in his life, looked for a means of livelihood. He remained
cheerful, unconcerned and full of humour. He had no wish
to make any one with whom he happened to be uncomfortable by the recital of his misfortune. Mr. Warburton was a
snob, but he was also a gentleman.

The only favour he asked of any of the great friends in
whose daily company he had lived for years was a recommendation. The able man who was at that time Sultan of
Sembulu took him into his service. The night before he sailed
he dined for the last time at his club.

"I hear you're going away, Warburton," the old Duke of
Hereford said to him.

"Yes, I'm going to Borneo."

"Good God, what are you going there for?"

"Oh, I'm broke."

"Are you? I'm sorry. Well, let us know when you come
back. I hope you have a good time."

"Oh, yes. Lots of shooting, you know."

The Duke nodded and passed on. A few hours later Mr.
Warburton watched the coast of England recede into the
mist, and he left behind everything which to him made life
worth living.

Twenty years had passed since then. He kept up a busy
correspondence with various great ladies and his letters were
amusing and chatty. He never lost his love for titled persons
and paid careful attention to the announcements in The
Times (which reached him six weeks after publication) of
their comings and goings. He perused the column which
records births, deaths, and marriages, and he was always
ready with his letter of congratulation or condolence. The
illustrated papers told him how people looked and on his

periodical visits to England, able to take up the threads as
though they had never been broken, he knew all about any
new person who might have appeared on the social surface.
His interest in the world of fashion was as vivid as when
himself had been a figure in it. It still seemed to him the only
thing that mattered.

But insensibly another interest had entered into his life.
The position he found himself in flattered his vanity; he was
no longer the sycophant craving the smiles of the great, he
was the master whose word was law. He was gratified by the
guard of Dyak soldiers who presented arms as he passed.
He liked to sit in judgment on his fellow men. It pleased
him to compose quarrels between rival chiefs. When the
head-hunters were troublesome in the old days he set out to
chastise them with a thrill of pride in his own behaviour. He
was too vain not to be of dauntless courage, and a pretty
story was told of his coolness in adventuring single-handed
into a stockaded village and demanding the surrender of a
bloodthirsty pirate. He became a skilful administrator. He
was strict, just and honest.

And little by little he conceived a deep love for the
Malays. He interested himself in their habits and customs.
He was never tired of listening to their talk. He admired
their virtues, and with a smile and a shrug of the shoulders
condoned their vices.

"In my day," he would say, "I have been on intimate
terms with some of the greatest gentlemen in England, but
I have never known finer gentlemen than some well-born
Malays whom I am proud to call my friends."

He liked their courtesy and their distinguished manners,
their gentleness and their sudden passions. He knew by instinct exactly how to treat them. He had a genuine tenderness for them. But he never forgot that he was an English
gentleman and he had no patience with the white men who
yielded to native customs. He made no surrenders. And he
did not imitate so many of the white men in taking a native
woman to wife, for an intrigue of this nature, however
sanctified by custom, seemed to him not only shocking but
undignified. A man who had been called George by Albert

Edward, Prince of Wales, could hardly be expected to have any connection with a native. And when he returned to Borneo from his visits to England it was now with something like relief. His friends, like himself, were no longer young, and there was a new generation which looked upon him as a tiresome old man. It seemed to him that the England of to-day had lost a good deal of what he had loved in the England of his youth. But Borneo remained the same. It was home to him now. He meant to remain in the service as long as was possible, and the hope in his heart was that he would die before at last he was forced to retire. He had stated in his will that wherever he died he wished his body to be brought back to Sembulu and buried among the people he loved within sound of the softly flowing river.

But these emotions he kept hidden from the eyes of men; and no one, seeing this spruce, stout, well-set-up man, with his clean-shaven strong face and his whitening hair, would have dreamed that he cherished so profound a sentiment.

He knew how the work of the station should be done, and during the next few days he kept a suspicious eye on his assistant. He saw very soon that he was painstaking and competent. The only fault he had to find with him was that he was brusque with the natives.

"The Malays are shy and very sensitive," he said to him. "I think you will find that you will get much better results if you take care always to be polite, patient and kindly."

Cooper gave a short, grating laugh.

"I was born in Barbadoes and I was in Africa in the war. I don't think there's much about niggers that I don't know."

"I know nothing," said Mr. Warburton acidly. "But we were not talking of them. We were talking of Malays."

"Aren't they niggers?"

"You are very ignorant," replied Mr. Warburton.

He said no more.

On the first Sunday after Cooper's arrival he asked him to dinner. He did everything ceremoniously, and though they had met on the previous day in the office and later, on the Fort verandah where they drank a gin and bitters together at six o'clock, he sent a polite note across to the bungalow by a boy. Cooper, however unwillingly, came in evening dress and Mr. Warburton, though gratified that his wish was respected, noticed with disdain that the young man's clothes were badly cut and his shirt ill-fitting. But Mr. Warburton was in a good temper that evening.

"By the way," he said to him, as he shook hands, "I've talked to my head-boy about finding you some one and he recommends his nephew. I've seen him and he seems a bright and willing lad. Would you like to see him?"

"I don't mind."

"He's waiting now."

Mr. Warburton called his boy and told him to send for his nephew. In a moment a tall, slender youth of twenty appeared. He had large dark eyes and a good profile. He was very neat in his sarong, a little white coat, and a fez, without a tassel, of plum-coloured velvet. He answered to the name of Abas. Mr. Warburton looked on him with approval, and his manner insensibly softened as he spoke to him in fluent and idiomatic Malay. He was inclined to be sarcastic with white people, but with the Malays he had a happy mixture of condescension and kindliness. He stood in the place of the Sultan. He knew perfectly how to preserve his own dignity, and at the same time put a native at his ease.

"Will he do?" said Mr. Warburton, turning to Cooper.

"Yes, I daresay he's no more of a scoundrel than any of the rest of them."

Mr. Warburton informed the boy that he was engaged and dismissed him.

"You're very lucky to get a boy like that," he told Cooper. "He belongs to a very good family. They came over from Malacca nearly a hundred years ago."

"I don't much mind if the boy who cleans my shoes and brings me a drink when I want it has blue blood in his veins or not. All I ask is that he should do what I tell him and look sharp about it."

Mr. Warburton pursed his lips, but made no reply.

They went in to dinner. It was excellent, and the wine was good. Its influence presently had its effect on them and they talked not only without acrimony, but even with friendliness. Mr. Warburton liked to do himself well, and on Sunday night he made it a habit to do himself even a little better than usual. He began to think he was unfair to Cooper. Of course he was not a gentleman, but that was not his fault, and when you got to know him it might be that he would turn out a very good fellow. His faults, perhaps, were faults of manner. And he was certainly good at his work, quick, conscientious and thorough. When they reached the dessert Mr. Warburton was feeling kindly disposed towards all mankind.

"This is your first Sunday and I'm going to give you a very special glass of port. I've only got about two dozen of it left and I keep it for special occasions."

He gave his boy instructions and presently the bottle was brought. Mr. Warburton watched the boy open it.

"I got this port from my old friend Charles Hollington. He'd had it for forty years and I've had it for a good many. He was well known to have the best cellar in England."

"Is he a wine merchant?"

"Not exactly," smiled Mr. Warburton. "I was speaking of Lord Hollington of Castle Reagh. He's one of the richest peers in England. A very old friend of mine. I was at Eton with his brother."

This was an opportunity that Mr. Warburton could never resist and he told a little anecdote of which the only point seemed to be that he knew an earl. The port was certainly very good; he drank a glass and then a second. He lost all caution. He had not talked to a white man for months. He began to tell stories. He showed himself in the company of the great. Hearing him you would have thought that at one time ministries were formed and policies decided on his suggestion whispered into the ear of a duchess or thrown over the dinner-table to be gratefully acted on by the confidential adviser of the sovereign. The old days at Ascot, Goodwood and Cowes lived again for him. Another glass of port. There were the great house-parties in Yorkshire and in Scotland to which he went every year.

"I had a man called Foreman then, the best valet I ever had, and why do you think he gave me notice? You know in the Housekeeper's Room the ladies' maids and the gentle-men's gentlemen sit according to the precedence of their masters. He told me he was sick of going to party after party at which I was the only commoner. It meant that he always had to sit at the bottom of the table and all the best bits were taken before a dish reached him. I told the story to the old Duke of Hereford and he roared. 'By God, sir,' he said, 'if I were King of England I'd make you a viscount just to give your man a chance.' 'Take him yourself, Duke,' I said. 'He's the best valet I've ever had.' 'Well, Warburton,' he said, 'if he's good enough for you he's good enough for me. Send him along.' "

Then there was Monte Carlo where Mr. Warburton and the Grand Duke Fyodor, playing in partnership, had broken the bank one evening; and there was Marienbad. At Marien-bad Mr. Warburton had played baccarat with Edward VII.

"He was only Prince of Wales then, of course. I remem-ber him saying to me, 'George, if you draw on a five you'll lose your shirt.' He was right; I don't think he ever said a truer word in his life. He was a wonderful man. I always said he was the greatest diplomatist in Europe. But I was a young fool in those days, I hadn't the sense to take his advice. If I had, if I'd never drawn on a five, I daresay I shouldn't be here to-day."

Cooper was watching him. His brown eyes, deep in their sockets, were hard and supercilious, and on his lips was a mocking smile. He had heard a good deal about Mr. War-burton in Kuala Solor. Not a bad sort, and he ran his district like clockwork, they said, but by heaven, what a snob! They laughed at him good-naturedly, for it was impossible to dis-like a man who was so generous and so kindly, and Cooper had already heard the story of the Prince of Wales and the game of baccarat. But Cooper listened without indulgence. From the beginning he had resented the Resident's manner. He was very sensitive and he writhed under Mr. Warbur-ton's polite sarcasms. Mr. Warburton had a knack of re-ceiving a remark of which he disapproved with a devastating silence. Cooper had lived little in England and he had a peculiar dislike of the English. He resented especially the public-school boy since he always feared that he was going to patronize him. He was so much afraid of others putting on airs with him that, in order as it were to get in first, he put on such airs as to make every one think him insufferably conceited.

"Well, at all events the war has done one good thing for us," he said at last. "It's smashed up the power of the aristocracy. The Boer War started it, and 1914 put the lid on."

"The great families of England are doomed," said Mr. Warburton with the complacent melancholy of an *émigré* who remembered the court of Louis XV. "They cannot afford any longer to live in their splendid palaces and their princely hospitality will soon be nothing but a memory."

"And a damned good job too in my opinion."

"My poor Cooper, what can you know of the glory that was Greece and the grandeur that was Rome?"

Mr. Warburton made an ample gesture. His eyes for an instant grew dreamy with a vision of the past.

"Well, believe me, we're fed up with all that rot. What we want is a business government by business men. I was born in a Crown Colony and I've lived practically all my life in the colonies. I don't give a row of pins for a lord. What's wrong with England is snobbishness. And if there's anything that gets my goat it's a snob."

A snob! Mr. Warburton's face grew purple and his eyes blazed with anger. That was a word that had pursued him all his life. The great ladies whose society he had enjoyed in his youth were not inclined to look upon his appreciation of themselves as unworthy, but even great ladies are sometimes out of temper and more than once Mr. Warburton had had the dreadful word flung in his teeth. He knew, he could not help knowing, that there were odious people who called him a snob. How unfair it was! Why, there was no vice he found so detestable as snobbishness. After all, he liked to mix with people of his own class, he was only at home in their company, and how in heaven's name could any one say that was snobbish? Birds of a feather.

"I quite agree with you," he answered. "A snob is a man who admires or despises another because he is of a higher social rank than his own. It is the most vulgar failing of our English middle class."

He saw a flicker of amusement in Cooper's eyes. Cooper put up his hand to hide the broad smile that rose to his lips, and so made it more noticeable. Mr. Warburton's hands trembled a little.

Probably Cooper never knew how greatly he had offended his chief. A sensitive man himself he was strangely insensitive to the feelings of others.

Their work forced them to see one another for a few minutes now and then during the day, and they met at six to have a drink on Mr. Warburton's verandah. This was an old-established custom of the country which Mr. Warburton would not for the world have broken. But they ate their meals separately, Cooper in his bungalow and Mr. Warburton at the Fort. After the office work was over they walked till dusk fell, but they walked apart. There were but few paths in this country, where the jungle pressed close upon the plantations of the village, and when Mr. Warburton caught sight of his assistant passing along with his loose stride, he would make a circuit in order to avoid him. Cooper, with his bad manners, his conceit in his own judgment and his intolerance, had already got on his nerves; but it was not till Cooper had been on the station for a couple of months that an incident happened which turned the Resident's dislike into bitter hatred.

Mr. Warburton was obliged to go up-country on a tour of inspection, and he left the station in Cooper's charge with more confidence, since he had definitely come to the conclusion that he was a capable fellow. The only thing he did not like was that he had no indulgence. He was honest, just and painstaking, but he had no sympathy for the natives. It bitterly amused Mr. Warburton to observe that this man, who looked upon himself as every man's equal, should look upon so many men as his own inferiors. He was hard, he had no patience with the native mind, and he was a bully. Mr. Warburton very quickly realized that the Malays disliked and feared him. He was not altogether displeased. He would not have liked it very much if his assistant had enjoyed a popularity which might rival his own. Mr. Warburton made his elaborate preparations, set out on his expedition, and in three weeks returned. Meanwhile the mail had arrived. The first thing that struck his eyes when he entered his sitting-room was a great pile of open newspapers. Cooper had met him, and they went into the room together. Mr. Warburton turned to one of the servants who had been left behind and sternly asked him what was the meaning of those open papers. Cooper hastened to explain.

"I wanted to read all about the Wolverhampton murder and so I borrowed your Times. I brought them back again. I knew you wouldn't mind."

Mr. Warburton turned on him, white with anger.

"But I do mind. I mind very much."

"I'm sorry," said Cooper, with composure. "The fact is, I simply couldn't wait till you came back."

"I wonder you didn't open my letters as well."

Cooper, unmoved, smiled at his chief's exasperation.

"Oh, that's not quite the same thing. After all, I couldn't imagine you'd mind my looking at your newspapers. There's nothing private in them."

"I very much object to any one reading my paper before me." He went up to the pile. There were nearly thirty numbers there. "I think it extremely impertinent of you. They're all mixed up."

"We can easily put them in order," said Cooper, joining him at the table.

"Don't touch them," cried Mr. Warburton.

"I say, it's childish to make a scene about a little thing like that."

"How dare you speak to me like that?"

"Oh, go to hell," said Cooper, and he flung out of the room.

Mr. Warburton, trembling with passion, was left contemplating his papers. His greatest pleasure in life had been destroyed by those callous, brutal hands. Most people living in out-of-the-way places when the mail comes tear open impatiently their papers and taking the last ones first glance at the latest news from home. Not so Mr. Warburton. His newsagent had instructions to write on the outside of the wrapper the date of each paper he despatched and when the great bundle arrived Mr. Warburton looked at these dates and with his blue pencil numbered them. His head-boy's orders were to place one on the table every morning in the verandah with the early cup of tea, and it was Mr. Warburton's especial delight to break the wrapper as he sipped his tea, and read the morning paper. It gave him the illusion of living at home. Every Monday morning he read the Monday Times of six weeks back and so went through the week. On Sunday he read The Observer. Like his habit of dressing for dinner it was a tie to civilization. And it was his pride that no matter how exciting the news was he had never yielded to the temptation of opening a paper before its allotted time. During the war the suspense sometimes had been intolerable, and when he read one day that a push was begun he had undergone agonies of suspense which he might have saved himself by the simple expedient of opening a later paper which lay waiting for him on a shelf. It had been the severest trial to which he had ever exposed himself, but he victoriously surmounted it. And that clumsy fool had broken open those neat tight packages because he wanted to know whether some horrid woman had murdered her odious husband.

Mr. Warburton sent for his boy and told him to bring wrappers. He folded up the papers as neatly as he could, placed a wrapper round each and numbered it. But it was a melancholy task.

"I shall never forgive him," he said. "Never."

Of course his boy had been with him on his expedition; he never travelled without him, for his boy knew exactly how he liked things, and Mr. Warburton was not the kind of jungle traveller who was prepared to dispense with his comforts; but in the interval since their arrival he had been gossiping in the servants' quarters. He had learnt that Cooper had had trouble with his boys. All but the youth Abas had left him. Abas had desired to go too, but his uncle had placed him there on the instructions of the Resident, and he was afraid to leave without his uncle's permission.

"I told him he had done well, Tuan," said the boy. "But he is unhappy. He says it is not a good house and he wishes to know if he may go as the others have gone."

"No, he must stay. The tuan must have servants. Have those who went been replaced?"

"No, Tuan, no one will go."

Mr. Warburton frowned. Cooper was an insolent fool, but he had an official position and must be suitably provided with servants. It was not seemly that his house should be improperly conducted.

"Where are the boys who ran away?"

"They are in the kampong, Tuan."

"Go and see them to-night and tell them that I expect them to be back at Tuan Cooper's house at dawn to-morrow."

"They say they will not go, Tuan."

"On my order?"

The boy had been with Mr. Warburton for fifteen years, and he knew every intonation of his master's voice. He was not afraid of him, they had gone through too much together, once in the jungle the Resident had saved his life and once, upset in some rapids, but for him the Resident would have been drowned; but he knew when the Resident must be obeyed without question.

"I will go to the kampong," he said.

Mr. Warburton expected that his subordinate would take the first opportunity to apologize for his rudeness, but Cooper had the ill-bred man's inability to express regret; and when they met next morning in the office he ignored the incident. Since Mr. Warburton had been away for three weeks it was necessary for them to have a somewhat prolonged interview. At the end of it Mr. Warburton dismissed him.

"I don't think there's anything else, thank you." Cooper turned to go, but Mr. Warburton stopped him. "I understand you've been having some trouble with your boys."

Cooper gave a harsh laugh.

"They tried to blackmail me. They had the damned cheek to run away, all except that incompetent fellow Abas—he knew when he was well off—but I just sat tight. They've all come to heel again."

"What do you mean by that?"

"This morning they were all back on their jobs, the Chinese cook and all. There they were, as cool as cucumbers; you would have thought they owned the place. I suppose they'd come to the conclusion that I wasn't such a fool as I looked."

"By no means. They came back on my express order."

Cooper flushed slightly.

"I should be obliged if you wouldn't interfere with my private concerns."

"They're not your private concerns. When your servants run away it makes you ridiculous. You are perfectly free to make a fool of yourself, but I cannot allow you to be made a fool of. It is unseemly that your house should not be properly staffed. As soon as I heard that your boys had left you, I had them told to be back in their places at dawn. That'll do."

Mr. Warburton nodded to signify that the interview was at an end. Cooper took no notice.

"Shall I tell you what I did? I called them and gave the whole bally lot the sack. I gave them ten minutes to get out of the compound."

Mr. Warburton shrugged his shoulders.

"What makes you think you can get others?"

"I've told my own clerk to see about it."

Mr. Warburton reflected for a moment.

"I think you behaved very foolishly. You will do well to remember in future that good masters make good servants."

"Is there anything else you want to teach me?"

"I should like to teach you manners, but it would be an arduous task, and I have not the time to waste. I will see that you get boys."

"Please don't put yourself to any trouble on my account. I'm quite capable of getting them for myself."

Mr. Warburton smiled acidly. He had an inkling that Cooper disliked him as much as he disliked Cooper, and he knew that nothing is more galling than to be forced to accept the favours of a man you detest.

"Allow me to tell you that you have no more chance of getting Malay or Chinese servants here now than you have of getting an English butler or a French chef. No one will come to you except on an order from me. Would you like me to give it?"

"No."

"As you please. Good morning."

Mr. Warburton watched the development of the situation with acrid humour. Cooper's clerk was unable to persuade Malay, Dyak or Chinese to enter the house of such a master. Abas, the boy who remained faithful to him, knew how to cook only native food, and Cooper, a coarse feeder, found his gorge rise against the everlasting rice. There was no water-carrier, and in that great heat he needed several baths a day. He cursed Abas, but Abas opposed him with sullen resistance and would not do more than he chose. It was galling to know that the lad stayed with him only because the Resident insisted. This went on for a fortnight and then, one morning, he found in his house the very servants whom he had previously dismissed. He fell into a violent rage, but he had learnt a little sense, and this time, without a word, he let them stay. He swallowed his humiliation, but the impatient contempt he had felt for Mr. Warburton's idiosyncrasies changed into a sullen hatred; the Resident with this malicious stroke had made him the laughing-stock of all the natives.

The two men now held no communication with one another. They broke the time-honoured custom of sharing, notwithstanding personal dislike, a drink at six o'clock with any white man who happened to be at the station. Each lived in his own house as though the other did not exist. Now that Cooper had fallen into the work, it was necessary for them to have little to do with one another in the office. Mr. Warburton used his orderly to send any message he had to give his assistant, and his instructions he sent by formal letter. They saw one another constantly, that was inevitable, but did not exchange half a dozen words in a week. The fact that they could not avoid catching sight of one another got on their nerves. They brooded over their antagonism and Mr.

Warburton, taking his daily walk, could think of nothing but how much he detested his assistant.

And the dreadful thing was that in all probability they would remain thus, facing each other in deadly enmity, till Mr. Warburton went on leave. It might be three years. He had no reason to send in a complaint to headquarters: Cooper did his work very well, and at that time men were hard to get. True, vague complaints reached him and hints that the natives found Cooper harsh. There was certainly a feeling of dissatisfaction among them. But when Mr. Warburton looked into specific cases, all he could say was that Cooper had shown severity where mildness would not have been misplaced and had been unfeeling when himself would have been sympathetic. He had done nothing for which he could be taken to task. But Mr. Warburton watched him. Hatred will often make a man clear-sighted, and he had a suspicion that Cooper was using the natives without consideration, yet keeping within the law, because he felt that thus he could exasperate his chief. One day perhaps he would go too far. None knew better than Mr. Warburton how irritable the incessant heat could make a man and how difficult it was to keep one's self-control after a sleepless night. He smiled softly to himself. Sooner or later Cooper would deliver himself into his hand.

When at last the opportunity came Mr. Warburton laughed aloud. Cooper had charge of the prisoners; they made roads, built sheds, rowed when it was necessary to send the prahu up- or down-stream, kept the town clean and otherwise usefully employed themselves. If well-behaved they even on occasion served as house-boys. Cooper kept them hard at it. He liked to see them work. He took pleasure in devising tasks for them; and seeing quickly enough that they were being made to do useless things the prisoners worked badly. He punished them by lengthening their hours. This was contrary to the regulations, and as soon as it was brought to the attention of Mr. Warburton, without referring the matter back to his subordinate, he gave instructions that the old hours should be kept; Cooper, going out for his walk, was astounded to see the prisoners strolling back to the jail; he had given instructions that they were not to knock off till dusk. When he asked the warder in charge why they had left off work he was told that it was the Resident's bidding.

White with rage he strode to the Fort. Mr. Warburton, in his spotless white ducks and his neat topee, with a walking-stick in his hand, followed by his dogs, was on the point of starting out on his afternoon stroll. He had watched Cooper go and knew that he had taken the road by the river. Cooper jumped up the steps and went straight up to the Resident.

"I want to know what the hell you mean by countermanding my order that the prisoners were to work till six," he burst out, beside himself with fury.

Mr. Warburton opened his cold blue eyes very wide and assumed an expression of great surprise.

"Are you out of your mind? Are you so ignorant that you do not know that that is not the way to speak to your official superior?"

"Oh, go to hell. The prisoners are my pidgin and you've got no right to interfere. You mind your business and I'll mind mine. I want to know what the devil you mean by making a damned fool of me. Every one in the place will know that you've countermanded my order."

Mr. Warburton kept very cool.

"You had no power to give the order you did. I counter-manded it because it was harsh and tyrannical. Believe me, I have not made half such a damned fool of you as you have made of yourself."

"You disliked me from the first moment I came here. You've done everything you could to make the place impossible for me because I wouldn't lick your boots for you. You got your knife into me because I wouldn't flatter you."

Cooper, spluttering with rage, was nearing dangerous ground, and Mr. Warburton's eyes grew on a sudden colder and more piercing.

"You are wrong. I thought you were a cad, but I was perfectly satisfied with the way you did your work."

"You snob. You damned snob. You thought me a cad because I hadn't been to Eton. Oh, they told me in K.S. what to expect. Why, don't you know that you're the laughing-stock of the whole country? I could hardly help bursting into a roar of laughter when you told your celebrated story about the Prince of Wales. My God, how they shouted at the club when they told it. By God, I'd rather be the cad I am than the snob you are."

He got Mr. Warburton on the raw.

"If you don't get out of my house this minute I shall knock you down," he cried.

The other came a little closer to him and put his face in his.

"Touch me, touch me," he said. "By God, I'd like to see you hit me. Do you want me to say it again? Snob. Snob."

Cooper was three inches taller than Mr. Warburton, a strong, muscular young man. Mr. Warburton was fat and fifty-four. His clenched fist shot out. Cooper caught him by the arm and pushed him back.

"Don't be a damned fool. Remember I'm not a gentleman. I know how to use my hands."

He gave a sort of hoot, and, grinning all over his pale, sharp face, jumped down the verandah steps. Mr. Warburton, his heart in his anger pounding against his ribs, sank exhausted into a chair. His body tingled as though he had prickly heat. For one horrible moment he thought he was going to cry. But suddenly he was conscious that his head-boy was on the verandah and instinctively regained control of himself. The boy came forward and filled him a glass of whisky and soda. Without a word Mr. Warburton took it and drank it to the dregs.

"What do you want to say to me?" asked Mr. Warburton, trying to force a smile on to his strained lips.

"Tuan, the assistant tuan is a bad man. Abas wishes again to leave him."

"Let him wait a little. I shall write to Kuala Solor and ask that Tuan Cooper should go elsewhere."

"Tuan Cooper is not good with the Malays."

"Leave me."

The boy silently withdrew. Mr. Warburton was left alone with his thoughts. He saw the club at Kuala Solor, the men sitting round the table in the window in their flannels, when the night had driven them in from golf and tennis, drinking whiskies and gin pahits and laughing when they told the celebrated story of the Prince of Wales and himself at Marienbad. He was hot with shame and misery. A snob! They all thought him a snob. And he had always thought them very good fellows, he had always been gentleman enough to let it make no difference to him that they were of very second-rate position. He hated them now. But his hatred for them was nothing compared with his hatred for Cooper. And if it had come to blows Cooper could have thrashed him. Tears of mortification ran down his red, fat face. He sat there for a couple of hours smoking cigarette after cigarette, and he wished he were dead.

At last the boy came back and asked him if he would dress for dinner. Of course! He always dressed for dinner. He rose wearily from his chair and put on his stiff shirt and the high collar. He sat down at the prettily decorated table and was waited on as usual by the two boys while two others waved their great fans. Over there in the bungalow, two hundred yards away, Cooper was eating a filthy meal clad only in a sarong and a baju. His feet were bare and while he ate he probably read a detective story. After dinner Mr. Warburton sat down to write a letter. The Sultan was away, but he wrote, privately and confidentially, to his representative. Cooper did his work very well, he said, but the fact was that he couldn't get on with him. They were getting dreadfully on each other's nerves and he would look upon it as a very great favour if Cooper could be transferred to another post.

He despatched the letter next morning by special messenger. The answer came a fortnight later with the month's mail. It was a private note and ran as follows:

My dear Warburton:—

I do not want to answer your letter officially and so I am writing you a few lines myself. Of course if you insist I will put the matter up to the Sultan, but I think you would be much wiser to drop it. I know Cooper is a rough diamond, but he is capable, and he had a pretty thin time in the war, and I think he should be given every chance. I think you are a little too much inclined to attach importance to a man's social position. You must remember that times have changed. Of course it's a very good thing for a man to be a gentleman, but it's better that he should be competent and hard-working. I think if you'll exercise a little tolerance you'll get on very well with Cooper.

Yours very sincerely

Richard Temple.

The letter dropped from Mr. Warburton's hand. It was easy to read between the lines. Dick Temple, whom he had known for twenty years, Dick Temple, who came from quite a good county family, thought him a snob and for that reason had no patience with his request. Mr. Warburton felt on a sudden discouraged with life. The world of which he was a part had passed away, and the future belonged to a meaner generation. Cooper represented it and Cooper he hated with all his heart. He stretched out his hand to fill his glass and at the gesture his head-boy stepped forward.

"I didn't know you were there."

The boy picked up the official letter. Ah, that was why he was waiting.

"Does Tuan Cooper go, Tuan?"

"No."

"There will be a misfortune."

For a moment the words conveyed nothing to his lassitude. But only for a moment. He sat up in his chair and looked at the boy. He was all attention.

"What do you mean by that?"

"Tuan Cooper is not behaving rightly with Abas."

Mr. Warburton shrugged his shoulders. How should a man like Cooper know how to treat servants? Mr. Warburton knew the type: he would be grossly familiar with them at one moment and rude and inconsiderate the next.

"Let Abas go back to his family."

"Tuan Cooper holds back his wages so that he may not run away. He has paid him nothing for three months. I tell him to be patient. But he is angry, he will not listen to reason. If the tuan continues to use him ill there will be a misfortune."

"You were right to tell me."

The fool! Did he know so little of the Malays as to think he could safely injure them? It would serve him damned well right if he got a kris in his back. A kris. Mr. Warburton's heart seemed on a sudden to miss a beat. He had only to let things take their course and one fine day he would be rid of Cooper. He smiled faintly as the phrase, a masterly inactivity, crossed his mind. And now his heart beat a little quicker, for he saw the man he hated lying on his face in a pathway of the jungle with a knife in his back. A fit end for the cad and the bully. Mr. Warburton sighed. It was his duty to warn him and of course he must do it. He wrote a brief and formal note to Cooper asking him to come to the Fort at once.

In ten minutes Cooper stood before him. They had not spoken to one another since the day when Mr. Warburton had nearly struck him. He did not now ask him to sit down.

"Did you wish to see me?" Cooper asked.

He was untidy and none too clean. His face and hands were covered with little red blotches where mosquitoes had bitten him and he had scratched himself till the blood came. His long, thin face bore a sullen look.

"I understand that you are again having trouble with your servants. Abas, my head-boy's nephew, complains that you have held back his wages for three months. I consider it a most arbitrary proceeding. The lad wishes to leave you, and I certainly do not blame him. I must insist on your paying what is due to him."

"I don't choose that he should leave me. I am holding back his wages as a pledge of his good behaviour."

"You do not know the Malay character. The Malays are very sensitive to injury and ridicule. They are passionate and revengeful. It is my duty to warn you that if you drive this boy beyond a certain point you run a great risk."

Cooper gave a contemptuous chuckle.

"What do you think he'll do?"

"I think he'll kill you."

"Why should you mind?"

"Oh, I wouldn't," replied Mr. Warburton, with a faint

laugh. "I should bear it with the utmost fortitude. But I feel the official obligation to give you a proper warning."

"Do you think I'm afraid of a damned nigger?"

"It's a matter of entire indifference to me."

"Well, let me tell you this, I know how to take care of myself; that boy Abas is a dirty, thieving rascal, and if he tries any monkey tricks on me, by God, I'll wring his bloody neck."

"That was all I wished to say to you," said Mr. Warburton. "Good evening."

Mr. Warburton gave him a little nod of dismissal. Cooper flushed, did not for a moment know what to say or do, turned on his heel and stumbled out of the room. Mr. Warburton watched him go with an icy smile on his lips. He had done his duty. But what would he have thought had he known that when Cooper got back to his bungalow, so silent and cheerless, he threw himself down on his bed and in his bitter loneliness on a sudden lost all control of himself? Painful sobs tore his chest and heavy tears rolled down his thin cheeks.

After this Mr. Warburton seldom saw Cooper, and never spoke to him. He read his Times every morning, did his work at the office, took his exercise, dressed for dinner, dined and sat by the river smoking his cheroot. If by chance he ran across Cooper he cut him dead. Each, though never for a moment unconscious of the propinquity, acted as though the other did not exist. Time did nothing to assuage their animosity. They watched one another's actions and each knew what the other did. Though Mr. Warburton had been a keen shot in his youth, with age he had acquired a distaste for killing the wild things of the jungle, but on Sundays and holidays Cooper went out with his gun: if he got something it was a triumph over Mr. Warburton; if not, Mr. Warburton shrugged his shoulders and chuckled. These counter-jumpers trying to be sportsmen! Christmas was a bad time for both of them: they ate their dinners alone, each in his own quarters, and they got deliberately drunk. They were the only white men within two hundred miles and they lived within shouting distance of each other. At the begin-

ning of the year Cooper went down with fever, and when
Mr. Warburton caught sight of him again he was surprised
to see how thin he had grown. He looked ill and worn. The
solitude, so much more unnatural because it was due to no
necessity, was getting on his nerves. It was getting on Mr.
Warburton's too, and often he could not sleep at night. He
lay awake brooding. Cooper was drinking heavily and surely
the breaking point was near; but in his dealings with the
natives he took care to do nothing that might expose him to
his chief's rebuke. They fought a grim and silent battle with
one another. It was a test of endurance. The months passed,
and neither gave sign of weakening. They were like men
dwelling in regions of eternal night, and their souls were
oppressed with the knowledge that never would the day
dawn for them. It looked as though their lives would continue for ever in this dull and hideous monotony of hatred.

And when at last the inevitable happened it came upon
Mr. Warburton with all the shock of the unexpected. Cooper
accused the boy Abas of stealing some of his clothes, and
when the boy denied the theft took him by the scruff of the
neck and kicked him down the steps of the bungalow. The
boy demanded his wages, and Cooper flung at his head every
word of abuse he knew. If he saw him in the compound in an
hour he would hand him over to the police. Next morning
the boy waylaid him outside the Fort when he was walking
over to his office, and again demanded his wages. Cooper
struck him in the face with his clenched fist. The boy fell to
the ground and got up with blood streaming from his nose.

Cooper walked on and set about his work. But he could
not attend to it. The blow had calmed his irritation, and he
knew that he had gone too far. He was worried. He felt ill,
miserable and discouraged. In the adjoining office sat Mr.
Warburton, and his impulse was to go and tell him what he
had done; he made a movement in his chair, but he knew
with what icy scorn he would listen to the story. He could see
his patronizing smile. For a moment he had an uneasy fear
of what Abas might do. Warburton had warned him all
right. He sighed. What a fool he had been! But he shrugged
his shoulders impatiently. He did not care; a fat lot he had

to live for. It was all Warburton's fault; if he hadn't put his back up nothing like this would have happened. Warburton had made life a hell for him from the start. The snob. But they were all like that: it was because he was a Colonial. It was a damned shame that he had never got his commission in the war; he was as good as any one else. They were a lot of dirty snobs. He was damned if he was going to knuckle under now. Of course Warburton would hear of what had happened; the old devil knew everything. He wasn't afraid. He wasn't afraid of any Malay in Borneo, and Warburton could go to blazes.

He was right in thinking that Mr. Warburton would know what had happened. His head-boy told him when he went in to tiffin.

"Where is your nephew now?"

"I do not know, Tuan. He has gone."

Mr. Warburton remained silent. After luncheon as a rule he slept a little, but to-day he found himself very wide awake. His eyes involuntarily sought the bungalow where Cooper was now resting.

The idiot! Hesitation for a little was in Mr. Warburton's mind. Did the man know in what peril he was? He supposed he ought to send for him. But each time he had tried to reason with Cooper, Cooper had insulted him. Anger, furious anger welled up suddenly in Mr. Warburton's heart, so that the veins on his temples stood out and he clenched his fists. The cad had had his warning. Now let him take what was coming to him. It was no business of his and if anything happened it was not his fault. But perhaps they would wish in Kuala Solor that they had taken his advice and transferred Cooper to another station.

He was strangely restless that night. After dinner he walked up and down the verandah. When the boy went away to his own quarters, Mr. Warburton asked him whether anything had been seen of Abas.

"No, Tuan, I think maybe he has gone to the village of his mother's brother."

Mr. Warburton gave him a sharp glance, but the boy was looking down and their eyes did not meet. Mr. Warburton went down to the river and sat in his arbour. But peace was denied him. The river flowed ominously silent. It was like a great serpent gliding with sluggish movement towards the sea. And the trees of the jungle over the water were heavy with a breathless menace. No bird sang. No breeze ruffled the leaves of the cassias. All around him it seemed as though something waited.

He walked across the garden to the road. He had Cooper's bungalow in full view from there. There was a light in his sitting-room and across the road floated the sound of rag-time. Cooper was playing his gramophone. Mr. Warburton shuddered; he had never got over his instinctive dislike of that instrument. But for that he would have gone over and spoken to Cooper. He turned and went back to his own house. He read late into the night, and at last he slept. But he did not sleep very long, he had terrible dreams, and he seemed to be awakened by a cry. Of course that was a dream too, for no cry—from the bungalow for instance—could be heard in his room. He lay awake till dawn. Then he heard hurried steps and the sound of voices, his head-boy burst suddenly into the room without his fez, and Mr. Warburton's heart stood still.

"Tuan, Tuan."

Mr. Warburton jumped out of bed.

"I'll come at once."

He put on his slippers, and in his sarong and pyjama-jacket walked across his compound and into Cooper's. Cooper was lying in bed, with his mouth open, and a kris sticking in his heart. He had been killed in his sleep. Mr. Warburton started, but not because he had not expected to see just such a sight, he started because he felt in himself a sudden glow of exultation. A great burden had been lifted from his shoulders.

Cooper was quite cold. Mr. Warburton took the kris out of the wound, it had been thrust in with such force that he had to use an effort to get it out, and looked at it. He recognized it. It was a kris that a dealer had offered him some weeks before and which he knew Cooper had bought.

"Where is Abas?" he asked sternly.

"Abas is at the village of his mother's brother."

The sergeant of the native police was standing at the foot of the bed.

"Take two men and go to the village and arrest him."

Mr. Warburton did what was immediately necessary. With set face he gave orders. His words were short and peremptory. Then he went back to the Fort. He shaved and had his bath, dressed and went into the dining-room. By the side of his plate The Times in its wrapper lay waiting for him. He helped himself to some fruit. The head-boy poured out his tea while the second handed him a dish of eggs. Mr. Warburton ate with a good appetite. The head-boy waited.

"What is it?" asked Mr. Warburton.

"Tuan, Abas, my nephew, was in the house of his mother's brother all night. It can be proved. His uncle will swear that he did not leave the kampong."

Mr. Warburton turned upon him with a frown.

"Tuan Cooper was killed by Abas. You know it as well as I know it. Justice must be done."

"Tuan, you would not hang him?"

Mr. Warburton hesitated an instant, and though his voice remained set and stern a change came into his eyes. It was a flicker which the Malay was quick to notice and across his own eyes flashed an answering look of understanding.

"The provocation was very great. Abas will be sentenced to a term of imprisonment." There was a pause while Mr. Warburton helped himself to marmalade. "When he has served a part of his sentence in prison I will take him into this house as a boy. You can train him in his duties. I have no doubt that in the house of Tuan Cooper he got into bad habits."

"Shall Abas give himself up, Tuan?"

"It would be wise of him."

The boy withdrew. Mr. Warburton took his Times and neatly slit the wrapper. He loved to unfold the heavy, rustling pages. The morning, so fresh and cool, was delicious and for a moment his eyes wandered out over his garden with a friendly glance. A great weight had been lifted from his mind. He turned to the columns in which were announced the births, deaths, and marriages. That was what he always looked at first. A name he knew caught his attention. Lady Ormskirk had had a son at last. By George, how pleased the old dowager must be! He would write her a note of congratulation by the next mail.

Abas would make a very good house-boy.

That fool Cooper!

THE
FRENCH GOVERNOR

I LEFT Bangkok on a shabby little boat of four or five hundred tons. The dingy saloon, which served as dining room, had two narrow tables down its length with swivel chairs on both sides of them. The cabins were in the bowels of the ship, and they were extremely dirty. Cockroaches walked about on the floor, and however placid your temperament it is difficult not to be startled when you go to the wash basin to wash your hands and a huge cockroach stalks leisurely out.

We dropped down the river, broad and lazy and smiling, and its green banks were dotted with little huts on piles standing at the water's edge. We crossed the bar, and the open sea, blue and still, spread before me. The look of it and the smell of it filled me with elation.

I had gone on board early in the morning and soon discovered that I was thrown amid the oddest collection of persons I had ever encountered. There were two French traders and a Belgian colonel, an Italian tenor, the American proprietor of a circus with his wife, and a retired French official with his. The circus proprietor was what is termed a good mixer, a type which according to your mood you fly from or welcome, but I happened to be feeling much pleased with life, and before I had been on board an hour we had shaken for drinks and he had shown me his animals. He was a very short fat man, and his *stengah-shifter*, white but none too clean, outlined the noble proportions of his abdomen, but the collar was so tight that you wondered he did not choke. He had a red, clean-shaven face, a merry blue eye, and short, untidy sandy hair. He wore a battered topee well on the back of his head. His name was Wilkins, and he was born in Portland, Oregon. It appears that the Oriental had a passion for the circus, and Mr. Wilkins for twenty years had been travelling up and down the East from Port Said to Yokohama (Aden, Bombay, Madras, Calcutta, Rangoon, Singapore, Penang, Bangkok, Saigon, Hue, Hanoi, Hong Kong, Shanghai, their names roll on the tongue savourily, crowding the imagination with sunshine and strange sounds and a multicoloured activity) with his menagerie and his merry-go-rounds. It was a strange life he led, unusual, and one that, one would have thought, must offer the occasion for all sorts of curious experiences, but the odd thing about him was that he was a perfectly commonplace little man, and you would have been prepared to find him running a garage or keeping a third-rate hotel in a second-rate town in California. The fact is, and I have noticed it so often that I do not know why it should always surprise me, that the extraordinariness of a man's life does not make him extraordinary, but contrariwise, if a man is extraordinary he will make extraordinariness out of a life as humdrum as that of a county curate. I wish I could feel it reasonable to tell here the story of the hermit I went to see on an island in the Torres Strait, a shipwrecked mariner who had lived there alone for thirty years; but when you are writing a book you are imprisoned by the four walls of your subject, and though for the entertainment of my digressing mind I set it down now, I should be forced in the end by my sense of what is fit to go between two covers, and by what is not, to cut it out. Anyhow, the long and short of it is that, notwithstanding this long and intimate communion with nature and his thoughts, the man was as dull, insensitive, and vulgar an oaf at the end of this experience as he must have been at the beginning.

The Italian singer passed us, and Mr. Wilkins told me that he was a Neapolitan who was on his way to Hong Kong to rejoin his company, which he had been forced to leave owing to an attack of malaria in Bangkok. He was an enormous fellow and very fat, and when he flung himself into a chair it creaked with dismay. He took off his topee, displaying a great head of long, curly, greasy hair, and ran podgy and beringed fingers through it.

"He ain't very sociable," said Mr. Wilkins. "He took the cigar I give him, but he wouldn't have a drink. I shouldn't wonder if there wasn't somethin' rather queer about him. Nasty lookin' guy, ain't he?"

Then a little fat woman in white came on deck holding by the hand a Wa-Wa monkey. It walked solemnly by her side.

"This is Mrs. Wilkins," said the circus proprietor, "and our youngest son. Draw up a chair, Mrs. Wilkins, and meet this gentleman. I don't know his name, but he's already paid for two drinks for me, and if he can't shake any better than he has yet he'll pay for one for you too."

Mrs. Wilkins sat down with an abstracted, serious look and with her eyes on the blue sea suggested that she did not see why she shouldn't have a lemonade.

"My, it's hot," she murmured, fanning herself with the topee which she took off.

"Mrs. Wilkins feels the heat," said her husband. "She's had twenty years of it now."

"Twenty-two and a half," said Mrs. Wilkins, still looking at the sea.

"And she's never got used to it yet."

"Nor never shall, you know it," said Mrs. Wilkins.

She was just the same size as her husband and just as fat, and she had a round red face like his and the same sandy, untidy hair. I wondered if they had married because they were so exactly alike, or if in the course of years they had acquired this astonishing resemblance. She did not turn her head but continued to look absently at the sea.

"Have you shown him the animals?" she asked.

"You bet your life I have."

"What did he think of Percy?"

"Thought him fine."

I could not but feel that I was being unduly left out of a conversation of which I was at all events partly the subject, so I asked:

"Who's Percy?"

"Percy's our eldest son. There's a flyin' fish, Elmer. He's the orang-utan. Did he eat his food well this morning?"

"Fine. He's the biggest orang-utan in captivity. I wouldn't take a thousand dollars for him."

"And what relation is the elephant?" I asked.

Mrs. Wilkins did not look at me, but with her blue eyes still gazed indifferently at the sea.

"He's no relation," she answered. "Only a friend."

The boy brought lemonade for Mrs. Wilkins, a whisky-and-soda for her husband, and a gin and tonic for me. We shook dice, and I signed the chit.

"It must come expensive if he always loses when he shakes," Mrs. Wilkins murmured to the coast line.

"I guess Egbert would like a sip of your lemonade, my dear," said Mr. Wilkins.

Mrs. Wilkins slightly turned her head and looked at the monkey sitting on her lap.

"Would you like a sip of Mother's lemonade, Egbert?"

The monkey gave a little squeak, and putting her arm round him she handed him a straw. The monkey sucked up a little lemonade and having drunk enough sank back against Mrs. Wilkins's ample bosom.

"Mrs. Wilkins thinks the world of Egbert," said her husband. "You can't wonder at it, he's her youngest."

Mrs. Wilkins took another straw and thoughtfully drank her lemonade.

"Egbert's all right," she remarked. "There's nothin' wrong with Egbert."

Just then the French official who had been sitting down got up and began walking up and down. He had been accompanied on board by the French minister at Bangkok, one or two secretaries, and a prince of the Royal Family. There had been a great deal of bowing and shaking of hands, and as the boat slipped away from the quay much waving of hats and handkerchiefs. He was evidently a person of consequence. I had heard the captain address him as Monsieur le Gouverneur.

"That's the big noise on this boat," said Mr. Wilkins.

"He was governor of one of the French colonies, and now he's making a tour of the world. He came to see my circus at Bangkok. I guess I'll ask him what he'll have. What shall I call him, my dear?"

Mrs. Wilkins slowly turned her head and looked at the Frenchman, with the rosette of the Legion of Honour in his buttonhole, pacing up and down.

"Don't call him anythin'," she said. "Show him a hoop and he'll jump right through it."

I could not but laugh. Monsieur le Gouverneur was a little man, well below the average height, and smally made, with a very ugly little face and thick, almost negroid features; and he had a bushy gray head, bushy gray eyebrows, and a bushy gray moustache. He did look a little like a poodle, and he had the poodle's soft, intelligent, and shining eyes. Next time he passed us Mr. Wilkins called out:

"*Monsoo. Qu'est-ce que vous prenez?*" I cannot reproduce the eccentricities of his accent. "*Une petite verre de porto?*" He turned to me. "Foreigners, they all drink porto. You're always safe with that."

"Not the Dutch," said Mrs. Wilkins, with a look at the sea. "They won't touch nothin' but schnapps."

The distinguished Frenchman stopped and looked at Mr. Wilkins with some bewilderment. Whereupon Mr. Wilkins tapped his breast and said:

"*Moa, proprietarre Cirque. Vous avez visité.*"

Then, for a reason that escaped me, Mr. Wilkins made his arms into a hoop and outlined the gestures that represented a poodle jumping through it. Then he pointed at the Wa-Wa that Mrs. Wilkins was still holding on her lap.

"*La petit fils de mon femme,*" he said.

Light broke upon the governor, and he burst into a peculiarly musical and infectious laugh. Mr. Wilkins began laughing too.

"*Oui, oui,*" he cried. "*Moa,* circus proprietor. *Une petite verre de porto. Oui, oui. N'est-ce pas?*"

"Mr. Wilkins talks French like a Frenchman," Mrs. Wilkins informed the passing sea.

"*Mais très volontiers,*" said the governor, still smiling. I drew him up a chair, and he sat down with a bow to Mrs. Wilkins.

"Tell poodle-face his name's Egbert," she said, looking at the sea.

I called the boy, and we ordered a round of drinks.

"You sign the chit, Elmer," she said. "It's not a bit of good Mr. What's-his-name shaking if he can't shake nothin' better than a pair of treys."

"*Vous comprenez le français, madame?*" asked the governor politely.

"He wants to know if you speak French, my dear."

"Where does he think I was raised? Naples?"

Then the governor, with exuberant gesticulation, burst into a torrent of English so fantastic that it required all my knowledge of French to understand what he was talking about.

Presently Mr. Wilkins took him down to look at his animals, and a little later we assembled in the stuffy saloon for luncheon. The governor's wife appeared and was put on the captain's right. The governor explained to her who we all were, and she gave us a gracious bow. She was a large woman, tall and of a robust build, of fifty-five, perhaps, and she was dressed somewhat severely in black silk. On her head she wore a huge round topee. Her features were so large and regular, her form so statuesque, that you were reminded of the massive females who take part in processions. She would have admirably suited the rôle of Columbia or Britannia in a patriotic demonstration. She towered over her diminutive husband like a skyscraper over a shack. He talked incessantly, with vivacity and wit, and when he said anything amusing her heavy features relaxed into a large fond smile.

"*Que tu es bête, mon ami,*" she said. She turned to the captain. "You must not pay any attention to him. He is always like that."

We had indeed a very amusing meal, and when it was over we separated to our various cabins to sleep away the heat of the afternoon. On such a small boat, having once made the acquaintance of my fellow passengers, it would have been impossible, even had I wished it, not to pass with them every

moment of the day that I was not in my cabin. The only person who held himself aloof was the Italian tenor. He spoke
to no one, but sat by himself as far forward as he could get,
twanging a guitar in an undertone so that you had to strain
your ears to catch the notes. We remained in sight of land,
and the sea was like a pail of milk. Talking of one thing and
another we watched the day decline, we dined, and then we
sat out again on deck under the stars. The two traders played
piquet in the hot saloon, but the Belgian colonel joined our
little group. He was shy and fat and opened his mouth only
to utter a civility. Soon, influenced perhaps by the night and
encouraged by the darkness that gave him, up there in the
bows, the sensation of being alone with the sea, the Italian
tenor, accompanying himself on his guitar, began to sing,
first in a low tone, and then a little louder, till presently, his
music captivating him, he sang with all his might. He had the
real Italian voice, all macaroni, olive oil, and sunshine, and
he sang the Neapolitan songs that I had heard in my youth
in the Piazza San Ferdinando, and fragments from *La Bohême,* and *Traviata* and *Rigoletto.* He sang with emotion
and false emphasis, and his tremolo reminded you of every
third-rate Italian tenor you had ever heard, but there in the
openness of that lovely night his exaggeration only made you
smile, and you could not but feel in your heart a lazy sensual
pleasure. He sang for an hour, perhaps, and we all fell silent; then he was still, but he did not move, and we saw his
huge bulk dimly outlined against the luminous sky.

I saw that the little French governor had been holding the
hand of his large wife, and the sight was absurd and touching.

"Do you know that this is the anniversary of the day on
which I first saw my wife," he said, suddenly breaking the
silence, which had certainly weighed on him, for I had never
met a more loquacious creature. "It is also the anniversary
of the day on which she promised to be my wife. And, which
will surprise you, they were one and the same."

"*Voyons, mon ami,*" said the lady, "you are not going to
bore our friends with that old story. You are really quite
insupportable."

But she spoke with a smile on her large, firm face and in a tone that suggested that she was quite willing to hear it again.

"But it will interest them, *mon petit chou*." It was in this way that he always addressed his wife and it was funny to hear this imposing and even majestic lady thus addressed by her small husband. "Will it not, monsieur?" he asked me. "It is a romance, and who does not like romance, especially on such a night as this?"

I assured the governor that we were all anxious to hear, and the Belgian colonel took the opportunity once more to be polite.

"You see, ours was a marriage of convenience, pure and simple."

"*C'est vrai*," said the lady. "It would be stupid to deny it. But sometimes love comes after marriage and not before, and then it is better. It lasts longer."

I could not but notice that the governor gave her hand an affectionate little squeeze.

"You see, I had been in the navy, and when I retired I was forty-nine. I was strong and active, and I was very anxious to find an occupation. I looked about; I pulled all the strings I could. Fortunately I had a cousin who had some political importance. It is one of the advantages of democratic government that if you have sufficient influence, merit, which otherwise might pass unnoticed, generally receives its due reward."

"You are modesty itself, *mon pauvre ami*," said she.

"And presently I was sent for by the Minister to the Colonies and offered the post of governor in a certain colony. It was a very distant spot that they wished to send me to, and a lonely one, but I had spent my life wandering from port to port, and that was not a matter that troubled me. I accepted with joy. The minister told me that I must be ready to start in a month. I told him that would be easy for an old bachelor who had nothing much in the world but a few clothes and a a few books.

" '*Comment, mon lieutenant*,' he cried. 'You are a bachelor?'

" 'Certainly,' I answered. 'And I have every intention of remaining one.'

" 'In that case I am afraid I must withdraw my offer. For this position it is essential that you should be married.'

"It is too long a story to tell you, but the gist of it was that owing to the scandal my predecessor, a bachelor, had caused by having native girls to live in the Residency and the consequent complaints of the white people, planters and the wives of functionaries, it had been decided that the next governor must be a model of respectability. I expostulated. I argued. I recapitulated my services to the country and the services my cousin could render at the next elections. Nothing would serve. The minister was adamant.

" 'But what can I do?' I cried with dismay.

" 'You can marry,' said the minister.

" '*Mais, voyons, monsieur le ministre,* I do not know any women. I am not a lady's man, and I am forty-nine. How do you expect me to find a wife?'"

" 'Nothing is more simple. Put an advertisement in the paper.'

"I was confounded. I did not know what to say.

" 'Well, think it over,' said the minister. 'If you can find a wife in a month you can go, but no wife no job. That is my last word.' He smiled a little, to him the situation was not without humour. 'And if you think of advertising I recommend the *Figaro*.'

"I walked away from the ministry with death in my heart. I knew the place to which they desired to appoint me, and I knew it would suit me very well to live there; the climate was tolerable, and the Residency was spacious and comfortable. The notion of being a governor was far from displeasing me, and, having nothing much but my pension as a naval officer, the salary was not to be despised. Suddenly I made up my mind. I walked to the offices of the *Figaro*, composed an advertisement, and handed it in for insertion. But I can tell you, when I walked up the Champs Elysées afterwards my heart was beating much more furiously than it had ever done when my ship was stripped for action."

The governor leaned forward and put his hand impressively on my knee.

"*Mon cher monsieur,* you will never believe it, but I had four thousand three hundred and seventy-two replies. It was an avalanche. I had expected half a dozen; I had to take a cab to take the letters to my hotel. My room was swamped with them. There were four thousand three hundred and seventy-two women who were willing to share my solitude and be a governor's lady. It was staggering. They were of all ages from seventeen to seventy. There were maidens of irreproachable ancestry and the highest culture; there were unmarried ladies who had made a little slip at one period of their career and now desired to regularize their situation; there were widows whose husbands had died in the most harrowing circumstances; and there were widows whose children would be a solace to my old age. They were blond and dark, tall and short, fat and thin; some could speak five languages and others could play the piano. Some offered me love and some craved for it; some could only give me a solid friendship but mingled with esteem; some had a fortune and others golden prospects. I was overwhelmed. I was bewildered. At last I lost my temper, for I am a passionate man, and I got up and I stamped on all those letters and all those photographs and I cried: 'I will marry none of them.' It was hopeless, I had less than a month now, and I could not see over four thousand aspirants to my hand in that time. I felt that if I did not see them all I should be tortured for the rest of my life by the thought that I had missed the one woman the fates had destined to make me happy. I gave it up as a bad job.

"I went out of my room, hideous with all those photographs and littered papers, and to drive care away went on to the boulevard and sat down at the Café de la Paix. After a time I saw a friend passing, and he nodded to me and smiled. I tried to smile, but my heart was sore; I realized that I must spend the years that remained to me in a cheap pension at Toulon or Brest as an *officier de marine en retrait. Zut!* My friend stopped and, coming up to me, sat down.

" 'What is making you look so glum, *mon cher?*' he asked me. 'You who are the gayest of mortals.'

"I was glad to have someone in whom I could confide my troubles and told him the whole story. He laughed consumedly. I have thought since that perhaps the incident had its comic side, but at the time, I assure you, I could see in it nothing to laugh at. I mentioned the fact to my friend not without asperity, and then, controlling his mirth as best he could, he said to me: 'But, my dear fellow, do you really want to marry?' At this I entirely lost my temper.

" 'You are completely idiotic,' I said. 'If I did not want to marry and what is more marry at once, within the next fortnight, do you imagine that I should have spent three days reading love letters from women I have never set eyes on?'

" 'Calm yourself and listen to me,' he replied. 'I have a cousin who lives in Geneva. She is Swiss, *du reste,* and she belongs to a family of the greatest respectability in the republic. Her morals are without reproach, she is of a suitable age, a spinster, for she has spent the last fifteen years nursing an invalid mother who has lately died, she is well educated and *pardessus le marché* she is not ugly.'

" 'It sounds as though she were a paragon,' I said.

" 'I do not say that, but she has been well brought up and would become the position you have to offer her.'

" 'There is one thing you forget. What inducement would there be for her to give up her friends and her accustomed life to accompany in exile a man of forty-nine who is by no means a beauty?' "

Monsieur le Gouverneur broke off his narrative and, shrugging his shoulders so emphatically that his head almost sank between them, turned to us.

"I am ugly. I admit it. I am of an ugliness that does not inspire terror or respect, but only ridicule, and that is the worst ugliness of all. When people see me for the first time they do not shrink with horror, there would evidently be something flattering in that, they burst out laughing. Listen, when the admirable Mr. Wilkins showed me his animals this morning Percy, the orang-utan, held out his arms and but for the bars of the cage would have clasped me to his bosom as a long lost brother. Once indeed when I was at the Jardin des Plantes in Paris and was told that one of the anthropoid apes had escaped I made my way to the exit as quickly as I could in fear that, mistaking me for the refugee, they would seize me and, notwithstanding my expostulation, shut me up in the monkey house."

"*Voyons, mon ami,*" said Madame, his wife, in her deep, slow voice, "you are talking even greater nonsense than usual. I do not say that you are an Apollo: in your position it is unnecessary that you should be; but you have dignity, you have poise, you are what any woman would call a fine man."

"I will resume my story. When I made this remark to my friend he replied: 'One can never tell with women. There is something about marriage that wonderfully attracts them. There would be no harm in asking her. After all, it is regarded as a compliment by a woman to be asked in marriage. She can but refuse.'

" 'But I do not know your cousin, and I do not see how I am to make her acquaintance. I cannot go to her house, ask to see her, and when I am shown into the drawing room say: *Voilà*, I have come to ask you to marry me. She would think I was a lunatic and scream for help. Besides, I am a man of an extreme timidity, and I could never take such a step.'

" 'I will tell you what to do,' said my friend. 'Go to Geneva and take her a box of chocolates from me. She will be glad to have news of me and will receive you with pleasure. You can have a little talk, and then, if you do not like the look of her, you take your leave and no harm is done. If, on the other hand, you do, we can go into the matter, and you can make a formal demand for her hand.'

"I was desperate. It seemed the only thing to do. We went to a shop at once and bought an enormous box of chocolates, and that night I took the train to Geneva. No sooner had I arrived than I sent her a letter to say that I was the bearer of a gift from her cousin and much wished to give myself the pleasure of delivering it in person. Within an hour I received her reply to the effect that she would be pleased to receive me at four o'clock in the afternoon. I spent the interval before my mirror, and seventeen times I tied and retied my tie.

As the clock struck four I presented myself at the door of her house and was immediately ushered into the drawing room. She was waiting for me. Her cousin said she was not ugly. Imagine my surprise to see a young woman, *enfin* a woman still young, of a noble presence, with the dignity of Juno, the features of Venus, and in her expression the intelligence of Minerva."

"You are too absurd," said Madame. "But by now these gentlemen know that one cannot believe all you say."

"I swear to you that I do not exaggerate. I was so taken aback that I nearly dropped the box of chocolates. But I said to myself: *'La garde meurt mais se ne rend pas.'* I presented the box of chocolates. I gave her news of her cousin. I found her amiable. We talked for a quarter of an hour. And then I said to myself: *'Allons-y.'* I said to her: 'Mademoiselle, I must tell you that I did not come here merely to give you a box of chocolates.'

"She smiled and remarked that evidently I must have had reasons to come to Geneva of more importance than that.

" 'I came to ask you to do me the honour of marrying me.' She gave a start.

" 'But, monsieur, you are mad,' she said.

" 'I beseech you not to answer till you have heard the facts,' I interrupted, and before she could say another word I told her the whole story. I told her about my advertisement in the *Figaro,* and she laughed till the tears ran down her face. Then I repeated my offer.

" 'You are serious?' she asked.

" 'I have never been more serious in my life.'

" 'I will not deny that your offer has come as a surprise. I had not thought of marrying, I have passed the age; but evidently your offer is not one that a woman should refuse without consideration. I am flattered. Will you give me a few days to reflect?'

" 'Mademoiselle, I am absolutely desolated,' I replied. 'But I have not time. If you will not marry me I must go back to Paris and resume my perusal of the fifteen or eighteen hundred letters that still await my attention.'

" 'It is quite evident that I cannot possibly give you an

answer at once. I had not set eyes on you a quarter of an hour
ago. I must consult my friends and my family.'

" 'What have they got to do with it? You are of full age.
The matter is pressing. I cannot wait. I have told you everything. You are an intelligent woman. What can prolonged
reflection add to the impulse of the moment?'

" 'You are not asking me to say "yes" or "no" this very
minute? That is outrageous.'

" 'That is exactly what I am asking. My train goes back
to Paris in a couple of hours.'

"She looked at me reflectively.

" 'You are quite evidently a lunatic. You ought to be shut
up both for your own safety and that of the public.'

" 'Well, which is it to be?' I said. 'Yes or no?'

"She shrugged her shoulders.

" '*Mon Dieu!*' She waited a minute, and I was on tenterhooks. 'Yes.' "

The governor waved his hand towards his wife.

"And there she is. We were married in a fortnight, and
I became governor of a colony. I married a jewel, my dear
sirs, a woman of the most charming character, one in a
thousand, a woman of a masculine intelligence and a feminine sensibility, an admirable woman."

"But hold your tongue, *mon ami*," his wife said. "You are
making me as ridiculous as yourself."

He turned to the Belgian colonel.

"Are you a bachelor, *mon colonel?* If so I strongly recommend you to go to Geneva. It is a nest (*une pepinière* was the
word he used) of the most adorable young women. You will
find a wife there as nowhere else. Geneva is besides a charming city. Do not waste a minute, but go there, and I will give
you a letter to my wife's nieces."

It was she who summed up the story.

"The fact is that in a marriage of convenience you expect
less and so you are less likely to be disappointed. As you do
not make senseless claims on one another there is no reason
for exasperation. You do not look for perfection, and so you
are tolerant to one another's faults. Passion is all very well,
but it is not a proper foundation for marriage. *Voyez-vous,*

for two people to be happy in marriage they must be able to respect one another, they must be of the same condition and their interests must be alike; then, if they are decent people and are willing to give and take, to live and let live, there is no reason why their union should not be as happy as ours." She paused. "But, of course, my husband is a very, very remarkable man."

OUR BETTERS

A Comedy in Three Acts

CHARACTERS

LADY GRAYSTON	FLEMING HARVEY
DUCHESSE DE SURENNES	ANTHONY PAXTON
PRINCIPESSA DELLA CERCOLA	LORD BLEANE
ELIZABETH SAUNDERS	POLE
ARTHUR FENWICK	ERNEST
THORNTON CLAY	

The action of the play takes place at LADY GRAYSTON's house in Grosvenor Street, Mayfair, and at her husband's place in Suffolk, Abbots Kenton.

ACT ONE

SCENE: *The drawing-room at* LADY GRAYSTON's *house in Grosvenor Street, Mayfair. It is a sumptuous double room, of the period of George II., decorated in green and gold, with a coromandel screen and lacquer cabinets; but the coverings of the chairs, the sofas and cushions, show the influence of Bakst and the Russian Ballet; they offer an agreeable mixture of rich plum, emerald green, canary and ultra-marine. On the floor is a Chinese carpet, and here and there are pieces of Ming pottery.*

It is about half-past four, early in the season, and a fine day.

When the curtain rises, from the street below is heard the melancholy chant of the lavender man.

Won't you buy my sweet lavender?
Sixteen blue branches for a penny.
If you buy it once,
You'll buy it twice,
For it makes your clothes
Smell very nice—
Sweet-scented lavender.

> BESSIE SAUNDERS *comes in. She is a very pretty Amer-*
> *ican girl, of twenty-two, with fair hair and blue eyes.*
> *She is dressed in the latest mode. She wears a hat and*
> *gloves, and carries a bag. She has just come in from*
> *the street. She has in her hand a telephone message,*
> *and going over to the telephone she takes up the*
> *receiver.*

BESSIE: Gerrard 4321. Is that the Berkeley? Put me through to Mr. Harvey, please. Fleming Harvey, that's right. [*She listens and smiles*] Yes. Who d'you think it is? [*She laughs*] I've just got your telephone message. Where have you sprung from? That's fine. How long are you staying in London? I see. I want to see you at once. Nonsense. This very minute. Now just jump into a taxi and come right away. Pearl will be in presently. Ring off, Fleming. No, I will not ring off first. [*A pause*] Are you there? How tiresome you are. You might be half-way here by now. Well, hustle.

> [*She puts down the receiver and begins to take off her*
> *gloves.* POLE, *the butler, comes in with a bunch of*
> *roses.*]

POLE: These flowers have just come for you, miss.

BESSIE: Oh! Thank you. Aren't they lovely? You must give me something to put them in, Pole.

POLE: I'll bring a vase, miss.

> [*He goes out. She buries her face in the flowers and*
> *inhales their fragrance. The* BUTLER *enters with a*
> *bowl filled with water.*]

BESSIE: Thank you. You're sure they *are* for me? There's no label.

POLE: Yes, miss. The person who brought them said they was for you, miss. I asked if there wasn't a card, and he said no, miss.

BESSIE [*With a faint smile*]: I think I know who they're from. [*She begins to arrange the flowers*] Her ladyship hasn't come in yet, has she?

POLE: Not yet, miss.

BESSIE: D'you know if anyone is coming in to tea?

POLE: Her ladyship didn't say, miss.

BESSIE: You'd better prepare for fifteen, then.

POLE: Very good, miss.

BESSIE: I was being funny, Pole.

POLE: Yes, miss? Shall I take the paper away, miss?

BESSIE [*With a slight sigh of resignation*]: Yes, do, will you? [*The telephone bell rings*] Oh, I forgot, I switched the telephone on here. See who it is.

[POLE *takes up the receiver and listens, then puts his hand over its mouth.*]

POLE: Will you speak to Lord Bleane, miss?

BESSIE: Say I'm not at home.

POLE: Miss Saunders hasn't come in yet. I beg pardon, my lord. I didn't recognise your lordship's voice. [*A pause*] Well, my lord, I did hear them say there was a private view they thought of going to at the Grosvenor. You might find Miss Saunders there.

BESSIE: You needn't elaborate, Pole.

POLE: I was only making it more convincing, miss. [*Listening*] I think so, my lord. Of course, I couldn't say for certain, my lord; they might have gone out to Ranelagh.

BESSIE: Really, Pole!

POLE: Very good, my lord. [*He puts down the receiver*] His lordship asked if you was expected in to tea, miss.

BESSIE: I see.

POLE: Is there anything else, miss?

BESSIE: No, Pole, thank you.

[*He goes out. She finishes arranging the flowers. The door is flung open and* LADY GRAYSTON *comes in, followed by* FLEMING HARVEY. PEARL—LADY GRAY-STON—*is a handsome, dashing creature, a woman of thirty-four, with red hair, and a face outrageously painted. She is dressed in a Paris frock, but of greater daring both in colour and cut than a Frenchwoman would wear.* FLEMING *is a nice-looking young American in clothes that were obviously made in New York.*]

PEARL: My dear Bessie, I've found an entirely strange young man on the doorstep who says he is a cousin.

BESSIE [*Giving him her hands enthusiastically*]: Fleming.

FLEMING: I introduced myself to Lady Grayston. She drove up just as they were opening the door. Please reassure your sister, Bessie. She looks upon me with suspicion.

BESSIE: You must remember Fleming Harvey, Pearl.

PEARL: I've never set eyes on him in my life. But he looks quite nice.

BESSIE: He is.

PEARL: He's apparently come to see you.

FLEMING: I rang up five minutes ago and Bessie ordered me to come round right away.

PEARL: Well, make him stop to tea. I've got to telephone. I've suddenly remembered that I've asked twelve people to dinner.

BESSIE: Does George know?

PEARL: Who is George?

BESSIE: Don't be absurd, Pearl. George—your husband.

PEARL: Oh! I couldn't make out who you meant. No, he doesn't know. But what's much more important, the cook doesn't know either. I'd forgotten George was in London.

[*She goes out.*]

BESSIE: George generally dines out when Pearl is giving a party, because he doesn't like people he doesn't know, and he seldom dines at home when we're alone, because it bores him.

FLEMING: It doesn't sound as if Sir George enjoyed many of the benefits of home life.

BESSIE: Now let's sit down and make ourselves comfortable. You are going to stay to tea, aren't you?

FLEMING: It's not a beverage that I'm in the habit of imbibing.

BESSIE: When you've been in England a month you won't be able to do without it. When did you land?

FLEMING: This morning. You see, I've lost no time in coming to see you.

BESSIE: I should think not. It *is* good to see someone straight from home.

FLEMING: Have you been having a good time, Bessie?

BESSIE: Wonderful! Since the beginning of the season, except when Pearl has had people here, I've been out to lunch and dinner every day, and I've been to a ball every night, generally two and sometimes three.

FLEMING: Gee!

BESSIE: If I stopped now I'd drop down dead.

FLEMING: D'you like England?

BESSIE: I adore it. I think it's too bad of dad never to have let me come over to London before. Rome and Paris are nothing. We're just trippers there, but here we're at home.

FLEMING: Don't get too much at home, Bessie.

BESSIE: Oh, Fleming, I never thanked you for sending me the roses. It was perfectly sweet of you.

FLEMING [*With a smile*]: I didn't send you any roses.

BESSIE: Didn't you? Well, why didn't you?

FLEMING: I hadn't time. But I will.

BESSIE: It's too late now. I naturally thought they were from you, because Englishmen don't send flowers in the same way as American boys do.

FLEMING: Is that so?

[*There is a slight pause.* BESSIE *gives him a quick look.*]

BESSIE: Fleming, I want to thank you for that charming letter you wrote me.

FLEMING: There's no occasion to do that, Bessie.

BESSIE: I was afraid you might feel badly about it. But we'll always be the greatest friends, won't we?

FLEMING: Always.

BESSIE: After all, you were eighteen when you asked me to marry you, and I was sixteen. It wasn't a very serious engagement. I don't know why we didn't break it off before.

FLEMING: I suppose it never occurred to us.

BESSIE: I'd almost forgotten it, but when I came over here I thought I'd better make everything quite clear.

FLEMING [*With a smile*]: Bessie, I believe you're in love.

BESSIE: No, I'm not. I tell you I'm having a wonderful time.

FLEMING: Well, who sent you the roses?

BESSIE: I don't know. Lord Bleane.

FLEMING: You're not going to marry a lord, Bessie?

BESSIE: Have you any objection?

FLEMING: Well, on first principles, I think American girls had better marry American men, but then I happen to be an American man.

[BESSIE *looks at him for a moment.*]

BESSIE: Pearl gave a dinner party last night. I was taken in by a cabinet minister, and on the other side of me I had an ambassador. Just opposite was a man who'd been Viceroy in India. Madame Angelotti dined with us, and she sang afterwards, and a lot of people came on from an official dinner in their stars and ribands. Pearl looked superb. She's a wonderful hostess, you know. Several people told me they would rather come here than to any house in London. Before Pearl married George Grayston she was engaged to a boy who was in business in Portland, Oregon.

FLEMING [*Smiling*]: I see you're quite determined to marry a lord.

BESSIE: No, I'm not. I'm keeping an open mind on the subject.

FLEMING: What d'you mean by that?

BESSIE: Well, Fleming, it hasn't escaped my notice that a certain noble lord is not unwilling to lay his beautiful coronet at my feet.

FLEMING: Don't talk like a novelette, Bessie.

BESSIE: But it feels just like a novelette. The poor dear is trying to propose to me every time he sees me, and I'm doing all I can to prevent him.

FLEMING: Why?

BESSIE: I don't want to refuse him, and then wish I hadn't.

FLEMING: You could easily make him ask you again. Women find that so simple.

BESSIE: Ah, but supposing he went right away to shoot big game in Africa. It's what they do, you know, in novelettes.

FLEMING: I'm reassured about one thing. You're not in the least in love with him.

BESSIE: I told you I wasn't. You don't mind my saying all this to you, Fleming?

FLEMING: Gracious, no; why should I?

BESSIE: You're sure you don't feel sore at my throwing you over?

FLEMING [*Cheerfully*]: Not a bit.

BESSIE: I am glad, because then I can tell you all about the noble lord.

FLEMING: Has it occurred to you that he wants to marry you for your money?

BESSIE: You can put it more prettily. You can say that he wants to marry me with my money.

FLEMING: And is that a prospect that allures you?

BESSIE: Poor dear, what else can he do? He's got a large place to keep up, and he simply hasn't a cent.

FLEMING: Really, Bessie, you amaze me.

BESSIE: I shan't when you've been here a month.

[PEARL *comes in.*]

PEARL: Now, Bessie, tell me all about this strange young man.

BESSIE: He's quite capable of telling you about himself.

PEARL [*To* FLEMING]: How long are you staying?

FLEMING: A couple of months. I want to see something of English life.

PEARL: I see. D'you want to improve your mind or d'you want to go into society?

FLEMING: I suppose I couldn't combine the two.

PEARL: Are you rich?

FLEMING: Not at all.

PEARL: It doesn't matter, you're good-looking. If one wants to be a success in London one must either have looks, wit, or a bank-balance. You know Arthur Fenwick, don't you?

FLEMING: Only by reputation.

PEARL: How superciliously you say that!

FLEMING: He provides bad food to the working classes of the United States at an exorbitant price. I have no doubt he makes a lot of money.

BESSIE: He's a great friend of Pearl's.

PEARL: When he first came over because they turned up their noses at him in New York, I said to him: My dear Mr. Fenwick, you're not good-looking, you're not amusing, you're not well-bred, you're only rich. If you want to get into society you must spend money.

FLEMING: It was evidently in the nature of a straight talk.

BESSIE: We must do what we can for Fleming, Pearl.

PEARL [*With a chuckle*]: We'll introduce him to Minnie Surennes.

FLEMING: Who in the world is she?

PEARL: The Duchesse de Surennes. Don't you remember? She was a Miss Hodgson. Chicago people. Of course, they're nobody in America, but that doesn't matter over here. She adores good-looking boys, and I daresay she's getting rather tired of Tony. [*To* BESSIE] By the way, they're coming in this afternoon.

BESSIE: I don't like Tony.

PEARL: Why not? I think he's charming. He's the most unprincipled ruffian I ever met.

FLEMING: Is Tony the duke?

PEARL: What duke? Her husband? Oh no, she divorced him years ago.

BESSIE: I think Fleming would like the Princess much better.

PEARL: Oh, well, he'll meet her here to-day, too.

BESSIE: She was a Miss van Hoog, Fleming.

FLEMING: Is she divorced too?

PEARL: Oh no, her husband's an Italian. It's very difficult to get a divorce in Italy. She's only separated. She's quite nice. She's one of my greatest friends. She bores me a little.

[POLE *comes in to announce* THORNTON CLAY *and then goes out.* THORNTON CLAY *is a stout American with a bald head and an effusive manner. He is somewhat overdressed. He speaks with a marked American accent.*]

POLE: Mr. Thornton Clay.

CLAY: How d'you do?

PEARL: You're the very person we want, Thornton. An entirely strange young man has suddenly appeared on my doorstep, and says he's my cousin.

CLAY: My dear Pearl, that is a calamity which we Americans must always be prepared for.

BESSIE: I won't have you say such things, Mr. Clay. Fleming is not only our cousin, but he's my very oldest friend. Aren't you, Fleming?

PEARL: Bessie has a charming nature. She really thinks that friendship puts one under an obligation.

FLEMING: Since you're talking of me, won't you introduce me to Mr. Clay?

PEARL: How American you are!

FLEMING [*Smiling*]: It's not unnatural, is it?

PEARL: Over here we haven't the passion that you have in America for introducing people. My dear Thornton, allow me to present to you my long-lost cousin, Mr. Fleming Harvey.

CLAY: It's so long since I was in America that I almost forget, but I believe the proper answer to that is: Mr. Fleming Harvey, I'm pleased to make your acquaintance.

FLEMING: Aren't you an American, Mr. Clay?

CLAY: I won't deny that I was born in Virginia.

FLEMING: I beg your pardon, I thought from the way you spoke . . .

CLAY [*Interrupting*]: But, of course, my home is London.

PEARL: Nonsense, Thornton, your home is wherever there's a first-class hotel.

CLAY: I went to America seven years ago. My father died and I had to go and settle up his affairs. Everyone took me for an Englishman.

FLEMING: That must have gratified you very much, Mr. Clay.

CLAY: Of course, I haven't a trace of an American accent I suppose that was the reason. And then my clothes.

[*He looks down at them with satisfaction.*]

PEARL: Fleming wants to see life in London, Thornton. He can't do better than put himself under your wing.

CLAY: I know everyone who's worth knowing. I can't deny that.

PEARL: Thornton calls more countesses by their Christian names than any man in town.

CLAY: I'll get him cards for some good balls, and I'll see that he's asked to one or two of the right parties.

PEARL: He's good-looking, and I'm sure he dances well. He'll be a credit to you, Thornton.

CLAY [*To* FLEMING]: But, of course, there's really nothing I *can* do for you. At Lady Grayston's you are in the very hub of society. I don't mean the stuffy, old-fashioned society, that goes about in barouches and bores itself stiff, but the society that counts, the society that figures in the newspapers. Pearl is the most wonderful hostess in London.

PEARL: What *do* you want, Thornton?

CLAY: In this house, sooner or later, you'll meet every remarkable man in England except one. That is George Grayston. And he's only remarkable because he's her husband.

PEARL [*With a chuckle*]: I might have known you were only saying a pleasant thing in order to make the next one more disagreeable.

CLAY: Of course, I can't make out why you never ask George to your parties. Personally I like him.

PEARL: That's all the nicer of you, Thornton, since he always speaks of you as that damned snob.

CLAY [*With a shrug of the shoulders*]: Poor George, he has such a limited vocabulary. I met Flora della Cercola at luncheon to-day. She told me she was coming to tea with you.

PEARL: She's getting up a concert in aid of something or other, and she wants me to help her.

CLAY: Poor Flora, with her good works! She takes philanthropy as a drug to allay the pangs of unrequited love.

PEARL: I always tell her she'd do much better to take a lover.

CLAY: You'll shock Mr. Harvey.

PEARL: It won't hurt him. It'll do him good.

CLAY: Did you ever know her husband?

PEARL: Oh yes, I met him. Just the ordinary little Dago. I cannot imagine why she should ever have been in love with him. She's an extraordinary creature. D'you know, I'm convinced that she's never had an affair.

CLAY: Some of these American women are strangely sexless.

FLEMING: I have an idea that some of them are even virtuous.

PEARL [*With a smile*]: It takes all sorts to make a world.
[POLE *enters to announce the* DUCHESSE DE SURENNES, *and then goes out.*]

POLE: The Duchess de Surennes.
[*The* DUCHESSE *is a large, dark woman of forty-five with scarlet lips and painted cheeks, a woman of opulent form, bold, self-assured and outrageously sensual. She suggests a drawing of a Roman Emperor by Aubrey Beardsley. She is gowned with a certain dashing magnificence, and wears a long string of large pearls round her neck. During the conversation* POLE *and two footmen bring in tea, and place it in the back drawing-room.*]

PEARL: My dear, how nice of you to come.

DUCHESSE: Isn't Tony here?

PEARL: No.

DUCHESSE: He said he was coming straight here.

PEARL: I daresay he's been delayed.

DUCHESSE: I can't understand it. He telephoned a quarter of an hour ago that he was starting at once.

PEARL [*Reassuringly*]: He'll be here presently.

DUCHESSE [*With an effort over herself*]: How pretty you're looking, Bessie. No wonder all the men I meet rave about you.

BESSIE: Englishmen are so shy. Why don't they rave *to* me?

DUCHESSE: They'll never let you go back to America.

PEARL: Of course, she's never going back. I'm determined that she shall marry an Englishman.

CLAY: She'll make a charming addition to our American peeresses.

PEARL: And there'll be another that you can call by her Christian name, Thornton.

BESSIE: I wish you wouldn't talk as if I hadn't a word to say in the matter.

CLAY: Of course, you've got a word to say, Bessie—a very important one.

BESSIE: Yes, I suppose?

CLAY: Exactly.

PEARL: Pour out the tea, darling, will you?

BESSIE: Surely. [*To* CLAY] I know you don't share Fleming's contempt for tea, Mr. Clay.

CLAY: I couldn't live a day without it. Why, I never travel without a tea basket.

FLEMING [*Ironically*]: Is that so?

CLAY: You Americans who live in America . . .

FLEMING [*Under his breath*]: So queer of us.

CLAY: Despise the delectable habit of drinking tea because you are still partly barbarous. The hour that we spend over it is the most delightful of the day. We do not make a business of eating as at luncheon or dinner. We are at ease with ourselves. We toy with pretty cakes as an excuse for conversation. We discuss the abstract, our souls, our morals; we play delicately with the concrete, our neighbour's new bonnet or her latest lover. We drink tea because we are a highly civilised nation.

FLEMING: I must be very stupid, but I don't follow.

CLAY: My dear fellow, the degree of a nation's civilisation is marked by its disregard for the necessities of existence. You have gone so far as to waste money, but we have gone farther; we waste what is infinitely more precious, more transitory, more irreparable—we waste time.

DUCHESSE: My dear Thornton, you fill me with despair. Compton Edwardes has cut me off my tea. I thought he was only depriving me of a luxury, now I see he's depriving me also of a religious rite.

FLEMING: Who in heaven's name is Compton Edwardes, that he should have such influence?

PEARL: My dear Fleming, he's the most powerful man in London. He's the great reducer.

FLEMING: Gracious! What does he reduce?

PEARL: Fat.

DUCHESSE: He's a perfect marvel, that man. Do you know, the Duchess of Arlington told me he'd taken nine pounds off her.

PEARL: My dear, that's nothing. Why, Clara Hollington gave me her word of honour she'd lost over a stone.

BESSIE [*From the tea-table*]: Anyone who wants tea must come and fetch it.

[*The men saunter over to the next room, while* PEARL *and the* DUCHESSE *go on with their conversation.*]

DUCHESSE: Who is that nice-looking young man, Pearl?

PEARL: Oh, he's a young American. He pretends to be a cousin of mine. He's come to see Bessie.

DUCHESSE: Does he want to marry her?

PEARL: Good heavens, I hope not. He's only an old friend. You know the funny ways they have in America.

DUCHESSE: I suppose nothing is really settled about Harry Bleane?

PEARL: No. But I shouldn't be surprised if you saw an announcement in the Morning Post one day.

DUCHESSE: Has she enough money for him?

PEARL: She has a million.

DUCHESSE: Not pounds?

PEARL: Oh no, dollars.

DUCHESSE: That's only eight thousand a year. I shouldn't have thought he'd be satisfied with that.

PEARL: People can't expect so much nowadays. There won't be any more enormous heiresses as there were in your time. Besides, Harry Bleane isn't such a catch as all that. Of course, it's better to be an English baron than an Italian count, but that's about all you can say for it.

DUCHESSE: Of course she'll accept him?

PEARL: Oh yes, she's crazy to live in England. And as I tell her, it's quite pleasant to be a peeress even now.

DUCHESSE: What on earth can have happened to Tony?

PEARL: My dear, he's not likely to have been run over by a motor-bus.

DUCHESSE: I'm not afraid of motor-buses running over him; I'm afraid of him running after Gaiety girls.

PEARL [*Drily*]: I should have thought you kept a very sharp eye on him.

DUCHESSE: You see, he hasn't got anything to do from morning till night.

PEARL: Why doesn't he get a job?

DUCHESSE: I've been trying to get him something, but it's so difficult. You've got such a lot of influence, Pearl. Can't you do something? I should be so grateful.

PEARL: What can he do?

DUCHESSE: Anything. And as you know he's very good-looking.

PEARL: Does he know French and German?

DUCHESSE: No, he has no gift for languages.

PEARL: Can he type and write shorthand?

DUCHESSE: Oh, no. Poor dear, you can hardly expect that.

PEARL: Can he do accounts?

DUCHESSE: No, he has no head for figures.

PEARL [*Reflectively*]: Well, the only thing I can see that he'd do for is a government office.

DUCHESSE: Oh, my dear, if you only could manage that. You can't think what a comfort it would be for me to know that he couldn't get into mischief at least from ten to four every day.

[POLE *announces* TONY PAXTON. TONY *is a handsome youth of twenty-five, in beautiful clothes, with engaging manners and a charming smile.*]

POLE: Mr. Paxton.

PEARL: Well, Tony, how is life?

TONY: Rotten. I haven't backed a winner or won a rubber this week.

PEARL: Ah well, that's the advantage of not having money, you can afford to lose it.

DUCHESSE [*Bursting in*]: Where have you been, Tony?

TONY: I? Nowhere.

DUCHESSE: You said you were coming straight here. It

doesn't take twenty-five minutes to get here from Dover Street.

TONY: I thought there wasn't any hurry. I was just hanging about the club.

DUCHESSE: I rang up the club again, and they said you'd gone.

TONY [*After a very slight pause*]: I was downstairs having a shave, and I suppose they never thought of looking for me in the barber's shop.

DUCHESSE: What on earth did you want to be shaved for at half-past four in the afternoon?

TONY: I thought you'd like me to look nice and clean.

PEARL: Go and get Bessie to give you some tea, Tony; I'm sure you want it after the strenuous day you've had.

[*He nods and walks into the inner room.*]

PEARL: Minnie, how can you be so silly? You can't expect to keep a man if you treat him like that.

DUCHESSE: I know he's lying to me, there's not a word of truth in anything he says: but he's so slim I can never catch him out. Oh, I'm so jealous.

PEARL: Are you really in love with him?

DUCHESSE: He's everything in the world to me.

PEARL: You shouldn't let yourself be carried away like this.

DUCHESSE: I'm not cold-blooded like you.

PEARL: You seem to have a passion for rotters, and they always treat you badly.

DUCHESSE: Oh, I don't care about the others. Tony is the only one I've ever really loved.

PEARL: Nonsense! You were just as much in love with Jack Harris. You did everything in the world for him. You taught him to wear his clothes. You got him into society. And the moment he could do without you he chucked you. Tony will do just the same.

DUCHESSE: I'm not going to be such a fool this time. I'm going to take care he can't do without me.

PEARL: I can't imagine what you see in him. You must know that . . .

DUCHESSE [*Interrupting*]: There's very little I don't

know. He's a liar, a gambler, an idler, a spendthrift, but in his way he is fond of me. [*Appealingly*] You can see he's fond of me, can't you?

PEARL: He's so much younger than you, Minnie.

DUCHESSE: I can't help it. I love him.

PEARL: Oh, well, I suppose it's no good talking. As long as he makes you happy.

DUCHESSE: He doesn't. He makes me miserable. But I love him. . . . He wants me to marry him, Pearl.

PEARL: You're not going to?

DUCHESSE: No, I won't be such a fool as that. If I married him I'd have no hold over him at all.

[*Enter* POLE *to announce the* PRINCESS DELLA CERCOLA. *She is a tall, thin woman of thirty-five, with a pale, haggard face and great dark eyes. She is a gentle, kind creature, but there is something pathetic, almost tragic, in her appearance. She is dressed, though very well, and obviously by a Paris dressmaker, more quietly than the* DUCHESSE *or* PEARL. *She has not only wealth, but distinction.*]

POLE: Princess della Cercola.

[*Exit.* PEARL *gets up to receive her. They kiss.*]

PEARL: Darling!

PRINCESS: D'you hate me for coming to bother you? I ran up because I know how difficult you are to catch. [*Kissing the* DUCHESSE] How are you, Minnie?

DUCHESSE: Don't ask me for a subscription, Flora. I'm so poor.

PRINCESS [*Smiling*]: Wait till I tell you what it's for, and then you'll remember that you had a father called Spencer Hodgson.

DUCHESSE [*With a little groan*]: As if I wanted to be reminded of it!

PEARL: You're so absurd, Minnie. You should make a joke of the pork. I always tell people about father's hardware store, and when I haven't got a funny story to tell about it, I invent one.

PRINCESS: You've made your father quite a character in London.

PEARL: That's why I never let him come over. He couldn't possibly live up to his reputation.

[FLEMING HARVEY *comes forward from the inner room.*]

FLEMING: I'm going to say good-bye to you.

PEARL: You musn't go before I've introduced you to Flora. Flora, this is Mr. Fleming Harvey. He's just come from America. He probably carries a six-shooter in his hip-pocket.

FLEMING: I'm told I mayn't say I'm pleased to make your acquaintance, Princess.

PRINCESS: When did you land?

FLEMING: This morning.

PRINCESS: I envy you.

FLEMING: Because I landed this morning?

PRINCESS: No, because a week ago you were in America.

DUCHESSE: Flora!

FLEMING: I was beginning to think it was something to be rather ashamed of.

PRINCESS: Oh, you mustn't pay any attention to Pearl and the Duchesse. They're so much more English than the English.

PEARL: I notice you show your devotion to the country of your birth by staying away from it, Flora.

PRINCESS: Last time I was in America it made me so unhappy that I vowed I'd never go there again.

DUCHESSE: I was there ten years ago, when I was divorcing Gaston. I hadn't been in America since my marriage, and I'd forgotten what it was like. Oh, it was so crude. Oh, it was so provincial. You don't mind my saying so, Mr. Harvey?

FLEMING: Not at all. You're just as American as I am, and there's no reason why among ourselves we shouldn't abuse the mother that bore us.

DUCHESSE: Oh, but I don't look upon myself as American. I'm French. After all, I haven't a trace of an American accent. To show you how it got on my nerves, I almost didn't divorce Gaston because I thought I couldn't bring myself to stay in America long enough.

PRINCESS: It's not because it was crude and provincial that

I was unhappy in America. I was unhappy because after all it was home, the only real home I've ever had, and I was a stranger.

PEARL: My dear Flora, you're being very sentimental.

PRINCESS [*Smiling*]: I'm sorry; I apologise. You're a New Yorker, Mr. Harvey?

FLEMING: I'm proud of it, madam.

PRINCESS: New York's wonderful, isn't it? It has something that no other city in the world has got. I like to think of Fifth Avenue on a spring day. The pretty girls in their smart frocks and neat shoes, who trip along so gaily, and all the good-looking boys.

DUCHESSE: I grant you that; some of the boys are too lovely for words.

PRINCESS: Everyone is so strong and confident. There's such an exaltation in the air. You feel in the passers-by a serene and unshakable belief in the future. Oh, it's very good to be alive in Fifth Avenue on a sunny day in April.

FLEMING: It's good for an American to hear another American say such pleasant things about his country.

PRINCESS: You must come and see me, and you shall tell me all the news of home.

PEARL: How high the newest building is, and how much money the latest millionaire has got.

FLEMING: Good-bye.

PEARL: Have you made friends with Thornton Clay?

FLEMING: I hope so.

PEARL: You must get him to give you the address of his tailor.

FLEMING: Aren't you pleased with my clothes?

PEARL: They're very American, you know.

FLEMING: So am I.

[THORNTON CLAY *comes forward. The* DUCHESSE *strolls over to the inner room and is seen talking with* BESSIE *and* TONY PAXTON.]

PEARL: Thornton, I was just telling Mr. Harvey that you'd take him to your tailor.

CLAY: I was going to suggest it.

FLEMING: My clothes are not at all a success.

PEARL: Who d'you go to? Stultz?

CLAY: Of course. He's the only tailor in London. [*To* FLEMING] Of course he's a German, but art has no nationality.

FLEMING: I'm pleased at all events to think that it's a German tailor who's going to make me look like an Englishman.

[*He goes out.* THORNTON *makes his farewells.*]

CLAY: Good-bye, Pearl.

PEARL: Are you going? Don't forget you're coming down to Kenton on Saturday.

CLAY: I won't, indeed. I adore your week-end parties, Pearl. I'm so exhausted by Monday morning that I'm fit for nothing for the rest of the week. Good-bye.

[*He shakes hands and goes out. As he is going,* POLE *opens the door to announce* LORD BLEANE. *He is a young man, very English in appearance, pleasant, clean and well-groomed.*]

[*Exit.*]

POLE: Lord Bleane.

PEARL: Dear Harry, how nice of you to come.

BLEANE: I'm in absolute despair.

PEARL: Good heavens, why?

BLEANE: They're sending a mission to Rumania to hand the Garter to some bigwig and I've got to go with it.

PEARL: Oh, but that'll be very interesting.

BLEANE: Yes, but we start to-morrow, and I shan't be able to come down to Kenton on Saturday.

PEARL: When do you come back?

BLEANE: In four weeks.

PEARL: Then come down to Kenton the Saturday after that.

BLEANE: May I?

PEARL: You must go and break the news to Bessie. She was so looking forward to your visit.

BLEANE: D'you think she'll give me some tea?

PEARL: I have no doubt, if you ask her nicely.

[*He goes over to the inner room.*]

PRINCESS: Now I've got you to myself for two minutes. You will help me with my concert, won't you?

PEARL: Of course. What do you want me to do? I'll make Arthur Fenwick take any number of tickets. You know how charitable he is.

PRINCESS: It's for a very good cause.

PEARL: I'm sure it is. But don't harrow me with revolting stories of starving children. I'm not interested in the poor.

PRINCESS [*Smiling*]: How can you say that?

PEARL: Are you? I often wonder if your philanthropy isn't an elaborate pose. You don't mind my saying that, do you?

PRINCESS [*Good-humouredly*]: Not at all. You have no heart, and you can't imagine that anyone else should have.

PEARL: I have plenty of heart, but it beats for people of my own class.

PRINCESS: I've only found one thing really worth doing with all this money I have, and that is to help a little those who need help.

PEARL [*With a shrug*]: So long as it makes you happy.

PRINCESS: It doesn't, but it prevents me from being utterly miserable.

PEARL: You make me so impatient, Flora. You've got more money than you know what to do with. You're a princess. You've practically got rid of your husband. I cannot imagine what more you want. I wish I could get rid of mine.

PRINCESS [*Smiling*]: I don't know what you've got to complain of in George.

PEARL: That's just it. I shouldn't mind if he beat me or made love to chorus girls. I could divorce him then. Oh, my dear, thank your stars that you had a husband who was grossly unfaithful to you. Mine wants me to live nine months of the year in the country and have a baby every five minutes. I didn't marry an Englishman for that.

PRINCESS: Why *did* you marry him?

PEARL: I made a mistake. I'd lived all my life in New York. I was very ignorant. I thought if you were a baronet you must be in society.

PRINCESS: I often wonder if you're happy, Pearl.

PEARL: Do you? Of course I'm happy.

PRINCESS: An ambassador told me the other day that you

were the most powerful woman in London. It's very wonderful how you've made your way. You had nothing very much to help you.

PEARL: Shall I tell you how it was done? By force of character, wit, unscrupulousness and push.

PRINCESS [*Smiling*]: You're very frank.

PEARL: That has always been my pose.

PRINCESS: I sometimes think there's positive genius in the way you've ignored the snubs of the great.

PEARL [*With a chuckle*]: You're being very unpleasant, Flora.

PRINCESS: And there's something very like heroism in the callousness with which you've dropped people when they've served your turn.

PEARL: You're driving me to the conclusion that you don't altogether approve of me.

PRINCESS: On the other hand I can't help admiring you. You've brought all the determination, insight, vigour, strength, which have made our countrymen turn America into what it is, to get what you wanted. In a way your life has been a work of art. And what makes it more complete is that what you've aimed at is trivial, transitory and worthless.

PEARL: My dear Flora, people don't hunt in order to catch a fox.

PRINCESS: Sometimes, doesn't it make you rather nervous, when you're sitting on the top of your ladder, in case anyone should give it a kick as he passes?

PEARL: It'll want more than a kick to topple my ladder over. D'you remember when that silly woman made such a fuss because her husband was in love with me? It wasn't till I only just escaped the divorce court that the duchesses really took me up.

[*The* DUCHESSE *comes forward with* TONY PAXTON.]

DUCHESSE: We really must be going, Pearl. I expect my masseur at six. Compton Edwardes told me about him. He's wonderful, but he's so run after, if you keep him waiting a moment he goes away.

PEARL: My dear, do be careful. Fanny Hallam got herself down to a mere nothing, but it made her look a hundred.

DUCHESSE: Oh, I know, but Compton Edwardes has recommended to me a wonderful woman who comes every morning to do my face.

PEARL: You are coming to my ball, aren't you?

DUCHESSE: Of course we're coming. Yours are almost the only parties in London where one amuses oneself as much as at a night club.

PEARL: I'm having Ernest to come in and dance.

DUCHESSE: I thought of having him one evening. How much does he charge for coming in socially?

PEARL: Twenty guineas.

DUCHESSE: Good heavens, I could never afford that.

PEARL: What nonsense! You're far richer than I am.

DUCHESSE: I'm not so clever, darling. I can't think how you do so much on your income.

PEARL [*Amused*]: I'm a very good manager.

DUCHESSE: One would never think it. Good-bye, dear. Are you coming, Tony?

TONY: Yes.

[*She goes out.*]

TONY [*Shaking hands with* PEARL]: I've not had a word with you to-day.

PEARL [*Chaffing him*]: What are we to do about it?

PRINCESS: I *must* get Minnie to go to my concert. Minnie.

[*She goes out.* TONY *is left face to face with* PEARL.]

TONY: You're looking perfectly divine to-day. I don't know what there is about you.

PEARL [*Amused, but not disconcerted*]: It is nice of you to say so.

TONY: I simply haven't been able to take my eyes off you.

PEARL: Are you making love to me?

TONY: That's nothing new, is it?

PEARL: You'll get into trouble.

TONY: Don't be disagreeable, Pearl.

PEARL: I don't remember that I ever told you you might call me Pearl.

TONY: It's how I think of you. You can't prevent me from doing that.

PEARL: Well, I think it's very familiar.

TONY: I don't know what you've done to me. I think of you all day long.

PEARL: I don't believe it for a minute. You're an unprincipled ruffian, Tony.

TONY: Do you mind?

PEARL [*With a chuckle*]: Shameless creature. I wonder what it is that Minnie sees in you.

TONY: I have all sorts of merits.

PEARL: I'm glad you think so. I can only discover one.

TONY: What is that?

PEARL: You're somebody else's property.

TONY: Oh!

PEARL [*Holding out her hand*]: Good-bye.

[*He kisses her wrist. His lips linger. She looks at him from under her eyelashes.*]

PEARL: It doesn't make you irresistible, you know.

TONY: There's always the future.

PEARL: The future's everybody's property.

TONY [*In an undertone*]: Pearl.

PEARL: Be quick and go. Minnie will be wondering why you don't come.

[*He goes out.* PEARL *turns away with a smile.* BESSIE *and* LORD BLEANE *advance into the room.*]

PEARL: Has Harry broken the news to you that he can't come down to us on Saturday?

[*The* PRINCESS *comes in.*]

PRINCESS: I've got my subscription.

PEARL: I kept Tony up here as long as I could so as to give you a chance.

PRINCESS [*With a laugh*]: That was really tactful.

PEARL: Poor Minnie, she's as mean as cat's meat. [*With a glance at* BESSIE *and* LORD BLEANE] If you'd like to come down to the morning-room we can go through my visitors' book and see who'll be useful to you.

PRINCESS: Oh, that would be kind of you.

PEARL [*To* BLEANE]: Don't go till I come back, will you? I haven't had a word with you yet.

BLEANE: All right.

[PEARL *and the* PRINCESS *go out.*]

BESSIE: I wonder if you sent me these flowers, Lord Bleane?

BLEANE: I did. I thought you wouldn't mind.

BESSIE: It was very kind of you.

[*She takes two of the roses and puts them in her dress.*
BLEANE *is overcome with shyness. He does not know
how to begin.*]

BLEANE: D'you mind if I light a cigarette?

BESSIE: Not at all.

BLEANE [*As he lights it*]: D'you know, this is the first time I've ever been alone with you. It was very tactful of Lady Grayston to leave us.

BESSIE: I'm not sure if it wasn't a trifle too tactful.

BLEANE: I was hoping most awfully to have the chance of getting a talk with you.

[*The song of the lavender is heard again in the street.*
BESSIE *welcomes the diversion.*]

BESSIE: Oh, listen, there's the lavender man come back again. [*She goes to the window and listens*] Throw him down a shilling, will you?

BLEANE: All right. [*He takes a coin from his pocket and throws it into the street.*]

BESSIE: I seem to feel all the charm of England in that funny little tune. It suggests cottage gardens, and hedges, and winding roads.

BLEANE: My mother grows lavender at home. When we were kids we were made to pick it, and my mother used to put it in little muslin bags and tie them up with pink ribbon. And she used to put them under the pillows of one's bed and in all the drawers. Shall I ask her to send you some?

BESSIE: Oh, that would be such a bother for her.

BLEANE: It wouldn't. She'd like to. And you know, it's not like the lavender you buy. It knocks spots off anything you can get in shops.

BESSIE: You must hate leaving London at this time of year.

BLEANE: Oh, I'm not very keen on London. [*Making a dash for it*] I hate leaving you.

BESSIE [*With comic desperation*]: Let's not talk about me, Lord Bleane.

BLEANE: But that's the only topic that occurs to me.

BESSIE: There's always the weather in England.

BLEANE: You see, I'm off to-morrow.

BESSIE: I never saw anyone so obstinate.

BLEANE: I shan't see you again for nearly a month. We haven't known one another very long, and if I hadn't been going away I expect I'd have thought it better to wait a bit.

BESSIE [*Clasping her hands*]: Lord Bleane, don't propose to me.

BLEANE: Why not?

BESSIE: Because I shall refuse you.

BLEANE: Oh!

BESSIE: Tell me about the part of the country you live in. I don't know Kent at all. Is it pretty?

BLEANE: I don't know. It's home.

BESSIE: I love those old Elizabethan houses that you have in England with all their chimneys.

BLEANE: Oh, ours isn't a show place, you know. It's just a rather ugly yellow brick house that looks like a box, and it's got a great big stucco portico in front of it. I think the garden's rather jolly.

BESSIE: Pearl hates Abbots Kenton. She'd sell it if George would. She's only really happy in London.

BLEANE: I don't know that I was so particularly struck on Bleane till I was over in France. When I was in hospital at Boulogne there didn't seem much to do but to think about things. . . . It didn't seem as if I *could* get well. I knew I should if they'd only let me come home, but they wouldn't; they said I couldn't be moved. . . . It's rather bleak in our part of the country. We've got an east wind that people find a bit trying, but if you've been used to it all your life it bucks you up wonderful. In summer it can be awfully hot down there, but there's always something fresh and salt in the air. You see, we're so near the marshes. . . . It was only just across the water, and it seemed such an awful long way off. I ain't boring you, am I?

BESSIE: No. I want you to tell me.

BLEANE: It's a funny sort of country. There are a lot of green fields and elm trees, and the roads wind about—it's rotten for motoring; and then you have the marshes, with dykes in them—we used to jump them when we were boys, and fall in mostly; and then there's the sea. It doesn't sound much, but I felt it was the most ripping thing I knew. And then there are hop-fields—I forgot them—and the oast-houses. They're rather picturesque, I suppose. I expect it's like the lavender to you. To me it's just England.

[BESSIE *gets up and walks towards the window. In the distance is heard the melancholy cry of the lavender man.*]

BLEANE: What are you thinking about?

BESSIE: It must be very wonderful to feel like that about one's home. I've never known anything but a red stone house in Nineteenth Street. As soon as dad can get a decent offer for it we're going to move further up town. Mother has a fancy for Seventy-Second Street, I don't know why.

BLEANE: Of course, I know it couldn't mean the same to a girl that it means to me. I shouldn't expect anyone to live there always. I can be quite happy in London.

BESSIE [*With a smile*]: You're determined to do it?

BLEANE: If you *could* bring yourself to marry me, I'd try and give you a good time.

BESSIE: Well, I suppose that's a proposal.

BLEANE: I've never made one before, and it makes me a bit nervous.

BESSIE: You haven't said anything that I can answer yes or no to.

BLEANE: I don't want to say anything that you *can* answer no to.

BESSIE [*With a chuckle*]: Let me say that I'll think it over, may I?

BLEANE: I'm going away to-morrow.

BESSIE: I'll give you an answer when you come back.

BLEANE: But that won't be for four weeks.

BESSIE: It'll give us both a chance to make up our minds. After all, it *is* rather a serious step. You may come to the conclusion that you don't really want to marry me.

BLEANE: There's no fear of that.

BESSIE: You're coming down to Kenton for the week-end after you get back. If you change your mind send Pearl a wire putting yourself off. I shall understand, and I shan't be in the least hurt or offended.

BLEANE: Then it's good-bye till then.

BESSIE: Yes. And . . . thank you very much for wishing to marry me.

BLEANE: Thank you very much for not refusing me outright.

[*They shake hands and he goes out. She walks over to the window to look at him, glances at the watch on her wrist, and then leaves the room. In a moment* POLE *shows in* ARTHUR FENWICK. *He is a tall, elderly man with a red face and grey hair.*]

POLE: I'll tell her ladyship you're here, sir.

FENWICK: That'll be very good of you.

[POLE *goes out.* FENWICK *takes a cigar from his case, and the evening paper from a table, and settles himself down comfortably to read and smoke. He makes himself very much at home.* PEARL *comes in.*]

PEARL: Aren't Bessie and Harry Bleane here?

FENWICK: No.

PEARL: That's very strange. I wonder what can have happened.

FENWICK: Never mind about Bessie and Harry Bleane. Give me your attention now.

PEARL: You're very late.

FENWICK: I like to come when I stand a chance of finding you alone, girlie.

PEARL: I wish you wouldn't call me girlie, Arthur. I do hate it.

FENWICK: That's how I think of you. When I'm present at one of your big set-outs, and watch you like a queen among all those lords and ambassadors and bigwigs, I just say to myself, She's my girlie, and I feel warm all over. I'm so proud of you then. You've got there, girlie, you've got there.

PEARL [*Smiling*]: You've been very kind to me, Arthur.

FENWICK: You've got brains, girlie, that's how you've done it. It's brains. Underneath your flighty ways and that casual air of yours, so that one might think you were just enjoying yourself and nothing more, I see you thinking it all out, pulling a string here and a string there; you've got them in the hollow of your hand all the time. You leave nothing to chance, Pearl, you're a great woman.

PEARL: Not great enough to make you obey your doctor's orders.

FENWICK [*Taking the cigar out of his mouth*]: You're not going to ask me to throw away the first cigar I've had to-day?

PEARL: To please me, Arthur. They're so bad for you.

FENWICK: If you put it like that I must give in.

PEARL: I don't want you to be ill.

FENWICK: You've got a great heart, girlie. The world just thinks you're a smart, fashionable woman, clever, brilliant, beautiful, a leader of fashion, but I know different. I know you've got a heart of gold.

PEARL: You're a romantic old thing, Arthur.

FENWICK: My love for you is the most precious thing I have in the world. You're my guiding star, you're my ideal. You stand to me for all that's pure and noble and clean in womanhood. God bless you, girlie. I don't know what I should do if you failed me. I don't believe I could live if I ever found out that you weren't what I think you.

PEARL [*With her tongue in her cheek*]: You shan't, if I can help it.

FENWICK: You do care for me a little, girlie?

PEARL: Of course I do.

FENWICK: I'm an old man, girlie.

PEARL: What nonsense! I look upon you as a mere boy.

FENWICK [*Flattered*]: Well, I expect a good many young men would be glad to have my physique. I can work fourteen hours on end and feel as fresh as a daisy at the end of it.

PEARL: Your vitality is wonderful.

FENWICK: I sometimes wonder what it is that first drew you to me, girlie.

PEARL: I don't know. I suppose it was the impression of strength you give.

FENWICK: Yes, I've often been told that. It's very difficult for people to be with me long without realising that—well, that I'm not just the man in the street.

PEARL: I always feel I can rely on you.

FENWICK: You couldn't have said anything to please me better. I want you to rely on me. I know you. I'm the only man who's ever understood you. I know that, deep down in that big, beating, human heart of yours, you're a timid, help-less little thing, with the innocence of a child, and you want a man like me to stand between you and the world. My God, how I love you, girlie!

PEARL: Take care, there's the butler.

FENWICK: Oh, damn it, there's always the butler.

[POLE *comes in with a telegram and a parcel of books.*]

PEARL [*Taking the telegram and glancing at the parcel*]: What's that, Pole?

POLE: They're books, my lady. They've just come from Hatchard's.

PEARL: Oh, I know. Undo them, will you? [POLE *cuts open the parcel and takes out a bundle of four or five books.* PEARL *opens the telegram*] Oh, bother! There's no answer, Pole.

POLE: Very good, my lady.

[*Exit.*]

FENWICK: Is anything the matter?

PEARL: That fool Sturrey was dining here to-night, and he's just wired to say he can't come. I do hate having my parties upset. I'd asked ten people to meet him.

FENWICK: That's too bad.

PEARL: Pompous owl. He's refused invitation after invi-tation. I asked him six weeks ago this time, and he hadn't the face to say he was engaged.

FENWICK: Well, I'm afraid you must give him up. I dare-say you can do without him.

PEARL: Don't be a fool, Arthur. I'll get hold of him some-how. He may be Prime Minister one of these days. [*She reflects a moment*] I wonder what his telephone number is.

[*She gets up and looks in a book, then sits down at the tele-phone*] Gerrard 7035. If he comes once because I force him to he'll come again because he likes it. This house is like the kingdom of heaven: I have to compel them to come in. . . . Is Lord Sturrey in? Lady Grayston. I'll hold the line. [*Making her voice sweet and charming*] Is that you, Lord Sturrey? It's Pearl Grayston·speaking. I just rang up to say it doesn't matter a bit about to-night. Of course, I'm disappointed you can't come. But you must come another day, will you? That's very nice of you. How about this day week? Oh, I'm sorry. Would Thursday suit you? Oh! Well, how about Friday? You're engaged every evening next week? You are in demand. Well, I'll tell you what, get your book and tell me what day you are free.

FENWICK: You're the goods, girlie. You'll get there.

PEARL: Tuesday fortnight. Yes, that'll suit me beautifully. 8:30. I'm so glad you chose that day, because I'm having Kreisler in to play. I shall look forward to seeing you. Good-bye. [*She puts down the receiver*] This time I've got him. The ape thinks he understands music.

FENWICK: Have you got Kreisler for Tuesday fortnight?

PEARL: No.

FENWICK: Are you sure you can get him?

PEARL: No, but I'm sure you can.

FENWICK: You shall have him, girlie. [*She takes the books that* POLE *brought in and puts them about the room. One she places face downwards, open*] What are you doing that for?

PEARL: They're Richard Twining's books. He's coming to dinner to-night.

FENWICK: Why d'you trouble about authors, girlie?

PEARL: London isn't like New York, you know. People like to meet them over here.

FENWICK: I should have thought your position was quite strong enough to do without them.

PEARL: We live in a democratic age. They take the place in society of the fools whom kings kept about their courts in the middle ages. They have the advantage that they don't presume on their position to tell one home truths. They're cheap. A dinner and a little flattery is all they want. And they provide their own clothes.

FENWICK: You litter up your house with their rotten books.

PEARL: Oh, but I don't keep them. These are on approval. I shall send them all back to the bookseller to-morrow morning.

FENWICK: Pearl, you're a little wonder. When you want to go into business you come to me and I'll take you into partnership.

PEARL: How is business?

FENWICK: Fine! I'm opening two new branches next week. They laughed at me when I first came over here. They said I'd go bankrupt. I've turned their silly old methods upside down. He laughs longest who laughs last.

PEARL [*Reflectively*]: Ah, I can't help thinking that's what my dressmaker said when she sent me in my bill.

[*He gives a slight start and looks at her shrewdly. He sees her blandly smiling.*]

FENWICK: Girlie, you promised me you wouldn't run up any more bills.

PEARL: That's like promising to love, honour, and obey one's husband, the kind of undertaking no one is really expected to carry out.

FENWICK: You naughty little thing.

PEARL: It's Suzanne—you know, the dressmaker in the Place Vendôme. The war has dislocated her business and she wants to get her money in. It isn't very convenient for me to pay just at present. It's rather a large sum. [*She gives him a sheaf of typewritten documents*]

FENWICK: This looks more like a five-act play than a bill.

PEARL: Clothes are expensive, aren't they? I wish I could dress in fig-leaves. It would be cheap, and I believe it would suit me.

FENWICK [*Putting the bill in his pocket*]: Well, I'll see what I can do about it.

PEARL: You are a duck, Arthur. . . . Would you like me to come and lunch with you to-morrow?

FENWICK: Why, sure.

PEARL: All right. Now you must go, as I want to lie down before I dress for dinner.

FENWICK: That's right. Take care of yourself, girlie, you're very precious to me.

PEARL: Good-bye, dear old thing.

FENWICK: Good-bye, girlie.

[*He goes out. As he goes to the door the telephone rings.* PEARL *takes up the receiver.*]

PEARL: You're speaking to Lady Grayston. Tony! Of course I knew your voice. Well, what is it? I'm not at all stern. I'm making my voice as pleasant as I can. I'm sorry you find it disagreeable. [*She gives a chuckle*] No, I'm afraid I couldn't come to tea to-morrow. I shall be engaged all the afternoon. What is the day after to-morrow? [*Smiling*] Well, I must ask Bessie. I don't know if she's free. Of course I'm not coming alone. It would be most compromising. A nice-looking young man like you. What would Minnie say? Oh, I know all about that. . . . I didn't promise anything. I merely said the future was everybody's property. A sleepless night. Fancy! Well, good-bye. . . . Tony, do you know the most enchanting word in the English language? Perhaps.

[*She puts down the telephone quickly, and the curtain falls.*]

THE END OF ACT ONE

ACT TWO

The Scene is a morning-room at Abbots Kenton, the Graystons' place in the country. It has an old-fashioned, comfortable look; nothing is very new; the chintzes are faded. Three long french windows lead on to a terrace.

It is after dinner, a fine night, and the windows are open.

The women of the party are sitting down, waiting for the men; they are PEARL *and* BESSIE, *the* DUCHESSE DE SURENNES *and the* PRINCESS DELLA CERCOLA.

PRINCESS: You must be exhausted after all the tennis you played this afternoon, Minnie.

DUCHESSE: Not a bit. I only played four sets.

PRINCESS: You played so vigorously. It made me quite hot to look at you.

DUCHESSE: If I didn't take exercise I should be enormous. Oh, Flora, how I envy you! You can eat anything you choose and it has no effect on you. And what makes it so unfair is that you don't care about food. I am a lazy and a greedy woman. I never eat any of the things I like, and I never miss a day without taking at least an hour's exercise.

PRINCESS [*Smiling*]: If mortification is the first step in sanctity, I'm sure you must be on the high road to it.

PEARL: One of these days you'll give up the struggle, Minnie, and, like Flora, take to good works.

DUCHESSE [*With immense decision*]: Never! I shall lie on my death-bed with my hair waved and a little rouge on my cheeks, and with my last breath murmur: Not gruel, it's so fattening.

PEARL: Well, you'll have more serious tennis to-morrow. Harry Bleane plays much better than Thornton.

DUCHESSE: It was very tiresome of him not to come till it was just time to dress.

PEARL: He only got back from Rumania yesterday, and he had to go down to see his mother. [*With an amused glance at her sister*] Bessie asked me not to put him next her at dinner.

BESSIE: Pearl, you are a cat! I do think it's hateful the way you discuss my private affairs with all and sundry.

DUCHESSE: My dear Bessie, they've long ceased to be your private affairs.

PEARL: I'm afraid Bessie misses her opportunities. Just before he went to Rumania I left them alone together, and nothing happened. All my tact was wasted.

BESSIE: Your tact was too obvious, Pearl.

DUCHESSE: Well, do be quick and bring him to the scratch, my dear. I'm growing tired of people asking me, Is he going to propose or is he not?

BESSIE: Don't they ever ask, Is she going to accept him or is she not?

DUCHESSE: Of course, you'll accept him.

BESSIE: I'm not so sure.

PRINCESS [*Smiling*]: Perhaps it depends on the way he asks.

PEARL: For heaven's sake, don't expect too much romance. Englishmen aren't romantic. It makes them feel absurd. George proposed to me when he was in New York for the Horse Show. I wasn't very well that day, and I was lying down. I was looking a perfect fright. He told me all about a mare he had, and he told me all about her father and her mother and her uncles and her aunts, and then he said: [*Imitating him*] Look here, you'd better marry me.

PRINCESS: How very sudden.

PEARL: Oh, I said, why didn't you tell me you were going to propose? I'd have had my hair waved. Poor George, he asked *Why?*

DUCHESSE: The French are the only nation who know how to make love. When Gaston proposed to me he went down on his knees, and he took my hand, and he said he couldn't live without me. Of course I knew that, because he hadn't a cent, but still it thrilled me. He said I was his guiding star and his guardian angel—oh, I don't know what! It was beautiful! I knew he'd been haggling with papa for a fortnight about having his debts paid; but it was beautiful.

PRINCESS: Were you quite indifferent to him?

DUCHESSE: Oh, quite. I'd made up my mind to marry a foreigner. People weren't very nice to us in Chicago. My cousin Mary had married the Count de Moret, and mother couldn't bear Aunt Alice. She said, If Alice has got hold of a Count for Mary, I'm determined that you shall have a Duke.

PEARL: And you did.

DUCHESSE: I wish you could have seen the fuss those Chicago people made of me when I went over last. It was hard to realise that I used to cry my eyes out because I wasn't asked to the balls I wanted to go to.

PRINCESS: Still, I hope Bessie won't marry any man she doesn't care for.

PEARL: My dear, don't put ideas in the child's head. The French are a much more civilised nation than we are, and they've come to the conclusion long ago that marriage is an affair of convenience rather than of sentiment. Think of the people you know who've married for love. After five years do they care for one another any more than the people who've married for money?

PRINCESS: They have the recollection.

PEARL: Nonsense! As if anyone remembered an emotion when he no longer felt it!

DUCHESSE: It's true. I've been in love a dozen times, desperately, and when I've got over it and look back, though I remember I was in love, I can't for the life of me remember my love. It always seems to me so odd.

PEARL: Believe me, Bessie, the flourishing state of father's hardware store is a much sounder basis for matrimonial happiness than any amount of passion.

BESSIE: Oh, Pearl, what is this you've been telling people about dad selling bananas?

PEARL: Bananas? Oh, I remember. They were saying that Mrs. Hanley used to wash the miners' clothes in California. That and her pearls are taking her everywhere. I wasn't going to be outdone, so I said father used to sell bananas in the streets of New York.

BESSIE: He never did anything of the kind.

PEARL: I know he didn't, but I thought people were getting rather tired of the hardware store, and I made a perfectly killing story out of it. I had a new Callot frock on and I thought I could manage the bananas.

DUCHESSE: A most unpleasant vegetable. So fattening.

[*The men come in.* THORNTON CLAY, ARTHUR FEN-
    WICK, *and* FLEMING. PEARL *and* BESSIE *get up.*]

BESSIE: You've been a long time.

DUCHESSE: Where is Tony?

CLAY: He and Bleane are finishing their cigars.

DUCHESSE: Well, Mr. Harvey, are you still enjoying life in London?

CLAY: He should be. I've got him invitations to all the nicest parties. But he *will* waste his time in sight-seeing. The other day—Thursday, wasn't it?—I wanted to take him to Hurlingham, and he insisted on going to the National Gallery instead.

PEARL [*Smiling*]: What an outrageous proceeding!

FLEMING: I don't see that it was any more outrageous for me than for you. I saw you coming in just as I was going out.

PEARL: I had a reason to go. Arthur Fenwick has just bought a Bronzino, and I wanted to see those in the National Gallery.

DUCHESSE: I think it's much more likely that you had an assignation. I've always heard it's a wonderful place for that. You never meet any of your friends, and if you do they're there for the same purpose, and pretend not to see you.

FLEMING: I certainly only went to see the pictures.

CLAY: But, good heavens, if you want to do that there's Christie's, and there you *will* meet your friends.

FLEMING: I'm afraid you'll never make a man of fashion out of me, Thornton.

CLAY: I'm beginning to despair. You have a natural instinct for doing the wrong thing. D'you know, the other day I caught him in the act of delivering half a bagful of letters of introduction? I implored him to put them in the waste-paper basket.

FLEMING: I thought as people had taken the trouble to give them to me, it was only polite to make use of them.

CLAY: Americans give letters so carelessly. Before you know where you are you'll know all the wrong people. And, believe me, the wrong people are very difficult to shake off.

FLEMING [*Amused*]: Perhaps some of my letters are to the right people.

CLAY: Then they'll take no notice of them.

FLEMING: It looks as though the wrong people had better manners than the right ones.

CLAY: The right people *are* rude. They can afford to be. I was a very young man when I first came to London, and I made mistakes. All of us Americans make mistakes. It wanted a good deal of character to cut people who'd taken me about, asked me to dine, stay with them in the country, and heaven knows what, when I found they weren't the sort of people one ought to know.

PEARL: Of course, one has to do it.

DUCHESSE: Of course. It shows that you have a nice nature, Thornton, to worry yourself about it.

CLAY: I'm curiously sentimental. Another of our American faults. I remember when I'd been in London two or three years, I knew pretty well everyone that was worth knowing, but I'd never been asked to Hereford House. The duchess doesn't like Americans anyway, and she'd been very disagreeable about me in particular. But I was determined to go to her ball. I felt it wasn't the sort of function I could afford to be left out of.

PEARL: They're very dull balls.

CLAY: I know, but they're almost the only ones you can't go to without an invitation. Well, I found out that the duchess had a widowed sister who lived in the country with her two daughters. Lady Helen Blair. My dear, she was a very stuffy, dowdy woman of fifty-five, and her two daughters were stuffier and dowdier still, and if possible, older. They were in the habit of coming up to London for the season. I got introduced to them, and I laid myself out. I took them to the play, I showed them round the Academy, I stood them luncheons, I gave them cards for private views, for a month I worked like a Trojan. Then the duchess sent out her invitations, and the Blair girls had half a dozen cards for their young men. I received one, and, by George, I'd earned it. Of course, as soon as I got my invitation I dropped them, but you know I felt quite badly about it.

DUCHESSE: I expect they're used to that.

CLAY: A strangely tactless woman, Lady Helen Blair. She wrote and asked me if I was offended about anything because I never went near them.

PEARL: I wish those men would come, and then we could dance.

DUCHESSE: Oh, that'll be charming! It's such good exercise, isn't it? I'm told that you dance divinely, Mr. Harvey.

FLEMING: I don't know about that. I dance.

DUCHESSE [To the PRINCESS]: Oh, my dear, who d'you think I danced with the other night? [Impressively] Ernest.

PRINCESS: Oh!

DUCHESSE: My dear, don't say, Oh! like that. Don't you know who Ernest is?

PEARL: Ernest is the most sought after man in London.

PRINCESS: You don't mean the dancing-master?

DUCHESSE: Oh, my dear, you mustn't call him that. He'd be furious. He isn't a professional. He gives lessons at ten guineas an hour, but only to oblige. He's invited to all the best dances.

FLEMING: One of the things that rather surprised me at balls was to see all these dancing-masters. Do English girls like to be pawed about by Greeks, Dagos and Bowery toughs?

CLAY: You Americans who live in America, you're so prudish.

DUCHESSE: Believe me, I would go to *any* dance where there was the remotest chance of meeting Ernest. It's a perfect dream to dance with him. He showed me a new step, and I can't get it quite right. I don't know what I shall do if I don't run across him again very soon.

PRINCESS: But why don't you let him give you a lesson?

DUCHESSE: My dear, ten guineas an hour! I couldn't possibly afford that. I'm sure to meet him at a dance in a day or two, and I shall get a lesson for nothing.

PEARL: You ought to make him fall in love with you.

DUCHESSE: Oh, my dear, if he only would! But he's so run after.

[BLEANE *and* TONY PAXTON *come in from the terrace.*]

DUCHESSE: At last!

TONY: We've been taking a stroll in the garden.

PEARL: I hope you showed him my tea-house.

BESSIE: It's Pearl's new toy. You must be sure to admire it.

PEARL: I'm very proud of it. You know, George won't let me do anything here. He says it's his house, and he isn't going to have any of my muck. He won't even have new chintzes. Well, there was an old summer-house just over there, and it was all worm-eaten and horrid and tumble-down, what they call picturesque, but it was rather a nice place to go and have tea in as it had a really charming view;

I wanted to pull it down and put up a smart Japanese tea-house instead, but George wouldn't hear of it because, if you please, his mother—a peculiarly plain woman—used to sit and sew there. Well, I bided my time, and the other day, when George was in London, I pulled down the old summer-house, got my Japanese tea-house down from town, put it up, and had everything finished by the time George came back twenty-four hours later. He very nearly had an apoplectic stroke. If he had I should have killed two birds with one stone.

BESSIE: Pearl!

PRINCESS: I don't know why you've furnished it so elaborately.

PEARL: Well, I thought in the hot weather I'd sleep there sometimes. It'll be just like sleeping in the open air.

FENWICK: These young people want to start dancing, Pearl.

PEARL: Where would you like to dance, in here with the gramophone, or in the drawing-room with the pianola?

BESSIE: Oh, in the drawing-room.

PEARL: Let's go there then.

BESSIE [*To* CLAY]: Come and help me get the rolls out.

CLAY: Right you are.

[*They go out, followed by the* DUCHESSE *and* PEARL, TONY, FENWICK, *and* BLEANE.]

FLEMING [*To the* PRINCESS]: Aren't you coming?

PRINCESS: No, I think I'll stay here for the present. But don't bother about me. You must go and dance.

FLEMING: There are enough men without me. I'm sure Thornton Clay is a host in himself.

PRINCESS: You don't like Thornton?

FLEMING: He's been very kind to me since I came to London.

PRINCESS: I was watching your face when he told that story about the Hereford ball. You must learn to conceal your feelings better.

FLEMING: Didn't you think it was horrible?

PRINCESS: I've known Thornton for ten years. I'm used to him. And as you say yourself, he's very kind.

FLEMING: That's what makes life so difficult. People don't seem to be good or bad as the squares on a chessboard are black or white. Even the worthless ones have got good traits, and it makes it so hard to know how to deal with them.

PRINCESS [*Smiling a little*]: You don't approve of poor Thornton?

FLEMING: What do you expect me to think of a man who's proud of having forced his way into a house where he knew he wasn't wanted? He reckons success by the number of invitations he receives. He holds himself up to me as an example. He tells me that if I want to get into society, I must work for it. What do they think of a man like Thornton Clay in England? Don't they despise him?

PRINCESS: Everywhere, in New York just as much as in London, there are masses of people struggling to get into society. It's so common a sight that one loses the sense of there being anything disgraceful in it. Pearl would tell you that English society is a little pompous; they welcome a man who can make them laugh. Thornton is very useful. He has high spirits, he's amusing, he makes a party go.

FLEMING: I should have thought a man could find some better use for his life than that.

PRINCESS: Thornton has plenty of money. Do you think there is any point in his spending his life making more? I sometimes think there's too much money in America already.

FLEMING: There are things a man can do beside making money.

PRINCESS: You know, American wealth has reached a pitch when it was bound to give rise to a leisured class. Thornton is one of the first members of it. Perhaps he doesn't play the part very well, but remember he hasn't had the time to learn it that they've had in Europe.

FLEMING [*Smiling*]: I'm afraid you don't think me very charitable.

PRINCESS: You're young. It's a real pleasure to me to know a nice clean American boy. And I'm so glad that you're not going to be dazzled by this English life that dazzles so many of our countrymen. Amuse yourself, learn what you can from it, take all the good it offers you, and go back to America.

FLEMING: I shall be glad to go back. Perhaps I ought never to have come.

PRINCESS: I'm afraid you're not very happy.

FLEMING: I don't know what makes you think that.

PRINCESS: It's not very hard to see that you're in love with Bessie.

FLEMING: Did you know that I was engaged to her?

PRINCESS [*Surprised*]: No.

FLEMING: I was engaged to her before I went to Harvard. I was eighteen then, and she was sixteen.

PRINCESS: How very early in life you young people settle things in America!

FLEMING: Perhaps it was rather silly and childish. But when she wrote and told me that she thought we'd better break it off, I discovered I cared more than I thought.

PRINCESS: What did you say to her?

FLEMING: I couldn't try to hold her to a promise she gave when she was a schoolgirl. I answered that I sympathised and understood.

PRINCESS: When did this happen?

FLEMING: A couple of months ago. Then I got the chance to go over to Europe and I thought I'd come to see what was going on. It didn't take me long to tumble.

PRINCESS: You're bearing it very well.

FLEMING: Oh, the only thing I could do was to be pleasant. I should only have bored her if I'd made love to her. She took our engagement as an amusing joke, and there wasn't anything for me to do but accept her view of it. She was having the time of her life. At first I thought perhaps she'd grow tired of all these balls and parties, and then if I was on the spot I might persuade her to come back to America with me.

PRINCESS: You may still.

FLEMING: No, I haven't a chance. The first day I arrived she told me how wonderful she thought this English life. She thinks it full and varied. She thinks it has beauty.

PRINCESS: That sounds rather satirical.

FLEMING: Pearl has been very nice to me. She's taken me about, I've driven with her constantly, I've sat in her box at the opera, I'm her guest at the moment. If I had any decency I'd hold my tongue.

PRINCESS: Well?

FLEMING [*Bursting out impetuously*]: There's something in these surroundings that makes me feel terribly uncomfortable. Under the brilliant surface I suspect all kinds of ugly and shameful secrets that everyone knows and pretends not to. This is a strange house in which the husband is never seen and Arthur Fenwick, a vulgar sensualist, acts as host; and it's an attractive spectacle, this painted duchess devouring with her eyes a boy young enough to be her son. And the conversation—I don't want to seem a prude, I daresay people over here talk more freely than the people I've known; but surely there are women who don't have lovers, there are such things as honour and decency and self-restraint. If Bessie is going to remain over here I wish to God she'd marry her lord at once and get out of it quickly.

PRINCESS: D'you think she'll be happy?

FLEMING: Are they any of them happy? How can they expect to be happy when they marry for . . . [*The* PRINCESS *gives a sudden start, and* FLEMING *stops short*] I beg your pardon. I was forgetting. Please forgive me. You see, you're so different.

PRINCESS: I'm sorry I interrupted you. What were you going to say?

FLEMING: It wasn't of any importance. You see, I've been thinking it over so much that it's rather got on my nerves. And I haven't been able to tell anyone what I was thinking about. I'm dreadfully sorry.

PRINCESS: You were going to say, how can they expect to be happy when they marry for a trumpery title? You thought, they're snobs, vulgar snobs, and the misery of their lives is the proper punishment for their ignoble desires.

FLEMING [*Very apologetically*]: Princess.

PRINCESS [*Ironically*]: Princess.

FLEMING: Believe me, I hadn't the smallest intention of saying anything to wound you.

PRINCESS: You haven't. It's too true. Most of us who marry foreigners are merely snobs. But I wonder if it's all our fault. We're not shown a better way of life. No one has even hinted to us that we have any duty towards our own country. We're blamed because we marry foreigners, but columns are written about us in the papers, and our photographs are in all the magazines. Our friends are excited and envious. After all, we are human. At first, when people addressed me as Princess, I couldn't help feeling thrilled. Of course it was snobbishness.

FLEMING: You make me feel a terrible cad.

PRINCESS: But sometimes there've been other motives, too. Has it ever occurred to you that snobbishness is the spirit of romance in a reach-me-down? I was only twenty when I married Marino. I didn't see him as a fortune-hunting Dago, but as the successor of a long line of statesmen and warriors. There'd been a pope in his family, and a dozen cardinals, one of his ancestors had been painted by Titian; for centuries they'd been men of war, with power of life and death; I'd seen the great feudal castle, with its hundred rooms, where they had ruled as independent sovereigns. When Marino came and asked me to marry him it was romance that stood in his shoes and beckoned to me. I thought of the palace in Rome, which I had visited as a tripper, and where I might reign as mistress. I thought it was splendid to take my place after all those great ladies, Orsinis, Colonnas, Gaetanis, Aldobrandinis. I loved him.

FLEMING: But there's no need to tell me that you could never do anything from an unworthy motive.

PRINCESS: My husband's family had been ruined by speculation. He was obliged to sell himself. He sold himself for five million dollars. And I loved him. You can imagine the rest. First he was indifferent to me, then I bored him, and at last he hated me. Oh, the humiliation I endured. When my child died I couldn't bear it any longer; I left him. I went back to America. I found myself a stranger. I was out of place, the life had become foreign to me; I couldn't live at home. I settled in England; and here we're strangers too. I've paid very heavily for being a romantic girl.

[BESSIE *comes in.*]

BESSIE: Really, Fleming, it's too bad of you to sit in here and flirt with the Princess. We want you to come and dance.

[*The* PRINCESS, *agitated, gets up and goes out into the garden.*]

BESSIE [*Looking after her*]: Is anything the matter?

FLEMING: No.

BESSIE: Are you coming to dance, or are you not?

FLEMING: I had quite a talk with Lord Bleane after dinner, Bessie.

BESSIE [*Smiling*]: Well?

FLEMING: Are you going to accept the coronet that he's dangling before your eyes?

BESSIE: It would be more to the point if you asked whether I'm going to accept the coronet that he's laying at my feet.

FLEMING: He's a very nice fellow, Bessie.

BESSIE: I know that.

FLEMING: I wanted to dislike him.

BESSIE: Why?

FLEMING: Well, I don't think much of these English lords who run after American girls for their money. I expected him to be a brainless loafer, with just enough cunning to know his market value, but he's a modest, unassuming fellow. To tell you the truth, I'm puzzled.

BESSIE [*Chaffing him*]: Fancy that!

FLEMING: I think it's a low-down thing that he's doing, and yet he doesn't seem a low-down fellow.

BESSIE: He might be in love with me, you know.

FLEMING: Is he?

BESSIE: No.

FLEMING: Are you going to marry him?

BESSIE: I don't know.

FLEMING: I suppose he's come here to ask you?

BESSIE [*After a short pause*]: He asked me a month ago. I promised to give him an answer when he came back from Rumania . . . I'm in a panic. He's waiting to get me alone. I was able to be quite flippant about it when I had a month before me, but now, when I've got to say yes or no, I'm so jumpy I don't know what to do with myself.

FLEMING: Don't marry him, Bessie.

BESSIE: Why not?

FLEMING: Well, first, you're no more in love with him than he is with you.

BESSIE: And then?

FLEMING: Isn't that enough?

BESSIE: I wonder if you realise what he offers me. Do you know what the position of an English peeress is?

FLEMING: Does it mean so much to be called Your Ladyship by tradesmen?

BESSIE: You donkey, Fleming. If I marry an American boy my life will be over; if I marry Harry Bleane it will be only just beginning. Look at Pearl. I could do what she's done; I could do more, because George Grayston isn't ambitious. I could make Harry do anything I liked. He would go into politics, and I should have a salon. Why, I could do anything.

FLEMING [*Dryly*]: I don't know why you should be in a panic. You've evidently made up your mind. You'll have a brilliant marriage with crowds outside the church, your photograph will be in all the papers, you'll go away for your honeymoon, and you'll come back. What will you do then?

BESSIE: Why, settle down.

FLEMING: Will you break your heart like the Princess because your husband has taken a mistress, or will you take lovers like the Duchesse de Surennes, or will you bore yourself to death like Pearl because your husband is virtuous, and wants you to do your duty?

BESSIE: Fleming, you've got no right to say things like that to me.

FLEMING: I'm sorry if I've made you angry. I had to say it.

BESSIE: Are you quite sure that it's for my sake you don't want me to marry Lord Bleane?

FLEMING: Yes, I think it is. When you broke off our engagement I didn't blame you. You wouldn't have done it if you'd cared for me, and it wasn't your fault if you didn't. When I came over I saw that I could expect nothing but friendship from you. You must do me the justice to acknowledge that during this month I haven't given the smallest sign that I wanted anything else.

BESSIE: Oh, you've been charming. You always were the best friend I've had.

FLEMING: If in a corner of my heart I kept my love for you, that is entirely my affair. I don't know that it puts you to any inconvenience, and it pleases me. I'm quite sure that I'm only thinking now of your happiness. Go back to America, and fall in love with some nice fellow, and marry him. You'll have all my best wishes. Perhaps your life won't be so brilliant or so exciting, but it will be simpler and wholesomer, and more becoming.

BESSIE: You're a dear, Fleming, and if I said anything disagreeable just now, forgive me. I didn't mean it. I shall always want you to be my dearest friend.

[LORD BLEANE *enters from the terrace.*]

BLEANE: I was looking for you everywhere. I wondered where you'd got to.

[*There is a moment's pause.* FLEMING HARVEY *looks from* BESSIE *to* BLEANE.]

FLEMING: I really must go and dance with the Duchesse or she'll never forgive me.

BLEANE: I've just been dancing with her. My dear fellow, it's the most violent form of exercise I've ever taken.

FLEMING: I'm in very good condition.

[*He goes out.*]

BLEANE: Blessings on him.

BESSIE: Why?

BLEANE: Because he's left us alone. Ask me another.

BESSIE: I don't think I will.

BLEANE: Then I'll ask you one.

BESSIE: Please don't. Tell me all about Rumania.

BLEANE: Rumania is a Balkan State. Its capital is Bucharest. It has long been known for its mineral springs.

BESSIE: You're in very high spirits to-night.

BLEANE: You may well wonder. Everything has conspired to depress them.

BESSIE: Oh, what nonsense!

BLEANE: First I was in England thirty-six hours before I

had a chance of seeing you; secondly, when I arrived you'd already gone up to dress; then, when I was expecting to sit next you at dinner, I was put between Lady Grayston and the Princess; and, lastly, you made me pound away at that beastly pianola when I wanted to dance with you.

BESSIE: Well, you survived it all.

BLEANE: What I want to point out to you is that if notwithstanding I'm in high spirits, I must have a most engaging nature.

BESSIE: I never dreamt of denying it.

BLEANE: So much to the good.

BESSIE: The man's going to propose to me.

BLEANE: No, I'm not.

BESSIE: I beg your pardon. My mistake.

BLEANE: I did that a month ago.

BESSIE: There's been a change of moon since then, and no proposal holds good after the new moon.

BLEANE: I never knew that.

BESSIE: You've been down to see your mother.

BLEANE: She sends you her love.

BESSIE: Have you told her?

BLEANE: I told her a month ago.

[BESSIE *does not speak for a moment; when she answers it is more gravely.*]

BESSIE: You know, I want to be frank with you. You won't think it disagreeable of me, will you? I'm not in love with you.

BLEANE: I know. But you don't positively dislike me?

BESSIE: No. I like you very much.

BLEANE: Won't you risk it then?

BESSIE [*Almost tragically*]: I can't make up my mind.

BLEANE: I'll do all I can to make you happy. I'll try not to make a nuisance of myself.

BESSIE: I know quite well that I wouldn't marry you if you weren't who you are, and I'm afraid I know that you wouldn't marry me if I hadn't a certain amount of money.

BLEANE: Oh, yes, I would.

BESSIE: It's nice of you to say so.

BLEANE: Don't you believe it?

BESSIE: I suppose I'm a perfect fool. I ought to play the game prettily. You see, I know that you can't afford to marry a girl who isn't well-to-do. Everyone knows what I have. Pearl has taken good care that they should. You wouldn't ever have thought of me otherwise. We're arranging a deal. You give your title and your position, and I give my money. It's a commonplace thing enough, but somehow it sticks in my throat.

[BLEANE *hesitates a moment, and walks up and down thinking.*]

BLEANE: You make me feel an awful swine. The worst of it is that some part of what you say is true. I'm not such a fool that I didn't see your sister was throwing us together. I don't want to seem a conceited ass, but a fellow in my sort of position can't help knowing that many people think him rather a catch. Mothers of marriageable daughters are very transparent sometimes, you know, and if they don't marry their daughters they're determined it shan't be for want of trying.

BESSIE: Oh, I can quite believe that. I have noticed it in American mothers, too.

BLEANE: I knew it would be a good thing if I married you. I don't suppose I should have thought about you if I hadn't been told you were pretty well off. It's beastly now, saying all that.

BESSIE: I don't see why.

BLEANE: Because after a bit I found out I'd fallen in love with you. And then I didn't care if you hadn't got a bob. I wanted to marry you because—because I didn't know what to do without you.

BESSIE: Harry!

BLEANE: Do believe me. I swear it's true. I don't care a hang about the money. After all, we could get along without it. And I love you.

BESSIE: It's very good to hear you say that. I'm so ab-surdly pleased and flattered.

BLEANE: You do believe it, don't you?

BESSIE: Yes.

BLEANE: And will you marry me?

BESSIE: If you like.

BLEANE: Of course I like. [*He takes her in his arms and kisses her*]

BESSIE: Take care, someone might come in.

BLEANE [*Smiling and happy*] : Come into the garden with me.

> [*He stretches out his hand, she hesitates a moment, smiles, takes it, and together they go out on to the terrace.*
>
> *For a moment the music of a one-step is heard more loudly, and then the* DUCHESSE *and* TONY PAXTON *come in. She sinks into a chair fanning herself, and he goes over to a table, takes a cigarette, and lights it.*]

DUCHESSE: Did you see? That was Harry Bleane and Bessie. I wondered where they were.

TONY: You've got eyes like a lynx.

DUCHESSE: I'm positive they were hand in hand.

TONY: It looks as if she'd worked it at last.

DUCHESSE: I don't know about that. It looks as if he'd worked it.

TONY: She's not such a catch as all that. If I were a peer I'd sell myself for a damned sight more than eight thousand pounds a year.

DUCHESSE: Don't stand so far away, Tony. Come and sit on the sofa by me.

TONY [*Going over to her*] : I say, I've been talking to Bleane about two-seaters.

DUCHESSE [*Very coldly*] : Oh!

TONY [*Giving her a look out of the corner of his eye*] : He says I can't do better than get a Talbot.

DUCHESSE: I don't see why you want a car of your own. You can always use one of mine.

TONY: That's not the same thing. After all, it won't cost much. I can get a ripper for just over twelve hundred pounds, with a really smart body.

DUCHESSE: You talk as though twelve hundred pounds were nothing at all.

TONY: Hang it all, it isn't anything to you.

DUCHESSE: What with the income tax and one thing and another, I'm not so terribly flush just now. No one knows the claims I have on me. Because one has a certain amount of money one's supposed to be made of it. They don't realise that if one spends it in one way one can't spend it in another. It cost me seven thousand pounds to have my house redecorated.

TONY [*Sulkily*]: You said I could buy myself a car.

DUCHESSE: I said I'd think about it. I wasn't under the impression that you'd go and order one right away.

TONY: I've practically committed myself now.

DUCHESSE: You only want a car so that you can be independent of me.

TONY: Well, hang it all, you can't expect me to be tied to your apron-strings always. It's a bit thick if whenever I want to take a man down to play golf I have to ring up and ask if I can have one of your cars. It makes me look such an ass.

DUCHESSE: If it's only to play golf you want it, I'm sure anyone would rather go down to the links in a comfortable Rolls-Royce than in a two-seater.

[*A silence.*]

TONY: If you don't want to give me a car, why on earth did you say you would?

DUCHESSE [*Putting her hand on him*]: Tony.

TONY: For goodness' sake don't touch me.

DUCHESSE [*Hurt and mortified*]: Tony!

TONY: I don't want to force you to make me presents. I can quite well do without a two-seater. I can go about in omnibuses if it comes to that.

DUCHESSE: Don't you love me?

TONY: I wish you wouldn't constantly ask me if I love you. It is maddening.

DUCHESSE: Oh, how can you be so cruel to me!

TONY [*Exasperated*]: D'you think this is quite the best place to choose to make a scene?

DUCHESSE: I love you with all my heart. I've never loved anybody as much as I love you.

TONY: No man could stand being loved so much. D'you think it's jolly for me to feel that your eyes are glued on me whatever I'm doing? I can never put my hand out without finding yours there ready to press it.

DUCHESSE: I can't help it if I love you. That's my temperament.

TONY: Yes, but you needn't show it so much. Why don't you leave me to do the love-making?

DUCHESSE: If I did that there wouldn't be any love-making.

TONY: You make me look such a fool.

DUCHESSE: Don't you know there's nothing in the world I wouldn't do for you?

TONY [Quickly]: Well, why don't you marry me?

DUCHESSE [With a gasp]: I can't do that. You know that I can't do that.

TONY: Why not? You could still call yourself Duchesse de Surennes.

DUCHESSE: No; I've always told you nothing would induce me to marry.

TONY: That shows how much you love me.

DUCHESSE: Marriage is so middle-class. It takes away all the romance of love.

TONY: You simply want to have your freedom and keep me bound hand and foot. D'you think it's jolly for me to know what people say about me? After all, I have got some pride.

DUCHESSE: I'm sure we shall be able to get you a job soon, and then no one will be able to say anything.

TONY: I'm getting fed up with the whole business; I tell you that straight. I'd just as soon chuck it.

DUCHESSE: Tony, you don't mean to say you want to leave me. I'll kill myself if you do. I couldn't bear it, I couldn't bear it. I'll kill myself.

TONY: For God's sake, don't make such a row.

DUCHESSE: Say you don't mean it, Tony. I shall scream.

TONY: After all, I've got my self-respect to think of. It seems to me the best thing would be if we put a stop to the whole thing now.

DUCHESSE: Oh, I can't lose you. I can't.

TONY: No one can say I'm mercenary, but hang it all, one has to think of one's future. I shan't be twenty-five for ever. I ought to be settling down.

DUCHESSE: Don't you care for me any more?

TONY: Of course I care for you. If I didn't, d'you think I'd have let you do all you have for me?

DUCHESSE: Then why d'you make me so unhappy?

TONY: I don't want to make you unhappy, but really sometimes you are unreasonable.

DUCHESSE: You mean about the car?

TONY: I wasn't thinking about the car then.

DUCHESSE: You can have it if you like.

TONY: I don't want it now.

DUCHESSE: Tony, don't be unkind.

TONY: I'm not going to take any more presents from you.

DUCHESSE: I didn't mean to be unreasonable. I'd like you to have the car, Tony. I'll give you a cheque for it to-morrow. [*Coaxingly*] Tell me what the body's like.

TONY [*Sulkily*]: Oh, it's a torpedo body.

DUCHESSE: You'll take me for drives in it sometimes?

[*He turns round and looks at her, she puts out her hand, he thaws, and smiles engagingly.*]

TONY: I say, you are awfully kind to me.

DUCHESSE: You do like me a little, don't you?

TONY: Of course I do.

DUCHESSE: You have a good heart, Tony. Kiss me.

TONY [*Kissing her, pleased and excited*]: I saw an awfully jolly body in a shop in Trafalgar Square the day before yesterday. I've got half a mind to get the people who made your body to copy it.

DUCHESSE: Why don't you get it at the shop you saw it at? My people are terribly expensive, and they aren't any better than anybody else.

TONY: Well, you see, I don't know anything about the firm. I just happened to catch sight of it as I was passing.

DUCHESSE: What on earth were you doing in Trafalgar Square on Thursday? I thought you were going to Ranelagh.

TONY: I was put off. I hadn't got anything to do, so I

thought I'd just slope round the National Gallery for half an hour.

DUCHESSE: That's the last place I should have expected you to go to.

TONY: I don't mind having a look at pictures now and then.

[*A sudden suspicion comes to the* DUCHESSE *that he was there with* PEARL, *but she makes no sign that he can see.*]

DUCHESSE [*Blandly*]: Did you look at the Bronzinos?

TONY [*Falling into the trap*]: Yes. Arthur Fenwick bought one the other day at Christie's. He paid a devil of a price for it too.

DUCHESSE [*Clenching her hands in the effort to hide her agitation*]: Oh?

TONY: I do think it's rot, the prices people pay for old masters. I'm blowed if I'd give ten thousand pounds for a picture.

DUCHESSE: We'll go to the National Gallery together one of these days, shall we?

TONY: I don't know that I want to make a habit of it, you know.

[PEARL *and* THORNTON CLAY *come in. During the conversation the* DUCHESSE *surreptitiously watches* PEARL *and* TONY *for signs of an intelligence between them.*]

PEARL: I've got great news for you. Bessie and Harry Bleane are engaged.

DUCHESSE: Oh, my dear, I'm so glad. How gratified you must be!

PEARL: Yes, I'm delighted. You must come and congratulate them.

CLAY: Above all we must congratulate one another. We've all worked for it, Pearl.

TONY: He hadn't much chance, poor blighter, had he?

PEARL: We're going to have one more dance, and then Arthur wants to play poker. You must come.

CLAY [*To the* DUCHESSE]: Will you dance this with me, Minnie?

DUCHESSE: I'd like to.

[CLAY *gives her his arm. She throws* TONY *and* PEARL *a glance, and purses her lips. She goes out with* CLAY.]

PEARL: You haven't danced with me yet, Tony. You should really pay some attention to your hostess.

TONY: I say, don't go.

PEARL: Why not?

TONY: Because I want to talk to you.

PEARL [*Flippantly*]: If you want to whisper soft nothings in my ear, you'll find the one-step exceedingly convenient.

TONY: You're a little beast, Pearl.

PEARL: You've been having a long talk with Minnie.

TONY: Oh, she's been making me a hell of a scene.

PEARL: Poor thing, she can't help it. She adores you.

TONY: I wish she didn't, and you did.

PEARL [*With a chuckle*]: My dear, it's your only attraction for me that she adores you. Come and dance with me.

TONY: You've got a piece of hair out of place.

PEARL: Have I? [*She takes a small glass out of her bag and looks at herself. As she does so* TONY *steps behind her and kisses her neck*] You fool, don't do that. Anyone might see us.

TONY: I don't care.

PEARL: I do. Arthur's as jealous as cats' meat.

TONY: Arthur's playing the pianola.

PEARL: There's nothing wrong with my hair.

TONY: Of course there isn't. You're perfectly divine to-night. I don't know what there is about you.

PEARL: You're a foolish creature, Tony.

TONY: Let's go in the garden.

PEARL: No, they'll be wondering where we are.

TONY: Hang it all, it's not so extraordinary to take a stroll instead of dancing.

PEARL: I don't want to take a stroll.

TONY: Pearl.

PEARL: Yes?

[*She looks at him. For a moment they stare at one another in silence. A hot flame of passion leaps up suddenly between them, and envelops them, so that they*

*forget everything but that they are man and woman.
The air seems all at once heavy to breathe.* PEARL,
*like a bird in a net, struggles to escape; their voices
sink, and unconsciously they speak in whispers.*]

PEARL: Don't be a fool, Tony.

TONY [*Hoarsely*]: Let's go down to the tea-house.

PEARL: No, I won't.

TONY: We shall be quite safe there.

PEARL: I daren't. It's too risky.

TONY: Oh, damn the risk!

PEARL [*Agitated*]: I can't!

TONY: I'll go down there and wait.

PEARL [*Breathlessly*]: But—if they wonder where I am.

TONY: They'll think you've gone up to your room.

PEARL: I won't come, Tony.

TONY: I'll wait for you.

[*As he goes out,* ARTHUR FENWICK *comes in.* PEARL
gives a slight start, but quickly recovers herself.]

FENWICK: Look here, I'm not going on pounding away
at that wretched pianola unless you come and dance, Pearl.

PEARL [*Exhausted*]: I'm tired, I don't want to dance any
more.

FENWICK: Poor child, you look quite pale.

PEARL: Do I? I thought I'd put plenty of rouge on. Am I
looking revolting?

FENWICK: You always look adorable. You're wonderful. I
can't think what you see in an old fellow like me.

PEARL: You're the youngest man I've ever known.

FENWICK: How well you know the thing to say to please
me!

[*He is just going to take her in his arms, but instinctively she draws back.*]

PEARL: Let's play poker now, shall we?

FENWICK: Not if you're tired, darling.

PEARL: I'm never too tired for that.

FENWICK: You don't know how I adore you. It's a privilege to be allowed to love you.

PEARL [*Sure of herself again*]: Oh, what nonsense! You'll
make me vain if you say things like that.

FENWICK: You do love me a little, don't you? I want your love so badly.

PEARL: Why, I dote on you, you silly old thing.

[*She takes his face in her hands and kisses him, avoids his arms that seek to encircle her, and goes towards the door.*]

FENWICK: Where are you going?

PEARL: I'm just going to my room to arrange my face.

FENWICK: My God, how I love you, girlie! There's nothing in the world I wouldn't do for you.

PEARL: Really?

FENWICK: Nothing.

PEARL: Then ring for Pole and tell him to set out the card-table and bring the counters.

FENWICK: And I was prepared to give you a sable coat or a diamond tiara.

PEARL: I much prefer chinchilla and emeralds.

PENWICK [*Taking her hand*]: Must you really go and arrange your face?

PEARL: Really!

FENWICK: Be quick then. I can hardly bear you out of my sight. [*He kisses her hand*]

PEARL [*Looking at him tenderly*]: Dear Arthur.

[*She goes out.* FENWICK *rings the bell. Then he goes on the terrace and calls out.*]

FENWICK: Thornton, we're going to play poker. Get them to come along, will you?

CLAY [*Outside*]: Right-ho!

[POLE *comes in.*]

FENWICK: Oh, Pole, get the card-table ready.

POLE: Very good, sir.

FENWICK: And we shall want the counters. Let's have those mother-o'-pearl ones that I brought down last time I was here.

POLE: Very good, sir.

[*The* PRINCESS *comes in.* POLE *proceeds to bring a card-table into the centre of the room and unfolds it. He gets a box of counters out of a drawer, and puts them on the table.*]

FENWICK: Pearl has just gone to her room. She'll be here in one minute.

PRINCESS [*Looking at the preparations*]: This looks like more dissipation.

FENWICK: We were going to have a little game of poker. I don't think we ought to play very long, Pearl is looking terribly tired.

PRINCESS: I don't wonder. She's so energetic.

FENWICK: She does too much. Just now when I came in she was quite white. I'm really very uneasy about her. You see, she never spares herself.

PRINCESS: Fortunately she's extremely strong.

FENWICK: She has a constitution of iron. She's a very wonderful woman. It's very seldom you meet a woman like Pearl. She's got a remarkable brain. I've frequently discussed business with her, and I've been amazed at her clear grasp of complicated matters. I owe a great deal to her. And she's good, Princess, she's good. She's got a heart of gold.

PRINCESS: I'm sure she has.

FENWICK: She'll always do a good turn to anybody. She's the most generous, the most open-handed woman I've ever met.

[*The* DUCHESSE *comes in as he says these words.*]

DUCHESSE: Who is this?

FENWICK: We were talking of our hostess.

DUCHESSE: I see.

[*She has her bag in her hand; when the others are not looking she hides it behind a sofa.*]

FENWICK: I have no hesitation in saying that Pearl is the most remarkable woman in England. Why, she's got half the Cabinet in her pocket. She's very powerful.

DUCHESSE: I have often thought that if she'd lived in the reign of Charles II she would have been a duchess in her own right.

FENWICK [*Innocently*]: Maybe. She would adorn any sphere. She's got everything—tact, brains, energy, beauty.

DUCHESSE: Virtue.

FENWICK: If I were the British people, I'd make her Prime Minister.

PRINCESS [*Smiling*]: You're an excellent friend, Mr. Fenwick.

FENWICK: Of course, you've heard of her hostel for young women alone in London?

DUCHESSE [*Sweetly*]: Yes, there was a great deal about it in the papers, wasn't there?

FENWICK: That's a thing I've always admired in Pearl. She has a thoroughly modern understanding of the value of advertisement.

DUCHESSE: Yes, she has, hasn't she?

FENWICK: Well, believe me, she conceived the idea of that hostel, built it, endowed it, organised it, all on her own. It cost twenty thousand pounds.

DUCHESSE: But surely, Mr. Fenwick, you paid the twenty thousand pounds. Pearl hasn't got sums like that to throw away on charity.

FENWICK: I gave the money, but the money isn't the important thing. The idea, the organisation, the success, are all due to Pearl.

DUCHESSE: It has certainly been one of the best advertised of recent philanthropic schemes.

[THORNTON CLAY, BESSIE, BLEANE and FLEMING *come in.*]

CLAY: We're all dying to play poker.

FENWICK: The table is ready.

BESSIE: Where is Pearl?

FENWICK: She's gone to her room. She'll be back in a minute.

[*They gather round the table and sit down.*]

BESSIE: You're going to play, Princess?

PRINCESS: Oh, I don't think so, I'll look on. I'm going to bed in a minute.

BESSIE: Oh, you must play.

[*The* PRINCESS *smiles, shrugs her shoulders and approaches the table.*]

FENWICK: Leave a place for Pearl.

DUCHESSE: You must leave one for Tony, too.

CLAY: What's he doing?

DUCHESSE: He'll be here presently.

FENWICK: Shall I give out the counters? What would you like to play for?

PRINCESS: Don't let it be too high.

DUCHESSE: How tiresome of you, Flora! I think I'm in luck to-night.

FENWICK: We don't want to ruin anyone. Shilling antes. Will that suit you?

PRINCESS: Very well.

FENWICK [*To* CLAY]: The whites are a shilling, Thornton, reds two, and blues five bob. Mr. Harvey, you might count some out, will you?

FLEMING: Sure.

[*The three of them start counting out the counters.*]

DUCHESSE: Oh, how stupid of me, I haven't got my bag.

FENWICK: Never mind, we'll trust you.

DUCHESSE: Oh, I'd rather pay at once. It saves so much bother. Besides, I hate not having my bag.

PRINCESS: One always wants to powder one's nose if one hasn't got it.

DUCHESSE: Bessie dear, I left it in Pearl's new tea-house. Do run and fetch it for me.

BESSIE: Certainly.

BLEANE: No, I'll go.

BESSIE: You don't know the way. I can go through the bushes. It's only twenty yards. You stop and count out the counters.

[*She goes out.*]

FENWICK: There's five pounds here. Will you take them, Princess?

PRINCESS: Thank you. Here's my money.

DUCHESSE: I'll give you my fiver as soon as Bessie brings my bag.

CLAY: How on earth came you to leave it in the tea-house?

DUCHESSE: I'm so careless. I'm always leaving my bag about.

FLEMING: Here's another five pounds.

PRINCESS: What beautiful counters they are!

FENWICK: I'm glad you like them. I gave them to Pearl. They've got her initials on them.

CLAY: Let's have a hand before Pearl comes. Lowest deals.

[*They all cut.*]

FLEMING: Table stakes, I suppose?

FENWICK: Oh yes, it makes it a much better game.

CLAY: Your deal, Fenwick.

FENWICK: Ante up, Princess.

PRINCESS: I beg your pardon.

[*She pushes forward a counter.* FENWICK *deals. The others take up their cards.*]

FENWICK: Two shillings to come in.

FLEMING: I'm coming in.

BLEANE: I always come in.

FENWICK: I oughtn't to, but I shall all the same. Are you going to make good your ante, Princess?

PRINCESS: I may just as well, mayn't I?

FENWICK: That's how I've made a fortune. By throwing good money after bad. Would you like a card?

PRINCESS: I'll have three.

[FENWICK *gives them to her.*]

CLAY: The Princess has got a pair of deuces.

FLEMING: I'll have one.

[FENWICK *gives it to him.*]

BLEANE: One never gets that straight, Harvey. I'll take five.

FENWICK: That's what I call a real sport.

CLAY: Nonsense. It just means he can't play.

BLEANE: It would be rather a sell for you if I got a flush.

CLAY: It would, but you haven't.

[FENWICK *has given him cards and* BLEANE *looks at them.*]

BLEANE: You're quite right. I haven't.

[*He flings them down. Through the next speeches the business with the cards follows the dialogue.*]

FENWICK: Don't you want any cards, Duchesse?

DUCHESSE: No, I'm out of it.

CLAY: I'll have three. I thought you were in luck.

DUCHESSE: Wait a minute. You'll be surprised.

FENWICK: Dealer takes two.

CLAY: Who bets?

PRINCESS: I'm out of it.

CLAY: I said it was a pair of deuces.

FLEMING: I'll bet five shillings.

CLAY: I'll take it and raise five shillings.

FENWICK: I suppose I must risk my money. What have I got to put down? Ten shillings?

FLEMING: There's five shillings, and I'll raise you five shillings more.

CLAY: No, I've had enough.

FENWICK: I'll take you and raise you again.

FLEMING: Very well. And once more.

FENWICK: I'll see you.

[BESSIE *comes in. The* DUCHESSE *has been watching for her.* BESSIE *is excessively disturbed.*]

DUCHESSE: Ah, there's Bessie.

FENWICK [*To* FLEMING]: What have you got?

DUCHESSE: Did you find my bag?

BESSIE [*With a gasp*]: No, it wasn't there.

DUCHESSE: Oh, but I remember distinctly leaving it there. I'll go and look for it myself. Mr. Fenwick, will you come with me.

BESSIE: No, don't—you can't go into the tea-house.

PRINCESS [*Surprised*]: Bessie, is anything the matter?

BESSIE [*In a strained voice*]: The door of the tea-house is locked.

DUCHESSE: Oh, it can't be. I saw Pearl and Tony go in there just now.

[BESSIE *suddenly hides her face and bursts into a flood of tears.*]

PRINCESS [*Starting to her feet*]: Minnie, you devil! What have you been doing?

DUCHESSE: Don't ask what I've been doing.

FENWICK: You must be mistaken. Pearl went up to her room.

DUCHESSE: Go and look for her. . . .

[FENWICK *is about to start from his chair. The* PRINCESS *puts her hand on his shoulders.*]

PRINCESS: Where are you going?

DUCHESSE: I saw her.

[*For a moment there is a pause.*]

CLAY [*In an embarrassed way*]: Well, we'd better go on with our game, hadn't we?

[*The* PRINCESS *and* BLEANE *are bending over* BESSIE, *trying to get her to control herself.*]

FLEMING: That was your money, Mr. Fenwick.

FENWICK [*Staring in front of him, with a red face and bloodshot eyes, under his breath*]: The slut. The slut.

[*The* DUCHESSE *takes her bag from behind the cushion, gets out the stick for her lips, and her mirror, and begins to paint them.*]

CLAY: You'd better deal, Fleming. The Princess won't play, I expect.

DUCHESSE: Deal me cards. I want to play.

CLAY: Bleane, come on. We'd better go on with our game. Take Bessie's chips.

[BLEANE *comes forward.* FLEMING *deals the cards. A stormy silence hangs over the party, broken only by the short speeches referring to the game; they play trying to relieve the tension. They are all anxiously awaiting* PEARL, *afraid she will come, knowing she must, and dreading the moment; they are nervous and constrained.*]

CLAY: Your ante, Bleane.

[BLEANE *puts forward a counter. The cards are dealt in silence.*]

CLAY: I'm coming in.

[FENWICK *looks at his cards, puts forward a couple of counters, but does not speak.* FLEMING *puts forward counters.*]

FLEMING: D'you want a card?

BLEANE: Three, please.

CLAY: Two.

FENWICK [*With an effort over himself*]: I'll have three.

[FLEMING *deals them as they ask. Just as he has given* FENWICK *his,* PEARL *comes in, followed by* TONY. TONY *is smoking a cigarette.*]

PEARL: Oh, have you started already?

FENWICK [*Violently*] : Where have you been?

PEARL : I? My head was aching a little and I went for a turn in the garden. I found Tony composing a sonnet to the moon.

FENWICK : You said you were going to your room.

PEARL : What are you talking about?

[*She looks round, sees the* DUCHESSE'S *look of angry triumph, and gives a slight start.*]

DUCHESSE : Once too often, my dear, once too often.

[PEARL *takes no notice. She sees* BESSIE. BESSIE *has been staring at her with miserable eyes, and now she hides her face.* PEARL *realises that everything is discovered. She turns coolly to* TONY.]

PEARL : You damned fool, I told you it was too risky.

THE END OF ACT TWO

ACT THREE

The Scene is the same as in the last act, the morning-room at Kenton.

It is next day, Sunday, about three in the afternoon, and the sun is shining brightly.

The PRINCESS, THORNTON CLAY *and* FLEMING *are sitting down.* FLEMING *lights another cigarette.*

PRINCESS : Is it good for you to smoke so many cigarettes?

FLEMING : I shouldn't think so.

CLAY : He must do something.

PRINCESS : Perhaps you can get up a game of tennis later on.

FLEMING : It's very hot for tennis.

CLAY : Besides, who will play?

PRINCESS : You two could have a single.

CLAY : If we only had the Sunday papers it would be something.

PRINCESS : You can hardly expect them in a place like this. I don't suppose there are many trains on Sunday.

CLAY : I wonder if dinner is going to be as cheerful as luncheon was.

FLEMING: Did Pearl send any explanation for not appearing at luncheon?

PRINCESS: I haven't an idea.

CLAY: I asked the butler where she was. He said she was lunching in bed. I wish I'd thought of that.

PRINCESS: I'm afraid we were rather silent.

CLAY: Silent! I shall never forget that luncheon. Minnie subdued—and silent. Tony sulky—and silent. Bessie frightened—and silent. Bleane embarrassed—and silent. Fenwick furious—and silent. I tried to be pleasant and chatty. It was like engaging the pyramids in small-talk. Both of you behaved very badly. You might have given me a little encouragement.

FLEMING: I was afraid of saying the wrong thing. The Duchesse and Bessie looked as if they'd burst into tears on the smallest provocation.

PRINCESS: I was thinking of Pearl. What a humiliation! What a horrible humiliation!

FLEMING: What d'you think she'll do now?

CLAY: That's what I'm asking myself. I have an idea that she won't appear again till we're all gone.

PRINCESS: I hope she won't. She's always so sure of herself, I couldn't bear to see her pale and mortified.

CLAY: She's got plenty of courage.

PRINCESS: I know. She may force herself to face us. It would be a dreadful ordeal for all of us.

FLEMING: D'you think she's feeling it very much?

PRINCESS: She wouldn't be human if she weren't. I don't suppose she slept any better last night than the rest of us. Poor thing, she must be a wreck.

FLEMING: It was a terrible scene.

PRINCESS: I shall never forget it. The things that Minnie said. I couldn't have believed such language could issue from a woman's throat. Oh, it was horrible.

CLAY: It was startling. I've never seen a woman so beside herself. And there was no stopping her.

FLEMING: And with Bessie there.

PRINCESS: She was crying so much, I doubt if she heard.

CLAY: I was thankful when Minnie had hysterics and

we were able to fuss over her and dab her face and slap her hands. It was a very welcome diversion.

FLEMING: Does she have attacks like that often?

CLAY: I know she did when the young man before Tony married an heiress. I think she has one whenever there's a crisis in the affairs of her heart.

FLEMING: For goodness' sake, Thornton, don't talk about it as if it were a joke.

CLAY [*Surprised*]: What's the matter, Fleming?

FLEMING: I think it's abominable to treat the whole thing so flippantly.

CLAY: Why, I was very sympathetic. I wasn't flippant. Who got the sal volatile? I got the sal volatile.

FLEMING [*With a shrug of the shoulders*]: I daresay my nerves are a bit on edge. You see, before, I only thought things were rather queer. It's come as, well, as a shock to discover exactly what the relations are between all these people. And what I can't very easily get over is to realise that I'm the only member of the party who doesn't take it as a matter of course.

CLAY: We shall never make a man of the world of you, Fleming.

FLEMING: I'm afraid that didn't sound very polite, Princess. I beg your pardon.

PRINCESS: I should have few friends if I demanded the standard that you do. I've learned not to judge my neighbours.

FLEMING: Is it necessary to condone their vices?

PRINCESS: You don't understand. It's not entirely their fault. It's the life they lead. They've got too much money and too few responsibilities. English women in our station have duties that are part of their birthright, but we, strangers in a strange land, have nothing to do but enjoy ourselves.

FLEMING: Well, I thank God Bleane is a decent man, and he'll take Bessie out of all this.

[*The* DUCHESSE *comes in. Unlike the* PRINCESS, *who is in a summer frock, suitable for the country, the* DUCHESSE *wears a town dress and a hat.*]

PRINCESS: You've been changing your frock, Minnie.

DUCHESSE: Yes. I'm leaving this house in half an hour. I'd have gone this morning, if I'd been able to get away. I always thought it a detestable hole, but now that I've discovered there are only two trains on Sunday, one at nine, and the other at half-past four, I have no words to express my opinion of it.

CLAY: Yet you have an extensive vocabulary, Minnie.

DUCHESSE: I've been just as much a prisoner as if I'd been shut up with lock and key. I've been forced to eat that woman's food. I thought every mouthful would choke me.

PRINCESS: Do keep calm, Minnie. You know how bad it is for you to upset yourself.

DUCHESSE: As soon as I found there wasn't a train I sent over to the garage and said I wanted to be taken to London at once. Would you believe it, I couldn't get a car.

CLAY: Why not?

DUCHESSE: One of the cars went up to town early this morning, and the other is being overhauled. There's nothing but a luggage cart. I couldn't go to London in a luggage cart. As it is I shall have to go to the station in it. I shall look ridiculous.

CLAY: Have you ordered it?

DUCHESSE: Yes. It's to be round at the door in a few minutes.

CLAY: What on earth can Pearl have sent the car up to London for?

DUCHESSE: To show her spite.

PRINCESS: That's not like her.

DUCHESSE: My dear, she's been my greatest friend for fifteen years. I know her through and through, and I tell you that she hasn't got a single redeeming quality. And why does she want to have the car overhauled to-day? When you're giving a party the least you can do is to see that your cars are in running order.

PRINCESS: Oh, well, that was an accident. You can't blame her for that.

DUCHESSE: I only have one thing to be thankful for, and that is that she has had the decency to keep to her room. I will be just. It shows at least that she has some sense of shame.

CLAY: You know, Minnie, Pearl has a good heart. She didn't mean to cause you pain.

DUCHESSE: Are you trying to excuse her, Thornton?

CLAY: No, I think her conduct is inexcusable.

DUCHESSE: So do I. I mean to have nothing more to do with her. It's a judgment on me. I disliked her the first time I saw her. One should always trust one's first impressions. Now my eyes are opened. I will never speak to her again. I will cut her dead. I hope you'll tell her that, Thornton.

CLAY: If that's a commission you're giving me, it's not a very pleasant one.

PRINCESS: Will you let me have a word or two with Minnie?

CLAY: Why, of course. Come along, Fleming.

[CLAY *and* FLEMING HARVEY *go into the garden.*]

DUCHESSE: My dear, if you're going to ask me to turn the other cheek, don't. Because I'm not going to. I'm going to do all I can to revenge myself on that woman. I'm going to expose her. I'm going to tell everyone how she's treated me. When I was her guest.

PRINCESS: You must take care what you say for your own sake, Minnie.

DUCHESSE: I know quite enough about her to make her position in London impossible. I'm going to ruin her.

PRINCESS: What about Tony?

DUCHESSE: Oh, I've finished with him. Ah! I'm not the kind of woman to stand that sort of treatment. I hope he'll end in the gutter.

PRINCESS: Don't you care for him any more?

DUCHESSE: My dear, if he was starving, and went down on his bended knees to me for a piece of bread, I wouldn't give it to him. He revolts me.

PRINCESS: Well, I'm very glad. It distressed me to see you on those terms with a boy like that. You're well rid of him.

DUCHESSE: My dear, you needn't tell me that. He's a thorough wrong 'un, and that's all there is about it. He hasn't even had the decency to try and excuse himself. He hasn't even made an attempt to see me.

PRINCESS [*Gives her a quick look*]: After all, he never really cared for you. Anyone could see that.

DUCHESSE [*Her voice breaking*]: Oh, don't say that, Flora. I couldn't bear it. He loved me. Until that woman came between us I know he loved me. He couldn't help loving me. I did everything in the world for him. [*She bursts into tears*]

PRINCESS: Minnie. My dear, don't give way. You know what a worthless creature he is. Haven't you any self-respect?

DUCHESSE: He's the only man I've ever loved. I could hardly bear him out of my sight. What shall I do without him?

PRINCESS: Take care, here he is.

[TONY *comes in. He is startled at seeing the* DUCHESSE. *She turns away and hurriedly dries her tears.*]

TONY: Oh, I beg your pardon. I didn't know anyone was here. I was looking for some cigarettes.

[*He stands there awkwardly, not knowing whether to go or stay. The* PRINCESS *looks at him reflectively. There is a moment's silence. Then she shrugs her shoulders and goes out. He looks at the* DUCHESSE *who stands with her back to him. He hesitates a moment, then, almost on the tips of his toes, walks over to the cigarettes, fills his case, takes another look at the* DUCHESSE, *and is in the act of tip-toeing out of the room when she stops him with her question.*]

DUCHESSE: Where are you going?

TONY: Nowhere in particular.

DUCHESSE: Then you'd better stay here.

TONY: I thought you wished to be alone.

DUCHESSE: Is that why you've kept away from me all day?

[*He sinks sulkily into an armchair. The* DUCHESSE *finally turns round and faces him.*]

DUCHESSE: Haven't you got anything to say for yourself at all?

TONY: What's the good of talking?

DUCHESSE: You might at least say you're sorry for the pain you've caused me. If you'd had any affection for me you wouldn't have done all you could to avoid me.

TONY: I knew you'd only make a scene.

DUCHESSE: Good heavens, you surely don't expect me not to make a scene.

TONY: The whole thing's very unfortunate.

DUCHESSE: Ha! Unfortunate. You break my heart and then you say it's unfortunate.

TONY: I didn't mean that. I meant it was unfortunate that you caught us out.

DUCHESSE: Oh, hold your stupid tongue. Every word you say is more unfortunate than the last.

TONY: It's because I knew you'd take offence at everything I said that I thought the best thing I could do was to keep out of the way.

DUCHESSE: You're heartless, heartless. If you'd had any decent feeling you couldn't have eaten the lunch you did. But you munched away, munched, munched, munched, till I could have killed you.

TONY: Well, I was hungry.

DUCHESSE: You oughtn't to have been hungry.

TONY: What are you going to do about it?

DUCHESSE: About your appetite? Pray to God your next mouthful chokes you.

TONY: No, about the other.

DUCHESSE: I'm going to leave this house this afternoon.

TONY: D'you want me to come, too?

DUCHESSE: What d'you suppose it matters to me whether you go or stay?

TONY: If you go I shall have to go, too.

DUCHESSE: You ought to start soon then. It's four miles to the station. I shall be obliged if you will not get in the same carriage as me.

TONY: I'm not going to walk. They can run me down in a car.

DUCHESSE: There's nothing but a luggage cart, and I'm going in that.

TONY: Isn't there room for me?

DUCHESSE: No.

TONY: When d'you want me to move out of my flat?

DUCHESSE: What has that got to do with me?

TONY: You know very well that *I* can't pay the rent.

DUCHESSE: That's your look-out.

TONY: I shall go to the colonies.

DUCHESSE: That's the very best thing you can do. I hope you'll have to break stones, and dig, and paint—with lead paint. I hope you're miserable.

TONY: Oh, well, it'll have its compensations.

DUCHESSE: Such as?

TONY: I shall be my own master. I was about fed up with this, I can tell you.

DUCHESSE: Yes, you can say that now.

TONY: D'you think it was all jam, never being able to call my soul my own? I was sick to death of it.

DUCHESSE: You cad!

TONY: Well, you may just as well know the truth.

DUCHESSE: D'you mean to say you never cared for me? Not even at the beginning?

[*He shrugs his shoulders, but does not answer. She speaks the next phrases in little gasps gradually weakening as her emotion overcomes her. He stands before her in sulky silence.*]

DUCHESSE: Tony, I've done everything in the world for you. I've been like a mother to you. How *can* you be so ungrateful. You haven't got any heart. If you had you'd have asked me to forgive you. You'd have made some attempt to . . . Don't you *want* me to forgive you?

TONY: What d'you mean by that?

DUCHESSE: If you'd only asked me, if you'd only shown you were sorry, I'd have been angry with you, I wouldn't have spoken to you for a week, but I'd have forgiven you— I'd have forgiven you, Tony. But you never gave me a chance. It's cruel of you, cruel!

TONY: Well, anyhow, it's too late now.

DUCHESSE: Do you want it to be too late?

TONY: It's no good grousing about the past. The thing's over now.

DUCHESSE: Aren't you sorry?

TONY: I don't know. I suppose I am in a way. I don't want to make you unhappy.

DUCHESSE: If you wanted to be unfaithful to me, why didn't you prevent me from finding out? You didn't even trouble to take a little precaution.

TONY: I was a damned fool, I know that.

DUCHESSE: Are you in love with that woman?

TONY: No.

DUCHESSE: Then why did you? Oh, Tony, how could you?

TONY: If one felt about things at night as one does next morning, life would be a dashed sight easier.

DUCHESSE: If I said to you, Let's let bygones be bygones and start afresh, what would you say, Tony?

[*She looks away. He rests his eyes on her reflectively.*]

TONY: We've made a break now. We'd better leave it at that. I shall go out to the colonies.

DUCHESSE: Tony, you don't mean that seriously. You could never stand it. You know, you're not strong. You'll only die.

TONY: Oh, well, one can only die once.

DUCHESSE: I'm sorry for all I said just now, Tony. I didn't mean it.

TONY: It doesn't matter.

DUCHESSE: I can't live without you, Tony.

TONY: I've made up my mind. It's no good talking.

DUCHESSE: I'm sorry I was horrid to you, Tony. I'll never be again. Won't you forget it? Oh, Tony, won't you forgive me? I'll do anything in the world for you if only you won't leave me.

TONY: It's a rotten position I'm in. I must think of the future.

DUCHESSE: Oh, but Tony, I'll make it all right for you.

TONY: It's very kind of you, but it's not good enough. Let's part good friends, Minnie. If I've got to walk to the station, it's about time I was starting.

[*He holds out his hand to her.*]

DUCHESSE: D'you mean to say it's good-bye? Good-bye for ever? Oh, how can you be so cruel!

TONY: When one's made up one's mind to do a thing, it's best to do it at once.

DUCHESSE: Oh, I can't bear it. I can't bear it. [*She begins to cry*] Oh, what a fool I was! I ought to have pretended not to see anything. I wish I'd never known. Then you wouldn't have thought of leaving me.

TONY: Come, my dear, pull yourself together. You'll get over it.

DUCHESSE [*Desperately*]: Tony, if you want to marry me—I'm willing to marry you.

[*A pause.*]

TONY: I should be just as dependent on you. D'you think it would be jolly for me having to come to you for every five pounds I wanted?

DUCHESSE: I'll settle something on you so that you'll be independent. A thousand a year. Will that do?

TONY: You are a good sort, Minnie.

[*He goes over and sits down beside her.*]

DUCHESSE: You will be kind to me, won't you?

TONY: Rather! And look here, you needn't give me that two-seater. I shall be able to drive the Rolls-Royce.

DUCHESSE: You didn't want to go to the colonies, did you?

TONY: Not much.

DUCHESSE: Oh, Tony, I do love you so.

TONY: That's right.

DUCHESSE: We won't stay another minute in this house. Ring the bell, will you? You'll come with me in the luggage cart?

TONY [*Touching the bell*]: I much prefer that to walking.

DUCHESSE: It's monstrous that there shouldn't be a motor to take luggage to the station. It's a most uncomfortable house to stay in.

TONY: Oh, beastly. D'you know that I didn't have a bath-room attached to my bedroom?

[POLE *comes in.*]

DUCHESSE: Is the luggage cart ready, Pole?

POLE: I'll enquire, your grace.

DUCHESSE: My maid is to follow in the morning with the luggage. Mr. Paxton will come with me. [*To* TONY] What about your things?

TONY: Oh, they'll be all right. I brought my man with me.

POLE: Her ladyship is just coming downstairs, your grace.

DUCHESSE: Oh, is she? Thank you, that'll do, Pole.

POLE: Very good, your grace.

[*He goes out. As soon as he closes the door behind him the* DUCHESSE *springs to her feet.*]

DUCHESSE: I won't see her. Tony, see if Thornton is on the terrace.

TONY: All right. [*He goes to the French window*] Yes. I'll call him, shall I? Clay, come here a minute, will you?

[*He goes out.* THORNTON CLAY *comes in, followed immediately by the* PRINCESS *and* FLEMING.]

DUCHESSE: Thornton, I'm told Pearl is coming downstairs.

CLAY: At last.

DUCHESSE: I won't see her. Nothing will induce me to see her.

PRINCESS: My dear, what is to be done? We can't make her remain upstairs in her own house.

DUCHESSE: No, but Thornton can speak to her. She's evidently ashamed of herself. I only ask one thing, that she should keep out of the way till I'm gone.

CLAY: I'll do my best.

DUCHESSE: I'm going to walk up and down till the luggage cart is ready. I haven't taken my exercise to-day.

[*She goes out.*]

CLAY: If Pearl is in a temper that's not a very pleasant message to give her.

PRINCESS: You won't find her in a temper. If she's dreadfully upset, tell her what Minnie says gently.

FLEMING: Here is Bessie. [*She comes in*] It appears that Pearl is just coming downstairs.

BESSIE: Is she?

PRINCESS: Have you seen her this morning, Bessie?

BESSIE: No. She sent her maid to ask me to go to her, but I had a headache and couldn't.

[*They look at her curiously. She is inclined to be abrupt and silent. It may be imagined that she has made up her mind to some course, but what that is the others cannot tell.* FLEMING *goes over and sits beside her.*]

FLEMING: I'm thinking of going back to America next Saturday, Bessie.

BESSIE: Dear Fleming, I shall be sorry to lose you.

FLEMING: I expect you'll be too busy to think about me. You'll have to see all kinds of people, and then there's your trousseau to get.

BESSIE: I wish you could come over to Paris with me, Princess, and help me with it.

PRINCESS: I? [*She gets an inkling of what* BESSIE *means*] Of course, if I could be of any help to you, dear child. . . . [*She takes* BESSIE's *hand and gives her a fond smile.* BESSIE *turns away to hide a tear that for a moment obscures her eyes*] Perhaps it's a very good idea. We must talk about it.

[PEARL *comes in. She is perfectly cool and collected, radiant in a wonderful, audacious gown; she is looking her best and knows it. There is nothing in her manner to indicate the smallest recollection of the episode that took place on the preceding evening.*]

PEARL [*Brightly*]: Good-morning.

CLAY: Good-afternoon.

PEARL: I knew everyone would abuse me for coming down so late. It was such a lovely day I thought it was a pity to get up.

CLAY: Don't be paradoxical, Pearl, it's too hot.

PEARL: The sun streamed into my room, and I said, It's a sin not to get up on a morning like this. And the more I said I ought to get up, the more delightful I found it to lie in bed. How is your head, Bessie?

BESSIE: Oh, it's better, thank you.

PEARL: I was sorry to hear you weren't feeling up to the mark.

BESSIE: I didn't sleep very well.

PEARL: What have you done with your young man?

BESSIE: Harry? He's writing letters.

PEARL: Spreading the glad tidings, I suppose. You ought to write to his mother, Bessie. It would be a graceful attention. A charming, frank little letter, the sort of thing one would expect an *ingénue* to write. Straight from the heart.

CLAY: I'm sure you'd love to write it yourself, Pearl.

PEARL: And we must think about sending an announcement to the Morning Post.

FLEMING: You think of everything, Pearl.

PEARL: I take my duties as Bessie's chaperon very seriously. I've already got a brilliant idea for the gown I'm going to wear at the wedding.

FLEMING: Gee!

PEARL: My dear Fleming, don't say Gee, it's so American. Say By Jove.

FLEMING: I couldn't without laughing.

PEARL: Laffing. Why can't you say laughing?

FLEMING: I don't want to.

PEARL: How obstinate you are. Of course, now that Bessie is going to marry an Englishman she'll have to take lessons. I know an excellent woman. She's taught all the American peeresses.

FLEMING: You surprise me.

PEARL: She's got a wonderful method. She makes you read aloud. And she has long lists of words that you have to repeat twenty times a day—half instead of haf, and barth instead of bath, and carnt instead of can't.

FLEMING: By Jove instead of Gee?

PEARL: Peeresses don't say By Jove, Fleming. She teaches them to say Good heavens instead of Mercy.

FLEMING: Does she make money by it?

PEARL: Pots. She's a lovely woman. Eleo Dorset had an accent that you could cut with a knife when she first came over, and in three months she hadn't got any more than I have.

BESSIE [*Getting up. To* FLEMING]: D'you think it's too hot for a turn in the garden?

FLEMING: Why, no.

BESSIE: Shall we go then?

[*They go out together.*]

PEARL: What's the matter with Bessie? She must have swallowed a poker last night. No wonder she couldn't sleep. It's enough to give anyone indigestion.

CLAY: You know that Minnie is going this afternoon, Pearl?

PEARL: Yes, so I heard. It's such a bore there are no cars to take her to the station. She'll have to go in the luggage cart.

CLAY: She doesn't wish to see you.

PEARL: Oh, but I wish to see her.

CLAY: I daresay.

PEARL: I must see her.

CLAY: She asked me to tell you that she only wished you to do one thing, and that is to keep out of the way till she's gone.

PEARL: Then you can go and tell her that unless she sees me she shan't have the luggage cart.

CLAY: Pearl!

PEARL: That's my ultimatum.

CLAY: Can you see me taking a message like that to the Duchesse?

PEARL: It's four miles to the station, and there's not a scrap of shade all the way.

CLAY: After all, it's not a very unreasonable request she's making.

PEARL: If she wants the luggage cart she must come and say good-bye to me like a lady.

CLAY [*To the* PRINCESS]: What am I to do? We used up all the sal volatile last night.

PRINCESS: I'll tell her if you like. D'you really insist on seeing her, Pearl?

PEARL: Yes, it's very important. [*The* PRINCESS *goes out.* PEARL *watches her go with a smile*] I'm afraid Flora is shocked. She shouldn't know such people.

CLAY: Really, Pearl, your behaviour is monstrous.

PEARL: Never mind about my behaviour. Tell me how luncheon went off.

CLAY: My dear, it was like a gathering of relations who hate one another, after the funeral of a rich aunt who's left all her money to charity.

PEARL: It must have been priceless. I'd have given anything to be there.

CLAY: Why weren't you?

PEARL: Oh, I knew there'd be scenes, and I'm never at my best in a scene before luncheon. One of the things I've learnt from the war is that a general should choose his own time for a battle.

CLAY: Minnie moved heaven and earth to get away this morning.

PEARL: I knew she couldn't. I knew none of them could go till the afternoon.

CLAY: The train service is atrocious.

PEARL: George says that is one of the advantages of the place. It keeps it rural. There's one at nine and another at half-past four. I knew that not even the most violent disturbances would get people up at eight who never by any chance have breakfast till ten. As soon as I awoke I took the necessary steps.

CLAY [Interrupting]: You slept?

PEARL: Oh yes, I slept beautifully. There's nothing like a little excitement to give me a good night.

CLAY: Well, you certainly had some excitement. I've rarely witnessed such a terrific scene.

PEARL: I sent out to the garage and gave instructions that the old Rolls-Royce was to be taken down at once and the other was to go to London.

CLAY: What for?

PEARL: Never mind. You'll know presently. Then I did a little telephoning.

CLAY: Why were you so anxious to prevent anybody from leaving the house?

PEARL: I couldn't have persuaded myself that my party was a success if half my guests had left me on Sunday morning. I thought they might change their minds by the afternoon.

CLAY: If that's your only reason, I don't think it's a very good one.

PEARL: It isn't. I will be frank with you, Thornton. I can imagine that a very amusing story might be made out of this episode. I never mind scandal, but I don't expose myself to ridicule if I can help it.

CLAY: My dear Pearl, surely you can trust the discretion of your guests. Who do you think will give it away?

PEARL: You.

CLAY: I? My dear Pearl, I give you my word of honour . . .

PEARL [*Calmly*]: My dear Thornton, I don't care twopence about your word of honour. You're a professional entertainer, and you'll sacrifice everything to a good story. Why, don't you remember that killing story about your father's death? You dined out a whole season on it.

CLAY: Well, it was a perfectly killing story. No one would have enjoyed it more than my poor old father.

PEARL: I'm not going to risk anything, Thornton. I think it's much better there should be no story to tell.

CLAY: No one can move the clock backwards, Pearl. I couldn't help thinking at luncheon that there were the elements of a very good story indeed.

PEARL: And you'll tell it, Thornton. Then I shall say: My dear, does it sound probable? They all stayed quite happily till Monday morning; Sturrey and the Arlingtons dined on the Sunday night, and we had a very merry evening. Besides, I was lunching with Minnie only two days afterwards. And I shall say: Poor Thornton, he *is* such a liar, isn't he?

CLAY: I confess that if you are reconciled with Minnie it will take a great deal of the point away from my story. What about Arthur Fenwick?

PEARL: He's a sensualist, and the sensual are always sentimental.

CLAY: He scared me dreadfully at luncheon. He was eating a dressed crab, and his face grew every minute more purple. I was expecting him to have an apoplectic fit.

PEARL: It's not an unpleasant death, you know, Thornton, to have a stroke while you're eating your favourite dish.

CLAY: You know, there are no excuses for you, Pearl.

PEARL: Human nature excuses so much, Thornton.

CLAY: You really might have left Tony alone. This habit you have of snitching has got you into trouble before.

PEARL: People are so selfish. It just happens that I find no man so desirable as one that a friend of mine is in love with. I make allowances for the idiosyncrasies of my friends. Why shouldn't they make allowances for mine?

[*The* DUCHESSE *comes in, erect and haughty, with the air of Boadicea facing the Roman legions.* PEARL *turns to her with an ingratiating smile.*]

PEARL: Ah, Minnie.

DUCHESSE: I'm told the only way I can leave this house is by submitting to the odious necessity of seeing you.

PEARL: I wish you wouldn't go, Minnie. Lord Sturrey is coming over to dinner to-night, and so are the Arlingtons. I always take a lot of trouble to get the right people together, and I hate it when anybody fails me at the last minute.

DUCHESSE: D'you think anything would have induced me to stay so long if there'd been any possibility of getting away?

PEARL: It wouldn't have been nice to go without saying good-bye to me.

DUCHESSE: Don't talk nonsense, Pearl.

PEARL: D'you know that you behaved very badly last night, and I ought to be extremely angry with you?

DUCHESSE: I? Thornton, the woman's as mad as a hatter.

PEARL: You really oughtn't to have made a scene before Harry Bleane. And, you know, to tell Arthur wasn't playing the game. If you wanted to tell anyone, why didn't you tell George?

DUCHESSE: In the first place, he wasn't here. He never is.

PEARL: I know. He says that now society has taken to coming down to the country for week-ends he prefers London.

DUCHESSE: I'll never forgive you. Never. Never. Never. You'd got Arthur Fenwick. Why weren't you satisfied with him? If you wanted to have an affair with anyone, why didn't you take Thornton? He's almost the only one of your friends with whom you haven't. The omission is becoming almost marked.

PEARL: Thornton never makes love to me except when other people are looking. He can be very passionate in the front seat of my box at the opera.

CLAY: This conversation is growing excessively personal. I'll leave you.

[*He goes out.*]

PEARL: I'm sorry I had to insist on your seeing me, but I had something quite important to say to you.

DUCHESSE: Before you go any further, Pearl, I wish to tell you that I'm going to marry Tony.

PEARL [*Aghast*]: Minnie! Oh, my dear, you're not doing it to spite me? You know, honestly, he doesn't interest me in the slightest. Oh, Minnie, do think carefully.

DUCHESSE: It's the only way I can keep him.

PEARL: D'you think you'll be happy?

DUCHESSE: What should you care if I'm happy?

PEARL: Of course I care. D'you think it's wise? You're giving yourself into his hands. Oh, my dear, how can you risk it?

DUCHESSE: He said he was going out to the colonies. I love him. . . . I believe you're really distressed. How strange you are, Pearl! Perhaps it's the best thing for me. He may settle down. I was very lonely sometimes, you know. Sometimes, when I had the blues, I almost wished I'd never left home.

PEARL: And I've been moving heaven and earth to get him a job. I've been on the telephone this morning to all the Cabinet Ministers I know, and at last I've done it. That's what I wanted to tell you. I thought you'd be so pleased. I suppose now he won't want it.

DUCHESSE: Oh, I'm sure he will. He's very proud, you know. That's one of the things I liked in him. He had to be dependent on me, and that's partly why he always wanted to marry me.

PEARL: Of course, you'll keep your title.

DUCHESSE: Oh yes, I shall do that.

PEARL [*Going towards her as if to kiss her*]: Well, darling, you have my very, very best wishes.

DUCHESSE [*Drawing back*]: I'm not going to forgive you, Pearl.

PEARL: But you've forgiven Tony.

DUCHESSE: I don't blame him. He was led away.

PEARL: Come, Minnie, don't be spiteful. You might let bygones be bygones.

DUCHESSE: Nothing will induce me to stay in this house another night.

PEARL: It's a very slow train, and you'll have to go without your tea.

DUCHESSE: I don't care.

PEARL: You won't arrive in London till half-past eight, and you'll have to dine in a restaurant.

DUCHESSE: I don't care.

PEARL: You'll be grubby and hot. Tony will be hungry and out of temper. And you'll look your age.

DUCHESSE: You promised me the luggage cart.

PEARL [*With a sigh*]: You shall have it; but you'll have to sit on the floor, because it hasn't got any seats.

DUCHESSE: Pearl, it's not going to break down on the way to the station?

PEARL: Oh, no. How can you suspect me of playing a trick like that on you? . . . [*With a tinge of regret*] It never occurred to me.

[THORNTON CLAY *comes in.*]

CLAY: Pearl, I thought you'd like to know that Fenwick is coming to say good-bye to you.

DUCHESSE: I'll go and tell Tony about the job you've got him. By the way, what is it?

PEARL: Oh, it's something in the Education Office.

DUCHESSE: How very nice. What do they do there?

PEARL: Nothing. But it'll keep him busy from ten to four.

[*The* DUCHESSE *goes out.*]

PEARL: She's going to marry him.

CLAY: I know.

PEARL: I'm a wonderful matchmaker. First Bessie and

Harry Bleane, and now Minnie and Tony Paxton. I shall have to find someone for you, Thornton.

CLAY: How on earth did you manage to appease her?

PEARL: I reasoned with her. After all, she should be glad the boy has sown his wild oats before he marries. And besides, if he were her husband, of course she wouldn't expect fidelity from him; it seems unnatural to expect it when he isn't.

CLAY: But she's going all the same.

PEARL: I've got a quarter of an hour yet. Give me your handkerchief, will you?

CLAY [*Handing it to her*]: You're not going to burst into tears?

PEARL [*She rubs her cheeks violently*]: I thought I ought to look a little wan and pale when Arthur comes in.

CLAY: You'll never love me, Pearl. You tell me all your secrets.

PEARL: Shall I tell you what to do about it? Take the advice I give to Americans who come over to London and want to see the Tower: say you've been, and don't go.

CLAY: D'you think you can bring Arthur round?

PEARL: I'm sure I could if he loved me.

CLAY: My dear, he dotes on you.

PEARL: Don't be a fool, Thornton. He loves his love for me. That's quite a different thing. I've only got one chance. He sees himself as the man of iron. I'm going to play the dear little thing racket.

CLAY: You're a most unscrupulous woman, Pearl.

PEARL: Not more than most. Please go. I think he ought to find me alone.

[CLAY *goes out.* PEARL *seats herself in a pensive attitude and looks down at the carpet; in her hand she holds dejectedly an open volume of poetry. Presently* ARTHUR FENWICK *comes in. She pretends not to see him. He is the strong man, battered but not beaten, struggling with the emotion which he tries to master.*]

FENWICK: Pearl!

PEARL [*With a jump*]: Oh, how you startled me. I didn't hear you come in.

FENWICK: I daresay you're surprised to see me. I thought it was necessary that we should have a short conversation before I left this house.

PEARL [*Looking away*]: I'm glad to see you once more.

FENWICK: You understand that everything is over between us.

PEARL: If you've made up your mind, there's nothing for me to say. I know that nothing can move you when you've once done that.

FENWICK [*Drawing himself up a little*]: No. That has always been part of my power.

PEARL: I wouldn't have you otherwise.

FENWICK: I don't want to part from you in anger, Pearl. Last night I could have thrashed you within an inch of your life.

PEARL: Why didn't you? D'you think I'd have minded that from the man I loved?

FENWICK: You know I could never hit a woman.

PEARL: I thought of you all through the long hours of the night, Arthur.

FENWICK: I never slept a wink.

PEARL: One would never think it. You must be made of iron.

FENWICK: I think I am sometimes.

PEARL: Am I very pale?

FENWICK: A little.

PEARL: I feel a perfect wreck.

FENWICK: You must go and lie down. It's no good making yourself ill.

PEARL: Oh, don't bother about me, Arthur.

FENWICK: I've bothered about you so long. It's difficult for me to get out of the habit all at once.

PEARL: Every word you say stabs me to the heart.

FENWICK: I'll get done quickly with what I had to tell you and then go. It's merely this. Of course, I shall continue the allowance I've always made you.

PEARL: Oh, I couldn't take it. I couldn't take it.

FENWICK: You must be reasonable, Pearl. This is a matter of business.

PEARL: It's a question I refuse to discuss. Nothing would have induced me to accept your help if I hadn't loved you. Now that there can be nothing more between us—no, no, the thought outrages me.

FENWICK: I was afraid that you'd take up that attitude. Remember that you've only got eight thousand pounds a year of your own. You can't live on that.

PEARL: I can starve.

FENWICK: I must insist, Pearl, for my own sake. You've adopted a style of living which you would never have done if you hadn't had me at the back of you. I'm morally responsible, and I must meet my obligations.

PEARL: We can only be friends in future, Arthur.

FENWICK: I haven't often asked you to do anything for me, Pearl.

PEARL: I shall return your presents. Let me give you my pearl necklace at once.

FENWICK: Girlie, you wouldn't do that.

PEARL [*Pretending to try and take the necklace off*]: I can't undo the clasp. Please help me.

[*She goes up to him and turns her back so that he may get at it.*]

FENWICK: I won't. I won't.

PEARL: I'll tear it off my neck.

FENWICK: Pearl, you break my heart. Do you care for me so little that you can't bear to wear the trifling presents I gave you.

PEARL: If you talk to me like that I shall cry. Don't you see that I'm trying to keep my self-control?

FENWICK: This is dreadful. This is even more painful than I anticipated.

PEARL: You see, strength is easy to you. I'm weak. That's why I put myself in your hands. I felt your power instinctively.

FENWICK: I know, I know, and it was because I felt you needed me that I loved you. I wanted to shelter you from the storms and buffets of the world.

PEARL: Why didn't you save me from myself, Arthur?

FENWICK: When I look at your poor, pale little face I wonder what you'll do without me, girlie.

PEARL [*Her voice breaking*]: It'll be very hard. I've grown so used to depending on you. Whenever anything has gone wrong, I've come to you and you've put it right. I was beginning to think there was nothing you couldn't do.

FENWICK: I've always welcomed obstacles. I like something to surmount. It excites me.

PEARL: You seemed to take all my strength from me. I felt strangely weak beside you.

FENWICK: It wasn't necessary that we should both be strong. I loved you because you were weak. I liked you to come to me in all your troubles. It made me feel so good to be able to put everything right for you.

PEARL: You've always been able to do the impossible.

FENWICK [*Impressively*]: I have never found anything impossible.

PEARL [*Deeply moved*]: Except to forgive.

FENWICK: Ah, I see you know me. I never forget. I never forgive.

PEARL: I suppose that's why people feel there's something strangely Napoleonic about you.

FENWICK: Maybe. And yet—though you're only a woman, you've broken me, Pearl, you've broken me.

PEARL: Oh no, don't say that. I couldn't bear that. I want you to go on being strong and ruthless.

FENWICK: Something has gone out of my life for ever. I almost think you've broken my heart. I was so proud of you. I took so much pleasure in your success. Why, whenever I saw your name in the society columns of the papers it used to give me a thrill of satisfaction. What's going to become of you now, girlie? What's going to become of you now?

PEARL: I don't know; I don't care.

FENWICK: This fellow, does he care for you? Will he make you happy?

PEARL: Tony? He's going to marry the Duchesse. [FENWICK *represses a start*] I shall never see him again.

FENWICK: Then if I leave you, you'll have nobody but your husband.

PEARL: Nobody.

FENWICK: You'll be terribly lonely, girlie.

PEARL: You will think of me sometimes, Arthur, won't you?

FENWICK: I shall never forget you, girlie. I shall never forget how you used to leave your fine house in Mayfair and come and lunch with me down town.

PEARL: You used to give me such delicious things to eat.

FENWICK: It was a treat to see you in your beautiful clothes sharing a steak with me and a bottle of beer. I can order a steak, Pearl, can't I?

PEARL: And d'you remember those delicious little onions that we used to have? [*She seems to taste them*] M . . . M . . . M . . . It makes my mouth water to think of them.

FENWICK: There are few women who enjoy food as much as you do, Pearl.

PEARL: D'you know, next time you dined with me, I'd made up my mind to give you an entirely English dinner. Scotch broth, herrings, mixed grill, saddle of lamb, and then enormous marrow bones.

[FENWICK *can hardly bear the thought, his face grows red, his eyes bulge, and he gasps.*]

FENWICK: Oh, girlie! [*With utter abandonment*] Let's have that dinner. [*He seizes her in his arms and kisses her*] I can't leave you. You need me too much.

PEARL: Arthur, Arthur, can you forgive me?

FENWICK: To err is human, to forgive divine.

PEARL: Oh, how like you that is!

FENWICK: If you must deceive me, don't let me ever find out. I love you too much.

PEARL: I won't, Arthur, I promise you I won't.

FENWICK: Come and sit on the sofa and let me look at you. I seem to see you for the first time.

PEARL: You know, you wouldn't have liked the walk to the station. It's four miles in the sun. You're a vain old thing, and your boots are always a little too small for you.

[BESSIE *comes in. She stops as she sees* PEARL *and*
FENWICK *sitting hand in hand.*]

PEARL: Are you going out, Bessie?

BESSIE: As soon as Harry has finished his letters, we're
going for a walk.

PEARL [*To* FENWICK]: You mustn't squeeze my hand in
Bessie's presence, Arthur.

FENWICK: You're a very lucky girl, Bessie, to have a sister like Pearl. She's the most wonderful woman in the world.

PEARL: You're talking nonsense, Arthur. Go and put
some flannels on. It makes me quite hot to look at you in
that suit. We'll try and get up a little tennis after tea.

FENWICK: Now, you mustn't tire yourself, Pearl. Remember those white cheeks of yours.

PEARL [*With a charming look at him*]: Oh, I shall soon
get my colour back now.

[*She gives him her hand to kiss and he goes out.* PEARL
*takes a little mirror out of her bag and looks at her-
self reflectively.*]

PEARL: Men are very trivial, foolish creatures. They have
kind hearts. But their heads. Oh dear, oh dear, it's lamentable. And they're so vain, poor dears, they're so vain.

BESSIE: Pearl, to-morrow, when we go back to London,
I'm going away.

PEARL: Are you? Where?

BESSIE: The Princess is going to take me over to Paris for
a few days.

PEARL: Oh, is that all? Don't stay away too long. You
ought to be in London just at present.

BESSIE: On my return I'm proposing to stay with the Princess.

PEARL [*Calmly*]: Nonsense.

BESSIE: I wasn't asking your permission, Pearl. I was telling you my plans.

PEARL [*Looks at her for a moment reflectively*]: Are you
going to make me a scene, too? I've already gone through
two this afternoon. I'm rather tired of them.

BESSIE: Please don't be alarmed. I've got nothing more to
say.

[*She makes as though to leave the room.*]

PEARL: Don't be a little fool, Bessie. You've been staying with me all the season. I can't allow you to leave my house and go and live with Flora. We don't want to go out of our way to make people gossip.

BESSIE: Please don't argue with me, Pearl. It's not my business to reproach you for anything you do. But it isn't my business, either, to stand by and watch.

PEARL: You're no longer a child, Bessie.

BESSIE: I've been blind and foolish. Because I was happy and having a good time, I never stopped to ask for explanations of this, that and the other. I never thought. . . . The life was so gay and brilliant—it never struck me that underneath it all—— Oh, Pearl, don't make me say what I have in my heart, but let me go quietly.

PEARL: Bessie, dear, you must be reasonable. Think what people would say if you suddenly left my house. They'd ask all sorts of questions, and heaven knows what explanations they'd invent. People aren't charitable, you know. I don't want to be hard on you, but I can't afford to let you do a thing like that.

BESSIE: Now that I know what I do, I should never respect myself again if I stayed.

PEARL: I don't know how you can be so unkind.

BESSIE: I don't want to be that, Pearl. But it's stronger than I am. I must go.

PEARL [*With emotion*]: I'm so fond of you, Bessie. You don't know how much I want you with me. After all, I've seen so little of you these last few years. It's been such a comfort to me to have you. You were so pretty and young and sweet, it was like a ray of April sunshine in the house.

BESSIE: I'm afraid you think women are as trivial, foolish creatures as men, Pearl.

[PEARL *looks up and sees that* BESSIE *is not in the least taken in by the pathetic attitude.*]

PEARL [*Icily*]: Take care you don't go too far, Bessie.

BESSIE: There's no need for us to quarrel. I've made up my mind, and there's the end of it.

PEARL: Flora's a fool. I shall tell her that I won't have her take you away from me. You'll stay with me until you're married.

BESSIE: D'you want me to tell you that I can hardly bear to speak to you? You fill me with shame and disgust. I want never to see you again.

PEARL: Really, you drive me beyond endurance. I think I must be the most patient woman in the world to put up with all I've had to put up with to-day. After all, what have I done? I was a little silly and incautious. By the fuss you all make one would think no one had ever been incautious and silly before. Besides, it hasn't got anything to do with you. Why don't you mind your own business?

BESSIE [Bitterly]: You talk as though your relations with Arthur Fenwick were perfectly natural.

PEARL: Good heavens, you're not going to pretend you didn't know about Arthur. After all, I'm no worse than anybody else. Why, one of the reasons we Americans like London is that we can live our own lives and people accept things philosophically. Eleo Gloster, Sadie Twickenham, Maimie Hartlepool—you don't imagine they're faithful to their husbands? They didn't marry them for that.

BESSIE: Oh, Pearl, how can you? How can you? Haven't you any sense of decency at all? When I came in just now and saw you sitting on the sofa with that gross, vulgar, sensual old man—oh! [She makes a gesture of disgust] You can't love him. I could have understood if . . . but—oh, it's so disgraceful, it's so hideous. What can you see in him? He's nothing but rich . . . [She pauses, and her face changes as a thought comes to her, and coming horrifies her] It's not because he's rich? Pearl! Oh!

PEARL: Really, Bessie, you're very silly, and I'm tired of talking to you.

BESSIE: Pearl, it's not that? Answer me. Answer me.

PEARL [Roughly]: Mind your own business.

BESSIE: He was right, then, last night, when he called you that. He was so right that you didn't even notice it. A few hours later you're sitting hand in hand with him. A slut. That's what he called you. A slut. A slut.

PEARL: How dare you! Hold your tongue. How dare you!

BESSIE: A kept woman. That's what you are.

PEARL [*Recovering herself*]: I'm a fool to lose my temper with you.

BESSIE: Why should you? I'm saying nothing but the truth.

PEARL: You're a silly little person, Bessie. If Arthur helps me a little, that's his affair, and mine. He's got more money than he knows what to do with, and it amuses him to see me spend it. I could have twenty thousand a year from him if I chose.

BESSIE: Haven't you got money of your own?

PEARL: You know exactly what I've got. Eight thousand pounds a year. D'you think I could have got the position I have on that? You're not under the impression all the world comes to my house because of my charm, are you? I'm not. You don't think the English want us here? You don't think they like us marrying their men? Good heavens, when you've known England as long as I have you'll realise that in their hearts they still look upon us as savages and Red Indians. We have to force ourselves upon them. They come to me because I amuse them. Very early in my career I discovered that the English can never resist getting something for nothing. If a dancer is the rage, they'll see her at my house. If a fiddler is in vogue, they'll hear him at my concert. I give them balls. I give them dinners. I've made myself the fashion, I've got power, I've got influence. But everything I've got—my success, my reputation, my notoriety—I've bought it, bought it, bought it.

BESSIE: How humiliating!

PEARL: And, finally, I've bought you a husband.

BESSIE: That's not true. He loves me.

PEARL: D'you think he'd have loved you if I hadn't shown you to him in these surroundings, if I hadn't dazzled him with the brilliant people among whom he found you. You don't know what love is made of. D'you think it's nothing that he should hear a Prime Minister pay you compliments. Of course I bought him.

BESSIE [*Aghast*]: It's horrible.

PEARL: You know the truth now. It'll be very useful to you in your married life. Run away and take your little walk with Harry Bleane. I'm going to arrange my face.

[*She goes out.* BESSIE *is left ashamed and stunned.* BLEANE *comes in.*]

BLEANE: I'm afraid I've kept you waiting. I'm so sorry.

BESSIE [*Dully*]: It doesn't matter at all.

BLEANE: Where shall we go? You know the way about these parts, and I don't.

BESSIE: Harry, I want you to release me. I can't marry you.

BLEANE [*Aghast*]: Why?

BESSIE: I want to go back to America. I'm frightened.

BLEANE: Of me?

BESSIE: Oh no, I know that you're a dear, good creature; I'm frightened of what I may become.

BLEANE: But I love you, Bessie.

BESSIE: Then that's all the more reason for me to go. I must tell you frankly. I'm not in love with you, I only like you. I would never have dreamt of marrying you, if you hadn't been who you are. I wanted to have a title. That's why Pearl married her husband, and that's why the Duchesse married. Let me go, Harry.

BLEANE: I knew you didn't love me, but I thought you might come to in time. I thought if I tried I could make you love me.

BESSIE: You didn't know that I was nothing but a self-seeking, heartless snob.

BLEANE: I don't care what you say of yourself, I know that you can be nothing but what is true and charming.

BESSIE: After what you've seen last night? After what you know of this house? Aren't you disgusted with all of us?

BLEANE: You can't think I could class you with the Duchesse and . . . [*He stops*]

BESSIE: Pearl at my age was no different from what I am. It's the life.

BLEANE: But perhaps you won't want to lead it. The set you've been living in here isn't the only set in England. It makes a stir because it's in the public eye. Its doings are announced in the papers. But it isn't a very good set, and there are plenty of people who don't very much admire it.

BESSIE: You must let me try and say what I have in my heart. And be patient with me. You think I can make myself at home in your life. I've had a hint of it now and then. I've seen a glimpse of it through Pearl's laughter and the Duchesse's sneers. It's a life of dignity, of responsibilities, and of public duty.

BLEANE [*With a rueful smile*]: You make it very strenuous.

BESSIE: It comes naturally to the English girls of your class. They've known it all their lives, and they've been brought up to lead it. But we haven't. To us it's just tedious, and its dignity is irksome. We're bored, and we fall back on the only thing that offers, pleasure. You've spoken to me about your house. It means everything to you because it's associated with your childhood and all your people before you. It could only mean something to me if I loved you. And I don't.

BLEANE: You've made me so wretched. I don't know what to say to you.

BESSIE: If I make you wretched now, it's so that we may both be saved a great deal of unhappiness later on. I'm glad I don't care for you, for it would make it so much harder for me to go. And I've got to go. I can't marry you. I want to go home. If I marry ever I want to marry in my own country. That is my place.

BLEANE: Don't you think you could wait a little before you decide finally?

BESSIE: Don't put difficulties in my way. Don't you see that we're not strong enough for the life over here? It goes to our heads; we lose our bearings; we put away our own code, and we can't adopt the code of the country we come to. We drift. There's nothing for us to do but amuse ourselves, and we fall to pieces. But in America we're safe. And perhaps America wants us. When we come over here we're like soldiers deserting our country in time of war. Oh, I'm homesick for America. I didn't know how much it meant to me till now. Let me go back, Harry.

BLEANE: If you don't want to marry me, of course, I'm not going to try and make you.

BESSIE: Don't be angry, and be my friend always.

BLEANE: Always.

BESSIE: After all, three months ago you didn't know me. In three months more you will have forgotten me. Then marry some English girl, who can live your life and share your thoughts. And be happy.

[PEARL *comes in. She has rouged her cheeks, and has once more the healthy colour which is usual with her. She is evidently jubilant.*]

PEARL: The car has just come back from London. [*She goes to the french window and calls*] Minnie!

BESSIE: I shall tell Pearl to-morrow.

BLEANE: I won't post my letters then. I'll go and get them out of the box.

BESSIE: Forgive me.

[*He goes out. The* DUCHESSE *and* CLAY *appear at the window.*]

DUCHESSE: Did you call me?

PEARL: The car has just come back from London, so it can take you to the station.

DUCHESSE: That's a mercy. I didn't at all like the idea of going to the station in the luggage cart. Where is Flora? I must say good-bye to her.

PEARL: Oh, there's plenty of time now. The car will run you down in ten minutes.

[TONY *comes in, then the* PRINCESS *and* FLEMING.]

DUCHESSE: Tony, the car has returned, and is going to take us to the station.

TONY: Thank God for that! I should have looked a perfect fool in that luggage cart.

CLAY: But what on earth did you send the car to London for, anyway?

PEARL: In one minute you'll see.

[ARTHUR FENWICK *comes in. He has changed into flannels.*]

FENWICK: Who is that gentleman that's just arrived, Pearl?

PEARL: The man of mystery.

[*The* BUTLER *comes in, followed by* ERNEST, *and after announcing him goes out.*]

POLE: Mr. Ernest.

DUCHESSE: Ernest!

CLAY: Ernest?

[*He is a little dark man, with large eyes, and long hair neatly plastered down. He is dressed like a tailor's dummy, in black coat, white gloves, silk hat, patent leather boots. He is a dancing master, and over-whelmingly gentlemanly. He speaks in mincing tones.*]

ERNEST: Dear Lady Grayston.

PEARL [*Shaking hands with him*]: I'm so glad you were able to come. [*To the others*] You were talking about Ernest last night, and I thought we would have nothing to do this evening and he would cheer and comfort us. I sent the car up to London with orders to bring him back dead or alive.

ERNEST: My dear Lady Grayston, I'm sure I'll get into no end of trouble. I had all sorts of calls to pay this afternoon, and I was dining out, and I'd promised to go to a little hop that the dear Duchess of Gloster was giving. But I felt I couldn't refuse *you*. You've always been such a good friend to me, dear Lady Grayston. You must excuse me coming in my town clothes, but your chauffeur said there wasn't a moment to lose, so I came just as I am.

PEARL: But you look a perfect picture.

ERNEST: Oh, don't say that, dear Lady Grayston; I know this isn't the sort of thing one ought to wear in the country.

PEARL: You remember the Duchesse de Surennes?

ERNEST: Oh, of course I remember the Duchesse.

DUCHESSE: Dear Ernest!

ERNEST: Dear Duchesse!

DUCHESSE: I thought I was never going to see you again, Ernest.

ERNEST: Oh, don't say that, it sounds too sad.

PEARL: It's such a pity you must go, Minnie. Ernest could have shown you all sorts of new steps.

ERNEST: Oh, dear Duchesse, you're not going the very moment I come down? That is unkind of you.

DUCHESSE [*With an effort*]: I must go. I must go.

ERNEST: Have you been practising that little step I showed you the other day? My dear friend, the Marchioness of Twickenham—not the *old* one, you know, the *new* one—is beginning to do it so well.

DUCHESSE [*Struggling with herself*]: Have we time, Pearl? I should like Ernest to dance just one two-step with me.

PEARL: Of course there's time. Thornton, set the gramophone.

[THORNTON CLAY *at once starts it, and the notes of the two-step tinkle out.*]

DUCHESSE: You don't mind, Ernest, do you?

ERNEST: I love dancing with you, Duchesse.

[*They take up their positions.*]

DUCHESSE: Just one moment. It always makes me so nervous to dance with you, Ernest.

ERNEST: Oh, now, don't be silly, dear Duchesse.

[*They begin to dance.*]

ERNEST: Now hold your shoulders like a lady. Arch your back, my dear, arch your back. Don't look like a sack of potatoes. If you put your foot there, I shall kick it.

DUCHESSE: Oh, Ernest, don't be cross with me.

ERNEST: I shall be cross with you, Duchesse. You don't pay any attention to what I say. You must give your mind to it.

DUCHESSE: I do! I do!

ERNEST: And don't dance like an old fish-wife. Put some vim into it. That's what I always say about these modern dances: you want two things, vim and nous.

DUCHESSE [*Plaintively*]: Ernest!

ERNEST: Now don't cry. I'm saying all this for your good, you know. What's wrong with you is that you've got no passion.

DUCHESSE: Oh, Ernest, how can you say such a thing. I've always looked upon myself as a very passionate woman.

ERNEST: I don't know anything about that, dear Duchesse,

but you don't get it into your dancing. That's what I said the other day to the dear Marchioness of Twickenham—not the *new* one, you know, the *old* one— You must put passion into it, I said. That's what these modern dances want—passion, passion.

DUCHESSE: I see exactly what you mean, Ernest.

ERNEST: And you must dance with your eyes as well, you know. You must look as if you had a knife in your garter, and as if you'd kill me if I looked at another woman. Don't you see how I'm looking, I'm looking as though I meant, Curse her! how I love her. There!

[*The music stops and they separate.*]

DUCHESSE: I have improved, Ernest, haven't I?

ERNEST: Yes, you've improved, dear Duchesse, but you want more practice.

PEARL: Minnie, why on earth don't you stay, and Ernest will give you a real lesson this evening.

ERNEST: That's what you want, Duchesse.

[*The* DUCHESSE *wrestles with her soul.*]

DUCHESSE: Tony, d'you think we can stop?

TONY: I didn't want to go away. It's rotten going up to town this evening. What on earth are we going to do with ourselves when we get there?

DUCHESSE: Very well, Pearl, if it'll please you, we'll stop.

PEARL: That is nice of you, Minnie.

DUCHESSE: You're very naughty sometimes, Pearl, but you have a good heart, and I can't help being fond of you.

PEARL [*With outstretched arms*]: Minnie!

DUCHESSE: Pearl!

[*They clasp one another and affectionately embrace.*]

ERNEST: What an exquisite spectacle—two ladies of title kissing one another.

BESSIE [*To* FLEMING]: They're not worth making a fuss about. I'm sailing for America next Saturday!

THE END

THE SUMMING UP

THIS is not an autobiography nor is it a book of recollections. In one way and another I have used in my writings whatever has happened to me in the course of my
life. Sometimes an experience I have had has served as a
theme and I have invented a series of incidents to illustrate
it; more often I have taken persons with whom I have been
slightly or intimately acquainted and used them as the
foundation for characters of my invention. Fact and fiction
are so intermingled in my work that now, looking back on it,
I can hardly distinguish one from the other. It would not interest me to record the facts, even if I could remember them,
of which I have already made a better use. They would
seem, moreover, very tame. I have had a varied, and often
an interesting, life, but not an adventurous one. I have a
poor memory. I can never remember a good story till I hear
it again and then I forget it before I have had a chance to tell
it to somebody else. I have never been able to remember even
my own jokes, so that I have been forced to go on making
new ones. This disability, I am aware, has made my company less agreeable than it might otherwise have been.

I have never kept a diary. I wish now that during the
year that followed my first success as a dramatist I had done
so, for I met then many persons of consequence and it might
have proved an interesting document. At that period the
confidence of the people in the aristocracy and the landed
gentry had been shattered by the muddle they had made of
things in South Africa, but the aristocracy and the landed
gentry had not realized this and they preserved their old
self-confidence. At certain political houses I frequented

they still talked as though to run the British Empire were their private business. It gave me a peculiar sensation to hear it discussed, when a general election was in the air, whether Tom should have the Home Office and whether Dick would be satisfied with Ireland. I do not suppose that anyone today reads the novels of Mrs. Humphry Ward, but dull though they may be, my recollection is that some of them give a very good picture of what the life of the ruling class was then. Novelists were still much concerned with it and even writers who had never known a lord thought it necessary to write largely about persons of rank. It would astonish anyone now who looked at the playbills of the day to see how many of the characters were titled. Managers thought that they attracted the public, and actors liked to portray them. But as the political importance of the aristocracy dwindled the public took less interest in it. Playgoers began to be ready to observe the actions of people of their own class, the well-to-do merchants and professional men who were then conducting the affairs of the country; and the rule, though never formulated, prevailed that the writer should not introduce persons of title unless they were essential to his theme. It was still impossible to interest the public in the lower classes. Novels and plays that dealt with them were very generally considered sordid. It will be curious to see if now that these classes have acquired political power the public at large will take the same interest in their lives that for so long it took in the lives of the titled, and for a while in those of the opulent bourgeoisie.

During this period I met persons who by their rank, fame or position might very well have thought themselves destined to become historical figures. I did not find them as brilliant as my fancy had painted them. The English are a political nation and I was often asked to houses where politics were the ruling interest. I could not discover in the eminent statesmen I met there any marked capacity. I concluded, perhaps rashly, that no great degree of intelligence was needed to rule a nation. Since then I have known in various countries a good many politicians who have attained high office. I have continued to be puzzled by what seemed to me the mediocrity of their minds. I have found them ill-informed upon the ordinary affairs of life and I have not often discovered in them either subtlety of intellect or liveliness of imagination. At one time I was inclined to think that they owed their illustrious position only to their gift of speech, for it must be next door to impossible to rise to power in a democratic community unless you can catch the ears of the public; and the gift of speech, as we know, is not often accompanied by the power of thought. But since I have seen statesmen who did not seem to me very clever conduct public affairs with reasonable success I cannot but think I was wrong: it must be that to govern a nation you need a specific talent and that this may very well exist without general ability. In the same way I have known men of affairs who have made great fortunes and brought vast enterprises to prosperity, but in everything unconcerned with their business appear to be devoid even of common sense.

Nor was the conversation that I heard then as clever as I had expected. It seldom gave you much to think about. It was easy, though not always; gay, amiable and superficial. Serious topics were not dealt with, for there was a feeling that to discuss them in general company was embarrassing, and the fear of "shop" seemed to prevent people from speaking of the subjects in which they were most interested. So far as I could judge conversation consisted in little more than a decorous badinage; but it was not often that you heard a witticism worth repeating. One might have thought that the only use of culture was to enable one to talk nonsense with distinction. On the whole I think the most interesting and consistently amusing talker I ever knew was Edmund Gosse. He had read a great deal, though not very carefully, it appears, and his conversation was extremely intelligent. He had a prodigious memory, a keen sense of humour, and malice. He had known Swinburne intimately and could talk about him in an entrancing fashion, but he could also talk of Shelley, whom after all he could not possibly have known, as if he had been a bosom friend. For many years he had been acquainted with eminent persons. I think he was a vain man and he had observed their absurdities with satisfaction.

I am sure he made them much more amusing then they really were.

ii

I HAVE always wondered at the passion many people have to meet the celebrated. The prestige you acquire by being able to tell your friends that you know famous men proves only that you are yourself of small account. The celebrated develop a technique to deal with the persons they come across. They show the world a mask, often an impressive one, but take care to conceal their real selves. They play the part that is expected from them and with practice learn to play it very well, but you are stupid if you think that this public performance of theirs corresponds with the man within.

I have been attached, deeply attached, to a few people; but I have been interested in men in general not for their own sakes, but for the sake of my work. I have not, as Kant enjoined, regarded each man as an end in himself, but as material that might be useful to me as a writer. I have been more concerned with the obscure than with the famous. They are more often themselves. They have had no need to create a figure to protect themselves from the world or to impress it. Their idosyncrasies have had more chance to develop in the limited circle of their activity, and since they have never been in the public eye it has never occurred to them that they have anything to conceal. They display their oddities because it has never struck them that they are odd. And after all it is with the common run of men that we writers have to deal; kings, dictators, commercial magnates are from our point of view very unsatisfactory. To write about them is a venture that has often tempted writers, but the failure that has attended their efforts shows that such beings are too exceptional to form a proper ground for a work of art. They cannot be made real. The ordinary is the writer's richer field. Its unexpectedness, its singularity, its infinite variety afford unending material. The great man is too often all of a piece; it is the little man that is a bundle of contradictory elements. He is inexhaustible. You never come to the end of the surprises he has in store for you. For my part I would much sooner spend a month on a desert island with a veterinary surgeon than with a prime minister.

iii

IN THIS book I am going to try to sort out my thoughts on the subjects that have chiefly interested me during the course of my life. But such conclusions as I have come to have drifted about my mind like the wreckage of a foundered ship on a restless sea. It has seemed to me that if I set them down in some sort of order I should see for myself more distinctly what they really were and so might get some kind of coherence into them. I have long thought I should like to make such an attempt and more than once, when starting on a journey that was to last for several months, have determined to set about it. The opportunity seemed ideal. But I have always found that I was assailed by so many impressions, I saw so many strange things and met so many people who excited my fancy, that I had no time to reflect. The experience of the moment was so vivid that I could not attune my mind to introspection.

I have been held back also by the irksomeness of setting down my thoughts in my own person. For though I have written a good deal from this standpoint I have written as a novelist and so in a manner have been able to regard myself as a character in the story. Long habit has made it more comfortable for me to speak through the creatures of my invention. I can decide what they would think more readily than I can decide what I think myself. The one has always been a pleasure to me; the other has been a labour that I have willingly put off. But now I can afford to put it off no longer. In youth the years stretch before one so long that it is hard to realize that they will ever pass, and even in middle age, with the ordinary expectation of life in these days, it is easy to find excuses for delaying what one would like to do but does not want to; but at last a time comes when death must be considered. Here and there one's contemporaries drop off. We know that all men are mortal (Socrates was a man; therefore—and so forth), but it remains for us little more than a logical premiss till we are forced to recognize that in the ordinary course of things our end can no longer be remote. An occasional glance at the obituary column of *The Times* has suggested to me that the sixties are very unhealthy; I have long thought that it would exasperate me to die before I had written this book and so it seemed to me that I had better set about it at once. When I have finished it I can face the future with serenity, for I shall have rounded off my life's work. I can no longer persuade myself that I am not ready to write it, since if I have not by now made up my mind about the things that seem of importance to me there is small likelihood that I shall ever do so. I am glad at last to collect all these thoughts that for so long have floated at haphazard on the various levels of my consciousness. When they are written down I shall have finished with them and my mind will be free to occupy itself with other things. For I hope that this will not be the last book I shall write. One does not die immediately one has made one's will; one makes one's will as a precaution. To have settled one's affairs is a very good preparation to leading the rest of one's life without concern for the future. When I have finished this book I shall know where I stand. I can afford then to do what I choose with the years that remain to me.

iv

IT IS inevitable that in it I should say many things that I have said before; that is why I have called it *The Summing Up*. When a judge sums up a case he recapitulates the facts that have been put before the jury and comments on the speeches of counsel. He does not offer new evidence. And since I have put the whole of my life into my books much of what I have to say will naturally have found a place in them. There are few subjects within the compass of my interests that I have not lightly or seriously touched upon. All I can attempt to do now is to give a coherent picture of my feelings and opinions; and here and there, maybe, to state with greater elaboration some idea which the limitations I have thought fit to accept in fiction and in the drama have only allowed me to hint at.

This book must be egotistic. It is about certain subjects that are important to me and it is about myself because I can only treat of these subjects as they have affected me. But it is not about my doings. I have no desire to lay bare my heart, and I put limits to the intimacy that I wish the reader to enter upon with me. There are matters on which I am content to maintain my privacy. No one can tell the whole truth about himself. It is not only vanity that has prevented those who have tried to reveal themselves to the world from telling the whole truth; it is direction of interest; their disappointment with themselves, their surprise that they can do things that seem to them so abnormal, make them place too great an emphasis on occurrences that are more common than they suppose. Rousseau in the course of his *Confessions* narrates incidents that have profoundly shocked the sensibility of mankind. By describing them so frankly he falsified his values and so gave them in his book a greater importance than they had in his life. There were events among a multitude of others, virtuous or at least neutral, that he omitted because they were too ordinary to seem worth recording. There is a sort of man who pays no attention to his good actions, but is tormented by his bad ones. This is the type that most often writes about himself. He leaves out his redeeming qualities and so appears only weak, unprincipled and vicious.

v

I WRITE this book to disembarrass my soul of certain notions that have hovered about in it too long for my comfort. I do not seek to persuade anybody. I am devoid of the pedagogic instinct and when I know a thing never feel in myself the desire to impart it to others. I do not much care if people agree with me. Of course I think I am right, otherwise I should not think as I do, and they are wrong, but it does not offend me that they should be wrong. Nor does it greatly disturb me to discover that my judgment is at variance with that of the majority. I have a certain confidence in my instinct.

I must write as though I were a person of importance; and indeed, I am—to myself. To myself I am the most important person in the world; though I do not forget that, not even taking into consideration so grand a conception as the Absolute, but from the standpoint of common sense, I am of no consequence whatever. It would have made small difference to the universe if I had never existed. Though I may seem to write as though significance must necessarily be attached to certain of my works, I mean only that they are of moment to me for the purpose of any discussion during which I may have occasion to mention them. I think few serious writers, by which I do not only mean writers of serious things, can be entirely indifferent to the fate that will befall their works after their death. It is pleasant to think, not that one may achieve immortality (immortality for literary productions lasts in any case but a few hundred years and then is seldom more than the immortality of the schoolroom) but that one may be read with interest by a few generations and find a place, however small, in the history of one's country's literature. But so far as I am concerned, I look upon this modest possibility with scepticism. Even in my life I have seen writers who made much more stir in the world of letters than ever I have, sink into oblivion. When I was young George Meredith and Thomas Hardy seemed certain of survival. They have ceased to mean very much to the youth of to-day. From time to time they will doubtless find a critic in search of a subject to write an article about them, which may cause readers here and there to get out one or other of their books from a library; but I think it is clear that neither of them wrote anything that will be read as *Gulliver's Travels*, *Tristram Shandy* or *Tom Jones* is read. If in the following pages I seem to express myself dogmatically, it is only because I find it very boring to qualify

every phrase with an "I think" or "to my mind." Everything
I say is merely an opinion of my own. The reader can take it
or leave it. If he has the patience to read what follows he
will see that there is only one thing about which I am certain,
and this is that there is very little about which one can be
certain.

vi

WHEN I began to write I did so as though it were the most
natural thing in the world. I took to it as a duck takes to
water. I have never quite got over my astonishment at being
a writer; there seems no reason for my having become one
except an irresistible inclination, and I do not see why such
an inclination should have arisen in me. For well over a hundred years my family has practised law. According to the
Dictionary of National Biography my grandfather was one
of the two founders of the Incorporated Law Society, and in
the catalogue of the library at the British Museum there is
a long list of his legal works. He wrote only one book that
was not of this character. It was a collection of essays that
he had contributed to the solid magazines of the day and he
issued it, as became his sense of decorum, anonymously.
I once had the book in my hands, a handsome volume bound
in calf, but I never read it and I have not been able to get
hold of a copy since. I wish I had, for I might have learnt
from it something of the kind of man he was. For many
years he lived in Chancery Lane, for he became secretary of
the society he had founded, and when he retired to a house
in Kensington Gore overlooking the Park, he was presented
with a salver, a tea and coffee service and an épergne, in
silver, so massive and ornate that they have been ever since
an embarrassment to his descendants. An old solicitor, whom
I knew when I was a boy, told me that as an articled clerk
he was once invited to dine with my grandfather. My grandfather carved the beef and then a servant handed him a dish
of potatoes baked in their skins. There are few things better
to eat than a potato in its skin, with plenty of butter, pepper
and salt, but apparently my grandfather did not think so. He

rose in his chair at the head of the table and took the potatoes out of the dish one by one and threw one at each picture
on the walls. Then without a word he sat down again and
went on with his dinner. I asked my friend what effect this
behaviour had on the rest of the company. He told me that
no one took any notice. He also told me that my grandfather
was the ugliest little man he ever saw. I went once to the
building of the Incorporated Society in Chancery Lane to
see for myself if he was really so ugly as all that, for there
is a portrait of him there. If what my old gentleman said was
true the painter must have grossly flattered my grandfather;
he has given him very fine dark eyes under black eyebrows,
and there is a faintly ironic twinkle in them; a firm jaw, a
straight nose and pouting red lips. His dark hair is windswept as becomingly as that of Miss Anita Loos. He is
holding a quill and there is a pile of books, doubtless his
own, by his side. Notwithstanding his black coat, he does
not look so respectable as I should have expected, but
slightly mischievous. Many years ago when I was destroy-
ing the papers of one of his sons, my uncle, who had died, I
came across the diary that my grandfather kept when as a
young man at the beginning of the nineteenth century he did
what I believe was called the Little Tour, France, Germany
and Switzerland; and I remember that when he described
the not very impressive fall of the Rhine at Schaffhausen he
offered thanks to God Almighty because in creating "this
stupendous cataract" he had given "His miserable creatures
occasion to realize their insignificance in comparison with the
prodigious greatness of His works."

vii

MY PARENTS died when I was so young, my mother when I
was eight, my father when I was ten, that I know little of
them but from hearsay. My father, I do not know why unless
he was drawn by some such restlessness for the unknown as
has consumed his son, went to Paris and became solicitor to
the British Embassy. He had offices just opposite, in the

Faubourg St. Honoré, but he lived in what was then called
the Avenue d'Antin, a broad street with chestnut trees on
each side of it that leads from the Rond Point. He was a
great traveller for those days. He had been to Turkey,
Greece and Asia Minor and in Morocco as far as Fez, which
was a place few people then visited. He had a considerable
library of travel books and the apartment in the Avenue
d'Antin was filled with the things he had brought back,
Tanagra statuettes, Rhodes ware and Turkish daggers in
hilts of richly decorated silver. He was forty when he married my mother, who was more than twenty years younger.
She was a very beautiful woman and he was a very ugly man.
I have been told that they were known in the Paris of that
day as Beauty and the Beast. Her father was in the army;
he died in India and his widow, my grandmother, after
squandering a considerable fortune, settled down in France
to live on her pension. She was a woman of character, I
suspect, and perhaps of some talent, for she wrote novels in
French *pour jeunes filles* and composed the music for drawing-room ballads. I like to think that the novels were read
and the ballads sung by Octave Feuillet's high-born heroines.
I have a little photograph of her, a middle-aged woman in a
crinoline with fine eyes and a look of good-humoured determination. My mother was very small, with large brown
eyes and hair of a rich reddish gold, exquisite features and a
lovely skin. She was very much admired. One of her great
friends was Lady Anglesey, an American woman who died
at an advanced age not very long ago, and she told me that
she had once said to my mother: "You're so beautiful and
there are so many people in love with you, why are you faithful to that ugly little man you've married?" And my mother
answered: "He never hurts my feelings."

The only letter of hers I ever saw was one that I came
across when I was going through my uncle's papers after his
death. He was a clergyman and she asked him to be god-
father to one of her sons. She expressed, very simply and
piously, the hope that by reason of his holy calling the relationship into which she invited him to enter would have
such an influence on the new-born child that he would grow

up to be a good, God-fearing man. She was a great novel-reader and in the billiard-room of the apartment in the Avenue d'Antin were two great bookcases filled with Tauchnitz. She suffered from tuberculosis of the lungs and I remember the string of donkeys that stopped at the door to provide her with asses' milk, which at that time was thought to be good for that malady. In the summer we used to take a house at Deauville, not then a fashionable spot, but a little fishing village overshadowed by the smarter Trouville, and towards the end of her life we spent winters at Pau. Once when she was lying in bed, I suppose after a hæmorrhage, and knew she could not live much longer, the thought came to her that her sons when they grew up would not know what she was like when she died, so she called her maid, had herself dressed in an evening gown of white satin and went to the photographer's. She had six sons and died in childbirth. The doctors of the period had a theory that to have a child was beneficial to women suffering from consumption. She was thirty-eight.

After my mother's death, her maid became my nurse. I had till then had French nurses and I had been sent to a French school for children. My knowledge of English must have been slight. I have been told that on one occasion, seeing a horse out of the window of a railway carriage, I cried: *"Regardez, Maman, voilà un 'orse."*

I think my father had a romantic mind. He took it into his head to build a house to live in during the summer. He bought a piece of land on the top of a hill at Suresnes. The view was splendid over the plain, and in the distance was Paris. There was a road down to the river and by the river lay a little village. It was to be like a villa on the Bosphorus and on the top floor it was surrounded by loggias. I used to go down with him every Sunday by the Seine on a *bateau-mouche* to see how it was getting on. When the roof was on, my father began to furnish it by buying a pair of antique fire irons. He ordered a great quantity of glass on which he had engraved a sign against the Evil Eye which he had found in Morocco and which the reader may see on the cover of this book. It was a white house and the shutters were painted red. The garden was laid out. The rooms were furnished and then my father died.

viii

I HAD been taken away from the French school and went for my lessons every day to the apartment of the English clergyman at the church attached to the Embassy. His method of teaching me English was to make me read aloud the police-court news in *The Standard* and I can still remember the horror with which I read the ghastly details of a murder in the train between Paris and Calais. I must then have been nine. I was for long uncertain about the pronunciation of English words and I have never forgotten the roar of laughter that abashed me when in my preparatory school I read out the phrase "unstable as water" as though unstable rhymed with Dunstable.

I have never had more than two English lessons in my life, for though I wrote essays at school, I do not remember that I ever received any instruction on how to put sentences together. The two lessons I have had were given me so late in life that I am afraid I cannot hope greatly to profit by them. The first was only a few years ago. I was spending some weeks in London and had engaged as temporary secretary a young woman. She was shy, rather pretty, and absorbed in a love affair with a married man. I had written a book called *Cakes and Ale* and, the typescript arriving one Saturday morning, I asked her if she would be good enough to take it home and correct it over the week-end. I meant her only to make a note of mistakes in spelling that the typist might have made and point out errors occasioned by a handwriting that is not always easy to decipher. But she was a conscientious young person and she took me more literally than I intended. When she brought back the typescript on Monday morning it was accompanied by four foolscap sheets of corrections. I must confess that at the first glance I was a trifle vexed; but then I thought that it would be silly of me not to profit, if I could, by the trouble she had taken and so sat me down to examine them. I suppose the young woman had taken a course at a secretarial college and she had gone through my novel in the same methodical way as her masters had gone through her essays. The remarks that filled the four neat pages of foolscap were incisive and severe. I could not but surmise that the professor of English at the secretarial college did not mince matters. He took a marked line, there could be no doubt about that; and he did not allow that there might be two opinions about anything. His apt pupil would have nothing to do with a preposition at the end of a sentence. A mark of exclamation betokened her disapproval of a colloquial phrase. She had a feeling that you must not use the same word twice on a page and she was ready every time with a synonym to put in its place. If I had indulged myself in the luxury of a sentence of ten lines, she wrote: "Clarify this. Better break it up into two or more periods." When I had availed myself of the pleasant pause that is indicated by a semicolon, she noted: "A full stop"; and if I had ventured upon a colon she remarked stingingly: "Obsolete." But the harshest stroke of all was her comment on what I thought was rather a good joke: "Are you sure of your facts?" Taking it all in all I am bound to conclude that the professor at her college would not have given me very high marks.

The second lesson I had was given me by a don, both intelligent and charming, who happened to be staying with me when I was myself correcting the typescript of another book. He was good enough to offer to read it. I hesitated, because I knew that he judged from a standpoint of excellence that is hard to attain; and though I was aware that he had a profound knowledge of Elizabethan literature, his inordinate admiration for *Esther Waters* made me doubtful of his discernment in the productions of our own day: no one could attach so great a value to that work who had an intimate knowledge of the French novel during the nineteenth century. But I was anxious to make my book as good as I could and I hoped to benefit by his criticisms. They were in point of fact lenient. They interested me peculiarly because I inferred that this was the way in which he dealt with the compositions of undergraduates. My don had, I think, a natural gift for language, which it has been his business to cultivate; his taste appeared to me faultless. I was much struck by his insistence on the force of individual words. He liked the stronger word rather than the euphonious. To give an example, I had written that a statue would be placed in a certain square and he suggested that I should write: the statue will stand. I had not done that because my ear was offended by the alliteration. I noticed also that he had a feeling that words should be used not only to balance a sentence but to balance an idea. This is sound, for an idea may lose its effect if it is delivered abruptly; but it is a matter of delicacy, since it may well lead to verbiage. Here a knowledge of stage dialogue should help. An actor will sometimes say to an author: "Couldn't you give me a word or two more in this speech? It seems to take away all the point of my line if I have nothing else to say." As I listened to my don's remarks I could not but think how much better I should write now if in my youth I had had the advantage of such sensible, broadminded and kindly advice.

ix

As it is, I have had to teach myself. I have looked at the stories I wrote when I was very young in order to discover what natural aptitude I had, my original stock-in-trade, before I developed it by taking thought. The manner had a superciliousness that perhaps my years excused and an irascibility that was a defect of nature; but I am speaking now only of the way in which I expressed myself. It seems to me that I had a natural lucidity and a knack for writing easy dialogue.

When Henry Arthur Jones, then a well-known playwright, read my first novel, he told a friend that in due course I should be one of the most successful dramatists of the day. I suppose he saw in it directness and an effective way of presenting a scene that suggested a sense of the theatre. My language was commonplace, my vocabulary limited, my

grammar shaky and my phrases hackneyed. But to write was
an instinct that seemed as natural to me as to breathe, and
I did not stop to consider if I wrote well or badly. It was
not till some years later that it dawned upon me that it
was a delicate art that must be painfully acquired. The
discovery was forced upon me by the difficulty I found in
getting my meaning down on paper. I wrote dialogue fluently, but when it came to a page of description I found
myself entangled in all sorts of quandaries. I would struggle for a couple of hours over two or three sentences
that I could in no way manage to straighten out. I made up
my mind to teach myself how to write. Unfortunately I
had no one to help me. I made many mistakes. If I had had
someone to guide me like the charming don of whom I
spoke just now I might have been saved much time. Such a
one might have told me that such gifts as I had lay in one
direction and that they must be cultivated in that direction;
it was useless to try to do something for which I had no
aptitude. But at that time a florid prose was admired. Richness of texture was sought by means of a jewelled phrase
and sentences stiff with exotic epithets: the ideal was a brocade so heavy with gold that it stood up by itself. The intelligent young read Walter Pater with enthusiasm. My common sense suggested to me that it was anæmic stuff; behind
those elaborate, gracious periods I was conscious of a tired,
wan personality. I was young, lusty and energetic; I wanted
fresh air, action, violence, and I found it hard to breathe that
dead, heavily scented atmosphere and sit in those hushed
rooms in which it was indecorous to speak above a whisper.
But I would not listen to my common sense. I persuaded
myself that this was the height of culture and turned a
scornful shoulder on the outside world where men shouted
and swore, played the fool, wenched and got drunk. I read
Intentions and *The Picture of Dorian Gray*. I was intoxicated by the colour and rareness of the fantastic words
that thickly stud the pages of *Salome*. Shocked by the poverty of my own vocabulary, I went to the British Museum
with pencil and paper and noted down the names of curious
jewels, the Byzantine hues of old enamels, the sensual feel

of textiles, and made elaborate sentences to bring them in.
Fortunately I could never find an opportunity to use them
and they lie there yet in an old notebook ready for anyone
who has a mind to write nonsense. It was generally thought
then that the Authorized Version of the Bible was the
greatest piece of prose that the English language has produced. I read it diligently, especially the Song of Solomon,
jotting down for future use turns of phrase that struck me
and making lists of unusual or beautiful words. I studied
Jeremy Taylor's *Holy Dying*. In order to assimilate his style
I copied out passages and then tried to write them down
from memory.

The first fruit of this labour was a little book about
Andalusia called *The Land of the Blessed Virgin*. I had occasion to read parts of it the other day. I know Andalusia
a great deal better now than I knew it then, and I have
changed my mind about a good many things of which I wrote.
Since it has continued in America to have a small sale it
occurred to me that it might be worth while to revise it. I
soon saw that this was impossible. The book was written
by someone I have completely forgotten. It bored me to
distraction. But what I am concerned with is the prose, for it
was as an exercise in style that I wrote it. It is wistful, allusive and elaborate. It has neither ease nor spontaneity. It
smells of hothouse plants and Sunday dinner like the air
in the greenhouse that leads out of the dining-room of a
big house in Bayswater. There are a great many melodious
adjectives. The vocabulary is sentimental. It does not remind
one of an Italian brocade, with its rich pattern of gold, but
of a curtain material designed by Burne-Jones and reproduced by Morris.

x

I DO not know whether it was a subconscious feeling that
this sort of writing was contrary to my bent or a naturally
methodical cast of mind that led me then to turn my attention to the writers of the Augustan Period. The prose of
Swift enchanted me. I made up my mind that this was the

perfect way to write and I started to work on him in the
same way as I had done with Jeremy Taylor. I chose *The
Tale of a Tub*. It is said that when the Dean re-read it in
his old age he cried: "What genius I had then!" To my
mind his genius was better shown in other works. It is a
tiresome allegory and the irony is facile. But the style is
admirable. I cannot imagine that English can be better written. Here are no flowery periods, fantastic turns of phrase
or high-flown images. It is a civilized prose, natural, discreet and pointed. There is no attempt to surprise by an
extravagant vocabulary. It looks as though Swift made do
with the first word that came to hand, but since he had an
acute and logical brain it was always the right one, and he
put it in the right place. The strength and balance of his
sentences are due to an exquisite taste. As I had done before I copied passages and then tried to write them out again
from memory. I tried altering words or the order in which
they were set. I found that the only possible words were
those Swift had used and that the order in which he had
placed them was the only possible order. It is an impeccable
prose.

But perfection has one grave defect: it is apt to be dull.
Swift's prose is like a French canal, bordered with poplars,
that runs through a gracious and undulating country. Its
tranquil charm fills you with satisfaction, but it neither excites the emotions nor stimulates the imagination. You go on
and on and presently you are a trifle bored. So, much as
you may admire Swift's wonderful lucidity, his terseness,
his naturalness, his lack of affectation, you find your attention wandering after a while unless his matter peculiarly
interests you. I think if I had my time over again I would
give to the prose of Dryden the close study I gave to that
of Swift. I did not come across it till I had lost the inclination to take so much pains. The prose of Dryden is delicious.
It has not the perfection of Swift nor the easy elegance of
Addison, but it has a springtime gaiety, a conversational
ease, a blithe spontaneousness that are enchanting. Dryden
was a very good poet, but it is not the general opinion that
he had a lyrical quality; it is strange that it is just this

that sings in his softly sparkling prose. Prose had never been written in England like that before; it has seldom been written like that since. Dryden flourished at a happy moment. He had in his bones the sonorous periods and the baroque massiveness of Jacobean language and under the influence of the nimble and well-bred felicity that he learnt from the French he turned it into an instrument that was fit not only for solemn themes but also to express the light thought of the passing moment. He was the first of the rococo artists. If Swift reminds you of a French canal Dryden recalls an English river winding its cheerful way round hills, through quietly busy towns and by nestling villages, pausing now in a noble reach and then running powerfully through a woodland country. It is alive, varied, windswept; and it has the pleasant open-air smell of England.

The work I did was certainly very good for me. I began to write better; I did not write well. I wrote stiffly and self-consciously. I tried to get a pattern into my sentences, but did not see that the pattern was evident. I took care how I placed my words, but did not reflect that an order that was natural at the beginning of the eighteenth century was most unnatural at the beginning of ours. My attempt to write in the manner of Swift made it impossible for me to achieve the effect of inevitable rightness that was just what I so much admired in him. I then wrote a number of plays and ceased to occupy myself with anything but dialogue. It was not till five years had passed that I set out again to write a novel. By then I no longer had any ambition to be a stylist; I put aside all thought of fine writing. I wanted to write without any frills of language, in as bare and unaffected a manner as I could. I had so much to say that I could afford to waste no words. I wanted merely to set down the facts. I began with the impossible aim of using no adjectives at all. I thought that if you could find the exact term a qualifying epithet could be dispensed with. As I saw it in my mind's eye my book would have the appearance of an immensely long telegram in which for economy's sake you had left out every word that was not necessary to make the sense clear. I have not read it since I corrected the proofs and do not know how near I came to doing what I tried. My impression is that it is written at least more naturally than anything I had written before; but I am sure that it is often slipshod and I daresay there are in it a good many mistakes in grammar.

Since then I have written many other books; and though ceasing my methodical study of the old masters (for though the spirit is willing, the flesh is weak), I have continued with increasing assiduity to try to write better. I discovered my limitations and it seemed to me that the only sensible thing was to aim at what excellence I could within them. I knew that I had no lyrical quality. I had a small vocabulary and no efforts that I could make to enlarge it much availed me. I had little gift of metaphor; the original and striking simile seldom occurred to me. Poetic flights and the great imaginative sweep were beyond my powers. I could admire them in others as I could admire their far-fetched tropes and the unusual but suggestive language in which they clothed their thoughts, but my own invention never presented me with such embellishments; and I was tired of trying to do what did not come easily to me. On the other hand, I had an acute power of observation and it seemed to me that I could see a great many things that other people missed. I could put down in clear terms what I saw. I had a logical sense, and if no great feeling for the richness and strangeness of words, at all events a lively appreciation of their sound. I knew that I should never write as well as I could wish, but I thought with pains I could arrive at writing as well as my natural defects allowed. On taking thought it seemed to me that I must aim at lucidity, simplicity and euphony. I have put these three qualities in the order of the importance I assigned to them.

xi

I HAVE never had much patience with the writers who claim from the reader an effort to understand their meaning. You have only to go to the great philosophers to see that it is possible to express with lucidity the most subtle re-

flections. You may find it difficult to understand the thought
of Hume, and if you have no philosophical training its implications will doubtless escape you; but no one with any
education at all can fail to understand exactly what the
meaning of each sentence is. Few people have written English with more grace than Berkeley. There are two sorts of
obscurity that you find in writers. One is due to negligence
and the other to wilfulness. People often write obscurely
because they have never taken the trouble to learn to write
clearly. This sort of obscurity you find too often in modern
philosophers, in men of science, and even in literary critics.
Here it is indeed strange. You would have thought that
men who passed their lives in the study of the great masters
of literature would be sufficiently sensitive to the beauty of
language to write if not beautifully at least with perspicuity.
Yet you will find in their works sentence after sentence that
you must read twice to discover the sense. Often you can
only guess at it, for the writers have evidently not said what
they intended.

Another cause of obscurity is that the writer is himself
not quite sure of his meaning. He has a vague impression
of what he wants to say, but has not, either from lack of
mental power or from laziness, exactly formulated it in
his mind and it is natural enough that he should not find a
precise expression for a confused idea. This is due largely
to the fact that many writers think, not before, but as they
write. The pen originates the thought. The disadvantage
of this, and indeed it is a danger against which the author
must be always on his guard, is that there is a sort of magic
in the written word. The idea acquires substance by taking
on a visible nature, and then stands in the way of its own
clarification. But this sort of obscurity merges very easily
into the wilful. Some writers who do not think clearly are
inclined to suppose that their thoughts have a significance
greater than at first sight appears. It is flattering to believe
that they are too profound to be expressed so clearly that
all who run may read, and very naturally it does not occur
to such writers that the fault is with their own minds which
have not the faculty of precise reflection. Here again the

magic of the written word obtains. It is very easy to persuade oneself that a phrase that one does not quite understand may mean a great deal more than one realizes. From this there is only a little way to go to fall into the habit of setting down one's impressions in all their original vagueness. Fools can always be found to discover a hidden sense in them. There is another form of wilful obscurity that masquerades as aristocratic exclusiveness. The author wraps his meaning in mystery so that the vulgar shall not participate in it. His soul is a secret garden into which the elect may penetrate only after overcoming a number of perilous obstacles. But this kind of obscurity is not only pretentious; it is short-sighted. For time plays it an odd trick. If the sense is meagre time reduces it to a meaningless verbiage that no one thinks of reading. This is the fate that has befallen the lucubrations of those French writers who were seduced by the example of Guillaume Apollinaire. But occasionally it throws a sharp cold light on what had seemed profound and thus discloses the fact that these contortions of language disguised very commonplace notions. There are few of Mallarmé's poems now that are not clear; one cannot fail to notice that his thought singularly lacked originality. Some of his phrases were beautiful; the materials of his verse were the poetic platitudes of his day.

xii

SIMPLICITY is not such an obvious merit as lucidity. I have aimed at it because I have no gift for richness. Within limits I admire richness in others, though I find it difficult to digest in quantity. I can read one page of Ruskin with delight, but twenty only with weariness. The rolling period, the stately epithet, the noun rich in poetic associations, the subordinate clauses that give the sentence weight and magnificence, the grandeur like that of wave following wave in the open sea; there is no doubt that in all this there is something inspiring. Words thus strung together fall on the ear like music. The appeal is sensuous rather than intellectual, and the

beauty of the sound leads you easily to conclude that you
need not bother about the meaning. But words are tyrannical
things, they exist for their meanings, and if you will not pay
attention to these, you cannot pay attention at all. Your
mind wanders. This kind of writing demands a subject that
will suit it. It is surely out of place to write in the grand
style of inconsiderable things. No one wrote in this manner
with greater success than Sir Thomas Browne, but even he
did not always escape this pitfall. In the last chapter of
Hydriotaphia the matter, which is the destiny of man, wonderfully fits the baroque splendour of the language, and
here the Norwich doctor produced a piece of prose that
has never been surpassed in our literature; but when he describes the finding of his urns in the same splendid manner
the effect (at least to my taste) is less happy. When a modern
writer is grandiloquent to tell you whether or no a little trollop shall hop into bed with a commonplace young man you
are right to be disgusted.

But if richness needs gifts with which everyone is not endowed, simplicity by no means comes by nature. To achieve
it needs rigid discipline. So far as I know ours is the only
language in which it has been found necessary to give a name
to the piece of prose which is described as the purple patch;
it would not have been necessary to do so unless it were
characteristic. English prose is elaborate rather than simple.
It was not always so. Nothing could be more racy, straight-
forward and alive than the prose of Shakespeare; but it
must be remembered that this was dialogue written to be
spoken. We do not know how he would have written if
like Corneille he had composed prefaces to his plays. It may
be that they would have been as euphuistic as the letters
of Queen Elizabeth. But earlier prose, the prose of Sir
Thomas More, for instance, is neither ponderous, flowery
nor oratorical. It smacks of the English soil. To my mind
King James's Bible has been a very harmful influence on
English prose. I am not so stupid as to deny its great beauty,
and it is obvious that there are passages in it of a simplicity
which is deeply moving. But the Bible is an oriental book. Its
alien imagery has nothing to do with us. Those hyperboles,

those luscious metaphors, are foreign to our genius. I cannot but think that not the least of the misfortunes that the Secession from Rome brought upon the spiritual life of our country is that this work for so long a period became the daily, and with many the only, reading of our people. Those rhythms, that powerful vocabulary, that grandiloquence, became part and parcel of the national sensibility. The plain, honest English speech was overwhelmed with ornament. Blunt Englishmen twisted their tongues to speak like Hebrew prophets. There was evidently something in the English temper to which this was congenial, perhaps a native lack of precision in thought, perhaps a naïve delight in fine words for their own sake, an innate eccentricity and love of embroidery, I do not know; but the fact remains that ever since, English prose has had to struggle against the tendency to luxuriance. When from time to time the spirit of the language has reasserted itself, as it did with Dryden and the writers of Queen Anne, it was only to be submerged once more by the pomposities of Gibbon and Dr. Johnson. When English prose recovered simplicity with Hazlitt, the Shelley of the letters and Charles Lamb at his best, it lost it again with De Quincey, Carlyle, Meredith and Walter Pater. It is obvious that the grand style is more striking than the plain. Indeed many people think that a style that does not attract notice is not style. They will admire Walter Pater's, but will read an essay by Matthew Arnold without giving a moment's attention to the elegance, distinction and sobriety with which he set down what he had to say.

The dictum that the style is the man is well known. It is one of those aphorisms that say too much to mean a great deal. Where is the man in Goethe, in his birdlike lyrics or in his clumsy prose? And Hazlitt? But I suppose that if a man has a confused mind he will write in a confused way, if his temper is capricious his prose will be fantastical, and if he has a quick, darting intelligence that is reminded by the matter in hand of a hundred things he will, unless he has great self-control, load his pages with metaphor and simile. There is a great difference between the magniloquence of the Jacobean writers, who were intoxicated with the new wealth that had lately been brought into the language, and the turgidity of Gibbon and Dr. Johnson, who were the victims of bad theories. I can read every word that Dr. Johnson wrote with delight, for he had good sense, charm and wit. No one could have written better if he had not wilfully set himself to write in the grand style. He knew good English when he saw it. No critic has praised Dryden's prose more aptly. He said of him that he appeared to have no art other than that of expressing with clearness what he thought with vigour. And one of his Lives he finished with the words: "Whoever wishes to attain an English style, familiar but not coarse, and elegant but not ostentatious, must give his days and nights to the volumes of Addison." But when he himself sat down to write it was with a very different aim. He mistook the orotund for the dignified. He had not the good breeding to see that simplicity and naturalness are the truest marks of distinction.

For to write good prose is an affair of good manners. It is, unlike verse, a civil art. Poetry is baroque. Baroque is tragic, massive and mystical. It is elemental. It demands depth and insight. I cannot but feel that the prose writers of the baroque period, the authors of King James's Bible, Sir Thomas Browne, Glanville, were poets who had lost their way. Prose is a rococo art. It needs taste rather than power, decorum rather than inspiration and vigour rather than grandeur. Form for the poet is the bit and the bridle without which (unless you are an acrobat) you cannot ride your horse; but for the writer of prose it is the chassis without which your car does not exist. It is not an accident that the best prose was written when rococo with its elegance and moderation, at its birth attained its greatest excellence. For rococo was evolved when baroque had become declamatory and the world, tired of the stupendous, asked for restraint. It was the natural expression of persons who valued a civilized life. Humour, tolerance and horse sense made the great tragic issues that had preoccupied the first half of the seventeenth century seem excessive. The world was a more comfortable place to live in and perhaps for the first time in centuries the cultivated classes could sit back and enjoy their leisure. It has been said that good prose should resemble the conversation of a well-bred man. Conversation is only possible when men's minds are free from pressing anxieties. Their lives must be reasonably secure and they must have no grave concern about their souls. They must attach importance to the refinements of civilization. They must value courtesy, they must pay attention to their persons (and have we not also been told that good prose should be like the clothes of a well-dressed man, appropriate but unobtrusive?), they must fear to bore, they must be neither flippant nor solemn, but always apt; and they must look upon "enthusiasm" with a critical glance. This is a soil very suitable for prose. It is not to be wondered at that it gave a fitting opportunity for the appearance of the best writer of prose that our modern world has seen, Voltaire. The writers of English, perhaps owing to the poetic nature of the language, have seldom reached the excellence that seems to have come so naturally to him. It is in so far as they have approached the ease, sobriety and precision of the great French masters that they are admirable.

xiii

WHETHER you ascribe importance to euphony, the last of the three characteristics that I mentioned, must depend on the sensitiveness of your ear. A great many readers, and many admirable writers, are devoid of this quality. Poets as we know have always made a great use of alliteration. They are persuaded that the repetition of a sound gives an effect of beauty. I do not think it does so in prose. It seems to me that in prose alliteration should be used only for a special reason; when used by accident it falls on the ear very disagreeably. But its accidental use is so common that one can only suppose that the sound of it is not universally offensive. Many writers without distress will put two rhyming words together, join a monstrous long adjective to a monstrous long noun, or between the end of one word and the beginning of another have a conjunction of consonants that almost breaks your jaw. These are trivial and obvious instances. I mention them only to prove that if careful writers can do such things it is only because they have no ear. Words have weight, sound and appearance; it is only by considering these that you can write a sentence that is good to look at and good to listen to.

I have read many books on English prose, but have found it hard to profit by them; for the most part they are vague, unduly theoretical, and often scolding. But you cannot say this of Fowler's Dictionary of Modern English Usage. It is a valuable work. I do not think anyone writes so well that he cannot learn much from it. It is lively reading. Fowler liked simplicity, straightforwardness and common sense. He had no patience with pretentiousness. He had a sound feeling that idiom was the backbone of a language and he was all for the racy phrase. He was no slavish admirer of logic and was willing enough to give usage right of way through the exact demesnes of grammar. English grammar is very difficult and few writers have avoided making mistakes in it. So heedful a writer as Henry James, for instance, on occasion wrote so ungrammatically that a schoolmaster, finding such errors in a schoolboy's essay, would be justly indignant. It is necessary to know grammar, and it is better to write grammatically than not, but it is well to remember that grammar is common speech formulated. Usage is the only test. I would prefer a phrase that was easy and unaffected to a phrase that was grammatical. One of the differences between French and English is that in French you can be grammatical with complete naturalness, but in English not invariably. It is a difficulty in writing English that the sound of the living voice dominates the look of the printed word. I have given the matter of style a great deal of thought and have taken great pains. I have written few pages that I feel I could not improve and far too many that I have left with dissatisfaction because, try as I would, I could do no better. I cannot say of myself what Johnson said of Pope: "He never passed a fault unamended by indifference, nor quitted it by despair." I do not write as I want to; I write as I can.

But Fowler had no ear. He did not see that simplicity may

sometimes make concessions to euphony. I do not think a
far-fetched, an archaic or even an affected word is out of
place when it sounds better than the blunt, obvious one or
when it gives a sentence a better balance. But, I hasten to
add, though I think you may without misgiving make this
concession to pleasant sound, I think you should make none
to what may obscure your meaning. Anything is better than
not to write clearly. There is nothing to be said against lucidity, and against simplicity only the possibility of dryness.
This is a risk that is well worth taking when you reflect how
much better it is to be bald than to wear a curly wig. But
there is in euphony a danger that must be considered. It
is very likely to be monotonous. When George Moore began
to write, his style was poor; it gave you the impression that
he wrote on wrapping paper with a blunt pencil. But he developed gradually a very musical English. He learnt to write
sentences that fall away on the ear with a misty languor
and it delighted him so much that he could never have enough
of it. He did not escape monotony. It is like the sound of
water lapping a shingly beach, so soothing that you presently
cease to be sensible of it. It is so mellifluous that you hanker
for some harshness, for an abrupt dissonance, that will interrupt the silky concord. I do not know how one can guard
against this. I suppose the best chance is to have a more lively
faculty of boredom than one's readers so that one is wearied
before they are. One must always be on the watch for mannerisms and when certain cadences come too easily to the
pen ask oneself whether they have not become mechanical. It
is very hard to discover the exact point where the idiom one
has formed to express oneself has lost its tang. As Dr. Johnson said: "He that has once studiously formed a style, rarely
writes afterwards with complete ease." Admirably as I think
Matthew Arnold's style was suited to his particular purposes, I must admit that his mannerisms are often irritating.
His style was an instrument that he had forged once for all;
it was not like the human hand capable of performing a
variety of actions.

If you could write lucidly, simply, euphoniously and yet
with liveliness you would write perfectly: you would write

like Voltaire. And yet we know how fatal the pursuit of liveliness may be: it may result in the tiresome acrobatics of
Meredith. Macaulay and Carlyle were in their different ways
arresting; but at the heavy cost of naturalness. Their flashy
effects distract the mind. They destroy their persuasiveness;
you would not believe a man was very intent on ploughing
a furrow if he carried a hoop with him and jumped through
it at every other step. A good style should show no sign of
effort. What is written should seem a happy accident. I
think no one in France now writes more admirably than
Colette, and such is the ease of her expression that you cannot bring yourself to believe that she takes any trouble over
it. I am told that there are pianists who have a natural technique so that they can play in a manner that most executants
can achieve only as the result of unremitting toil, and I am
willing to believe that there are writers who are equally
fortunate. Among them I was much inclined to place Colette.
I asked her. I was exceedingly surprised to hear that she
wrote everything over and over again. She told me that she
would often spend a whole morning working upon a single
page. But it does not matter how one gets the effect of ease.
For my part, if I get it at all, it is only by strenuous effort.
Nature seldom provides me with the word, the turn of
phrase, that is appropriate without being far-fetched or commonplace.

xiv

I HAVE read that Anatole France tried to use only the constructions and the vocabulary of the writers of the seventeenth century whom he so greatly admired. I do not know if
it is true. If so, it may explain why there is some lack of
vitality in his beautiful and simple French. But simplicity
is false when you do not say a thing that you should say because you cannot say it in a certain way. One should write
in the manner of one's period. The language is alive and
constantly changing; to try to write like the authors of a
distant past can only give rise to artificiality. I should not
hesitate to use the common phrases of the day, knowing that

their vogue was ephemeral, or slang, though aware that in ten years it might be incomprehensible, if they gave vividness and actuality. If the style has a classical form it can support the discreet use of a phraseology that has only a local and temporary aptness. I would sooner a writer were vulgar than mincing; for life is vulgar, and it is life he seeks.

I think that we English authors have much to learn from our fellow authors in America. For American writing has escaped the tyranny of King James's Bible and American writers have been less affected by the old masters whose mode of writing is part of our culture. They have formed their style, unconsciously perhaps, more directly from the living speech that surrounds them; and at its best it has a directness, a vitality and a drive that give our more urbane manner an air of languor. It has been an advantage to American writers, many of whom at one time or another have been reporters, that their journalism has been written in a more trenchant, nervous, graphic English than ours. For we read the newspaper now as our ancestors read the Bible. Not without profit either; for the newspaper, especially when it is of the popular sort, offers us a part of experience that we writers cannot afford to miss. It is raw material straight from the knacker's yard, and we are stupid if we turn up our noses because it smells of blood and sweat. We cannot, however willingly we would, escape the influence of this workaday prose. But the journalism of a period has very much the same style; it might all have been written by the same hand; it is impersonal. It is well to counteract its effect by reading of another kind. One can do this only by keeping constantly in touch with the writing of an age not too remote from one's own. So can one have a standard by which to test one's own style and an ideal which in one's modern way one can aim at. For my part the two writers I have found most useful to study for this purpose are Hazlitt and Cardinal Newman. I would try to imitate neither. Hazlitt can be unduly rhetorical; and sometimes his decoration is as fussy as Victorian Gothic. Newman can be a trifle flowery. But at their best both are admirable. Time has little touched their style; it is almost contemporary. Hazlitt is vivid, bracing and energetic; he has strength and liveliness. You feel the man in his phrases, not the mean, querulous, disagreeable man that he appeared to the world that knew him, but the man within of his own ideal vision. (And the man within us is as true in reality as the man, pitiful and halting, of our outward seeming.) Newman had an exquisite grace, music, playful sometimes and sometimes grave, a woodland beauty of phrase, dignity and mellowness. Both wrote with extreme lucidity. Neither is quite as simple as the purest taste demands. Here I think Matthew Arnold excels them. Both had a wonderful balance of phrase and both knew how to write sentences pleasing to the eye. Both had an ear of extreme sensitiveness.

If anyone could combine their merits in the manner of writing of the present day he would write as well as it is possible for anyone to write.

xv

FROM time to time I have asked myself whether I should have been a better writer if I had devoted my whole life to literature. Somewhat early, but at what age I cannot remember, I made up my mind that, having but one life, I should like to get the most I could out of it. It did not seem to me enough merely to write. I wanted to make a pattern of my life, in which writing would be an essential element, but which would include all the other activities proper to man, and which death would in the end round off in complete fulfilment. I had many disabilities. I was small; I had endurance but little physical strength; I stammered; I was shy; I had poor health. I had no facility for games, which play so great a part in the normal life of Englishmen; and I had, whether for any of these reasons or from nature I do not know, an instinctive shrinking from my fellow men that has made it difficult for me to enter into any familiarity with them. I have loved individuals; I have never much cared for men in the mass. I have none of that engaging come-hitherness that makes people take to one another on first acquaintance. Though in the course of years I have learnt to assume an air of heartiness when forced into contact with a stranger, I have never liked anyone at first sight. I do not think I have ever addressed someone I did not know in a railway carriage or spoken to a fellow-passenger on board ship unless he first spoke to me. The weakness of my flesh has prevented me from enjoying that communion with the human race that is engendered by alcohol; long before I could reach the state of intoxication that enables so many, more happily constituted, to look upon all men as their brothers, my stomach has turned upon me and I have been as sick as a dog. These are grave disadvantages both to the writer and the man. I have had to make the best of them. I have followed the pattern I made with persistence. I do not claim that it was a perfect one. I think it was the best that I could hope for in the circumstances and with the very limited powers that were granted to me by nature.

Looking for the special function of man Aristotle decided that since he shares growth with the plants and perception with the beasts, and alone has a rational element, his function is the activity of the soul. From this he concluded, not as you would have thought sensible, that man should cultivate the three forms of activity which he ascribed to him, but that he should pursue only that which is especial to him. Philosophers and moralists have looked at the body with misgiving. They have pointed out that its satisfactions are brief. But a pleasure is none the less a pleasure because it does not please forever. It is delightful to plunge into cold water on a hot day even though in a moment your skin is no longer sensitive to the coldness. White is no whiter if it lasts for a year or a day. I looked upon it then as a part of the pattern I was attempting to draw to experience all the pleasures of sense. I have not been afraid of excess: excess on occasion is exhilarating. It prevents moderation from acquiring the deadening effect of a habit. It tonifies the system and rests the nerves. The spirit is often most free when the body is satiated with pleasure; indeed, sometimes the stars shine more brightly seen from the gutter than from the hilltop. The keenest pleasure to which the body is susceptible is that of sexual congress. I have known men who gave up their whole lives to this; they are grown old now, but I have noticed, not without surprise, that they look upon them as well spent. It has been my misfortune that a native fastidiousness has prevented me from indulging as much in this particular delight as I might have. I have exercised moderation because I was hard to please. When from time to time I have seen the persons with whom the great lovers satisfied their desires I have been more often astonished by the robustness of their appetites than envious of their successes. It is obvious that you need not often go hungry if you are willing to dine off mutton hash and turnip tops.

Most people live haphazard lives subject to the varying winds of fortune. Many are forced by the situation in which they were born and the necessity of earning a living to keep to a straight and narrow road in which there is no possibility of turning to the right or to the left. Upon these the pattern is imposed. Life itself has forced it on them. There is no reason why such a pattern should not be as complete as that which anyone has tried self-consciously to make. But the artist is in a privileged position. I use the word artist, not meaning to attach any measure of value to what he produces, but merely to signify someone who is occupied with the arts. I wish I could find a better word. Creator is pretentious and seems to make a claim to originality that can seldom be justified. Craftsman is not enough. A carpenter is a craftsman, and though he may be in the narrower sense an artist, he has not as a rule the freedom of action which the most incompetent scribbler, the poorest dauber, possesses. The artist can within certain limits make what he likes of his life. In other callings, in medicine for instance or the law, you are free to choose whether you will adopt them or not, but having chosen, you are free no longer. You are bound by the rules of your profession; a standard of conduct is imposed upon you. The pattern is predetermined. It is only the artist, and maybe the criminal, who can make his own.

Perhaps it was a natural sense of tidiness that engaged

me, when still so young, to design a pattern for my life; perhaps it was due to something I discovered in myself about which I shall have a little to say later. The defect of such an undertaking is that it may kill spontaneity. One great difference between the persons of real life and the persons of fiction is that the persons of real life are creatures of impulse. It has been said that metaphysics is the finding of bad reasons for what we believe upon instinct; and it might be said also that in the conduct of life we make use of deliberation to justify ourselves in doing what we want to do. And to surrender to impulse is part of the pattern. I think a greater defect is that it leads you to live too much in the future. I have long known that this was a fault of mine and have in vain tried to correct it. I have never, except by an effort of will, wished that the passing moment might linger so that I could get more enjoyment from it, for even when it has brought me something I had immensely looked forward to, my imagination in the very moment of fulfilment has been busy with the problematical delight of whatever was to come. I have never walked down the south side of Piccadilly without being all in a dither about what was happening on the north. This is folly. The passing moment is all we can be sure of; it is only common sense to extract its utmost value from it; the future will one day be the present and will seem as unimportant as the present does now. But common sense avails me little. I do not find the present unsatisfactory; I merely take it for granted. It is interwoven in the pattern and what interests me is what remains to come.

I have made a great many mistakes. I have at times fallen victim to a snare to which the writer is peculiarly liable, the desire to carry out in my own life certain actions which I made the characters of my invention do. I have attempted things that were foreign to my nature and obstinately persevered in them because in my vanity I would not confess myself beaten. I have paid too much attention to the opinion of others. I have made sacrifices to unworthy objects because I had not the courage to inflict pain. I have committed follies. I have a sensitive conscience, and I have done certain things in my life that I am unable entirely to forget; if I had been fortunate enough to be a Catholic I could have delivered myself of them at confession and after performing the penance imposed received absolution and put them out of my mind forever. I have had to deal with them as my common sense suggested. I do not regret them, for I think it is because of my own grave faults that I have learnt indulgence for others. It took me a long time. In youth I was harshly intolerant. I remember my indignation upon hearing someone make the remark, not an original one, but new to me then, that hypocrisy was the tribute that vice paid to virtue. I thought that one should have the courage of one's vices. I had ideals of honesty, uprightness, truth; I was impatient not of human weakness, but of cowardice, and I would make no allowances for those who hedged and temporized. It never occurred to me that no one stood in greater need of indulgence than I.

xvi

AT FIRST sight it is curious that our own offences should seem to us so much less heinous than the offences of others. I suppose the reason is that we know all the circumstances that have occasioned them and so manage to excuse in ourselves what we cannot excuse in others. We turn our attention away from our own defects, and when we are forced by untoward events to consider them find it easy to condone them. For all I know we are right to do this; they are part of us and we must accept the good and the bad in ourselves together. But when we come to judge others it is not by ourselves as we really are that we judge them, but by an image that we have formed of ourselves from which we have left out everything that offends our vanity or would discredit us in the eyes of the world. To take a trivial instance: how scornful we are when we catch someone out telling a lie; but who can say that he has never told not one, but a hundred? We are shocked when we discover that great men were weak and petty, dishonest or selfish, sexually vicious, vain or intemperate; and many people think it disgraceful to disclose to the public its heroes' failings. There is not much to choose between men. They are all a hotchpotch of greatness and littleness, of virtue and vice, of nobility and baseness. Some have more strength of character, or more opportunity, and so in one direction or another give their instincts freer play, but potentially they are the same. For my part I do not think I am any better or any worse than most people, but I know that if I set down every action in my life and every thought that has crossed my mind the world would consider me a monster of depravity.

I wonder how anyone can have the face to condemn others when he reflects upon his own thoughts. A great part of our lives is occupied in reverie, and the more imaginative we are, the more varied and vivid this will be. How many of us could face having our reveries automatically registered and set before us? We should be overcome with shame. We should cry that we could not really be as mean, as wicked, as petty, as selfish, as obscene, as snobbish, as vain, as sentimental, as that. Yet surely our reveries are as much part of us as our actions, and if there were a being to whom our inmost thoughts were known we might just as well be held responsible for them as for our deeds. Men forget the horrible thoughts that wander through their own minds, and are indignant when they discover them in others. In Goethe's *Wahrheit und Dichtung* he relates how in his youth he could not bear the idea that his father was a middle-class lawyer in Frankfurt. He felt that noble blood must flow in his veins. So he sought to persuade himself that some prince travelling through the city had met and loved his mother, and that he was the offspring of the union. The editor of the copy I read wrote an indignant footnote on the subject. It seemed to him unworthy of so great a poet that he should impugn the undoubted virtue of his mother in order snobbishly to plume himself on his bastard aristocracy. Of course it was disgraceful, but it was not unnatural and I venture to say not uncommon. There must be few romantic, rebellious and imaginative boys who have not toyed with the idea that they could not be the son of their dull and respectable father, but ascribe the superiority they feel in themselves, according to their own idiosyncrasies, to an unknown poet, great statesman or ruling prince. The Olympian attitude of Goethe's later years inspires me with esteem; this confession arouses in me a warmer feeling. Because a man can write great works he is none the less a man.

It is, I suppose, these lewd, ugly, base and selfish thoughts, dwelling in their minds against their will, that have tormented the saints when their lives were devoted to good works and repentance had redeemed the sins of their past. St. Ignatius Loyola, as we know, when he went to Monserrat made a general confession and received absolution; but he continued to be obsessed by a sense of sin so that he was on the point of killing himself. Till his conversion he had led the ordinary life of the young man of good birth at that time; he was somewhat vain of his appearance, he had wenched and gambled; but at least on one occasion he had shown rare magnanimity and he had always been honourable, loyal, generous and brave. If peace was still denied him it looks as though it was his thoughts that he could not forgive himself. It would be a comfort to know that even the saints were thus afflicted. When I have seen the great ones of the earth, so upright and dignified, sitting in state I have often asked myself whether at such moments they ever remembered how their minds in solitude were sometimes occupied and whether it ever made them uneasy to think of the secrets that their subliminal self harboured. It seems to me that the knowledge that these reveries are common to all men should inspire one with tolerance to oneself as well as to others. It is well also if they enable us to look upon our fellows, even the most eminent and respectable, with humour and if they lead us to take ourselves not too seriously. When I have heard judges on the bench moralizing with unction I have asked myself whether it was possible for them to have forgotten their humanity so completely as their words suggested. I have wished that beside his bunch of flowers at the Old Bailey, his lordship had a packet of toilet paper. It would remind him that he was a man like any other.

xvii

I HAVE been called cynical. I have been accused of making men out worse than they are. I do not think I have done this. All I have done is to bring into prominence certain traits that many writers shut their eyes to. I think what has chiefly struck me in human beings is their lack of consistency. I have never seen people all of a piece. It has amazed me that the most incongruous traits should exist in the same person and for all that yield a plausible harmony. I have often asked myself how characteristics, seemingly irreconcilable, can exist in the same person. I have known crooks who were capable of self-sacrifice, sneak-thieves who were sweet-natured and harlots for whom it was a point of honour to give good value for money. The only explanation I can offer is that so instinctive is each one's conviction that he is unique in the world, and privileged, that he feels that, however wrong it might be for others, what he for his part does, if not natural and right, is at least venial. The contrast that I have found in people has interested me, but I do not think I have unduly emphasized it. The censure that has from time to time been passed on me is due perhaps to the fact that I have not expressly condemned what was bad in the characters of my invention and praised what was good. It must be a fault in me that I am not gravely shocked at the sins of others unless they personally affect me, and even when they do I have learnt at last generally to excuse them. It is meet not to expect too much of others. You should be grateful when they treat you well, but unperturbed when they treat you ill. "For every one of us," as the Athenian Stranger said, "is made pretty much what he is by the bent of his desires and the nature of his soul." It is want of imagination that prevents people from seeing things from any point of view but their own, and it is unreasonable to be angry with them because they lack this faculty.

I think I could be justly blamed if I saw only people's faults and were blind to their virtues. I am not conscious that this is the case. There is nothing more beautiful than goodness and it has pleased me very often to show how much of it there is in persons who by common standards would be relentlessly condemned. I have shown it because I have seen it. It has seemed to me sometimes to shine more brightly in them because it was surrounded by the darkness of sin. I take the goodness of the good for granted and I am amused when I discover their defects or their vices; I am touched when I see the goodness of the wicked and I am willing enough to shrug a tolerant shoulder at their wickedness. I am not my brother's keeper. I cannot bring myself to judge my fellows; I am content to observe them. My observation has led me to believe that, all in all, there is not so much difference between the good and the bad as the moralists would have us believe.

I have not on the whole taken people at their face value. I do not know if this coolness of scrutiny has been inherited from my fathers; they could hardly have been successful lawyers if they had not possessed a shrewdness that prevented them from being deceived by appearances; or if I owe it to the lack in me of that joyful uprush of emotion on meeting people that makes many, as the saying is, take their geese for swans. It was certainly encouraged by my training as a medical student. I did not want to be a doctor. I did not want to be anything but a writer, but I was much too shy to say so, and in any case at that time it was unheard of that a boy of eighteen, belonging to a respectable family, should adopt literature as a profession. The notion was so preposterous that I never even dreamt of imparting it to anybody. I had always supposed that I should enter the law, but my three brothers, much older than I, were practising it and there did not seem room for me too.

xviii

I LEFT school early. I had been unhappy at the preparatory school to which I was sent on my father's death because it was at Canterbury and only six miles from Whitstable of which my uncle and guardian was vicar. It was an annex of the King's School, an ancient foundation, and to this when I was thirteen I duly went. After I had got out of the lower forms, the masters of which were frightening bullies, I was contented enough, and I was miserable when an illness forced me to spend a term in the South of France. My mother and her only sister had died of tuberculosis and when it was found that my lungs were affected my uncle and aunt were concerned. I was placed at a tutor's at Hyères. When I went back to Canterbury I did not like it so well. My friends had made new friends. I was lonely. I had been moved into a higher form in which, with three months lost, I could not find my place. My form-master nagged me. I persuaded my uncle that it would be very good for my lungs if instead of staying at school I spent the following winter on the Riviera and that it would be of value to me after that to go to Germany and learn German. I could continue to work there on the subjects which were necessary for me to get into Cambridge. He was a weak man and my arguments were specious. He did not much like me, for which I cannot blame him, since I do not think I was a likeable boy, and as it was my own money that was being spent on my education, he was willing enough to let me do as I chose. My aunt greatly favoured my plan. She was herself German, penniless but of noble birth; her family had a coat of arms with supporters and a great number of quarterings, of which she was primly arrogant. I have related elsewhere how, though but a poor clergyman's wife, she would not call on the wife of an opulent banker who had taken a house for the summer near by because he was in trade. It was she who arranged that I should go to a family in Heidelberg whom she had heard of through her relations in Munich.

But when I came back from Germany, aged eighteen, I had very decided views of my own about my future. I had been happier than ever before. I had for the first time tasted freedom and I could not bear the thought of going to Cambridge and being subjected once more to restraint. I felt myself a man and I had a great eagerness to enter at once upon life. I felt that there was not a moment to waste. My uncle had always hoped that I would go into the church, though he should have known that, stammering as I did, no profession could have been more unsuitable; and when I told him that I wouldn't, he accepted with his usual indifference my refusal to go to Cambridge. I still remember the rather absurd arguments that were held about the calling I should adopt. A suggestion was made that I should become a civil servant and my uncle wrote to an old Oxford friend of his who held an important position in the Home Office for his advice. It was that, owing to the system of examinations and the class of persons it had introduced into the government service, it was now no place for a gentleman. That settled that. It was finally decided that I should become a doctor.

The medical profession did not interest me, but it gave me the chance of living in London and so gaining the experience of life that I hankered after. I entered St. Thomas's Hospital in the autumn of 1892. I found the first two years of the curriculum very dull and gave my work no more attention than was necessary to scrape through the examinations. I was an unsatisfactory student. But I had the freedom I yearned for. I liked having lodgings of my own, where I could be by myself; I took pride in making them pretty and comfortable. All my spare time, and much that I should have devoted to my medical studies, I spent reading and writing. I read enormously; I filled notebooks with ideas for stories and plays, scraps of dialogue and reflections, very ingenuous ones, on what my reading and the various experiences that I was undergoing suggested to me. I entered little into the life of the hospital and made few friends there, for I was occupied with other things; but when, after two years, I became a clerk in the out-patients' departments I began to grow interested. In due course I started to work in the wards and then my interest so much increased that when I caught septic tonsillitis through doing a post-mortem on a corpse that was in an unreasonable state of decomposition and had to take to my bed, I could not wait to get well to resume my duties. I had to attend a certain number of confinements to get a certificate and this meant going into the slums of Lambeth, often into foul courts that the police hesitated to enter, but in which my black bag amply protected me: I found the work absorbing. For a short period I was on accident duty day and night to give first aid to urgent cases. It left me tired out but wonderfully exhilarated.

xix

FOR here I was in contact with what I most wanted, life in the raw. In those three years I must have witnessed pretty well every emotion of which man is capable. It appealed to my dramatic instinct. It excited the novelist in me. Even now that forty years have passed I can remember certain people so exactly that I could draw a picture of them. Phrases that I heard then still linger on my ears. I saw how men died. I saw how they bore pain. I saw what hope looked like, fear and relief; I saw the dark lines that despair drew on a face; I saw courage and steadfastness. I saw faith shine in the eyes of those who trusted in what I could only think was an illusion and I saw the gallantry that made a man greet the prognosis of death with an ironic joke because he was too proud to let those about him see the terror of his soul.

At that time (a time to most people of sufficient ease, when peace seemed certain and prosperity secure) there was a school of writers who enlarged upon the moral value of suffering. They claimed that it was salutary. They claimed that it increased sympathy and enhanced the sensibilities. They claimed that it opened to the spirit new avenues of beauty and enabled it to get into touch with the mystical kingdom of God. They claimed that it strengthened the character, purified it from its human grossness and brought to him who did not avoid but sought it a more perfect happiness. Several books on these lines had a great success and their authors, who lived in comfortable homes, had three meals a day and were in robust health, gained much reputation. I set down in my notebook, not once or twice, but in a dozen places, the facts that I had seen. I knew that suffering did not ennoble; it degraded. It made men selfish, mean, petty and suspicious. It absorbed them in small things. It did not make them more than men; it made them less than men; and I wrote ferociously that we learn resignation not by our own suffering, but by the suffering of others.

All this was a valuable experience to me. I do not know a better training for a writer than to spend some years in the medical profession. I suppose that you can learn a good deal about human nature in a solicitor's office; but there on the whole you have to deal with men in full control of themselves. They lie perhaps as much as they lie to the doctor, but they lie more consistently, and it may be that for the solicitor it is not so necessary to know the truth. The interests he deals with, besides, are usually material. He sees human nature from a specialized standpoint. But the doctor, especially the hospital doctor, sees it bare. Reticences can generally be undermined; very often there are none. Fear for the most part will shatter every defence; even vanity is unnerved by it. Most people have a furious itch to talk about themselves and are restrained only by the disinclination of others to listen. Reserve is an artificial quality that is developed in most of us but as the result of innumerable rebuffs. The doctor is discreet. It is his business to listen and no details are too intimate for his ears.

But of course human nature may be displayed before you and if you have not the eyes to see you will learn nothing. If you are hidebound with prejudice, if your temper is sentimental, you can go through the wards of a hospital and be as ignorant of man at the end as you were at the beginning. If you want to get any benefit from such an experience you must have an open mind and an interest in human beings. I look upon myself as very fortunate in that though I have never much liked men I have found them so interesting that I am almost incapable of being bored by them. I do not particularly want to talk and I am very willing to listen. I do not care if people are interested in me or not. I have no desire to impart any knowledge I have to others nor do I feel the need to correct them if they are wrong. You can get a great deal of entertainment out of tedious people if you keep your head. I remember being taken for a drive in a foreign country by a kind lady who wanted to show me round. Her conversation was composed entirely of truisms and she had so large a vocabulary of hackneyed phrases that I despaired of remembering them. But one remark she made has stuck in my memory as have few witticisms; we passed a row of little houses by the sea and she said to me: "Those are week-end bungalows, if you understand what I mean; in other words they're bungalows that people go to on Saturdays and leave on Mondays." I should have been sorry to miss that.

I do not want to spend too long a time with boring people, but then I do not want to spend too long a time with amusing ones. I find social intercourse fatiguing. Most persons, I think, are both exhilarated and rested by conversation; to me it has always been an effort. When I was young and stammered, to talk for long singularly exhausted me, and even now that I have to some extent cured myself, it is a strain. It is a relief to me when I can get away and read a book.

xx

I would not claim for a moment that those years I spent at St. Thomas's Hospital gave me a complete knowledge of human nature. I do not suppose anyone can hope to have that. I have been studying it, consciously and subconsciously, for forty years and I still find men unaccountable; people I know intimately can surprise me by some action of which I never thought them capable or by the discovery of some trait exhibit a side of themselves that I never even suspected. It is possible that my training gave me a warped view, for at St. Thomas's the persons I came in contact with were for the most part sick and poor and ill-educated. I have tried to guard against this. I have tried also to guard against my own prepossessions. I have no natural trust in others. I am more inclined to expect them to do ill than to do good. This is the price one has to pay for having a sense of humour. A sense of humour leads you to take pleasure in the discrepancies of human nature; it leads you to mistrust great professions and look for the unworthy motive that they conceal; the disparity between appearance and reality diverts you and you are apt when you cannot find it to create it. You tend to close your eyes to truth, beauty and goodness because they give no scope to your sense of the ridiculous. The humorist has a quick eye for the humbug; he does not always recognize the saint. But if to see men one-sidedly is a heavy price to pay for a sense of humour there is a compensation that has a value too. You are not angry with people when you laugh at them. Humour teaches tolerance, and the humourist, with a smile and perhaps a sigh, is more likely to shrug his shoulders than to condemn. He does not moralize, he is content to understand; and it is true that to understand is to pity and forgive.

But I must admit that, with these reservations that I have tried always to remember, the experience of all the years that have followed has only confirmed the observations on human nature that I made, not deliberately, for I was too young, but unconsciously, in the out-patients' departments and in the wards of St. Thomas's Hospital. I have seen men since as I saw them then, and thus have I drawn them. It may not be a true picture and I know that many have thought it an unpleasant one. It is doubtless partial, for naturally I have seen men through my own idosyncrasies. A buoyant, optimistic, healthy and sentimental person would have seen the same people quite differently. I can only claim to have seen them coherently. Many writers seem to me not to observe at all, but to create their characters in stock sizes from images in their own fancy. They are like draughtsmen who draw their figures from recollections of the antique and have never attempted to draw from the living model. At their best they can only give living shape to the fantasies of their own minds. If their minds are noble they can give you noble figures and perhaps it does not matter if they lack the infinite complication of common life.

I have always worked from the living model. I remember that once in the dissecting room when I was going over my "part" with the demonstrator, he asked me what some nerve was and I did not know. He told me; whereupon I remonstrated, for it was in the wrong place. Nevertheless he insisted that it was the nerve I had been in vain looking for.

I complained of the abnormality and he, smiling, said that in anatomy it was the normal that was uncommon. I was only annoyed at the time, but the remark sank into my mind and since then it has been forced upon me that it was true of man as well as of anatomy. The normal is what you find but rarely. The normal is an ideal. It is a picture that one fabricates of the average characteristics of men, and to find them all in a single man is hardly to be expected. It is this false picture that the writers I have spoken of take as their model and it is because they describe what is so exceptional that they seldom achieve the effect of life. Selfishness and kindliness, idealism and sensuality, vanity, shyness, disinterestedness, courage, laziness, nervousness, obstinacy, and diffidence, they can all exist in a single person and form a plausible harmony. It has taken a long time to persuade readers of the truth of this.

I do not suppose men in past centuries were any different from the men we know, but they must surely have appeared to their contemporaries more of a piece than they do to us now, or writers would not have thus represented them. It seemed reasonable to describe every man in his humour. The miser was nothing but miserly, the fop foppish, and the glutton gluttonous. It never occurred to anyone that the miser might be foppish and gluttonous; and yet we see constantly people who are; still less, that he might be an honest and upright man with a disinterested zeal for public service and a genuine passion for art. When novelists began to disclose the diversity that they had found in themselves or seen in others they were accused of maligning the human race. So far as I know the first novelist who did this with deliberate intention was Stendhal in *Le Rouge et le Noir*. Contemporary criticism was outraged. Even Sainte-Beuve, who needed only to look into his own heart to discover what contrary qualities could exist side by side in some kind of harmony, took him to task. Julien Sorel is one of the most interesting characters that a novelist has ever created. I do not think that Stendhal has succeeded in making him entirely plausible, but that, I believe, is due to causes that I shall mention in another part of this book. For the first three quarters of the novel he is perfectly consistent. Sometimes he fills you with horror; sometimes he is entirely sympathetic; but he has an inner coherence, so that though you often shudder you accept.

But it was long before Stendhal's example bore fruit. Balzac, with all his genius, drew his characters after the old models. He gave them his own immense vitality so that you accept them as real; but in fact they are humours as definitely as are the characters of old comedy. His people are unforgettable, but they are seen from the standpoint of the ruling passion that affected those with whom they were brought in contact. I suppose it is a natural prepossession of mankind to take people as though they were homogeneous. It is evidently less trouble to make up one's mind about a man one way or the other and dismiss suspense with the phrase, he's one of the best or he's a dirty dog. It is disconcerting to find that the saviour of his country may be stingy or that the poet who has opened new horizons to our consciousness may be a snob. Our natural egoism leads us to judge people by their relations to ourselves. We want them to be certain things to us, and for us that is what they are; because the rest of them is no good to us, we ignore it.

These reasons perhaps explain why there is so great a disinclination to accept the attempts to portray man with his incongruous and diverse qualities and why people turn away with dismay when candid biographers reveal the truth about famous persons. It is distressing to think that the composer of the quintet in the *Meistersinger* was dishonest in money matters and treacherous to those who had benefited him. But it may be that he could not have had great qualities if he had not also had great failings. I do not believe they are right who say that the defects of famous men should be ignored; I think it is better that we should know them. Then, though we are conscious of having faults as glaring as theirs, we can believe that that is no hindrance to our achieving also something of their virtues.

BESIDES teaching me something about human nature my training in a medical school furnished me with an elementary knowledge of science and scientific method. Till then I had been concerned only with art and literature. It was a very limited knowledge, for the demands of the curriculum at that time were small, but at all events it showed me the road that led to a region of which I was completely ignorant. I grew familiar with certain principles. The scientific world of which I thus obtained a cursory glimpse was rigidly materialistic and because its conceptions coincided with my own pre-possessions I embraced them with alacrity; "For men," as Pope observed, "let them say what they will, never approve any other's sense, but as it squares with their own." I was glad to learn that the mind of man (himself the product of natural causes) was a function of the brain subject like the rest of his body to the laws of cause and effect and that these laws were the same as those that governed the move-ments of star and atom. I exulted at the thought that the universe was no more than a vast machine in which every event was determined by a preceding event so that nothing could be other than it was. These conceptions not only appealed to my dramatic instinct; they filled me besides with a very delectable sense of liberation. With the ferocity of youth I welcomed the hypothesis of the Survival of the Fittest. It gave me much satisfaction to learn that the earth was a speck of mud whirling round a second-rate star which was gradually cooling; and that evolution, which had pro-duced man, would by forcing him to adapt himself to his environment deprive him of all the qualities he had acquired but those that were necessary to enable him to combat the increasing cold till at last the planet, an icy cinder, would no longer support even a vestige of life. I believed that we were wretched puppets at the mercy of a ruthless fate; and that, bound by the inexorable laws of nature, we were doomed to take part in the ceaseless struggle for existence with nothing to look forward to but inevitable defeat. I learnt that men were moved by a savage egoism, that love was only the dirty trick nature played on us to achieve the continuation of the species, and I decided that, whatever aims men set themselves, they were deluded, for it was impossible for them to aim at anything but their own selfish pleasures. When once I happened to do a friend a good turn (for what reasons, since I knew that all our actions were purely selfish, I did not stop to think) and wanting to show his gratitude (which of course he had no business to feel, for my apparent kindness was rigidly determined) he asked me what I would like as a present, I answered without hesitation Herbert Spencer's *First Principles*. I read it with complacency. But I was impatient of Spencer's maudlin belief in progress: the world I knew was going from bad to worse and I was as pleased as Punch at the thought of my remote descendants, having long forgotten art and science and handicraft, cowering skin-clad in caverns as they watched the approach of the cold and eternal night. I was violently pessimistic. All the same, having abundant vitality, I was getting on the whole a lot of fun out of life. I was ambitious to make a name for myself as a writer. I exposed myself to every vicissitude that seemed to offer a chance of gaining the greater experience that I wanted and I read everything I could lay my hands on.

xxii

I LIVED at this time in a group of young men who had by nature gifts that seemed to me much superior to mine. They could write and draw and compose with a facility that aroused my envy. They had an appreciation of art and a critical instinct that I despaired of attaining. Of these some died without fulfilling the promise I thought they had and the rest have lived on without distinction. I know now that all they had was the natural creativity of youth. To write prose and verse, to hammer out little tunes on the piano and to draw and paint, are instinctive with a great many young persons. It is a form of play, due merely to the exuberance of their years, and is no more significant than a child's building of a castle on the sands. I suspect that it was my own ingenuousness that led me to admire so much the gifts of my friends. If I had been less ignorant I might have seen that the opinions that seemed to me so original were theirs only at second-hand and that their verses and their music owed more to a retentive memory than to a lively imagination. The point I want to make is that this facility is, if not universal, so common that one can draw no conclusions from it. Youth is the inspiration. One of the tragedies of the arts is the spectacle of the vast number of persons who have been misled by this passing fertility to devote their lives to the effort of creation. Their invention deserts them as they grow older, and they are faced with the long years before them in which, unfitted by now for a more humdrum calling, they harass their wearied brain to beat out material it is incapable of giving them. They are lucky when, with what bitterness we know, they can make a living in ways, like journalism or teaching, that are allied to the arts.

Of course it is from among those who possess by nature this facility that the artist is produced. Without it he cannot have talent; but it is only a part of talent. We start by living, each one of us, in the solitariness of our own minds and from the data given us and our communications with other minds we construct the outside world to suit our needs. Because we are all the result of one evolutionary process, and our environment is more or less the same, the constructions we make are roughly similar. For convenience and simplicity we accept them as identical and speak of a common world. The peculiarity of the artist is that he is in some particular different from other men and so the world of his construction is different too. It is this idiosyncrasy that is the better part of his equipment. When the picture he draws of his private world appeals to a certain number of persons, either by its strangeness, its intrinsic interest or its correspondence with their own prepossessions (for none of us is quite the same as his neighbour, only rather like, and not everyone accepts the world common to us all in every respect) his talent will be acknowledged. If he is a writer he will fulfill some need in the nature of his readers and they will lead with him a life of the spirit that satisfies them better than the life circumstances have forced on them. But there are others to whom this idiosyncrasy does not appeal. They have no patience with the world constructed by its instrumentality. It may actually revolt them. Then the artist has nothing to say to them and they will deny his talent.

I do not believe that genius is an entirely different thing from talent. I am not even sure that it depends on any great difference in the artist's natural gifts. For example, I do not think that Cervantes had an exceptional gift for writing; few people would deny him genius. Nor would it be easy in English literature to find a poet with a happier gift than Herrick and yet no one would claim that he had more than a delightful talent. It seems to me that what makes genius is the combination of natural gifts for creation with an idiosyncrasy that enables its possessor to see the world personally in the highest degree and yet with such catholicity that his appeal is not to this type of man or to that type, but to all men. His private world is that of common men, but ampler and more pithy. His communication is universal and though men may not be able to tell exactly what it signifies they feel that it is important. He is supremely normal. By a happy accident of nature seeing life with immense vivacity, as it were at concert pitch, he sees it, with its infinite diversity, in the healthy way that mankind at large sees it. In Matthew Arnold's phrase he sees it steadily and sees it whole. But genius arises once or twice in a century. The lesson of anatomy applies: there is nothing so rare as the normal. It is foolish to do as many do now and call a man a genius because he has written half-a-dozen clever plays or painted a score of good pictures. It is very well to have talent; few people have. With talent the artist will only reach the second class, but that need not disturb him for it contains the names of many whose works have uncommon merit. When you think it has produced such novels as *Le Rouge et le Noir,* such poems as *The Shropshire Lad,* such paintings as those of Watteau, there is not much to be ashamed of. Talent cannot reach the utmost heights, but it can show you many an

unexpected and delicious view, an unfrequented dell, a bubbling brook or a romantic cavern, on the way that leads to
them. The frowardness of human nature is such that it
falters sometimes when it is bidden to take the broadest of
all surveys of human nature. It will shrink from the splendour of Tolstoi's *War and Peace* to turn with complacency
to Voltaire's *Candide*. It would be hard to live always with
Michelangelo's ceiling in the Sistine Chapel, but anyone
could do with one of Constable's pictures of Salisbury Cathedral.

My sympathies are limited. I can only be myself, and
partly by nature, partly by the circumstances of my life, it is
a partial self. I am not a social person. I cannot get drunk
and feel a great love for my fellow men. Convivial amusement has always somewhat bored me. When people sit in an
ale house or drifting down the river in a boat start singing I
am silent. I have never even sung a hymn. I do not much like
being touched and I have always to make a slight effort over
myself not to draw away when someone links his arm in
mine. I can never forget myself. The hysteria of the world
repels me and I never feel more aloof than when I am in the
midst of a throng surrendered to a violent feeling of mirth
or sorrow. Though I have been in love a good many times I
have never experienced the bliss of requited love. I know that
this is the best thing that life can offer and it is a thing that
almost all men, though perhaps only for a short time, have
enjoyed. I have most loved people who cared little or nothing
for me and when people have loved me I have been embarrassed. It has been a predicament that I have not quite known
how to deal with. In order not to hurt their feelings I have
often acted a passion that I did not feel. I have tried, with
gentleness when possible, and if not, with irritation, to
escape from the trammels with which their love bound me.
I have been jealous of my independence. I am incapable of
complete surrender. And so, never having felt some of the
fundamental emotions of normal men, it is impossible that
my work should have the intimacy, the broad human touch
and the animal serenity which the greatest writers alone can
give.

xxiii

IT IS dangerous to let the public behind the scenes. They are easily disillusioned and then they are angry with you, for it was the illusion they loved; they do not understand that what interests you is the way in which you have created the illusion. Anthony Trollope ceased to be read for thirty years because he confessed that he wrote at regular hours and took care to get the best price he could for his work.

But for me the race now is nearly run and it would ill become me to conceal the truth. I do not want anyone to think better of me than I deserve. Let those who like me take me as I am and let the rest leave me. I have more character than brains and more brains than specific gifts. I said something of this sort many years ago to a charming and distinguished critic. I do not know what led me to do so, since I am not much inclined to talk about myself in general company. It was at Montdidier, during the first months of the war, and we were lunching there on our way to Péronne. We had been very hard-worked for some days and it was a pleasure to linger over a meal that seemed to our healthy appetites uncommonly good. I suppose I was flushed with wine and I daresay excited by the discovery, from a statue in the market-place, that Montdidier was the birthplace of Parmentier, who introduced the potato into France. Anyhow as we idled over our coffee and liqueurs I was moved to give an acute and candid analysis of my talent. I was disconcerted some years later to read it, almost in my very words, in the columns of an important paper. I was a trifle vexed, for it is a very different thing to tell the truth about yourself and to have somebody else tell it, and I should have liked the critic to do me the compliment of saying that he had heard it all from my own lips. But I chid myself. I thought it very natural that he should like to think that he had so much perspicacity. And it was the truth. It has been a little unfortunate for me, since the critic is deservedly influential and what he said in this article has been very generally repeated. In another moment of frankness I informed my readers that

I was unusually competent. One would think that except for this the critics would never have discovered it; but since then the adjective has been much and depreciatingly applied to me. It has seemed strange to me that so many people concerned, though only at second hand, with the arts should regard competence with so little favour.

I am told that there are natural singers and made singers. Though of course he must have something of a voice the made singer owes the better part of his accomplishment to training; with taste and musical ability he can eke out the relative poverty of his organ and his singing can afford a great deal of pleasure, especially to the connoisseur; but he will never move you as you are moved to ecstasy by the pure, birdlike notes of the natural singer. The natural singer may be inadequately trained, he may have neither tact nor knowledge, he may outrage all the canons of art, but such is the magic of his voice that you are captivated. You forgive the liberties he takes, his vulgarities, his appeals to obvious emotion, when those heavenly sounds enchant your ear. I am a made writer. But it would be vanity if I thought that such results as I have achieved on myself were due to a design that I deliberately carried out. I was drawn to various courses by very simple motives and it is only on looking back that I discover myself subconsciously working to a certain end. The end was to develop my character and so make up for the deficiencies in my natural gifts.

I have a clear and logical brain, but not a very subtle nor a very powerful one. For long I wished it were better. I used to get exasperated because it would not do for me nearly as much as I wished. I was like a mathematician who could do no more than add and subtract and though he wanted to tackle all manner of complicated operations knew that he simply had not the capacity. It took me a long time to resign myself to making the best of what I had. I think it was a good enough brain to have brought me success in whatever profession I had adopted. I am not one of those persons who is a fool at everything but his own specialty. In law, medicine and politics a clear mind and insight into men are useful.

I have had one advantage; I have never wanted a subject.

I have always had more stories in my head than I ever had time to write. I have often heard writers complain that they wanted to write but had nothing to write about, and I remember one distinguished author telling me that she was reading through some books in which were epitomized all the plots that had ever been used in order to find a theme. I have never found myself in such a predicament. Swift, as we know, who claimed that he could write on any subject whatever, when he was challenged to write a discourse on a broomstick acquitted himself very creditably. I am almost inclined to say that I could not spend an hour in anyone's company without getting the material to write at least a readable story about him. It is pleasant to have so many stories in mind that whatever your mood you have one upon which, for an hour or two, for a week or so, you can let your fancy linger. Reverie is the groundwork of creative imagination; it is the privilege of the artist that with him it is not as with other men an escape from reality, but the means by which he accedes to it. His reverie is purposeful. It affords him a delight in comparison with which the pleasures of sense are pale and it affords him the assurance of his freedom. One cannot wonder if sometimes he is unwilling to exchange its enjoyment for the drudgery and loss of execution.

But though I have had variety of invention, and this is not strange since it is the outcome of the variety of mankind, I have had small power of imagination. I have taken living people and put them into the situations, tragic or comic, that their characters suggested. I might well say that they invented their own stories. I have been incapable of those great, sustained flights that carry the author on broad pinions into a celestial sphere. My fancy, never very strong, has been hampered by my sense of probability. I have painted easel pictures, not frescoes.

xxiv

I HEARTILY wish that in my youth I had had someone of good sense to direct my reading. I sigh when I reflect on the amount of time I have wasted on books that were of no great profit to me. What little guidance I had I owe to a young man who came to live with the same family in Heidelberg as I was living with. I will call him Brown. He was then twenty-six. After leaving Cambridge he was called to the bar, but he had a little money, enough to live on in those inexpensive days, and finding the law distasteful he had made up his mind to devote himself to literature. He came to Heidelberg to learn German. I knew him till his death forty years later. For twenty years he amused himself with thinking what he would write when he really got down to it and for another twenty with what he could have written if the fates had been kinder. He wrote a good deal of verse. He had neither imagination, nor passion; and he had a defective ear. He spent some years translating those dialogues of Plato that already had been most often translated. I doubt, however, if he ever got to the end of one. He was completely devoid of will-power. He was sentimental and vain. Though short he was handsome, with finely cut features and curly hair; he had pale blue eyes and a wistful expression. He looked as one imagines a poet should look. As an old man, after a life of complete indolence, bald and emaciated, he had an ascetic air so that you might have taken him for a don who had spent long years in ardent and disinterested research. The spirituality of his expression suggested the tired scepticism of a philosopher who had plumbed the secrets of existence and discovered nothing but vanity. Having gradually wasted his small fortune, he preferred to live on the generosity of others rather than work, and often he found it difficult to make both ends meet. His self-complacency never deserted him. It enabled him to endure poverty with resignation and failure with indifference. I do not think he ever had an inkling that he was an outrageous sham. His whole life was a lie, but when he was dying, if he had known he was going to, which mercifully he didn't, I am convinced he would have looked upon it as well-spent. He had charm, he was devoid of envy, and though too selfish to do anyone a good turn, he was incapable of unkindness. He had a real appreciation of literature. During the long walks we

took together over the hills of Heidelberg he talked to me
of books. He talked to me of Italy and Greece, neither of
which in point of fact he knew, but he fired my young imagination and I began to learn Italian. I accepted everything
he told me with the fervour of the proselyte. I should not
blame him because he inspired me with a passionate admiration for certain works that time has shown to be not so
admirable. When he arrived he found me reading *Tom
Jones,* which I had got out of the public library, and he told
me that of course there was no harm in it, but I should do
better to read *Diana of the Crossways.* Even then he was a
Platonist and he gave me Shelley's translation of the Sym-
posium. He talked to me of Renan, Cardinal Newman and
Matthew Arnold. But Matthew Arnold, he thought, was a
bit of a philistine himself. He talked to me of Swinburne's
Poems and Ballads and of *Omar Khayyám.* He knew a great
many of the quatrains by heart and recited them to me on
our walks. I was divided between enthusiasm for the romantic epicureanism of the matter and the embarrassment
occasioned by Brown's delivery, for he recited poetry like a
high-church curate intoning the Litany in an ill-lit crypt. But
the two writers that it was really necessary to admire if you
would be a person of culture and not a British philistine were
Walter Pater and George Meredith. I was very ready to do
what I was told to achieve this desirable end and incredible
as it must seem I read *The Shaving of Shagpat* with roars of
laughter. It seemed to me superlatively funny. Then I read
the novels of George Meredith one after the other. I thought
them wonderful; but not so wonderful as even to myself I
pretended. My admiration was factitious. I admired because
it was the part of a cultured young man to admire. I intoxicated myself with my own enthusiasm. I would not listen to
the still small voice within me that carped. Now I know that
there is a great deal of fustian in these novels. But the
strange thing is that, reading them again, I recapture the
days when I first read them. They are rich for me now with
sunny mornings and my awakening intelligence and the delicious dreams of youth, so that even as I close a novel of
Meredith's, *Evan Harrington* for instance, and decide that

its insincerity is exasperating, its snobbishness loathsome, its verbosity intolerable and I will never read another, my heart melts and I think it's grand.

On the other hand I have no such feeling about Walter Pater whom I read at the same time and with a similar excitement. No pleasant associations give him for me a merit to which he has no claim. I find him as dull as a picture of Alma Tadema. It is strange that one can ever have admired that prose. It does not flow. There is no air in it. A careful mosaic constructed by someone without great technical skill to decorate the walls of a station dining-room. Pater's attitude towards the life about him, cloistered, faintly supercilious, gentlemanly, donnish in short, repels me. Art should be appreciated with passion and violence, not with a tepid, deprecating elegance that fears the censoriousness of a common room. But Walter Pater was a feeble creature: it is unnecessary to condemn him with intensity. I dislike him not for himself, but because he is an example of a type in the literary world that is common and detestable. This is the person who is filled with the conceit of culture.

The value of culture is its effect on character. It avails nothing unless it ennobles and strengthens that. Its use is for life. Its aim is not beauty but goodness. Too often, as we know, it gives rise to self-complacency. Who has not seen the scholar's thin-lipped smile when he corrects a misquotation and the connoisseur's pained look when someone praises a picture he does not care for? There is no more merit in having read a thousand books than in having ploughed a thousand fields. There is no more merit in being able to attach a correct description to a picture than in being able to find out what is wrong with a stalled motorcar. In each case it is special knowledge. The stockbroker has his knowledge too and so has the artizan. It is a silly prejudice of the intellectual that his is the only one that counts. The True, the Good and the Beautiful are not the perquisites of those who have been to expensive schools, burrowed in libraries and frequented museums. The artist has no excuse when he uses others with condescension. He is a fool if he thinks his knowledge is more important than theirs and an oaf if he cannot comfortably meet them on an equal footing. Matthew Arnold did a great disservice to culture when he insisted on its opposition to philistinism.

xxv

AT EIGHTEEN I knew French, German and some Italian, but I was extremely uneducated and I was deeply conscious of my ignorance. I read everything that came my way. My curiosity was such that I was as willing to read a history of Peru or the reminiscences of a cowboy as a treatise on Provençal poetry or the *Confessions* of St. Augustine. I suppose it gained me a certain amount of general knowledge which is useful for the novelist to have. One never knows when an out-of-the-way bit of information will come in handy. I made lists of what I read and one of these lists by some accident I still have. It is my reading for two months and, but that I made it only for myself, I could not believe that it was veracious. It shows that I read three of Shakespeare's plays, two volumes of Mommsen's *History of Rome,* a large part of Lanson's *Littérature Française,* two or three novels, some of the French classics, a couple of scientific works and a play of Ibsen's. I was indeed the industrious apprentice. During the time I was at St. Thomas's Hospital I went systematically through English, French, Italian and Latin literature. I read a lot of history, a little philosophy and a good deal of science. My curiosity was too great to allow me to give much time to reflect upon what I read; I could hardly wait to finish one book, so eager was I to begin another. This was always an adventure, and I would start upon a famous work as excitedly as a reasonable young man would go in to bat for his side or a nice girl go to a dance. Now and then journalists in search of copy ask me what is the most thrilling moment of my life. If I were not ashamed to, I might answer that it is the moment when I began to read Goethe's *Faust.* I have never quite lost this feeling, and even now the first pages of a book sometimes send the blood racing through my veins. To me reading is a rest as to other people conversation or a game of cards. It is more than that; it is a necessity, and if I am deprived of it for a little while I find myself as irritable as the addict deprived of his drug. I would sooner read a time-table or a catalogue than nothing at all. That is putting it too low. I have spent many delightful hours poring over the price list of the Army and Navy Stores, the lists of second-hand booksellers and the A.B.C. All these are redolent of romance. They are much more entertaining than half the novels that are written.

I have put books aside only because I was conscious that time was passing and that it was my business to live. I have gone into the world because I thought it was necessary in order to get the experience without which I could not write, but I have gone into it also because I wanted experience for its own sake. It did not seem to me enough only to be a writer. The pattern I had designed for myself insisted that I should take the utmost part I could in this fantastic affair of being a man. I desired to feel the common pains and enjoy the common pleasures that are part of the common human lot. I saw no reason to subordinate the claims of sense to the tempting lure of spirit and I was determined to get whatever fulfilment I could out of social intercourse and human relations, out of food, drink and fornication, luxury, sport, art, travel, and as Henry James says, whatever. But it was an effort and I have always returned to my books and my own company with relief.

And yet, though I have read so much, I am a bad reader. I read slowly and I am a poor skipper. I find it difficult to leave a book, however bad and however much it bores me, unfinished. I could count on my fingers the number of books that I have not read from cover to cover. On the other hand there are few books that I have read twice. I know very well that there are many of which I cannot get the full value on a single reading, but in that they have given me all I was capable of getting at the time, and this, though I may forget their details, remains a permanent enrichment. I know people who read the same book over and over again. It can only be that they read with their eyes and not with their sensibility. It is a mechanical exercise like the Tibetan's turning of a

praying-wheel. It is doubtless a harmless occupation, but they are wrong if they think it an intelligent one.

xxvi

In my youth, when my instinctive feeling about a book differed from that of authoritative critics I did not hesitate to conclude that I was wrong. I did not know how often critics accept the conventional view and it never occurred to me that they could talk with assurance of what they did not know very much about. It was long before I realized that the only thing that mattered to me in a work of art was what I thought about it. I have acquired now a certain confidence in my own judgment, for I have noticed that what I felt instinctively forty years ago about the writers I read then, and what I would not heed because it did not agree with current opinion, is now pretty generally accepted. For all that I still read a great deal of criticism, for I think it a very agreeable form of literary composition. One does not always want to be reading to the profit of one's soul and there is no pleasanter way of idling away an hour or two than reading a volume of criticism. It is diverting to agree; it is diverting to differ; and it is always interesting to know what an intelligent man has to say about some writer, Henry More, for instance, or Richardson, whom you have never had occasion to read.

But the only important thing in a book is the meaning it has for you; it may have other and much more profound meanings for the critic, but at second hand they can be of small service to you. I do not read a book for the book's sake, but for my own. It is not my business to judge it, but to absorb what I can of it, as the amœba absorbs a particle of a foreign body, and what I cannot assimilate has nothing to do with me. I am not a scholar, a student or a critic; I am a professional writer and now I read only what is useful to me professionally. Anyone can write a book that will revolutionize the ideas that have been held for centuries on the Ptolemies and I shall contentedly leave it unread; he can

describe an incredibly adventurous journey in the heart of
Patagonia and I shall remain ignorant of it. There is no need
for the writer of fiction to be an expert on any subject but
his own; on the contrary, it is hurtful to him, since, human
nature being weak, he is hard put to it to resist the temptation of inappositely using his special knowledge. The novelist is ill-advised to be too technical. The practice, which came
into fashion in the nineties, of using a multitude of cant
terms is tiresome. It should be possible to give verisimilitude
without that, and atmosphere is dearly bought at the price
of tediousness. The novelist should know something about
the great issues that occupy men, who are his topics, but it is
generally enough if he knows a little. He must avoid ped-
antry at all costs. But even at that the field is vast and I have
tried to limit myself to such works as were significant to my
purpose. You can never know enough about your characters.
Biographies and reminiscences, technical works, will give you
often an intimate detail, a telling touch, a revealing hint, that
you might never have got from a living model. People are
hard to know. It is a slow business to induce them to tell you
the particular thing about themselves that can be of use to
you. They have the disadvantage that often you cannot look
at them and put them aside, as you can a book, and you have
to read the whole volume, as it were, only to learn that it
had nothing much to tell you.

xxvii

YOUNG persons, who are anxious to write, sometimes pay me
the compliment of asking me to tell them of certain books
necessary for them to read. I do. They seldom read them,
for they seem to have little curiosity. They do not care what
their predecessors have done. They think they know everything that it is necessary to know of the art of fiction when
they have read two or three novels by Mrs. Woolf, one by
E. M. Forster, several by D. H. Lawrence and, oddly
enough, the *Forsyte Saga*. It is true that contemporary literature has a vividness of appeal that classical literature can

never have and it is well for a young writer to know what his contemporaries are writing about and how. But there are fashions in literature and it is not easy to tell what intrinsic value there is in a style of writing that happens to be the vogue at the moment. An acquaintance with the great works of the past serves as a very good standard of comparison. I have sometimes wondered whether it is due to their ignorance that many young writers, notwithstanding their facility and cleverness, their skilful technique, so frequently fizzle out. They write two or three books that are not only brilliant, but mature, and then they are done for. But that is not what enriches the literature of a country. For that you must have writers who can produce not just two or three books, but a great body of work. Of course it will be uneven, because so many fortunate circumstances must go together to produce a masterpiece; but a masterpiece is more likely to come as the culminating point of a laborious career than as the lucky fluke of untaught genius. The writer can only be fertile if he renews himself and he can only renew himself if his soul is constantly enriched by fresh experience. There is no more fruitful source of this than the enchanting exploration of the great literatures of the past.

For the production of a work of art is not the result of a miracle. It requires preparation. The soil, be it ever so rich, must be fed. By taking thought, by deliberate effort, the artist must enlarge, deepen and diversify his personality. Then the soil must lie fallow. Like the bride of Christ, the artist waits for the illumination that shall bring forth a new spiritual life. He goes about his ordinary avocations with patience; the subconscious does its mysterious business; and then, suddenly springing, you might think from nowhere, the idea is produced. But like the corn that was sown on stony ground it may easily wither away; it must be tended with anxious care. All the power of the artist's mind must be set to work on it, all his technical skill, all his experience, and whatever he has in him of character and individuality, so that with infinite pains he may present it with the completeness that is fitting to it.

But I am not impatient with the young when, only at their

request, I insist, I advise them to read Shakespeare and Swift, and they tell me that they read *Gulliver's Travels* in their nursery and *Henry IV* at school; and if they find *Vanity Fair* unendurable and *Anna Karenina* footling it is their own affair. No reading is worth while unless you enjoy it. There is at least this to be said for them that they do not suffer from the self-conceit of knowledge. They are not withdrawn by a wide culture from sympathy with the common run of men who are after all their material. They are nearer to their fellows and the art they practise is not a mystery, but a craft on the same footing as any other. They write novels and plays as unaffectedly as other men build motorcars. This is much to the good. For the artist, the writer especially, in the solitariness of his own mind constructs a world that is different from other men's; the idiosyncrasy that makes him a writer separates him from them and the paradox emerges that though his aim is to describe them truthfully his gift prevents him from knowing them as they really are. It is as though he wanted urgently to see a certain thing and by the act of looking at it drew before it a veil that obscured it. The writer stands outside the very action he is engaged in. He is the comedian who never quite loses himself in the part, for he is at the same time spectator and actor. It is all very well to say that poetry is emotion remembered in tranquillity; but a poet's emotion is specific, a poet's rather than a man's, and it is never quite disinterested. That is why women with their instinctive common sense have so often found the love of poets unsatisfying. It may be that the writers of the present day, who seem to be so much nearer to their raw material, ordinary men among ordinary men, rather than artists in an alien crowd, may break down the barrier that their peculiar gift cannot but raise and so come nearer to the plain truth than has ever been done before. But then you have to make up your mind about the relations between truth and art.

xxviii

I HAD my full share of the intellectual's arrogance and if, as I hope, I have lost it, I must ascribe it not to my own virtue or wisdom but to the chance that made me more of a traveller than most writers. I am attached to England, but I have never felt myself very much at home there. I have always been shy with English people. To me England has been a country where I had obligations that I did not want to fulfil and responsibilities that irked me. I have never felt entirely myself till I had put at least the Channel between my native country and me. Some fortunate persons find freedom in their own minds; I, with less spiritual power than they, find it in travel. While still at Heidelberg I managed to visit a good many places in Germany (at Munich I saw Ibsen drinking a glass of beer at the Maximilianerhof and with a scowl on his face reading the paper) and I went to Switzerland; but the first real journey I made was to Italy. I went primed with much reading of Walter Pater, Ruskin and John Addington Symonds. I had the six weeks of the Easter vacation at my disposal and twenty pounds in my pocket. After going to Genoa and Pisa, where I trudged the interminable distance to sit for a while in the pine wood in which Shelley read Sophocles and wrote verses on a guitar, I settled down for the inside of a month in Florence in the house of a widow lady, with whose daughter I read the *Purgatorio,* and spent laborious days, Ruskin in hand, visiting the sights. I admired everything that Ruskin told me to admire (even that horrible tower of Giotto) and turned away in disgust from what he condemned. Never can he have had a more ardent disciple. After that I went to Venice, Verona and Milan. I returned to England very much pleased with myself and actively contemptuous of anyone who did not share my views (and Ruskin's) of Botticelli and Bellini. I was twenty.

A year later I went to Italy again, travelling as far down as Naples, and discovered Capri. It was the most enchanting spot I had ever seen and the following summer I spent the whole of my vacation there. Capri was then little known.

There was no funicular from the beach to the town. Few people went there in summer and you could get board and lodging, with wine included, and from your bedroom window a view of Vesuvius, for four shillings a day. There was a poet there then, a Belgian composer, my friend from Heidelberg, Brown, a painter or two, a sculptor (Harvard Thomas) and an American colonel who had fought on the Southern side in the Civil War. I listened with transport to conversations, up at Anacapri at the colonel's house, or at Morgano's, the wine shop just off the Piazza, when they talked of art and beauty, literature and Roman history. I saw two men fly at one another's throats because they disagreed over the poetic merit of Heredia's sonnets. I thought it all grand. Art, art for art's sake, was the only thing that mattered in the world; and the artist alone gave this ridiculous world significance. Politics, commerce, the learned professions—what did they amount to from the standpoint of the Absolute? They might disagree, these friends of mine (dead, dead every jack one of them), about the value of a sonnet or the excellence of a Greek bas-relief (Greek, my eye! I tell you it's a Roman copy and if I tell you a thing it is so); but they were all agreed about this, that they burned with a hard, gemlike flame. I was too shy to tell them that I had written a novel and was halfway through another and it was a great mortification to me, burning as I was too with a hard, gemlike flame, to be treated as a philistine who cared for nothing but dissecting dead bodies and would seize an unguarded moment to give his best friend an enema.

xxix

PRESENTLY I was qualified. I had already published a novel and it had had an unexpected success. I thought my fortune was made, and, abandoning medicine to become a writer, I went to Spain. I was then twenty-three. I was much more ignorant than are, it seems to me, young men of that age at the present day. I settled down in Seville. I grew a moustache, smoked Filipino cigars, learnt the guitar, bought a broad-brimmed hat with a flat crown, in which I swaggered down the Sierpes, and hankered for a flowing cape, lined with green and red velvet. But on account of the expense I did not buy it. I rode about the countryside on a horse lent me by a friend. Life was too pleasant to allow me to give an undivided attention to literature. My plan was to spend a year there till I had learnt Spanish, then go to Rome which I knew only as a tripper and perfect my superficial knowledge of Italian, follow that up with a journey to Greece where I intended to learn the vernacular as an approach to ancient Greek, and finally go to Cairo and learn Arabic. It was an ambitious programme, but I am glad now that I did not carry it out. I duly went to Rome (where I wrote my first play) but then I went back to Spain; for something had occurred that I had not anticipated. I fell in love with Seville and the life one led there and incidentally with a young thing with green eyes and a gay smile (but I got over that) and I could not resist its lure. I returned year after year. I wandered through the white and silent streets and strolled along the Guadalquivir, I dawdled about the Cathedral, I went to bullfights and made light love to pretty little creatures whose demands on me were no more than my exiguous means could satisfy. It was heavenly to live in Seville in the flower of one's youth. I postponed my education to a more convenient moment. The result is that I have never read the *Odyssey* but in English and I have never achieved my ambition to read *A Thousand Nights and a Night* in Arabic.

When the intelligentsia took up Russia I, remembering that Cato had begun to learn Greek when he was eighty, set about learning Russian, but I had by then lost my youthful enthusiasm; I never got farther than being able to read the plays of Chekhov and have long since forgotten the little I knew. I think now that these schemes of mine were a trifle nonsensical. Words are not important, but their meanings, and it is of no spiritual advantage that I can see to know half-a-dozen languages. I have met polyglots; I have not noticed that they were wiser than the rest of us. It is convenient if you are travelling in a country to have a sufficient smattering of its speech to find your way about and get what you want to eat; and if it has a considerable literature it is pleasant to be able to read it. But such a knowledge as this can be acquired easily. To attempt to learn more is futile. Unless you devote your whole life to it, you will never learn to speak the language of another country to perfection; you will never know its people and its literature with complete intimacy. For they, and the literature which is their expression, are wrought, not only of the actions they perform and the words they use, neither of which offer great difficulty, but of ancestral instincts, shades of feeling that they have absorbed with their mothers' milk, and innate attitudes which the foreigner can never quite seize. It is hard enough for us to know our own people; we deceive ourselves, we English especially, if we think we can know those of other lands. For the sea-girt isle sets us apart and the link that a common religion gave, which once mitigated our insularity, was snapped with the Reformation. It seems hardly worth while to take much trouble to acquire a knowledge that can never be more than superficial. I think then it is merely waste of time to learn more than a smattering of foreign tongues. The only exception I would make to this is French. For French is the common language of educated men and it is certainly convenient to speak it well enough to be able to treat of any subject of discourse that may arise. It has a great literature; other countries, with the exception of England, have great writers, rather than a great literature; and its influence on the rest of the world has, till the last twenty years, been profound. It is very well to be able to read French as easily as if it were your native tongue. There are limits, however, to the excellence with which you should allow yourself to speak it. As a matter of practice it is good to be on your guard against an Englishman who speaks French perfectly; he is very likely to be a card-sharper or an attaché in the diplomatic service.

xxx

I WAS never stage-struck. I have known dramatists who wandered in every night to the theatre in which their play was being acted. They said they did it in order to see that the cast was not getting slack: I suspect it was because they could never hear their own words spoken often enough. Their delight was to sit in a dressing-room during the intervals and talk over this scene or the other, wondering why it had fallen flat that night or congratulating themselves on how well it had gone, and watch an actor make up. They never ceased to find the theatrical gossip of the day absorbing. They loved the theatre and everything connected with it. They had grease-paint in their bones.

I have never been like that. I like a theatre best when it is under dust-sheets, the auditorium in darkness, and the unset stage, with the flats stacked against the back wall, is lit only by footlights. I have passed many happy hours at rehearsals; I have liked their easy camaraderie, the hurried lunch at a restaurant round the corner with a member of the cast and the cup of strong bitter tea, with thick bread and butter, brought in by the charwoman at four o'clock. I have never quite lost that little thrill of surprised amusement I felt when in my first play I heard grown men and women repeat the lines that had come so easily to my pen. It has interested me to watch the way in which a part grows in the actor's hands from the first lifeless reading of the typescript to something like the character that I have seen in my mind's eye. I have been diverted by the important discussions about the exact place where a piece of furniture should stand, the self-sufficiency of the director, the tantrums of an actress displeased with her positions, the artfulness of old players determined to get the centre of the stage for their scene, and the desultory talk about any subject that came to hand. But the consummation is the dress rehearsal. There are half-a-dozen people in the front-row of the dress circle. They are the dressmakers, subdued as though they were in church, but very businesslike; they exchange short, sharp whispers with

one another during the performance and make little significant gestures. You know that they are speaking of the length
of a skirt, the cut of a sleeve or the feather in a hat; and the
moment the curtain falls, the pins already in their mouths,
they hurry through the door on to the stage. The director
shouts "curtain up" and when it rises an actress snatches herself away from an agitated colloquy with two grim ladies in
black.

"Oh, Mr. Thing," she calls out, "I know that passemen-
terie is wrong, but Madame Floss says she'll take it off and
put a bit of lace instead."

In the stalls are the photographers, the management and
the man from the box office, the mothers of the actresses in
the cast and the wives of the actors, your own agent, a girl
friend of yours, and three or four old actors who haven't had
a part for twenty years. It is the perfect audience. After each
act the director reads out the remarks he has jotted down.
There is a row with the electrician who, with nothing to do
but attend to his switches, has turned on the wrong ones; and
the author is indignant with him for being so careless and at
the same time indulgent because he has a notion that the
electrician only forgot his work because he was so absorbed
in the play. Perhaps a little scene is repeated; then effective
positions are arranged and with sudden blares of flashlight
photographs are taken. The curtain is lowered to set the
scene for the next act and the cast separate to their dressing-
rooms to change. The dressmakers vanish and the old actors
slink round the corner to have a drink. The management
despondently smoke gaspers, the wives and mothers of the
cast talk to one another in undertones and the author's agent
reads the racing news in the evening paper. It is all unreal
and exciting. At last the dressmakers filter through the fire-
proof door and resume their seats, the representatives of
rival firms at a haughty distance from one another, and the
stage manager puts his head round the curtain.

"All ready, Mr. Thing," he says.

"All right. Fire away. Curtain up."

But the dress rehearsal was the last pleasure my play ever
had to give me. At the first nights of my early plays I was

on tenterhooks, for on their result my future depended.
When *Lady Frederick* was produced I had reached the end
of the little money I had come into when I was twenty-one,
my novels did not bring me in enough to live upon, and I
could earn nothing by journalism. I had been given a little
reviewing now and then and once persuaded an editor to let
me do the notice of a play, but I evidently had no gifts in
that direction; indeed, the editor in question told me that I
had no sense of the theatre. If *Lady Frederick* was a failure
it seemed to me that there was nothing for me but to go back
to the hospital for a year to refresh my knowledge of medicine and then get a post as surgeon on a ship. At that time
this was a position not much sought after and few men with
London degrees applied for it. Later, when I had become a
successful dramatist, I went to first nights with my senses
alert to discern from the reactions of the public whether
there was any falling off in my ability. I did my best to lose
myself in the audience. For the audience a first night is a
more or less interesting event which they take between a
snack at seven-thirty and supper at eleven, and the success or
failure of which is no great matter. I tried to go to my own
first nights as though they were somebody else's; but even
at that I found it a disagreeable experience. It did me no
good to hear the laughter that rewarded a happy jest or the
applause that broke out on the fall of the curtain when an
act had pleased. The fact is that, even in my lightest pieces,
I had put in so much of myself that I was embarrassed to
hear it disclosed to a crowd of people. Because they were
words I had written myself they had for me an intimacy that
I shrank from sharing with all and sundry. This unreasonable feeling I have had even when I have gone to see a play
of mine in a translation and have sat in the theatre as an
entirely unknown member of the public. Indeed I should
never have gone to see my plays at all, on the first night or
any other, if I had not thought it necessary to see the effect
they had on the audience in order to learn how to write them.

xxxi

THE actor's calling is a hard one. I am not speaking now of the young women who go on the stage because they have a pretty face and if good looks were a qualification for typists might just as well have gone into an office, or of the young men who do so because they have a good figure and no particular aptitude for anything else. They drift in and out of the profession; the women marry and the men get into a wine-merchant's office or take up interior decoration. I am speaking of the actors by vocation. They have a natural gift and the desire to use it. It is a profession that requires assiduous labour to achieve proficiency, so that by the time an actor knows how to act any sort of part he is often too old to act any but a few; it requires boundless patience; it is fraught with disappointments. Long stretches of enforced idleness must be endured. The prizes are few and can be held but for a brief period. The rewards are inadequate. The actor is at the mercy of fortune and the inconstant favour of the public. He is forgotten as soon as he ceases to please. Then it will avail him nothing to have been the idol of the crowd. He can starve for all they care. It is when I think of this that I find it easy to be indulgent to the actor's airs and graces, his exigence and vanity, when he is on the crest of the wave. Let him be flamboyant and absurd if he likes. It all lasts such a little while. And after all his egotism is part of his talent.

There was a period when the stage was the doorway to romance and everyone connected with it seemed exciting and mysterious. In the civilized world of the eighteenth century the actors gave life a touch of fantasy. Their disorderly existence was a lure to the imagination in the Age of Reason and the heroic parts they played, the verse they spoke, invested them with a halo. In Goethe's *Wilhelm Meister,* that wonderful and neglected book, you can see with what tenderness the poet regarded what can have been nothing but a second-rate touring company. And in the nineteenth century the actors offered an escape from the respectability of an industrial era. The bohemianism that was ascribed to them excited the imagination of young men who were forced to earn their living in an office. They were extravagant persons in a sober world, thoughtless in a careful one, and fancy clothed them with glamour. There is in Victor Hugo's *Choses Vues* a passage, touching in its unconscious humour, in which with awe, astonishment and a spark of envy for such wildness, the sensible little man describes a supper party with an actress. For once in his life he felt a devil of a fellow. Good gracious, how the champagne flowed and what luxury, what silver, what tiger skins, were to be seen in her apartment!

This glory has vanished. The actors have become settled, respectable and well-to-do. It offended them to be thought a race apart and they have done their best to be like everybody else. They have shown themselves to us without their make up in the broad light of day, and besought us to see for ourselves that they are golfers and taxpayers and thinking men and women. To my mind this is all stuff and nonsense.

I have known a number of actors very well. I have found them good company. Their gift of mimicry, their knack of telling a story, their quick wit, make them often highly entertaining. They are generous, kindly and courageous. But I have never quite been able to look upon them as human beings. I have never succeeded in achieving any intimacy with them. They are like crossword puzzles in which there are no words to fit the clues. The fact is, I suppose, that their personality is made up of the parts they play and that the basis of it is something amorphous. It is a soft, malleable thing that is capable of taking any shape and being painted in any colour. An ingenious writer has suggested that it is not surprising if for so long they were refused burial in consecrated ground because it is preposterous to suppose that they have souls. This is probably an extravagance. They are certainly very interesting. And the novelist, if he is sincere, cannot but acknowledge that there is between him and them a certain affinity: their character, like his, is a harmony that is none too plausible; they are all the persons they can mirror, while he is all the persons he can beget. The writer and the actor represent emotions they do not, at the moment at all events, feel; and standing with one side of themselves outside life portray it for the satisfaction of their creative instincts. Make-believe is their reality, and the public, which is at once their material and their judge, is also their dupe. Because make-believe is their reality they can look upon reality as make-believe.

xxxii

I BEGAN to write plays, as do most young writers, I expect, because it seemed less difficult to set down on paper the things people said than to construct a narrative. Dr. Johnson remarked long ago that it is much more easy to form dialogues than to contrive adventures. Looking through the old notebooks in which from eighteen to twenty I wrote down scenes for the plays I had in mind I find the dialogue on the whole easy and probable. The jokes no longer make me smile, but they are said in the words people would have used then. I caught the colloquial note by instinct. But the jokes are few and savage. The themes of my plays were sombre; and they ended in gloom, despair and death. On my first journey to Florence, I took *Ghosts* with me, and by way of relaxation, for I was seriously studying Dante, translated it into English from a German version in order to acquire a knowledge of technique. I remember that with all my admiration for Ibsen I could not help thinking Pastor Manders a bit of a bore. The *Second Mrs. Tanqueray* was then running at the St. James's Theatre.

During the next two or three years I finished several curtain-raisers and sent them to various managers. One or two were never returned and since I had no copies were lost; the others I got discouraged over and put away or destroyed. At that time, and for long after, it was much more difficult than it is now for an unknown playwright to get a production. Runs were long, for expenses were small, and a small band of authors, headed by Pinero and Henry Arthur Jones, could be counted upon to provide the principal theatres with a play whenever one was needed. The French stage was still flourishing and adaptations from the French in bowdlerized versions were popular. I got it into my head, I think from the fact that George Moore's *Strike at Arlingford* was done by the Independent Theatre, that my only chance of being acted was by making a reputation for myself as a novelist. So I put the drama aside and set myself to writing fiction. The reader may think that this methodical fashion of going to work was unbecomingly businesslike in a young author. It suggests a matter-of-fact turn of mind rather than a heavensent compulsion to enrich the world with works of art. When I had published a couple of novels and had a volume of short stories ready for the press, I sat down and wrote my first full-length play. It was called *A Man of Honour*. I sent it to Forbes-Robertson, who was then a popular actor, with the reputation of having artistic inclinations, and when he returned it to me after three or four months, to Charles Frohman. He also returned it. I rewrote it and at last, having by then published two more novels, one of which (*Mrs. Craddock*) had a considerable success, so that I was beginning to be looked upon as a serious and promising novelist, I sent it to the Stage Society. They accepted it and W. L. Courtney, a member of the committee, liked it well enough to print it in *The Fortnightly Review*. He had only published one play before, Mrs. Clifford's *The Likeness of the Night,* so that it was a great honour.

Since the Stage Society was at that time the only organization of its kind, its productions attracted a good deal of attention and my play was treated by the critics as seriously as though it had been put on for a run in an important theatre. The old hacks, with Clement Scott at their head, abused it soundly; the critic of the *Sunday Times* stated that it showed no sign of any talent for the stage. I have forgotten who he was. But the critics who had succumbed to the influence of Ibsen treated it as a work worthy of consideration. They were sympathetic and encouraging.

I thought I had taken such a step forward that my course from then on would offer no great difficulties. It did not take me long to discover that, beyond learning a good deal about the technique of playwriting, I had achieved nothing. After its two performances my play was dead. My name was known to the small body of people who were interested in the experimental theatre and if I had written suitable plays I have no doubt that the Stage Society would have performed them. But that seemed to me unsatisfactory. During the rehearsals I had come in contact with the people who were interested in the society and especially with Granville Barker, who played the leading part in my play. The attitude I found there was antagonistic to me. It seemed to me patronizing and narrow. Granville Barker was very young; I was only twenty-eight, and he, I think, was a year younger. He had charm and gaiety and a coltish grace. He was brimming over with other people's ideas. But I felt in him a fear of life which he sought to cheat by contempt of the common herd. It was difficult to find anything he did not despise. He lacked spiritual vitality. I thought that an artist needed more force, more go, more bluntness, more guts, more beef. He had written a play, *The Marriage of Ann Leete,* which seemed to me anæmic and affected. I liked life and wanted to enjoy it. I wanted to get all I possibly could out of it. I was not satisfied with the appreciation of a small band of intellectuals. I had my doubts about their quality, for I had been to a stupid and rather common little farce that the Stage Society had unaccountably given and had seen its members consumed with laughter. I was not at all certain that there was not a great deal of pose in their concern for the higher drama. I wanted no such audience as this, but the great public. Moreover I was poor. I had no notion of living on a crust in a garret if I could help it. I had found out that money was like a sixth sense without which you could not make the most of the other five.

During the rehearsals of *A Man of Honour* I had discovered that some scenes of flirtatious badinage in the first act were amusing and I decided that I could write a comedy. I made up my mind to write one now. I called it *Loaves and Fishes.* Its hero was a worldly, ambitious parson and the story dealt with his courtship of a rich widow, his intrigues to get a bishopric and his final capture of a pretty heiress. No manager would consider it; it was thought impossible that a play that held a clergyman up to ridicule would be tolerated. I came to the conclusion then that my best chance was to write a comedy with a big part for an actress, who, if she liked it, might induce a manager to give the play a trial. I asked myself what sort of part would be likely to appeal to a leading lady, and having made up my mind on this point, wrote *Lady Frederick*. But its most effective scene, the scene that afterwards made it so successful, was one in which the heroine in order to disillusion a young lover let him come into her dressing-room and discover her without any make up on her face and with her hair dishevelled. At that distant time make up was not universal and most women wore false hair. But no actress would consent to let an audience see her in this condition and manager after manager refused it. I made up my mind then to devise a play in which no one could find anything to object to. I wrote *Mrs. Dot*. It suffered the same fate as the others. The managers thought it too slight. They complained that there was not enough action and Miss Mary Moore, then a popular actress, suggested that I should insert a burglary to make it more exciting. I began to think that I should never be able to write a piece that a leading lady liked well enough to insist on playing and so tried my hand at a man's play. I wrote *Jack Straw*.

I had been under the impression that the small success I had had with the Stage Society would impress managers in my favour. To my mortification I found that this was not so. In fact my connection with that body prejudiced me with them, for they decided that I could only write gloomy and unprofitable plays. They could not say that my comedies were gloomy; but they felt them vaguely unpleasant and were convinced that they were uncommercial. I should certainly have given up in despair the attempt to get acted, for one rejection of a manuscript has always discouraged me; but fortunately for me Golding Bright thought that my plays were marketable and took them in hand. He submitted them to manager after manager and at last, in 1907, when I had written six full-length pieces, after ten years' waiting, *Lady Frederick* was produced at the Court Theatre. Three months later

Mrs. Dot was being played at the Comedy and *Jack Straw* at the Vaudeville. In June Lewis Waller put on at the Lyric a play called *The Explorer* which I had written immediately after *A Man of Honour*. I had achieved what I wanted.

xxxiii

The first three had long runs. *The Explorer* was only just not a failure. I did not make a great deal of money, for in those days the takings of a popular play were much less than they are now, and my royalties were small, but I was at all events relieved from financial anxiety and my future seemed sure. The fact that I had four plays running at once brought me great notoriety and Bernard Partridge drew a cartoon for *Punch* in which William Shakespeare was shown biting his fingers in front of the boards that advertised my plays. I was much photographed and much interviewed. Distinguished people sought my acquaintance. My success was spectacular and unexpected. I was more relieved than excited. I think I lack the quality of being surprised, and just as in my journeys I have accepted the most curious sights and the most novel circumstances as perfectly ordinary, so that I have had to force myself to notice that they were remarkable, so now I took all this to-do as natural. One evening when I was dining alone at my club a fellow member, but a stranger to me, was entertaining a guest at the next table to mine; they were going to one of my plays and began to talk of me. The stranger mentioned that I was a member of the club, whereupon his guest said:

"D'you know him at all? I suppose he's about as swollen-headed as he can be."

"Oh, yes, I know him well," answered my fellow member. "He can't get a hat big enough to fit him."

He did me an injustice. I took the success as my due. I was amused at my notoriety, but not impressed by it. The only definite reaction that I can recall of that period was a reflection that occurred to me when I was walking along Panton Street one evening. Passing the Comedy Theatre I happened to look up and saw the clouds lit by the setting sun. I paused to look at the lovely sight and I thought to myself: Thank God, I can look at a sunset now without having to think how to describe it. I meant then never to write another book, but to devote myself for the rest of my life to the drama.

Though the public accepted my plays with enthusiasm, not only in England and America, but on the Continent, critical opinion was by no means unanimous. The more popular organs praised their wit, gaiety and theatrical effectiveness, but found fault with their cynicism; the more serious critics, on the other hand, fell very foul of them. They found them cheap and trivial. They told me that I had sold my soul to mammon; and the intelligentsia, of which I had been a modest but respected member, not only turned a cold shoulder on me, that would have been bad enough, but flung me, like Lucifer, headlong into the bottomless pit. I was taken aback and a trifle mortified, but I bore my disgrace with fortitude, for I knew it was not the end of the story. I had desired a certain end and had taken what I thought were the only possible means to attain it; I could only shrug my shoulders if there were people so stupid as not to see that. If I had continued to write plays as bitter as *A Man of Honour* or as sardonic as *Loaves and Fishes* I should never have been given the opportunity of producing certain pieces to which not even the most severe have refused praise. The critics accused me of writing down to the public; I did not exactly do that; I had then very high spirits, a facility for amusing dialogue, an eye for a comic situation and a flippant gaiety; there was more in me than that, but this I put away for the time, and wrote my comedies with those sides of myself only that were useful to my purpose. They were designed to please and they achieved their aim.

I had no intention of fizzling out with a passing success and I wrote my next two plays to consolidate my hold on the public. They were a little bolder and, mild and unsophisticated as they must seem now, they were attacked by the more strait-laced for their indecency. One of them, *Penelope,* must have had some merit, for when it was revived in Berlin twenty years later it filled the theatre for a whole season.

I had by now learnt all that I was ever able to learn of the technique of the drama, and with the exception of *The Explorer,* which for a reason I saw very clearly had failed to please so well, I had had an uninterrupted series of successes. I thought it time to try my hand at more serious work. I wanted to see what I could do with more complicated subjects, I wanted to make one or two small technical experiments which I thought would be theatrically effective, and I wanted to see how far I could go with the public. I wrote *The Tenth Man* and *Landed Gentry,* and finally, after it had been lying in my desk a dozen years, produced *Loaves and Fishes.* None of them was a failure; none of them was a success. The managers neither made nor lost money on them. *Loaves and Fishes* failed to have a long run because the public of that day was uneasy at seeing a clergyman made fun of. The play is written somewhat extravagantly, so that it suggests farce rather than comedy, but it has some amusing scenes in it. The others fell between two stools. One portrayed the narrow, hidebound life of country gentlefolk; the other, the political and financial world; with both of which I had some acquaintance. I knew that I must interest, move and amuse, and I heightened the note. They were neither frankly realistic nor frankly theatrical. My indecision was fatal. The audiences found them rather disagreeable and not quite real. Then I took a rest for two years and at the end of it wrote *The Land of Promise.* This had been played to crowded houses for some months when the war broke out. I had produced ten plays in seven years. The intelligentsia, having passed judgment, ignored me, but I was securely fixed in the public favour.

xxxiv

FROM time to time I had a good deal of leisure during the war; at first because the work I was doing took up but part of my day and to write plays was a convenient means of distracting attention from the activities I was engaged in; and later, when, having contracted tuberculosis, I had to lie long in bed, because it was a pleasant way of passing the time. I wrote a series of plays in quick succession. It began with *Our Betters,* which was written in 1915, and ended with *The Constant Wife,* which was written in 1927.

Most of these plays were comedies. They are written in the tradition which flourished so brightly in the Restoration Period, which was carried on by Goldsmith and Sheridan, and which, since it has had so long a vogue, may be supposed to have something in it that peculiarly appeals to the English temper. The people who do not like it describe it as artificial comedy and by the epithet foolishly think they condemn it. It is drama not of action, but of conversation. It treats with indulgent cynicism the humours, follies and vices of the world of fashion. It is urbane, sentimental at times, for that is in the English character, and a trifle unreal. It does not preach: sometimes it draws a moral, but with a shrug of the shoulders as if to invite you to lay no too great stress on it. When the busy Monsieur de Voltaire went to see Congreve to discuss the current drama with him, Mr. Congreve pointed out to him that he was a gentleman rather than a dramatist. The interviewer answered: "If you were nothing but a gentleman I should not have troubled to call upon you." Monsieur de Voltaire was certainly the wittiest man of his age, but here he showed want of intelligence. Mr. Congreve's remark was profound. It showed that he knew very well that the first person the author of comedy must consider from the standpoint of comedy is himself.

xxxv

I HAD by then made up my mind on many things connected with the drama.

One of the conclusions I had come to was that a prose play was scarcely less ephemeral than a news sheet. The playwright and the journalist need very similar gifts, a quick eye for a good story and a telling point, animation and a vivid way of writing. All the dramatist needs besides is a specific knack. I do not know that anyone has been able to discover what this knack consists of. It cannot be learnt. It can exist without education or culture. It is a faculty that enables the playwright so to put words that they carry across the footlights and to tell a story, as it were stereoscopically, so that it visibly moves before an audience. It is a very rare faculty: that is why dramatists are so much more highly paid than other artists. It has nothing to do with literary ability as we know from the fact that the most distinguished novelists have generally failed lamentably when they have tried to write plays. It is a faculty, like that of being able to play by ear, of no spiritual importance. But without it, though your ideas may be profound, your theme original and your characterization acute, you will never be able to write a play.

A good deal has been written about the technique of playwriting. I have read most of the books on the subject with interest. The best way of learning how to write a play is to see one of your own produced. That will teach you how to write lines that the actors find easy to say and, if you have an ear, how far you can carry the rhythm of a sentence without losing the spontaneity of conversation. It will show you what sort of speech and what sort of scene are effective. But I think the secret of playwriting can be given in two maxims: stick to the point and whenever you can, cut. The first of these demands a logical mind. Few of us have it. One idea suggests another; it is very pleasant to pursue it, even though it is not directly concerned with the subject. The inclination to digress is human. But the dramatist must avoid it even more strenuously than the saint must avoid sin, for while sin may be venial, digression is mortal. The principle is that of direction of interest. It is important in a novel too, but here greater space permits of greater latitude and, just as according to the idealists evil is transformed into the perfect good of the Absolute, so certain digressions may take their necessary part in the development of the main theme. (A very good example of this is the early history of the Elder Zossima in the *Brothers Karamazov*.) Perhaps I should explain what I mean by direction of interest. It is the method by which an author causes you to concern yourself with the fortunes of certain people under certain conditions and keeps you attached to them till he has reached his solution. If he lets you wander from the main point it is very likely that he will never recapture your attention. It is a psychological trait in human nature that interest is established in the persons whom the playwright introduces at the beginning of his play so firmly that if the interest is then switched off to other persons who enter upon the scene later, a sense of disappointment ensues. The astute dramatist presents his subject as early as possible, and if for theatrical effectiveness he does not introduce his principal characters till later, the conversation of the persons on the stage at the rising of the curtain concentrates the attention of the audience on them so that the delay in their appearance increases the expectation. No one followed this practice more scrupulously than that very competent dramatist William Shakespeare.

It is the difficulty of directing the interest that makes it so hard to write the plays that are known as plays of atmosphere. The best known of them, of course, are Chekhov's. Since the interest is not concentrated on two or three persons, but on a group, and since the theme is their relations with one another and the environment, the author must take care to counteract the natural inclination of the audience to concern themselves with one character or two more than with the rest. With the interest thus dispersed it is possible that the audience will not feel warmly about any of the persons of the play, and since the author must beware that none of his threads is more important than the other, and thus attracts more vividly the attention of the audience, every incident must be subdued to the minor key. So it is very difficult to prevent the audience from feeling a certain monotony and because nothing, either incident or character, has been very forcibly impressed upon them they are very likely to take away with them, when the play is over, some confusion of spirit. In practice it has been shown that such plays are only tolerable when they are perfectly acted.

Now I come to my second maxim. However brilliant a scene may be, however witty a line or profound a reflection, if it is not essential to his play the dramatist must cut it. Here it may serve him if he is also a man of letters. The pure dramatist looks upon it as something of a miracle that he should be able to put words on paper at all, and when they are there, out of his own brain, if not straight from heaven, he looks upon them as sacred. He cannot bear to sacrifice one of them. I well remember Henry Arthur Jones showing me one of his manuscripts and my surprise on noticing that he had written such a simple sentence as, will you have sugar in your tea? in three different ways. It is no wonder that people to whom words come so reluctantly should attach an inordinate importance to them. The man of letters is accustomed to writing; he has learnt how to express himself without intolerable labour and so can cut with fortitude. Of course every writer hits now and then upon a thought that seems to him so happy, a repartee that amuses him so much, that to cut it is worse than having a tooth out: it is then that it is well to have engraved on his heart the maxim, if you can, cut.

To do so is now more than ever necessary, for audiences are at once quicker-witted and more impatient than ever before in the history of the theatre. Plays have been written in such and such a way because they satisfied audiences. Audiences in the past seem to have been willing to sit out scenes that were elaborately developed and to listen to speeches in which the characters fully explained themselves. It is very different now, and the difference has been occasioned, I suppose, by the advent of the cinema. Today, audiences, especially in English-speaking countries, have learnt to see the point of a scene at once and having seen it want to pass on to the next; they catch the gist of a speech in a few words and having caught it, their attention quickly wanders. The author must curb his natural desire to get the full value out of a scene or to let his characters display themselves in ample expression. Indications are enough. They will be seized. His dialogue must be a sort of spoken shorthand. He must cut and cut till he has arrived at the maximum of concentration.

xxxvi

A PLAY is the result of a collaboration between the author, the actors, the audience, and, I suppose one must add now, the director. For the moment I will consider the audience. All the best dramatists have written with their eye on it and though they have more often spoken of it with contempt than with good will they have known that they were dependent on it. It is the public that pays, and if it is not pleased with the entertainment that is offered it, stays away. A play does not exist without an audience. Indeed the definition of a play is a piece of writing in dialogue devised to be spoken by actors and heard by an indefinite number of persons. A play written to be read in the study is a form of the novel in dialogue in which the author for some reason of his own (obscure to most of us) has eschewed the ordinary advantages of narrative. A play that does not appeal to an audience may have merits, but it is no more a play than a mule is a horse. (Alas, all of us dramatists from time to time give birth to these unsatisfactory hybrids.) Everyone who has had to do with the theatre knows how strangely audiences affect plays; a matinée audience and an evening audience may see quite different plays. We are told that the Norwegian public looks upon Ibsen's plays as comedies rich in laughter; the English public has never seen anything to laugh at in those harassing dramas. The emotion of the audience, its interests, its laughter, are part of the action of the play. It creates it in the same way as we through our senses from the objective data create the beauty of the sunrise and the peace of the sea. The audience is not the least important actor in the play and if it will not do its allotted share the play falls to pieces. The dramatist then is in the position of a tennis player who is left on the court with nobody to play with.

Now the audience is a very curious animal. It is shrewd rather than intelligent. Its mental capacity is less than that of its most intellectual members. If these were graded from A to Z, decreasing with succeeding letters to the zero of the hysterical shop-girl, I should say its mental capacity would come round about the letter O. It is immensely suggestible; individuals will laugh at a joke they have not seen because others who see it do. It is emotional; but it instinctively resents having its emotions stirred and is always ready to escape with a giggle. It is sentimental; but will only accept sentimentality of its own brand: thus in England it will accept the emotions attached to the concept of home, but the concept of a son's love for his mother only excites its ridicule. It is careless of probability if the situation excites its interest, a trait of which Shakespeare made extravagant use; but jibs at a lack of plausibility. Individuals know that they constantly give way to impulse, but an audience insists that every action must have its cogent reason. Its morality is the average morality of the crowd and it will be sincerely shocked by a sentiment that will offend none of its members taken one by one. It does not think with its brain, but with its solar plexus. It is easily bored. It likes novelty, but a novelty that will fit in with old notions, so that it excites but does not alarm. It likes ideas, so long as they are put in dramatic form, only they must be ideas that it has itself had, but for want of courage has never expressed. It will not play if it is hurt or affronted. Its chief desire is to be assured that the make-believe is real.

In essentials audiences never change, but at different periods and in different countries at the same period they rise to different levels of sophistication. The drama pictures the manners and customs of the day, and in its turn affects them, and as these change minor changes follow both in the trappings of a play and in its themes. The invention of the telephone, for instance, has made many scenes redundant, has quickened the pace of plays and has made it possible to avoid certain improbabilities. Probability is a variable factor. It is merely what the audience is prepared to accept. Often there is no rhyme nor reason for this. People leave compromising letters about or accidentally hear things they are not supposed to hear as often as they did in Elizabethan times and it is merely a convention that rejects such incidents as improbable. But what is more important is that there has been a change of heart among us, owing to changes in civilization, and so certain themes that dramatists favoured have now fallen into desuetude. We are less revengeful than we were and now a play devoted to revenge would be scarcely plausible. Perhaps because our passions are less strong, perhaps even because the teaching of Christ has at last penetrated our thick heads, we look upon revenge as discreditable. I ventured once to suggest that the liberation of women and their new-won sexual freedom had so altered men's views on the importance of chastity that jealousy was no longer a theme for tragedy, but only for comedy; but this observation was received with so much indignation that I will not enlarge upon it.

xxxvii

I HAVE given this little analysis of an audience because the nature of the audience is for the dramatist the most important of the conventions within which he must work. Every artist must accept the conventions of the art which he pursues, but it may be that these are of such a nature as to make the art a minor one. It was a poetic convention in the eighteenth century that enthusiasm was objectionable and that imagination must be curbed by reasonableness; so it was only minor poetry that was produced. Now, the fact that the general mentality of an audience is so very much lower than that of its more intellectual members is a factor that the author must deal with. I think it definitely reduces prose drama to a minor place. It has been noticed over and over again that, intellectually, the theatre is thirty years behind the times, and the intelligent, owing to its poverty of thought, have largely ceased to frequent it. I have a notion that when the intelligent look for thought in a playhouse, they show less intelligence than one would have expected of them. Thought is a private thing. It is the offspring of reason. It depends on the mental capacity of the individual and on his education. Its communication is private from the mind that conceives it to the mind that is prepared to receive it, and if one man's meat is another man's poison, still more is one man's thought another man's truism. But an audience is affected by mass suggestion and mass suggestion is excited by emotion. I have hazarded the opinion that if you classified the members of an audience from A to Z, starting, say, with the critic of *The Times* and ending with the girl who sells sweet-stuffs in a shop off the Tottenham Court Road, its mental capacity would stand about the letter O. How can you write a play of which the ideas are so significant that they will make the critic of *The Times* sit up in his stall and at the same time induce the shop-girl in the gallery to forget the young man who is holding her hand? The only ideas that can affect them when they are welded together in that unity which is an audience, are those commonplace, fundamental ideas that are almost feelings. These, the root ideas of poetry, are love, death and the destiny of man. It is not any sort of dramatist who can find anything to say about them that has not been said a thousand times already; the great truths are too important to be new.

Besides, ideas do not grow on a gooseberry bush and few people in a generation can devise new ones. It is very unlikely that the dramatist who is lucky enough to have been born with the faculty of putting things so that they carry across the footlights will also be an original thinker. He would not be a dramatist if his mind did not work in the concrete. He has a quick eye for the instance; there is no reason to expect that he will have a faculty for conceptual thinking. He may have a meditative cast of mind and be interested in the speculations of his time, but there is a long way between this and having the power of creative thought. It might be very well if dramatists were philosophers, but in point of fact they are as little likely to be so as are kings. The only two dramatists in our time who have made their mark as thinkers are Ibsen and Shaw. Both were fortunate in the time of their appearance. Ibsen's advent coincided with the movement for the liberation of women from the inferior position in which they had so long stood; Shaw's with the revolt of youth from the conventionality of the Victorian epoch and the trammels that age had set upon it. They had to their hands subjects new to the theatre

that could be displayed with dramatic effectiveness. Shaw
had the advantage, useful to any dramatist, of high spirits,
rollicking humour, wit and fertility of comic invention. Ibsen
as we know had a meagre power of invention; his characters
under different names are very dully repeated and his intrigue from play to play is little varied. It is not a gross exaggeration to say that his only gambit is the sudden arrival
of a stranger who comes into a stuffy room and opens the
windows; whereupon the people who were sitting there catch
their death of cold and everything ends unhappily. When
you consider the mental content of what these authors had
to offer, you can, unless you are but ill educated, hardly
fail to see that it consisted of no more than the common
culture of the day. Shaw's ideas were expressed with great
vivacity. They could only have surprised because the intellectual capacity of the audience was inconsiderable. They
surprise no longer; indeed, the young tend to look on them
now as antiquated buffooneries. The disadvantage of ideas
in the theatre is that if they are acceptable, they are accepted and so kill the play that helped to diffuse them. For
nothing is so tiresome in the theatre as to be forced to listen
to the exposition of ideas that you are willing to take for
granted. Now that everyone admits the right of a woman
to her own personality it is impossible to listen to *A Doll's
House* without impatience. The dramatist of ideas loads
the dice against himself. Plays are ephemeral enough in any
case, because they must be dressed in the fashion of the
moment and fashions change so that they lose the actuality
which is one of their attractive features; it seems a pity to
make them more ephemeral still by founding them on ideas
that will be stale the day after tomorrow. When I say that
plays are ephemeral, I am of course not speaking of plays
in verse; the greatest and noblest of the arts can lend its
own life to the humble partner; I am speaking of the plays
in prose with which our modern theatre is alone occupied.
I can think of no serious prose play that has survived the
generation that gave it birth. A few comedies have hap-
hazardly travelled down a couple of centuries or so. They
are revived now and then because a famous part tempts

a leading actor, or a manager in want of a stop-gap thinks he will put on a play on which he has no royalties to pay. They are museum pieces. The audience laughs at their wit with politeness and at their farce with embarrassment. They are not held nor taken out of themselves. They cannot believe and so are never caught by the illusion of the theatre.

But if a play is naturally ephemeral why, the dramatist may ask, should he not look upon himself as a journalist, a journalist of the better class who writes for the sixpenny weeklies, and produce plays of the current topics, political and social, of the day? His ideas will be neither more nor less original than those of the serious young men who write in these journals. There is no reason why they should be less interesting; and if by the time the play has run its course they are out of date, what of it? The play is dead anyway. Now to this question the answer is that there is no reason at all, if he can get away with it and if he thinks it worth while. But he must be warned that he will get little thanks from the critics. For though they clamour for the play of ideas, when he presents it to them they sniff at it if the ideas are familiar to them, thinking modestly that what they know already is commonplace, and if the ideas are unfamiliar to them, they think them perfect nonsense and come down on him like a thousand of bricks. Even the licensed Shaw has not escaped the horns of this dilemma.

Societies have been founded in order to produce plays that people may go to who disdain the commercial theatre. They languish. The intelligentsia cannot be persuaded to patronize these performances, and if they do, want to go without paying. There are a number of dramatists who spend their whole careers writing plays which are only produced by these societies. They are trying to do something for which the drama is unsuited; once they have got a number of persons into the playhouse, these become an audience, and then, even though their average mentality is higher than the ordinary, they are subject to the reactions by which an audience is governed. They are swayed by emotion rather than by reasoning. They demand action rather than debate. (By action of course I do not mean merely physical action:

from the standpoint of the theatre a character who says, I have a headache, performs an action as much as one who falls off a steeple.) When the plays these authors write fail, they claim it is because audiences have not the sense to appreciate them. I do not think they are right. Their plays fail because they have no dramatic value. Let no one think that commercial plays succeed because they are bad plays. The story they tell may be hackneyed, the dialogue commonplace and the characterization ordinary, they succeed notwithstanding because they have the essential, though doubtless trivial, merit of holding their audiences by the specific appeal of drama. But that this need not be the only merit of the commercial play is shown by those of Lope de Vega, Shakespeare and Molière.

xxxviii

IF I have thus enlarged on the play of ideas, it is because I think the demand for it is responsible for the lamentable decadence of our theatre. The critics clamour for them. Now, the critics are of necessity the worst judges of plays. For consider, the play appeals to the audience as a unity, the current that passes infectiously from one person to another is essential to the dramatist; he wants to excite a contagion; he must take people out of themselves so that they become an instrument for him to play on, and what they give back, the resonance, the tone, the emotion, is part of his play. But the critic is there not to feel but to judge. He must hold aloof from the contagion that has captured the group and keep his self-possession. He must not allow his heart to carry him away; his head must remain well screwed on his shoulders. He must take care not to become part of the audience. He is not there to play his part in the play, but to watch it from the outside. The result is that he does not see the play they see because he has not, as they have, acted in it. It is natural enough then that he should ask for different things in a play from those the audience asks for. There is no reason why he should get it. Plays are not written for critics. Or at least, they should not be. But playwrights are sensitive creatures, and when they are told that the plays they write are an insult to the adult intelligence, they are distressed. They would like to do better, and so the young, aspiring ones, still trailing clouds of glory, sit down to write plays of ideas. That it can be done, and bring fame and fortune, the example of Bernard Shaw is there to show them.

The influence of Shaw on the English stage of today has been devastating. The public have not always liked his plays, any more than they liked Ibsen's, but after seeing them they have liked those written according to the old conventions even less. Disciples arose who sought to follow in his steps, but the event has proved that it was impossible to do so without his great gifts. The most talented of these was Granville Barker. As many scenes in his plays show, Granville Barker had it in him to be a very good playwright; he had a dramatic gift, facility for writing easy, natural and amusing dialogue, and an eye for theatrically effective character. The influence of Shaw led him to attach importance to ideas that were somewhat commonplace and to suppose that the natural discursiveness of his mind was a virtue. If he had not been persuaded that the public were fools, who must be bullied rather than cajoled, he would by the usual method of trial and error have learnt to correct his faults, and then might have added to the drama of this country a number of popular plays of great excellence. The lesser followers of Bernard Shaw have only copied his defects. Shaw has succeeded on the stage not because he is a dramatist of ideas, but because he is a dramatist. But he is inimitable. He owes his originality to an idiosyncrasy, not of course peculiar to himself, that had never before found expression on the stage. The English, whatever they were in the Elizabethan era, are not an amorous race. Love with them is more sentimental than passionate. They are of course sufficiently sexual for the purpose of reproducing their species, but they cannot control the instinctive feeling that the sexual act is disgusting. They are more inclined to look upon love as affection or benevolence than as passion.

They regard with approval its sublimations which dons describe in scholarly books, and with repulsion or with ridicule its frank expression. English is the only modern language in which it has been found necessary to borrow from the Latin a word with a depreciatory meaning, the word uxorious, for a man's devoted love for his wife. That love should absorb a man has seemed to them unworthy. In France a man who has ruined himself for women is generally regarded with sympathy and admiration; there is a feeling that it was worth while, and the man who has done it feels even a certain pride in the fact; in England he will be thought and will think himself a damned fool. That is why *Antony and Cleopatra* has always been the least popular of Shakespeare's greater plays. Audiences have felt that it was contemptible to throw away an empire for a woman's sake. Indeed if it were not founded on an accepted legend they would be unanimous in asserting that such a thing was incredible.

To audiences who had been forced to sit through plays in which love was the motive of the intrigue, but who had an instinctive feeling that love, though all very well in its way, was not really quite so important as the dramatists pretended, for after all there were politics, golf, getting on with one's job and all sorts of other things, it was a welcome relief to come upon a dramatist for whom love was a tiresome, secondary business, a quick gratification of a momentary impulse whose consequences were generally awkward. Though put as things must be put on the stage in an exaggerated way (and it should never be forgotten that Shaw is an extremely skilful dramatist) there was enough truth in this attitude to impress. It responded to the deep-seated puritanism of the Anglo-Saxon race. But, if not amorous, the English are sentimental and emotional, and they felt that it was not the whole truth. When other dramatists repeated it, not because it was, as with Shaw, a natural expression of a personality, but because it was striking and effective, its onesidedness became tediously apparent. The author describes for you his private world, and if it interests you, you will give him your attention. There is no rea-

son why you should trouble yourself with a description of it
at second hand. It is inept to say again what Shaw has said
so well.

xxxix

To MY mind, the drama took a wrong turning when the
demand for realism led it to abandon the ornament of verse.
Verse has a specific dramatic value as anyone can see by
observing in himself the thrilling effect of a tirade in one
of Racine's plays or of any of Shakespeare's great set pieces;
and this is independent of the sense; it is due to the emotional power of rhythmical speech. But more than that: verse
forces on the matter a conventional form that heightens
the æsthetic effect. It enables the drama to achieve a beauty
that is out of the question in a prose play. However much
you may admire *The Wild Duck, The Importance of Being
Earnest* or *Man and Superman,* you cannot without abuse
of the word claim that they are beautiful. But the chief value
of verse is that it delivers a play from sober reality. It puts
it on another level, at one remove from life, and so makes
it easier for the audience to attune themselves to that state
of feeling in which they are most susceptible to the drama's
specific appeal. In that artificial medium life is not presented
in a word-for-word translation, but in a free rendering, and
thus the dramatist has ample scope for the effects of which
his art is capable. For the drama is make-believe. It does
not deal with truth but with effect. That willing suspension
of disbelief of which Coleridge wrote is essential to it. The
importance of truth to the dramatist is that it adds to interest, but to the dramatist truth is only verisimilitude. It
is what he can persuade his audience to accept. If they will
believe that a man can doubt his wife's fidelity because someone tells him he has found her handkerchief in somebody
else's possession, well and good, that is sufficient motive for
his jealousy; if they will believe that a six-course dinner can
be eaten in ten minutes, well and good again, the dramatist
can get on with his play. But when a greater and greater
realism, both in motive and in action, is demanded of him

and he is asked not to embroider gaily or romantically upon
life but to copy it, he is robbed of great part of his resources.
He is forced to forego asides because people do not naturally
talk to themselves out loud; he may not telescope events,
by which he was able to accelerate his action, but must cause
them to occur as deliberately as in real life; he must eschew
accident and chance, for we know (in the theatre) that things
do not happen like that. The result has shown that realism
too often can only produce plays that are drab and dull.

When the movies learnt to talk the prose play was powerless to defend itself. The movies could represent action much
more effectively, and action is the essence of drama. The
screen gave that artificiality which verse had once given to
drama so that a different standard of verisimilitude was set
and improbability was acceptable if only it gave rise to
situation. It gave the opportunity for all manner of novel,
picturesque and dramatic effects that stimulated and excited
the public. The dramatist of ideas had to swallow the bitter
pill that the intelligentsia for which he wrote would have
nothing to do with his plays, but roared with laughter at the
farce and wallowed in the thrills and spectacle of the moving pictures. The fact was of course that they had succumbed
to the atmosphere the stage play has taken pains to lose
and were delivered to the sway of make-believe that had
held the audiences who first saw the plays of Lope de Vega
and William Shakespeare.

I have always eschewed the prophetic role and have left
to others the reformation of my fellows, but I cannot but
state my belief that the prose drama to which I have given
so much of my life will soon be dead. The minor arts, which
depend on the manners and customs of the time rather than
on deep-seated human necessities, come and go. The madrigal
which was once a popular form of musical entertainment,
exciting composers to write for it and producing an elaborate school of performers, succumbed when musical instruments were invented that produced more beautifully the
peculiar effects it sought; and there is no reason why prose
drama should not suffer the same fate. It may be said that
the screen can never give exactly the sympathetic thrill you

feel when you see living persons in flesh and blood before you. It might very well have been said that strings and wood could never make up for the intimate quality of the human voice. The event has proved that they could.

One thing seems certain, and that is that if the stage play has any chance at all of survival, it is not by trying to do any longer what the pictures can do better. Those dramatists have followed a false trail who by a multitude of little scenes have tried to reproduce the rapid action and varied setting of the cinematograph. It has occurred to me that possibly the dramatist would be wise now to go back to the origins of modern drama and call to his aid verse, dancing, music and pageantry so that he might appeal to all possible sources of entertainment; but I am conscious that here again the cinema with its great resources can do better whatever the spoken theatre can do; and of course a play of this kind would need a dramatist who was also a poet. Perhaps the best chance the realistic dramatist has today is to occupy himself with what, till now at all events, the screen has not succeeded very well in presenting—the drama in which the action is inner rather than outer and the comedy of wit. The screen demands physical action. Emotion which cannot be translated into this, and the humour whose appeal is mental, have little value for it. It may be that, for some time at all events, such plays would have their appeal.

But so far as comedy is concerned, it should be recognized that the demand for realism is unjustified. Comedy is an artificial thing and so only the appearance, not the reality, of naturalism is in place. The laugh must be sought for its own sake. The playwright's aim is not now to represent life as it is (a tragic business) but to comment on it satirically and amusingly. The audience should not be allowed to ask, do such things happen? They should be content to laugh. In comedy more than ever must the playwright exact a willing suspension of disbelief. So the critics are wrong when they complain that a comedy now and then "degenerates" into farce. It has been found in practice that it is impossible to hold the attention of an audience through three acts of pure comedy. For comedy appeals to the collective mind of the audience and this grows fatigued; while farce appeals to a more robust organ, their collective belly. The great writers of comedy, Shakespeare, Molière and Bernard Shaw, have never jibbed at the farcical. It is the life blood that makes the body of comedy viable.

xl

THESE ideas floating vaguely in my mind had little by little made me increasingly dissatisfied with the theatre and at last I decided to have done with it. I have never taken very comfortably to collaboration, and as I have pointed out, a play is more than any other artistic product a matter of collective effort. I found it more and more difficult to work in harmony with my collaborators.

It is often said that good actors can get out of a play more than the author has put into it. That is not true. A good actor, bringing to a part his own talent, often gives it a value that the layman on reading the play had not seen in it, but at the utmost he can do no more than reach the ideal that the author has seen in his mind's eye. He has to be an actor of address to do this; for the most part the author has to be satisfied with an approximation to the performance he visualized. In all my plays I have been fortunate enough to have some of the parts acted as I wanted; but in none have I had all the parts so acted. This is obviously inevitable, for the actor who is suited to a certain role may very well be engaged and you have to put up with the second or the third best, because there is no help for it. In recent years, as everyone knows who has had to do with the casting of plays, the competition of New York and of the pictures both in England and America has made it more than ever difficult to get the right person for a certain part; and over and over again a manager finds himself obliged to engage an actor who he knows is mediocre because no one else can be got. Another difficulty is that of salaries. A small part often wants clever playing and so an actor of experience, but from the standpoint of the management it will only stand a certain salary and it is impracticable to engage for it the proper person. The part then is inadequately acted and the balance of the play jeopardized; a scene that has a definite value is thrown away because it is improperly played. It often happens also that the perfect actor for a part will not play it because it is too small or too unsympathetic.

In saying all this, I have no intention of minimizing my obligation to the distinguished actors and actresses to whom is due so much of the success many of my plays have had. My debt to them is great. The list of those who fulfilled all my hopes is so long that it would be tedious to give it, but there is one actor whom, since he has never reached the rank of a star and so has hardly received the recognition that he deserves, I should like to mention. This is C. V. France. He has acted in several of my plays. He has never played a part in which he has not been admirable. He has represented to the smallest particular the character that I had in my mind's eye. It would be difficult to find on the English stage a more competent, intelligent and versatile actor. On the other hand, I have had plays produced in which I was conscious that the audience were not seeing anything like what I wanted them to see. Errors of casting, especially when they occur with actors of reputation, can often not be rectified, and then the author has the mortification of being judged by something that is merely a misrepresentation of his intent. There is no such thing as an actor-proof part. There are effective parts, and parts, often very important ones, that are the reverse, but however effective a part is, it is only fully realized when it is perfectly played. The funniest line in the world is only funny if it is said in the right way; however tender a scene is it will go for nothing if it is played without tenderness. Another pitfall that the actors prepare for the dramatist is one that is not often realized. The system of choosing actors to play themselves makes it very difficult to avoid. An author devises a character, then an actor is chosen because he has the traits the author has indicated; but the addition of his idiosyncrasies to those the author has already given his character results in an absurd exaggeration; the person of the author's invention, who was plausible and natural, is in this way turned into a grotesque. I have often sought to cast an actor contrary to his type, but I do not know that the notion has proved successful; it needs a greater adaptability than modern actors have. Probably the dramatist's best way to cope with this difficulty is to underwrite his parts, lightly sketching the characters and counting on the actors to fill them in with their own individualities. But then he must be certain of getting actors who can do this.

Exaggeration of this kind, wrong casting, inevitable sometimes, already sufficiently distort the author's intention and this is too often further distorted by the director. When I first began to write for the stage, directors took a more modest view of their functions than they have lately done. Then they confined themselves to cutting where the author had been long-winded and disguising by their ingenuity his errors of construction; they arranged the positions of the actors and helped them to get the best out of their parts. I think it must have been Reinhardt who first exacted for the director a preponderating share in the collaboration. His example was followed by directors who lacked his talent and more than once since the preposterous claim has been made that the author's script is to be looked upon merely as a vehicle for the director to express his own ideas. Instances have been known of directors who imagined that they were playwrights. Gerald du Maurier, a very good director, told me himself that he took no interest in directing a play that he could not partly rewrite. This was an extreme case. But it has certainly become very hard to find a director who is content to interpret his author's play; he has too often come to look upon it as an opportunity for an original creation of his own. The public would be surprised if they knew how often an author's purport is misrepresented by the director's stupid obstinacy and how much vulgarity and silliness for which they blame him are due to the director. The director is a man of ideas, but of few, and that is a disastrous thing. To conceive ideas is exhilarating, but it is only safe when you conceive so many that you ascribe no undue consequence to them and can take them for what they are worth. People who conceive few find it very difficult not to regard them with inordinate respect. A director who thinks of a scrap of dialogue, a bit of business or a scenic effect, will attach so much importance to it that he will cheerfully hang up the action of the play or distort its meaning in order to introduce it. Too often the director is vain, self-opinionated and unimaginative; he is sometimes so autocratic that he will force the cast to reproduce his own intonations and his own mannerisms; the actors, dependent on his good word to get parts and on their docility to gain his favour, can but slavishly do as they are told, thus taking all spontaneity from their performance. The best director is the one who does least. I have been lucky enough now and then to be given directors who were honestly anxious to do their best by the play and who have tried to fulfil my wishes; but it is very difficult to enter into somebody else's mind and the most sympathetic director can hardly do more than give an adumbration of the author's intention. I think he often gives the audience something that they like more than they would have liked what the author meant. But that is not to the author's purpose.

The remedy of course is for the author to direct his own play. Few can but those who have themselves been actors. It is not enough to be able to tell an actor that an intonation or a gesture is wrong, you must be able to show him by word and deed what is right. This is more than ever necessary now that the players of minor parts have an inadequate technique. Gerald du Maurier used often to do this by the mortifying, but efficacious, expedient of caricaturing the manner in which an actor had done something and then showing him how it should be done. He could do this only because he was a very good mimic and a very good actor. But this is a small matter. Direction is a complicated affair. It is a business, or if you like an art, of its own that has to be acquired with pains. The director deals with the mechanics of the play, the entrances and exits, the positions assigned to various characters so that their grouping may be seemly and that they may be so placed that at the proper time the attention of the audience is easily turned on them; he takes into consideration the peculiarities of individual actors and when one is asked to do something that is not within his powers by subterfuge gets over the difficulty; he is mindful also of the peculiarities of actors in general, such as that no English player can now say a speech of more than twenty lines without feeling self-conscious, and devises means of overcoming their diffidence; he directs the audience's interest to the main points of the play and lures them by ingenuity to support the necessarily dull passages of exposition and the joins, the introductions to dramatic episodes, that no play can avoid; he takes account of the facility with which their attention wanders and by the invention of "business" holds it at dangerous points; he considers the susceptibilities, the jealousy and vanity of actors and takes care that natural egoism does not disturb the balance of the play; he sees that every part is given its appropriate value and that no actor to make his own more important encroaches on somebody else's. He decides when to go quick and when to go slow; when to emphasize, when to slur; when to play up and when to play down. He deals with the sets and sees that they are suitable and practicable to the action; he chooses the clothes to fit the parts and keeps a close watch on the actresses who would sooner be beautifully than aptly dressed; he concerns himself with lighting. Direction is a business, or an art, that needs technical knowledge of an elaborate order. It needs moreover tact, patience, good humour, firmness and pliability. For myself, I have been well aware that I possessed none of the knowledge and few of the qualities that are needed to direct a play. I was hampered besides by my stammer and by the unfortunate accident that after I had written a play and finally corrected the typescript I could no longer take any great interest in it. I was curious to see how it would act, but when once I had given it over to others, like a bitch who takes no more concern in her puppies when others have handled them, I could no longer look upon it any more as intimately my own. I have been blamed often for yielding too easily to directors and accepting their opinions when they were contrary to my own; the fact is that I have always been inclined to think that others knew better than I; I have never liked rows unless I was in a temper and I am seldom in a temper, and lastly, I did not very much care. What added to my growing distaste for the theatre was not that directors were sometimes incompetent, but that they were necessary at all.

xli

AND now the audience. It must seem ungracious that I should express anything but gratitude to the public that has given me, if not fame, at least notoriety and a fortune that has enabled me to live in the same style as my father lived in before me. I have travelled; I live in a house with a view of the sea, silent and apart from other habitations, in the middle of a garden, with spacious rooms. I have always thought life too short to do anything for oneself that one can pay others to do for one and I have been rich enough to afford myself the luxury of only doing for myself what I alone can do. I have been able to entertain my friends and to help people whom I wanted to help. All this I owe to the favour of the public. I found myself, notwithstanding, growing more and more impatient with that section of it that makes up the theatrical audience. I have mentioned the fact that from the first I felt a singular embarrassment at witnessing one of my own plays, and this, instead of growing less with each play I produced, as I might have expected, grew greater. The feeling that a mass of people were seeing my plays became a sort of horror of distaste, so that I found myself going out of my way to avoid the street in which the theatre was situated where they were acting one of my plays.

I had long come to the conclusion that there was not much point in a play that was not successful and I thought I knew exactly how to write a successful play. I knew, that is to say, what I could expect from an audience. Without their collaboration I could do nothing and I knew how far their collaboration could go. I found myself increasingly dissatisfied with this. The dramatist must share the prepossess-

sions of his audience, the example of Lope de Vega and
Shakespeare is there to prove it, and at his boldest he can do
no more than put into words what they from cowardice or
laziness have been contented only to feel and not to express.
I was tired of giving half a truth because that was all they
were prepared to take. I grew tired of the absurdity that
admits in conversation all manner of facts that must be denied on the stage. I wearied of the necessity of fitting my
theme into a certain compass, drawing it out to an unnecessary length or unduly constricting it because a play to attract
had to be of a definite length. I grew bored with trying never
to be boring. In fact, I did not want to conform any longer
to the necessary conventions of the drama. I suspected that
I was out of touch with the taste of the public and to decide
the matter went to a number of plays that were drawing
the town. I found them tedious. I could not laugh at the jokes
that amused the delighted audience and the scenes that
moved them to tears left me stone cold. That settled it.

I sighed for the liberty of fiction and I thought with pleasure of the lonely reader who was willing to listen to all I
had to say and with whom I could effect an intimacy that I
could never hope for in the garish publicity of the theatre.
I had known too many dramatists who had survived their
popularity. I had seen them pitifully writing their own plays
over and over again without an inkling that the times had
changed; I had seen others desperately attempting to capture
the modern spirit and dismayed when their efforts were
treated with derision. I had seen famous authors treated
with contumely, when they offered a play to managers who
had once pestered them with contracts. I had heard actors'
scornful comments on them. I had seen the bewilderment,
the consternation, the bitterness with which they realized
at last that the public was finished with them. I had heard
Arthur Pinero and Henry Arthur Jones, both celebrated in
their day, say to me identically the same words, one with a
grim, sardonic humour, the other with a puzzled exasperation; the words were: "They don't want me any more." I
thought I would go while the going was good.

xlii

BUT I had several plays still in my head. Two or three of these were little more than vague schemes and I was willing enough to let them go, but there were four that were lying pigeon-holed in my fancy all ready to be written, and I knew myself well enough to be aware that they would continue to pester me till I wrote them. I had been thinking of them all for a good many years; I had done nothing about them because I did not think they would please. I have always had a dislike to managers losing money over me, due, I suppose, to my bourgeois instincts, and on the whole they have not. It is generally accepted that it is four to one against a play being profitable to a management; I do not think I am exaggerating when I say that the event has proved that with me it has been four to one on. I wrote these four plays in the order in which I expected them to be increasingly unsuccessful. I did not want to destroy my reputation with the public till I was definitely finished with it. The first two surprised me by having a considerable success. The last two had as little as I expected. I will speak but of one of them, *The Sacred Flame,* and of this only because in it I tried an experiment that some readers of this book may think interesting enough to merit a few minutes' consideration. I tried in this play to write a more formal dialogue than I had been in the habit of using. I wrote my first full-length play in 1898, my last in 1933. In that time I have seen dialogue change from the turgid, pedantic speech of Pinero, from the elegant artificiality of Oscar Wilde, to the extreme colloquialism of the present day. The demand for realism has inveigled dramatists into a naturalism ever greater and greater, a style that has been cultivated to its utmost limit, as we know, by Noel Coward. Not only is the "literary" avoided, but actuality has been so much sought after that grammar is eschewed, sentences are broken, for it is said that in ordinary life people speak ungrammatically and in short or unfinished sentences, and a vocabulary has been employed in which only the simplest and most ordinary words are allowed. This dialogue is eked out with shrugs, waves of the hand and grimaces. In thus yielding to the fashion it seems to me that dramatists have gravely handicapped themselves. For this slangy, clipped, broken speech they reproduce is only the speech of a class, the speech of the young, ill-educated well-to-do, who are described in the papers as the smart set. They are the persons who figure in the gossip columns and in the pages of illustrated weeklies. It may be a fact that the English are tongue-tied, but I do not think they are so tongue-tied as we are now asked to believe. There are a great many people, members of the various professions and cultured women, who clothe their thoughts in grammatical, well-chosen language and can say what they want to in the right words, put in the right order, with distinction. The present mode, which forces a judge or an eminent physician to express himself as inadequately as a barlounger, grossly misrepresents the truth. It has narrowed the range of character that the dramatist can deal with, for he can only show this by speech, and it is impossible to portray people of any subtlety of mind or intricacy of emotion when his dialogue is but a sort of spoken hieroglyph. He is insensibly led to choose as his characters persons who talk naturally in the way his audience have come to think natural and these inevitably are very simple and obvious. It has restricted his themes since it is hard to deal with the fundamental issues of human life, it is impossible to analyze the complexities of human nature (dramatic subjects both) when you confine yourself to a naturalistic dialogue. It has killed comedy, which depends on verbal wit, which in turn depends on the well-turned phrase. It has thus knocked another nail in the coffin of prose drama.

I thought then that in *The Sacred Flame* I would try to make my characters speak not the words they would actually have spoken, but in a more formal manner, using the phrases they would have used if they had been able to prepare them beforehand and had known how to put what they wanted to say in exact and well-chosen language. It may be that I did not manage it very well. During rehearsals I found that the actors, no longer used to speeches of this sort, had an uncomfortable feeling that they were delivering a recitation and I had to simplify and break up my sentences. I left enough to give the critics grounds for animadversion, and my dialogue was, in some quarters, blamed because it was "literary." I was told that people did not speak like that. I never thought they did. But I did not insist. I was in the position of a man in a rented house, whose lease is expiring; it is not worth his while to make structural alterations. In my last two plays I reverted to the naturalistic dialogue I had hitherto used.

When for days you have been going through a mountain pass, a moment comes when you are sure that after winding round the great mass of rock in front of you, you will come upon the plain; but instead you are faced with another huge crag and the weary trail continues; surely after this you will see the plain; no; the path winds on and another mountain bars your way. And then suddenly it lies before you. Your heart exults; there it stretches wide and sunny; the oppression of the mountains is lifted from your shoulders and with exhilaration you breathe the more spacious air. You have a wonderful sense of freedom. So I felt when I had done with my last play.

I could not tell whether I was free from the theatre for good and all, for the author is the slave of what, for want of a more modest word, I am forced to call his inspiration, and I could not be certain that a theme would not some day occur to me that I could not but write in the form of a play. I hoped not. For I was possessed of a notion which I cannot expect the reader to think other than foolishly arrogant. I had had all the experience that it seemed possible the theatre could give me. I had made as much money as I needed to live in the sort of way that pleased me and to provide for such as had claims on me. I had won a great notoriety and perhaps even a passing fame. I might have been satisfied. But there was one thing more I wanted to achieve and this it seemed to me I could not hope to reach in the drama. Perfection. I looked not at my own plays, of whose faults no one could be more irritably conscious than I, but at the plays that have come down to us from the past. Even

the greatest have grave defects. You have to make excuses
for them by considering the conventions of the time and
the conditions of the stage for which they were written.
The great Greek tragedies are so far from us and interpret
a civilization that is now so strange that it is hard to judge
them candidly. It has seemed to me that perhaps *Antigone*
came very near perfection. In the modern drama I think
no one on occasion approached it more closely than Racine.
But at the cost of how many a limitation! It was a cherry
stone that he carved with infinite skill. Only idolatry can
refuse to see the great shortcomings in the conduct and
sometimes in the characterization of Shakespeare's plays;
and this is very comprehensible, since, as we know, he sacrificed everything to effective situation. All these plays were
written in imperishable verse. When you come to the modern prose drama and look for perfection you will not find
it. I suppose it will be admitted that Ibsen is the greatest
dramatist the last hundred years have seen. For all the vast
merits of his plays, how poverty-stricken was his invention,
how repetitive his characters, and how silly, when you go
a little below the surface, are too many of his subjects! It
looks as though defects of one sort or another were inherent
in the art of drama. To get one result you must sacrifice
another, so that to write a play perfect in all its particulars,
in the interest and significance of its theme, in the subtlety
and originality of its characterization, in the plausibility of
its intrigue and in the beauty of its dialogue, is impossible.
It seemed to me that in the novel and in the short story
perfection had been sometimes achieved, and though I could
scarcely hope to reach it, I had a notion that in those medi-
ums I could come nearer to it than I had any chance of doing
in the drama.

xliii

THE first novel I wrote was called *Liza of Lambeth*. It was
accepted by the first publisher to whom I sent it. For some
time Fisher Unwin had been bringing out in what he called

The Pseudonym Series a number of short novels which had attracted a good deal of attention; among them were those of John Oliver Hobbs. They were thought witty and audacious. They made the author's name and confirmed the prestige of the series. I wrote two short stories which together, I thought, would make a volume of a size suitable for this collection and sent them to Fisher Unwin. After some time he returned them, but with a letter asking me if I had not a novel I could submit to him. This was so great an encouragement that I immediately sat down and wrote one. Since I was working at the hospital all day I could only write in the evening. I used to get home soon after six, read my *Star,* which I bought at the corner of Lambeth Bridge, and as soon as the table was cleared after an early meal, set to work.

Fisher Unwin was hard on his authors. He took advantage of my youth, my inexperience, and my delight at having a book accepted, to make a contract with me whereby I was to get no royalty at all till he had sold so many copies; but he know how to push his wares and he sent my novel to a number of influential persons. It was widely, though diversely, reviewed, and Basil Wilberforce, afterwards Archdeacon of Westminster, preached about it in the Abbey. The senior obstetric physician at St. Thomas's Hospital was sufficiently impressed by it to offer me a minor appointment under him, for soon after it appeared I passed my final examinations; but this, exaggerating its success and determined to abandon the medical profession, I unwisely refused. A second edition was called for within a month of publication and I had no doubt that I could easily earn my living as a writer. I was somewhat shaken when, a year later, on my return from Seville, I received from Fisher Unwin a cheque for my royalties. It amounted to twenty pounds. If I may judge by its continuing sales *Liza of Lambeth* is still readable, but any merit it may have is due to the luck I had in being, by my work as a medical student, thrown into contact with a side of life that at that time had been little exploited by novelists. Arthur Morrison with his *Tales of Mean Streets* and *A Child of the Jago* had drawn the attention of the public to what were then known as the lower classes and I profited by the interest he had aroused.

I knew nothing about writing. Though for my age I had read a good deal, I had read without discrimination, devouring one after the other books I had heard of to find out what they were about, and though I suppose I got something out of them, it was the novels and short stories of Guy de Maupassant that had most influence on me when I set myself to write. I began to read them when I was sixteen. Whenever I went to Paris I spent my afternoons in the galleries of the Odéon browsing among the books there. A certain number of Maupassant's books had been reissued in little volumes at seventy-five centimes and these I bought; but the others cost three francs fifty, a sum that I could not afford, so I used to take a book out of the shelves and read what I could of it. The attendants in their pale grey smocks took no notice of me and it was often possible when none of them was looking to cut a page and continue the narrative without interruption. Thus I managed to read most of Maupassant before I was twenty. Though he does not enjoy now the reputation he did then it must be admitted that he had great merits. He was lucid and direct, he had a sense of form, and he knew how to get the utmost dramatic value out of the story he had to tell. I cannot but think that he was a better master to follow than the English novelists who at that time influenced the young. In *Liza of Lambeth* I described without addition or exaggeration the people I had met in the out-patients' department at the hospital and in the district during my service as an obstetric clerk, the incidents that had struck me when I went from house to house as the work called, or, when I had nothing to do, had seen on my idle saunterings. My lack of imagination (for imagination grows by exercise and contrary to common belief is more powerful in the mature than in the young) obliged me to set down quite straightforwardly what I had seen with my own eyes and heard with my own ears. Such success as the book had was due to a lucky chance. It augured nothing for my future. But this I did not know.

Fisher Unwin pressed me to write another much longer book about the slums. He told me that was what the public wanted from me and prophesied that it would have, now that I had broken the ice, a far greater success than *Liza of Lambeth*. But this was not in my ideas at all. I was ambitious. I had a feeling, I do not know where I got it, that you must not pursue a success, but fly from it; and I had learnt from the French to set no great store on the *roman régional*. I was no longer interested in the slums once I had written a book about them, and I had indeed already finished a novel of a very different sort. Fisher Unwin must have been dismayed when he received it. It was a novel set in Italy during the Renaissance and it was founded on a story I had read in Machiavelli's *History of Florence*. I wrote it because of some articles by Andrew Lang that I had read on the art of fiction. In one of them he argued, very convincingly to me, that the historical novel was the only one that the young author could hope to write with success. For he could not have sufficient experience of life to write of contemporary manners; history provided him with a story and characters and the romantic fervour of his young blood gave him the dash that was needed for this sort of composition. I know now that this was nonsense. In the first place it is not true that the young author has not sufficient knowledge to write about his contemporaries. I do not suppose one ever in after life knows people so intimately as those with whom one's childhood and early youth have been passed. One's family, the servants with whom so much of a child's life is spent, one's masters at school, other boys and girls—the boy knows a great deal about them. He sees them with directness. Adults discover themselves, consciously and unconsciously, to the very young as they never do to other adults. And the child, the boy, is aware of his environment, the house he lives in, the countryside or the streets of the town, in a detail that he can never realize again when a multitude of past impressions has blurred his sensibilities. The historical novel calls surely for a profound experience of men to create living people out of those persons who with their different manners and different notions at first sight seem so alien to us; and to recreate the past needs not only a vast knowledge but an effort of imagination that is hardly to be expected in the young. I should have said that the truth was exactly contrary to what Andrew Lang said. The novelist should turn to the historical novel towards the end of his career, when thought and the vicissitudes of his own life have brought him knowledge of the world, and when, having for years explored the personalities of people around him, he has acquired an intuition into human natur␣ that will enable him to understand and so to recreate the figures of a past age. I had written my first novel of what I knew, but now, seduced by this bad advice, set to work on a historical romance. I wrote it in Capri, during the long vacation, and such was my ardour that I had myself awakened every morning at six and wrote with perseverance till hunger forced me to break off and have breakfast. I had at least the sense to spend the rest of the morning in the sea.

xliv

THERE is no need for me to speak of the novels I wrote during the next few years. One of them, *Mrs. Craddock,* was not unsuccessful and I have reprinted it in the collected edition of my works. Of the others two were novelizations of plays that I had failed to get produced and for long they lay on my conscience like a discreditable action; I would have given much to suppress them. But I know now that my qualms were unnecessary. Even the greatest authors have written a number of very poor books, Balzac himself left a good many out of the *Comédie Humaine,* and of those he inserted there are several that only the student troubles to read; the writer can rest assured that the books he would like to forget will be forgotten. I wrote one of these books because I had to have enough money to carry me on for the following year; the other because I was at the time much taken with a young person of extravagant tastes and the gratification of my desires was frustrated by the attentions of more opulent admirers who were able to provide the luxuries that her frivolous soul hankered after. I had nothing much to offer but a serious disposition and a sense of humour. I determined to write a book that would enable me to earn three or four hundred pounds with which I could hold my own with my rivals. For the young person was attractive. But even if you work hard it takes a long time to write a novel; you have to get it published; then publishers do not pay you till many months have elapsed. The result was that by the time I received the money the passion that I had thought would last forever was extinct and I had no longer the slightest wish to spend it in the way I had intended. I went to Egypt on it.

With these two exceptions the books I wrote during the first ten years after I became a professional writer were the exercises by which I sought to learn my business. For one of the difficulties that beset the professional writer is that he must acquire his craft at the expense of the public. He is constrained to write by the instinct within him and his brain teems with subjects. He has not the skill to cope with them. His experience is narrow. He is crude and he does not know how to make the best of such gifts as he has. And when he has finished his book he must publish it if he can, partly of course to get the money to live on; but also because he does not know what it is like till it is in print, and he can only find out his errors from the opinions of his friends and the criticisms of the reviewers. I have always heard that Guy de Maupassant submitted whatever he wrote to Flaubert and it was not till he had been writing for some years that Flaubert allowed him to publish his first story. As all the world knows it was that little masterpiece called *Boule de Suif*. But this is an exceptional case. Maupassant had a post in a government office that provided him both with a living and with sufficient leisure to write. There are few people who would have the patience to wait so long before trying their luck with the public and fewer still who can have had the good fortune to find so conscientious and great a writer as Flaubert to direct them. For the most part writers waste in this way subjects that they could have made good use of if they had not treated them till they had a greater knowledge of life and a more intimate acquaintance with the technique of their art. I sometimes wish that I had not had the good fortune to get my first book accepted immediately, for then I should have continued with medicine; I should have got the usual hospital appointments, gone as assistant to general practitioners in various parts of the country, and done locums; I should thus have acquired a mass of valuable experience. If my books had been refused one after the other I should have come before the public at last with work less imperfect. I regret that I had no one to guide me; I might have been spared much misdirected effort. I knew a few literary people, not many, for even then I had a feeling that their company, though pleasant enough, was unprofitable to the author, and I was too shy, too arrogant and too diffident, to seek their counsel. I studied the French novelists more than the English, and having got what I was capable of getting from Maupassant, turned to Stendhal, Balzac, the Goncourts, Flaubert and Anatole France.

I tried various experiments. One of them at that time had a certain novelty. The experience of life I was forever eagerly seeking suggested to me that the novelist's method of taking two or three people, or even a group, and describing their adventures, spiritual and otherwise, as though no one else existed and nothing else was happening in the world, gave a very partial picture of reality. I was myself living in several sets that had no connection with one another, and it occurred to me that it might give a truer picture of life if one could carry on at the same time the various stories, of equal importance, that were enacted during a certain period in different circles. I took a larger number of persons than I had ever sought to cope with before and devised four or five independent stories. They were attached to one another by a very thin thread, an elderly woman who knew at least one person in each group. The book was called *The Merry-Go-Round*. It was rather absurd because owing to the influence on me of the æsthetic school of the nineties I made everyone incredibly beautiful, and it was written in a tight and affected manner. But its chief defect was that it lacked the continuous line that directs the reader's interest; the stories were not after all of equal importance and it was tiresome to divert one's attention from one set of people to another. I failed from my ignorance of the very simple device of seeing the diverse events and the characters that took part in them through the eyes of a single person. It is a device which of course the autobiographical novel has used for centuries, but which Henry James has very usefully developed. By the simple process of writing *he* for *I* and stepping down from the omniscience of an all-knowing narrator to the imperfect acquaintance of a participator he showed how to give unity and verisimilitude to a story.

xlv

I HAVE a notion that I was more slow to develop than most writers. Around the years that ended the old century and began the new one I was looked upon as a clever young writer, rather precocious, harsh and somewhat unpleasant, but worth consideration. Though I made little money out of them my books were reviewed at length and conscientiously. But when I compare my early novels with those that are written by young men now I cannot but see that theirs are vastly more accomplished. The ageing writer does well to keep in touch with what the young do and from time to time I read their novels. Girls still in their teens, youths at the university, produce books that seem to me well-written, well-composed and ripe with experience. I do not know whether the young mature sooner than they did forty years ago or whether it is that the art of fiction has in that time so much advanced that it is now as easy to write a good novel as then it was difficult to write even a mediocre one. If one takes the trouble to look through the volumes of *The Yellow Book*, which at that time seemed the last thing in sophisticated intelligence, it is startling to discover how thoroughly bad the majority of its contributions were. For all their parade these writers were no more than an eddy in a backwater and it is unlikely that the history of English literature will give them more than a passing glance. I shiver a little when I turn those musty pages and ask myself whether in another forty years the bright young things of current letters will appear as jejune as do now their maiden aunts of *The Yellow Book*.

It was fortunate for me that I suddenly achieved popularity as a dramatist and so was relieved of the necessity of writing a novel once a year to earn my living. I found plays easy to write; the notoriety they brought me was not unpleasing; and they earned for me enough money to enable me to live less straitly than I had been obliged to. I have never had the bohemian trait of being unconcerned for the morrow. I have never liked to borrow money. I have hated to be in debt. Nor has the squalid life had any attraction for me. I was not born in squalid circumstances. As soon as I could afford it I bought a house in Mayfair.

There are people who despise possessions. Of course when they say that it ill becomes the artist thus to cumber himself they may be right, but it is not a view that artists themselves have held. They have never lived from choice in the garrets in which their admirers like to see them. They have much more often ruined themselves by the extravagance with which they conducted themselves. After all they are creatures of imagination and state appeals to them, fine houses, servants to do their bidding, rich carpets, lovely pictures, and sumptuous furniture. Titian and Rubens lived like princes. Pope had his Grotto and his Quincunx and Sir Walter his Gothic Abbotsford. El Greco with his suites of rooms, his musicians to play to him while he ate, his library and his grand clothes, died bankrupt. It is unnatural for the artist to live in a semi-detached villa and eat cottage pie cooked by a maid of all work. It shows, not disinterestedness, but an arid, petty soul. For of course to the artist the luxury with which he likes to surround himself is but a diversion. His house, his grounds, his cars, his pictures, are playthings to amuse his fancy; they are visible tokens of his power; they do not penetrate to his essential aloofness. For myself I can say that, having had every good thing that money can buy, an experience like another, I could part without a pang with every possession I have. We live in uncertain times and our all may yet be taken from us. With enough plain food to satisfy my small appetite, a room to myself, books from a public library, pens and paper, I should regret nothing. I was glad to earn a great deal of money as a dramatist. It gave me liberty. I was careful with it because I did not want ever again to be in a position when for want of it I could not do anything I had really a mind to.

xlvi

I AM a writer as I might have been a doctor or a lawyer. It is so pleasant a profession that it is not surprising if a vast number of persons adopt it who have no qualifications for it. It is exciting and various. The writer is free to work in whatever place and at whatever time he chooses; he is free to idle if he feels ill or dispirited. But it is a profession that has disadvantages. One is that though the whole world, with everyone in it and all its sights and events, is your material, you yourself can only deal with what corresponds to some secret spring in your own nature. The mine is incalculably rich, but each one of us can get from it only a definite amount of ore. Thus in the midst of plenty the writer may starve to death. His material fails him and we say that he has written himself out. I think there are few writers who are not haunted by the fear of this. Another disadvantage is that the professional writer must please. Unless a sufficient number of persons can be found to read him he will starve. Sometimes the stress of circumstances is too great for him and with rage in his heart he yields to the demand of the public. One must not expect too much of human nature and an occasional pot-boiler may be accepted from him with lenity. The writers who are in independent circumstances should sympathize with, rather than sneer at, those of their brethren whom hard necessity sometimes forces to do hack work. One of the minor sages of Chelsea has remarked that the writer who wrote for money did not write for him.

He has said a good many wise things (as indeed a sage should) but this was a very silly one; for the reader has nothing to do with the motive from which the author writes. He is only concerned with the result. Many writers need the spur of necessity to write at all (Samuel Johnson was one of them), but they do not write for money. It would be foolish of them if they did, for there are few avocations in which with equal ability and industry you cannot earn more money than by writing. Most of the great portraits of the world have been painted because their painters were paid to do them. In painting as in writing the excitement of the work is such that when it is once started the artist is absorbed in doing it as well as he can. But just as the painter will not get commissions unless on the whole he satisfies his patrons, so the writer's books will not be read unless on the whole they interest his readers. Yet there is in writers a feeling that the public ought to like what they write and if their books do not sell the fault is not with them but with the public. I have never met an author who admitted that people did not buy his book because it was dull. There are many instances of artists whose work for long has been little appreciated and who yet in the end achieved fame. We do not, however, hear of those whose work has continued to be ignored. Their number is far greater. Where are the votive offerings of those who perished? If it is true that talent consists in a certain facility combined with a peculiar outlook on the world it is very understandable that originality should not at first be welcomed. In this perpetually changing world people are suspicious of novelty and it takes them some time before they can accustom themselves to it. A writer with an idiosyncrasy has to find little by little the people to whom it appeals. Not only does it take him time to be himself, for the young are themselves only with timidity, but it takes him time to convince that body of persons, whom he will eventually rather pompously call his public, that he has something to give them that they want. The more individual he is the harder will he find it to achieve this and the longer will it take him to earn his living. Nor can he be sure that the result will be lasting, for it may be that with all his individuality he has but one or two things to give and then he will soon sink back into the obscurity from which he with difficulty emerged.

It is easy to say that the writer should have an occupation that provides him with his bread and butter and write in such leisure as this occupation affords him. This course, indeed, was forced upon him very generally in the past, when the author, however distinguished and popular, could not earn enough money by writing to keep body and soul together. It is forced upon him still in countries with a small reading public; he must eke out his livelihood by work in an office, preferably under the government, or by journalism. But the English-speaking writer has the potentiality of such an enormous public that writing can very reasonably be adopted as a profession. It would be more overcrowded than it is if in English-speaking countries the cultivation of the arts were not slightly despised. There is a healthy feeling that to write or to paint is not a man's work, and the social force of this keeps many from entering the ranks. You have to have a very decided urge to enter a profession which exposes you to at least a small degree of moral obloquy. In France and in Germany writing is an honourable occupation, and so is adopted with the consent of parents even though its financial rewards are unsatisfactory. You can often run across a German mother who, when you ask her what her young son is going to be, will answer with complacency, a poet; and in France the family of a girl with a large *dot* will look upon her marriage with a young novelist of talent as a suitable alliance.

But the author does not only write when he is at his desk; he writes all day long, when he is thinking, when he is reading, when he is experiencing; everything he sees and feels is significant to his purpose and, consciously or unconsciously, he is forever storing and making over his impressions. He cannot give an undivided attention to any other calling. He will not follow it to his own satisfaction or that of his employers. The most common one for him to adopt is journalism, because it seems to have a closer connection with his proper work. It is the most dangerous. There is an impersonality in a newspaper that insensibly affects the writer.

People who write much for the press seem to lose the faculty of seeing things for themselves; they see them from a generalized standpoint, vividly often, sometimes with hectic brightness, yet never with that idiosyncrasy which may give only a partial picture of the facts, but is suffused by the personality of the observer. The press, in fact, kills the individuality of those who write for it. Nor is reviewing less harmful; the writer has not the time to read any books but those that directly concern him, and this reading of hundreds of books haphazard, not for the spiritual advantage he may gain from them but to give a reasonably honest account of them, deadens his sensibilities and impedes the free flow of his own imagination. Writing is a whole-time job. To write must be the main object of the author's life; that is to say, he must be a professional writer. He is lucky if he has sufficient fortune to make him independent of his earnings, but that does not prevent him from being a professional writer. Swift with his deanery, Wordsworth with his sinecure, were just as much professional writers as Balzac and Dickens.

xlvii

It is acknowledged that the technique of painting and of musical composition can only be acquired by assiduous labour, and the productions of dilettantes are rightly regarded with good-humoured or exasperated contempt. We all congratulate ourselves that the radio and the gramophone have driven from our drawing-rooms the amateur pianist and the amateur singer. The technique of writing is no less difficult than that of the other arts and yet, because he can read and write a letter, there is a notion that anyone can write well enough to write a book. Writing seems now the favourite relaxation of the human race. Whole families will take to it as in happier times they entered religious houses. Women will write novels to while away their pregnancies; bored noblemen, axed officers, retired civil servants, fly to the pen as one might fly to the bottle. There is an impression abroad that everyone has it in him to write one book; but if by this is implied a good book the impression is false. It is true that the amateur may sometimes produce a work of merit. By a lucky chance he may have a natural facility for writing well, he may have had experiences that are in themselves interesting, or he may have a charming or quaint personality that his very inexpertness helps him to get down on the printed page. But let him remember that the saying asserts only that everyone has it in him to write one book; it says nothing about a second. The amateur is wise not to try his luck again. His next book is pretty sure to be worthless.

For one of the great differences between the amateur and the professional is that the latter has the capacity to progress. The literature of a country is made not by a few excellent books, I repeat, but by a great body of work, and this can only be produced by professional writers. The literature of those countries that has been produced chiefly by amateurs is thin in comparison with that of the countries in which a number of men, with difficulty trying to make their living, have followed it as a profession. A body of work, an *œuvre,* is the result of long-continued and resolute effort. The author, like other men, learns by the method of trial and error. His early works are tentative; he tries his hand at various subjects and various methods and at the same time develops his character. By a simultaneous process he discovers himself, which is what he has to give, and learns how to display this discovery to the best advantage. Then, in full possession of his faculties, he produces the best of which he is capable. Since writing is a healthy occupation, he will probably go on living long after he has done this, and since by this time writing will have become an ingrained habit he will doubtless continue to produce works of no great consequence. These the public may legitimately neglect. From the standpoint of the reader, very little that the writer produces in the whole course of his life is essential. (By essential, I mean only that small part of him which expresses his individuality, and I attach no implication of absolute value to the word.) But I think he can only give this as the result of a long apprenticeship and at the cost of a good many failures.

To do it he must make literature his life's work. He must be a professional author.

xlviii

I HAVE spoken of the disadvantages of the author's profession: now I should like to speak of its dangers.

It is evident that no professional writer can afford only to write when he feels like it. If he waits till he is in the mood, till he has the inspiration as he says, he waits indefinitely and ends by producing little or nothing. The professional writer creates the mood. He has his inspiration too, but he controls and subdues it to his bidding by setting himself regular hours of work. But in time writing becomes a habit, and like the old actor in retirement, who gets restless when the hour arrives at which he has been accustomed to go down to the theatre and make up for the evening performance, the writer itches to get to his pens and paper at the hours at which he has been used to write. Then he writes automatically. Words come easily to him and words suggest ideas. They are old and empty ideas, but his practised hand can turn out an acceptable piece. He goes down to luncheon or goes to bed with the assurance that he has done a good day's work. Every production of an artist should be the expression of an adventure of his soul. This is a counsel of perfection and in an imperfect world a certain indulgence should be bestowed on the professional writer; but this surely is the aim he should keep before him. He does well only to write to liberate his spirit of a subject that he has so long meditated that it burdens him and if he is wise he will take care to write only for the sake of his own peace. Perhaps the simplest way to break the habit of writing is by changing the environment to one that gives no opportunity for the daily task. You cannot write well or much (and I venture the opinion that you cannot write well unless you write much) unless you form a habit; but habits in writing as in life are only useful if they are broken as soon as they cease to be advantageous. But the greatest danger that besets the professional author is one that unfortunately only a few have to guard against. Success. It is the most difficult thing the writer has to cope with. When after a long and bitter struggle he has at last achieved it he finds that it spreads a snare to entangle and destroy him. Few of us have the determination to avoid its perils. It must be dealt with warily. The common idea that success spoils people by making them vain, egotistic and self-complacent is erroneous; on the contrary it makes them, for the most part, humble, tolerant and kind. Failure makes people bitter and cruel. Success improves the character of the man; it does not always improve the character of the author. It may very well deprive him of that force which has brought him success. His individuality has been formed by his experiences; his struggles, his frustrated hopes, his efforts to adapt himself to a hostile world; it must be very stubborn if it is not modified by the softening influences of success.

Success besides often bears within itself the seed of destruction, for it may very well cut the author off from the material that was its occasion. He enters a new world. He is made much of. He must be almost super-human if he is not captivated by the notice taken of him by the great and remains insensible to the attentions of beautiful women. He grows accustomed to another way of life, probably more luxurious than that to which he has been used, and to people who have more of the social graces than those with whom he has consorted before. They are more intellectual and their superficial brilliance is engaging. How difficult it is for him then to move freely still in the circles with which he has been familiar and which have given him his subjects! His success has changed him in the eyes of his old associates and they are no longer at home with him. They may look upon him with envy or with admiration, but no longer as one of themselves. The new world into which his success has brought him excites his imagination and he writes about it; but he sees it from the outside and can never so penetrate it as to become a part of it. No better example of this can be given than Arnold Bennett. He never knew anything intimately but the life of the Five Towns in which he had been born and bred, and it was only when he dealt with them that his work had character. When success brought him into the society of literary people, rich men and smart women, and he sought to deal with them, what he wrote was worthless. Success destroyed him.

xlix

THE writer is wise then who is wary of success. He must look with dread on the claims that others make on him because of it, the responsibilities it forces on him, and the hindering activities that it brings in its wake. It can only give him two good things: one, the more important by far, is the freedom to follow his own bent, and the other is confidence in himself. Notwithstanding his pretension and his susceptible vanity the author when he compares his work with what he intended it to be is never free from misgiving. There is so great a distance between what he saw in his mind's eye and the best he has been able to do that for him the result is no more than a makeshift. He may be pleased with a page here or there and regard an episode or a character with approval; I think it must be very seldom that he looks upon any work of his as a whole with complete satisfaction. At the back of his mind is the suspicion that it is not good at all and the praises of the public, even if he is inclined to doubt their value, are a heaven-sent reassurance.

That is why praise is important to him. It is a weakness that he should hanker for it; though perhaps a pardonable one. For the artist should be indifferent to praise and blame, since he is concerned with his work only in its relation to himself, and how it affects the public is a matter in which he is materially perhaps, but not spiritually, concerned. The artist produces for the liberation of his soul. It is his nature to create as it is the nature of water to run down hill. It is not for nothing that artists have called their works the children of their brains and likened the pains of production to the pains of childbirth. It is something like an organic thing that develops, not of course only in their brains, but in their heart, their nerves and their viscera, something that their creative instinct evolves out of the experiences of their soul and their body, and that at last becomes so oppressive that they must rid themselves of it. When this happens they enjoy a sense of liberation and for one delicious moment rest in peace. But unlike human mothers, they lose interest very soon in the child that is born. It is no longer a part of them. It has given them its satisfaction and now their souls are open to a new impregnation.

In the production of his work, the author has fulfilled himself. But that is not to say that it has any value for anyone else. The reader of a book, the observer of a picture, is not concerned with the artist's feelings. The artist has sought release, but the layman seeks for a communication, and he alone can judge whether the communication is valuable to him. To the artist the communication he offers is a by-product. I am not speaking now of those who practise an art to teach; they are propagandists and with them art is a side issue. Artistic creation is a specific activity that is satisfied by its own exercise. The work created may be good art or bad art. That is a matter for the layman to decide. He forms his decision from the æsthetic value of the communication that is offered to him. If it yields escape from the reality of the world he will welcome it, but is very likely at best to describe it only as minor art; if it enriches his soul and enlarges his personality he will rightly describe it as great. But this, I insist, has nothing to do with the artist; it is human that he should be pleased if he has given others pleasure or greater strength; but he should not take it amiss if they find nothing to their purpose in the results of his production. He has already had his reward in the satisfaction of his creative instinct. Now this is no counsel of perfection; it is the only condition on which the artist can work his way towards the unattainable perfection that is his aim. If he is a novelist he uses his experience of people and places, his apprehension of himself, his love and hate, his deepest thoughts, his passing fancies, to draw in one work after another a picture of life. It can never be more than a partial one, but if he is fortunate he will succeed in the end in doing something else; he will draw a complete picture of himself.

At all events to think thus is a consolation when you cast your eye over the publishers' advertisements. When you read those long lists of books and when you discover that reviewers have extolled their wit, profundity, originality and beauty your heart sinks; what chance have you in comparison with so much genius? The publishers will tell you that the average life of a novel is ninety days. It is hard to reconcile yourself to the fact that a book into which you have put, besides your whole self, several months of anxious toil, should be read in three or four hours and after so short a period forgotten. Though it will do him no good, there is no author so small-minded as not to have a secret hope that some part at least of his work will survive him for a generation or two. The belief in posthumous fame is a harmless vanity which often reconciles the artist to the disappointments and failure of his life. How unlikely he is to attain it we see when we look back on the writers who only twenty years ago seemed assured of immortality. Where are their readers now? And with the mass of books that are constantly produced and the ceaseless competition of those that have lived on, how small is the likelihood that work that has been once forgotten will ever be again remembered! There is one very odd, and some may think very unfair, thing about posterity; it seems to choose the works to which it gives attention from those of authors who have been popular in their lifetime. The writers who delight a clique and never reach the great public will never delight posterity, for posterity will never hear about them. It is a consolation to the popular authors who have had it impressed upon them that their popularity was sufficient proof of their worthlessness. It may be that Shakespeare, Scott and Balzac did not write for the minor sage of Chelsea, but it looks as though they did write for after ages. The writer's only safety is to find his satisfaction in his own performance. If he can realize that in the liberation of soul which his work has brought him and in the pleasure of shaping it in such a way as to satisfy to some extent at least his æsthetic sense, he is amply rewarded for his labours, he can afford to be indifferent to the outcome.

l

FOR the disadvantages and dangers of the author's calling are offset by an advantage so great as to make all its difficulties, disappointments, and maybe hardships, unimportant. It gives him spiritual freedom. To him life is a tragedy and by his gift of creation he enjoys the catharsis, the purging of pity and terror, which Aristotle tells us is the object of art. For his sins and his follies, the unhappiness that befalls him, his unrequited love, his physical defects, illness, privation, his hopes abandoned, his griefs, humiliations, everything is transformed by his power into material and by writing it he can overcome it. Everything is grist to his mill, from the glimpse of a face in the street to a war that convulses the civilized world, from the scent of a rose to the death of a friend. Nothing befalls him that he cannot transmute into a stanza, a song or a story, and having done this be rid of it. The artist is the only free man.

Perhaps that is why the world on the whole has had the profound suspicion of him that we know. It is not sure that he can be trusted when he reacts to the common impulses of men so unaccountably. And indeed the artist, to the indignation of mankind, has never felt himself bound by ordinary standards. Why should he? With men in general the primary end of thought and action is to satisfy their needs and preserve their being; but the artist satisfies his needs and preserves his being by the pursuit of art: their pastime is his grim earnest and so his attitude to life can never be the same as theirs. He creates his own values. Men think him cynical because he does not attach importance to the virtues and is not revolted by the vices that move them. He is not cynical. But what they call virtue and what they call vice are not the sort of things that he takes any particular interest in. They are indifferent elements in the scheme of things out of which he constructs his own freedom. Of course common men are quite right to be indignant with him. But that isn't going to do him any good. He is incorrigible.

li

WHEN, having achieved success as a dramatist, I determined to devote the rest of my life to playwriting I reckoned without my host. I was happy, I was prosperous, I was busy, my head was full of plays that I wanted to write; I do not know whether it was that success did not bring me all I had expected or whether it was a natural reaction from success: I was but just firmly established as a popular playwright when I began to be obsessed by the teeming memories of my past life. The loss of my mother and then the break-up of my home, the wretchedness of my first years at school for which my French childhood had so ill-prepared me and which my stammering made so difficult, the delight of those easy, monotonous and exciting days in Heidelberg, when I first entered upon the intellectual life, the irksomeness of my few years at the hospital and the thrill of London; it all came back to me so pressingly, in my sleep, on my walks, when I was rehearsing plays, when I was at a party, it became such a burden to me that I made up my mind that I could only regain my peace by writing it all down in the form of a novel. I knew it would be a long one and I wanted to be undisturbed, so I refused the contracts managers were anxious to give me and temporarily retired from the stage.

I had written a novel on the same themes when, after taking my medical degrees, I went to Seville. Luckily for me Fisher Unwin refused to give me the hundred pounds I wanted for it and no other publisher would have it at any price; or I should have lost a subject which I was then too young to make proper use of. The manuscript still exists, but I have not looked at it since I corrected the typescript; I have no doubt it is very immature. I was not far enough away from the events I described to see them reasonably and I had not had a number of experiences that later went to enrich the book I finally wrote. It seems to me that if the writing of this first novel did not finally repress into my subconscious the unhappy memories with which it was concerned it is because the writer is not finally disembarrassed of his subject till his work is published. When it is delivered to the public, however heedless the public be, it is his no longer and he is free from the burden that oppressed him. I called my book *Beauty from Ashes,* which is a quotation from Isaiah, but finding that this title had been recently used, I chose instead the title of one of the books in Spinoza's *Ethics* and called it *Of Human Bondage.* It is not an autobiography, but an autobiographical novel; fact and fiction are inextricably mingled; the emotions are my own, but not all the incidents are related as they happened and some of them are transferred to my hero not from my own life but from that of persons with whom I was intimate. The book did for me what I wanted, and when it was issued to the world (a world in the throes of a terrible war and too much concerned with its own sufferings to bother with the adventures of a creature of fiction) I found myself free forever from those pains and unhappy recollections. I put into it everything I then knew and having at last finished it prepared to make a fresh start.

lii

I WAS tired. I was tired not only of the people and thoughts that had so long occupied me; I was tired of the people I lived with and the life I was leading. I felt that I had got all that I was capable of getting out of the world in which I had been moving; my success as a playwright and the luxurious existence it had brought me; the social round, the grand dinners at the houses of the great, the brilliant balls and the week-end parties at country houses; the company of clever and brilliant people, writers, painters, actors; the love affairs I had had and the easy companionship of my friends; the comfortableness and security of life. It was stifling me and I hankered after a different mode of existence and new experiences. But I did not know where to turn for them. I thought of travelling. I was tired of the man I was, and it seemed to me that by a long journey to some far-distant country I might renew myself. Russia was very much in the thoughts of people then and I had a mind to go there for a year, learn the language of which I already knew the elements and immerse myself in the emotion and mystery of that vast country. I thought that there perhaps I might find something that would give sustenance and enrichment to my spirit. I was forty. If I meant to marry and have children it was high time I did so and for some time I had amused my imagination with pictures of myself in the married state. There was no one I particularly wanted to marry. It was the condition that attracted me. It seemed a necessary motif in the pattern of life that I had designed, and to my ingenuous fancy (for though no longer young and thinking myself so worldly wise, I was still in many ways incredibly naïve) it offered peace; peace from the disturbance of love affairs, casual it might be in the beginning, but bringing in their train such troublesome complications (for it takes two to make a love affair and a man's meat is too often a woman's poison); peace that would enable me to write all I wanted to write without the loss of precious time or disturbance of mind; peace and a settled and dignified way of life. I sought freedom and thought I could find it in marriage. I conceived these notions when I was still at work on *Of Human Bondage,* and turning my wishes into fiction, as writers will, towards the end of it I drew a picture of the marriage I should have liked to make. Readers on the whole have found it the least satisfactory part of my book.

But my uncertainties were resolved by an event over which I had no control. The war broke out. A chapter of my life had finished. A new chapter began.

liii

I HAD a friend who was a cabinet minister and I wrote and asked him to help me to do something, whereupon I was invited to present myself at the War Office; but fearing that I should be set to clerical work in England and anxious to get out to France at once I joined a unit of ambulance cars. Though I do not think I was less patriotic than another my patriotism was mingled with the excitement the new experience offered me and I began keeping a notebook the moment I landed in France. I kept it till the work got heavy and then at the end of the day I was too tired to do anything but go to bed. I enjoyed the new life I was thrown into and the lack of responsibility. It was a pleasure to me who had never been ordered about since I was at school to be told to do this and that and when it was done to feel that my time was my own. As a writer I had never felt that; I had felt on the contrary that I had not a minute to lose. Now with a clear conscience I wasted long hours at *estaminets* in idle chatter. I liked meeting a host of people, and, though writing no longer, I treasured their peculiarities in my memory. I was never in any particular danger. I was anxious to see how I should feel when exposed to it; I have never thought myself very courageous nor did I think there was any necessity for me to be so. The only occasion upon which I might have examined myself was when in the Grande Place at Ypres a shell blew up a wall against which I had been standing just as I had moved over to get a view of the ruined Cloth Makers' Hall from the other side; but I was too much surprised to observe my state of mind.

Later on I joined the Intelligence Department where it looked as though I could be more useful than in somewhat inadequately driving an ambulance. The work appealed both to my sense of romance and my sense of the ridiculous. The methods I was instructed to use in order to foil persons who were following me; the secret interviews with agents in unlikely places; the conveying of messages in a mysterious fashion; the reports smuggled over a frontier; it was all doubtless very necessary but so reminiscent of what was then known as the shilling shocker that for me it took most of its reality away from the war and I could not but look upon it as little more than material that might one day be of use to me. But it was so hackneyed that I doubted whether I should ever be able to profit by it. After a year in Switzerland my work there came to an end. It had entailed a good deal of exposure, the winter was bitter and I had to take journeys across the Lake of Geneva in all weathers. I was in very poor health. There seemed nothing much for me to do at the mo ment, so I went to America where two of my plays were about to be produced. I wanted to recover my peace of mind shattered through my own foolishness and vanity by occurrences upon which I need not dwell and so made up my mind to go to the South Seas. I had wanted to go ever since as a youth I had read *The Ebb-Tide* and *The Wrecker* and I wanted besides to get material for a novel I had long been thinking over based on the life of Paul Gauguin.

I went, looking for beauty and romance and glad to put a great ocean between me and the trouble that harassed me. I found beauty and romance, but I found also something I had never expected. I found a new self. Ever since I left St. Thomas's Hospital I had lived with people who attached value to culture. I had come to think that there was nothing in the world more important than art. I looked for a meaning in the universe and the only one I could find was the beauty that men here and there produced. On the surface my life was varied and exciting; but beneath it was narrow. Now I entered a new world, and all the instinct in me of a novelist went out with exhilaration to absorb the novelty. It was not only the beauty of the islands that took me, Herman Melville and Pierre Loti had prepared me for that, and though it is a different beauty it is not a greater beauty than that of Greece or Southern Italy; nor was it their ramshackle, slightly adventurous, easy life; what excited me was to meet one person after another who was new to me. I was like a naturalist who comes into a country where the fauna are of an unimaginable variety. Some I recognized; they were old types that I had read of and they gave me just the same feeling of delighted surprise that I had once in the Malayan Archipelago when I saw sitting on the branch of a tree a bird that I had never seen before but in a zoo. For the first moment I thought it must have escaped from a cage. Others were strange to me and they thrilled me as Wallace was thrilled when he came upon a new species. I found them easy to get on with. They were of all sorts; indeed, the variety would have been bewildering but that my powers of observation were by now well trained and I found it possible without conscious effort to pigeon-hole each one in my awareness. Few of them had culture. They had learnt life in a different school from mine and had come to different conclusions. They led it on a different plane; I could not, with my sense of humour, go on thinking mine a higher one. It was different. Their lives too formed themselves to the discerning eye into a pattern that had order and finally coherence.

I stepped off my pedestal. It seemed to me that these men had more vitality than those I had known hitherto. They did not burn with a hard, gemlike flame, but with a hot, smoky, consuming fire. They had their own narrownesses. They had their prejudices. They were often dull and stupid. I did not care. They were different. In civilized communities men's idiosyncrasies are mitigated by the necessity of conforming to certain rules of behaviour. Culture is a mask that hides their faces. Here people showed themselves bare. These heterogeneous creatures thrown into a life that had preserved a great deal of its primitiveness had never felt the need to adapt themselves to conventional standards. Their peculiarities had been given opportunity to develop unchecked. In great cities men are like a lot of stones thrown together in a bag; their jagged corners are rubbed off till in the end they are as smooth as marbles. These men had never had their jagged corners rubbed away. They seemed to me nearer to the elementals of human nature than any of the people I had been living with for so long and my heart leapt towards them as it had done years before to the people who filed into the out-patients' room at St. Thomas's. I filled my notebook with brief descriptions of their appearance and their character, and presently, my imagination excited by these multitudinous impressions, from a hint or an incident or a happy invention, stories began to form themselves round certain of the most vivid of them.

liv

I RETURNED to America and shortly afterwards was sent on a mission to Petrograd. I was diffident of accepting the post, which seemed to demand capacities that I did not think I

THE SUMMING UP 609

possessed; but there seemed to be no one more competent available at the moment and my being a writer was very good "cover" for what I was asked to do. I was not very well. I still knew enough medicine to guess the meaning of the hæmorrhages I was having. An X-ray photograph showed clearly that I had tuberculosis of the lungs. But I could not miss the opportunity of spending certainly a considerable time in the country of Tolstoi, Dostoievski and Chekhov; I had a notion that in the intervals of the work I was being sent to do I could get something for myself that would be of value; so I set my foot hard on the loud pedal of patriotism and persuaded the physician I consulted that under the tragic circumstances of the moment I was taking no undue risk. I set off in high spirits with unlimited money at my disposal and four devoted Czechs to act as liaison officers between me and Professor Masaryk who had under his control in various parts of Russia something like sixty thousand of his compatriots. I was exhilarated by the responsibility of my position. I went as a private agent, who could be disavowed if necessary, with instructions to get in touch with parties hostile to the government and devise a scheme that would keep Russia in the war and prevent the Bolsheviks, supported by the Central Powers, from seizing power. It is not necessary for me to inform the reader that in this I failed lamentably and I do not ask him to believe me when I state that it seems to me at least possible that if I had been sent six months before I might quite well have succeeded. Three months after my arrival in Petrograd the crash came and put an end to all my plans.

I returned to England. I had had some interesting experiences and had got to know fairly well one of the most extraordinary men I have ever met. This was Boris Savinkov, the terrorist who had assassinated Trepov and the Grand Duke Sergius. But I came away disillusioned. The endless talk when action was needed, the vacillations, the apathy when apathy could only result in destruction, the high-flown protestations, the insincerity and halfheartedness that I found everywhere sickened me with Russia and the Russians. I also came back very ill indeed, for in the position I was in

I could not profit by the abundant supplies that made it possible for the embassies to serve their countries on a full
stomach and I was (like the Russians themselves) reduced
to a meagre diet. (When I arrived in Stockholm, where I
had a day to wait for the destroyer that was to take me
across the North Sea, I went into a confectioner's, bought a
pound of chocolates and ate them in the street.) A scheme to
send me to Rumania in connection with some Polish intrigue,
the details of which I now forget, fell through. I was not
sorry, for I was coughing my head off and constant fever
made my nights very uncomfortable. I went to see the most
eminent specialist I could find in London. He packed me off
to a sanatorium in the North of Scotland, Davos and St.
Moritz at that time being inconvenient to go to, and for the
next two years I led an invalid life.

I had a grand time. I discovered for the first time in my
life how very delightful it is to lie in bed. It is astonishing
how varied life can be when you stay in bed all day and how
much you find to do. I delighted in the privacy of my room
with the immense window wide open to the starry winter
night. It gave me a delicious sense of security, aloofness and
freedom. The silence was enchanting. Infinite space seemed
to enter it and my spirit, alone with the stars, seemed capable
of any adventure. My imagination was never more nimble;
it was like a barque under press of sail scudding before the
breeze. The monotonous days, whose only excitement was
the books I read and my reflections, passed with inconceivable rapidity. I left my bed with a pang.

It was a strange world that I entered when I grew well
enough to mix during part of the day with my fellow-
patients. In their different ways these people, some of whom
had been in the sanatorium for years, were as singular as any
of those I had met in the South Seas. Illness and the queer,
sheltered life affected them strangely, twisting, strengthen-
ing, deteriorating their character just as in Samoa or Tahiti
it was deteriorated, strengthened or twisted by the languor-
ous climate and the alien environment. I think I learnt a good
deal about human nature in that sanatorium that otherwise
I should never have known.

lv

WHEN I recovered from my illness the war was over. I went to China. I went with the feelings of any traveller interested in art and curious to see what he could of the manners of a strange people whose civilization was of great antiquity; but I went also with the notion that I must surely run across men of various sorts whose acquaintance would enlarge my experience. I did. I filled notebooks with descriptions of places and persons and the stories they suggested. I became aware of the specific benefit I was capable of getting from travel; before, it had been only an instinctive feeling. This was freedom of the spirit on the one hand, and on the other, the collection of all manner of persons who might serve my purposes. After that I travelled to many countries. I journeyed over a dozen seas, in liners, in tramps, in schooners; I went by train, by car, by chair, on foot or on horseback. I kept my eyes open for character, oddness and personality. I learnt very quickly when a place promised me something and then I waited till I had got it. Otherwise I passed on. I accepted every experience that came my way. When I could I travelled as comfortably as my ample means allowed, for it seemed to me merely silly to rough it for the sake of roughing it; but I do not think I ever hesitated to do anything because it was uncomfortable or dangerous.

I have never been much of a sightseer. So much enthusiasm has been expended over the great sights of the world that I can summon up very little when I am confronted with them. I have preferred common things, a wooden house on piles nestling among fruit trees, the bend of a little bay lined with coconuts, or a group of bamboos by the wayside. My interest has been in men and the lives they led. I am shy of making acquaintance with strangers, but I was fortunate enough to have on my journeys a companion who had an inestimable social gift. He had an amiability of disposition that enabled him in a very short time to make friends with people in ships, clubs, bar-rooms and hotels, so that through him I was able to get into easy contact with an immense number of persons whom otherwise I should have known only from a distance.

I made acquaintance with them with just the degree of intimacy that suited me. It was an intimacy born on their side of ennui or loneliness, that withheld few secrets, but one that separation irrevocably broke. It was close because its limits were settled in advance. Looking back on that long procession I cannot think of anyone who had not something to tell me that I was glad to know. I seemed to myself to develop the sensitiveness of a photographic plate. It did not matter to me if the picture I formed was true; what mattered was that with the help of my imagination I could make of each person I met a plausible harmony. It was the most entrancing game in which I had ever engaged.

One reads that no one exactly resembles anyone else, and that every man is unique, and in a way this is true, but it is a truth easy to exaggerate: in practice men are very much alike. They are divided into comparatively few types. The same circumstances mould them in the same way. Certain characteristics infer certain others. You can, like the palæontologist, reconstruct the animal from a single bone. The "characters" which have been a popular form of letters since Theophrastus, and the "humours" of the seventeenth century, prove that men sort themselves into a few marked categories. Indeed this is the foundation of realism, which depends for its attractiveness on recognition. The romantic method turns its attention to the exceptional; the realistic to the usual. The slightly abnormal circumstances in which men live in the countries where life is primitive or the environment alien to them, emphasize their ordinariness so that it gains a character of its own; and when they are in themselves extraordinary, which of course they sometimes are, the want of the usual restraints permits them to develop their kinks with a freedom that in more civilized communities can be but hardly won. Then you have creatures that realism can scarcely cope with. I used to stay away till my receptivity was exhausted and I found that when I met people I had no longer the power to make the imaginative effort to give them shape and coherence; then I returned to England to sort out my impressions and rest till I felt my powers of assimilation restored. At last, after seven, I think, of these long journeys I found a certain sameness in people. I met more and more often types that I had met before. They ceased to interest me so much. I concluded that I had come to the end of my capacity for seeing with passion and individuality the people I went so far to find, for I had never doubted that it was I who gave them the idiosyncrasy that I discovered in them, and so I decided that there was no further profit for me in travel. I had twice nearly died of fever, I had been nearly drowned, I had been shot at by bandits. I was glad to resume a more ordered way of life.

I came back from each of my journeys a little different. In my youth I had read a great deal, not because I supposed that it would benefit me, but from curiosity and the desire to learn; I travelled because it amused me, and to get material that would be of use to me: it never occurred to me that my new experiences were having an effect on me, and it was not till long afterwards that I saw how they had formed my character. In contact with all these strange people I lost the smoothness that I had acquired when, leading the humdrum life of a man of letters, I was one of the stones in a bag. I got back my jagged edges. I was at last myself. I ceased to travel because I felt that travel could give me nothing more. I was capable of no new development. I had sloughed the arrogance of culture. My mood was complete acceptance. I asked from nobody more than he could give me. I had learnt toleration. I was pleased with the goodness of my fellows; I was not distressed by their badness. I had acquired independence of spirit. I had learnt to go my own way without bothering with what others thought about it. I demanded freedom for myself and I was prepared to give freedom to others. It is easy to laugh and shrug your shoulders when people act badly to others; it is much more difficult when they act badly to you. I have not found it impossible. The conclusion I came to about men I put into the mouth of a man I met on board ship in the China Seas. "I'll give you my opinion of the human race in a nutshell, brother," I made him say. "Their heart's in the right place, but their head is a thoroughly inefficient organ."

lvi

I HAVE always liked to let things simmer in my mind for a long time before setting them down on paper, and it was not till four years after I had made my notes for it that I wrote the first of the stories I had conceived in the South Seas. I had not written short stories for many years. I began my literary career by writing them and my third book was a collection of six. They were not good. After that I tried now and then to write stories for the magazines; my agents pressed me to write humorously, but for this I had no aptitude; I was grim, indignant or satirical. My efforts to satisfy editors and thus earn a little money rarely succeeded. The first story I wrote now was called *Rain* and it looked for a while as though I should have no better luck with it than with those I had written in my youth, for editor after editor refused it; but I no longer minded and I went on. When I had written six, all of which eventually found their way into magazines, I published them in a book. The success they had was pleasant and unexpected. I liked the form. It was very agreeable to live with the personages of my fancy for two or three weeks and then be done with them. One had no time to grow sick of them as one easily may during the months one has to spend in their company when writing a novel. This sort of story, one of about twelve thousand words, gave me ample room to develop my theme, but forced upon me a concision that my practice as a dramatist had made grateful to me.

It was unlucky for me that I set about writing short stories seriously when the better-class writers in England and America were delivered over to the influence of Chekhov. The literary world somewhat lacks balance, and when a fancy takes it, is apt to regard it not as a passing fashion, but as Heaven's first law; and the notion prevailed that anyone who had artistic leanings and wanted to write short stories must write stories like Chekhov. Several writers transplanted Russian melancholy, Russian mysticism, Russian fecklessness, Russian despair, Russian futility, Russian infirmity of purpose, to Surrey or Michigan, Brooklyn or Clapham and made quite a reputation for themselves. It must be admitted that Chekhov is not hard to imitate. As I know to my cost there are dozens of Russian refugees who do it quite well: to my cost, because they send me their stories so that I may correct the English and then are offended with me when I cannot get vast sums of money for them from American magazines. Chekhov was a very good short story writer, but he had his limitations and he very wisely made them the basis of his art. He had no gift for devising a compact, dramatic story, such a story as you could tell with effect over the dinner-table, like *L'Héritage* or *La Parure*. As a man, he seems to have been of a cheerful and practical disposition, but as a writer, he was of a depressed melancholic nature that made him turn away with distaste from violent action or exuberance. His humour, often so painful, is the exasperated reaction of a man whose shuddering sensibilities have been rubbed the wrong way. He saw life in a monotone. His people are not sharply individualized. He does not seem to have been much interested in them as persons. Perhaps that is why he is able to give you the feeling that they are all part of one another, strange groping ectoplasms that melt into each other, the sense of the mystery of life and its futility, which give him his unique quality. It is a quality that has escaped his followers.

I do not know if I could ever have written stories in the Chekhov manner. I did not want to. I wanted to write stories that proceeded, tightly knit, in an unbroken line from the exposition to the conclusion. I saw the short story as a narrative of a single event, material or spiritual, to which by the elimination of everything that was not essential to its elucidation a dramatic unity could be given. I had no fear of what is technically known as "the point." It seemed to me that it was reprehensible only if it was not logical, and I thought that the discredit that had been attached to it was due only to the fact that it had been too often tacked on, merely for effect, without legitimate reason. In short, I preferred to end my short stories with a full-stop rather than with a straggle of dots.

It is this, I imagine, that has led to their being better appreciated in France than in England. Our great novels are shapeless and unwieldy. It has pleased the English to lose themselves in these huge, straggling, intimate works; and this laxity of construction, this haphazard conduct of a rambling story, this wandering in and out of curious characters who have nothing much to do with the theme, have given them a peculiar sense of reality. It is this, however, that has given the French an acute sense of discomfort. The sermons that Henry James preached to the English on form in the novel aroused their interest, but have little affected their practice. The fact is that they are suspicious of form. They find in it a sort of airlessness; its constraint irks them; they feel that when the author has fixed upon his material a wilful shape life has slipped through his fingers. The French critic demands that a piece of fiction should have a beginning, a middle and an end; a theme that is clearly developed to a logical conclusion; and that it should tell you all that is of moment to the point at issue. From the familiarity with Maupassant that I gained at an early age, from my training as a dramatist, and perhaps from personal idiosyncrasy, I have, it may be, acquired a sense of form that is pleasing to the French. At all events they find me neither sentimental nor verbose.

lvii

IT IS very seldom that life provides the writer with a ready-made story. Facts indeed are often very tiresome. They will give a suggestion that excites the imagination, but then are apt to exercise an authority that is only pernicious. The classic example of this is to be found in *Le Rouge et le Noir*. This is a very great novel, but it is generally acknowledged that the end is unsatisfactory. The reason is not hard to find. Stendhal got the idea for it from an incident that at the time made a great stir: a young seminarist shot his mistress, was tried and guillotined. But Stendhal put into Julien Sorel, his hero, not only a great deal of himself, but much more of what he would have liked to be and was miserably conscious that he was not; he created one of the most interesting personages of fiction and for fully three quarters of his book made him behave with coherence and probability; but then he found himself forced to return to the facts that had been his inspiration. He could only do this by causing his hero to act incongruously with his character and his intelligence. The shock is so great that you no longer believe, and when you do not believe in a novel you are no longer held. The moral is that you must have the courage to throw your facts overboard if they fail to comply with the logic of your character. I do not know how Stendhal could have ended his novel; but I think it would have been hard to find a more unsatisfactory end than the one he chose.

I have been blamed because I have drawn my characters from living persons, and from criticisms that I have read one might suppose that nobody had ever done this before. That is nonsense. It is the universal custom. From the beginning of literature authors have had originals for their creations. Scholars, I believe, give a name to the rich glutton who served as a model to Petronius for his Trimalchio and Shakespearean students find an original for Mr. Justice Shallow. The very virtuous and upright Scott drew a bitter portrait of his father in one book and a pleasanter one, when the passage of years had softened his asperity, in another. Stendhal, in one of his manuscripts, has written the names of the persons who had suggested his characters; Dickens, as we all know, portrayed his father in Mr. Micawber and Leigh Hunt in Harold Skimpole. Turgenev stated that he could not create a character at all unless as a starting point he could fix his imagination on a living person. I suspect that the writers who deny that they use actual persons deceive themselves (which is not impossible, since you can be a very good novelist without being very intelligent) or deceive us. When they tell the truth and have in fact had no particular person in mind, it will be found, I think, that they owe their characters rather to their memory than to their creative instinct. How many times have we met d'Artagnan, Mrs. Proudie, Archdeacon Grantley, Jane Eyre and Jérome Coignard with other names and in other dress! I should say that the practice of drawing characters from actual models is not only universal but necessary. I do not see why any writer should be ashamed to acknowledge it. As Turgenev said, it is only if you have a definite person in your mind that you can give vitality and idiosyncrasy to your own creation.

I insist that it is a creation. We know very little even of the persons we know most intimately; we do not know them enough to transfer them to the pages of a book and make human beings of them. People are too elusive, too shadowy, to be copied; and they are also too incoherent and contradictory. The writer does not copy his originals; he takes what he wants from them, a few traits that have caught his attention, a turn of mind that has fired his imagination, and therefrom constructs his character. He is not concerned whether it is a truthful likeness; he is concerned only to create a plausible harmony convenient for his own purposes. So different may be the finished product from the original that it must be a common experience of authors to be accused of having drawn a lifelike portrait of a certain person when they had in mind someone quite different. Further, it is just chance whether the author chooses his models from persons with whom he is intimately connected or not. It is often enough for him to have caught a glimpse of someone in a tea-shop or chatted with him for a quarter of an hour in a ship's smoking-room. All he needs is that tiny, fertile substratum which he can then build up by means of his experience of life, his knowledge of human nature and his native intuition.

The whole business would be plain sailing if it were not for the susceptibilities of the persons who serve as models for the author's characters. So colossal is human egotism that people who have met an author are constantly on the lookout for portraits of themselves in his works and if they can persuade themselves that such and such a character is drawn from them they are bitterly affronted if it is drawn with any imperfections. Though they will find fault with their friends freely and ridicule their absurdities, their vanity is so outrageous that they cannot reconcile themselves to the fact that they too have faults and absurdities. The matter is made worse for them by their friends who with malicious indignation offer them feigned sympathy for the outrage they have suffered. Of course there is a lot of humbug about it all. I do not suppose I am the only author who has been vilified by women who claimed that I had stayed with them and abused their hospitality by writing about them when not only had I not stayed with them, but neither knew nor had ever heard of them. The poor drabs were so vain and their lives so empty that they deliberately identified themselves with a creature of odious character in order in some small circle to give themselves a petty notoriety.

Sometimes the author takes a very commonplace person and from him invents a character who is noble, self-controlled and courageous. He has seen in that person a significance that had escaped those he lived with. Then oddly enough the original goes unrecognized; it is only when you show somebody with faults or ridiculous foibles that a name is at once assigned. I have been forced to conclude from this that we know our friends by their defects rather than by their merits. The author seldom has the wish to give offence and he uses what means he can to protect his originals; he puts the persons of his invention in different places, gives them another means of livelihood, situates them perhaps in a different class; what he cannot so easily do is to change their appearance. The physical traits of a man influence his character and contrariwise his character is expressed, at least in the rough, in his appearance. You cannot make a tall man short and otherwise keep him the same. A man's height gives him a different outlook on his environment and so changes his character. Nor to cover your tracks can you make a little brunette into a massive blonde. You have to leave them very much as they are or you will lose what it was that moved you to draw a character from them. But no one has the right to take a character in a book and say, this is meant for me. All he may say is, I provided the suggestion for this character. If he has any common sense he will be interested rather than vexed; and the author's inventiveness and intuition may suggest to him things about himself that it is useful for him to know.

lviii

I HAVE no illusions about my literary position. There are but
two important critics in my own country who have troubled
to take me seriously and when clever young men write essays
about contemporary fiction they never think of considering
me. I do not resent it. It is very natural. I have never been a
propagandist. The reading public has enormously increased
during the last thirty years and there is a large mass of ignorant people who want knowledge that can be acquired with
little labour. They have thought that they were learning
something when they read novels in which the characters delivered their views on the burning topics of the day. A bit of
love-making thrown in here and there made the information
they were given sufficiently palatable. The novel was regarded
as a convenient pulpit for the dissemination of ideas and a
good many novelists were willing enough to look upon themselves as leaders of thought. The novels they wrote were
journalism rather than fiction. They had a news value. Their
disadvantage was that after a little while they were as un-
readable as last week's paper. But the demand of this great
new public for knowledge has of late given rise to the production of a number of books in which subjects of common
interest, science, education, social welfare and I know not
what, are treated in non-technical language. Their success
has been very great and has killed the propaganda novel. But
it is evident that while its vogue lasted it seemed much more
significant and so offered a better subject of discourse than
the novel of character or adventure.

The intelligent critics, the more serious novel readers,
have since then given most of their attention to the writers
who seemed to offer something new in technique, and this is
very comprehensible, for the novelties they presented gave a
sort of freshness to well-worn material and were a fruitful
matter of discussion.

It seems strange that so much attention has been paid to
these things. The method that Henry James devised and
brought to a high degree of perfection of telling his story

through the sensibilities of an observer who had some part in its action was an ingenious dodge that gave the dramatic effect he sought in fiction, a verisimilitude grateful to an author much influenced by the French naturalists and a means of getting round some of the difficulties of the novelist who takes up the attitude of an all-seeing and all-wise narrator. What this observer did not know could be left conveniently mysterious. It was, however, only a slight variation from the autobiographical form that has many of the same advantages, and to speak of it as though it were a great æsthetic discovery is somewhat absurd. Of the other experiments that have been made the most important is the use of the stream of thought. Writers have always been attracted by the philosophers who had an emotional value and who were not too hard to understand. They were taken in turn by Schopenhauer, Nietzsche and Bergson. It was inevitable that psycho-analysis should captivate their fancy. It had great possibilities for the novelist. He knew how much he owed to his own subconscious for the best of what he wrote and it was tempting to explore greater depths of character by an imaginative picture of the subconscious of the persons of his invention. It was a clever and amusing trick, but nothing more. When writers, instead of using it as an occasional device for a particular purpose, ironical, dramatic or explanatory, made it the basis of their work it proved tedious. I conjecture that what is useful in this and similar devices will be absorbed into the general technique of fiction, but that the works that introduced them will soon lose their interest. It seems to have escaped the attention of those who have been taken by these curious experiments that the matter treated of in the books in which they are made use of is of an extreme triviality. It almost looks as though their authors had been driven to these contrivances by an uneasy consciousness of their own emptiness. The persons they describe with all this ingenuity are intrinsically uninteresting and the subjects at issue unimportant. This might be expected. For the artist is absorbed by his technique only when his theme is of no pressing interest to him. When he is obsessed by his topic he has not much time over to think of the artfulness of his presentation. So in the seventeenth century the writers, exhausted by the mental effort of the Renaissance and prevented by the tyranny of kings and the domination of the church from occupying themselves with the great issues of life, turned their minds to gongorism, concettism and such-like toys. It may be that the interest that has been taken during recent years in every form of technical experiment in the arts points to the fact that our civilization is crumbling; the subjects that seemed important to the nineteenth century have lost their interest, and artists do not yet see what the great issues are that will affect the generation which will create the civilization that is in course of displacing our own.

lix

I LOOK upon it as very natural then that the world of letters should have attached no great importance to my work. In the drama I have found myself at home in the traditional moulds. As a writer of fiction I go back, through innumerable generations, to the teller of tales round the fire in the cavern that sheltered neolithic men. I have had some sort of story to tell and it has interested me to tell it. To me it has been a sufficient object in itself. It has been my misfortune that for some time now a story has been despised by the intelligent. I have read a good many books on the art of fiction and all ascribe very small value to the plot. (In passing I should like to say that I cannot understand the sharp distinction some clever theorists make between story and plot. A plot is merely the pattern on which the story is arranged.) From these books you would judge that it is only a hindrance to the intelligent author and a concession that he makes to the stupid demands of the public. Indeed, sometimes you might think that the best novelist is the essayist, and that the only perfect short stories have been written by Charles Lamb and Hazlitt.

But the delight in listening to stories is as natural to human nature as the delight in looking at the dancing and miming out of which drama arose. That it exists unimpaired is shown by the vogue of the detective novel. The most intellectual persons read them, with condescension of course, but they read them, and why, if not because the psychological, the pedagogic, the psycho-analytic novels which alone their minds approve do not give them the satisfaction of this particular need? There are a number of clever writers who, with all sorts of good things in their heads to say and a gift for creating living people, do not know what on earth to do with them when they have created them. They cannot invent a plausible story. Like all writers (and in all writers there is a certain amount of humbug) they make a merit of their limitations and either tell the reader that he can imagine for himself what happens or else berate him for wanting to know. They claim that in life stories are not finished, situations are not rounded off and loose ends are left hanging. This is not always true, for at least death finishes all our stories; but even if it were it would not be a good argument.

For the novelist claims to be an artist and the artist does not copy life, he makes an arrangement out of it to suit his own purposes. Just as the painter thinks with his brush and paints the novelist thinks with his story; his view of life, though he may be unconscious of it, his personality, exist as a series of human actions. When you look back on the art of the past you can hardly fail to notice that artists have seldom attached great value to realism. On the whole they have used nature to make a formal decoration and they have only copied it directly from time to time when their imagination had taken them so far from it that a return was felt necessary. In painting and sculpture it might even be argued that a very close approximation to reality has always announced the decadence of a school. In the sculpture of Phidias you see already the dullness of the Apollo Belvedere and in Raphael's Miracle at Bolsano the vapidity of Bouguereau. Then art can only gain new vigour by forcing on nature a new convention.

But that is by the way.

It is a natural desire in the reader to want to know what happens to the people in whom his interest has been aroused and the plot is the means by which you gratify this desire. A good story is obviously a difficult thing to invent, but its difficulty is a poor reason for despising it. It should have coherence and sufficient probability for the needs of the theme; it should be of a nature to display the development of character, which is the chief concern of fiction at the present day, and it should have completeness, so that when it is finally unfolded no more questions can be asked about the persons who took part in it. It should have like Aristotle's tragedy a beginning, a middle and an end. The chief use of a plot is one that many people do not seem to have noticed. It is a line to direct the reader's interest. That is possibly the most important thing in fiction, for it is by direction of interest that the author carries the reader along from page to page and it is by direction of interest that he induces in him the mood he desires. The author always loads his dice, but he must never let the reader see that he has done so, and by the manipulation of his plot he can engage the reader's attention so that he does not perceive what violence has been done him. I am not writing a technical treatise on the novel, so I need not enumerate the various devices that novelists have used to achieve this. But how efficacious this direction of interest may be and how injurious its neglect is well shown in *Sense and Sensibility* and in *L'Education Sentimentale*. Jane Austen leads the reader so firmly along the line of the simple story that he does not stop to reflect that Elinor is a prig, Marianne a fool, and the three men lifeless dummies. Flaubert, aiming at a rigid objectivity, directs the reader's interest so little that he is perfectly indifferent to the fortunes of the various characters. This makes the novel very difficult to read. I cannot think of another that has so many merits and leaves so shadowy an impression.

lx

IN MY twenties the critics said I was brutal, in my thirties they said I was flippant, in my forties they said I was cynical, in my fifties they said I was competent, and now in my sixties they say I am superficial. I have gone my way, following the course I had mapped out for myself, and trying with my works to fill out the pattern I looked for. I think authors are unwise who do not read criticisms. It is salutary to train oneself to be no more affected by censure than by praise; for of course it is easy to shrug one's shoulders when one finds oneself described as a genius, but not so easy to be unconcerned when one is treated as a nincompoop. The history of criticism is there to show that contemporary criticism is fallible. It is a nice point to decide how far the author should consider it and how far ignore it. And such is the diversity of opinion that it is very difficult for an author to arrive at any conclusion about his merit. In England there is a natural tendency to despise the novel. The autobiography of an insignificant politician, the life of a royal courtesan will receive serious critical consideration, whereas half-a-dozen novels will be reviewed in a bunch by a reviewer who is concerned only too often to be amusing at their expense. The fact is simply that the English are more interested in works of information than in works of art. This makes it difficult for the novelist to get from criticisms of his work anything that will be useful to his own development.

It is a great misfortune to English letters that we have not had in this century a critic of the class, say, of Sainte-Beuve, Matthew Arnold or even Brunetière. It is true that he would not have occupied himself much with current literature, and if we may judge by the three I have mentioned, had he done so it would have been of no direct service to contemporary writers. For Sainte-Beuve, as we know, was too envious of a form of success he hankered after, but never achieved, to treat his contemporaries with fairness; and Matthew Arnold's taste was so much at fault when he dealt with French writers of his day that there is no reason to suppose it would have been any better if he had dealt with English ones. Brunetière had no tolerance; he measured writers by hard-and-fast rules and was incapable of seeing merit in those who had aims with which he did not sympathize. His force of character gave him an influence that his talents did not warrant. But notwithstanding, writers benefit by a critic who is gravely concerned with literature; even if they resent him they may be incited by antagonism to a clearer definition of their own aims. He can provoke in them an excitement that calls them to more conscious effort and his example urges them to take their art with a more intense seriousness.

In one of his dialogues Plato seemingly has tried to show the impossibility of criticism; but in fact he has only shown to what extravagance the Socratic method may sometimes lead. There is one sort of criticism that is evidently futile. This is that which is written by the critic to compensate himself for humiliations he has suffered in his early youth. Criticism affords him a means of regaining his self-esteem. Because at school, unable to adapt himself to the standards of that narrow world, he has been kicked and cuffed, he will when grown up cuff and kick in his turn in order to assuage his wounded feelings. His interest is in his reaction to the work he is considering, not in the reaction it has to him.

There can seldom have been a greater need than now of a critic of authority, for the arts are at sixes and sevens. We see composers telling stories, painters philosophizing, and novelists preaching sermons; we see poets impatient with their own harmony trying to fit with their verse the other harmony of prose, and see the writers of prose trying to force on it the rhythms of verse. Someone is badly wanted to define once more the characters peculiar to the several arts and to point out to those who go astray that their experiments can lead only to their own confusion. It is too much to expect that anyone may be found who can speak with equal competence in all the arts; but, the demand producing the supply, we may still hope that one of these days a critic will arise to ascend the throne once occupied by Sainte-Beuve and Matthew Arnold. He could do much. I have read lately two or three books in which a claim is made to form an exact science of criticism. They have not convinced me that such a thing is possible. Criticism to my mind is a personal matter, but there is nothing against that if the critic has a great personality. It is dangerous for him to look upon his activity as creative. His business is to guide, to appraise, and to point to new avenues of creation, but if he looks upon himself as creative he will be more occupied with creation, the most enthralling of human activities, than with the functions proper to him. It is perhaps well for him to have written a play, a novel and some verse, for thus as in no other way can he acquire the technique of letters; but he cannot be a great critic unless he has realized that to create is not his affair. One of the reasons why current criticism is so useless is that it is done as a side-issue by creative writers. It is only natural that they should think the sort of thing they do the thing best worth doing. The great critic should have a sympathy as wide as his knowledge is universal. It should be grounded not on a general indifference, such as makes men tolerant of things they care nothing about, but on an active delight in diversity. He must be a psychologist and a physiologist, for he must know how the basic elements of literature are related to the minds and bodies of men; and he must be a philosopher, for from philosophy he will learn serenity, impartiality, and the transitoriness of human things. He must be familiar not only with the literature of his native land. With standards founded on the literature of the past, and studious of contemporary literature in other countries, he will see clearly the trend that literature in its evolution is pursuing and so be enabled profitably to direct that of his own countrymen. He must support himself on tradition, for tradition is the expression of the inevitable idiosyncrasies of a nation's literature, but he must do everything he can to encourage its development in its natural direction. Tradition is a guide and not a jailer. He must have patience, firmness and enthusiasm. Each book he reads should be a new and thrilling adventure; he judges it by the universality of his knowledge and the strength of his character. In fact the great critic must be a great man. He must be great enough to recognize with good-humoured resignation that his work, though so important, can have but an ephemeral value; for his merit is that he responds to the needs of, and points the way to, his own generation. A new generation arises with other needs, a new way stretches before it; he has nothing more to say and is thrown with all his works into the dust-heap.

To spend his life to such an end can only be worth his while if he thinks literature one of the most important of human pursuits.

lxi

THAT is a claim that the author has always made and to this he has added another claim: he has asserted that he was not as other men and in consequence not amenable to their rules. Other men have received it with obloquy, derision and contempt. This he has met in different ways according to his idiosyncrasy. Sometimes he has flaunted his difference from what he was inclined to call the common herd by wilful eccentricity and to *épater le bourgeois* has paraded the red waistcoat of Théophile Gautier or, like Gérard de Nerval, led a lobster tied by a pink ribbon down the street; sometimes he has taken an ironic pleasure in pretending to be the same as every one else and with Browning has dressed the poet within him in the likeness of a prosperous banker. It may be that we are all of us a bundle of mutually contradictory selves, but the writer, the artist, is deeply conscious of it. With other men, the life they lead makes one side of them predominant, so that, except perhaps in the depths of the subconscious, it ends by being the whole man. But the painter, the writer, the saint, is always looking in himself for new facets; he is bored at repeating himself and seeks, though it may be without actually knowing it, to prevent himself from becoming one-sided. He never gets the opportunity to grow into a self-consistent, coherent creature.

Other men have been outraged on discovering, as they so often have, the discrepancy between the artist's life and his work. They have not been able to reconcile Beethoven's idealism with his meanness of spirit, Wagner's heavenly rapture with his selfishness and dishonesty, Cervantes' moral obliquity with his tenderness and magnanimity. Sometimes, in their indignation, they have sought to persuade themselves that the work of such men could not possess the value they thought. When it has been brought to their knowledge that great and pure poets had left behind them a large body of obscene verse they have been horrified. They have had an uneasy feeling that the whole thing was a sham. "What arrant humbugs these people are!" they say. But the point of the writer is that he is not one man but many. It is because he is many that he can create many and the measure of his greatness is the number of selves that he comprises. When he fashions a character that does not carry conviction it is because there is in himself nothing of that person; he has had to fall back on observation, and so has only described, not begotten. The writer does not feel with; he feels in. It is not sympathy that he has, that too often results in sentimentality; he has what the psychologists call empathy. It is because Shakespeare had this to so great a degree that he was at once the most living and the least sentimental of authors. I think Goethe was the first writer to grow conscious of this multiple personality and it troubled him all his life. He was always comparing the writer that he was with the man and he could not quite reconcile the discongruity. But the end of the artist and the end of other men are different, for the end of the artist is production while the end of other men is right action. And so the artist's attitude to life is in a certain way peculiar to himself. The psychologists tell us that with the ordinary man an image is less vivid than a sensation. It is an attenuated experience that serves to give information about objects of sense and in the world of sense is a guide to action. His day-dreams satisfy emotional needs and fulfil desires that in the world of affairs are frustrated. But they are pale shadows of real life and at the back of his mind is the awareness that the demands of the world of sense have another validity. To the writer this is not so. The images, free ideas that throng his mind, are not guides but materials for action. They have all the vividness of sensation. His day-dreams are so significant to him that it is the world of sense that is shadowy and he has to reach out for it by an effort of will. His castles in Spain are no baseless fabric, but real castles that he lives in.

The artist's egoism is outrageous: it must be; he is by nature a solipsist and the world exists only for him to exercise upon it his powers of creation. He partakes of life only with part of him and never feels the common emotions of men with his whole being, for however urgent the necessity he is an observer as well as an actor. It often makes him seem heartless. Women with their shrewd sense are on their guard against him; they are attracted by him, but instinctively feel that they can never completely dominate him, which is their desire, for they know that somehow he escapes them. Has not Goethe, that great lover, himself told us how he composed verses in the arms of his beloved and with singing fingers softly tapped the beat of his hexameters on her shapely back? The artist is ill to live with. He can be perfectly sincere in his creative emotion and yet there is someone else within him who is capable of cocking a snook at its exercise. He is not dependable.

But the gods never make any of their gifts without adding to it a drawback and this multiplicity of the writer that enables him, like the gods, to create human beings prevents him from achieving perfect truth in their creation. Realism is relative. The most realistic writer by the direction of his interests falsifies his creatures. He sees them through his own eyes. He makes them more self-conscious than they really are. He makes them more reflective and more complicated. He throws himself into them, trying to make them ordinary men, but he never quite succeeds; for the peculiarity that gives him his talent and makes him a writer forever prevents him from knowing exactly what ordinary men are. It is not truth he attains, but merely a transposition of his own personality. And the greater his talent, the more powerful his individuality, the more fantastic is the picture of life he draws. It has sometimes seemed to me that if posterity wants to know what the world of today was like it will not go to those writers whose idiosyncrasy has impressed our contemporaries, but to the mediocre ones whose ordinariness has allowed them to describe their surroundings with a greater faithfulness. I do not mention them since, even though they may be assured of the appreciation of after ages, people do not like to be labelled as mediocre. But I think it may be admitted that one gets the impression of a truer picture of life in the novels of Anthony Trollope than in those of Charles Dickens.

lxii

SOMETIMES the writer must ask himself whether what he has written has any value except to himself and the question is perhaps urgent now when the world seems, at least to us who live in it, in such a condition of unrest and wretchedness as it has not often been in before. For me the question has had a special import for I have never wished to be nothing but a writer; I have wished to live life completely. I have been uneasily conscious that it was a duty I owed myself to take some part, however small, in the business of the common weal. My natural inclination has been to keep aloof from every kind of public activity and it has been with the greatest reluctance that I have even served on committees formed to effect some aim of passing interest. Thinking that not the whole of life was long enough to learn to write well, I have been unwilling to give to other activities time that I so much needed to achieve the purpose I had in mind. I have never been able intimately to persuade myself that anything else mattered. Notwithstanding, when men in millions are living on the border-line of starvation, when freedom in great parts of the inhabited globe is dying or dead, when a terrible war has been succeeded by years during which happiness has been out of the reach of the great mass of the human race, when men are distraught because they can see no value in life and the hopes that had enabled them for so many centuries to support its misery seem illusory; it is hard not to ask oneself whether it is anything but futility to write plays and stories and novels. The only answer I can think of is that some of us are so made that there is nothing else we can do. We do not write because we want to; we write because we must. There may be other things in the world that more pressingly want doing: we must liberate our souls of the burden of creation. We must go on though Rome burns. Others may despise us because we do not lend a hand with a bucket of water; we cannot help it; we do not know how to handle a bucket. Besides, the conflagration thrills us and charges our mind with phrases.

From time to time, however, writers have engaged in politics. Its effect on them as writers has been injurious. I have not noticed that their counsel has had much influence on the conduct of affairs. The only exception I can recall is Disraeli; but in his case, it it not unfair to say, writing was not an end in itself, but a means to political advancement. At the present day, living as we do in an age of specialization, I have a notion that on the whole the cobbler does best to stick to his last.

Because I had heard that Dryden had learnt to write English from his study of Tillotson, I read certain passages of this author and I came across a piece that gave me some consolation in this matter. It ran as follows: "We ought to be glad, when those that are fit for government, and called to it, are willing to take the burden of it upon them; yea, and to be very thankful to them too, that they will be at the pains, and can have the patience, to govern and live publicly. Therefore it is happy for the world that there are some who are born and bred up to it; and that custom hath made it easy, or at least tolerable to them. . . . The advantage which men have by a more devout and retired and contemplative life, is, that they are not distracted about many things; their minds and affections are set upon one thing; and the whole stream and force of their affections run one way. All their thoughts and endeavours are united in one great end and design, which makes their life all of a piece, and to be consistent with itself throughout."

lxiii

WHEN I started this book I warned the reader that perhaps the only thing of which I was certain was that I was certain of nothing else. I was trying to put my thoughts on sundry subjects in order and I asked no one to agree with me in my opinions. On revising what I have written, I have cut out the words, I think, in a great many places because, though they came to my pen naturally, I found them tedious, but they are to be understood as qualifying my every statement. And now that I come to this last section of my book, I am constrained more anxiously than ever to repeat that what I give are my own private convictions. It may be that they are superficial. It may be that some of them are contradictory. It is unlikely that surmises that are the outcome of thoughts, feelings, and desires built up out of all sorts of haphazard experiences and coloured by a particular personality should fit with the logical precision of a proposition of Euclid. When I wrote of the drama and of fiction I wrote of what by practice I had some cognizance of, but now that I come to deal with matters of which philosophers treat I have no more special knowledge than can be acquired by any man who has lived for many years a busy and varied life. Life also is a school of philosophy, but it is like one of those modern kindergartens in which children are left to their own devices and work only at the subjects that arouse their interest. Their attention is drawn to what seems to have a meaning for them and they take no notice of what does not immediately concern them. In psychological laboratories rats are trained to find their way through a maze and presently by trial and error they learn the path that leads to the food they seek. In the matters with which I now occupy myself I am like one of these rats scurrying along the pathways of the complicated maze, but I do not know that it has a centre where I shall find what I seek. For all I know all the alleys are blind.

I was introduced to philosophy by Kuno Fischer whose lectures I attended when I was at Heidelberg. He had a great reputation there and he was giving that winter a course of lectures on Schopenhauer. They were crowded and one had to queue up early in order to get a good seat. He was a dapper, short, stoutish man, neat in his dress, with a bullet head, white hair *en brosse* and a red face. His little eyes were quick and shining. He had a funny, flattened snub nose that looked as if it had been bashed in, and you would have been much more likely to take him for an old prize-fighter than for a philosopher. He was a humourist; he had indeed written a book on wit which I read at the time, but which I have completely forgotten, and every now and then a great guffaw broke from his audience of students as he made a joke. His voice was powerful and he was a vivid, impressive and exciting speaker. I was too young and too ignorant to understand much of what he said, but I got a very clear impression of Schopenhauer's odd and original personality and a confused feeling of the dramatic value and the romantic quality of his system. I hesitate to make any statement after so many years, but I have a notion that Kuno Fischer treated it as a work of art rather than as a serious contribution to metaphysics.

Since then I have read a great deal of philosophy. I have found it very good reading. Indeed, of the various great subjects that afford reading matter to the person for whom reading is a need and a delight it is the most varied, the most copious and the most satisfying. Ancient Greece is thrilling, but from this point of view there is not enough in it; a time comes when you have read the little that remains of its literature and all of significance that has been written about it. The Italian Renaissance is fascinating too, but the subject, comparatively, is small; the ideas that informed it were few, and you get tired of its art which has been long since drained of its creative value so that you are left only with grace, charm and symmetry (qualities of which you can have enough) and you get tired of its men, whose versatility falls into too uniform a pattern. You can go on reading about the Italian Renaissance forever, but your interest fails before the material is exhausted. The French Revolution is another subject that may well engage the attention and it has the advantage that its significance is actual. It is close to us in point of time so that with a very small effort of imagination we can put ourselves into the men who made it. They are almost contemporaries. And what they did and what they thought affect the lives we lead today; after a fashion we are all descendants of the French Revolution. And the material is abundant. The documents that relate to it are countless and the last thing has never been said about it. You can always find something fresh and interesting to read. But it does not satisfy. The art and literature it directly produced are negligible so that you are driven to the study of the men who made it, and the more you read about them the more are you dismayed by their pettiness and vulgarity. The actors in one of the greatest dramas in the world's history were pitifully inadequate to their parts. You turn away from the subject at last with a faint disgust.

But metaphysics never lets you down. You can never come to the end of it. It is as various as the soul of man. It has greatness, for it deals with nothing less than the whole of knowledge. It treats of the universe, of God and immortality, of the properties of human reason and the end and purpose of life, of the power and limitations of man; and if it cannot answer the questions that assail him on his journey through this dark and mysterious world it persuades him to support his ignorance with good humour. It teaches resignation and inculcates courage. It appeals to the imagination as well as to the intelligence; and to the amateur, much more, I suppose, than to the professional it affords matter for that reverie which is the most delicious pleasure with which man can beguile his idleness.

Since, inspired by Kuno Fischer's lectures, I began to read Schopenhauer I have read pretty well all the most important works of the great classical philosophers. Though there is in them a great deal that I did not understand, and perhaps I did not even understand as much as I thought, I have read them with passionate interest. The only one who has consistently bored me is Hegel. This is doubtless my own fault, for his influence on philosophical thought during the nineteenth century proves his importance. I found him terribly longwinded and I could never reconcile myself to the jugglery with which it seemed to me he proved whatever he had a mind to. Perhaps I was prejudiced against him by the scorn with which Schopenhauer always spoke of him. But to the others, from Plato onwards, I surrendered myself, one after the other, with the pleasure of a traveller adventuring into an unknown country. I did not read critically, but as I might have read a novel, for the excitement and delight of it. (I have already confessed that I read a novel not for instruction, but for pleasure. I crave my reader's indulgence.) A student of character, I got an immense amount of pleasure out of the self-revelation which these various writers offered to my survey. I saw the man behind his philosophy and I was exalted by the nobility I found in some and amused by the queerness I discerned in others. I felt a wonderful exhilaration when I dizzily followed Plotinus in his flight from the alone to the alone, and though I have learnt since that Descartes drew preposterous conclusions from his effective premiss I was entranced by the lucidity of his expression. To read him was like swimming in a lake so clear that you could see the bottom; that crystalline water was wonderfully refreshing. I look upon my first reading of Spinoza as one of the signal experiences of my life. It filled me with just that feeling of majesty and exulting power that one has at the sight of a great mountain range.

And when I came to the English philosophers, with perhaps a slight prejudice, for it had been impressed upon me in Germany that, with the possible exception of Hume, they were quite negligible and Hume's only importance was that Kant had demolished him, I found that besides being philosophers they were uncommonly good writers. And though they might not be very great thinkers, of this I could not presume to judge, they were certainly very curious men. I should think that few could read Hobbes' *Leviathan* without being taken by the gruff, downright John Bullishness of his personality and surely no one could read Berkeley's *Dialogues* without being ravished by the charm of that delightful bishop. And though it may be true that Kant made hay of Hume's theories it would be impossible, I think, to write philosophy with more elegance, urbanity and clearness. They all, and Locke too for the matter of that, wrote English that the student of style could do much worse than study. Before I start writing a novel I read *Candide* over again so that I may have in the back of my mind the touchstone of that lucidity, grace and wit; I have a notion that it would not hurt the English philosophers of our own day if before they set about a work they submitted themselves to the discipline of reading Hume's *Inquiry Concerning the Human Understanding.* For it is not invariably that they write now with distinction. It may be that their thoughts are so much more subtle than those of their predecessors that they are obliged to use a technical vocabulary of their own invention; but it is a dangerous procedure, and when they deal with matters that are of pressing concern to all reflective persons, one can only regret that they cannot make their meaning so plain that all who read may understand. They tell me that Professor Whitehead has the most ingenious brain of anyone who is now engaged in philosophic thought. It seems to me a pity then that he should not always take pains to make his sense clear. It was a good rule of Spinoza's to indicate the nature of things by words whose customary meanings should not be altogether opposed to the meanings he desired to bestow upon them.

lxiv

THERE is no reason why philosophers should not be also men of letters. But to write well does not come by instinct; it is an art that demands arduous study. The philosopher does not speak only to other philosophers and to undergraduates working for a degree; he speaks also to the men of letters, politicians and reflective persons who directly mould the ideas of the coming generation. They, naturally enough, are taken by a philosophy that is striking and not too difficultly assimilated. We all know how the philosophy of Nietzsche has affected some parts of the world and few would assert that its influence has been other than disastrous. It has prevailed, not by such profundity of thought as it may have, but by a vivid style and an effective form. The philosopher who will not take the trouble to make himself clear shows only that he thinks his thought of no more than academic value.

It has, however, been a consolation to me to discover that sometimes even the professional philosophers do not understand one another. Bradley frequently confesses that he is at a loss to understand what someone with whom he is arguing means and Professor Whitehead in one place states that something Bradley says is beyond his comprehension. When the most eminent philosophers cannot always understand one another the layman may well feel resigned if he often does not understand them. Of course metaphysics is difficult. One must expect that. The layman walks a tight-rope without a pole to balance him and he must be thankful if he can scramble somehow to safety. The feat is exciting enough to make it worth his while to risk a tumble.

I was much disconcerted by the claim that I found here and there advanced that philosophy was the province of the higher mathematicians; and though it seemed hard to me to believe that, if knowledge, as the doctrine of evolution suggests, has been developed for practical reasons in the struggle for existence, the sum total of it, something that is essential to the well-being of man in general, could be reserved only for a small body of men who are gifted by nature with a rare faculty, I might very well have been deterred from pursuing my pleasant studies in this direction, since I have no head for mathematics, if I had not luckily come across an admission of Bradley's that he knew very little of this abstruse science. And Bradley was no mean philosopher. We know that the sense of taste differs in various persons; but without it men would perish. It seems as unlikely that you may not hold reasonable theories about the universe and man's place in it, the mystery of evil and the meaning of reality, unless you are a mathematical physicist, as that you cannot enjoy a bottle of wine unless you have the trained sensibility that enables you without error to ascribe a year to twenty different clarets.

For philosophy is not a subject that has to do only with philosophers and mathematicians. It is one that concerns us all. It is true that most of us accept our opinions on the matters with which it deals at second hand and most do not know that they have any philosophy at all. But it is implicit even in the most thoughtless. The old woman who first said, "it's no good crying over spilt milk" was a philosopher in her way. For what did she mean by this except that regret was useless? A complete system of philosophy is implied. The determinist thinks that you cannot take a step in life that is not motivated by what you are at the moment; and you are not only your muscles, your nerves, your entrails and your brain; you are your habits, your opinions and your ideas. However little you may be aware of them, however contradictory, unreasonable and prejudiced they may be, they are there, influencing your actions and reactions. Even if you have never put them into words they are your philosophy. Perhaps it is well enough that most people should leave this unformulated. It is hardly thoughts they have, at least not conscious thoughts, it is a kind of vague feeling, a sort of experience like that muscular sense that the physiologists not so long ago discovered, which they have absorbed from the notions current in the society in which they live and which has been faintly modified by their own experience. They lead their ordered lives and this confused body of ideas and feelings is enough. Since it includes something of the wisdom of the ages, it is adequate for the ordinary purposes of the ordinary life. But I have sought to make a pattern of mine and from an early age tried to find out what were the elements I had to deal with. I wanted to get what knowledge I could about the general structure of the universe; I wanted to make up my mind whether I had to consider only this life or a life to come; I wanted to discover whether I was a free agent or whether my feeling that I could mould myself according to my will was an illusion; I wanted to know whether life had any meaning or whether it was I that must strive to give it one. So in a desultory way I began to read.

lxv

THE first subject that attracted my attention was religion. For it seemed to me of the greatest importance to decide whether this world I lived in was the only one I had to reckon with or whether I must look upon it as no more than a place of trial which was to prepare me for a life to come. When I wrote *Of Human Bondage* I gave a chapter to my hero's loss of the faith in which he had been brought up. The book was read in typescript by a very clever woman who at that time was good enough to be interested in me. She told me that this chapter was inadequate. I rewrote it; but I do not think I much improved it. For it described my own experience and I have no doubt that my reasons for coming to the conclusion I came to were inadequate. They were the reasons of an ignorant boy. They were of the heart rather than of the head. When my parents died I went to live with my uncle who was a clergyman. He was a childless man of fifty, and I am sure that it was a great nuisance to have the charge of a small boy thrust upon him. He read prayers morning and evening, and we went to church twice on Sundays. Sunday was the busy day. My uncle always said that he was the only man in his parish who worked seven days a week. In point of fact he was incredibly idle and left the work of his parish to his curate and his churchwardens. But I was impressionable and soon became very religious. I accepted what I was taught, both in my uncle's vicarage and afterwards at school, with unquestioning trust.

There was one point that immediately affected me. I had not been long at school before I discovered, through the ridicule to which I was exposed and the humiliations I suffered, how great a misfortune it was to me that I stammered; and I had read in the Bible that if you had faith you could move mountains. My uncle assured me that it was a literal fact. One night, when I was going back to school next day, I prayed to God with all my might that he would take away my impediment; and, such was my faith, I went to sleep quite certain that when I awoke next morning I should be able to speak like everybody else. I pictured to myself the surprise of the boys (I was still at a preparatory school) when they found that I no longer stammered. I woke full of exultation and it was a real, a terrible shock, when I discovered that I stammered as badly as ever.

I grew older. I went to the King's School. The masters were clergymen; they were stupid and irascible. They were impatient of my stammering and if they did not ignore me completely, which I preferred, they bullied me. They seemed to think it was my fault that I stammered. Presently I discovered that my uncle was a selfish man who cared for nothing but his own comfort. The neighbouring clergy sometimes came to the vicarage. One of them was fined in the county court for starving his cows; another had to resign his living because he was convicted of drunkenness. I was taught that we lived in the presence of God and that the chief business of man was to save his soul. I could not help seeing that none of these clergymen practised what they preached. Fervent though my faith was, I had been terribly bored by all the church-going that was forced upon me, both at home and at school, and on going to Germany I welcomed the freedom that enabled me to stay away. But two or three times out of curiosity I went to High Mass at the Jesuit Church in Heidelberg. Though my uncle had a natural sympathy for Catholics (he was a High Churchman and at election time they painted on the garden fence, "This way to Rome"), he had no doubt that they would frizzle in hell. He believed implicitly in eternal punishment. He hated the dissenters in his parish and indeed thought it a monstrous thing that the state tolerated them. His consolation was that they too would suffer eternal damnation. Heaven was reserved for the members of the Church of England. I accepted it as a great mercy of God that I had been bred in that communion. It was as wonderful as being born an Englishman.

But when I went to Germany I discovered that the Germans were just as proud of being Germans as I was proud of being English. I heard them say that the English did not understand music and that Shakespeare was only appreciated in Germany. They spoke of the English as a nation of shopkeepers and had no doubt in their minds that as artists, men of science and philosophers they were greatly superior. It shook me. And now at High Mass in Heidelberg I could not but notice that the students, who filled the church to its doors, seemed very devout. They had, indeed, all the appearance of believing in their religion as sincerely as I believed in mine. It was queer that they could, for of course I knew that theirs was false and mine was true. I think I can have had by nature no strong religious feeling, or else in the intolerance of my youth I must have been so shocked by the contrast of the practice with the professions of the various clergymen with whom I had to do, that I was already inclined to doubt; otherwise I can hardly think that such a simple little notion as then occurred to me could have had consequences that were to me of so much importance. It struck me that I might very well have been born in South Germany, and then I should naturally have been brought up as a Catholic. I found it very hard that thus through no fault of my own I should have been condemned to everlasting torment. My ingenuous nature revolted at the injustice. The next step was easy; I came to the conclusion that it could not matter a row of pins what one believed; God could not condemn people just because they were Spaniards or Hottentots. I might have stopped there and if I had been less ignorant adopted some form of deism like that which was current in the eighteenth century. But the beliefs that had been instilled into me hung together and when one of them came to seem outrageous the others participated in its fate. The whole horrible structure, based not on the love of God but on the fear of Hell, tumbled down like a house of cards.

With my mind at all events I ceased to believe in God; I felt the exhilaration of a new freedom. But we do not believe only with our minds; in some deep recess of my soul there lingered still the old dread of hell-fire, and for long my exultation was tempered by the shadow of that ancestral anxiety. I no longer believed in God; I still, in my bones, believed in the Devil.

lxvi

IT WAS this fear that I sought to banish when, becoming a medical student, I entered a new world. I read a great many books. They told me that man was a machine subject to mechanical laws; and when the machine ran down that was the end of him. I saw men die at the hospital and my startled

sensibilities confirmed what my books had taught me. I
was satisfied to believe that religion and the idea of God
were constructions that the human race had evolved as a
convenience for living, and represented something that had
at one time, and for all I was prepared to say still had,
value for the survival of the species, but that must be his-
torically explained and corresponded to nothing real. I
called myself an agnostic, but in my blood and my bones I
looked upon God as a hypothesis that a reasonable man
must reject.

But if there was no God who could consign me to eternal
flames and no soul that could be thus consigned, if I was the
plaything of mechanical forces and the struggle for life
was the impelling force, I could not see that there was any
meaning in good such as I had been taught it. I began to
read Ethics. I waded conscientiously through many formidable tomes. I came to the conclusion that man aimed
at nothing but his own pleasure and that when he sacrificed
himself for others it was only an illusion that led him to
believe that he was seeking anything but his own gratification. And since the future was uncertain it was only common
sense to seize every pleasure that the moment offered. I
decided that right and wrong were merely words and that
the rules of conduct were no more than conventions that
men had set up to serve their own selfish purposes. The
free man had no reason to follow them except in so far
as they suited his convenience. Having then an epigram-
matic turn, and epigrams being the fashion, I put my conviction into a phrase and said to myself: follow your inclinations with due regard to the policeman round the corner.
By the time I was twenty-four I had constructed a complete
system of philosophy. It rested on two principles: The Rela-
tivity of Things and The Circumferentiality of Man. I have
learnt since that the first of these was not a very original
discovery. It may be that the other was profound, but though
I have racked my brains I cannot for the life of me remember what on earth it meant.

On a certain occasion I read a little story that greatly
took my fancy. It is to be found in one of the volumes of

Anatole France's *La Vie Littéraire*. It is many years since I read it, but it has remained in my recollection as follows: a young king of the East, anxious on his ascent of the throne to rule his kingdom justly, sent for the wise men of his country and ordered them to gather the wisdom of the world in books so that he might read them and learn how best to conduct himself. They went away and after thirty years returned with a string of camels laden with five thousand tomes. Here, they told him, is collected everything that wise men have learnt of the history and destiny of man. But the king was immersed in affairs of state and could not read so many books, so he bade them go and condense this knowledge into a smaller number. Fifteen years later they returned and their camels carried but five hundred works. In these volumes, they told the king, you will find all the wisdom of the world. But there were still too many and the king sent them away again. Ten years passed and they came back and now they brought no more than fifty books. But the king was old and tired. He had no time now even to read so few and he ordered his wise men once more to reduce their number and in a single volume give him an epitome of human knowledge so that he might learn at last what it was so important for him to know. They went away and set to work and in five years returned. They were old men when for the last time they came and laid the result of their labours in the king's hands, but now the king was dying and he had no time any more to read even the one book they brought him.

It was some such book as this that I sought, a book that would answer once for all the questions that puzzled me, so that, everything being settled for good and all, I could pursue the pattern of my life without let or hindrance. I read and read. From the classical philosophers I turned to the moderns, thinking that among them, perhaps, I should find what I wanted. I could not discover much agreement among them. I found myself convinced by the critical parts of their works, but when I came to the constructive, though often I failed to see the flaws, I could not but be conscious that they did not compel my assent. The impression suggested itself to me that notwithstanding their learning, their logic and their classifications, philosophers embraced such-and-such beliefs not because they were led to them by their reason, but because their temperaments forced these beliefs upon them. Otherwise I could not understand how after all this time they differed from one another so profoundly. When I read, I do not know where, that Fichte had said that the kind of philosophy a man adopts depends on the kind of man he is, it occurred to me that perhaps I was looking for something that could not be found. It seemed to me then that if there was in philosophy no universal truth that everyone could accept, but only a truth that agreed with the personality of the individual, the only thing for me was to narrow my search and look for some philosopher whose system suited me because I was the same sort of man that he was. The answers that he would provide to the questions that puzzled me must satisfy me because they would be the only possible answers to fit my humour.

For some time I was much attracted by the pragmatists. I had not got as much profit as I expected from the metaphysical writings of the dons at the great English universities. They seemed to me too gentlemanlike to be very good philosophers and I could not resist the suspicion that sometimes they failed to pursue an argument to its logical conclusion for fear of offending the susceptibilities of colleagues with whom they were in social relations. The pragmatists had vigour. They were very much alive. The most important of them wrote well, and they gave an appearance of simplicity to problems which I had not been able to make head or tail of. But much as I should have liked to I could not bring myself to believe, as they did, that truth is fashioned by us to meet our practical needs. The sense-datum, on which I thought all knowledge was based, seemed to me something given, which had to be accepted whether it suited the convenience or not. Nor did I feel comfortable with the argument that God existed if it consoled me to believe that he did. The pragmatists ceased to interest me so much. I found Bergson good to read, but singularly unconvincing; nor did I find in Benedetto Croce anything to my purpose.

On the other hand, in Bertrand Russell I discovered a writer who greatly pleased me; he was easy to understand and his English was good. I read him with admiration.

I was very willing to accept him as the guide I sought. He had worldly wisdom and common sense. He was tolerant of human weakness. But I discovered in time that he was a guide none too certain of the way. His mind was restless. He was like an architect who, when you want a house to live in, having persuaded you to build it of brick, then sets before you good reasons why it should be built of stone; but when you have agreed to this produces reasons just as good to prove that the only material to use is reinforced concrete. Meanwhile you have not a roof to your head. I was looking for a system of philosophy as coherent and self-contained as Bradley's, in which one part hung necessarily on another, so that nothing could be altered without the whole fabric falling to pieces. This Bertrand Russell could not give me.

At last I came to the conclusion that I could never find the one, complete and satisfying book I sought, because that book could only be an expression of myself. So with more courage than discretion I made up my mind that I must write it for myself. I found out what were the books set for the undergraduate to read in order to take a philosophical degree and laboriously perused them. I thought I should thus have at least a foundation for my own work. It seemed to me that with this, the knowledge of the world I had acquired during the forty years of my life (for I was forty when I conceived this idea) and the industrious study of philosophical literature to which I was prepared to devote some years, I should be competent to write such a book as I had in mind. I was aware that except to myself it could have no value beyond such a coherent portrait as it might give of the soul (for want of a more exact word) of a reflective person who had led a fuller life and been subject to more varied experiences than generally fall to the lot of professional philosophers. I knew very well that I had no gift for metaphysical speculation. I meant to take from here and there theories that satisfied not only my mind but, what I could not but think more important than my mind, the whole body of my instincts, feelings and deep-rooted prejudices, the prejudices that are so intimate a part of one that they can hardly be distinguished from instincts; and out of them make a system that would be valid for me and enable me to pursue the course of my life.

But the more I read the more complicated the subject seemed to me and the more conscious I grew of my ignorance. I was peculiarly discouraged by the philosophical magazines in which I found topics discussed at great length which were evidently of importance but which seemed to me in my darkness very trivial; and the manner in which they were handled, the logical apparatus, the care with which each point was argued and the possible objections met, the terms which each writer defined when he first used them, the authorities he quoted, proved to me that philosophy, at all events now, was a business for the experts to deal with between them. The layman could little hope to comprehend its subtleties. I should need twenty years to prepare myself to write the book I proposed and by the time it was done I might, like the king in Anatole France's story, be on my death bed and to me at least the labour I had taken would no longer be of use.

I abandoned the idea and all I have to show for my efforts now are the few desultory notes that follow. I claim no originality for them, or even for the words in which I have put them. I am like a tramp who has rigged himself up as best he could with a pair of trousers from a charitable farmer's wife, a coat off a scarecrow, odd boots out of a dustbin, and a hat that he has found in the road. They are just shreds and patches, but he has fitted himself into them pretty comfortably and, uncomely as they may be, he finds that they suit him well enough. When he passes a gentleman in a smart blue suit, a new hat and well-polished shoes, he thinks he looks very grand, but he is not so sure that in that neat and respectable attire he would be nearly so much at his ease as in his own rags and tatters.

lxvii

WHEN I read Kant I found myself obliged to abandon the
materialism in which in my youth I had exulted and the
physiological determinism that went with it. I did not then
know the objections that have riddled Kant's system and
I found an emotional satisfaction in his philosophy. It excited me to contemplate that unknowable "thing in itself"
and I was content with a world that man had constructed
from appearances. It gave me a peculiar sense of liberation. I jibbed at his maxim that you should so act that your
action may be a universal rule. I was too much convinced
of the diversity of human nature to believe that this was
reasonable. I thought that what was right for one person
might very well be wrong for another. For my part I chiefly
wanted to be let alone, but I had discovered that not many
wanted that, and if I let them alone they thought me unkind, indifferent and selfish. But one cannot study the idealistic philosophers long without coming into touch with
solipsism. Idealism is always trembling on the brink of it.
The philosophers shy away from it like startled fawns, but
their arguments continue to lead them back to it and so
far as I can judge they escape it only because they will not
pursue them to the end. It is a theory that can hardly fail
to allure the writer of fiction. The claims it makes are his
common practice. It has a completeness and an elegance
that make it infinitely attractive. Since I cannot suppose
that everyone who reads this book will know all about the
various philosophical systems, the instructed reader will
perhaps forgive me if I state briefly what solipsism is. The
solipsist believes only in himself and his experience. He
creates the world as the theatre of his activity, and the world
he creates consists of himself and his thoughts and feelings;
and beyond that nothing has being. Everything knowable,
every fact of experience, is an idea in his mind, and without
his mind does not exist. There is no possibility and no necessity for him to postulate anything outside himself. For him
dream and reality are one. Life is a dream in which he creates

the objects that come before him, a coherent and consistent dream, and when he ceases to dream, the world, with its beauty, its pain and sorrow and unimaginable variety, ceases to be. It is a perfect theory; it has but one defect; it is unbelievable.

When I cherished the ambition of writing a book on these matters, thinking I must start at the beginning, I studied epistemology. I found none of the theories that I examined very convincing. It seemed to me that the plain man (that object of the philosopher's contempt, except when it happens that his views agree with the philosopher's, in which case quite a lot of value is attached to them) incompetent to judge of their value was perhaps entitled to choose that one which most satisfied his prepossessions. If one is unwilling to suspend one's judgment it appears to me that there is a good deal of plausibility in the theory which holds that, beyond certain fundamental data which they call the given, and the existence of other minds, which they infer, men can be sure of nothing. All the rest of their knowledge is fiction, the construction of their minds, that they have devised for the convenience of living. Having to fit themselves, in the course of evolution, to a constantly changing environment, they have made a picture from fragments that they took here and there because they suited their purposes. This is the world of phenomena that they know. Reality is merely the hypothesis they have suggested as its occasion. It may be that they might have taken other fragments and combined them into another picture. This different world would have been as coherent and as true as the one we imagine we know.

It would be difficult to persuade an author that there was not a close interaction between the body and the mind. The experience of Flaubert when he suffered from the symptoms of arsenical poisoning while writing of Emma Bovary's suicide is but an extreme instance of what every novelist has undergone. Most writers have chills and fevers, aches and pains, nausea at times, when they are engaged in composition; and contrariwise they are aware to what morbid states of their body they owe many of their happiest inventions. Knowing that many of their deepest emotions, many of the reflections seem to come straight from heaven, may be due to want of exercise or a sluggish liver, they can hardly fail to regard their spiritual experiences with a certain irony; which is all to the good, for thus they can manage and manipulate them. For my part, of the various theories of the relations between matter and spirit that are offered by the philosophers for the consideration of the plain man that which still seems to me most satisfactory is Spinoza's conception that substance thinking and substance extended are one and the same substance. But of course today it is more convenient to call it energy. Unless I misunderstand him Bertrand Russell had expressed in his modern fashion an idea not very dissimilar when he speaks of a neutral stuff which is the raw material of the mental and physical worlds. Trying to form for myself some sort of picture of this, I have seen spirit in the likeness of a river that forces its way through the jungle of matter; but river is jungle and jungle is river, for river and jungle are one. It does not seem impossible that the biologists will in the future succeed in creating life in their laboratories and then it may be that we shall know more of these matters.

lxviii

BUT the plain man's interest in philosophy is practical. He wants to know what is the value of life, how he should live and what sense he can ascribe to the universe. When philosophers stand back and refuse to give even tentative answers to these questions they shirk their responsibilities. Now, the most urgent problem that confronts the plain man is the problem of evil.

It is curious to notice that when they speak of evil, philosophers so often use toothache as their example. They point out with justice that you cannot feel my toothache. In their sheltered, easy lives it looks as though this were the only pain that had much afflicted them and one might almost conclude that with the improvement of American dentistry the

whole problem could be conveniently shelved. I have sometimes thought that it would be a very good thing if before
philosophers were granted the degrees that will enable them
to impart their wisdom to the young, they had to spend a
year in social service in the slums of a great city or earn
their living by manual labour. If they had ever seen a child
die of meningitis they would face some of the problems that
concern them with other eyes.

If the subject were not of such pressing moment it would
be difficult to read the chapter on evil in *Appearance and
Reality* without ironic amusement. It is appallingly gentlemanlike. It leaves you with the impression that it is really
rather bad form to attach any great importance to evil, and
though its existence must be admitted it is unreasonable to
make a fuss about it. In any case it is much exaggerated
and it is evident that there is a lot of good in it. Bradley
held that there was no pain on the whole. The Absolute is
the richer for every discord and for all diversity which it
embraces. Just as in a machine, he tells us, the resistance
and pressure of the parts subserve an end beyond any of
them, so at a much higher level it may be with the Absolute; and if this is possible it is indubitably real. Evil and
error subserve a wider scheme and in this are realized. They
play a part in a higher good and in this sense unknowingly
are good. Evil in short is a deception of our senses and nothing more.

I have tried to find out what philosophers of other schools
had to say on this question. This is not very much. It may
be that there is not very much to be said about it, and philosophers quite naturally attach importance to subjects upon
which they can discourse at length. And in the little they
have said I can find less to satisfy me. It may be that the
evils we endure educate us and so make us better; but observation does not allow us to think that this is a universal
rule. It may be that courage and sympathy are excellent
and that they could not come into existence without danger
and suffering. It is hard to see how the Victoria Cross that
rewards the soldier who has risked his life to save a blinded
man is going to solace *him* for the loss of his sight. To give

alms shows charity, and charity is a virtue, but does *that* good compensate for the evil of the cripple whose poverty has called it forth? Evils are there, omnipresent; pain and disease, the death of those we love, poverty, crime, sin, frustrated hope: the list is interminable. What explanations have the philosophers to offer? Some say that evil is logically necessary so that we may know good; some say that by the nature of the world there is an opposition between good and evil and that each is metaphysically necessary to the other. What explanations have the theologians to offer? Some say that God has placed evils here for our training; some say that he has sent them upon men to punish them for their sins. But *I* have seen a child die of meningitis. I have only found one explanation that appealed equally to my sensibility and to my imagination. This is the doctrine of the transmigration of souls. As everyone knows, it assumes that life does not begin at birth or end at death, but is a link in an indefinite series of lives each one of which is determined by the acts done in previous existences. Good deeds may exalt a man to the heights of heaven and evil deeds degrade him to the depths of hell. All lives come to an end, even the life of the gods, and happiness is to be sought in release from the round of births and repose in the changeless state called Nirvana. It would be less difficult to bear the evils of one's own life if one could think that they were but the necessary outcome of one's errors in a previous existence, and the effort to do better would be less difficult too when there was the hope than in another existence a greater happiness would reward one. But if one feels one's own woes in a more forcible way than those of others (I cannot feel your toothache, as the philosophers say) it is the woes of others that arouse one's indignation. It is possible to achieve resignation in regard to one's own, but only philosophers obsessed with the perfection of the Absolute can look upon those of others, which seem so often unmerited, with an equal mind. If Karma were true one could look upon them with pity, but with fortitude. Revulsion would be out of place and life would be robbed of the meaninglessness of pain which is pessimism's unanswered argument. I can only regret that I find the doctrine as impossible to believe as the solipsism of which I spoke just now.

lxix

BUT I have not done with evil yet. The problem presses when you come to consider whether God exists, and if he does, what nature must be ascribed to him. The time came when, like everybody else, I read the engaging works of the physicists. I was seized with awe at the contemplation of the immense distances that separated the stars and the vast stretches of time that light traversed in order to come from them to us. I was staggered by the unimaginable extent of the nebulæ. If I understood aright what I read, I must suppose that at the beginning the two forces of cosmical attraction and repulsion balanced so that the universe remained for untold ages in a state of perfect equilibrium. Then at some moment this was disturbed and the universe, toppling off its balance, gave rise to the universe the astronomers tell us of and the little earth we know. But what caused the original act of creation and what upset the balance of equilibrium? I seemed inevitably drawn to the conception of a creator, and what could create this vast, this stupendous universe but a being all-powerful? But the evil of the world then forces on us the conclusion that this being cannot be all-powerful and all-good. A God who is all-powerful may be justly blamed for the evil of the world and it seems absurd to consider him with admiration or accord him worship. But mind and heart revolt against the conception of a God who is not all-good. We are forced then to accept the supposition of a God who is not all-powerful: such a God contains within himself no explanation of his own existence or of that of the universe he creates.

It is singular when you read the documents on which the great religions of the world are founded, to note how much more succeeding ages have read into them than was there. Their teaching, their example, have created an ideal greater than themselves. Most of us find it embarrassing when flowery compliments are paid to us. It is strange that the devout should think God can be pleased when they slavishly pay them to him. When I was young I had an elderly friend who used often to ask me to stay with him in the country. He was a religious man and he read prayers to the assembled household every morning. But he had crossed out in pencil all the passages in the Book of Common Prayer that praised God. He said that there was nothing so vulgar as to praise people to their faces and, himself a gentleman, he could not believe that God was so ungentlemanly as to like it. At the time it seemed to me a curious eccentricity. I think now that my friend showed very good sense.

Men are passionate, men are weak, men are stupid, men are pitiful; to bring to bear on them anything so tremendous as the wrath of God seems strangely inept. It is not very difficult to forgive other people their sins. When you put yourself into their shoes it is generally easy to see what has caused them to do things they should not have done and excuses can be found for them. There is a natural instinct to anger when some harm is done one that leads one to revengeful action, and it is hard in what concerns oneself to take up an attitude of detachment; but a little reflection enables one to look upon the situation from the outside and with practice it is no more difficult to forgive the harm that is done one than any other. It is much harder to forgive people the harm one has done them; that indeed requires a singular power of mind.

Every artist wishes to be believed in, but he is not angry with those who will not accept the communication he offers. God is not so reasonable. He craves so urgently to be believed in that you might think he needed your belief in order to reassure himself of his own existence. He promises rewards to those who believe in him and threatens with horrible punishment those who do not. For my part I cannot believe in a God who is angry with me because I do not believe in him. I cannot believe in a God who is less tolerant than I. I cannot believe in a God who has neither humour nor common sense. Plutarch long ago put the matter succinctly. "I would much rather," he writes, "have men say of me that there never was a Plutarch, nor is now, than to say that Plutarch is a man inconstant, fickle, easily moved to anger, revengeful for trifling provocations and vexed at small things."

But though men have ascribed to God imperfections that they would deplore in themselves that does not prove that God does not exist. It proves only that the religions that men have accepted are but blind alleys cut into an impenetrable jungle and none of them leads to the heart of the great mystery. Arguments have been adduced to prove the existence of God, and I will ask the reader to have patience with me while I briefly consider them. One of them assumes that man has an idea of a perfect being; and since perfection includes existence a perfect being must exist. Another maintains that every event has a cause and since the universe exists it must have a cause and this cause is the Creator. A third, the argument from design, which Kant said was the clearest, oldest and best suited to human reason, is thus stated by one of the characters in Hume's great dialogues: "the order and arrangement of nature, the curious adjustment of final causes, the plain use and intention of every part and organ; all these bespeak in the clearest language an intelligent cause or Author." But Kant showed conclusively that there was no more to be said in favour of this argument than in that of the other two. In their place he propounded another. In a few words it is to the effect that without God there is no guarantee that the sense of duty, which presupposes a free and real self, is not an illusion and therefore that it is morally necessary to believe in God. This has been generally thought more creditable to Kant's amiable nature than to his subtle intelligence. The argument which to me seems more persuasive than any of these is one that has now fallen out of favour. It is known as the proof *e consensu gentium*. It asserts that all men from the remotest origins have had some sort of belief in God and it is hard to think that a belief that has grown up with the human race, a belief that has been accepted by the wisest men, the sages of the East, the philosophers of

Greece, the great Scholastics, should not have a foundation in fact. It has seemed to many instinctive and it may be (one can only say, it may be, for it is far from certain) that an instinct does not exist unless there is a possibility of its being satisfied. Experience has shown that the prevalence of a belief, no matter for how long it has been held, is no guarantee of its truth. It appears, then, that none of the arguments for the existence of God is valid. But of course you do not disprove his existence because you cannot prove it. Awe remains, man's sense of helplessness, and his desire to attain harmony between himself and the universe at large. These, rather than the worship of nature or of ancestors, magic or morality, are the sources of religion. There is no reason to believe that what you desire exists, but it is a hard saying that you have no right to believe what you cannot prove; there is no reason why you should not believe so long as you are aware that your belief lacks proof. I suppose that if your nature is such that you want comfort in your trials and a love that sustains and encourages you, you will neither ask for proofs nor have need of them. Your intuition suffices.

Mysticism is beyond proof and indeed demands no more than an indwelling conviction. It is independent of the creeds, for it finds sustenance in all of them, and it is so personal that it satisfies every idiosyncrasy. It is the feeling that the world we live in is but part of a spiritual universe and from this gains its significance; it is the sense of a present God who supports and comforts us. The mystics have narrated their experience so often, and in terms so similar, that I do not see how one can deny its reality. Indeed, I have myself had on one occasion an experience that I could only describe in the words the mystics have used to describe their ecstasy. I was sitting in one of the deserted mosques near Cairo when suddenly I felt myself rapt as Ignatius of Loyola was rapt when he sat by the river at Manresa. I had an overwhelming sense of the power and import of the universe, and an intimate, a shattering sense of communion with it. I could almost bring myself to say that I felt the presence of God. It is doubtless a common enough

sensation and the mystics have been careful to ascribe value
to it only if its influence was clearly seen in its results. I
have a notion that it can be occasioned by other causes than
the religious. The saints themselves have been willing to
admit that the artists may have it, and love, as we know,
can produce a state so like it that the mystics have found
themselves drawn to use the phrases of lovers to express
the beatific vision. I do not know that it is more mysterious
than that condition, which the psychologists have not yet
explained, when you have a strong feeling that you have at
some past time been through an experience that you are
in the act of undergoing. The ecstasy of the mystic is real
enough, but it is valid only for himself. Mystic and sceptic
agree in this, that at the end of all our intellectual efforts
there remains a great mystery.

Faced with this, awed by the greatness of the universe
and malcontent with what the philosophers told me, and
what the saints, I have sometimes gone back, beyond Mo-
hammed, Jesus and Buddha, beyond the gods of Greece,
Jehovah and Baal, to the Brahman of the Upanishads. That
spirit, if spirit it may be called, self-created and independent
of all other existence, though all that exists, exists in it,
the sole source of life in all that lives, has at least a grandeur
that satisfies the imagination. But I have been busy with
words too long not to be suspicious of them, and when I
look at those I have just written I cannot but see that their
meaning is tenuous. In religion above all things the only
thing of use is an objective truth. The only God that is
of use is a being who is personal, supreme and good, and
whose existence is as certain as that two and two make four.
I cannot penetrate the mystery. I remain an agnostic, and
the practical outcome of agnosticism is that you act as
though God did not exist.

lxx

BELIEF in God is not essential to belief in immortality, but
it is difficult to dissociate one from the other. Even in that

shadowy form of survival which looks forward to the dissolution of human consciousness, once divorced from the body, into the general consciousness, it is only possible to refuse the name of God to this general consciousness if you deny that it has either efficacy or value. And practically, as we know, the two notions have been so inseparably connected that a life after death has always been looked upon as the most powerful instrument to God's hand in his dealings with the human race. It has offered a merciful God the happiness of rewarding the good and a revengeful one the satisfaction of punishing the wicked. The arguments for immortality are simple enough, but, if not meaningless, they have no great force unless the premiss of God's existence is accepted first. I will nevertheless enumerate them. One is based on the incompleteness of life: we have a craving to fulfil ourselves, but the force of events, and our own limitations, leave us with a sense of frustration and this a future life will counterbalance. So Goethe, though he did so much, felt that there was still more for him to do. Akin to this is the argument from desire: if we can conceive immortality and if we desire it, does not that indicate that it exists? Our immortal longings can be understood only by the possibility of their satisfaction. Another argument insists upon the indignation, the anguish and perplexity that beset men when they consider the injustice and the inequality that reign in this world. The wicked flourish like the green bay tree. Justice demands another life in which the guilty may be punished and the innocent rewarded. Evil can be condoned only if in the beyond it is compensated by good and God himself needs immortality to vindicate his ways to man. Then there is the idealistic argument: consciousness cannot be extinguished by death; for the annihilation of consciousness is inconceivable, since only consciousness can conceive the annihilation of consciousness; it goes on to assert that values exist only for mind and point to a supreme mind in which they are completely realized. If God is love, men are values to him, and it cannot be believed that what is of value to God can be allowed to perish. But at this point a certain hesitation has betrayed itself. Common experience, especially the common experience of philosophers, shows that a great many men are no great shakes. Immortality is too stupendous a notion to be entertained in connection with common mortals. They are too insignificant to deserve eternal punishment or to merit eternal bliss. So philosophers have been found to suggest that such as have the possibility of spiritual fulfilment will enjoy a limited survival till they have had the opportunity of reaching the perfection of which they are capable and will then suffer a welcome extinction, while those who have no such possibility will be forthwith mercifully annihilated. But when one comes to enquire into the qualities which in this case will admit the chosen few into the blessings of this limited survival one makes the disconcerting discovery that they are those that few but philosophers possess. One cannot but wonder, however, in what manner the philosophers will pass their time when their virtue has received its due reward, for the questions that occupied them during their sojourn on earth will presumably have received their adequate replies. One can only suppose that they will take piano lessons from Beethoven or learn to paint in water colour under the guidance of Michelangelo. Unless these two great men have much changed they will find them irascible masters.

A very good test of the force of arguments on which you accept a belief is to ask yourself whether for reasons of equal weight you would embark on a practical operation of any importance. Would you for example buy a house on hearsay without having the title examined by a lawyer and the drains tested by a surveyor? The arguments for immortality, weak when you take them one by one, are no more cogent when you take them together. They are alluring, like a house-agent's advertisement in the daily paper, but to me at least no more convincing. For my part I cannot see how consciousness can persist when its physical basis has been destroyed and I am too sure of the interconnection of my body and my mind to think that any survival of my consciousness apart from my body would be in any sense the survival of myself. Even if one could persuade oneself that there was any truth in the suggestion that the human consciousness survives in some general consciousness, there would be small comfort in it, and to be satisfied with the notion that one survives in such spiritual force as one has produced is merely to cheat oneself with idle words. The only survival that has any value is the complete survival of the individual.

lxxi

IF THEN one puts aside the existence of God and the possibility of survival as too doubtful to have any effect on one's behaviour, one has to make up one's mind what is the meaning and use of life. If death ends all, if I have neither to hope for good to come nor to fear evil, I must ask myself what I am here for and how in these circumstances I must conduct myself. Now the answer to one of these questions is plain, but it is so unpalatable that most men will not face it. There is no reason for life and life has no meaning. We are here, inhabitants for a little while of a small planet, revolving round a minor star which in its turn is a member of one of unnumbered galaxies. It may be that this planet alone can support life, or it may be that in other parts of the universe other planets have had the possibility of forming a suitable environment to that substance from which, we suppose, along the vast course of time the men we are have been gradually created. And if the astronomer tells us truth this planet will eventually reach a condition when living things can no longer exist upon it and at long last the universe will attain that final stage of equilibrium when nothing more can happen. Æons and æons before this man will have disappeared. Is it possible to suppose that it will matter then that he ever existed? He will have been a chapter in the history of the universe as pointless as the chapter in which is written the life stories of the strange monsters that inhabited the primæval earth.

I must ask myself then what difference all this makes to me and how I am to deal with these circumstances if I want to make the best use of my life and to get the utmost that I can out of it. Here it is not I that speak, it is the craving within me, which is in every man, to persevere in my own being; it is the egoism that we all inherit from that remote energy which in the unplumbed past first set the ball rolling; it is the need of self-assertion which is in every living thing and which keeps it alive. It is the very essence of man. Its satisfaction is the self-satisfaction which Spinoza has told us is the highest thing for which we can hope, "for no one endeavours to preserve his being for the sake of any end." We may suppose that consciousness was kindled in man as an instrument to enable him to deal with his environment and that for long ages it reached no higher development than was needed to deal with the vital problems of his practice. But it seems in course of time to have outgrown his immediate needs, and with the rise of imagination man widened his environment to include the unseen. We know with what answers he satisfied the questions that he put to himself then. The energy that flamed within him was so intense that he could admit no doubt of his significance; his egoism was so all-embracing that he could not conceive the possibility of his extinction. To many these answers are satisfactory still. They give meaning to life and comfort to human vanity.

Most people think little. They accept their presence in the world; blind slaves of the striving which is their mainspring they are driven this way and that to satisfy their natural impulses, and when it dwindles they go out like the light of a candle. Their lives are purely instinctive. It may be that theirs is the greater wisdom. But if your consciousness has so far developed that you find certain questions pressing upon you and you think the old answers wrong, what are you going to do? What answers will you give? To at least one of these questions two of the wisest men who ever lived have given their own answers. When you come to look at them they seem to mean pretty much the same thing and I am not so sure that that is very much. Aristotle has said that the end of human activity is right action, and Goethe that the secret of life is living. I suppose that Goethe means that man makes the most of his life when he arrives at self-realization;

he had small respect for a life governed by passing whims and uncontrolled instincts. But the difficulty of self-realization, that bringing to the highest perfection every faculty of which you are possessed, so that you can get from life all the pleasure, beauty, emotion and interest you can wring from it, is that the claims of other people constantly limit your activity; and moralists, taken by the reasonableness of the theory, but frightened of its consequences, have spilt much ink to prove that in sacrifice and selflessness a man most completely realizes himself. That is certainly not what Goethe meant and it does not seem to be true. That there is a singular delight in self-sacrifice few would deny, and in so far as it offers a new field for activity and the opportunity to develop a new side of the self, it has value in self-realization; but if you aim at self-realization only in so far as it interferes with no one else's attempts at the same thing you will not get very far. Such an aim demands a good deal of ruthlessness and an absorption in oneself which is offensive to others and thus often stultifies itself. As we well know many of those who came in contact with Goethe were outraged by his frigid egotism.

lxxii

IT MAY seem arrogant that I should not have been content to walk in the steps of men much wiser than myself. But much as we resemble one another we are none of us exactly alike (our finger-prints are there to show it), and I have seen no reason why I should not, so far as I could, choose my own course. I have sought to make a pattern of my life. This, I suppose, might be described as self-realization tempered by a lively sense of irony; making the best of a bad job. But a question presents itself which I shirked when, at the beginning of my book, I dealt with this subject; and now that I can avoid it no longer I cannot but draw back. I am conscious that here and there I have taken free-will for granted; I have spoken as though I had power to mould my intentions and direct my actions as the whim took me. In other places I have spoken as though I accepted determinism. Such shilly-shallying would have been deplorable had I been writing a philosophical work. I make no such pretension. But how can I, an amateur, be expected to settle a question which the philosophers have not yet ceased to argue?

It might seem only sensible to leave the matter alone, but it happens to be one in which the writer of fiction is peculiarly concerned. For as a writer he finds himself compelled by his readers to rigid determination. I pointed out earlier in these pages how unwilling an audience is to accept impulse on the stage. Now an impulse is merely an urge to action of whose motive the agent is not conscious; it is analogous to an intuition, which is a judgment you make without being aware of its grounds. But though an impulse has its motive, an audience, because it is not obvious, will not accept it. The spectators of a play and the readers of a book insist on knowing the reasons of action and they will not admit its probability unless the reasons are cogent. Each person must behave in character; that means that he must do what from their knowledge of him they expect him to do. Cunning must be exercised in order to persuade them to accept the coincidences and accidents which in real life they swallow without a second thought. They are determinists to a man and the writer who trifles with their obstinate prejudice is lost.

But when I look back upon my own life I cannot but notice how much that vitally affected me has been due to circumstances that it is hard not to regard as pure chance. Determinism tells us that choice follows the line of least resistance or the strongest motive. I am not conscious that I have always followed the line of least resistance, and if I have followed the strongest motive that motive has been an idea of myself that I have gradually evolved. The metaphor of chess, though frayed and shop-worn, is here wonderfully apposite. The pieces were provided and I had to accept the mode of action that was characteristic of each one; I had to accept the moves of the persons I played with; but it has seemed to me that I had the power to make on my side, in accordance perhaps with my likes and dislikes and the ideal that I set before me, moves that I freely willed. It has seemed to me that I have now and then been able to put forth an effort that was not wholly determined. If it was an illusion it was an illusion that had its own efficacy. The moves I made, I know now, were often mistaken, but in one way and another they have tended to the end in view. I wish that I had not committed a great many errors, but I do not deplore them nor would I now have them undone.

I do not think it unreasonable to hold the opinion that everything in the universe combines to cause every one of our actions, and this naturally includes all our opinions and desires; but whether an action, once performed, was inevitable from all eternity can only be decided when you have made up your mind whether or no there are events, the events that Dr. Broad calls casual progenitors, which are not completely determined. Hume long ago showed that there was no intrinsic connection between cause and effect which could be perceived by the mind; and of late the Principle of Indeterminacy, by bringing to view certain events to which apparently no causes can be assigned, has cast a doubt on the universal efficacy of those laws upon which science has hitherto been based. It looks as if chance must once more be reckoned with. But if we are not certainly bound by the law of cause and effect, then perhaps it is not an illusion that our wills are free. The bishops and the deans have snatched at this new notion as though it were the devil's tail by which they hoped to drag the old devil himself back into existence. There has been great rejoicing, if not in the courts of heaven, at all events in the palaces of the episcopacy. Perhaps the Te Deum has been sung too soon. It is well to remember that the two most eminent scientists of our day regard Heisenberg's principle with scepticism. Planck has started his belief that further research will sweep away the anomaly, and Einstein has described the philosophical ideas that have been based upon it as "literature"; I am afraid that this is only his civil way of calling them nonsense. The physicists themselves tell us that physics is making such rapid progress that it is only possible to keep abreast of it by close study of the periodical literature

It is surely rash to found a theory on principles suggested by a science that is so unstable. Schrödinger himself has stated that a final and comprehensive judgment on the matter is at present impossible. The plain man is justified in sitting on the fence, but perhaps he is prudent to keep his legs dangling on the side of determinism.

lxxiii

THE life force is vigorous. The delight that accompanies it counter-balances all the pains and hardships that confront men. It makes life worth living, for it works from within and lights with its own bright flame each one's circumstances so that, however intolerable, they yet seem tolerable to him. Much pessimism is caused by ascribing to others the feelings you would feel if you were in their place. It is this (among much else) that makes novels so false. The novelist constructs a public world out of his own private world and gives to the characters of his fancy a sensitiveness, a power of reflection and an emotional capacity, which are peculiar to himself. Most people have little imagination and they do not suffer from circumstances that to the imaginative would be unbearable. The lack of privacy, to take an instance, in which the very poor live seems frightful to us who value it; but it does not seem so to the very poor. They hate to be alone; it gives them a sense of security to live in company. No one who has dwelt among them can fail to have noticed how little they envy the well-to-do. The fact is that they do not want many of the things that to others of us appear essential. It is fortunate for the well-to-do. For he is blind who will not see that in the lives of the proletariat in the great cities all is misery and confusion. It is hard to reconcile oneself to the fact that men should have no work to do, that work should be so dreary, that they should live, they, their wives and their children, on the edge of starvation, and in the end have nothing to look forward to but destitution. If only revolution can remedy this, then let revolution come and come quickly. When we see the cruelty with which men even now treat one another in countries that we have been in the habit of calling civilized, it would be rash to say that they are any better than they were, but for all that it does not seem fatuous to think that the world is on the whole a better place to live in than it was in the past that history sets before us, and that the lot of the great majority, bad as it is, is less dreadful than it was then; and one may reasonably hope that with the increase of knowledge, with the discarding of many cruel superstitions and outworn conventions, with a livelier sense of loving-kindness, many of the evils from which men suffer will be removed. But many evils must continue to exist. We are the playthings of nature. Earthquakes will continue to wreak havoc, droughts to ruin crops and unforeseen floods to destroy the prudent constructions of men. Human folly, alas, will continue to devastate the nations with war. Men will continue to be born who are not fitted for life and life will be a burden to them. So long as some are strong and some are weak, the weak will be driven to the wall. So long as men are cursed with the sense of possession, and that I presume is as long as they exist, they will wrest what they can from those who are powerless to hold it. So long as they have the instinct of self-assertion, they will exercise it at the expense of others' happiness. In short, so long as man is man he must be prepared to face all the woes that he can bear.

There is no explanation for evil. It must be looked upon as a necessary part of the order of the universe. To ignore it is childish; to bewail it senseless. Spinoza called pity woman-ish; the epithet has a harsh sound on the lips of that tender and austere spirit. I suppose he thought that it was but waste of emotion to feel strongly about what you could not alter.

I am not a pessimist. Indeed, it would be nonsensical of me to be so, for I have been one of the lucky ones. I have often wondered at my good fortune. I am well aware that many who were more deserving than I have not had the happy fate that has befallen me. An accident here, an accident there, might have changed everything and frustrated me as so many with talents equal to, or greater than, mine, with equal opportunities, have been frustrated. Should any of them chance to read these pages, I would ask them to believe that I do not arrogantly ascribe to my merits what has come to me, but to some concatenation of unlikely circumstances for which I can offer no explanation. With all my limitations, physical and mental, I have been glad to live. I would not live my life over again. There would be no point in that. Nor would I care to pass again through the anguish I have suffered. It is one of the faults of my nature that I have suffered more from the pains, than I have enjoyed the pleasures of my life. But without my physical imperfections, with a stronger body and a better brain, I would not mind entering upon the world afresh. The years that now stretch immediately in front of us look as if they would be interesting. The young enter upon life now with advantages that were denied to the young of my generation. They are hampered by fewer conventions and they have learnt how great is the value of youth. The world of my twenties was a middle-aged world and youth was something to be got through as quickly as possible so that maturity might be reached. The young things of the present day, at least in that middle class to which I belong, seem to me better prepared. They are taught now many things that are useful to them, whereas we had to pick them up as best we could. The relation between the sexes is more normal. Young women have learnt now to be the companions of young men. One of the difficulties that my generation had to face, the generation that saw the emancipation of women, was this: women had ceased to be the housekeepers and mothers of an earlier age, who led a life apart from men, with their own interests and particular concerns, and were trying to participate in men's affairs without the capacity to do so; they demanded the consideration that had been their due when they were content to look upon themselves as men's inferiors and withal insisted on their right, their new-won right, to join in all the masculine activities in which they knew only enough to make a nuisance of themselves. They were no longer housewives and had not yet learnt to be good fellows. There is no more pleasant spectacle for an elderly gentleman than that of the young girl of the present day, so competent and so self-assured, who can run an office and play a hard game of tennis, who is intelligently concerned with public affairs and can appreciate the arts, and, prepared to stand on her own feet, faces life with cool, shrewd and tolerant eyes.

Far be it from me to don the prophet's mantle, but I think it is clear that these young folk who are now taking the stage must look forward to economic changes that will transform civilization. They will not know the easy, sheltered life which makes many who were at their prime before the war look upon those years as did the survivors of the French Revolution when they look back on the Ancien Régime. They will not know the *douceur de vivre*. We live now on the eve of great revolutions. I cannot doubt that the proletariat, increasingly conscious of its rights, will eventually seize power in one country after the other, and I never cease to marvel that the governing classes of today, rather than continue a vain struggle against these overwhelming forces, do not use every effort to train the masses for their future tasks so that when they are dispossessed their fate may be less cruel than that which befell them in Russia. Years ago Disraeli told them what to do. For my part I must candidly say that I hope the present state of things will last my time. But we live in an era of rapid change and I may yet see the countries of the west given over to the rule of communism. A Russian exile of my acquaintance told me that when he lost his estates and his wealth, he was overcome with despair; but at the end of a fortnight he regained his serenity and never since gave a thought to what he had been deprived of. I do not think I have such an attachment to my various possessions as to regret their loss for long. If such a condition of things came to pass in my world I should make an attempt to adapt myself and then, if I found life intolerable, I think I should not lack the courage to quit a stage on which I could no longer play my part to my own satisfaction. I wonder why so many people turn with horror from the thought of suicide. To speak of it as cowardly is nonsense. I can only approve the man who makes an end of himself of his own will when life has nothing to offer him but pain and misfortune. Did not Pliny say that the power of dying when you please is the best thing that God has given to man amid all the sufferings of life? Putting aside those who regard suicide as sinful because it breaks a divine law, I think the reason of the indignation which it seems to arouse in so many is that the suicide flouts the life-force, and by setting at nought the strongest instinct of human beings casts a terrifying doubt on its power to preserve them.

With this book I shall have completed in sufficient outline the pattern I set myself to make. If I live I shall write other books, for my amusement and I hope for the amusement of my readers, but I do not think they will add anything essential to my design. The house is built. There will be additions, a terrace from which one has a pretty view, or an arbour in which to meditate in the heat of summer; but should death prevent me from producing them, the house, though the housebreakers may set to work on it the day after I am buried in an obituary notice, will have been built.

I look forward to old age without dismay. When Lawrence of Arabia was killed I read in an article contributed by a friend that it was his habit to ride his motorbicycle at an excessive speed with the notion than an accident would end his life while he was still in full possession of his powers and so spare him the indignity of old age. If this is true it was a great weakness in that strange and somewhat theatrical character. It showed want of sense. For the complete life, the perfect pattern, includes old age as well as youth and maturity. The beauty of the morning and the radiance of noon are good, but it would be a very silly person who drew the curtains and turned on the light in order to shut out the tranquillity of the evening. Old age has its pleasures, which, though different, are not less than the pleasures of youth. The philosophers have always told us that we are the slaves of our passions, and is it so small a thing to be liberated from their sway? The fool's old age will be foolish, but so was his youth. The young man turns away from it with horror because he thinks that when he reaches it, he will still yearn for the things that give variety and gusto to his youth. He is mistaken. It is true that the old man will no longer be able to climb an Alp or tumble a pretty girl on a bed; it is true that he can no longer arouse the concupiscence of others. It is something to be free from the pangs of unrequited love and the torment of jealousy. It is something that envy, which so often poisons youth, should be assuaged by the extinction of desire. But these are negative compensations; old age has positive compensations also. Paradoxical as it may sound it has more time. When I was young I was amazed at Plutarch's statement that the elder Cato began at the age of eighty to learn Greek. I am amazed no longer. Old age is ready to undertake tasks that youth shirked because they would take too long. In old age the taste improves and it is possible to enjoy art and literature without the personal bias that in youth warps the judgment. It has the satisfaction of its own fulfillment. It is liberated from the trammels of human egoism; free at last, the soul delights in the passing moment, but does not bid it stay. It has completed the pattern. Goethe asked for survival after death so that he might realize those sides of himself which he felt that in his life he had not had time to develop. But did he not say that he who would accomplish anything must learn to limit himself? When you read his life you cannot but be struck by the way in which he wasted time in trivial pursuits. Perhaps if he had limited himself more carefully he would have developed everything that properly belonged to his special individuality and so found no need of a future life.

lxxiv

SPINOZA says that a free man thinks of nothing less than of death. It is unnecessary to dwell upon it, but it is foolish, as so many do, to shrink from all consideration of it. It is well to make up one's mind about it. It is impossible to know till death is there facing one whether one will fear it. I have often tried to imagine what my feelings would be if a doctor told me I had a fatal disease and had no more than a little time to live. I have put them into the mouths of various characters of my invention, but I am aware that thus I dramatized them and I cannot tell whether they would be those I should actually feel. I do not think I have a very strong instinctive hold on life. I have had a good many serious illnesses, but have only once known myself to be within measurable distance of death; then I was so tired that I could not fear, I only wanted to be done with the struggle. Death is inevitable and it does not much matter how one meets it. I do not think one can be blamed if one hopes that one will not be aware of its imminence and be fortunate enough to undergo it without pain.

I have always lived so much in the future that now, though the future is so short, I cannot get out of the habit and my mind looks forward with a certain complacency to the completion within an indefinite number of years of the pattern that I have tried to make. There are moments when I have so palpitating an eagerness for death that I could fly to it as to the arms of a lover. It gives me the same passionate thrill as years ago was given me by life. I am drunk with the thought of it. It seems to me then to offer me the final and absolute freedom. Notwithstanding, I am willing enough to go on living so long as the doctors can keep me in tolerable health; I enjoy the spectacle of the world and it interests me to see what is going to happen. The consummation of many lives that have run their course parallel with my own gives me continual food for reflection and sometimes for the confirmation of theories that I formed long ago. I shall be sorry to part from my friends. I cannot be indifferent to the welfare of some whom I have guided and protected, but it is well that after depending on me so long they should enjoy their liberty whithersoever it leads them. Having held a certain place in the world for a long time I am content that others soon should occupy it. After all the point of a pattern is that it should be completed. When nothing can be added without spoiling the design the artist leaves it.

But now if anyone should ask me what is the use or sense of this pattern I should have to answer, none. It is merely something I have imposed on the senselessness of life because I am a novelist. For my own satisfaction, for my amusement

and to gratify what feels to me like an organic need, I have
shaped my life in accordance with a certain design, with a beginning, a middle and an end, as from people I have met here
and there I have constructed a play, a novel or a short story.
We are the product of our natures and our environment. I
have not made the pattern I thought best, or even the pattern I should have liked to make, but merely that which
seemed feasible. There are better patterns than mine. I do
not believe that I am influenced only by an illusion natural
to the man of letters to think that the best pattern of all is
the husbandman's, who ploughs his land and reaps his crop,
who enjoys his toil and enjoys his leisure, loves, marries,
begets children and dies. When I have observed the peas-
antry in those favoured lands in which the earth produces
her plenty without excessive labour, where the pleasures and
pains of the individual are those incidental to the human
race, it has seemed to me that there the perfect life was
perfectly realized. There life, like a good story, pursues its
way from beginning to end in a firm and unbroken line.

lxxv

THE egoism of man makes him unwilling to accept the meaninglessness of life and when he has unhappily found himself
no longer able to believe in a higher power whose ends he
could flatter himself that he subserved he has sought to give
it significance by constructing certain values beyond those
that seem to further his immediate welfare. The wisdom
of the ages has chosen three of these as most worthy. To
aim at them for their own sake has seemed to give life some
kind of sense. Though it can hardly be doubted that they too
have a biologic utility, they have superficially an appearance
of disinterestedness which gives man the illusion that through
them he escapes from human bondage. Their nobility
strengthens his wavering sense of his spiritual significance
and, whatever the result, the pursuit of them appears to
justify his efforts. Oases in the vast desert of existence, since
he knows no other end to his journey, man persuades him-

self that they at all events are worth reaching and that there
he will find rest and the answer to his question. These three
values are Truth, Beauty and Goodness.

I have a notion that Truth finds a place in this list for
rhetorical reasons. Man invests it with ethical qualities, such
as courage, honour and independence of spirit, which indeed
are often shown by his insistence on truth, but which in effect
have nothing whatever to do with it. Finding in it so great
an occasion for his own self-assertion he will be indifferent
to any sacrifice that it entails. But then his interest is in himself and not in the truth. If truth is a value it is because it is
true and not because it is brave to speak it. But truth is a
character of judgments and so one would suppose that its
value lay in the judgments it characterizes rather than in
itself. A bridge that joined two great cities would be more
important than a bridge that led from one barren field to another. And if truth is one of the ultimate values, it seems
strange that no one seems quite to know what it is. Philosophers still quarrel about its meaning and the upholders of
rival doctrines say many sarcastic things of one another. In
these circumstances the plain man must leave them to it and
content himself with the plain man's truth. This is a very
modest affair and merely asserts something about particular
existents. It is a bare statement of the facts. If this is a value
one must admit that none is more neglected. The books on
ethics give long lists of occasions on which it may be legitimately withheld; their authors might have saved themselves
the trouble. The wisdom of the ages has long since decided
that *toutes vérités ne sont pas bonnes à dire*. Man has always sacrificed truth to his vanity, comfort and advantage.
He lives not by truth but by make-believe, and his idealism,
it has sometimes seemed to me, is merely his effort to attach
the prestige of truth to the fictions he has invented to satisfy
his self-conceit.

lxxvi

BEAUTY stands in a better case. For many years I thought
that it was beauty alone that gave significance to life and

that the only purpose that could be assigned to the teeming generations that succeed one another on the face of the earth was to produce now and then an artist. The work of art, I decided, was the crowning product of human activity, and the final justification for all the misery, the endless toil and the frustrated strivings of humanity. So that Michelangelo might paint certain figures on the ceiling of the Sistine Chapel, so that Shakespeare might write certain speeches and Keats his odes, it seemed to me worth while that untold millions should have lived and suffered and died. And though I modified this extravagance later by including the beautiful life among the works of art that alone gave a meaning to life, it was still beauty that I valued. All these notions I have long since abandoned.

In the first place I discovered that beauty was a full stop. When I considered beautiful things I found that there was nothing for me to do but to gaze and admire. The emotion they gave me was exquisite, but I could not preserve it, nor could I indefinitely repeat it; the most beautiful things in the world finished by boring me. I noticed that I got a more lasting satisfaction from works of a more tentative character. Because they had not achieved complete success they gave more scope for the activity of my imagination. In the greatest of all works of art everything had been realized, I could give nothing, and my restless mind tired of passive contemplation. It seemed to me that beauty was like the summit of a mountain peak; when you had reached it there was nothing to do but to come down again. Perfection is a trifle dull. It is not the least of life's ironies that this, which we all aim at, is better not quite achieved.

I suppose that we mean by beauty that object, spiritual or material, more often material, which satisfies our æsthetic sense. That, however, tells you just about as much as you would know about water if you were told that it was wet. I have read a good many books to discover what the authorities had to say that made the matter a little plainer. I have known intimately a great many persons who were absorbed in the arts. I am afraid that neither from them nor from books have I learnt much that greatly profited me. One of the most curious things that has forced itself on my notice is that there is no permanence in the judgment of beauty. The museums are full of objects which the most cultivated taste of a period considered beautiful, but which seem to us now worthless; and in my own lifetime I have seen the beauty evaporate from poems and pictures, exquisite not so long ago, like hoar frost before the morning sun. Vain as we may be we can hardly think our own judgment ultimate; what we think beautiful will doubtless be scorned in another generation, and what we have despised may be raised to honour. The only conclusion is that beauty is relative to the needs of a particular generation, and that to examine the things we consider beautiful for qualities of absolute beauty is futile. If beauty is one of the values that give life significance it is something that is constantly changing and thus cannot be analyzed, for we can as little feel the beauty our ancestors felt as we can smell the roses they smelt.

I have tried to find out from the writers on æsthetics what it is in human nature that makes it possible for us to get the emotion of beauty and what exactly this emotion is. It is usual enough to talk of the æsthetic instinct: the term seems to give it a place among the mainsprings of the human being, like hunger and sex, and at the same time to endow it with a specific quality that flatters the philosophic craving for unity. So æsthetics have been derived from an instinct of expression, an exuberance of vitality, a mystical sense of the absolute and I know not what. For my part I should have said it was not an instinct at all, but a state of the body-mind, founded in part on certain powerful instincts, but combined with human characteristics, which are the result of the evolutionary process, and with the common circumstances of life. That it has a great deal to do with the sexual instinct seems to be shown by the fact, commonly admitted, that those who possess an æsthetic sense of unusual delicacy diverge sexually from the norm to an extreme and often pathological degree. There may be in the constitution of the body-mind something that renders certain tones, certain rhythms and certain colours peculiarly attractive to man, so that there may be a physiological reason for the elements of what we consider beautiful. But we also find things beautiful because they remind us of objects, people or places, that we have loved or to which the passage of time has lent a sentimental value. We find things beautiful because we recognize them and contrariwise we find things beautiful because their novelty surprises us. All this means that association, by likeness or contrast, enters largely into the æsthetic emotion. It is only association that can explain the æsthetic value of the ugly. I do not know that anyone has studied the effect of time on the creation of beauty. It is not only that we grow to see the beauty of things as we know them better; it is rather that the delight that succeeding ages take in them somehow adds to their beauty. That, I suppose, is why certain works whose beauty now seems manifest should, when first given to the world, have attracted no great attention. I have a notion that the odes of Keats are more beautiful than when he wrote them. They are enriched by the emotion of all who have found solace and strength in their loveliness. Far then from thinking the æsthetic emotion a specific, simple affair, I think it is a very complicated one, which is made up of various, often discordant elements. It is no good for the æstheticians to say that you ought not to be moved by a picture or a symphony because it fills you with erotic excitement or melts you to tears by reminding you of some long-forgotten scene, or through its associations exalts you to mystic rapture. It does; and these sides of it are just as much part and parcel of the æsthetic emotion as the disinterested satisfaction in balance and composition.

What exactly is one's reaction to a great work of art? What does one feels when for instance one looks at Titian's Entombment in the Louvre or listens to the quintet in the *Meistersinger?* I know what mine is. It is an excitement that gives me a sense of exhilaration, intellectual but suffused with sensuality, a feeling of well-being in which I seem to discern a sense of power and of liberation from human ties; at the same time I feel in myself a tenderness which is rich with human sympathy; I feel rested, at peace and yet spiritually aloof. Indeed on occasion, looking at certain pictures or statues, listening to certain music, I have had an emotion so strong that I could only describe it in the same words as those the mystics use to describe the union with God. That is why I have thought that this sense of communion with a larger reality is not only the privilege of the religious, but may be reached by other paths than prayer and fasting. But I have asked myself what was the use of this emotion. Of course it is delightful and pleasure in itself is good, but what is there in it that makes it superior to any other pleasure, so superior that to speak of it as pleasure at all seems to depreciate it? Was Jeremy Bentham so foolish after all when he said that one sort of happiness was as good as another, and if the amount of pleasure was equal pushpin as good as poetry? The answer the mystics gave to this question was unequivocal. They said that rapture was worthless unless it strengthened the character and rendered man more capable of right action. The value of it lay in works.

It has been my lot to live much among persons of æsthetic sensibility. I am not speaking now of the creators: to my mind there is a great difference between those who create art and those who enjoy it; the creators produce because of that urge within them that forces them to exteriorize their personality. It is an accident if what they produce has beauty; that is seldom their special aim. Their aim is to disembarrass their souls of the burdens that oppress them and they use the means, their pen, their paints or their clay, for which they have by nature a facility. I am speaking now of those to whom the contemplation and appreciation of art is the main business of life. I have found little to admire in them. They are vain and self-complacent. Inapt for the practical affairs of life, they disdain those who with humility perform the modest offices to which their destiny has constrained them. Because they have read a great many books or seen a great many pictures they think themselves superior to other men. They use art to escape the realities of life and in their imbecile contempt for common things deny value to the essential activities of humanity. They are no better really than drug-fiends; worse rather, for the drug-fiend at all events does not set himself on a pedestal from which to look down on his fellow-men. The value of art, like the value of the Mystic Way, lies in its effects. If it can only give pleasure, however spiritual that pleasure may be, it is of no great consequence or at least of no more consequence than a dozen oysters and a pint of Montrachet. If it is a solace, that is well enough; the world is full of inevitable evils and it is good that man should have some hermitage to which from time to time he may withdraw himself; but not to escape them, rather to gather fresh strength to face them. For art, if it is to be reckoned as one of the great values of life, must teach men humility, tolerance, wisdom and magnanimity. The value of art is not beauty, but right action.

If beauty is one of the great values of life, then it seems hard to believe that the æsthetic sense which enables men to appreciate it should be the privilege only of a class. It is not possible to maintain that a form of sensibility that is shared but by the elect can be a necessity of human life. Yet that is what the æsthetics claim. I must confess that in my foolish youth when I considered that art (in which I included the beauties of nature, for I was very much of opinion, as indeed I still am, that their beauty was constructed by men as definitely as they constructed pictures or symphonies) was the crown of human endeavour and the justification of man's existence, it gave me a peculiar satisfaction to think that it could be appreciated only by the chosen few. But this notion has long stuck in my gizzard. I cannot believe that beauty is the appanage of a set and I am inclined to think that a manifestation of art that has a meaning only to persons who have undergone a peculiar training is as inconsiderable as the set to which it appeals. An art is only great and significant if it is one that all may enjoy. The art of a clique is but a plaything. I do not know why distinctions are made between ancient art and modern art. There is nothing but art. Art is living. To attempt to give an object of art life by dwelling on its historical, cultural, or archæological associations is senseless. It does not matter whether a statue was hewn by an archaic Greek or a modern Frenchman. Its only importance is that it should give us here and now the æsthetic thrill and that this æsthetic thrill should move us to works. If it is to be anything more than a self-indulgence and an occasion of self-complacency, it must strengthen your character and make it more fitted for right action. And little as I like the deduction, I cannot but accept it; and this is that the work of art must be judged by its fruits, and if these are not good it is valueless. It is an odd fact, which must be accepted as in the nature of things and for which I know no explanation, that the artist achieves this effect only when he does not intend it. His sermon is most efficacious if he has no notion that he is preaching one. The bee produces wax for her own purposes and is unaware that man will put it to diverse uses.

lxxvii

IT APPEARS then impossible to say that either truth or beauty has intrinsic value. What about goodness? But before I speak of goodness I would speak of love; for there are philosophers who, thinking that it embraced every other, have accepted it as the highest of human values. Platonism and Christianity have combined to give it a mystical significance. The associations of the word lend it an emotion that makes it more exciting than plain goodness. Goodness in comparison is a trifle dull. But love has two meanings, love pure and simple, sexual love, namely; and loving-kindness. I do not think that even Plato distinguished them with exactness. He seems to me to ascribe the exultation, the sense of power, the feeling of heightened vitality which accompany sexual love to that other love which he calls the heavenly love and which I should prefer to call loving-kindness; and by doing so infects it with the ineradicable vice of earthly love. For love passes. Love dies. The great tragedy of life is not that men perish, but that they cease to love. Not the least of the evils of life, and one for which there is small help, is that someone whom you love no longer loves you; when La Rochefoucauld discovered that between two lovers there is one who loves and one who lets himself be loved he put in an epigram the discord that must ever prevent men from achieving in love perfect happiness. However much people may resent the fact and however angrily deny it, there can surely be no doubt that love depends on certain secretions of the sexual glands. In the immense majority these do not continue indefinitely to be excited by the same object and with advancing years they atrophy. People are very hypocritical in this matter and will not face the truth. They so deceive themselves that they can accept it with complacency when their love dwindles into what they describe as a solid and enduring affection. As if affection had anything to do with love! Affection is created by habit, community of interests, convenience and the desire of companionship. It is a comfort rather than an exhilaration. We are creatures of change, change is the atmosphere we breathe, and is it likely that the strongest but one of all our instincts should be free from the law? We are not the same persons this year as last; nor are those we love. It is a happy chance if we, changing, continue to love a changed person. Mostly, different ourselves, we make a desperate, pathetic effort to love in a different person the person we once loved. It is only because the power of love when it seizes us seems so mighty that we persuade ourselves that it will last forever. When it subsides we are ashamed, and, duped, blame ourselves for our weakness, whereas we should accept our change of heart as a natural effect of our humanity. The experience of mankind has led them to regard love with mingled feelings. They have been suspicious of it. They have as often cursed as praised it. The soul of man, struggling to be free, has except for brief moments looked upon the self-surrender that it claims as a fall from grace. The happiness it brings may be the greatest of which man is capable, but it is seldom, seldom unalloyed. It writes a story that generally has a sad ending. Many have resented its power and angrily prayed to be delivered from its burden. They have hugged their chains, but knowing they were chains hated them too. Love is not always blind and there are few things that cause greater wretchedness than to love with all your heart someone who you know is unworthy of love.

But loving-kindness is not coloured with that transitoriness which is the irremediable defect of love. It is true that it is not entirely devoid of the sexual element. It is like dancing; one dances for the pleasure of the rhythmic movement, and it is not necessary that one should wish to go to bed with one's partner; but it is a pleasant exercise only if to do so would not be disgusting. In loving-kindness the sexual instinct is sublimated, but it lends the emotion something of its own warm and vitalizing energy. Loving-kindness is the better part of goodness. It lends grace to the sterner qualities of which this consists and makes it a little less difficult to practice those minor virtues of self-control and self-restraint, patience, discipline and tolerance, which are the passive and not very exhilarating elements of goodness. Goodness is the only value that seems in this world of appearances to have any claim to be an end in itself. Virtue is its own reward. I am ashamed to have reached so commonplace a conclusion. With my instinct for effect I should have liked to end my book with some startling and paradoxical announcement or with a cynicism that my readers would have recognized with a chuckle as characteristic. It seems I have little more to say than can be read in any copybook or heard from any pulpit. I have gone a long way round to discover what everyone knew already.

I have little sense of reverence. There is a great deal too much of it in the world. It is claimed for many objects that do not deserve it. It is often no more than the conventional homage we pay to things in which we are not willing to take an active interest. The best homage we can pay to the great figures of the past, Dante, Titian, Shakespeare, Spinoza, is to treat them not with reverence, but with the familiarity we should exercise if they were our contemporaries. Thus we pay them the highest compliment we can; our familiarity acknowledges that they are alive for us. But when now and then I have come across real goodness I have found reverence rise naturally in my heart. It has not seemed to matter then that its rare possessors were perhaps sometimes a trifle less intelligent than I should have liked them to be. When I was a small boy and unhappy I used to dream night after night that my life at school was all a dream and that I should wake to find myself at home again with my mother. Her death was a wound that fifty years have not entirely healed. I have long ceased to have that dream; but I have never quite lost the sense that my living life was a mirage in which I did this and that because that was how it fell out, but which, even while I was playing my part in it, I could look at from a distance and know for the mirage it was. When I look back on my life, with its successes and its failures, its endless errors, its deceptions and its fulfilments, its joys and miseries, it seems to me strangely lacking in reality. It is shadowy and unsubstantial. It may be that my heart, having found rest nowhere, had some deep ancestral craving for God and immortality which my reason would have no truck with. In default of anything better it has seemed to me sometimes that I might pretend to myself that the goodness I have not so seldom after all come across in many of those I have encountered on my way had reality. It may be that in goodness we may see, not a reason for life nor an explanation of it, but an extenuation. In this indifferent universe, with its inevitable evils that surround us from the cradle to the grave, it may serve, not as a challenge or a reply, but as an affirmation of our own independence. It is the retort that humour makes to the tragic absurdity of fate. Unlike beauty, it can be perfect without being tedious, and, greater than love, time does not wither its delight. But goodness is shown in right action and who can tell in this meaningless world what right action is? It is not action that aims at happiness; it is a happy chance if happiness results. Plato, as we know, enjoined upon his wise man to abandon the serene life of contemplation for the turmoil of practical affairs and thereby set the claim of duty above the desire for happiness; and we have all of us, I suppose, on occasion adopted a course because we thought it right though we well knew that it could bring us happiness neither then nor in the future. What then is right action? For my own part the best answer I know is that given by Fray Luis de Leon. To follow it does not look so difficult that human weakness quails before it as beyond its strength. With it I can end my book. The beauty of life, he says, is nothing but this, that each should act in conformity with his nature and his business.

THE CONSTANT WIFE

To
ETHEL BARRYMORE

CHARACTERS

CONSTANCE
JOHN MIDDLETON, F.R.C.S.
BERNARD KERSAL
MRS. CULVER

MARIE-LOUISE
MARTHA
BARBARA
MORTIMER DURHAM

BENTLEY

The action of the play takes place in John's house in Harley Street.

ACT ONE

SCENE: CONSTANCE'S *drawing room. It is a room furnished with singularly good taste.* CONSTANCE *has a gift for decoration and has made this room of hers both beautiful and comfortable.*
   It is afternoon.
   MRS. CULVER *is seated alone. She is an elderly lady with a pleasant face and she is dressed in walking costume. The door is opened and* BENTLEY *the butler introduces* MARTHA CULVER. *This is her daughter and a fine young woman.*

BENTLEY: Miss Culver.
   [*He goes out.*]
MARTHA [*With astonishment*]: Mother.
MRS. CULVER [*Very calmly*]: Yes, darling.

MARTHA: You're the last person I expected to find here. You never told me you were coming to see Constance.

MRS. CULVER [*Good humouredly*]: I didn't intend to till I saw in your beady eye that *you* meant to. I thought I'd just as soon be here first.

MARTHA: Bentley says she's out.

MRS. CULVER: Yes. . . . Are you going to wait?

MARTHA: Certainly.

MRS. CULVER: Then I will too.

MARTHA: That'll be very nice.

MRS. CULVER: Your words are cordial, but your tone is slightly frigid, my dear.

MARTHA: I don't know what you mean by that, mother.

MRS. CULVER: My dear, we've known one another a great many years, haven't we? More than we always find it convenient to mention.

MARTHA: Not at all. I'm thirty-two. I'm not in the least ashamed of my age. Constance is thirty-six.

MRS. CULVER: And yet we still think it worth while to be a trifle disingenuous with one another. Our sex takes a natural pleasure in dissimulation.

MARTHA: I don't think any one can accuse me of not being frank.

MRS. CULVER: Frankness of course is the pose of the moment. It is often a very effective screen for one's thoughts.

MARTHA: I think you're being faintly disagreeable to me, mother.

MRS. CULVER: I, on the other hand, think you're inclined to be decidedly foolish.

MARTHA: Because I want to tell Constance something she ought to know?

MRS. CULVER: Ah, I *was* right then. And it's to tell her that you've broken an engagement, and left three wretched people to play cutthroat.

MARTHA: It is.

MRS. CULVER: And may I ask why you think Constance ought to know?

MARTHA: Why? Why? Why? That's one of those questions that really don't need answering.

MRS. CULVER: I've always noticed that the questions that really don't need answering are the most difficult to answer.

MARTHA: It isn't at all difficult to answer. She ought to know the truth becaues it's the truth.

MRS. CULVER: Of course truth is an excellent thing, but before one tells it one should be quite sure that one does so for the advantage of the person who hears it rather than for one's own self-satisfaction.

MARTHA: Mother, Constance is a very unhappy person.

MRS. CULVER: Nonsense. She eats well, sleeps well, dresses well and she's losing weight. No woman can be unhappy in those circumstances.

MARTHA: Of course if you won't understand it's no use my trying to make you. You're a darling, but you're the most unnatural mother. Your attitude simply amazes me.

[*The door opens and* BENTLEY *ushers in* MRS. FAWCETT. MRS. FAWCETT *is a trim, business-like woman of forty.*]

BENTLEY: Mrs. Fawcett.

MRS. CULVER: Oh, Barbara, how very nice to see you.

BARBARA [*Going up to her and kissing her*]: Bentley told me you were here and Constance was out. What are you doing?

MRS. CULVER: Bickering.

BARBARA: What about?

MRS. CULVER: Constance.

MARTHA: I'm glad you've come, Barbara. . . . Did you know that John was having an affair with Marie-Louise?

BARBARA: I hate giving a straight answer to a straight question.

MARTHA: I suppose every one knows but us. How long have you known? They say it's been going on for months. I can't think how it is we've only just heard it.

MRS. CULVER [*Ironically*]: It speaks very well for human nature that with the masses of dear friends we have it's only to-day that one of them broke the news to us.

BARBARA: Perhaps the dear friend only heard it this morning.

MARTHA: At first I refused to believe it.

MRS. CULVER: Only quite, quite at first, darling. You surrendered to the evidence with an outraged alacrity that took my breath away.

MARTHA: Of course I put two and two together. After the first shock I understood everything. I'm only astonished that it never occurred to me before.

BARBARA: Are you very much upset, Mrs. Culver?

MRS. CULVER: Not a bit. I was brought up by a very strict mother to believe that men were naturally wicked. I am seldom surprised at what they do and never upset.

MARTHA: Mother has been simply maddening. She treats it as though it didn't matter a row of pins.

MRS. CULVER: Constance and John have been married for fifteen years. John is a very agreeable man. I've sometimes wondered whether he was any more faithful to his wife than most husbands, but as it was really no concern of mine I didn't let my mind dwell on it.

MARTHA: Is Constance your daughter or is she not your daughter?

MRS. CULVER: You certainly have a passion for straight questions, my dear. The answer is yes.

MARTHA: And are you prepared to sit there quietly and let her husband grossly deceive her with her most intimate friend?

MRS. CULVER: So long as she doesn't know I can't see that she's any the worse. Marie-Louise is a nice little thing, silly of course, but that's what men like, and if John is going to deceive Constance it's much better that it should be with some one we all know.

MARTHA [*To* BARBARA]: Did you ever hear a respectable woman—and mother is respectable. . . .

MRS. CULVER [*Interrupting*]: Oh, quite.

MARTHA: Talk like that?

BARBARA: You think that something ought to be done about it?

MARTHA: I am determined that something shall be done about it.

MRS. CULVER: Well, my dear, I'm determined that there's at least one thing you shan't do and that is to tell Constance.

BARBARA [*A trifle startled*] : Is that what you want to do?

MARTHA : Somebody ought to tell her. If mother won't I must.

BARBARA : I'm extremely fond of Constance. Of course I've known what was going on for a long time and I've been dreadfully worried.

MARTHA : John has put her into an odious position. No man has the right to humiliate his wife as he has humiliated Constance. He's made her perfectly ridiculous.

MRS. CULVER : If women were ridiculous because their husbands are unfaithful to them there would surely be a great deal more merriment in the world than there is.

BARBARA [*Delighted to have a good gossip*] : You know they were lunching together to-day?

MARTHA : We hadn't heard that. But they were dining together the night before last.

MRS. CULVER [*Brightly*] : We know what they had to eat for dinner. Do you know what they had to eat for luncheon?

MARTHA : Mother.

MRS. CULVER : Well, I thought she seemed rather uppish about the lunch.

MARTHA : You have no sense of decency, mother.

MRS. CULVER : Oh, my dear, don't talk to me about decency. Decency died with dear Queen Victoria.

BARBARA [*To* MRS. CULVER] : But you can't approve of John having an open and flagrant intrigue with Constance's greatest friend.

MRS. CULVER : It may be that with advancing years my arteries have hardened. I am unable to attach any great importance to the philanderings of men. I think it's their nature. John is a very hard-working surgeon. If he likes to lunch and dine with a pretty woman now and then I don't think he's much to blame. It must be very tiresome to have three meals a day with the same woman for seven days a week. I'm a little bored myself at seeing Martha opposite me at the dinner-table. And men can't stand boredom as well as women.

MARTHA : I'm sure I'm very much obliged to you, mother.

BARBARA [*Significantly*]: But they're not only lunching and dining together.

MRS. CULVER: You fear the worst, my dear?

BARBARA [*With solemnity*]: I know the worst.

MRS. CULVER: I always think that's such a comfort. With closed doors and no one listening to us, so long as a man is kind and civil to his wife do you blame him very much if he strays occasionally from the narrow path of virtue?

MARTHA: Do you mean to say that you attach no importance to husbands and wives keeping their marriage vows?

MRS. CULVER: I think wives should.

BARBARA: But that's grossly unfair. Why should *they* any more than men?

MRS. CULVER: Because on the whole they like it. We ascribe a great deal of merit to ourselves because we're faithful to our husbands. I don't believe we deserve it for a minute. We're naturally faithful creatures and we're faithful because we have no particular inclination to be anything else.

BARBARA: I wonder.

MRS. CULVER: My dear, you are a widow and perfectly free. Have you really had any great desire to do anything that the world might say you shouldn't?

BARBARA: I have my business. When you work hard eight hours a day you don't much want to be bothered with love. In the evening the tired business woman wants to go to a musical comedy or play cards. She doesn't want to be worried with adoring males.

MARTHA: By the way, how is your business?

BARBARA: Growing by leaps and bounds. As a matter of fact I came here to-day to ask Constance if she would like to come in with me.

MRS. CULVER: Why should she? John earns plenty of money.

BARBARA: Well, I thought if things came to a crisis she might like to know that her independence was assured.

MRS. CULVER: Oh, you want them to come to a crisis too?

BARBARA: No, of course I don't. But, you know, they can't go on like this. It's a miracle that Constance hasn't heard yet. She's bound to find out soon.

MRS. CULVER: I suppose it's inevitable.

MARTHA: I hope she'll find out as quickly as possible. I still think it's mother's duty to tell her.

MRS. CULVER: Which I have no intention of doing.

MARTHA: And if mother won't I think I ought.

MRS. CULVER: Which I have no intention of permitting.

MARTHA: He's humiliated her beyond endurance. Her position is intolerable. I have no words to express my opinion of Marie-Louise, and the first time I see her I shall tell her exactly what I think of her. She's a horrid, ungrateful, mean and contemptible little cat.

BARBARA: Anyhow I think it would be a comfort to Constance to know that if anything happened she has me to turn to.

MRS. CULVER: But John would make her a handsome allowance. He's a very generous man.

MARTHA [*Indignantly*]: Do you think Constance would accept it?

BARBARA: Martha's quite right, Mrs. Culver. No woman in those circumstances would take a penny of his money.

MRS. CULVER: That's what she'd say. But she'd take care that her lawyer made the best arrangement he could. Few men know with what ingenuity we women can combine the disinterested gesture with a practical eye for the main chance.

BARBARA: Aren't you rather cynical, Mrs. Culver?

MRS. CULVER: I hope not. But when women are alone together I don't see why they shouldn't tell the truth now and then. It's a rest from the weary round of pretending to be something that we quite well know we're not.

MARTHA [*Stiffly*]: I'm not aware that I've ever pretended to be anything I wasn't.

MRS. CULVER: I dare say not, my dear. But I've always thought you were a little stupid. You take after your poor father. Constance and I have the brains of the family.

[CONSTANCE *comes into the room. She is a handsome woman of six and thirty. She has been out and wears a hat.*]

BARBARA [*Eagerly*]: Constance.

CONSTANCE: I'm so sorry I wasn't in. How nice of you all to wait. How are you, mother darling?

[*She kisses them one after another.*]

MARTHA: What have you been doing all day, Constance?

CONSTANCE: Oh, I've been shopping with Marie-Louise. She's just coming up.

BARBARA [*With dismay*]: Is she here?

CONSTANCE: Yes. She's telephoning.

MARTHA [*Ironically*]: You and Marie-Louise are quite inseparable.

CONSTANCE: I like her. She amuses me.

MARTHA: Were you lunching together?

CONSTANCE: No, she was lunching with a beau.

MARTHA [*With a glance at* MRS. CULVER]: Oh, really. [*Breezily*] John always comes home to luncheon, doesn't he?

CONSTANCE [*With great frankness*]: When he doesn't have to be at the hospital too early.

MARTHA: Was he lunching with you to-day?

CONSTANCE: No. He was engaged.

MARTHA: Where?

CONSTANCE: Good heavens, I don't know! When you've been married as long as I have you never ask your husband where he's going.

MARTHA: I don't know why not.

CONSTANCE [*Smiling*]: Because he might take it into his head to ask *you*.

MRS. CULVER: And also because if you're a wise woman you have confidence in your husband.

CONSTANCE: John has never given me a moment's uneasiness yet.

MARTHA: You're lucky.

CONSTANCE [*With her tongue in her cheek*]: Or wise.

[MARIE-LOUISE *appears. She is a very pretty little thing, beautifully dressed, of the clinging, large-eyed type.*]

MARIE-LOUISE: Oh, I didn't know there was a party.

MRS. CULVER: Martha and I are just going.

CONSTANCE: You know my mother, Marie-Louise.

MARIE-LOUISE: Of course I do.

CONSTANCE: She's a very nice mother.

MRS. CULVER: With her head screwed on the right way and very active for her years.

[MARIE-LOUISE *kisses* BARBARA *and* MARTHA.]

MARIE-LOUISE: How do you do.

MARTHA [*Looking at her dress*]: That's new, isn't it, Marie-Louise?

MARIE-LOUISE: Yes, I've never had it on before.

MARTHA: Oh, did you put it on because you were lunching with a beau?

MARIE-LOUISE: What makes you think I was lunching with a beau?

MARTHA: Constance told me so.

CONSTANCE: It was only a guess on my part. [*To* MARIE-LOUISE] When we met I noticed that your eyes were shining and you had that pleased, young look a woman always gets when some one has been telling her she's the most adorable thing in the world.

MARTHA: Tell us who it was, Marie-Louise.

CONSTANCE: Do nothing of the kind, Marie-Louise. Keep it a secret and give us something to gossip about.

BARBARA: How is your husband, dear?

MARIE-LOUISE: Oh, he's very well. I've just been telephoning to him.

BARBARA: I never saw any one adore his wife so obviously as he adores you.

MARIE-LOUISE: Yes, he's sweet, isn't he?

BARBARA: But doesn't it make you a little nervous sometimes? It must be nerve-racking to be obliged to live up to such profound devotion. It would be a dreadful shock if he ever found out that you were not everything he thought you.

CONSTANCE [*Charmingly*]: But Marie-Louise is everything he thinks her.

MARIE-LOUISE: And even if I weren't I think it would require more than the evidence of his eyes to persuade him.

CONSTANCE: Listen. There's John. [*She goes to the door and calls*] John! John!

JOHN [*Downstairs*]: Hulloa.

CONSTANCE: Are you coming up? Marie-Louise is here.

JOHN: Yes, I'm just coming.

CONSTANCE: He's been operating all the afternoon. I expect he's tired out.

MARTHA [*With a look at* MARIE-LOUISE]: I dare say he only had a sandwich for luncheon.

[JOHN *comes in. He is a tall, spare man of about forty.*]

JOHN: Good Lord, I never saw such a lot of people. How is my mother-in-law?

MRS. CULVER: Mother-in-lawish.

JOHN [*Kissing her—to* BARBARA]: You know, I only married Constance because her mother wouldn't have me.

MRS. CULVER: I was too young at the time to marry a boy twenty years younger than myself.

CONSTANCE: It hasn't prevented you from flirting outrageously with the creature ever since. It's lucky I'm not a jealous woman.

JOHN: What have you been doing all day, darling?

CONSTANCE: I've been shopping with Marie-Louise.

JOHN [*Shaking hands with* MARIE-LOUISE]: Oh, how do you do. Did you lunch together?

MARTHA: No, she lunched with a beau.

JOHN: I wish it had been me. [*To* MARIE-LOUISE] What have you been doing with yourself lately? We haven't seen you for ages.

MARIE-LOUISE: You're never about. Constance and I almost live in one another's pockets.

JOHN: How's that rich husband of yours?

MARIE-LOUISE: I've just been speaking to him. Isn't it a bore, he's got to go down to Birmingham for the night.

CONSTANCE: You'd better come and dine with us.

MARIE-LOUISE: Oh, it's awfully nice of you. But I'm tired out. I shall just go to bed and have an egg.

JOHN: I was just going to tell you, Constance. I shan't be in this evening. I've got an acute appendix to do.

CONSTANCE: Oh, what a nuisance.

MARTHA: You've got a wonderful profession, John. If you ever want to do anything or go anywhere you've only got to say you've got an operation and no one can prove it's a lie.

CONSTANCE: Oh, my dear, you mustn't put suspicions into my innocent head. It would never occur to John to be so deceitful. [*To* JOHN] Would it?

JOHN: I think I'd have to go an awful long way before I managed to deceive you, darling.

CONSTANCE [*With a little smile*]: Sometimes I think you're right.

MARIE-LOUISE: I do like to see a husband and wife so devoted to one another as you and John. You've been married fifteen years, haven't you?

JOHN: Yes. And it doesn't seem a day too much.

MARIE-LOUISE: Well, I must be running along. I'm late already. Good-bye, darling. Good-bye, Mrs. Culver.

CONSTANCE: Good-bye, darling. We've had such a nice afternoon.

MARIE-LOUISE [*Giving her hand to* JOHN]: Good-bye.

JOHN: Oh, I'll come downstairs with you.

MARTHA: I was just going, Marie-Louise. I'll come with you.

MARIE-LOUISE [*With presence of mind*]: John, I wonder if you'd mind looking at my knee for a minute. It's been rather painful for the last day or two.

JOHN: Of course not. Come into my consulting-room. These knee-caps are troublesome things when you once get them out of order.

MARTHA [*Firmly*]: I'll wait for you. You won't be long, will you? We might share a taxi.

MARIE-LOUISE: I've got my car.

MARTHA: Oh, how nice! You can give me a lift then.

MARIE-LOUISE: Of course. I shall be delighted.

[JOHN *opens the door for* MARIE-LOUISE. *She goes out and he follows her.* CONSTANCE *has watched this little scene coolly, but with an alert mind.*]

MARTHA: What is the matter with her knee?

CONSTANCE: It slips.

MARTHA: What happens then?

CONSTANCE: She slips too.

MARTHA: Are you never jealous of these women who come and see John in his consulting-room?

CONSTANCE: He always has a nurse within call in case they should attempt to take liberties with him.

MARTHA [*Amiably*]: Is the nurse there now?

CONSTANCE: And anyway I can't help thinking that the sort of woman who wants to be made love to in a consulting-room with a lively odour of antiseptics is the sort of woman who wears horrid undies. I could never bring myself to be jealous of her.

MARTHA: Marie-Louise gave me two of her chemises to copy only the other day.

CONSTANCE: Oh, did she give you the cerise one with the Irish lace insertions? I thought that sweet. I've copied that.

BARBARA: It's true that Marie-Louise is very pretty.

CONSTANCE: Marie-Louise is a darling. But she and John have known each other far too long. John likes her of course, but he says she has no brain.

MARTHA: Men don't always say what they think.

CONSTANCE: Fortunately, or we shouldn't always know what they feel.

MARTHA: Don't you think John has any secrets from you?

CONSTANCE: I'm sure of it. But of course a good wife always pretends not to know the little things her husband wishes to keep hidden from her. That is an elementary rule in matrimonial etiquette.

MARTHA: Don't forget that men were deceivers ever.

CONSTANCE: My dear, you talk like a confirmed spinster. What woman was ever deceived that didn't want to be? Do you really think that men are mysterious? They're children. Why, my dear, John at forty isn't nearly so grown up as Helen at fourteen.

BARBARA: How is your girl, Constance?

CONSTANCE: Oh, she's very well. She loves boarding-school, you know. They're like little boys, men. Sometimes of course they're rather naughty and you have to pretend to be angry with them. They attach so much importance to such entirely unimportant things that it's really touching. And they're so helpless. Have you never nursed a man when he's ill? It wrings your heart. It's just like a dog or a horse. They haven't got the sense to come in out of the rain, poor darlings. They have all the charming qualities that accompany general incompetence. They're sweet and good and silly, and tiresome and selfish. You can't help liking them, they're so ingenuous, and so simple. They have no complexity or finesse. I think they're sweet, but it's absurd to take them seriously. You're a wise woman, mother. What do you think?

MRS. CULVER: I think you're not in love with your husband.

CONSTANCE: What nonsense.

[JOHN *comes in.*]

JOHN: Marie-Louise is waiting for you, Martha. I've just put a little bandage round her knee.

CONSTANCE: I hope you weren't rough.

MARTHA [*To* CONSTANCE]: Good-bye, dear. Are you coming, mother?

MRS. CULVER: Not just yet.

MARTHA: Good-bye, Barbara.

[MARTHA *and* JOHN *go out.*]

BARBARA: Constance, I've got a suggestion to make to you. You know that my business has been growing by leaps and bounds and I simply cannot get along alone any more. I was wondering if you'd like to come in with me.

CONSTANCE: Oh, my dear, I'm not a business woman.

BARBARA: You've got marvellous taste and you have ideas. You could do all the decorating and I'd confine myself to buying and selling furniture.

CONSTANCE: But I've got no capital.

BARBARA: I've got all the capital I want. I must have help and I know no one more suitable than you. We'd go fifty-fifty and I think I can promise that you'd make a thousand to fifteen hundred a year.

CONSTANCE: I've been an idle woman so long. I think I'd find it dreadfully hard to work eight hours a day.

BARBARA: Won't you think it over? It's very interesting, you know. You're naturally energetic. Don't you get bored with doing nothing all the time?

CONSTANCE: I don't think John would like it. After all, it would look as though he couldn't afford to support me.

BARBARA: Oh, not nowadays surely. There's no reason that a woman shouldn't have a career just as much as a man.

CONSTANCE: I think my career is looking after John— running a house for him, entertaining his friends and making him happy and comfortable.

BARBARA: Don't you think it rather a mistake to put all your eggs in one basket? Supposing that career failed you?

CONSTANCE: Why should it?

BARBARA: Of course I hope it won't. But men, you know, are fluctuating and various. Independence is a very good thing, and a woman who stands on her own feet financially can look upon the future with a good deal of confidence.

CONSTANCE: It's sweet of you, but so long as John and I are happy together I think I should be a fool to do anything that would vex him.

BARBARA: Of course I'm in no immediate hurry. One never knows what the future will bring forth. I want you to know that if you change your mind the job is open to you. I don't think I shall ever find any one so competent as you. You have only to say the word.

CONSTANCE: Oh, Barbara, you are kind to me. It's a splendid offer and I'm ever so grateful to you. Don't think me horrid if I say I hope I shall never need to accept it.

BARBARA: Of course not. Good-bye, darling.

CONSTANCE: Good-bye, dear.

[*They kiss, and* BARBARA *goes out.* CONSTANCE *rings the bell.*]

MRS. CULVER: Are you quite happy, dear?

CONSTANCE: Oh, quite. Don't I look it?

MRS. CULVER: I'm bound to say you do. So far as I can judge by the look of you I should say you haven't a trouble in the world.

CONSTANCE: You'd be wrong. My cook has given notice and she makes the best meringues I've ever eaten.

MRS. CULVER: I like John.

CONSTANCE: So do I. He has all the solid qualities that

make a man a good husband, an agreeable temper, a sense of humour and an entire indifference to petty extravagance.

MRS. CULVER: How right you are, darling, to realise that those are the solid qualities.

CONSTANCE: It's not the seven deadly virtues that make a man a good husband, but the three hundred pleasing amiabilities.

MRS. CULVER: Of course one has to compromise in life. One has to make the best of things. One mustn't expect too much from people. If one wants to be happy in one's own way one must let others be happy in theirs. If one can't get this, that and the other the wise thing is to make up one's mind to do without it. The great thing is not to let vanity warp one's reasonable point of view.

CONSTANCE: Mother, mother, pull yourself together.

MRS. CULVER: Everybody's so clever nowadays. They see everything but the obvious. I've discovered that I only have to say it quite simply in order to be thought a most original and amusing old lady.

CONSTANCE: Spare me, darling.

MRS. CULVER [*Affectionately*]: If at any time anything went wrong with you, you would tell your mother, wouldn't you?

CONSTANCE: Of course.

MRS. CULVER: I hate the thought that you might be unhappy and let a foolish pride prevent you from letting me console and advise you.

CONSTANCE [*With feeling*]: It wouldn't, mother dear.

MRS. CULVER: I had rather an odd experience the other day. A little friend of mine came to see me and told me that her husband was neglecting her. I asked her why she told me and not her own mother. She said that her mother had never wanted her to marry and it would mortify her now to have to say that she had made a mistake.

CONSTANCE: Oh, well, John never neglects me, mother.

MRS. CULVER: Of course I gave her a good talking to. She didn't get much sympathy from me.

CONSTANCE [*With a smile*]: That was very unkind, wasn't it?

MRS. CULVER: I have my own ideas about marriage. If a man neglects his wife it's her own fault, and if he's systematically unfaithful to her in nine cases out of ten she only has herself to blame.

CONSTANCE [*Ringing the bell*]: Systematically is a grim word.

MRS. CULVER: No sensible woman attaches importance to an occasional slip. Time and chance are responsible for that.

CONSTANCE: And shall we say, masculine vanity?

MRS. CULVER: I told my little friend that if her husband was unfaithful to her it was because he found other women more attractive. Why should she be angry with him for that? Her business was to be more attractive than they.

CONSTANCE: You are not what they call a feminist, mother, are you?

MRS. CULVER: After all, what is fidelity?

CONSTANCE: Mother, do you mind if I open the window?

MRS. CULVER: It is open.

CONSTANCE: In that case do you mind if I shut it? I feel that when a woman of your age asks such a question I should make some sort of symbolic gesture.

MRS. CULVER: Don't be ridiculous. Of course I believe in fidelity for women. I suppose no one has ever questioned the desirability of that. But men are different. Women should remember that they have their homes and their name and position and their family, and they should learn to close their eyes when it's possible they may see something they are not meant to.

[*The butler comes in.*]

BENTLEY: Did you ring, Madam?

CONSTANCE: Yes. I am expecting Mr. Bernard Kersal. I'm not at home to anybody else.

BENTLEY: Very good, Madam.

CONSTANCE: Is Mr. Middleton in?

BENTLEY: Yes, Madam. He's in the consulting-room.

CONSTANCE: Very well.

[*The butler goes out.*]

MRS. CULVER: Is that a polite way of telling me that I had better take myself off?

CONSTANCE: Of course not. On the contrary I particularly want you to stay.

MRS. CULVER: Who is this mysterious gentleman?

CONSTANCE: Mother. Bernard.

MRS. CULVER: That says nothing to me at all. Not Saint Bernard, darling?

CONSTANCE: Pull yourself together, my pet. You must remember Bernard Kersal. He proposed to me.

MRS. CULVER: Oh, my dear, you cannot expect me to remember the names of all the young men who proposed to you.

CONSTANCE: Yes, but he proposed more than any of the others.

MRS. CULVER: Why?

CONSTANCE: I suppose because I refused him. I can't think of any other reason.

MRS. CULVER: He made no impression on me.

CONSTANCE: I don't suppose he tried to.

MRS. CULVER: What did he look like?

CONSTANCE: He was tall.

MRS. CULVER: They were all tall.

CONSTANCE: He had brown hair and brown eyes.

MRS. CULVER: They all had brown hair and brown eyes.

CONSTANCE: He danced divinely.

MRS. CULVER: They all danced divinely.

CONSTANCE: I very nearly married him, you know.

MRS. CULVER: Why didn't you?

CONSTANCE: I think he was a trifle too much inclined to lie down on the floor and let me walk over him.

MRS. CULVER: In short he had no sense of humour.

CONSTANCE: I was quite certain that he loved me, and I was never absolutely sure that John did.

MRS. CULVER: Well, you're sure now, dear, aren't you?

CONSTANCE: Oh, yes. John adores me.

MRS. CULVER: And what's this young man coming for to-day?

CONSTANCE: He's not such a very young man any more. He was twenty-nine then and so he must be nearly forty-five now.

MRS. CULVER: He isn't still in love with you?

CONSTANCE: I shouldn't think so. Do you think it possible after fifteen years? It's surely very unlikely. Don't look at me like that, mother. I don't like it.

MRS. CULVER: Don't talk stuff and nonsense to me, child. Of course you know if he's in love with you or not.

CONSTANCE: But I haven't seen him since I married John. You see he lives in Japan. He's a merchant or something in Kobe. He was here during the war on leave. But that was when I was so dreadfully ill and I didn't see him.

MRS. CULVER: Oh! Why's he here now then? Have you been corresponding with him?

CONSTANCE: No. One can't write letters to any one one never sees for fifteen years. He always sends me flowers on my birthday.

MRS. CULVER: That's rather sweet of him.

CONSTANCE: And the other day I had a letter from him saying he was in England and would like to see me. So I asked him to come to-day.

MRS. CULVER: I wondered why you were so smart.

CONSTANCE: Of course he may be terribly changed. Men go off so dreadfully, don't they? He may be bald and fat now.

MRS. CULVER: He may be married.

CONSTANCE: Oh, if he were I don't think he'd want to come and see me, would he?

MRS. CULVER: I see you're under the impression that he's still in love with you.

CONSTANCE: Oh, I'm not.

MRS. CULVER: Then why are you so nervous?

CONSTANCE: It's only natural that I shouldn't want him to think me old and haggard. He adored me, mother. I suppose he still thinks of me as I was then. It wouldn't be very nice if his face fell about a yard and a half when he came into the room.

MRS. CULVER: I think I'd much better leave you to face the ordeal alone.

CONSTANCE: Oh, no, mother, you must stay. I particularly want you. You see, he may be awful and I may wish I'd never seen him again. It'll be so much easier if you're here. I may not want to be alone with him at all.

MRS. CULVER: Oh.

CONSTANCE [*With a twinkle in her eye*]: On the other hand I may.

MRS. CULVER: It seems to me you're putting me in a slightly embarrassing situation.

CONSTANCE: Now listen. If I think he's awful we'll just talk about the weather and the crops for a few minutes and then we'll have an ominous pause and stare at him. That always makes a man feel a perfect fool and the moment a man feels a fool he gets up and goes.

MRS. CULVER: Sometimes they don't know how to, poor dears, and the earth will never open and swallow them up.

CONSTANCE: On the other hand if I think he looks rather nice I shall just take out my handkerchief and carelessly place it on the piano.

MRS. CULVER: Why?

CONSTANCE: Darling, in order that you may rise to your aged feet and say, well, you really must be running along.

MRS. CULVER: Yes, I know that, but why should you carelessly place your handkerchief on the piano?

CONSTANCE: Because I am a creature of impulse. I shall have an impulse to place my handkerchief on the piano.

MRS. CULVER: Oh, very well. But I always mistrust impulses.

[BENTLEY *enters and announces* BERNARD KERSAL. *He is a tall good-looking man, sunburned and of healthy appearance. He is evidently very fit and he carries his forty-five years well.*]

BENTLEY: Mr. Kersal.

CONSTANCE: How do you do. Do you remember my mother?

BERNARD [*Shaking hands with her*]: I'm sure she doesn't remember me.

[CONSTANCE *takes a small handkerchief out of her bag.*]

MRS. CULVER: That is the soft answer that turneth away wrath.

CONSTANCE: It's rather late for tea, isn't it? Would you like a drink?

[*As she says this she goes towards the bell and places her handkerchief on the piano.*]

BERNARD: No, thanks. I've just this moment had one.

CONSTANCE: To brace you for seeing me?

BERNARD: I was nervous.

CONSTANCE: Have I changed as much as you expected?

BERNARD: Oh, that's not what I was nervous about.

MRS. CULVER: Is it really fifteen years since you saw Constance?

BERNARD: Yes. I didn't see her when I was last in England. When I got demobbed I had to go out to Japan again and get my business together. I haven't had a chance to come home before.

[CONSTANCE *has been giving her mother significant looks, but her mother does not notice them.* CONSTANCE *takes a second handkerchief out of her bag and when the opportunity arises places it neatly on the piano beside the first one.*]

MRS. CULVER: And are you home for long?

BERNARD: A year.

MRS. CULVER: Have you brought your wife with you?

BERNARD: I'm not married.

MRS. CULVER: Oh, Constance said you were married to a Japanese lady.

CONSTANCE: Nonsense, mother. I never said anything of the sort.

MRS. CULVER: Oh, perhaps I was thinking of Julia Linton. She married an Egyptian pasha. I believe she's very happy. At all events he hasn't killed her yet.

BERNARD: How is your husband?

CONSTANCE: He's very well. I dare say he'll be in presently.

BERNARD: Haven't you got a little sister? I suppose she's out now?

MRS. CULVER: He means Martha. She's come out and gone in again.

CONSTANCE: She was not so very much younger than me, you know. She's thirty-two now.

[MRS. CULVER *has taken no notice of the handkerchiefs and in desperation* CONSTANCE *takes a third from her bag and places it beside the other two.*]

MRS. CULVER: Do you like the East, Mr. Kersal?

BERNARD: One has a pretty good time there, you know.

[*Now* MRS. CULVER *catches sight of the three handkerchiefs and starts.*]

MRS. CULVER: I wonder what the time is.

CONSTANCE: It's late, mother. Are you dining out tonight? I suppose you want to have a lie-down before you dress for dinner.

MRS. CULVER: I hope I shall see you again, Mr. Kersal.

BERNARD: Thank you very much.

[CONSTANCE *accompanies her to the door.*]

MRS. CULVER: Good-bye, darling. [*In a whisper*] I couldn't remember if the handkerchiefs meant go or stay.

CONSTANCE: You had only to use your eyes. You can see at a glance that he is the kind of man one would naturally want to have a heart-to-heart talk with after fifteen years.

MRS. CULVER: You only confused me by putting more and more handkerchiefs on the piano.

CONSTANCE: For goodness' sake, go, mother. [*Aloud*] Good-bye, my sweet. I'm sorry you've got to run away so soon.

MRS. CULVER: Good-bye.

[*She goes out and* CONSTANCE *comes back into the room.*]

CONSTANCE: Did you think it very rude of us to whisper? Mother has a passion for secrets.

BERNARD: Of course not.

CONSTANCE: Now let's sit down and make ourselves comfortable. Let me look at you. You haven't changed much. You're a little thinner and perhaps a little more lined. Men are so lucky, if they have any character they grow better-looking as they grow older. Do you know I'm thirty-six now?

BERNARD: What does that matter?

CONSTANCE: Shall I tell you something? When you wrote

and suggested coming here I was delighted at the thought of seeing you again and wrote at once making a date. And then I was panic-stricken. I would have given almost anything not to have sent that letter. And all to-day I've had such a horrible feeling at the pit of my stomach. Didn't you see my knees wobble when you came into the room?

BERNARD: In God's name, why?

CONSTANCE: Oh, my dear, I think you must be a little stupid. I should be a perfect fool if I didn't know that when I was a girl I was very pretty. It's rather a pang when you are forced to the conclusion that you're not quite so pretty as you were. People don't tell one. One tries to hide it from oneself. Anyhow I thought I'd rather know the worst. That's one of the reasons I asked you to come.

BERNARD: Whatever I thought you can hardly imagine that I should be deliberately rude.

CONSTANCE: Of course not. But I watched your face. I was afraid I'd see there: By God, how she's gone off.

BERNARD: And did you?

CONSTANCE: You were rather shy when you came in. You weren't thinking of me.

BERNARD: It's quite true, fifteen years ago you were a pretty girl. Now you're lovely. You're ten times more beautiful than you were then.

CONSTANCE: It's nice of you to say so.

BERNARD: Don't you believe it?

CONSTANCE: I think you do. And I confess that's sufficiently gratifying. Now tell me, why aren't you married? It's time you did, you know, or it'll be too late. You'll have a very lonely old age if you don't.

BERNARD: I never wanted to marry any one but you.

CONSTANCE: Oh, come, you're not going to tell me that you've never been in love since you were in love with me?

BERNARD: No, I've been in love half a dozen times, but when it came to the point I found I still loved you best.

CONSTANCE: I like you for saying that. I shouldn't have believed it if you'd said you'd never loved anybody else and I should have been vexed with you for thinking me such a fool as to believe it.

BERNARD: You see, it was you I loved in the others. One because she had hair like yours and another because her smile reminded me of your smile.

CONSTANCE: I hate to think that I've made you unhappy.

BERNARD: But you haven't. I've had a very good time; I've enjoyed my work; I've made a bit of money and I've had a lot of fun. I don't blame you for having married John instead of me.

CONSTANCE: Do you remember John?

BERNARD: Of course I do. He was a very nice fellow. I dare say he's made you a better husband than I should have. I've had my ups and downs. I'm very irritable sometimes. John's been able to give you everything you wanted. You were much safer with him. By the way, I suppose I can still call you Constance.

CONSTANCE: Of course. Why not? Do you know, I think you have a very nice nature, Bernard.

BERNARD: Are you happy with John?

CONSTANCE: Oh, very. I don't say that he has never given me a moment's uneasiness. He did once, but I took hold of myself and saw that I mustn't be silly. I'm very glad I did. I think I can quite honestly say that ours has been a very happy and successful marriage.

BERNARD: I'm awfully glad to hear that. Do you think it's cheek to ask if John loves you?

CONSTANCE: I'm sure he loves me.

BERNARD: And do you love him?

CONSTANCE: Very much.

BERNARD: May I make you a short speech?

CONSTANCE: If I may interrupt at suitable moments.

BERNARD: I hope you're going to let me see a great deal of you during this year I've got at home.

CONSTANCE: I want to see a great deal of you.

BERNARD: There's just one thing I want to get off my chest and then I needn't refer to it again. I am just as madly in love with you as I was when I asked you to marry me fifteen years ago. I think I shall remain in love with you all my life. I'm too old a dog to learn new tricks. But I want you to know that you needn't have the smallest fear that I shall make a nuisance of myself. I should think it an awfully caddish thing to try to come between you and John. I suppose we all want to be happy, but I don't believe the best way of being that is to try to upset other people's happiness.

CONSTANCE: That's not such a very long speech after all. At a public dinner they would hardly even call it a few remarks.

BERNARD: All I ask for is your friendship and if in return I care to give you my love I don't see that it's any one's business but my own.

CONSTANCE: I don't think it is. I think I can be a very good friend, Bernard.

[*The door opens and* JOHN *comes in.*]

JOHN: Oh, I'm sorry. I didn't know you were engaged.

CONSTANCE: I'm not. Come in. This is Bernard Kersal.

JOHN: How do you do?

BERNARD: I'm afraid you don't remember me.

JOHN: If you ask me point-blank I think it's safer to confess I don't.

CONSTANCE: Don't be so silly, John. He used to come to mother's.

JOHN: Before we were married, d'you mean?

CONSTANCE: Yes. You spent several week-ends with us together.

JOHN: My dear, that was fifteen years ago. I'm awfully sorry not to remember you, but I'm delighted to see you now.

CONSTANCE: He's just come back from Japan.

JOHN: Oh, well, I hope we shall see you again. I'm just going along to the club to have a rubber before dinner, darling. [*To* BERNARD] Why don't you dine here with Constance? I've got an acute appendix and she'll be all alone, poor darling.

BERNARD: Oh, that's awfully kind of you.

CONSTANCE: It would be a friendly act. Are you free?

BERNARD: Always to do a friendly act.

CONSTANCE: Very well. I shall expect you at eight-fifteen.

THE END OF ACT ONE

ACT TWO

The Scene is the same as in the First Act.
A fortnight has passed.
MARTHA *in walking costume and a hat is looking at an illustrated paper.*
BENTLEY *comes in.*

BENTLEY: Mr. Kersal is here, Miss.

MARTHA: Oh! Ask him if he won't come up.

BENTLEY: Very good, Miss. [*He goes out and in a moment comes in again to announce* BERNARD, *and then goes*] Mr. Kersal.

MARTHA: Constance is dressing. She won't be very long.

BERNARD: Oh, I see. Well, there's no violent hurry.

MARTHA: You're taking her to Ranelagh, aren't you?

BERNARD: That was the idea. I know some of the fellows who are playing to-day.

MARTHA: Are you having a good time in London?

BERNARD: Marvellous. When a man's lived in the East as long as I have, he's apt to feel rather out of it when he comes home. But Constance and John have been ripping to me.

MARTHA: Do you like John?

BERNARD: Yes. He's been awfully kind.

MARTHA: Do you know, I remember you quite well.

BERNARD: Oh, you can't. You were a kid when I used to come down and stay with your mother.

MARTHA: I was sixteen. Do you imagine I wasn't thrilled to the marrow by Constance's young men?

BERNARD: There were a good many of them. I should have thought your marrow got callous.

MARTHA: But you were one of the serious ones. I always thought you terribly romantic.

BERNARD: I was terribly romantic. I think it's becoming in the young.

MARTHA: I don't think it's unbecoming in the not quite as young.

BERNARD: Don't think I'm romantic now. I make a considerable income and I'm putting on weight. The price of silk has ousted love's young dream in my manly bosom.

MARTHA: You're an unconscionable liar.

BERNARD: To which I can only retort that you're excessively rude.

MARTHA: You were madly in love with Constance in those days, weren't you?

BERNARD: You know, it's so long ago I forget.

MARTHA: I advised her to marry you rather than John.

BERNARD: Why?

MARTHA: Well, for one thing you lived in Japan. I would have married any one who would take me there.

BERNARD: I live there still.

MARTHA: Oh, I don't want to marry you.

BERNARD: I couldn't help suspecting that.

MARTHA: I could never really quite understand what she saw in John.

BERNARD: I suppose she loved him.

MARTHA: I wonder if she ever regrets that she married John rather than you.

BERNARD: Well, don't. She's perfectly satisfied with John and wouldn't change him for anything in the world.

MARTHA: It's exasperating, isn't it?

BERNARD: I don't think so. It must make it much more comfortable for a husband and wife to be content with one another.

MARTHA: You're in love with her still, aren't you?

BERNARD: Not a bit.

MARTHA: Upon my soul, you've got a nerve. Why, you donkey, you're giving it away all the time. Do you know what you look like when she's in the room? Have you any idea how your eyes change when they rest on her? When you speak her name it sounds as though you were kissing it.

BERNARD: I thought you were an odious child when you were sixteen, Martha, and now that you're thirty-two I think you're a horrible woman.

MARTHA: I'm not really. But I'm very fond of Constance and I'm inclined to be rather fond of you.

BERNARD: Don't you think you could show your attachment by minding your own business?

MARTHA: Why does it make you angry because I've told you that no one can see you with Constance for five minutes without knowing that you adore her?

BERNARD: My dear, I'm here for one year. I want to be happy. I don't want to give trouble or cause trouble. I value my friendship with Constance and I hate the idea that anything should interfere with it.

MARTHA: Hasn't it occurred to you that she may want more than your friendship?

BERNARD: No, it has not.

MARTHA: You need not jump down my throat.

BERNARD: Constance is perfectly happy with her husband. You must think me a damned swine if you think I'm going to butt in and try to smash up a perfectly wonderful union.

MARTHA: But, you poor fool, don't you know that John has been notoriously unfaithful to Constance for ages?

BERNARD: I don't believe it.

MARTHA: Ask any one you like. Mother knows it. Barbara Fawcett knows it. Every one knows it but Constance.

BERNARD: That certainly isn't true. Mrs. Durham told me when I met her at dinner two or three days ago that John and Constance were the most devoted couple she'd ever known.

MARTHA: Did Marie-Louise tell you that?

BERNARD: She did.

[MARTHA *begins to laugh. She can hardly restrain herself.*]

MARTHA: The nerve. Marie-Louise. Oh, my poor Bernard. Marie-Louise is John's mistress.

BERNARD: Marie-Louise is Constance's greatest friend.

MARTHA: Yes.

BERNARD: If this is a pack of lies I swear I'll damned well wring your neck.

MARTHA: All right.

BERNARD: That was a silly thing to say. I'm sorry.

MARTHA: Oh, I don't mind. I like a man to be violent. I think you're just the sort of man Constance needs.

BERNARD: What the devil do you mean by that?

MARTHA: It can't go on. Constance is being made perfectly ridiculous. Her position is monstrous. I thought she ought to be told and as every one else seemed to shirk the job I was prepared to do it myself. My mother was so disagreeable about it, I've had to promise not to say a word.

BERNARD: You're not under the delusion that I'm going to tell her?

MARTHA: No, I don't really think it would come very well from you. But things can't go on. She's bound to find out. All I want you to do is to . . . well, stand by.

BERNARD: But Marie-Louise has got a husband. What about him?

MARTHA: His only ambition in life is to make a million. He's the sort of a fool who thinks a woman loves him just because he loves her. Marie-Louise can turn him round her little finger.

BERNARD: Has Constance never suspected?

MARTHA: Never. You've only got to look at her. Really, her self-confidence sometimes is positively maddening.

BERNARD: I wonder if it wouldn't be better that she never did find out. She's so happy. She's entirely carefree. You've only got to look at that open brow and those frank, trustful eyes.

MARTHA: I thought you loved her.

BERNARD: Enough to want her happiness above all things.

MARTHA: You *are* forty-five, aren't you? I forgot that for a moment.

BERNARD: Dear Martha. You have such an attractive way of putting things.

[CONSTANCE's *voice on the stairs is heard calling:* BENTLEY, BENTLEY.]

MARTHA: Oh, there's Constance. I can't imagine where mother is. I think I'll go into the brown room and write a letter.

[BERNARD *takes no notice of what she says nor does he make any movement when she goes out. A moment later* CONSTANCE *comes in.*]

CONSTANCE: Have I kept you waiting?

BERNARD: It doesn't matter.

CONSTANCE: Hulloa! What's up?

BERNARD: With me? Nothing. Why?

CONSTANCE: You look all funny. Why are your eyes suddenly opaque?

BERNARD: I didn't know they were.

CONSTANCE: Are you trying to hide something from me?

BERNARD: Of course not.

CONSTANCE: Have you had bad news from Japan?

BERNARD: No. Far from it. Silk is booming.

CONSTANCE: Then you're going to tell me that you've just got engaged to a village maiden.

BERNARD: No, I'm not.

CONSTANCE: I hate people who keep secrets from me.

BERNARD: I have no secrets from you.

CONSTANCE: Do you think I don't know your face by now?

BERNARD: You'll make me vain. I would never have ventured to think that you took the trouble to look twice at my ugly face.

CONSTANCE [*With sudden suspicion*]: Wasn't Martha here when you came? She hasn't gone, has she?

BERNARD: She's waiting for her mother. She's gone into another room to write letters.

CONSTANCE: Did you see her?

BERNARD [*Trying to be very casual*]: Yes. We had a little chat about the weather.

CONSTANCE [*Immediately grasping what has happened*]: Oh—— Don't you think we ought to be starting?

BERNARD: There's plenty of time. It's no good getting there too early.

CONSTANCE: Then I'll take off my hat.

BERNARD: And it's jolly here, isn't it? I love your room.

CONSTANCE: Do you think it's a success? I did it myself. Barbara Fawcett wants me to go into the decorating business. She's in it, you know, and she's making quite a lot of money.

BERNARD [*Smiling to hide his anxiety in asking the question*]: Aren't you happy at home?

CONSTANCE [*Breezily*]: I don't think it necessarily means

one's unhappy at home because one wants an occupation. One may very easily grow tired of going to parties all the time. But as a matter of fact I refused Barbara's offer.

BERNARD [*Insisting*]: You are happy, aren't you?

CONSTANCE: Very.

BERNARD: You've made *me* very happy during this last fortnight. I feel as though I'd never been away. You've been awfully kind to me.

CONSTANCE: I'm very glad you think so. I don't know that I've done anything very much for you.

BERNARD: Yes, you have. You've let me see you.

CONSTANCE: I let the policeman at the corner do that, you know.

BERNARD: You mustn't think that because I take care only to talk to you of quite casual things I don't still love you with all my heart.

CONSTANCE [*Quite coolly*]: We agreed when first you came back that your feelings were entirely your business.

BERNARD: Do you mind my loving you?

CONSTANCE: Oughtn't we all to love one another?

BERNARD: Don't tease me.

CONSTANCE: My dear, I can't help being pleased and flattered and rather touched. It is rather wonderful that any one should care for me. . . .

BERNARD [*Interrupting*]: So much—?

CONSTANCE: After so many years.

BERNARD: If any one had asked me fifteen years ago if I could love you more than I loved you then I should have said it was impossible. I love you ten times more than I ever loved you before.

CONSTANCE [*Going on with her own speech*]: But I don't in the least want you to make love to me now.

BERNARD: I know. I'm not going to. I know you far too well.

CONSTANCE [*Amused and a trifle taken aback*]: I don't quite know what you've been doing for the last five minutes.

BERNARD: I was merely stating a few plain facts.

CONSTANCE: Oh, I beg your pardon. I thought it was something quite different. I'm afraid you might mistake my meaning if I said I'm quite curious to see how you *do* make love.

BERNARD [*Good-humouredly*] : I have a notion that you're laughing at me.

CONSTANCE : In the hope of teaching you to laugh at yourself.

BERNARD : I've been very good during the last fortnight, haven't I?

CONSTANCE : Yes, I kept on saying to myself, I wonder if a pat of butter really would melt in his mouth.

BERNARD : Well, for just a minute I'm going to let myself go.

CONSTANCE : I wouldn't if I were you.

BERNARD : Yes, but you're not. I want to tell you just once that I worship the ground you tread on. There's never been any one in the world for me but you.

CONSTANCE : Oh, nonsense. There have been half a dozen. We are seven.

BERNARD : They were all you. I love you with all my heart. I admire you more than any woman I've ever met. I respect you. I'm an awful fool when it comes to the point. I don't know how to say all I've got in my heart without feeling like a perfect ass. I love you. I want you to know that if ever you're in trouble I should look upon it as the greatest possible happiness to be allowed to help you.

CONSTANCE : That's very kind of you. I don't see why I should be in any great trouble.

BERNARD : Always and in all circumstances you can count on me absolutely. I will do anything in the world for you. If ever you want me you have only to give me a sign. I should be proud and happy to give my life for you.

CONSTANCE : It's sweet of you to say so.

BERNARD : Don't you believe it?

CONSTANCE [*With a charming smile*] : Yes.

BERNARD : I should like to think that it meant—oh, not very much, but just a little to you.

CONSTANCE [*Almost shaken*] : It means a great deal. I thank you.

BERNARD : Now we won't say anything more about it.

CONSTANCE [*Recovering her accustomed coolness*]: But why did you think it necessary to say all this just now?

BERNARD: I wanted to get it off my chest.

CONSTANCE: Oh, really.

BERNARD: You're not angry with me?

CONSTANCE: Oh, Bernard, I'm not that kind of a fool at all. . . . It's a pity that Martha doesn't marry.

BERNARD: Don't think that I'm going to marry her.

CONSTANCE: I don't. I merely thought that a husband would be a pleasant and useful occupation for her. She's quite a nice girl, you know. A liar, of course, but otherwise all right.

BERNARD: Oh?

CONSTANCE: Yes, a terrible liar, even for a woman. . . . Shall we start now? It's no good getting there when the polo is over.

BERNARD: All right. Let's start.

CONSTANCE: I'll put my hat on again. By the way, you haven't had a taxi waiting all this time, have you?

BERNARD: No, I've got a car. I thought I'd like to drive you down myself.

CONSTANCE: Open or shut?

BERNARD: Open.

CONSTANCE: Oh, my dear, then I must get another hat. A broad brim like this is such a bore in an open car.

BERNARD: Oh, I'm sorry.

CONSTANCE: It doesn't matter a bit. I shall only be a minute. And why on earth shouldn't one be comfortable if one can!

[*She goes out. In a moment* BENTLEY *shows in* MARIE-LOUISE.]

MARIE-LOUISE: Oh, how do you do. [*To* BENTLEY] Will you tell Mr. Middleton at once?

BENTLEY: Yes, Madam.

[*Exit* BENTLEY.]

MARIE-LOUISE [*Rather flustered*]: I particularly wanted to see John for a minute and there are patients waiting to see him, so I asked Bentley if he couldn't come here.

BERNARD: I'll take myself off.

MARIE-LOUISE: I'm awfully sorry, but it's rather urgent. John hates to be disturbed like this.

BERNARD: I'll go into the next room.

MARIE-LOUISE: Are you waiting for Constance?

BERNARD: Yes, I'm taking her to Ranelagh. She's changing her hat.

MARIE-LOUISE: I see. Bentley told me she was upstairs. Good-bye. I shall only be a minute. [BERNARD *goes into the adjoining room just as* JOHN *comes in*] Oh, John, I'm sorry to drag you away from your patients.

JOHN: There's nothing urgent. They can wait for a few minutes. [BERNARD *has closed the door behind him, and* JOHN'S *tone changes. They speak now in a low voice and quickly*] Is anything the matter?

MARIE-LOUISE: Mortimer.

JOHN: What about Mortimer?

MARIE-LOUISE: I'm convinced he suspects.

JOHN: Why?

MARIE-LOUISE: He was so funny last night. He came into my room to say good-night to me. He sat on my bed. He was chatting nicely and he was asking what I'd been doing with myself all the evening. . . .

JOHN: Presumably you didn't tell him.

MARIE-LOUISE: No, I said I'd been dining here. And suddenly he got up and just said good-night and went out. His voice was so strange that I couldn't help looking at him. He was as red as a turkey cock.

JOHN: Is that all?

MARIE-LOUISE: He never came in to say good-morning to me before he went to the City.

JOHN: He may have been in a hurry.

MARIE-LOUISE: He's never in too much of a hurry for that.

JOHN: I think you're making a mountain of a mole heap.

MARIE-LOUISE: Don't be stupid, John. Can't you see I'm as nervous as a cat?

JOHN: I can. But I'm trying to persuade you there's nothing to be nervous about.

MARIE-LOUISE: What fools men are. They never will see

that it's the small things that matter. I tell you I'm frightened out of my wits.

JOHN: You know there's a devil of a distance between suspicion and proof.

MARIE-LOUISE: Oh, I don't think he could prove anything. But he can make himself awfully unpleasant. Supposing he put ideas in Constance's head?

JOHN: She'd never believe him.

MARIE-LOUISE: If the worst came to worst I could manage Mortimer. He's awfully in love with me. That always gives one such an advantage over a man.

JOHN: Of course you can twist Mortimer round your little finger.

MARIE-LOUISE: I should die of shame if Constance knew. After all, she's my greatest friend and I'm absolutely devoted to her.

JOHN: Constance is a peach. Of course I don't believe there's anything in this at all, but if there were, I'd be in favour of making a clean breast of it to Constance.

MARIE-LOUISE: Never!

JOHN: I expect she'd kick up a row. Any woman would. But she'd do anything in the world to help us out.

MARIE-LOUISE: A lot you know about women. She'd help you out, I dare say. But she'd stamp on me with both feet. That's only human nature.

JOHN: Not Constance's.

MARIE-LOUISE: Upon my word, it's lucky I'm fairly sure of you, John, or the way you talk of Constance would really make me jealous.

JOHN: Thank God you can smile. You're getting your nerve back.

MARIE-LOUISE: It's been a comfort to talk it over. It doesn't seem so bad now.

JOHN: I'm sure you've got nothing to be frightened about.

MARIE-LOUISE: I dare say it was only my fancy. It was a stupid risk to take all the same.

JOHN: Perhaps. Why did you look so devilish pretty?

MARIE-LOUISE: Oughtn't you to be getting back to your wretched patients?

JOHN: I suppose so. Will you stop and see Constance?

MARIE-LOUISE: I may as well. It would look rather odd if I went away without saying how d'you do to her.

JOHN [*Going*]: I'll leave you then. And don't worry.

MARIE-LOUISE: I won't. I dare say it was only a guilty conscience. I'll go and have my hair washed.

[*As* JOHN *is about to go,* MARTHA *comes in followed by* BERNARD.]

MARTHA [*With an almost exaggerated cordiality*]: I had no idea you were here, Marie-Louise.

MARIE-LOUISE: It's not very important.

MARTHA: I was just writing letters, waiting for mother, and Bernard's only just told me.

MARIE-LOUISE: I wanted to see John about something.

MARTHA: I hope you haven't got anything the matter with you, darling.

MARIE-LOUISE: No. Mortimer's been looking rather run-down lately and I want John to persuade him to take a holiday.

MARTHA: Oh, I should have thought he'd be more likely to take a physician's advice than a surgeon's in a thing like that.

MARIE-LOUISE: He's got a tremendous belief in John, you know.

MARTHA: In which I'm sure he's justified. John is so very reliable.

JOHN: What can I do for you, Martha? If you'd like me to cut out an appendix or a few tonsils I shall be happy to oblige you.

MARTHA: My dear John, you've only left me the barest necessities of existence as it is. I don't think I could manage with anything less than I have.

JOHN: My dear, as long as a woman has a leg to stand on she need not despair of exciting her surgeon's sympathy and interest.

[CONSTANCE *comes in with* MRS. CULVER.]

MARIE-LOUISE [*Kissing her*]: Darling.

CONSTANCE: How is your knee, still slipping?

MARIE-LOUISE: It always gives me more or less trouble, you know.

CONSTANCE: Yes, of course. I think you're very patient. In your place I should be furious with John. Of course I would never dream of consulting him if I had anything the matter with me.

MRS. CULVER: I'm sorry I've been so long, Martha. Have you been very impatient?

MARTHA: No, I've been passing the time very pleasantly.

MRS. CULVER: For others, darling, or only for yourself?

CONSTANCE: I met mother on the stairs and she came up with me while I changed my hat. Bernard is taking me down to Ranelagh.

JOHN: Oh, that'll be jolly.

BERNARD: We shall be dreadfully late.

CONSTANCE: Does it matter?

BERNARD: No.

[BENTLEY *comes in with a card on a small salver and takes it to* CONSTANCE. *She looks at the card and hesitates.*]

CONSTANCE: How very odd.

JOHN: What's the matter, Constance?

CONSTANCE: Nothing. [*For an instant she reflects*] Is he downstairs?

BENTLEY: Yes, Madam.

CONSTANCE: I don't know why he should send up a card. Show him up.

BENTLEY: Very good, Madam.

[*Exit* BENTLEY.]

JOHN: Who is it, Constance?

CONSTANCE: Come and sit down, Marie-Louise.

MARIE-LOUISE: I must go and so must you.

CONSTANCE: There's plenty of time. Do you like this hat?

MARIE-LOUISE: Yes. I think it's sweet.

CONSTANCE: What are *you* doing here, John? Haven't you got any patients to-day?

JOHN: Yes, there are two or three waiting. I'm just going down. As a matter of fact I thought I deserved a cigarette. [*He puts his hand to his hip pocket*] Hang, I've mislaid my cigarette case. You haven't seen it about, Constance?

CONSTANCE: No, I haven't.

JOHN: I looked for it everywhere this morning. I can't think where I left it. I must ring up the nursing-home and ask if I left it there.

CONSTANCE: I hope you haven't lost it.

JOHN: Oh, no. I'm sure I haven't. I've just put it somewhere.

[*The door opens and* BENTLEY *announces the visitor.*]

BENTLEY: Mr. Mortimer Durham.

MARIE-LOUISE [*Startled out of her wits*]: Oh!

CONSTANCE [*Quickly, seizing her wrist*]: Sit still, you fool. [MORTIMER DURHAM *comes in. He is a stoutish, biggish man of about forty, with a red face and an irascible manner. At the moment he is a prey to violent emotion.* BENTLEY *goes out*] Hulloa, Mortimer. What are you doing in these parts at this hour? Why on earth did you send up a card?

[*He stops and looks around.*]

MARIE-LOUISE: What is the matter, Mortimer?

MORTIMER [*To* CONSTANCE, *with difficulty restraining his fury*]: I thought you might like to know that your husband is my wife's lover.

MARIE-LOUISE: Morty!

CONSTANCE [*Keeping a firm hand on* MARIE-LOUISE *and very coolly to* MORTIMER]: Oh? What makes you think that?

MORTIMER [*Taking a gold cigarette case out of his pocket*]: Do you recognize this? I found it under my wife's pillow last night.

CONSTANCE: Oh, I am relieved. I couldn't make out where I'd left it. [*Taking it from him*] Thank you so much.

MORTIMER [*Angrily*]: It's not yours.

CONSTANCE: Indeed it is. I was sitting on Marie-Louise's bed and I must have slipped it under the pillow without thinking.

MORTIMER: It has John's initials on it.

CONSTANCE: I know. It was presented to him by a grateful patient and I thought it much too nice for him, so I just took it.

MORTIMER: What sort of fool do you take me for, Constance?

CONSTANCE: My dear Morty, why should I say it was my cigarette case if it wasn't?

MORTIMER: They had dinner together.

CONSTANCE: My poor Morty, I know that. You were going to a City banquet or something, and Marie-Louise rang up and asked if she might come and take potluck with us.

MORTIMER: Do you mean to say she dined here?

CONSTANCE: Isn't that what she told you?

MORTIMER: Yes.

CONSTANCE: It's quite easy to prove. If you won't take my word for it we can ring for the butler and you can ask him yourself. . . . Ring the bell, John, will you?

MORTIMER [Uneasily]: No, don't do that. If you give me your word, of course I must take it.

CONSTANCE: That's very kind of you. I'm grateful to you for not exposing me to the humiliation of making my butler corroborate my statement.

MORTIMER: If Marie-Louise was dining here why were you sitting on her bed?

CONSTANCE: John had to go out and do an operation, and Marie-Louise wanted to show me the things she'd got from Paris, so I walked round to your house. It was a lovely night. You remember that, don't you?

MORTIMER: Damn it, I've got more important things to do than look at the night.

CONSTANCE: We tried them all on and then we were rather tired, so Marie-Louise got into bed and I sat down and we talked.

MORTIMER: If you were tired why didn't you go home and go to bed?

CONSTANCE: John had promised to come round and fetch me.

MORTIMER: And did he? At what time did he come?

JOHN: I couldn't manage it. The operation took much longer than I expected. It was one of those cases where when you once start cutting you really don't know where to stop. You know the sort of thing, don't you, Mortimer?

MORTIMER: No, I don't. How the devil should I?

CONSTANCE: All that is neither here nor there. This is a

terrible accusation you've made against John and Marie-Louise and I'm very much upset. But I will remain perfectly calm till I've heard everything. Now let me have your proofs.

MORTIMER: My proofs? What d'you mean? The cigarette case. When I found the cigarette case I naturally put two and two together.

CONSTANCE [*With her eyes flashing*] : I quite understand, but why did you make them five?

MORTIMER [*Emphatically, in order not to show that he is wavering*] : It isn't possible that I should have made a mistake.

CONSTANCE: Even the richest of us may err. I remember when Mr. Pierpont Morgan died, he was found to own seven million dollars' of worthless securities.

MORTIMER [*Uneasily*] : You don't know what a shock it was, Constance. I had the most implicit confidence in Marie-Louise. I was knocked endways. I've been brooding over it ever since till I was afraid I should go mad.

CONSTANCE: And do you mean to say that you've come here and made a fearful scene just because you found my cigarette case in Marie-Louise's room? I can't believe it. You're a man of the world and a business man. You're extremely intelligent. Surely you have something to go upon. You must be holding something back. Don't be afraid of hurting my feelings. You've said so much now that I must insist on your saying everything. I want the truth and the whole truth.

[*There is a pause.* MORTIMER *looks from* MARIE-LOUISE, *who is quietly weeping, to* CONSTANCE, *with the utmost bewilderment.*]

MORTIMER: I'm afraid I've made a damned fool of myself.

CONSTANCE: I'm afraid you have.

MORTIMER: I'm awfully sorry, Constance. I beg your pardon.

CONSTANCE: Oh, don't bother about me. You've exposed me to the most bitter humiliation. You've sown seeds of distrust between me and John which can never be. . . .

[*She looks for a word.*]

MRS. CULVER [*Supplying it*] : Fertilized.

CONSTANCE [*Ignoring it*] : Uprooted. But I don't matter. It's Marie-Louise's pardon you must beg.

MORTIMER [*Humbly*] : Marie-Louise.

MARIE-LOUISE : Don't touch me. Don't come near me.

MORTIMER [*To* CONSTANCE, *miserably*] : You know what jealousy is.

CONSTANCE : Certainly not. I think it's a most ugly and despicable vice.

MORTIMER [*To* MARIE-LOUISE] : Marie-Louise, I'm sorry. Won't you forgive me?

MARIE-LOUISE : You've insulted me before all my friends. You know how devotedly I love Constance. You might have accused me of having an affair with any one else—but not John.

CONSTANCE : Not her greatest friend's husband. The milkman or the dustman if you like, but not her greatest friend's husband.

MORTIMER : I've been a perfect swine. I don't know what came over me. I really wasn't responsible for my actions.

MARIE-LOUISE : I've loved you all these years. No one has ever loved you as I've loved you. Oh, it's cruel, cruel.

MORTIMER : Come away, darling. I can't say here what I want to say.

MARIE-LOUISE : No, no, no.

CONSTANCE [*Putting her hand on his arm, gently*] : I think you'd better leave her here for a little while, Morty. I'll talk to her when you've gone. She's naturally upset. A sensitive little thing like that.

MORTIMER : We're dining with the Vancouvers at 8.15.

CONSTANCE : For eight-thirty. I promise I'll send her home in good time to dress.

MORTIMER : She'll give me another chance?

CONSTANCE : Yes, yes.

MORTIMER : I'd do anything in the world for her. [CONSTANCE *puts her fingers to her lips and then points significantly to the pearl chain she is wearing. For a second* MORTIMER *does not understand, but as soon as her notion dawns on him he gives a pleased nod*] You're the cleverest woman in the world. [*As he goes out he stops and holds out his hand to* JOHN] Will you shake hands with me, old man? I made a mistake and I'm man enough to acknowledge it.

JOHN [*Very cordially*]: Not at all, old boy. I quite agree that it did look fishy, the cigarette case. If I'd dreamt that Constance was going to leave an expensive thing like that lying about all over the place, I'm hanged if I'd have let her pinch it.

MORTIMER: You don't know what a weight it is off my mind. I felt a hundred when I came here, and now I feel like a two-year-old.

[*He goes out. The moment the door is closed behind him there is a general change in every attitude. The tension disappears and there is a feeling of relief.*]

JOHN: Constance, you're a brick. I shall never forget this. Never, so long as I live. And by George, what presence of mind you showed. I went hot and cold all over, and you never batted an eye-lash.

CONSTANCE: By the way, here is your cigarette case. You'd better have a ring made and hang it on your key-chain.

JOHN: No, no. Keep it. I'm too old to take these risks.

CONSTANCE: By the way, did any one see you go into Morty's house last night?

JOHN: No, we let ourselves in with Marie-Louise's latch key.

CONSTANCE: That's all right then. If Mortimer asks the servants they can tell him nothing. I had to take that chance.

MARIE-LOUISE [*With a little gesture of ashamed dismay*]: Oh, Constance, what must you think of me?

CONSTANCE: I? Exactly the same as I thought before. I think you're sweet, Marie-Louise.

MARIE-LOUISE: You have every right to be angry with me.

CONSTANCE: Perhaps, but not the inclination.

MARIE-LOUISE: Oh, it's not true. I've treated you shamefully. You've made me feel such a pig. And you had your chance to get back on me and you didn't take it. I'm so ashamed.

CONSTANCE [*Amused*]: Because you've been having an affair with John, or because you've been found out?

MARIE-LOUISE: Oh, Constance, don't be heartless. Say anything you like, curse me, stamp on me, but don't smile at me. I'm in a terrible position.

CONSTANCE: And you want me to make a scene. I know and I sympathize. [*Very calmly*] But the fact is that Mortimer told me nothing I didn't know before.

MARIE-LOUISE [*Aghast*]: Do you mean to say that you've known all along?

CONSTANCE: All along, darling. I've been spending the last six months in a desperate effort to prevent my friends and relations from telling me your ghastly secret. It's been very difficult sometimes. Often mother's profound understanding of life, Martha's passion for truth at any price, and Barbara's silent sympathy, have almost worn me down. But until to-day the t's were not definitely crossed nor the i's distinctly dotted, and I was able to ignore the facts that were staring at me—rather rudely, I must say—in the face.

MARIE-LOUISE: But why, why? It's not human. Why didn't you do anything?

CONSTANCE: That, darling, is my affair.

MARIE-LOUISE [*Thinking she understands*]: Oh, I see.

CONSTANCE [*Rather tartly*]: No, you don't. I have always been absolutely faithful to John. I have not winked at your intrigue in order to cover my own.

MARIE-LOUISE [*Beginning to be a little put out*]: I almost think you've been laughing at me up your sleeve all the time.

CONSTANCE [*Good-humouredly*]: Oh, my dear, you mustn't be offended just because I've taken away from you the satisfaction of thinking that you have been deceiving me all these months. I should hate you to think me capable of an intentional meanness.

MARIE-LOUISE: My head's going round and round.

CONSTANCE: Such a pretty head, too. Why don't you go and lie down? You want to look your best if you're dining with the Vancouvers.

MARIE-LOUISE: I wonder where Mortimer is?

CONSTANCE: You know that pearl necklace you showed me the other day and you said that Mortimer thought it cost a lot of money—well, he's gone to Cartier's to buy it for you.

MARIE-LOUISE [*Excitedly*]: Oh, Constance, do you think he has?

CONSTANCE: I think all men are born with the knowledge that when they have wounded a woman's soul—and our souls are easily wounded—the only cure is a trifling, but expensive, jewel.

MARIE-LOUISE: Do you think he'll have the sense to bring it home with him so that I can wear it to-night?

CONSTANCE: Oh, my dear, don't be such a fool as to accept it with alacrity. Remember that Mortimer has grievously insulted you, he's made the most shocking accusation that a man can make against his wife, he's trampled on your love and now he's destroyed your trust in him.

MARIE-LOUISE: Oh, how right you are, Constance.

CONSTANCE: Surely I need not tell you what to do. Refuse to speak to him, but never let him get a word of defense in edgeways. Cry enough to make him feel what a brute he is, but not enough to make your eyes swell. Say you'll leave him and run sobbing to the door, but take care to let him stop you before you open it. Repeat yourself. Say the same thing over and over again—it wears them down—and if he answers you take no notice, but just say it again. And at last when you've reduced him to desperation, when his head is aching as though it would split, when he's sweating at every pore, when he's harassed and miserable and haggard and broken—then consent as an unmerited favor, as a sign of your forgiving temper and the sweetness of your nature, to accept, no, don't consent, *deign* to accept the pearl necklace for which the wretch has just paid ten thousand pounds.

MARIE-LOUISE [*With peculiar satisfaction*]: Twelve, darling.

CONSTANCE: And don't thank him. That wouldn't be playing the game. Let him thank *you* for the favour you do him in allowing him to make you a paltry gift. Have you got your car here?

MARIE-LOUISE: No, I was in such a state when I came I took a taxi.

CONSTANCE: John, do take Marie-Louise down and put her in a taxi.

JOHN: All right.

MARIE-LOUISE: No, not John. I couldn't. After all, I have some delicacy.

CONSTANCE: Oh, have you? Well, let Bernard go.

BERNARD: I shall be pleased.

CONSTANCE [*To* BERNARD]: But come back, won't you?

BERNARD: Certainly.

MARIE-LOUISE [*Kissing* CONSTANCE]: This has been a lesson to me, darling. I'm not a fool, Constance. I can learn.

CONSTANCE: At least prudence, I hope.

[MARIE-LOUISE *goes out followed by* BERNARD KERSAL.]

JOHN: How did you guess that Marie-Louise had said she was dining here?

CONSTANCE: She's too crafty a woman to invent a new lie when an old one will serve.

JOHN: It would have been awkward if Mortimer had insisted on asking Bentley if it was true.

CONSTANCE: I knew he wouldn't dare. It's only if a man's a gentleman that he won't hesitate to do an ungentlemanly thing. Mortimer is on the boundary line and it makes him careful.

MARTHA [*Significantly*]: Don't you imagine your patients are growing a trifle restless, John?

JOHN: I like to keep them waiting. They grow more and more nervous as the minutes pass and when I recommend an operation that will cost them two hundred and fifty pounds they are too shaken to protest.

MARTHA [*Pursing her lips*]: I can't imagine you'll very much like to hear what I'm determined to say to Constance.

JOHN: It's because I shrewdly suspect that you have some very unpleasant things to say about me that I am prepared reluctantly to neglect the call of duty and listen to you with my own ears.

CONSTANCE: She's been exercising miracles of restraint for the last three months, John. I think she has a right to let herself go now.

JOHN: If she's suffering from suppressed desires she's

come to the wrong establishment. She ought to go to a psycho-analyst.

MARTHA: I've only got one thing to say, John, and I'm perfectly willing that you should hear it. [*To* CONSTANCE] I don't know what your reasons were for shielding that abominable woman. I can only suppose you wanted to avoid more scandal than was necessary. . . .

MRS. CULVER [*Interrupting*]: Before you go any further, my dear, you must let me put my word in. [*To* CONSTANCE] My dear child, I beg you not to decide anything in a hurry. We must all think things over. First of all you must listen to what John has to say for himself.

MARTHA: What can he have to say for himself?

CONSTANCE [*Ironically*]: What indeed?

JOHN: Not the right thing anyway. I've seen too much of married life. . . .

CONSTANCE [*Interrupting, with a smile*]: Let us be just. Other people's rather than your own.

JOHN [*Going on*]: To imagine that even the Archangel Gabriel could say the right thing.

CONSTANCE: I've no reason, however, to suppose that the Archangel Gabriel could ever find himself in such a predicament.

JOHN: I'm for it and I'm prepared to take what's coming to me.

CONSTANCE [*To the world in general*]: No man could say handsomer than that.

JOHN: I'm expecting you to make a scene, Constance. It's your right and your privilege. I'm willing to bear it. Give me hell. I deserve it. Drag me up and down the room by the hair of the head. Kick me in the face. Stamp on me. I'll grovel. I'll eat the dust. My name is mud. Mud.

CONSTANCE: My poor John, what is there to make a scene about?

JOHN: I know how badly I've treated you. I had a wife who was good, loving and faithful, devoted to my interests, a perfect mother and an excellent housekeeper. A woman ten times too good for me. If I'd had the smallest spark of decency I couldn't have treated you like this. I haven't a word to say for myself.

MARTHA [*Interrupting him*]: You've humiliated her to all her friends.

JOHN: I've behaved neither like a gentleman nor a sportsman.

MARTHA: Your conduct is inexcusable.

JOHN: I haven't a leg to stand on.

MARTHA: Even if you didn't love her, you might have treated her with respect.

JOHN: I've been as heartless as a crocodile and as unscrupulous as a typhoid bacillus.

CONSTANCE: Between you, of course, you're leaving me very little to say.

MARTHA: There *is* nothing to say. You're quite right. This is the sort of occasion when it's beneath a woman's dignity to make a scene. It just shows how little John knows women to think that you could demean yourself to vulgar abuse. [*To* JOHN] I suppose you'll have the decency to put no obstacle in the way of Constance's getting her freedom.

MRS. CULVER: Oh, Constance, you're not going to divorce him?

MARTHA: Mother, you're so weak. How can she go on living with a man for whom she has no respect? What would her life be with this creature whom she can only mistrust and despise? Besides, you have to think of their child. How can Constance allow her daughter to be contaminated by the society of a person of this character?

CONSTANCE: John has always been an excellent father. Let us give the devil his due.

MRS. CULVER: Don't be too hard, darling. I can understand that at the moment you feel bitter, but it would be very sad if you let your bitterness warp your judgment.

CONSTANCE: I don't feel in the least bitter. I wish I looked as sweet as I feel.

MRS. CULVER: You can't deceive a mother, my dear. I know the angry resentment that you feel. Under the unfortunate circumstances it's only too natural.

CONSTANCE: When I look into my heart I can't find a

trace of resentment, except perhaps for John's being so stupid as to let himself be found out.

JOHN: Let me say this in justification for myself, Constance. I did my little best to prevent it. Angels could do no more.

CONSTANCE: And angels presumably have not the pernicious habit of smoking straight-cut cigarettes.

JOHN: When you once get the taste for them, you prefer them to gippies.

MRS. CULVER: Don't be cynical, darling. That is the worst way to ease an aching heart. Come to your mother's arms, my dear, and let us have a good cry together. And then you'll feel better.

CONSTANCE: It's sweet of you, mother, but honestly I couldn't squeeze a tear out of my eyes if my life depended on it.

MRS. CULVER: And don't be too hard. Of course John is to blame. I admit that. He's been very, very naughty. But men are weak and women are so unscrupulous. I'm sure he's sorry for all the pain he's caused you.

MARTHA: What puzzles me is that you didn't do something the moment you discovered that John was having an affair.

CONSTANCE: To tell you the truth, I thought it no business of mine.

MARTHA [*Indignantly*]: Aren't you his wife?

CONSTANCE: John and I are very lucky people. Our marriage has been ideal.

MARTHA: How can you say that?

CONSTANCE: For five years we adored each other. That's much longer than most people do. Our honeymoon lasted five years and then we had a most extraordinary stroke of luck: we ceased to be in love with one another simultaneously.

JOHN: I protest, Constance. I've never ceased to be absolutely devoted to you.

CONSTANCE: I never said you had, darling. I'm convinced of it. I've never ceased to be devoted to you. We've shared one another's interests, we've loved to be together, I've exulted in your success and you've trembled in my illness. We've laughed at the same jokes and sighed over the same worries. I don't know any couple that's been bound together by a more genuine affection. But honestly, for the last ten years have you been in love with me?

JOHN: You can't expect a man who's been married for fifteen years. . . .

CONSTANCE: My dear, I'm not asking for excuses. I'm only asking for a plain answer.

JOHN: In the long run I enjoy your society much more than anybody else's. There's no one I like so much as you. You're the prettiest woman I've ever known and I shall say the same when you're a hundred.

CONSTANCE: But does your heart leap into your mouth when you hear my footstep on the stairs, and when I come into the room, is your first impulse to catch me in your manly arms? I haven't noticed it.

JOHN: I don't want to make a fool of myself.

CONSTANCE: Then I think you've answered my question. You're no more in love with me than I am with you.

JOHN: You never said a word of this before.

CONSTANCE: I think most married couples tell one another far too much. There are some things that two people may know very well, but which it's much more tactful for them to pretend they don't.

JOHN: How did you find out?

CONSTANCE: I'll tell you. One night as we were dancing together, all at once I noticed that we weren't keeping such good step as we generally did. It was because my mind was wandering. I was thinking how it would suit me to do my hair like a woman who was dancing alongside of us. Then I looked at you and I saw you were thinking what pretty legs she'd got. I suddenly realized that you weren't in love with me any more and at the same moment I realized that it was a relief, because I wasn't in love with you.

JOHN: I must say it never occurred to me for a moment.

CONSTANCE: I know. A man thinks it quite natural that he should fall out of love with a woman, but it never strikes him for a moment that a woman can do anything so unnatural as to fall out of love with him. Don't be upset at that, darling, that is one of the charming limitations of your sex.

MARTHA: Do you mean mother and me to understand that since then John has been having one affair after another and you haven't turned a hair?

CONSTANCE: Since this is the first time he's been found out, let us give him the benefit of the doubt and hope that till now he has never strayed from the strict and narrow path. You're not angry with me, John?

JOHN: No, darling, not angry. But I *am* a little taken aback. I think you've been making rather a damned fool of me. It never struck me that your feelings for me had changed so much. You can't expect me to like it.

CONSTANCE: Oh, come now, you must be reasonable. You surely wouldn't wish me to have languished for all these years in a hopeless passion for you when you had nothing to give me in return but friendship and affection. Think what a bore it is to have some one in love with you whom you're not in love with.

JOHN: I can't conceive of your ever being a bore, Constance.

CONSTANCE [*Kissing her hand to him*]: Don't you realize that we must thank our lucky stars? We are the favoured of the gods. I shall never forget those five years of exquisite happiness you gave me when I loved you, and I shall never cease to be grateful to you, not because you loved me, but because you inspired me with love. Our love never degenerated into weariness. Because we ceased loving one another at the very same moment we never had to put up with quarrels and reproaches, recriminations and all the other paraphernalia of a passion that has ceased on one side and is still alive and eager on the other. Our love was like a cross-word puzzle in which we both hit upon the last word at the same moment. That is why our lives since have been so happy; that is why ours is a perfect marriage.

MARTHA: Do you mean to say that it meant nothing to you when you found out that John was carrying on with Marie-Louise?

CONSTANCE: Human nature is very imperfect. I'm afraid

I must admit that at the first moment I was vexed. But only at the first moment. Then I reflected that it was most unreasonable to be angry with John for giving to another something that I had no use for. That would be too much like a dog in the manger. And then I was fond enough of John to be willing that he should be happy in his own way. And if he was going to indulge in an intrigue . . . isn't that the proper phrase, John?

JOHN: I have not yet made up my mind whether it really is an indulgence.

CONSTANCE: Then it was much better that the object of his affections should be so intimate a friend of mine that I could keep a maternal eye on him.

JOHN: Really, Constance.

CONSTANCE: Marie-Louise is very pretty so that my self-esteem was not offended, and so rich that it was certain John would have no reason to squander money on her to the inconvenience of myself. She's not clever enough to acquire any ascendency over him, and so long as I kept his heart I was quite willing that she should have his senses. If you wanted to deceive me, John, I couldn't have chosen any one with whom I would more willingly be deceived than Marie-Louise.

JOHN: I don't gather that you have been very grossly deceived, darling. You have such penetration that when you look at me I feel as though I were shivering without a stitch of clothing on.

MRS. CULVER: I don't approve of your attitude, Constance. In my day when a young wife discovered that her husband had been deceiving her, she burst into a flood of tears and went to stay with her mother for three weeks, not returning to her husband till he had been brought to a proper state of abjection and repentance.

MARTHA: Are we to understand then that you are not going to divorce John?

CONSTANCE: You know, I can never see why a woman should give up a comfortable home, a considerable part of her income and the advantage of having a man about to do all the tiresome and disagreeable things for her, because he has been unfaithful to her. She's merely cutting off her nose to spite her face.

MARTHA: I am at a loss for words. I cannot conceive how a woman of any spirit can sit down and allow her husband to make a perfect damned fool of her.

CONSTANCE: You've been very stupid, my poor John. In the ordinary affairs of life stupidity is much more tiresome than wickedness. You can mend the vicious, but what in Heaven's name are you to do with the foolish?

JOHN: I've been a fool, Constance. I know it, but I'm capable of learning by experience, so I can't be a damned fool.

CONSTANCE: You mean that in the future you'll be more careful to cover your tracks?

MRS. CULVER: Oh, no, Constance, he means that this has been a lesson to him, and that in the future you'll have no cause for complaint.

CONSTANCE: I've always been given to understand that men only abandon their vices when advancing years have made them a burden rather than a pleasure. John, I'm happy to say, is still in the flower of his age. I suppose you give yourself another fifteen years, John, don't you?

JOHN: Really, Constance, I don't know what you mean. The things you say sometimes are positively embarrassing.

CONSTANCE: I think at all events we may take it that Marie-Louise will have more than one successor.

JOHN: Constance, I give you my word of honour. . . .

CONSTANCE [Interrupting]: That is the only gift you can make for which I can find no use. You see, so long as I was able to pretend a blissful ignorance of your goings-on we could all be perfectly happy. You were enjoying yourself and I received a lot of sympathy as the outraged wife. But now I do see that the position is very difficult. You have put me in a position that is neither elegant nor dignified.

JOHN: I'm awfully sorry, Constance.

MARTHA: You're going to leave him?

CONSTANCE: No, I'm not going to leave him. John, you remember that Barbara offered to take me into her business?

I refused. Well, I've changed my mind and I'm going to accept.

JOHN: But why? I don't see your point.

CONSTANCE: I'm not prepared any more to be entirely dependent upon you, John.

JOHN: But, my dear, everything I earn is at your disposal. It's a pleasure for me to provide for your wants. Heaven knows, they're not very great.

CONSTANCE: I know. Come, John, I've been very reasonable, haven't I? Don't try and thwart me when I want to do something on which I've set my heart.

[*There is an instant's pause.*]

JOHN: I don't understand. But if you put it like that, I haven't a word to say. Of course, you must do exactly as you wish.

CONSTANCE: That's a dear. Now go back to your patients or else I shall have to keep you as well as myself.

JOHN: Will you give me a kiss?

CONSTANCE: Why not?

JOHN [*Kissing her*]: It's peace between us?

CONSTANCE: Peace and good-will. [JOHN *goes out*] He is rather sweet, isn't he?

MRS. CULVER: What have you got on your mind, Constance?

CONSTANCE: I, mother? [*Teasing her*] What do you suspect?

MRS. CULVER: I don't like the look of you.

CONSTANCE: I'm sorry for that. Most people find me far from plain.

MRS. CULVER: You've got some deviltry in mind, but for the life of me I can't guess it.

MARTHA: I can't see what you expect to get out of working with Barbara.

CONSTANCE: Between a thousand and fifteen hundred a year, I believe.

MARTHA: I wasn't thinking of the money, and you know it.

CONSTANCE: I'm tired of being the modern wife.

MARTHA: What do you mean by the modern wife?

CONSTANCE: A prostitute who doesn't deliver the goods.

MRS. CULVER: My dear, what would your father say if he heard you say such things?

CONSTANCE: Darling, need we conjecture the remarks of a gentleman who's been dead for five and twenty years? Had he any gift for repartee?

MRS. CULVER: None whatever. He was good, but he was stupid. That is why the gods loved him and he died young.

[BERNARD KERSAL *opens the door and looks in.*]

BERNARD: May I come in?

CONSTANCE: Oh, there you are. I wondered what had become of you.

BERNARD: When Marie-Louise saw my two-seater at the door she asked me to drive her. I couldn't very well refuse.

CONSTANCE: So you took her home.

BERNARD: No, she said she was in such a state she must have her hair washed. I drove her to a place in Bond Street.

CONSTANCE: And what did she say to you?

BERNARD: She said, "I don't know what you must think of me."

CONSTANCE: That is what most women say to a man when his opinion doesn't matter two straws to them. And what did you answer?

BERNARD: Well, I said, "I prefer not to offer an opinion on a matter which is no business of mine."

CONSTANCE: Dear Bernard, one of the things I like most in you is that you always remain so perfectly in character. If the heavens fell you would still remain the perfect English gentleman.

BERNARD: I thought it the most tactful thing to say.

CONSTANCE: Well, mother, I won't detain you any longer. I know that you and Martha have a thousand things to do.

MRS. CULVER: I'm glad you reminded me. Come, Martha. Good-bye, darling. Good-bye, Mr. Kersal.

BERNARD: Good-bye.

CONSTANCE [*To* MARTHA]: Good-bye, dear. Thank you for all your sympathy. You've been a great help in my hour of need.

MARTHA: I don't understand and it's no good saying I do.

CONSTANCE: Bless you. [MRS. CULVER *and* MARTHA *go*

out. BERNARD *closes the door after them*] Shall we be very late?

BERNARD: So late that it doesn't matter if we're a little later. I have something important to say to you.

CONSTANCE [*Teasing him a little*]: Important to me or important to you?

BERNARD: I can't tell you how distressed I was at that terrible scene.

CONSTANCE: Oh, didn't you think it had its lighter moments?

BERNARD: It's only this afternoon I learned the truth, and then I never imagined for a moment that you knew it too. I can't tell you how brave I think it of you to have borne all this torture with a smiling face. If I admired you before, I admire you ten times more now.

CONSTANCE: You're very sweet, Bernard.

BERNARD: My heart bleeds when I think of what you've gone through.

CONSTANCE: It's not a very good plan to take other people's misfortunes too much to heart.

BERNARD: Hardly an hour ago I told you that if ever you wanted me I was only too anxious to do anything in the world for you. I little thought then that the time would come so soon. There's no reason now why I shouldn't tell you of the love that consumes me. Oh, Constance, come to me. You know that if things were as I thought they were between you and John nothing would have induced me to say a word. But now he has no longer any claims on you. He doesn't love you. Why should you go on wasting your life with a man who is capable of exposing you to all this humiliation? You know how long and tenderly I've loved you. You can trust yourself to me. I'll give my whole life to making you forget the anguish you've endured. Will you marry me, Constance?

CONSTANCE: My dear, John may have behaved very badly but he's still my husband.

BERNARD: Only in name. You've done everything in your power to save a scandal and now if you ask him to let himself be divorced he's bound to consent.

CONSTANCE: Do you really think John has behaved so very badly to me?

BERNARD [*Astonished*]: You don't mean to say that you have any doubts in your mind about his relationship with Marie-Louise?

CONSTANCE: None.

BERNARD: Then what in God's name do you mean?

CONSTANCE: My dear Bernard, have you ever considered what marriage is among well-to-do people? In the working classes a woman cooks her husband's dinner, washes for him and darns his socks. She looks after the children and makes their clothes. She gives good value for the money she costs. But what is a wife in our class? Her house is managed by servants, nurses look after her children, if she has resigned herself to having any, and as soon as they are old enough she packs them off to school. Let us face it, she is no more than the mistress of a man of whose desire she has taken advantage to insist on a legal ceremony that will prevent him from discarding her when his desire has ceased.

BERNARD: She's also his companion and his helpmate.

CONSTANCE: My dear, any sensible man would sooner play bridge at his club than with his wife, and he'd always rather play golf with a man than with a woman. A paid secretary is a far better helpmate than a loving spouse. When all is said and done, the modern wife is nothing but a parasite.

BERNARD: I don't agree with you.

CONSTANCE: You see, my poor friend, you are in love and your judgment is confused.

BERNARD: I don't understand what you mean.

CONSTANCE: John gives me board and lodging, money for my clothes and my amusements, a car to drive in and a certain position in the world. He's bound to do all that because fifteen years ago he was madly in love with me, and he undertook it; though, if you'd asked him, he would certainly have acknowledged that nothing is so fleeting as that particular form of madness called love. It was either very generous of him or very imprudent. Don't you think it would be rather shabby of me to take advantage now of his generosity or his want of foresight?

BERNARD: In what way?

CONSTANCE: He paid a very high price for something that he couldn't get cheaper. He no longer wants that. Why should I resent it? I know as well as anybody else that desire is fleeting. It comes and goes and no man can understand why. The only thing that's certain is that when it's gone it's gone forever. So long as John continues to provide for me what right have I to complain that he is unfaithful to me? He bought a toy and if he no longer wants to play with it why should he? He paid for it.

BERNARD: That might be all right if a man had only to think about himself. What about the woman?

CONSTANCE: I don't think you need waste too much sympathy on her. Like ninety-nine girls out of a hundred when I married I looked upon it as the only easy, honourable and lucrative calling open to me. When the average woman who has been married for fifteen years discovers her husband's infidelity it is not her heart that is wounded but her vanity. If she had any sense, she would regard it merely as one of the necessary inconveniences of an otherwise pleasant profession.

BERNARD: Then the long and short of it is that you don't love me.

CONSTANCE: You think that my principles are all moonshine?

BERNARD: I don't think they would have much influence if you were as crazy about me as I am about you. Do you still love John?

CONSTANCE: I'm very fond of him, he makes me laugh, and we get on together like a house on fire, but I'm not in love with him.

BERNARD: And is that enough for you? Isn't the future sometimes a trifle desolate? Don't you want love?

[*A pause. She gives him a long reflective look.*]

CONSTANCE [*Charmingly*]: If I did I should come to you for it, Bernard.

BERNARD: Constance, what do you mean? Is it possible

that you could ever care for me? Oh, my darling, I worship the ground you tread on.

. [*He seizes her in his arms and kisses her passionately.*]

CONSTANCE [*Releasing herself*]: Oh, my dear, don't be so sudden. I should despise myself entirely if I were unfaithful to John so long as I am entirely dependent on him.

BERNARD: But if you love me?

CONSTANCE: I never said I did. But even if I did, so long as John provides me with all the necessities of existence I wouldn't be unfaithful. It all comes down to the economic situation. He has bought my fidelity and I should be worse than a harlot if I took the price he paid and did not deliver the goods.

BERNARD: Do you mean to say there's no hope for me at all?

CONSTANCE: The only hope before you at the moment is to start for Ranelagh before the game is over.

BERNARD: Do you still want to go?

CONSTANCE: Yes.

BERNARD: Very well. [*With a burst of passion*] I love you.

CONSTANCE: Then go down and start up the car, put a spot of oil in the radiator or something, and I'll join you in a minute. I want to telephone.

BERNARD: Very well.

[*He goes out.* CONSTANCE *takes up the telephone.*]

CONSTANCE: Mayfair 2646. . . . Barbara? It's Constance. That offer you made me a fortnight ago—is it still open? Well, I want to accept it. . . . No, no, nothing has happened. John is very well. He's always sweet, you know. It's only that I want to earn my own living. When can I start? The sooner the better.

THE END OF ACT TWO

ACT THREE

The scene is the same as in the preceding acts. A year has passed. It is afternoon.

CONSTANCE *is seated at a desk writing letters.* THE BUTLER *shows in* BARBARA FAWCETT *and* MARTHA.

BENTLEY: Mrs. Fawcett and Miss Culver.

CONSTANCE: Oh! Sit down, I'm just finishing a note.

BARBARA: We met on the doorstep.

MARTHA: I thought I'd just look round and see if there was anything I could do to help you before you start.

CONSTANCE: That's very nice of you, Martha. I really don't think there is. I'm packed and ready, and for once I don't believe I've forgotten one of the things I shan't want.

BARBARA: I felt I must run in to say good-bye to you.

CONSTANCE: Now, my dear, you mustn't neglect your work the moment my back is turned.

BARBARA: Well, it's partly the work that's brought me. An order has just come in for a new house and they want an Italian room.

CONSTANCE: I don't like that look in your beady eye, Barbara.

BARBARA: Well, it struck me that as you're going to Italy you might go round the shops and buy any nice pieces that you can find.

CONSTANCE: Perish the thought. I've worked like a dog for a year and last night at six o'clock I downed tools. I stripped off my grimy overalls, wrung the sweat from my honest brow and scrubbed my horny hands. You said I could take six weeks' holiday.

BARBARA: I admit that you've thoroughly earned it.

CONSTANCE: When I closed the shop-door behind me, I ceased to be a British workingman and resumed the position of a perfect English lady.

MARTHA: I never saw you in such spirits.

CONSTANCE: Something accomplished, something done. But what I was coming to was this: for the next six weeks I refuse to give a moment's thought to bathrooms or wall-papers, kitchen sinks, scullery floors, curtains, cushions and refrigerators.

BARBARA: I wasn't asking you to. I only wanted you to get some of that painted Italian furniture and a few mirrors.

CONSTANCE: No, I've worked hard and I've enjoyed my work, and now I'm going to enjoy a perfect holiday.

BARBARA: Oh, well, have it your own way.

MARTHA: Constance dear, I think there's something you ought to know.

CONSTANCE: I should have thought you had discovered by now that I generally know the things I ought to know.

MARTHA: You'll never guess whom I saw in Bond Street this morning.

CONSTANCE: Yes, I shall. Marie-Louise.

MARTHA: Oh!

CONSTANCE: I'm sorry to disappoint you, darling. She rang me up an hour ago.

MARTHA: But I thought she wasn't coming back for another month. She was going to stay away a year.

CONSTANCE: She arrived last night and I'm expecting her every minute.

MARTHA: Here?

CONSTANCE: Yes. She said she simply must run in and see me before I left.

MARTHA: I wonder what she wants.

CONSTANCE: Perhaps to pass the time of day. I think it's rather sweet of her, considering how busy she must be on getting back after so long.

BARBARA: She's been all over the place, hasn't she?

CONSTANCE: Yes, she's been in Malaya; Mortimer has interests there, you know, and in China, and now they've just come from India.

MARTHA: I often wondered if it was at your suggestion that they set off on that long tour immediately after that unfortunate scene.

CONSTANCE: Which, you must confess, no one enjoyed more than you, darling.

BARBARA: It was certainly the most sensible thing they could do.

MARTHA: Of course you know your own business best, darling, but don't you think it's a little unfortunate that you should be going away for six weeks just as she comes back?

CONSTANCE: We workingwomen have to take our holidays when we can.

BARBARA: Surely John has had his lesson. He's not going to make a fool of himself a second time.

MARTHA: Do you think he has really got over his infatuation, Constance?

CONSTANCE: I don't know at all. But here he is, you'd better ask him.

[*As she says these words,* JOHN *enters.*]

JOHN: Ask him what?

MARTHA [*Not at all at a loss*]: I was just wondering what you'd do with yourself during Constance's absence.

JOHN: I've got a lot of work, you know, and I shall go to the club a good deal.

MARTHA: It seems a pity that you weren't able to arrange things so that you and Constance should take your holidays together.

BARBARA: Don't blame me for that. I was quite willing to make my arrangements to suit Constance.

CONSTANCE: You see, I wanted to go to Italy and the only places John likes on the Continent are those in which it's only by an effort of the imagination that you can tell you're not in England.

MARTHA: What about Helen?

CONSTANCE: We've taken a house at Henley for August. John can play golf and go on the river and I shall be able to come up to town every day to look after the business.

BARBARA: Well, dear, I'll leave you. I hope you'll have a wonderful holiday. I know you've deserved it. Do you know, I think I'm a very clever woman, John, to have persuaded Constance to work. She's been absolutely invaluable to me.

JOHN: I never liked the idea and I'm not going to say I did.

BARBARA: Haven't you forgiven me yet?

JOHN: She insisted on it and I had to make the best of a bad job.

BARBARA: Good-bye.

CONSTANCE [*Kissing her*]: Good-bye, dear. Take care of yourself.

MARTHA: I'll come with you, Barbara. Mother said she'd look in for a minute to say good-bye to you.

CONSTANCE: Oh, all right. Good-bye.

[*She kisses the two and accompanies them to the door. They go out.*]

JOHN: I say, Constance, I thought you had to go now because Barbara couldn't possibly get away.

CONSTANCE: Did I say that?

JOHN: Certainly.

CONSTANCE: Oh!

JOHN: If I'd dreamt that you could just as easily take your holiday when I take mine. . . .

CONSTANCE [*Interrupting*]: Don't you think it's a mistake for husbands and wives to take their holidays together? The only reason one takes a holiday is for rest and change and recreation. Do you think a man really gets that when he goes away with his wife?

JOHN: It depends on the wife.

CONSTANCE: I know nothing more depressing than the sight of all those couples in a hotel dining room, one little couple to one little table, sitting opposite to one another without a word to say.

JOHN: Oh, nonsense. You often see couples who are very jolly and cheerful.

CONSTANCE: Yes, I know, but look closely at the lady's wedding-ring and you'll see that it rests uneasily on the hand it adorns.

JOHN: We always get on like a house on fire and when I slipped a wedding-ring on your finger a bishop supervised the process. You're not going to tell me that I bore *you*.

CONSTANCE: On the contrary, you tickle me to death. It's that unhappy modesty of mine: I was afraid that you could have too much of my society. I thought it would refresh you if I left you to your own devices for a few weeks.

JOHN: If you go on pulling my leg so persistently I shall be permanently deformed.

CONSTANCE: Anyhow it's too late now. My bags are packed, my farewells made and nothing bores people so much as to see you to-morrow when they've made up their minds to get on without you for a month.

JOHN: H'm. Eyewash. . . . Look here, Constance, there's something I want to say to you.

CONSTANCE: Yes?

JOHN: Do you know that Marie-Louise has come back?

CONSTANCE: Yes. She said she'd try and look in to say how do you do before I started. It'll be nice to see her again after so long.

JOHN: I want you to do something for me, Constance.

CONSTANCE: What is it?

JOHN: Well, you've been a perfect brick to me, and hang it all, I can't take advantage of your good nature. I must do the square thing.

CONSTANCE: I'm afraid I don't quite understand.

JOHN: I haven't seen Marie-Louise since that day when Mortimer came here and made such a fool of himself. She's been away for nearly a year and taking all things into consideration I think it would be a mistake to resume the relations that we were on then.

CONSTANCE: What makes you think she wishes to?

JOHN: The fact that she rang you up the moment she arrived looks ominous to me.

CONSTANCE: Ominous? You know some women can't see a telephone without taking the receiver off and then, when the operator says, "Number, please," they have to say something. I dare say ours was the first that occurred to Marie-Louise.

JOHN: It's no good blinking the fact that Marie-Louise was madly in love with me.

CONSTANCE: Well, we can neither of us blame her for that.

JOHN: I don't want to be unkind, but after all, circumstances have forced a break upon us and I think we had better look upon it as permanent.

CONSTANCE: Of course you must please yourself.

JOHN: I'm not thinking of myself, Constance. I'm thinking partly of course of Marie-Louise's good, but, I confess, chiefly of you. I could never look you in the face again if everything between Marie-Louise and me were not definitely finished.

CONSTANCE: I should hate you to lose so harmless and inexpensive a pleasure.

JOHN: Of course it'll be painful, but if one's made up one's mind to do a thing I think it's much better to do it quickly.

CONSTANCE: I think you're quite right. I'll tell you what I'll do, as soon as Marie-Louise comes I'll make an excuse and leave you alone with her.

JOHN: That wasn't exactly my idea.

CONSTANCE: Oh?

JOHN: It's the kind of thing that a woman can do so much better than a man. It struck me that it would come better from you than from me.

CONSTANCE: Oh, did it?

JOHN: It's a little awkward for me, but it would be quite easy for you to say—well, you know the sort of thing, that you have your self-respect to think of, and to cut a long story short, she must either give me up or you'll raise hell.

CONSTANCE: But you know what a soft heart I have. If she bursts into tears and says she can't live without you I shall feel so sorry for her that I shall say, "Well, damn it all, keep him."

JOHN: You wouldn't do me a dirty trick like that, Constance.

CONSTANCE: You know that your happiness is my chief interest in life.

JOHN [*After a moment's hesitation*]: Constance, I will be perfectly frank with you. I'm fed up with Marie-Louise.

CONSTANCE: Darling, why didn't you say that at once?

JOHN: Be a sport, Constance. You know that's not the kind of thing one can say to a woman.

CONSTANCE: I admit it's not the kind of thing she's apt to take very well.

JOHN: Women are funny. When they're tired of you they tell you so without a moment's hesitation and if you don't like it you can lump it. But if you're tired of them you're a brute and a beast and boiling oil's too good for you.

CONSTANCE: Very well, leave it to me. I'll do it.

JOHN: You're a perfect brick. But you'll let her down gently, won't you? I wouldn't hurt her feelings for the world. She's a nice little thing, Constance.

CONSTANCE: Sweet.

JOHN: And it's hard luck on her.

CONSTANCE: Rotten.

JOHN: Make her understand that I'm more sinned against than sinning. I don't want her to think too badly of me.

CONSTANCE: Of course not.

JOHN: But be quite sure it's definite.

CONSTANCE: Leave it to me.

JOHN: You're a ripper, Constance. By George, no man could want a better wife.

[*The butler introduces* MARIE-LOUISE.]

BUTLER: Mrs. Durham.

[*The two women embrace warmly.*]

MARIE-LOUISE: Darling, how perfectly divine to see you again. It's too, too wonderful.

CONSTANCE: My dear, how well you're looking. Are those the new pearls?

MARIE-LOUISE: Aren't they sweet? But Mortimer bought me the most heavenly emeralds when we were in India. Oh, John, how are you?

JOHN: Oh, I'm all right, thanks.

MARIE-LOUISE: Aren't you a little fatter than when I saw you last?

JOHN: Certainly not.

MARIE-LOUISE: I've lost pounds. [*To* CONSTANCE] I'm so glad I caught you. I should have been so disappointed to miss you. [*To* JOHN] Where are you going?

JOHN: Nowhere. Constance is going alone.

MARIE-LOUISE: Is she? How perfectly divine. I suppose you can't get away. Are you making pots of money?

JOHN: I get along. Will you forgive me if I leave you? I've got to be off.

MARIE-LOUISE: Of course. You're always busy, aren't you?

JOHN: Good-bye.

MARIE-LOUISE: I hope we shall see something of you while Constance is away.

JOHN: Thank you very much.

MARIE-LOUISE: Mortimer's golf has improved. He'd love to play with you.

JOHN: Oh, yes, I should love it.

[*He goes out.*]

MARIE-LOUISE: I did so hope to find you alone. Constance, I've got heaps and heaps to tell you. Isn't it tactful of John to leave us? First of all I want to tell you how splendidly everything has turned out. You know you were quite right. I'm so glad I took your advice and made Mortimer take me away for a year.

CONSTANCE: Mortimer is no fool.

MARIE-LOUISE: Oh, no, for a man he's really quite clever. I gave him hell, you know, for ever having suspected me, and at last he was just eating out of my hand. But I could see he wasn't quite sure of me. You know what men are— when they once get an idea in their heads it's dreadfully difficult for them to get it out again. But the journey was an inspiration; I was absolutely angelic all the time, and he made a lot of money, so everything in the garden was rosy.

CONSTANCE: I'm very glad.

MARIE-LOUISE: I owe it all to you, Constance. I made Mortimer buy you a perfectly divine star sapphire in Ceylon. I told him he owed you some sort of reparation for the insult he'd put upon you. It cost a hundred and twenty pounds, darling, and we're taking it to Cartier's to have it set.

CONSTANCE: How thrilling.

MARIE-LOUISE: You mustn't think I'm ungrateful. Now listen, Constance, I want to tell you at once that you needn't distress yourself about me and John.

CONSTANCE: I never did.

MARIE-LOUISE: I know I behaved like a little beast, but I never thought you'd find out. If I had, well, you know me well enough to be positive that nothing would have induced me to have anything to do with him.

CONSTANCE: You're very kind.

MARIE-LOUISE: I want you to do something for me, Constance. Will you?

CONSTANCE: I'm always eager to oblige a friend.

MARIE-LOUISE: Well, you know what John is. Of course he's a dear and all that kind of thing, but the thing's over and it's best that he should realize it at once.

CONSTANCE: Over?

MARIE-LOUISE: Of course I know he's head over heels in love with me still. I saw that the moment I came into the room. One can't blame him for that, can one?

CONSTANCE: Men do find you fascinating.

MARIE-LOUISE: But one has to think of oneself sometimes in this world. He must see that it could never be the same after we discovered that you knew all about it.

CONSTANCE: I kept it from you as long as I could.

MARIE-LOUISE: One couldn't help feeling then that you were rather making fools of us. It seemed to take the romance away if you see what I mean.

CONSTANCE: Dimly.

MARIE-LOUISE: You know, I wouldn't hurt John's feelings for the world, but it's no good beating around the bush and I'm quite determined to have the thing finished and done with before you go.

CONSTANCE: This is very sudden. I'm afraid it'll be an awful shock to John.

MARIE-LOUISE: I've quite made up my mind.

CONSTANCE: There isn't much time for a very long and moving scene, but I'll see if John is in still. Could you manage it in ten minutes?

MARIE-LOUISE: Oh, but *I* can't see him. I want you to tell him.

CONSTANCE: Me!

MARIE-LOUISE: You know him so well, you know just the sort of things to say to him. It's not very nice telling a man who adores you that you don't care for him in that way any more. It's so much easier for a third party.

CONSTANCE: Do you really think so?

MARIE-LOUISE: I'm positive of it. You see, you can say that for your sake I've made up my mind that from now on we can be nothing but friends. You've been so wonderful to both of us, it would be dreadful if we didn't play the game now. Say that I shall always think of him tenderly and that he's the only man I've ever really loved, but that we must part.

CONSTANCE: But if he insists on seeing you?

MARIE-LOUISE: It's no good, Constance, I can't see him. I shall only cry and get my eyes all bunged up. You will do it for me, darling. Please.

CONSTANCE: I will.

MARIE-LOUISE: I got the most divine evening frock in pale green satin on my way through Paris and it would look too sweet on you. Would you like me to give it to you? I've only worn it once.

CONSTANCE: Now tell me the real reason why you're so determined to get rid of John without a moment's delay.

[MARIE-LOUISE *looks at her and gives a little roguish smile.*]

MARIE-LOUISE: Swear you won't tell.

CONSTANCE: On my honour.

MARIE-LOUISE: Well, my dear, we met a perfectly divine young man in India. He was A.D.C. to one of the governors and he came home on the same boat with us. He simply adores me.

CONSTANCE: And of course you adore him.

MARIE-LOUISE: My dear, I'm absolutely mad about him. I don't know what's going to happen.

CONSTANCE: I think we can both give a pretty shrewd guess.

MARIE-LOUISE: It's simply awful to have a temperament like mine. Of course you can't understand, you're cold.

CONSTANCE [*Very calmly*]: You're an immoral little beast, Marie-Louise.

MARIE-LOUISE: Oh, I'm not. I have affairs—but I'm not promiscuous.

CONSTANCE: I should respect you more if you were an

honest prostitute. She at least does what she does to earn her bread and butter. You take everything from your husband and give him nothing that he pays for. You are no better than a vulgar cheat.

MARIE-LOUISE [*Surprised and really hurt*]: Constance, how can you say such things to me? I think it's terribly unkind of you. I thought you liked me.

CONSTANCE: I do. I think you a liar, a humbug and a parasite, but I like you.

MARIE-LOUISE: You can't if you think such dreadful things about me.

CONSTANCE: I do. You're good-tempered and generous and sometimes amusing. I even have a certain affection for you.

MARIE-LOUISE [*Smiling*]: I don't believe you mean a word you say. You know how devoted I am to you.

CONSTANCE: I take people as they are and I dare say that in another twenty years you'll be the pink of propriety.

MARIE-LOUISE: Darling, I knew you didn't mean it, but you will have your little joke.

CONSTANCE: Now run along, darling, and I'll break the news to John.

MARIE-LOUISE: Well, good-bye, and be gentle with him. There is no reason why we shouldn't spare him as much as possible. [*She turns to go and at the door—stops*] Of course I've often wondered why with your looks you don't have more success than you do. I know now.

CONSTANCE: Tell me.

MARIE-LOUISE: You see—you're a humourist and that always puts men off. [*She goes out. In a moment the door is cautiously opened and* JOHN *puts his head in*]

JOHN: Has she gone?

CONSTANCE: Come in. A fine night and all's well.

JOHN [*Entering*]: I heard the door bang. You broke it to her?

CONSTANCE: I broke it.

JOHN: Was she awfully upset?

CONSTANCE: Of course it was a shock, but she kept a stiff upper lip.

JOHN: Did she cry?

CONSTANCE: No. Not exactly. To tell you the truth I think she was stunned by the blow. But of course when she gets home and realises the full extent of her loss, she'll cry like anything.

JOHN: I hate to see a woman cry.

CONSTANCE: It is painful, isn't it? But of course it's a relief to the nerves.

JOHN: I think you're rather cool about it, Constance. I am not feeling any too comfortable. I shouldn't like her to think I'd treated her badly.

CONSTANCE: I think she quite understands that you're doing it for my sake. She knows that you have still a very great regard for her.

JOHN: But you made it quite definite, didn't you?

CONSTANCE: Oh, quite.

JOHN: I'm really very much obliged to you, Constance.

CONSTANCE: Not at all.

JOHN: At all events I'm glad to think that you'll be able to set out on your holiday with a perfectly easy mind. By the way, do you want any money? I'll write you a cheque at once.

CONSTANCE: Oh, no, thank you. I've got plenty. I've earned fourteen hundred pounds during this year that I've been working.

JOHN: Have you, by Jove! That's a very considerable sum.

CONSTANCE: I'm taking two hundred of it for my holiday. I've spent two hundred on my clothes and on odds and ends and the remaining thousand I've paid into your account this morning for my board and lodging during the last twelve months.

JOHN: Nonsense, darling. I won't hear of such a thing. I don't want you to pay for your board and lodging.

CONSTANCE: I insist.

JOHN: Don't you love me any more?

CONSTANCE: What has that to do with it? Oh, you think a woman can only love a man if he keeps her. Isn't that rating your powers of fascination too modestly? What about your charm and good humour?

JOHN: Don't be absurd, Constance. I can perfectly well afford to support you in your proper station. To offer me a thousand pounds for your board and lodging is almost insulting.

CONSTANCE: Don't you think it's the kind of insult you could bring yourself to swallow? One can do a lot of amusing things with a thousand pounds.

JOHN: I wouldn't dream of taking it. I never liked the idea of your going into business. I thought you had quite enough to do looking after the house and so forth.

CONSTANCE: Have you been less comfortable since I began working?

JOHN: No, I can't say I have.

CONSTANCE: You can take my word for it, a lot of incompetent women talk a great deal of nonsense about housekeeping. If you know your job and have good servants it can be done in ten minutes a day.

JOHN: Anyhow you wanted to work and I yielded. I thought in point of fact it would be a very pleasant occupation for you, but heavens knows, I wasn't expecting to profit financially by it.

CONSTANCE: No, I'm sure you weren't.

JOHN: Constance, I could never help thinking that your determination had something to do with Marie-Louise.

[*There is a moment's pause and when* CONSTANCE *speaks it is not without seriousness.*]

CONSTANCE: Haven't you wondered why I never reproached you for your affair with Marie-Louise?

JOHN: Yes. I could only ascribe it to your unfathomable goodness.

CONSTANCE: You were wrong. I felt I hadn't the right to reproach you.

JOHN: What do you mean, Constance? You had every right. We behaved like a couple of swine. I may be a dirty dog, but, thank God, I know I'm a dirty dog.

CONSTANCE: You no longer desired me. How could I blame you for that? But if you didn't desire me, what use was I to you? You've seen how small a share I take in providing you with the comfort of a well-ordered home.

JOHN: You were the mother of my child.

CONSTANCE: Let us not exaggerate the importance of that, John. I performed a natural and healthy function of my sex. And all the tiresome part of looking after the child when she was born I placed in the hands of much more competent persons. Let us face it, I was only a parasite in your house. You had entered into legal obligations that prevented you from turning me adrift, but I owe you a debt of gratitude for never letting me see by word or gesture that I was no more than a costly and at times inconvenient ornament.

JOHN: I never looked upon you as an inconvenient ornament. And I don't know what you mean by being a parasite. Have I ever in any way suggested that I grudged a penny that I spent on you?

CONSTANCE [*With mock amazement*]: Do you mean to say that I ascribed to your beautiful manners what was only due to your stupidity? Are you as great a fool as the average man who falls for the average woman's stupendous bluff that just because he's married her he must provide for her wants and her luxuries, sacrifice his pleasures and comfort and convenience, and that he must look upon it as a privilege that she allows him to be her slave and bondman? Come, come, John, pull yourself together. You're a hundred years behind the times. Now that women have broken down the walls of the harem they must take the rough-and-tumble of the street.

JOHN: You forget all sorts of things. Don't you think a man may have gratitude to a woman for the love he has had for her in the past?

CONSTANCE: I think gratitude is often very strong in men so long as it demands from them no particular sacrifices.

JOHN: Well, it's a curious way of looking at things, but obviously I have reason to be thankful for it. But after all you knew what was going on long before it came out. What happened then that made you make up your mind to go into business?

CONSTANCE: I am naturally a lazy woman. So long as appearances were saved I was prepared to take all I could get and give nothing in return. I was a parasite, but I knew

it. But when we reached a situation where only your politeness or your lack of intelligence prevented you from throwing the fact in my teeth I changed my mind. I thought that I
should very much like to be in a position where, if I felt inclined to, I could tell you, with calm, courtesy, but with determination—to go to hell.

JOHN: And are you in that position now?

CONSTANCE: Precisely. I owe you nothing. I am able to
keep myself. For the last year I have paid my way. There is
only one freedom that is really important and that is economic freedom, for in the long run the man who pays the
piper calls the tune. Well, I have that freedom and upon my
soul it's the most enjoyable sensation I can remember since
I ate my first strawberry ice.

JOHN: You know, I would sooner you had made me scenes
for a month on end like any ordinary woman and nagged my
life out than that you should harbour this cold rancour
against me.

CONSTANCE: My poor darling, what are you talking
about? Have you known me for fifteen years and do you
think me capable of the commonness of insincerity? I harbour no rancour. Why, my dear, I'm devoted to you.

JOHN: Do you mean to tell me that you've done all this
without any intention of making me feel a perfect cad?

CONSTANCE: On my honour. If I look in my heart I can
only find in it affection for you and the most kindly and
charitable feelings. Don't you believe me?

[*He looks at her for a moment and then makes a little
gesture of bewilderment.*]

JOHN: Yes, oddly enough, I do. You are a remarkable
woman, Constance.

CONSTANCE: I know, but keep it to yourself. You don't
want to give a dog a bad name.

JOHN [*With an affectionate smile*]: I wish I could get
away. I don't half like the idea of your travelling by yourself.

CONSTANCE: Oh, but I'm not. Didn't I tell you?

JOHN: No.

CONSTANCE: I meant to. I'm going with Bernard.

JOHN: Oh. You never said so. Who else?

CONSTANCE: Nobody.

JOHN: Oh! [*He is rather taken aback at the news*] Isn't that rather odd?

CONSTANCE: No. Why?

JOHN [*Not knowing at all how to take it*]: Well, it's not usual for a young woman to take a six weeks' holiday with a man who can hardly be described as old enough to be her father.

CONSTANCE: Bernard's just about the same age as you.

JOHN: Don't you think it'll make people gossip a bit?

CONSTANCE: I haven't gone out of my way to spread the news. In fact, now I come to think of it, I haven't told any one but you, and you, I am sure, will be discreet.

[JOHN *suddenly feels that his collar is a little too tight for him, and with his fingers he tries to loosen it.*]

JOHN: You're pretty certain to be seen by some one who knows you and they're bound to talk.

CONSTANCE: Oh, I don't think so. You see we're motoring all the way and we neither of us care for frequented places. One of the advantages of having really nice friends like ours is that you can always be certain of finding them at the fashionable resorts at the very moment when everybody you know is there.

JOHN: Of course I am not so silly as to think that because a man and a woman go away together it is necessary to believe the worst about them, but you can't deny that it is rather unconventional. I wouldn't for a moment suggest that there'll be anything between you, but it's inevitable that ordinary persons should think there was.

CONSTANCE [*As cool as a cucumber*]: I've always thought that ordinary persons had more sense than the clever ones are ready to credit them with.

JOHN [*Deliberately*]: What on earth do you mean?

CONSTANCE: Why, of course we're going as man and wife, John.

JOHN: Don't be a fool, Constance. You don't know what you're talking about. That's not funny at all.

CONSTANCE: But, my poor John, whom do you take us for? Am I so unattractive that what I'm telling you is incredible? Why else should I go with Bernard? If I merely wanted a companion I'd go with a woman. We could have headaches together and have our hair washed at the same place and copy one another's nightdresses. A woman's a much better travelling companion than a man.

JOHN: I may be very stupid, but I don't seem to be able to understand what you're saying. Do you really mean me to believe that Bernard Kersal is your lover?

CONSTANCE: Certainly not.

JOHN: Then what *are* you talking about?

CONSTANCE: My dear, I can't put it any plainer. I'm going away for six weeks' holiday and Bernard has very kindly offered to come with me.

JOHN: And where do I come in?

CONSTANCE: You don't come in. You stay at home and look after your patients.

JOHN [*Trying his best to control himself*]: I flatter myself I'm a sensible man. I'm not going to fly into a passion. Many men would stamp and rave or break the furniture. I have no intention of being melodramatic, but you must allow me to say that what you've just told me is very surprising.

CONSTANCE: Just for a moment, perhaps, but I'm sure you have only to familiarize yourself with the notion in order to become reconciled to it.

JOHN: I'm doubtful whether I shall have time to do that, for I feel uncommonly as though I were about to have an apoplectic stroke.

CONSTANCE: Undo your collar then. Now I come to look at you I confess that you are more than usually red in the face.

JOHN: What makes you think that I am going to allow you to go?

CONSTANCE [*Good-humouredly*]: Chiefly the fact that you can't prevent me.

JOHN: I can't bring myself to believe that you mean what you say. I don't know what ever put such an idea into your head.

CONSTANCE [*Casually*]: I thought a change might do me good.

JOHN: Nonsense.

CONSTANCE: Why? You did. Don't you remember? You were getting rather flat and stale. Then you had an affair with Marie-Louise and you were quite another man. Gay and amusing, full of life, and much more agreeable to live with. The moral effect on you was quite remarkable.

JOHN: It's different for a man than for a woman.

CONSTANCE: Are you thinking of the possible consequences? We have long passed the Victorian Era when asterisks were followed after a certain interval by a baby.

JOHN: That never occurred to me. What I meant was that if a man's unfaithful to his wife she's an object of sympathy, whereas if a woman's unfaithful to her husband he's merely an object of ridicule.

CONSTANCE: That is one of those conventional prejudices that sensible people must strive to ignore.

JOHN: Do you expect me to sit still and let this man take my wife away from under my very nose? I wonder you don't ask me to shake hands with him and wish him good luck.

CONSTANCE: That's just what I am going to do. He's coming here in a few minutes to say good-bye to you.

JOHN: I shall knock him down.

CONSTANCE: I wouldn't take any risks in your place. He's pretty hefty and I'm under the impression that he's very nippy with his left.

JOHN: I shall have great pleasure in telling him exactly what I think of him.

CONSTANCE: Why? Have you forgotten that I am charming to Marie-Louise? We were the best of friends. She never bought a hat without asking me to go and help her choose it.

JOHN: I have red blood in my veins.

CONSTANCE: I'm more concerned at the moment with the grey matter in your brain.

JOHN: Is he in love with you?

CONSTANCE: Madly. Didn't you know?

JOHN: I? How should I?

CONSTANCE: He's been here a great deal during the last year. Were you under the impression that he only came to see you?

JOHN: I never paid any attention to him. I thought him rather dull.

CONSTANCE: He is rather dull. But he's very sweet.

JOHN: What sort of a man is it who eats a fellow's food and drinks his wine and then makes love to his wife behind his back?

CONSTANCE: A man very like you, John, I should say.

JOHN: Not at all. Mortimer is the sort of man who was born to be made a fool of.

CONSTANCE: None of us know for certain the designs of providence.

JOHN: I see you're bent on driving me to desperation. I shall break something in a minute.

CONSTANCE: There's that blue-and-white bowl that your Uncle Henry gave us as a wedding present. Break that, it's only a modern imitation.

[*He takes the bowl and hurls it on the floor so that it is shattered.*]

JOHN: There.

CONSTANCE: Do you feel better?

JOHN: Not a bit.

CONSTANCE: It's a pity you broke it then. You might have given it away as a wedding present to one of your colleagues at the hospital.

[*The butler shows in* MRS. CULVER.]

BUTLER: Mrs. Culver.

CONSTANCE: Oh, mother, how sweet of you to come. I was so hoping I'd see you before I left.

MRS. CULVER: Oh, you've had an accident.

CONSTANCE: No, John's in a temper and he thought it would relieve him if he broke something.

MRS. CULVER: Nonsense, John's never in a temper.

JOHN: That's what you think, Mrs. Culver. Yes, I am in a temper. I'm in a filthy temper. Are you a party to this plan of Constance's?

CONSTANCE: No, mother doesn't know.

JOHN: Can't you do something to stop it? You have some influence over her. You must see that the thing's preposterous.

MRS. CULVER: My dear boy, I haven't the ghost of an idea what you're talking about.

JOHN: She's going to Italy with Bernard Kersal. Alone.

MRS. CULVER [*With a stare*]: It's not true; how d'you know?

JOHN: She's just told me so, as bold as brass, out of a blue sky. She mentioned it in the course of conversation as if she were saying: "Darling, your coat wants brushing."

MRS. CULVER: Is it true, Constance?

CONSTANCE: Quite.

MRS. CULVER: But haven't you been getting on with John? I always thought you two were as happy as the day is long.

JOHN: So did I. We've never had the shadow of a quarrel. We've always got on.

MRS. CULVER: Don't you love John any more, darling?

CONSTANCE: Yes, I'm devoted to him.

JOHN: How can you be devoted to a man when you're going to do him the greatest injury that a woman can do to a man?

CONSTANCE: Don't be idiotic, John. I'm going to do you no more injury than you did me a year ago.

JOHN [*Striding up to her, thinking quite erroneously that he sees light*]: Are you doing this in order to pay me out for Marie-Louise?

CONSTANCE: Don't be such a fool, John. Nothing is further from my thoughts.

MRS. CULVER: The circumstances are entirely different. It was very naughty of John to deceive you, but he's sorry for what he did and he's been punished for it. It was all very dreadful and caused us a great deal of pain. But a man's a man and you expect that kind of thing from him. There are excuses for him. There are none for a woman. Men are naturally polygamous and sensible women have always made allowances for their occasional lapse from a condition which modern civilisation has forced on them. Women are monogamous. They do not naturally desire more than one man and that is why the common sense of the world has heaped obloquy upon them when they have overstepped the natural limitations of their sex.

CONSTANCE [*Smiling*] : It seems rather hard that what is sauce for the gander shouldn't also be sauce for the goose.

MRS. CULVER : We all know that unchastity has no moral effect on men. They can be perfectly promiscuous and remain upright, industrious and reliable. It's quite different with women. It ruins their character. They become untruthful and dissipated, lazy, shiftless and dishonest. That is why the experience of ten thousand years has demanded chastity in women. Because it has learnt that this virtue is the key to all others.

CONSTANCE : They were dishonest because they were giving away something that wasn't theirs to give. They had sold themselves for board, lodging and protection. They were chattel. They were dependent on their husbands and when they were unfaithful to them they were liars and thieves. I'm not dependent on John. I am economically independent and therefore I claim my sexual independence. I have this afternoon paid into John's account one thousand pounds for my year's keep.

JOHN : I refuse to take it.

CONSTANCE : Well, you'll damned well have to.

MRS. CULVER : There's no object in losing your temper.

CONSTANCE : I have mine under perfect control.

JOHN : If you think what they call free love is fun, you're mistaken. Believe me, it's the most overrated amusement that was ever invented.

CONSTANCE : In that case, I wonder why people continue to indulge in it.

JOHN : I ought to know what I'm talking about, hang it all. It has all the inconveniences of marriage and none of its advantages. I assure you, my dear, the game is not worth the candle.

CONSTANCE : You may be right, but you know how hard it is to profit by anybody's experience. I think I'd like to see for myself.

MRS. CULVER : Are you in love with Bernard?

CONSTANCE : To tell you the truth I haven't quite made up my mind. How does one know if one's in love?

MRS. CULVER: My dear, I only know one test. Could you use his tooth-brush?

CONSTANCE: No.

MRS. CULVER: Then you're not in love with him.

CONSTANCE: He's adored me for fifteen years. There's something in that long devotion which gives me a funny little feeling in my heart. I should like to do something to show him that I'm not ungrateful. You see, in six weeks he goes back to Japan. There is no chance of his coming to England again for seven years. I'm thirty-six now and he adores me; in seven years I shall be forty-three. A woman of forty-three is often charming, but it's seldom that a man of fifty-five is crazy about her. I came to the conclusion that it must be now or never and so I asked him if he'd like me to spend these last six weeks with him in Italy. When I wave my handkerchief to him as the ship that takes him sails out of the harbour at Naples I hope that he will feel that all those years of unselfish love have been well worth the while.

JOHN: Six weeks. Do you intend to leave him at the end of six weeks?

CONSTANCE: Oh, yes, of course. It's because I'm putting a limit to our love that I think it may achieve the perfection of something that is beautiful and transitory. Why, John, what is it that makes a rose so lovely but that its petals fall as soon as it is full blown?

JOHN: It's all come as such a shock and a surprise that I hardly know what to say. You've got me at a complete disadvantage.

[MRS. CULVER, *who has been standing at the window, gives a little cry.*]

CONSTANCE: What is it?

MRS. CULVER: Here is Bernard. He's just driven up to the door.

JOHN: Do you expect me to receive him as if I were blissfully unconscious of your plans?

CONSTANCE: It would be more comfortable. It would be stupid to make a scene and it wouldn't prevent my going on this little jaunt with him.

JOHN: I have my dignity to think of.

CONSTANCE: One often preserves that best by putting it in one's pocket. It would be kind of you, John, to treat him just as pleasantly as I treated Marie-Louise when I knew she was your mistress.

JOHN: Does he know that I know?

CONSTANCE: Of course not. He's a little conventional, you know, and he couldn't happily deceive a friend if he thought there was no deception.

MRS. CULVER: Constance, is there nothing I can say to make you reconsider your decision?

CONSTANCE: Nothing, darling.

MRS. CULVER: Then I may just as well save my breath. I'll slip away before he comes.

CONSTANCE: Oh, all right. Good-bye, mother. I'll send you a lot of picture post-cards.

MRS. CULVER: I don't approve of you, Constance, and I can't pretend that I do. No good will come of it. Men were meant by nature to be wicked and delightful and deceive their wives, and women were meant to be virtuous and forgiving and to suffer verbosely. That was ordained from all eternity and none of your new-fangled notions can alter the decrees of Providence.

[*The butler enters, followed by* BERNARD.]

BENTLEY: Mr. Kersal.

MRS. CULVER: How do you do, Bernard, and good-bye. I'm just going.

BERNARD: Oh, I'm sorry. Good-bye.

[*She goes out.*]

CONSTANCE [*To* BERNARD]: How d'you do. Just one moment. [*To the butler*] Oh, Bentley, get my things downstairs and put them in a taxi, will you?

BENTLEY: Very good, madam.

BERNARD: Are you just starting? It's lucky I came when I did. I should have hated to miss you.

CONSTANCE: And let me know when the taxi's here.

BENTLEY: Yes, madam.

CONSTANCE: Now I can attend to you. [*The butler goes out.*]

BERNARD: Are you looking forward to your holiday?

CONSTANCE: Immensely. I've never gone on a jaunt like this before, and I'm really quite excited.

BERNARD: You're going alone, aren't you?

CONSTANCE: Oh, yes, quite alone.

BERNARD: It's rotten for you not to be able to get away, old man.

JOHN: Rotten.

BERNARD: I suppose these are the penalties of greatness. I can quite understand that you have to think of your patients first.

JOHN: Quite.

CONSTANCE: Of course John doesn't very much care for Italy.

BERNARD: Oh, are you going to Italy? I thought you said Spain.

JOHN: No, she always said Italy.

BERNARD: Oh, well, that's hardly your mark, is it, old boy? Though I believe there are some sporting links on the Lake of Como.

JOHN: Are there?

BERNARD: I suppose there's no chance of your being anywhere near Naples towards the end of July?

CONSTANCE: I don't really know. My plans are quite vague.

BERNARD: I was only asking because I'm sailing from Naples. It would be fun if we met there.

JOHN: Great fun.

CONSTANCE: I hope you'll see a lot of John while I'm away. I'm afraid he'll be a trifle lonely, poor darling. Why don't you dine together one day next week?

BERNARD: I'm terribly sorry, but you know I'm going away.

CONSTANCE: Oh, are you? I thought you were going to stay in London till you had to start for Japan.

BERNARD: I meant to, but my doctor has ordered me to go and do a cure.

JOHN: What sort of a cure?

BERNARD: Oh, just a cure. He says I want bucking up.

JOHN: Oh, does he? What's the name of your doctor?

BERNARD: No one you ever heard of. A man I used to know in the war.

JOHN: Oh!

BERNARD: So I'm afraid this is good-bye. Of course, it's a wrench leaving London, especially as I don't expect to be in Europe again for some years, but I always think it rather silly not to take a man's advice when you've asked for it.

JOHN: More especially when he's charged you three guineas.

CONSTANCE: I'm sorry. I was counting on you to keep John out of mischief during my absence.

BERNARD: I'm not sure if I could guarantee to do that. But we might have done a few theatres together and had a game of golf or two.

CONSTANCE: It would have been jolly, wouldn't it, John?

JOHN: Very jolly.

[*The butler comes in.*]

BENTLEY: The taxi's waiting, madam.

CONSTANCE: Thank you.

[*The butler goes out.*]

BERNARD: I'll take myself off. In case I don't see you again I'd like to thank you now for all your kindness to me during the year I've spent in London.

CONSTANCE: It's been very nice to see you.

BERNARD: You and John have been most awfully good to me. I never imagined I was going to have such a wonderful time.

CONSTANCE: We shall miss you terribly. It's been a great comfort to John to think that there was some one to take me out when he had to be away on one of his operations. Hasn't it, darling?

JOHN: Yes, darling.

CONSTANCE: When he knew I was with you he never worried. Did you, darling?

JOHN: No, darling.

BERNARD: I'm awfully glad if I've been able to make myself useful. Don't forget me entirely, will you?

CONSTANCE: We're not likely to do that, are we, darling?

JOHN: No, darling.

BERNARD: And if you ever have a moment to spare you will write to me, won't you? You don't know how much it means to us exiles.

CONSTANCE: Of course we will. We'll both write. Won't we, darling?

JOHN: Yes, darling.

CONSTANCE: John writes such a good letter. So chatty, you know, and amusing.

BERNARD: That's a promise. Well, good-bye, old boy. Have a good time.

JOHN: Thanks, old bean.

BERNARD: Good-bye, Constance. There's so much I want to say to you that I don't know where to begin.

JOHN: I don't want to hurry you, but the taxi is just ticking its head off.

BERNARD: John is so matter-of-fact. Well, I'll say nothing then but God bless you.

CONSTANCE: Au revoir.

BERNARD: If you do go to Naples you will let me know, won't you? If you send a line to my club, it'll be forwarded at once.

CONSTANCE: Oh, all right.

BERNARD: Good-bye.

[*He gives them both a friendly nod and goes out.* CON-STANCE *begins to giggle and soon is seized with uncontrollable laughter.*]

JOHN: Will you kindly tell what there is to laugh at? If you think it amuses me to stand here like patience on a monument and have my leg pulled you're mistaken. What did you mean by all that balderdash about meeting you by chance in Naples?

CONSTANCE: He was throwing you off the scent.

JOHN: The man's a drivelling idiot.

CONSTANCE: D'you think so? I thought he was rather ingenious. Considering he hasn't had very much practice in this sort of thing I thought he did very well.

JOHN: Of course if you're determined to find him a pattern of perfection it's useless for me to attempt to argue. But honestly, speaking without prejudice for or against, I'm sorry to think of you throwing yourself away on a man like that.

CONSTANCE: Perhaps it's natural that a man and his wife should differ in their estimate of her prospective lover.

JOHN: You're not going to tell me he's better-looking than I am.

CONSTANCE: No. You have always been my ideal of manly beauty.

JOHN: He's no better dressed than I am.

CONSTANCE: He could hardly expect to be. He goes to the same tailor.

JOHN: I don't think you can honestly say he's more amusing than I am.

CONSTANCE: No, I honestly can't.

JOHN: Then in Heaven's name why do you want to go away with him?

CONSTANCE: Shall I tell you? Once more before it's too late I want to feel about me the arms of a man who adores the ground I walk on. I want to see his face light up when I enter the room. I want to feel the pressure of his hand when we look at the moon together and the pleasantly tickling sensation when his arm tremulously steals around my waist. I want to let my hand fall on his shoulder and feel his lips softly touch my hair.

JOHN: The operation is automatically impossible, the poor devil would get such a crick in the neck he wouldn't know what to do.

CONSTANCE: I want to walk along country lanes holding hands and I want to be called by absurd pet names. I want to talk baby-talk by the hour together.

JOHN: Oh, God.

CONSTANCE: I want to know that I'm eloquent and witty when I'm dead silent. For ten years I've been very happy in your affections, John, we've been the best and dearest friends, but now just for a little while I hanker for something else. Do you grudge it me? I want to be loved.

JOHN: But, my dear, I'll love you. I've been a brute, I've neglected you, it's not too late and you're the only woman I've ever really cared for. I'll chuck everything and we'll go away together.

CONSTANCE: The prospect does not thrill me.

JOHN: Come, darling, have a heart. I gave up Marie-Louise. Surely you can give up Bernard.

CONSTANCE: But you gave up Marie-Louise to please yourself, not to please me.

JOHN: Don't be a little beast, Constance. Come away with me. We'll have such a lark.

CONSTANCE: Oh, my poor John, I didn't work so hard to gain my economic independence in order to go on a honeymoon with my own husband.

JOHN: Do you think I can't be a lover as well as a husband?

CONSTANCE: My dear, no one can make yesterday's cold mutton into to-morrow's lamb cutlets.

JOHN: You know what you're doing. I was determined in future to be a model husband and you're driving me right into the arms of Marie-Louise. I give you my word of honour that the moment you leave this house I shall drive straight to her door.

CONSTANCE: I should hate you to have a fruitless journey. I'm afraid you won't find her at home. She has a new young man and she says he's too divine.

JOHN: What!

CONSTANCE: He's the A.D.C. of a Colonial Governor. She came here to-day to ask me to break the news to you that henceforth everything was over between you.

JOHN: I hope you told her first that I was firmly resolved to terminate a connection that could only cause you pain.

CONSTANCE: I couldn't. She was in such a blooming hurry to give me her message.

JOHN: Really, Constance, for your own pride I should have thought you wouldn't like her to make a perfect fool of me. Any other woman would have said: "What a strange coincidence. Why it's only half an hour since John told me he had made up his mind never to see you again." But of course you don't care two straws for me any more, that's quite evident.

CONSTANCE: Oh, don't be unjust, darling. I shall always care for you. I may be unfaithful, but I am constant. I always think that's my most endearing quality.

[*The butler opens the door.*]

JOHN [*Irritably*]: What is it?

BENTLEY: I thought madam had forgotten that the taxi was at the door.

JOHN: Go to hell.

BENTLEY: Very good, sir.

[*He goes out.*]

CONSTANCE: I don't see why you should be rude to him. Bernard will pay the taxi. Anyhow I must go now or he'll begin to think I'm not coming. Good-bye, darling. I hope you'll get on all right in my absence. Just give the cook her head and you'll have no trouble. Won't you say good-bye to me?

JOHN: Go to the devil.

CONSTANCE: All right. I shall be back in six weeks.

JOHN: Back? Where?

CONSTANCE: Here.

JOHN: Here? Here? Do you think I'm going to take you back?

CONSTANCE: I don't see why not. When you've had time to reflect you'll realise that you have no reason to blame me. After all, I'm taking from you nothing that you want.

JOHN: Are you aware that I can divorce you for this?

CONSTANCE: Quite. But I married very prudently. I took the precaution to marry a gentleman and I know that you could never bring yourself to divorce me for doing no more than you did yourself.

JOHN: I wouldn't divorce you. I wouldn't expose my worst enemy to the risk of marrying a woman who's capable of treating her husband as you're treating me.

CONSTANCE [*At the door*]: Well, then, shall I come back?

JOHN [*After a moment's hesitation*]: You are the most maddening, wilful, capricious, wrong-headed, delightful and enchanting woman man was ever cursed with having for a wife. Yes, damn you, come back.

[*She lightly kisses her hand to him and slips out, slamming the door behind her.*]

THE END

RED

THE skipper thrust his hand into one of his trouser pockets and with difficulty, for they were not at the sides but in front and he was a portly man, pulled out a large silver watch. He looked at it and then looked again at the declining sun. The Kanaka at the wheel gave him a glance, but did not speak. The skipper's eyes rested on the island they were approaching. A white line of foam marked the reef. He knew there was an opening large enough to get his ship through, and when they came a little nearer he counted on seeing it. They had nearly an hour of daylight still before them. In the lagoon the water was deep and they could anchor comfortably. The chief of the village which he could already see among the coconut trees was a friend of the mate's, and it would be pleasant to go ashore for the night. The mate came forward at that minute and the skipper turned to him.

"We'll take a bottle of booze along with us and get some girls in to dance," he said.

"I don't see the opening," said the mate.

He was a Kanaka, a handsome, swarthy fellow, with somewhat the look of a later Roman emperor, inclined to stoutness; but his face was fine and clean-cut.

"I'm dead sure there's one right here," said the captain, looking through his glasses. "I can't understand why I can't pick it up. Send one of the boys up the mast to have a look."

The mate called one of the crew and gave him the order. The captain watched the Kanaka climb and waited for him to speak. But the Kanaka shouted down that he could see nothing but the unbroken line of foam. The captain spoke Samoan like a native, and he cursed him freely.

"Shall he stay up there?" asked the mate.

"What the hell good does that do?" answered the captain. "The blame fool can't see worth a cent. You bet your sweet life I'd find the opening if I was up there."

He looked at the slender mast with anger. It was all very well for a native who had been used to climbing up coconut trees all his life. He was fat and heavy.

"Come down," he shouted. "You're no more use than a dead dog. We'll just have to go along the reef till we find the opening."

It was a seventy-ton schooner with paraffin auxiliary, and it ran, when there was no head wind, between four and five knots an hour. It was a bedraggled object; it had been painted white a very long time ago, but it was now dirty, dingy, and mottled. It smelt strongly of paraffin and of the copra which was its usual cargo. They were within a hundred feet of the reef now and the captain told the steersman to run along it till they came to the opening. But when they had gone a couple of miles he realised that they had missed it. He went about and slowly worked back again. The white foam of the reef continued without interruption and now the sun was setting. With a curse at the stupidity of the crew the skipper resigned himself to waiting till next morning.

"Put her about," he said. "I can't anchor here."

They went out to sea a little and presently it was quite dark. They anchored. When the sail was furled the ship began to roll a good deal. They said in Apia that one day she would roll right over; and the owner, a German-American who managed one of the largest stores, said that no money was big enough to induce him to go out in her. The cook, a Chinese in white trousers, very dirty and ragged, and a thin white tunic, came to say that supper was ready, and when the skipper went into the cabin he found the engineer already seated at table. The engineer was a long, lean man with a scraggy neck. He was dressed in blue overalls and a sleeveless jersey which showed his thin arms tattooed from elbow to wrist.

"Hell, having to spend the night outside," said the skipper.

The engineer did not answer, and they ate their supper in silence. The cabin was lit by a dim oil lamp. When they had eaten the canned apricots with which the meal finished the Chink brought them a cup of tea. The skipper lit a cigar and went on the upper deck. The island now was only a darker mass against the night. The stars were very bright. The only sound was the ceaseless breaking of the surf. The skipper sank into a deck-chair and smoked idly. Presently three or four members of the crew came up and sat down. One of them had a banjo and another a concertina. They began to play, and one of them sang. The native song sounded strange on these instruments. Then to the singing a couple began to dance. It was a barbaric dance, savage and primeval, rapid, with quick movements of the hands and feet and contortions of the body; it was sensual, sexual even, but sexual without passion. It was very animal, direct, weird without mystery, natural in short, and one might almost say childlike. At last they grew tired. They stretched themselves on the deck and slept, and all was silent. The skipper lifted himself heavily out of his chair and clambered down the companion. He went into his cabin and got out of his clothes. He climbed into his bunk and lay there. He panted a little in the heat of the night.

But next morning, when the dawn crept over the tranquil sea, the opening in the reef which had eluded them the night before was seen a little to the east of where they lay. The schooner entered the lagoon. There was not a ripple on the surface of the water. Deep down among the coral rocks you saw little coloured fish swim. When he had anchored his ship the skipper ate his breakfast and went on deck. The sun shone from an unclouded sky, but in the early morning the air was grateful and cool. It was Sunday, and there was a feeling of quietness, a silence as though nature were at rest, which gave him a peculiar sense of comfort. He sat, looking at the wooded coast, and felt lazy and well at ease. Presently a slow smile moved his lips and he threw the stump of his cigar into the water.

"I guess I'll go ashore," he said. "Get the boat out."

He climbed stiffly down the ladder and was rowed to a little cove. The coconut trees came down to the water's edge, not in rows, but spaced out with an ordered formality. They were like a ballet of spinsters, elderly but flippant, standing in affected attitudes with the simpering graces of a bygone age. He sauntered idly through them, along a path that could be just seen winding its tortuous way, and it led him presently to a broad creek. There was a bridge across it, but a bridge constructed of single trunks of coconut trees, a dozen of them, placed end to end and supported where they met by a forked branch driven into the bed of the creek. You walked on a smooth, round surface, narrow and slippery, and there was no support for the hand. To cross such a bridge required sure feet and a stout heart. The skipper hesitated. But he saw on the other side, nestling among the trees, a white man's house; he made up his mind and, rather gingerly, began to walk. He watched his feet carefully, and where one trunk joined on to the next and there was a difference of level, he tottered a little. It was with a gasp of relief that he reached the last tree and finally set his feet on the firm ground of the other side. He had been so intent on the difficult crossing that he never noticed anyone was watching him, and it was with surprise that he heard himself spoken to.

"It takes a bit of nerve to cross these bridges when you're not used to them."

He looked up and saw a man standing in front of him. He had evidently come out of the house which he had seen.

"I saw you hesitate," the man continued, with a smile on his lips, "and I was watching to see you fall in."

"Not on your life," said the captain, who had now recovered his confidence.

"I've fallen in myself before now. I remember, one evening I came back from shooting, and I fell in, gun and all. Now I get a boy to carry my gun for me."

He was a man no longer young, with a small beard, now somewhat grey, and a thin face. He was dressed in a singlet, without arms, and a pair of duck trousers. He wore neither shoes nor socks. He spoke English with a slight accent.

"Are you Neilson?" asked the skipper.

"I am."

"I've heard about you. I thought you lived somewheres round here."

The skipper followed his host into the little bungalow and sat down heavily in the chair which the other motioned him to take. While Neilson went out to fetch whisky and glasses he took a look round the room. It filled him with amazement. He had never seen so many books. The shelves reached from floor to ceiling on all four walls, and they were closely packed. There was a grand piano littered with music, and a large table on which books and magazines lay in disorder. The room made him feel embarrassed. He remembered that Neilson was a queer fellow. No one knew very much about him, although he had been in the islands for so many years, but those who knew him agreed that he was queer. He was a Swede.

"You've got one big heap of books here," he said, when Neilson returned.

"They do no harm," answered Neilson with a smile.

"Have you read them all?" asked the skipper.

"Most of them."

"I'm a bit of a reader myself. I have the *Saturday Evening Post* sent me regler."

Neilson poured his visitor a good stiff glass of whisky and gave him a cigar. The skipper volunteered a little information.

"I got in last night, but I couldn't find the opening, so I had to anchor outside. I never been this run before, but my people had some stuff they wanted to bring over here. Gray, d'you know him?"

"Yes, he's got a store a little way along."

"Well, there was a lot of canned stuff that he wanted over, an' he's got some copra. They thought I might just as well come over as lie idle at Apia. I run between Apia and Pago-Pago mostly, but they've got smallpox there just now, and there's nothing stirring."

He took a drink of his whisky and lit a cigar. He was a taciturn man, but there was something in Neilson that made him nervous, and his nervousness made him talk. The Swede was looking at him with large dark eyes in which there was an expression of faint amusement.

"This is a tidy little place you've got here."

"I've done my best with it."

"You must do pretty well with your trees. They look fine. With copra at the price it is now. I had a bit of a plantation myself once, in Upolu it was, but I had to sell it."

He looked round the room again, where all those books gave him a feeling of something incomprehensible and hostile.

"I guess you must find it a bit lonesome here though," he said.

"I've got used to it. I've been here for twenty-five years."

Now the captain could think of nothing more to say, and he smoked in silence. Neilson had apparently no wish to break it. He looked at his guest with a meditative eye. He was a tall man, more than six feet high, and very stout. His face was red and blotchy, with a network of little purple veins on the cheeks, and his features were sunk into its fatness. His eyes were bloodshot. His neck was buried in rolls of fat. But for a fringe of long curly hair, nearly white, at the back of his head, he was quite bald; and that immense, shiny surface of forehead, which might have given him a false look of intelligence, on the contrary gave him one of peculiar imbecility. He wore a blue flannel shirt, open at the neck and showing his fat chest covered with a mat of reddish hair, and a very old pair of blue serge trousers. He sat in his chair in a heavy ungainly attitude, his great belly thrust forward and his fat legs uncrossed. All elasticity had gone from his limbs. Neilson wondered idly what sort of man he had been in his youth. It was almost impossible to imagine that this creature of vast bulk had ever been a boy who ran about. The skipper finished his whisky, and Neilson pushed the bottle towards him.

"Help yourself."

The skipper leaned forward and with his great hand seized it.

"And how come you in these parts anyways?" he said.

"Oh, I came out to the islands for my health. My lungs

were bad and they said I hadn't a year to live. You see they were wrong."

"I meant, how come you to settle down right here?"

"I am a sentimentalist."

"Oh!"

Neilson knew that the skipper had not an idea what he meant, and he looked at him with an ironical twinkle in his dark eyes. Perhaps just because the skipper was so gross and dull a man the whim seized him to talk further.

"You were too busy keeping your balance to notice, when you crossed the bridge, but this spot is generally considered rather pretty."

"It's a cute little house you've got here."

"Ah, that wasn't here when I first came. There was a native hut, with its beehive roof and its pillars, over-shadowed by a great tree with red flowers; and the croton bushes, their leaves yellow and red and golden, made a pied fence around it. And then all about were the coconut trees, as fanciful as women, and as vain. They stood at the water's edge and spent all day looking at their reflections. I was a young man then—Good Heavens, it's a quarter of a century ago—and I wanted to enjoy all the loveliness of the world in the short time allotted to me before I passed into the darkness. I thought it was the most beautiful spot I had ever seen. The first time I saw it I had a catch at my heart, and I was afraid I was going to cry. I wasn't more than twenty-five, and though I put the best face I could on it, I didn't want to die. And somehow it seemed to me that the very beauty of this place made it easier for me to accept my fate. I felt when I came here that all my past life had fallen away, Stockholm and its University, and then Bonn: it all seemed the life of somebody else, as though now at last I had achieved the reality which our doctors of philosophy—I am one myself, you know—had discussed so much. 'A year,' I cried to myself. 'I have a year. I will spend it here and then I am content to die.'

"We are foolish and sentimental and melodramatic at twenty-five, but if we weren't perhaps we should be less wise at fifty."

"Now drink, my friend. Don't let the nonsense I talk interfere with you."

He waved his thin hand towards the bottle, and the skipper finished what remained in his glass.

"You ain't drinking nothin'," he said, reaching for the whisky.

"I am of a sober habit," smiled the Swede. "I intoxicate myself in ways which I fancy are more subtle. But perhaps that is only vanity. Anyhow, the effects are more lasting and the results less deleterious."

"They say there's a deal of cocaine taken in the States now," said the captain.

Neilson chuckled.

"But I do not see a white man often," he continued, "and for once I don't think a drop of whisky can do me any harm."

He poured himself out a little, added some soda, and took a sip.

"And presently I found out why the spot had such an unearthly loveliness. Here love had tarried for a moment like a migrant bird that happens on a ship in mid-ocean and for a little while folds its tired wings. The fragrance of a beautiful passion hovered over it like the fragrance of hawthorn in May in the meadows of my home. It seems to me that the places where men have loved or suffered keep about them always some faint aroma of something that has not wholly died. It is as though they had acquired a spiritual significance which mysteriously affects those who pass. I wish I could make myself clear." He smiled a little. "Though I cannot imagine that if I did you would understand."

He paused.

"I think this place was beautiful because here I had been loved beautifully." And now he shrugged his shoulders. "But perhaps it is only that my æsthetic sense is gratified by the happy conjunction of young love and a suitable setting."

Even a man less thick-witted than the skipper might have been forgiven if he were bewildered by Neilson's words. For he seemed faintly to laugh at what he said. It was as though he spoke from emotion which his intellect found ridiculous. He had said himself that he was a sentimentalist, and when sentimentality is joined with scepticism there is often the devil to pay.

He was silent for an instant and looked at the captain with eyes in which there was a sudden perplexity.

"You know, I can't help thinking that I've seen you before somewhere or other," he said.

"I couldn't say as I remember you," returned the skipper.

"I have a curious feeling as though your face were familiar to me. It's been puzzling me for some time. But I can't situate my recollection in any place or at any time."

The skipper massively shrugged his heavy shoulders.

"It's thirty years since I first come to the islands. A man can't figure on remembering all the folk he meets in a while like that."

The Swede shook his head.

"You know how one sometimes has the feeling that a place one has never been to before is strangely familiar. That's how I seem to see you." He gave a whimsical smile. "Perhaps I knew you in some past existence. Perhaps, perhaps you were the master of a galley in ancient Rome and I was a slave at the oar. Thirty years have you been here?"

"Every bit of thirty years."

"I wonder if you knew a man called Red?"

"Red?"

"That is the only name I've ever known him by. I never knew him personally. I never even set eyes on him. And yet I seem to see him more clearly than many men, my brothers, for instance, with whom I passed my daily life for many years. He lives in my imagination with the distinctness of a Paolo Malatesta or a Romeo. But I daresay you have never read Dante or Shakespeare?"

"I can't say as I have," said the captain.

Neilson, smoking a cigar, leaned back in his chair and looked vacantly at the ring of smoke which floated in the still air. A smile played on his lips, but his eyes were grave. Then he looked at the captain. There was in his gross obesity something extraordinarily repellent. He had the plethoric self-satisfaction of the very fat. It was an outrage. It set

Neilson's nerves on edge. But the contrast between the man before him and the man he had in mind was pleasant.

"It appears that Red was the most comely thing you ever saw. I've talked to quite a number of people who knew him in those days, white men, and they all agree that the first time you saw him his beauty just took your breath away. They called him Red on account of his flaming hair. It had a natural wave and he wore it long. It must have been of that wonderful colour that the pre-Raphaelites raved over. I don't think he was vain of it, he was much too ingenuous for that, but no one could have blamed him if he had been. He was tall, six feet and an inch or two—in the native house that used to stand here was the mark of his height cut with a knife on the central trunk that supported the roof—and he was made like a Greek god, broad in the shoulders and thin in the flanks; he was like Apollo, with just that soft roundness which Praxiteles gave him, and that suave, feminine grace which has in it something troubling and mysterious. His skin was dazzling white, milky, like satin; his skin was like a woman's."

"I had kind of a white skin myself when I was a kiddie," said the skipper, with a twinkle in his bloodshot eyes.

But Neilson paid no attention to him. He was telling his story now and interruption made him impatient.

"And his face was just as beautiful as his body. He had large blue eyes, very dark, so that some say they were black, and unlike most red-haired people he had dark eyebrows and long dark lashes. His features were perfectly regular and his mouth was like a scarlet wound. He was twenty."

On these words the Swede stopped with a certain sense of the dramatic. He took a sip of whisky.

"He was unique. There never was anyone more beautiful. There was no more reason for him than for a wonderful blossom to flower on a wild plant. He was a happy accident of nature.

"One day he landed at that cove into which you must have put this morning. He was an American sailor, and he had deserted from a man-of-war in Apia. He had induced some good-humoured native to give him a passage on a cutter that happened to be sailing from Apia to Safoto, and he had been put ashore here in a dugout. I do not know why he deserted. Perhaps life on a man-of-war with its restrictions irked him, perhaps he was in trouble, and perhaps it was the South Seas and these romantic islands that got into his bones. Every now and then they take a man strangely, and he finds himself like a fly in a spider's web. It may be that there was a softness of fibre in him, and these green hills with their soft airs, this blue sea, took the northern strength from him as Delilah took the Nazarite's. Anyhow, he wanted to hide himself, and he thought he would be safe in this secluded nook till his ship had sailed from Samoa.

"There was a native hut at the cove and as he stood there, wondering where exactly he should turn his steps, a young girl came out and invited him to enter. He knew scarcely two words of the native tongue and she as little English. But he understood well enough what her smiles meant, and her pretty gestures, and he followed her. He sat down on a mat and she gave him slices of pineapple to eat. I can speak of Red only from hearsay, but I saw the girl three years after he first met her, and she was scarcely nineteen then. You cannot imagine how exquisite she was. She had the passionate grace of the hibiscus and the rich colour. She was rather tall, slim, with the delicate features of her race, and large eyes like pools of still water under the palm trees; her hair, black and curling, fell down her back, and she wore a wreath of scented flowers. Her hands were lovely. They were so small, so exquisitely formed, they gave your heartstrings a wrench. And in those days she laughed easily. Her smile was so delightful that it made your knees shake. Her skin was like a field of ripe corn on a summer day. Good Heavens, how can I describe her? She was too beautiful to be real.

"And these two young things, she was sixteen and he was twenty, fell in love with one another at first sight. That is the real love, not the love that comes from sympathy, common interests, or intellectual community, but love pure and simple. That is the love that Adam felt for Eve when he awoke and found her in the garden gazing at him with dewy eyes. That is the love that draws the beasts to one another, and the

Gods. That is the love that makes the world a miracle. That is the love which gives life its pregnant meaning. You have never heard of the wise, cynical French duke who said that with two lovers there is always one who loves and one who lets himself be loved; it is a bitter truth to which most of us have to resign ourselves; but now and then there are two who love and two who let themselves be loved. Then one might fancy that the sun stands still as it stood when Joshua prayed to the God of Israel.

"And even now after all these years, when I think of these two, so young, so fair, so simple, and of their love, I feel a pang. It tears my heart just as my heart is torn when on certain nights I watch the full moon shining on the lagoon from an unclouded sky. There is always pain in the contemplation of perfect beauty.

"They were children. She was good and sweet and kind. I know nothing of him, and I like to think that then at all events he was ingenuous and frank. I like to think that his soul was as comely as his body. But I daresay he had no more soul than the creatures of the woods and forests who made pipes from reeds and bathed in the mountain streams when the world was young, and you might catch sight of little fauns galloping through the glade on the back of a bearded centaur. A soul is a troublesome possession and when man developed it he lost the Garden of Eden.

"Well, when Red came to the island it had recently been visited by one of those epidemics which the white man has brought to the South Seas, and one third of the inhabitants had died. It seems that the girl had lost all her near kin and she lived now in the house of distant cousins. The household consisted of two ancient crones, bowed and wrinkled, two younger women, and a man and a boy. For a few days he stayed there. But perhaps he felt himself too near the shore, with the possibility that he might fall in with white men who would reveal his hiding-place; perhaps the lovers could not bear that the company of others should rob them for an instant of the delight of being together. One morning they set out, the pair of them, with the few things that belonged to the girl, and walked along a grassy path under the coco-

nuts, till they came to the creek you see. They had to cross
the bridge you crossed, and the girl laughed gleefully because
he was afraid. She held his hand till they came to the end of
the first tree, and then his courage failed him and he had to
go back. He was obliged to take off all his clothes before he
could risk it, and she carried them over for him on her head.
They settled down in the empty hut that stood here.
Whether she had any rights over it (land tenure is a complicated business in the islands), or whether the owner had died
during the epidemic, I do not know, but anyhow no one
questioned them, and they took possession. Their furniture
consisted of a couple of grass-mats on which they slept, a
fragment of looking-glass, and a bowl or two. In this pleasant land that is enough to start housekeeping on.

"They say that happy people have no history, and certainly a happy love has none. They did nothing all day long
and yet the days seemed all too short. The girl had a native
name, but Red called her Sally. He picked up the easy language very quickly, and he used to lie on the mat for hours
while she chattered gaily to him. He was a silent fellow, and
perhaps his mind was lethargic. He smoked incessantly the
cigarettes which she made him out of the native tobacco and
pandanus leaf, and he watched her while with deft fingers
she made grass mats. Often natives would come in and tell
long stories of the old days when the island was disturbed
by tribal wars. Sometimes he would go fishing on the reef,
and bring home a basket full of coloured fish. Sometimes at
night he would go out with a lantern to catch lobster. There
were plantains round the hut and Sally would roast them for
their frugal meal. She knew how to make delicious messes
from coconuts, and the breadfruit tree by the side of the
creek gave them its fruit. On feast-days they killed a little
pig and cooked it on hot stones. They bathed together in the
creek; and in the evening they went down to the lagoon and
paddled about in a dugout, with its great outrigger. The sea
was deep blue, wine-coloured at sundown, like the sea of
Homeric Greece; but in the lagoon the colour had an infinite
variety, aquamarine and amethyst and emerald; and the setting sun turned it for a short moment to liquid gold. Then

there was the colour of the coral, brown, white, pink, red, purple; and the shapes it took were marvellous. It was like a magic garden, and the hurrying fish were like butterflies. It strangely lacked reality. Among the coral were pools with a floor of white sand and here, where the water was dazzling clear, it was very good to bathe. Then, cool and happy, they wandered back in the gloaming over the soft grass road to the creek, walking hand in hand, and now the mynah birds filled the coconut trees with their clamour. And then the night, with that great sky shining with gold, that seemed to stretch more widely than the skies of Europe, and the soft airs that blew gently through the open hut, the long night again was all too short. She was sixteen and he was barely twenty. The dawn crept in among the wooden pillars of the hut and looked at those lovely children sleeping in one another's arms. The sun hid behind the great tattered leaves of the plantains so that it might not disturb them, and then, with playful malice, shot a golden ray, like the outstretched paw of a Persian cat, on their faces. They opened their sleepy eyes and they smiled to welcome another day. The weeks lengthened into months, and a year passed. They seemed to love one another as—I hesitate to say passionately, for passion has in it always a shade of sadness, a touch of bitterness or anguish, but as whole heartedly, as simply and naturally as on that first day on which, meeting, they had recognised that a god was in them.

"If you had asked them I have no doubt that they would have thought it impossible to suppose their love could ever cease. Do we not know that the essential element of love is a belief in its own eternity? And yet perhaps in Red there was already a very little seed, unknown to himself and unsuspected by the girl, which would in time have grown to weariness. For one day one of the natives from the cove told them that some way down the coast at the anchorage was a British whaling-ship.

" 'Gee,' he said, 'I wonder if I could make a trade of some nuts and plantains for a pound or two of tobacco.'

"The pandanus cigarettes that Sally made him with untiring hands were strong and pleasant enough to smoke, but they left him unsatisfied; and he yearned on a sudden for real tobacco, hard, rank, and pungent. He had not smoked a pipe for many months. His mouth watered at the thought of it. One would have thought some premonition of harm would have made Sally seek to dissuade him, but love possessed her so completely that it never occurred to her any power on earth could take him from her. They went up into the hills together and gathered a great basket of wild oranges, green, but sweet and juicy; and they picked plantains from around the hut, and coconuts from their trees, and breadfruit and mangoes; and they carried them down to the cove. They loaded the unstable canoe with them, and Red and the native boy who had brought them the news of the ship paddled along outside the reef.

"It was the last time she ever saw him.

"Next day the boy came back alone. He was all in tears. This is the story he told. When after their long paddle they reached the ship and Red hailed it, a white man looked over the side and told them to come on board. They took the fruit they had brought with them and Red piled it up on the deck. The white man and he began to talk, and they seemed to come to some agreement. One of them went below and brought up tobacco. Red took some at once and lit a pipe. The boy imitated the zest with which he blew a great cloud of smoke from his mouth. Then they said something to him and he went into the cabin. Through the open door the boy, watching curiously, saw a bottle brought out and glasses. Red drank and smoked. They seemed to ask him something, for he shook his head and laughed. The man, the first man who had spoken to them, laughed too, and he filled Red's glass once more. They went on talking and drinking, and presently, growing tired of watching a sight that meant nothing to him, the boy curled himself up on the deck and slept. He was awakened by a kick; and, jumping to his feet, he saw that the ship was slowly sailing out of the lagoon. He caught sight of Red seated at the table, with his head resting heavily on his arms, fast asleep. He made a movement towards him, intending to wake him, but a rough hand seized his arm, and a man, with a scowl and words which he did not understand, pointed to the side. He shouted to Red, but in a moment he was seized and flung overboard. Helpless, he swam round to his canoe which was drifting a little way off, and pushed it on to the reef. He climbed in and, sobbing all the way, paddled back to shore.

"What had happened was obvious enough. The whaler, by desertion or sickness, was short of hands, and the captain when Red came aboard had asked him to sign on; on his refusal he had made him drunk and kidnapped him.

"Sally was beside herself with grief. For three days she screamed and cried. The natives did what they could to comfort her, but she would not be comforted. She would not eat. And then, exhausted, she sank into a sullen apathy. She spent long days at the cove, watching the lagoon, in the vain hope that Red somehow or other would manage to escape. She sat on the white sand, hour after hour, with the tears running down her cheeks, and at night dragged herself wearily back across the creek to the little hut where she had been happy. The people with whom she had lived before Red came to the island wished her to return to them, but she would not; she was convinced that Red would come back, and she wanted him to find her where he had left her. Four months later she was delivered of a still-born child, and the old woman who had come to help her through her confinement remained with her in the hut. All joy was taken from her life. If her anguish with time became less intolerable it was replaced by a settled melancholy. You would not have thought that among these people, whose emotions, though so violent, are very transient, a woman could be found capable of so enduring a passion. She never lost the profound conviction that sooner or later Red would come back. She watched for him, and every time someone crossed this slender little bridge of coconut trees she looked. It might at last be he."

Neilson stopped talking and gave a faint sigh.

"And what happened to her in the end?" asked the skipper.

Neilson smiled bitterly.

"Oh, three years afterwards she took up with another white man."

The skipper gave a fat, cynical chuckle.

"That's generally what happens to them," he said.

The Swede shot him a look of hatred. He did not know why that gross, obese man excited in him so violent a repulsion. But his thoughts wandered and he found his mind filled with memories of the past. He went back five and twenty years. It was when he first came to the island, weary of Apia, with its heavy drinking, its gambling and coarse sensuality, a sick man, trying to resign himself to the loss of the career which had fired his imagination with ambitious thoughts. He set behind him resolutely all his hopes of making a great name for himself and strove to content himself with the few poor months of careful life which was all that he could count on. He was boarding with a half-caste trader who had a store a couple of miles along the coast at the edge of a native village; and one day, wandering aimlessly along the grassy paths of the coconut groves, he had come upon the hut in which Sally lived. The beauty of the spot had filled him with a rapture so great that it was almost painful, and then he had seen Sally. She was the loveliest creature he had ever seen, and the sadness in those dark, magnificent eyes of hers affected him strangely. The Kanakas were a handsome race, and beauty was not rare among them, but it was the beauty of shapely animals. It was empty. But those tragic eyes were dark with mystery, and you felt in them the bitter complexity of the groping, human soul. The trader told him the story and it moved him.

"Do you think he'll ever come back?" asked Neilson.

"No fear. Why, it'll be a couple of years before the ship is paid off, and by then he'll have forgotten all about her. I bet he was pretty mad when he woke up and found he'd been shanghaied, and I shouldn't wonder but he wanted to fight somebody. But he'd got to grin and bear it, and I guess in a month he was thinking it the best thing that had ever happened to him that he got away from the island."

But Neilson could not get the story out of his head. Per-

haps because he was sick and weakly, the radiant health of
Red appealed to his imagination. Himself an ugly man, insignificant of appearance, he prized very highly comeliness
in others. He had never been passionately in love, and certainly he had never been passionately loved. The mutual
attraction of those two young things gave him a singular
delight. It had the ineffable beauty of the Absolute. He went
again to the little hut by the creek. He had a gift for languages and an energetic mind, accustomed to work, and he
had already given much time to the study of the local tongue.
Old habit was strong in him and he was gathering together
material for a paper on the Samoan speech. The old crone
who shared the hut with Sally invited him to come in and sit
down. She gave him *kava* to drink and cigarettes to smoke.
She was glad to have someone to chat with and while she
talked he looked at Sally. She reminded him of the Psyche
in the museum at Naples. Her features had the same clear
purity of line, and though she had borne a child she had still
a virginal aspect.

It was not till he had seen her two or three times that he
induced her to speak. Then it was only to ask him if he had
seen in Apia a man called Red. Two years had passed since
his disappearance, but it was plain that she still thought of
him incessantly.

It did not take Neilson long to discover that he was in love
with her. It was only by an effort of will now that he prevented himself from going every day to the creek, and when
he was not with Sally his thoughts were. At first, looking
upon himself as a dying man, he asked only to look at her,
and occasionally hear her speak, and his love gave him a
wonderful happiness. He exulted in its purity. He wanted
nothing from her but the opportunity to weave around her
graceful person a web of beautiful fancies. But the open air,
the equable temperature, the rest, the simple fare, began to
have an unexpected effect on his health. His temperature did
not soar at night to such alarming heights, he coughed less
and began to put on weight; six months passed without his
having a hæmorrhage; and on a sudden he saw the possibility
that he might live. He had studied his disease carefully, and

the hope dawned upon him that with great care he might arrest its course. It exhilarated him to look forward once more to the future. He made plans. It was evident that any active life was out of the question, but he could live on the islands, and the small income he had, insufficient elsewhere, would be ample to keep him. He could grow coconuts; that would give him an occupation; and he would send for his books and a piano; but his quick mind saw that in all this he was merely trying to conceal from himself the desire which obsessed him.

He wanted Sally. He loved not only her beauty, but that dim soul which he divined behind her suffering eyes. He would intoxicate her with his passion. In the end he would make her forget. And in an ecstasy of surrender he fancied himself giving her too the happiness which he had thought never to know again, but had now so miraculously achieved.

He asked her to live with him. She refused. He had expected that and did not let it depress him, for he was sure that sooner or later she would yield. His love was irresistible. He told the old woman of his wishes, and found somewhat to his surprise that she and the neighbours, long aware of them, were strongly urging Sally to accept his offer. After all, every native was glad to keep house for a white man, and Neilson according to the standards of the island was a rich one. The trader with whom he boarded went to her and told her not to be a fool; such an opportunity would not come again, and after so long she could not still believe that Red would ever return. The girl's resistance only increased Neilson's desire, and what had been a very pure love now became an agonising passion. He was determined that nothing should stand in his way. He gave Sally no peace. At last, worn out by his persistence and the persuasions, by turns pleading and angry, of everyone around her, she consented. But the day after when, exultant, he went to see her he found that in the night she had burnt down the hut in which she and Red had lived together. The old crone ran towards him full of angry abuse of Sally, but he waved her aside; it did not matter; they would build a bungalow on the place where the hut had stood. A European house would really be more convenient if he wanted to bring out a piano and a vast number of books.

And so the little wooden house was built in which he had now lived for many years, and Sally became his wife. But after the first few weeks of rapture, during which he was satisfied with what she gave him he had known little happiness. She had yielded to him, through weariness, but she had only yielded what she set no store on. The soul which he had dimly glimpsed escaped him. He knew that she cared nothing for him. She still loved Red, and all the time she was waiting for his return. At a sign from him, Neilson knew that, notwithstanding his love, his tenderness, his sympathy, his generosity, she would leave him without a moment's hesitation. She would never give a thought to his distress. Anguish seized him and he battered at that impenetrable self of hers which sullenly resisted him. His love became bitter. He tried to melt her heart with kindness, but it remained as hard as before; he feigned indifference, but she did not notice it. Sometimes he lost his temper and abused her, and then she wept silently. Sometimes he thought she was nothing but a fraud, and that soul simply an invention of his own, and that he could not get into the sanctuary of her heart because there was no sanctuary there. His love became a prison from which he longed to escape, but he had not the strength merely to open the door—that was all it needed—and walk out into the open air. It was torture and at last he became numb and hopeless. In the end the fire burnt itself out and, when he saw her eyes rest for an instant on the slender bridge, it was no longer rage that filled his heart but impatience. For many years now they had lived together bound by the ties of habit and convenience, and it was with a smile that he looked back on his old passion. She was an old woman, for the women on the islands age quickly, and if he had no love for her any more he had tolerance. She left him alone. He was contented with his piano and his books.

His thoughts led him to a desire for words.

"When I look back now and reflect on that brief passionate love of Red and Sally, I think that perhaps they should thank the ruthless fate that separated them when their love seemed still to be at its height. They suffered, but they suffered in beauty. They were spared the real tragedy of love."

"I don't know exactly as I get you," said the skipper.

"The tragedy of love is not death or separation. How long do you think it would have been before one or other of them ceased to care? Oh, it is dreadfully bitter to look at a woman whom you have loved with all your heart and soul, so that you felt you could not bear to let her out of your sight, and realise that you would not mind if you never saw her again. The tragedy of love is indifference."

But while he was speaking a very extraordinary thing happened. Though he had been addressing the skipper he had not been talking to him, he had been putting his thoughts into words for himself, and with his eyes fixed on the man in front of him he had not seen him. But now an image presented itself to them, an image not of the man he saw, but of another man. It was as though he were looking into one of those distorting mirrors that make you extraordinarily squat or outrageously elongate, but here exactly the opposite took place, and in the obese, ugly old man he caught the shadowy glimpse of a stripling. He gave him now a quick, searching scrutiny. Why had a haphazard stroll brought him just to this place? A sudden tremor of his heart made him slightly breathless. An absurd suspicion seized him. What had occurred to him was impossible, and yet it might be a fact.

"What is your name?" he asked abruptly.

The skipper's face puckered and he gave a cunning chuckle. He looked then malicious and horribly vulgar.

"It's such a damned long time since I heard it that I almost forget it myself. But for thirty years now in the islands they've always called me Red."

His huge form shook as he gave a low, almost silent laugh. It was obscene. Neilson shuddered. Red was hugely amused, and from his bloodshot eyes tears ran down his cheeks.

Neilson gave a gasp, for at that moment a woman came in. She was a native, a woman of somewhat commanding presence, stout without being corpulent, dark, for the natives grow darker with age, with very grey hair. She wore a black Mother Hubbard, and its thinness showed her heavy breasts. The moment had come.

She made an observation to Neilson about some household matter and he answered. He wondered if his voice sounded as unnatural to her as it did to himself. She gave the man who was sitting in the chair by the window an indifferent glance, and went out of the room. The moment had come and gone.

Neilson for a moment could not speak. He was strangely shaken. Then he said:

"I'd be very glad if you'd stay and have a bit of dinner with me. Pot luck."

"I don't think I will," said Red. "I must go after this fellow Gray. I'll give him his stuff and then I'll get away. I want to be back in Apia tomorrow."

"I'll send a boy along with you to show you the way."

"That'll be fine."

Red heaved himself out of his chair, while the Swede called one of the boys who worked on the plantation. He told him where the skipper wanted to go, and the boy stepped along the bridge. Red prepared to follow him.

"Don't fall in," said Neilson.

"Not on your life."

Neilson watched him make his way across and when he had disappeared among the coconuts he looked still. Then he sank heavily in his chair. Was that the man who had prevented him from being happy? Was that the man whom Sally had loved all these years and for whom she had waited so desperately? It was grotesque. A sudden fury seized him so that he had an instinct to spring up and smash everything around him. He had been cheated. They had seen each other at last and had not known it. He began to laugh, mirthlessly, and his laughter grew till it became hysterical. The Gods had played him a cruel trick. And he was old now.

At last Sally came in to tell him dinner was ready. He sat down in front of her and tried to eat. He wondered what she would say if he told her now that the fat old man sitting in the chair was the lover whom she remembered still with the passionate abandonment of her youth. Years ago, when he hated her because she made him so unhappy, he would have been glad to tell her. He wanted to hurt her then as she hurt him, because his hatred was only love. But now he did not care. He shrugged his shoulders listlessly.

"What did that man want?" she asked presently.

He did not answer at once. She was old too, a fat old native woman. He wondered why he had ever loved her so madly. He had laid at her feet all the treasures of his soul, and she had cared nothing for them. Waste, what waste! And now, when he looked at her, he felt only contempt. His patience was at last exhausted. He answered her question.

"He's the captain of a schooner. He's come from Apia."

"Yes."

"He brought me news from home. My eldest brother is very ill and I must go back."

"Will you be gone long?"

He shrugged his shoulders.

A STRING OF BEADS

"W HAT a bit of luck that I'm placed next to you," said
Laura, as we sat down to dinner.

"For me," I replied politely.

"That remains to be seen. I particularly wanted to have
the chance of talking to you. I've got a story to tell you."

At this my heart sank a little.

"I'd sooner you talked about yourself," I answered. "Or
even about me."

"Oh, but I must tell you the story. I think you'll be able
to use it."

"If you must, you must. But let's look at the menu first."

"Don't you want me to?" she said, somewhat aggrieved.
"I thought you'd be pleased."

"I am. You might have written a play and wanted to read
me that."

"It happened to some friends of mine. It's perfectly true."

"That's no recommendation. A true story is never quite
so true as an invented one."

"What does that mean?"

"Nothing very much," I admitted. "But I thought it
sounded well."

"I wish you'd let me get on with it."

"I'm all attention. I'm not going to eat the soup. It's
fattening."

She gave me a pinched look and then glanced at the menu.
She uttered a little sigh.

"Oh, well, if you're going to deny yourself I suppose I
must too. Heaven knows, I can't afford to take liberties with
my figure."

"And yet is there any soup more heavenly than the sort of soup in which you put a great dollop of cream?"

"Bortsch," she sighed. "It's the only soup I really like."

"Never mind. Tell me your story and we'll forget about food till the fish comes."

"Well, I was actually there when it happened. I was dining with the Livingstones. Do you know the Livingstones?"

"No, I don't think I do."

"Well, you can ask them and they'll confirm every word I say. They'd asked their governess to come in to dinner because some woman had thrown them over at the last moment—you know how inconsiderate people are—and they would have been thirteen at table. Their governess was a Miss Robinson, quite a nice girl, young, you know, twenty or twenty-one, and rather pretty. Personally I would never engage a governess who was young and pretty. One never knows."

"But one hopes for the best."

Laura paid no attention to my remark.

"The chances are that she'll be thinking of young men instead of attending to her duties and then, just when she's got used to your ways, she'll want to go and get married. But Miss Robinson had excellent references, and I must allow that she was a very nice, respectable person. I believe in point of fact she was a clergyman's daughter.

"There was a man at dinner whom I don't suppose you've ever heard of, but who's quite a celebrity in his way. He's a Count Borselli and he knows more about precious stones than anyone in the world. He was sitting next to Mary Lyngate, who rather fancies herself on her pearls, and in the course of conversation she asked him what he thought of the string she was wearing. He said it was very pretty. She was rather piqued at this and told him it was valued at eight thousand pounds.

" 'Yes, it's worth that,' he said.

"Miss Robinson was sitting opposite to him. She was looking rather nice that evening. Of course I recognized her dress, it was one of Sophie's old ones; but if you hadn't known Miss Robinson was the governess you would never have suspected it.

" 'That's a very beautiful necklace that young lady has on,' said Borselli.

" 'Oh, but that's Mrs. Livingstone's governess,' said Mary Lyngate.

" 'I can't help that,' he said. 'She's wearing one of the finest strings of pearls for its size that I've ever seen in my life. It must be worth fifty thousand pounds.'

" 'Nonsense.'

" 'I give you my word it is.'

"Mary Lyngate leant over. She has rather a shrill voice.

" 'Miss Robinson, do you know what Count Borselli says?' she exclaimed. 'He says that string of pearls you're wearing is worth fifty thousand pounds.'

"Just at that moment there was a sort of pause in the conversation so that everybody heard. We all turned and looked at Miss Robinson. She flushed a little and laughed.

" 'Well, I made a very good bargain,' she said, 'because I paid fifteen shillings for it.'

" 'You certainly did.'

"We all laughed. It was of course absurd. We've all heard of wives palming off on their husbands as false a string of pearls that was real and expensive. That story is as old as the hills."

"Thank you," I said, thinking of a little narrative of my own.

"But it was too ridiculous to suppose that a governess would remain a governess if she owned a string of pearls worth fifty thousand pounds. It was obvious that the Count had made a bloomer. Then an extraordinary thing happened. The long arm of coincidence came in."

"It shouldn't," I retorted. "It's had too much exercise. Haven't you seen that charming book called A Dictionary of English Usage?"

"I wish you wouldn't interrupt just when I'm really getting to the exciting point."

But I had to do so again, for just then a young grilled salmon was insinuated round my left elbow.

"Mrs. Livingstone is giving us a heavenly dinner," I said.

"Is salmon fattening?" asked Laura.

"Very," I answered as I took a large helping.

"Bunk," she said.

"Go on," I begged her. "The long arm of coincidence was about to make a gesture."

"Well, at that very moment the butler bent over Miss Robinson and whispered something in her ear. I thought she turned a trifle pale. It's such a mistake not to wear rouge; you never know what tricks nature will play on you. She certainly looked startled. She leant forwards.

" 'Mrs. Livingstone, Dawson says there are two men in the hall who want to speak to me at once.'

" 'Well, you'd better go,' said Sophie Livingstone.

"Miss Robinson got up and left the room. Of course the same thought flashed through all our minds, but I said it first.

" 'I hope they haven't come to arrest her,' I said to Sophie. 'It would be too dreadful for you, my dear.'

" 'Are you sure it was a real necklace, Borselli?' she asked.

" 'Oh, quite.'

" 'She could hardly have had the nerve to wear it tonight if it were stolen,' I said.

"Sophie Livingstone turned as pale as death under her make-up and I saw she was wondering if everything was all right in her jewel case. I only had on a little chain of diamonds, but instinctively I put my hand up to my neck to feel if it was still there.

" 'Don't talk nonsense,' said Mr. Livingstone. 'How on earth would Miss Robinson have had the chance of sneaking a valuable string of pearls?'

" 'She may be a receiver,' I said.

" 'Oh, but she had such wonderful references,' said Sophie.

" 'They always do,' I said."

I was positively forced to interrupt Laura once more.

"You don't seem to have been determined to take a very bright view of the case," I remarked.

"Of course I knew nothing against Miss Robinson and

I had every reason to think her a very nice girl, but it would have been rather thrilling to find out that she was a notorious thief and a well-known member of a gang of international crooks."

"Just like a film. I'm dreadfully afraid that it's only in films that exciting things like that happen."

"Well, we waited in breathless suspense. There was not a sound. I expected to hear a scuffle in the hall or at least a smothered shriek. I thought the silence very ominous. Then the door opened and Miss Robinson walked in. I noticed at once that the necklace was gone. I could see that she was pale and excited. She came back to the table, sat down and with a smile threw on it——"

"On what?"

"On the table, you fool. A string of pearls."

" 'There's my necklace,' she said.

"Count Borselli leant forwards.

" 'Oh, but those are false,' he said.

" 'I told you they were,' she laughed.

" 'That's not the same string you had on a few moments ago,' he said.

"She shook her head and smiled mysteriously. We were all intrigued. I don't know that Sophie Livingstone was so very much pleased at her governess making herself the centre of interest like that and I thought there was a suspicion of tartness in her manner when she suggested that Miss Robinson had better explain. Well, Miss Robinson said that when she went into the hall she found two men who said they'd come from Jarrot's Stores. She'd bought her string there, as she said, for fifteen shillings, and she'd taken it back because the clasp was loose and had only fetched it that afternoon. The men said they had given her the wrong string. Someone had left a string of real pearls to be restrung and the assistant had made a mistake. Of course I can't understand how anyone could be so stupid as to take a really valuable string to Jarrot's, they aren't used to dealing with that sort of thing, and they wouldn't know real pearls from false; but you know what fools some women are. Anyhow it was the string Miss Robinson was wearing and it was valued at fifty thousand pounds. She naturally gave it back to them—she couldn't do anything else, I suppose, though it must have been a wrench—and they returned her own string to her; then they said that although of course they were under no obligation—you know the silly, pompous way men talk when they're trying to be businesslike—they were instructed, as a solatium or whatever you call it, to offer her a cheque for three hundred pounds. Miss Robinson actually showed it to us. She was as pleased as Punch."

"Well, it was a piece of luck, wasn't it?"

"You'd have thought so. As it turned out it was the ruin of her."

"Oh, how was that?"

"Well, when the time came for her to go on her holiday she told Sophie Livingstone that she'd made up her mind to go to Deauville for a month and blow the whole three hundred pounds. Of course Sophie tried to dissuade her, and begged her to put the money in the savings bank, but she wouldn't hear of it. She said she'd never had such a chance before and would never have it again and she meant for at least four weeks to live like a duchess. Sophie couldn't really do anything and so she gave way. She sold Miss Robinson a lot of clothes that she didn't want; she'd been wearing them all through the season and was sick to death of them; she says she gave them to her, but I don't suppose she quite did that—I dare say she sold them very cheap—and Miss Robinson started off, entirely alone, for Deauville. What do you think happened then?"

"I haven't a notion," I replied. "I hope she had the time of her life."

"Well, a week before she was due to come back she wrote to Sophie and said that she'd changed her plans and had entered another profession and hoped Mrs. Livingstone would forgive her if she didn't return. Of course poor Sophie was furious. What had actually happened was that Miss Robinson had picked up a rich Argentine in Deauville and had gone off to Paris with him. She's been in Paris ever since. I've seen her myself at Florence's, with bracelets right up to her elbow and ropes of pearls round her neck.

Of course I cut her dead. They say she has a house in the Bois de Boulogne and I know she has a Rolls. She threw over the Argentine in a few months and then got hold of a Greek; I don't know who she's with now, but the long and short of it is that she's far and away the smartest cocotte in Paris."

"When you say she was ruined you use the word in a purely technical sense, I conclude," said I.

"I don't know what you mean by that," said Laura. "But don't you think you could make a story out of it?"

"Unfortunately I've already written a story about a pearl necklace. One can't go on writing stories about pearl necklaces."

"I've got half a mind to write it myself. Only of course I should change the end."

"Oh, how would you end it?"

"Well, I should have had her engaged to a bank clerk who had been badly knocked about in the war, with only one leg, say, or half his face shot away: and they'd be dreadfully poor and there would be no prospect of their marriage for years, and he would be putting all his savings into buying a little house in the suburbs and they'd have arranged to marry when he had saved the last instalment. And then she takes him the three hundred pounds and they can hardly believe it, they're so happy, and he cries on her shoulder. He just cries like a child. And they get the little house in the suburbs and they marry, and they have his old mother to live with them, and he goes to the bank every day, and if she's careful not to have babies she can still go out as a daily governess, and he's often ill—with his wound, you know —and she nurses him, and it's all very pathetic and sweet and lovely."

"It sounds rather dull to me," I ventured.

"Yes, but moral," said Laura.

THE
DOOR OF OPPORTUNITY

THEY got a first-class carriage to themselves. It was lucky, because they were taking a good deal in with them, Alban's suit-case and a hold-all, Anne's dressing-case and her hat-box. They had two trunks in the van, containing what they wanted immediately, but all the rest of their luggage Alban had put in the care of an agent who was to take it up to London and store it till they had made up their minds what to do. They had a lot, pictures and books, curios that Alban had collected in the East, his guns and saddles. They had left Sondurah for ever. Alban, as was his way, tipped the porter generously and then went to the book-stall and bought papers. He bought The New Statesman and The Nation, and The Tatler and The Sketch, and the last number of The London Mercury. He came back to the carriage and threw them on the seat.

"It's only an hour's journey," said Anne.

"I know, but I wanted to buy them. I've been starved so long. Isn't it grand to think that to-morrow morning we shall have to-morrow's Times, and The Express and The Mail?"

She did not answer and he turned away, for he saw coming towards them two persons, a man and his wife, who had been fellow-passengers from Singapore.

"Get through the customs all right?" he cried to them cheerily.

The man seemed not to hear, for he walked straight on, but the woman answered.

"Yes, they never found the cigarettes."

She saw Anne, gave her a friendly little smile, and passed on. Anne flushed.

"I was afraid they'd want to come in here," said Alban. "Let's have the carriage to ourselves if we can."

She looked at him curiously.

"I don't think you need worry," she answered. "I don't think anyone will come in."

He lit a cigarette and lingered at the carriage door. On his face was a happy smile. When they had passed through the Red Sea and found a sharp wind in the Canal, Anne had been surprised to see how much the men who had looked presentable enough in the white ducks in which she had been accustomed to see them, were changed when they left them off for warmer clothes. They looked like nothing on earth then. Their ties were awful and their shirts all wrong. They wore grubby flannel trousers and shabby old golf-coats that had too obviously been bought off the nail, or blue serge suits that betrayed the provincial tailor. Most of the passengers had got off at Marseilles, but a dozen or so, either because after a long period in the East they thought the trip through the Bay would do them good, or, like themselves, for economy's sake, had gone all the way to Tilbury, and now several of them walked along the platform. They wore solar topis or double-brimmed terais, and heavy greatcoats, or else shapeless soft hats or bowlers, not too well brushed, that looked too small for them. It was a shock to see them. They looked suburban and a trifle second-rate. But Alban had already a London look. There was not a speck of dust on his smart greatcoat, and his black Homburg hat looked brand-new. You would never have guessed that he had not been home for three years. His collar fitted closely round his neck and his foulard tie was neatly tied. As Anne looked at him she could not but think how good-looking he was. He was just under six feet tall, and slim, and he wore his clothes well, and his clothes were well cut. He had fair hair, still thick, and blue eyes and the faintly yellow skin common to men of that complexion after they have lost the pink and white freshness of early youth. There was no colour in his cheeks. It was a fine head, well-set on rather a long neck, with a somewhat prominent Adam's apple; but you were more impressed with the distinction than with the beauty of his face. It was because his features were so regular, his nose so straight, his brow so broad that he photographed so well. Indeed, from his photographs you would have thought him extremely handsome. He was not that, perhaps because his eyebrows and his eyelashes were pale, and his lips thin, but he looked very intellectual. There was refinement in his face and a spirituality that was oddly moving. That was how you thought a poet should look; and when Anne became engaged to him she told her girl friends who asked her about him that he looked like Shelley. He turned to her now with a little smile in his blue eyes. His smile was very attractive.

"What a perfect day to land in England!"

It was October. They had steamed up the Channel on a grey sea under a grey sky. There was not a breath of wind. The fishing boats seemed to rest on the placid water as though the elements had forever forgotten their old hostility. The coast was incredibly green, but with a bright cosy greenness quite unlike the luxuriant, vehement verdure of Eastern jungles. The red towns they passed here and there were comfortable and homelike. They seemed to welcome the exiles with a smiling friendliness. And when they drew into the estuary of the Thames they saw the rich levels of Essex and in a little while Chalk Church on the Kentish shore, lonely in the midst of weather-beaten trees, and beyond it the woods of Cobham. The sun, red in a faint mist, set on the marshes, and night fell. In the station the arc-lamps shed a light that spotted the darkness with cold hard patches. It was good to see the porters lumbering about in their grubby uniforms and the stationmaster fat and important in his bowler hat. The stationmaster blew a whistle and waved his arm. Alban stepped into the carriage and seated himself in the corner opposite to Anne. The train started.

"We're due in London at six-ten," said Alban. "We ought to get to Jermyn Street by seven. That'll give us an hour to bath and change and we can get to the Savoy for dinner by eight-thirty. A bottle of pop to-night, my pet, and a slap-up dinner." He gave a chuckle. "I heard the Strouds and the Maundys arranging to meet at the Trocadero Grill-Room."

He took up the papers and asked if she wanted any of them. Anne shook her head.

"Tired?" he smiled.

"No."

"Excited?"

In order not to answer she gave a little laugh. He began to look at the papers, starting with the publishers' advertisements, and she was conscious of the intense satisfaction it was to him to feel himself through them once more in the middle of things. They had taken in those same papers in Sondurah, but they arrived six weeks old, and though they kept them abreast of what was going on in the world that interested them both, they emphasised their exile. But these were fresh from the press. They smelt different. They had a crispness that was almost voluptuous. He wanted to read them all at once. Anne looked out of the window. The country was dark, and she could see little but the lights of their carriage reflected on the glass, but very soon the town encroached upon it, and then she saw little sordid houses, mile upon mile of them, with a light in a window here and there, and the chimneys made a dreary pattern against the sky. They passed through Barking and East Ham and Bromley —it was silly that the name on the platform as they went through the station should give her such a tremor—and then Stepney. Alban put down his papers.

"We shall be there in five minutes now."

He put on his hat and took down from the racks the things the porter had put in them. He looked at her with shining eyes and his lips twitched. She saw that he was only just able to control his emotion. He looked out of the window, too, and they passed over brightly lighted thoroughfares, close packed with tram-cars, buses and motor-vans, and they saw the streets thick with people. What a mob! The shops were all lit up. They saw the hawkers with their barrows at the curb.

"London," he said.

He took her hand and gently pressed it. His smile was so

sweet that she had to say something. She tried to be facetious.

"Does it make you feel all funny inside?"

"I don't know if I want to cry or if I want to be sick."

Fenchurch Street. He lowered the window and waved his
arm for a porter. With a grinding of brakes the train came
to a standstill. A porter opened the door and Alban handed
him out one package after another. Then in his polite way,
having jumped out, he gave his hand to Anne to help her
down to the platform. The porter went to fetch a barrow
and they stood by the pile of their luggage. Alban waved to
two passengers from the ship who passed them. The man
nodded stiffly.

"What a comfort it is that we shall never have to be civil
to those awful people any more," said Alban lightly.

Anne gave him a quick glance. He was really incomprehensible. The porter came back with his barrow, the luggage
was put on and they followed him to collect their trunks.
Alban took his wife's arm and pressed it.

"The smell of London. By God, it's grand."

He rejoiced in the noise and the bustle, and the crowd of
people who jostled them; the radiance of the arc-lamps and
the black shadows they cast, sharp but full-toned, gave him a
sense of elation. They got out into the street and the porter
went off to get them a taxi. Alban's eyes glittered as he
looked at the buses and the policemen trying to direct the
confusion. His distinguished face bore a look of something
like inspiration. The taxi came. Their luggage was stowed
away and piled up beside the driver, Alban gave the porter
half-a-crown, and they drove off. They turned down Grace-
church Street and in Cannon Street were held up by a block
in the traffic. Alban laughed out loud.

"What's the matter?" said Anne.

"I'm so excited."

They went along the Embankment. It was relatively quiet
there. Taxis and cars passed them. The bells of the trams
were music in his ears. At Westminster Bridge they cut
across Parliament Square and drove through the green silence of St. James's Park. They had engaged a room at a

hotel just off Jermyn Street. The reception clerk took them upstairs and a porter brought up their luggage. It was a room with twin beds and a bathroom.

"This looks all right," said Alban. "It'll do us till we can find a flat or something."

He looked at his watch.

"Look here, darling, we shall only fall over one another if we try to unpack together. We've got oodles of time and it'll take you longer to get straight and dress than me. I'll clear out. I want to go to the club and see if there's any mail for me. I've got my dinner-jacket in my suit-case and it'll only take me twenty minutes to have a bath and dress. Does that suit you?"

"Yes. That's all right."

"I'll be back in an hour."

"Very well."

He took out of his pocket the little comb he always carried and passed it through his long fair hair. Then he put on his hat. He gave himself a glance in the mirror.

"Shall I turn on the bath for you?"

"No, don't bother."

"All right. So long."

He went out.

When he was gone Anne took her dressing-case and her hat-box and put them on the top of her trunk. Then she rang the bell. She did not take off her hat. She sat down and lit a cigarette. When a servant answered the bell she asked for the porter. He came. She pointed to the luggage.

"Will you take those things and leave them in the hall for the present. I'll tell you what to do with them presently."

"Very good, ma'am."

She gave him a florin. He took the trunk out and the other packages and closed the door behind him. A few tears slid down Anne's cheeks, but she shook herself; she dried her eyes and powdered her face. She needed all her calm. She was glad that Alban had conceived the idea of going to his club. It made things easier and gave her a little time to think them out.

Now that the moment had come to do what she had for

weeks determined, now that she must say the terrible things
she had to say, she quailed. Her heart sank. She knew exactly
what she meant to say to Alban, she had made up her mind
about that long ago, and had said the very words to herself
a hundred times, three or four times a day every day of the
long journey from Singapore, but she was afraid that she
would grow confused. She dreaded an argument. The
thought of a scene made her feel slightly sick. It was something at all events to have an hour in which to collect herself.
He would say she was heartless and cruel and unreasonable.
She could not help it.

"No, no, no," she cried aloud.

She shuddered with horror. And all at once she saw herself again in the bungalow, sitting as she had been sitting
when the whole thing started. It was getting on towards tiffin
time and in a few minutes Alban would be back from the
office. It gave her pleasure to reflect that it was an attractive
room for him to come back to, the large verandah which
was their parlour, and she knew that though they had been
there eighteen months he was still alive to the success she
had made of it. The jalousies were drawn now against the
midday sun and the mellowed light filtering through them
gave an impression of cool silence. Anne was house-proud,
and though they were moved from district to district according to the exigencies of the Service and seldom stayed anywhere very long, at each new post she started with new enthusiasm to make their house cosy and charming. It amused
her to devise fresh schemes of decoration. She was very
modern. People were surprised because there were no knick-
knacks. They were taken aback by the bold colour of her curtains and they could not at all make out the tinted reproductions of pictures by Marie Laurencin and Gauguin in silvered
frames which were placed on the walls with such cunning
skill. She was conscious that few of them quite approved
and the good ladies of Port Wallace and Pemberton thought
such arrangements odd, affected and out of place; but this
left her calm. They would learn. It did them good to get a
bit of a jolt. And now she looked round the long, spacious
verandah with the complacent sigh of the artist satisfied

with his work. It was gay. It was bare. It was restful. It refreshed the spirit and gently excited the fancy. Three immense bowls of yellow cannas completed the colour scheme. Her eyes lingered for a moment on the bookshelves filled with books; that was another thing that disconcerted the colony, all the books they had, and strange books too, heavy they thought them for the most part; and she gave them a little affectionate look as though they were living things. Then she gave the piano a glance. A piece of music was still open on the rack, it was something of Debussy, and Alban had been playing it before he went to the office.

Her friends in the colony had condoled with her when Alban was appointed D.O. at Daktar, for it was the most isolated district in Sondurah. It was connected with the town which was the headquarters of the government neither by telegraph nor telephone. But she liked it. They had been there for some time and she hoped they would remain till Alban went home on leave in another twelve months. It was as large as an English county, with a long coast line, and the sea was dotted with little islands. A broad, winding river ran through it and on each side of this stretched hills densely covered with virgin forest. The station, a good way up the river, consisted of a row of Chinese shops and a little native village nestling amid coconut trees, the District Office, the D.O.'s bungalow, the Clerk's quarters and the barracks. Their only neighbours were the manager of a rubber estate a few miles up the river and the manager and his assistant, Dutchmen both, of a timber camp on one of the river's tributaries. The rubber estate's launch went up and down twice a month and was their only means of regular communication with the outside world. But though they were lonely they were not dull. Their days were full. Their ponies waited for them at dawn and they rode while the day was still fresh and in the bridle-paths through the jungle lingered the mystery of the tropical night. They came back, bathed, changed and had breakfast, and Alban went to the office. Anne spent the morning writing letters and working. She had fallen in love with the country from the first day she arrived in it and had taken pains to master the common language spoken.

Her imagination was inflamed by the stories she heard of love and jealousy and death. She was told romantic tales of a time that was only just past. She sought to steep herself in the lore of those strange people. Both she and Alban read a great deal. They had for the country a considerable library and new books came from London by nearly every mail. Little that was noteworthy escaped them. Alban was fond of playing the piano. For an amateur he played very well. He had studied rather seriously, and he had an agreeable touch and a good ear; he could read music with ease, and it was always a pleasure to Anne to sit by him and follow the score when he tried something new. But their great delight was to tour the district. Sometimes they would be away for a fortnight at a time. They would go down the river in a prahu and then sail from one little island to another, bathe in the sea, and fish, or else row upstream till it grew shallow and the trees on either bank were so close to one another that you only saw a slim strip of sky between. Here the boatmen had to pole and they would spend the night in a native house. They bathed in a river pool so clear that you could see the sand shining silver at the bottom and the spot was so lovely, so peaceful and remote, that you felt you could stay there for ever. Sometimes, on the other hand, they would tramp for days along the jungle paths, sleeping under canvas, and notwithstanding the mosquitoes that tormented them and the leeches that sucked their blood, enjoy every moment. Who ever slept so well as on a camp bed? And then there was the gladness of getting back, the delight in the comfort of the well-ordered establishment, the mail that had arrived with letters from home and all the papers, and the piano.

Alban would sit down to it then, his fingers itching to feel the keys, and in what he played, Stravinsky, Ravel, Darius Miehaud, she seemed to feel that he put in something of his own, the sounds of the jungle at night, dawn over the estuary, the starry nights, and the crystal clearness of the forest pools.

Sometimes the rain fell in sheets for days at a time. Then Alban worked at Chinese. He was learning it so that he could communicate with the Chinese of the country in their own language, and Anne did the thousand and one things for which she had not had time before. Those days brought them even more closely together; they always had plenty to talk about, and when they were occupied with their separate affairs they were pleased to feel in their bones that they were near to one another. They were wonderfully united. The rainy days that shut them up within the walls of the bungalow made them feel as if they were one body in face of the world.

On occasion they went to Port Wallace. It was a change, but Anne was always glad to get home. She was never quite at her ease there. She was conscious that none of the people they met liked Alban. They were very ordinary people, middle-class and suburban and dull, without any of the intellectual interests that made life so full and varied to Alban and her, and many of them were narrow-minded and ill-natured; but since they had to pass the better part of their lives in contact with them, it was tiresome that they should feel so unkindly towards Alban. They said he was conceited. He was always very pleasant with them, but she was aware that they resented his cordiality. When he tried to be jovial they said he was putting on airs, and when he chaffed them they thought he was being funny at their expense.

Once they stayed at Government House, and Mrs. Hannay, the Governor's wife, who liked her, talked to her about it. Perhaps the Governor had suggested that she should give Anne a hint.

"You know, my dear, it's a pity your husband doesn't try to be more come-hither with people. He's very intelligent; don't you think it would be better if he didn't let others see he knows it quite so clearly? My husband said to me only yesterday: of course I know that Alban Torel is the cleverest young man in the Service, but he does manage to put my back up more than anyone I know. I am the Governor, but when he talks to me he always gives me the impression that he looks upon me as a damned fool."

The worst of it was that Anne knew how low an opinion Alban had of the Governor's parts.

"He doesn't mean to be superior," Anne answered, smiling. "And he really isn't in the least conceited. I think it's only because he has a straight nose and high cheek-bones."

"You know, they don't like him at the club. They call him Powder-Puff Percy."

Anne flushed. She had heard that before and it made her very angry. Her eyes filled with tears.

"I think it's frightfully unfair."

Mrs. Hannay took her hand and gave it an affectionate little squeeze.

"My dear, you know I don't want to hurt your feelings. Your husband can't help rising very high in the Service. He'd make things so much easier for himself if he were a little more human. Why doesn't he play football?"

"It's not his game. He's always only too glad to play tennis."

"He doesn't give that impression. He gives the impression that there's no one here who's worth his while to play with."

"Well, there isn't," said Anne, stung.

Alban happened to be an extremely good tennis player. He had played a lot of tournaments in England and Anne knew that it gave him a grim satisfaction to knock those beefy, hearty men all over the court. He could make the best of them look foolish. He could be maddening on the tennis court and Anne was aware that sometimes he could not resist the temptation.

"He does play to the gallery, doesn't he?" said Mrs. Hannay.

"I don't think so. Believe me, Alban has no idea he isn't popular. As far as I can see he's always pleasant and friendly with everybody."

"It's then he's most offensive," said Mrs. Hannay dryly.

"I know people don't like us very much," said Anne, smiling a little. "I'm very sorry, but really I don't know what we can do about it."

"Not you, my dear," cried Mrs. Hannay. "Everybody adores you. That's why they put up with your husband. My dear, who could help liking you?"

"I don't know why they should adore me," said Anne.

But she did not say it quite sincerely. She was deliberately playing the part of the dear little woman and within her she bubbled with amusement. They disliked Alban because he had such an air of distinction, and because he was interested in art and literature; they did not understand these things and so thought them unmanly; and they disliked him because his capacity was greater than theirs. They disliked him because he was better bred than they. They thought him superior; well, he was superior, but not in the sense they meant. They forgave her because she was an ugly little thing. That was what she called herself, but she wasn't that, or if she was it was with an ugliness that was most attractive. She was like a little monkey, but a very sweet little monkey and very human. She had a neat figure. That was her best point. That and her eyes. They were very large, of a deep brown, liquid and shining; they were full of fun, but they could be tender on occasion with a charming sympathy. She was dark, her frizzy hair was almost black, and her skin was swarthy; she had a small fleshy nose, with large nostrils, and much too big a mouth. But she was alert and vivacious. She could talk with a show of real interest to the ladies of the colony about their husbands and their servants and their children in England, and she could listen appreciatively to the men who told her stories that she had often heard before. They thought her a jolly good sort. They did not know what clever fun she made of them in private. It never occurred to them that she thought them narrow, gross and pretentious. They found no glamour in the East because they looked at it vulgarly with material eyes. Romance lingered at their threshold and they drove it away like an importunate beggar. She was aloof. She repeated to herself Landor's line:

"Nature I loved, and next to nature, art."

She reflected on her conversation with Mrs. Hannay, but on the whole it left her unconcerned. She wondered whether she should say anything about it to Alban; it had always seemed a little odd to her that he should be so little aware of his unpopularity; but she was afraid that if she told him of it he would become self-conscious.

He never noticed the coldness of the men at the club. He made them feel shy and therefore uncomfortable. His appearance there caused a sort of awkwardness, but he, happily insensible, was breezily cordial to all and sundry. The fact was that he was strangely unconscious of other people. She was in a class by herself, she and a little group of friends they had in London, but he could never quite realise that the people of the colony, the government officials and the planters and their wives, were human beings. They were to him like pawns in a game. He laughed with them, chaffed them, and was amiably tolerant of them; with a chuckle Anne told herself that he was rather like a master of a preparatory school taking little boys out on a picnic and anxious to give them a good time.

She was afraid it wasn't much good telling Alban. He was incapable of the dissimulation which, she happily realised, came so easily to her. What was one to do with these people? The men had come out to the colony as lads from second-rate schools, and life had taught them nothing. At fifty they had the outlook of hobbledehoys. Most of them drank a great deal too much. They read nothing worth reading. Their ambition was to be like everybody else. Their highest praise was to say that a man was a damned good sort. If you were interested in the things of the spirit you were a prig. They were eaten up with envy of one another and devoured by petty jealousies. And the women, poor things, were obsessed by petty rivalries. They made a circle that was more provincial than any in the smallest town in England. They were prudish and spiteful. What did it matter if they did not like Alban? They would have to put up with him because his ability was so great. He was clever and energetic. They could not say that he did not do his work well. He had been successful in every post he had occupied. With his sensitiveness and his imagination he understood the native mind and he was able to get the natives to do things that no one in his position could. He had a gift for languages, and he spoke all the local dialects. He knew not only the common tongue that most of the government officials spoke, but was acquainted with the niceties of the language and on occasion could make use of a ceremonial speech that flattered and impressed the chiefs. He had a gift for organisation. He was not afraid of responsibility. In due course he was bound to be made a Resident. Alban had some interest in England; his father was a brigadier-general killed in the war, and though he had no private means he had influential friends. He spoke of them with pleasant irony.

"The great advantage of democratic government," he said, "is that merit, with influence to back it, can be pretty sure of receiving its due reward."

Alban was so obviously the ablest man in the Service that there seemed no reason why he should not eventually be made Governor. Then, thought Anne, his air of superiority, of which they complained, would be in place. They would accept him as their master and he would know how to make himself respected and obeyed. The position she foresaw did not dazzle her. She accepted it as their right. It would be fun for Alban to be Governor and for her to be the Governor's wife. And what an opportunity! They were sheep, the government servants and the planters; when Government House was the seat of culture they would soon fall into line. When the best way to the Governor's favour was to be intelligent, intelligence would become the fashion. She and Alban would cherish the native arts and collect carefully the memorials of a vanished past. The country would make an advance it had never dreamed of. They would develop it, but along lines of order and beauty. They would instil into their subordinates a passion for that beautiful land and a loving interest in these romantic races. They would make them realise what music meant. They would cultivate literature. They would create beauty. It would be the golden age.

Suddenly she heard Alban's footstep. Anne awoke from her day-dream. All that was far away in the future. Alban was only a District Officer yet and what was important was the life they were living now. She heard Alban go into the bath-house and splash water over himself. In a minute he came in. He had changed into a shirt and shorts. His fair hair was still wet.

"Tiffin ready?" he asked.

"Yes."

He sat down at the piano and played the piece that he had played in the morning. The silvery notes cascaded coolly down the sultry air. You had an impression of a formal garden with great trees and elegant pieces of artificial water and of leisurely walks bordered with pseudo-classical statues. Alban played with an exquisite delicacy. Lunch was announced by the head boy. He rose from the piano and gave her his hand. They walked into the dining-room hand in hand. A punkah lazily fanned the air. Anne gave the table a glance. With its bright-coloured tablecloth and the amusing plates it looked very gay.

"Anything exciting at the office this morning?" she asked.

"No, nothing much. A buffalo case. Oh, and Prynne has sent along to ask me to go up to the estate. Some coolies have been damaging the trees and he wants me to come along and look into it."

Prynne was manager of the rubber estate up the river and now and then they spent a night with him. Sometimes when he wanted a change he came down to dinner and slept at the D.O.'s bungalow. They both liked him. He was a man of five and thirty, with a red face, with deep furrows in it, and very black hair. He was quite uneducated, but cheerful and easy, and being the only Englishman within two days' journey they could not but be friendly with him. He had been a little shy of them at first. News spreads quickly in the East and long before they arrived in the district he heard that they were highbrows. He did not know what he would make of them. He probably did not know that he had charm, which makes up for many more commendable qualities, and Alban with his almost feminine sensibilities was peculiarly susceptible to this. He found Alban much more human than he expected, and of course Anne was stunning. Alban played ragtime for him, which he would not have done for the Governor, and played dominoes with him. When Alban was making his first tour of the district with Anne, and suggested that they would like to spend a couple of nights on the estate, he had thought it as well to warn him that he lived with a native woman and had two children by her. He would do his best to keep them out of Anne's sight, but he could not send them away, there was nowhere to send them. Alban laughed.

"Anne isn't that sort of woman at all. Don't dream of hiding them. She loves children."

Anne quickly made friends with the shy, pretty little native woman and soon was playing happily with the children. She and the girl had long confidential chats. The children took a fancy to her. She brought them lovely toys from Port Wallace. Prynne, comparing her smiling tolerance with the disapproving acidity of the other white women in the colony, described himself as knocked all of a heap. He could not do enough to show his delight and gratitude.

"If all highbrows are like you," he said, "give me highbrows every time."

He hated to think that in another year they would leave the district for good and the chances were that, if the next D.O. was married, his wife would think it dreadful that, rather than live alone, he had a native woman to live with him and, what was more, was much attached to her.

But there had been a good deal of discontent on the estate of late. The coolies were Chinese and infected with communist ideas. They were disorderly. Alban had been obliged to sentence several of them for various crimes to terms of imprisonment.

"Prynne tells me that as soon as their term is up he's going to send them all back to China and get Javanese instead," said Alban. "I'm sure he's right. They're much more amenable."

"You don't think there's going to be any serious trouble?"

"Oh, no. Prynne knows his job and he's a pretty determined fellow. He wouldn't put up with any nonsense and with me and our policemen to back him up I don't imagine they'll try any monkey tricks." He smiled. "The iron hand in the velvet glove."

The words were barely out of his mouth when a sudden shouting arose. There was a commotion and the sound of steps. Loud voices and cries.

"Tuan, Tuan."

"What the devil's the matter?"

Alban sprang from his chair and went swiftly on to the verandah. Anne followed him. At the bottom of the steps was a group of natives. There was the sergeant, and three or four policemen, boatmen and several men from the kampong.

"What is it?" called Alban.

Two or three shouted back in answer. The sergeant pushed others aside and Alban saw lying on the ground a man in a shirt and khaki shorts. He ran down the steps. He recognised the man as the assistant manager of Prynne's estate. He was a half-caste. His shorts were covered with blood and there was clotted blood all over one side of his face and head. He was unconscious.

"Bring him up here," called Anne.

Alban gave an order. The man was lifted up and carried on to the verandah. They laid him on the floor and Anne put a pillow under his head. She sent for water and for the medicine-chest in which they kept things for emergency.

"Is he dead?" asked Alban.

"No."

"Better try to give him some brandy."

The boatmen brought ghastly news. The Chinese coolies had arisen suddenly and attacked the manager's office. Prynne was killed and the assistant manager, Oakley by name, had escaped only by the skin of his teeth. He had come upon the rioters when they were looting the office, he had seen Prynne's body thrown out of the window, and had taken to his heels. Some of the Chinese saw him and gave chase. He ran for the river and was wounded as he jumped into the launch. The launch managed to put off before the Chinese could get on board and they had come down stream for help as fast as they could go. As they went they saw flames rising from the office buildings. There was no doubt that the coolies had burned down everything that would burn.

Oakley gave a groan and opened his eyes. He was a little, dark-skinned man, with flattened features and thick coarse hair. His great native eyes were filled with terror.

"You're all right," said Anne. "You're quite safe."

He gave a sigh and smiled. Anne washed his face and swobbed it with antiseptics. The wound on his head was not serious.

"Can you speak yet?" said Alban.

"Wait a bit," she said. "We must look at his leg."

Alban ordered the sergeant to get the crowd out of the verandah. Anne ripped up one leg of the shorts. The material was clinging to the coagulated wound.

"I've been bleeding like a pig," said Oakley.

It was only a flesh wound. Alban was clever with his fingers, and though the blood began to flow again they stanched it. Alban put on a dressing and a bandage. The sergeant and a policeman lifted Oakley on to a long chair. Alban gave him a brandy and soda, and soon he felt strong enough to speak. He knew no more than the boatmen had already told. Prynne was dead and the estate was in flames.

"And the girl and the children?" asked Anne.

"I don't know."

"Oh, Alban."

"I must turn out the police. Are you sure Prynne is dead?"

"Yes, sir. I saw him."

"Have the rioters got fire-arms?"

"I don't know, sir."

"How d'you mean, you don't know?" Alban cried irritably. "Prynne had a gun, hadn't he?"

"Yes, sir."

"There must have been more on the estate. You had one, didn't you? The head overseer had one."

The half-caste was silent. Alban looked at him sternly.

"How many of those damned Chinese are there?"

"A hundred and fifty."

Anne wondered that he asked so many questions. It seemed waste of time. The important thing was to collect coolies for the transport up river, prepare the boats and issue ammunition to the police.

"How many policemen have you got, sir?" asked Oakley.

"Eight and the sergeant."

"Could I come too? That would make ten of us. I'm sure I shall be all right now I'm bandaged."

"I'm not going," said Alban.

"Alban, you must," cried Anne. She could not believe her ears.

"Nonsense. It would be madness. Oakley's obviously useless. He's sure to have a temperature in a few hours. He'd only be in the way. That leaves nine guns. There are a hundred and fifty Chinese and they've got firearms and all the ammunition in the world."

"How d'you know?"

"It stands to reason they wouldn't have started a show like this unless they had. It would be idiotic to go."

Anne stared at him with open mouth. Oakley's eyes were puzzled.

"What are you going to do?"

"Well, fortunately we've got the launch. I'll send it to Port Wallace with a request for reinforcements."

"But they won't be here for two days at least."

"Well, what of it? Prynne's dead and the estate burned to the ground. We couldn't do any good by going up now. I shall send a native to reconnoitre so that we can find out exactly what the rioters are doing." He gave Anne his charming smile. "Believe me, my pet, the rascals won't lose anything by waiting a day or two for what's coming to them."

Oakley opened his mouth to speak, but perhaps he hadn't the nerve. He was a half-caste assistant manager and Alban, the D.O., represented the power of the Government. But the man's eyes sought Anne's and she thought she read in them an earnest and personal appeal.

"But in two days they're capable of committing the most frightful atrocities," she cried. "It's quite unspeakable what they may do."

"Whatever damage they do they'll pay for. I promise you that."

"Oh, Alban, you can't sit still and do nothing. I beseech you to go yourself at once."

"Don't be so silly. I can't quell a riot with eight policemen and a sergeant. I haven't got the right to take a risk of that sort. We'd have to go in boats. You don't think we could get

up unobserved. The lalang along the banks is perfect cover
and they could just take pot shots at us as we came along.
We shouldn't have a chance."

"I'm afraid they'll only think it weakness if nothing is
done for two days, sir," said Oakley.

"When I want your opinion I'll ask for it," said Alban
acidly. "So far as I can see when there was danger the only
thing you did was to cut and run. I can't persuade myself
that your assistance in a crisis would be very valuable."

The half-caste reddened. He said nothing more. He
looked straight in front of him with troubled eyes.

"I'm going down to the office," said Alban. "I'll just write
a short report and send it down the river by launch at once."

He gave an order to the sergeant who had been standing
all this time stiffly at the top of the steps. He saluted and ran
off. Alban went into a little hall they had to get his topi.
Anne swiftly followed him.

"Alban, for God's sake listen to me a minute," she whispered.

"I don't want to be rude to you, darling, but I am pressed
for time. I think you'd much better mind your own business."

"You can't do nothing, Alban. You must go. Whatever
the risk."

"Don't be such a fool," he said angrily.

He had never been angry with her before. She seized his
hand to hold him back.

"I tell you I can do no good by going."

"You don't know. There's the woman and Prynne's children. We must do something to save them. Let me come
with you. They'll kill them."

"They've probably killed them already."

"Oh, how can you be so callous! If there's a chance of
saving them it's your duty to try."

"It's my duty to act like a reasonable human being. I'm
not going to risk my life and my policemen's for the sake of
a native woman and her half-caste brats. What sort of a
damned fool do you take me for?"

"They'll say you were afraid."

"Who?"

"Everyone in the colony."

He smiled disdainfully.

"If you only knew what a complete contempt I have for the opinion of everyone in the colony."

She gave him a long searching look. She had been married to him for eight years and she knew every expression of his face and every thought in his mind. She stared into his blue eyes as if they were open windows. She suddenly went quite pale. She dropped his hand and turned away. Without another word she went back on to the verandah. Her ugly little monkey face was a mask of horror.

Alban went to his office, wrote a brief account of the facts, and in a few minutes the motor launch was pounding down the river.

The next two days were endless. Escaped nahois brought them news of happenings on the estate. But from their excited and terrified stories it was impossible to get an exact impression of the truth. There had been a good deal of bloodshed. The head overseer had been killed. They brought wild tales of cruelty and outrage. Anne could hear nothing of Prynne's woman and the two children. She shuddered when she thought of what might have been their fate. Alban collected as many natives as he could. They were armed with spears and swords. He commandeered boats. The situation was serious, but he kept his head. He felt that he had done all that was possible and nothing remained but for him to carry on normally. He did his official work. He played the piano a great deal. He rode with Anne in the early morning. He appeared to have forgotten that they had had the first serious difference of opinion in the whole of their married life. He took it that Anne had accepted the wisdom of his decision. He was as amusing, cordial and gay with her as he had always been. When he spoke of the rioters it was with grim irony: when the time came to settle matters a good many of them would wish they had never been born.

"What'll happen to them?" asked Anne.

"Oh, they'll hang." He gave a shrug of distaste. "I hate having to be present at executions. It always makes me feel rather sick."

He was very sympathetic to Oakley, whom they had put to bed and whom Anne was nursing. Perhaps he was sorry that in the exasperation of the moment he had spoken to him offensively, and he went out of his way to be nice to him.

Then on the afternoon of the third day, when they were drinking their coffee after luncheon, Alban's quick ears caught the sound of a motor boat approaching. At the same moment a policeman ran up to say that the government launch was sighted.

"At last," cried Alban.

He bolted out of the house. Anne raised one of the jalousies and looked out at the river. Now the sound was quite loud and in a moment she saw the boat come round the bend. She saw Alban on the landing-stage. He got into a prahu and as the launch dropped her anchor he went on board. She told Oakley that the reinforcements had come.

"Will the D.O. go up with them when they attack?" he asked her.

"Naturally," said Anne coldly.

"I wondered."

Anne felt a strange feeling in her heart. For the last two days she had had to exercise all her self-control not to cry. She did not answer. She went out of the room.

A quarter of an hour later Alban returned to the bungalow with the captain of constabulary who had been sent with twenty Sikhs to deal with the rioters. Captain Stratton was a little red-faced man with a red moustache and bow legs, very hearty and dashing, whom she had met often at Port Wallace.

"Well, Mrs. Torel, this is a pretty kettle of fish," he cried, as he shook hands with her, in a loud jolly voice. "Here I am, with my army all full of pep and ready for a scrap. Up, boys, and at 'em. Have you got anything to drink in this benighted place?"

"Boy," she cried, smiling.

"Something long and cool and faintly alcoholic, and then I'm ready to discuss the plan of campaign."

His breeziness was very comforting. It blew away the sullen apprehension that had seemed ever since the disaster to brood over the lost peace of the bungalow. The boy came in with a tray and Stratton mixed himself a stengah. Alban put him in possession of the facts. He told them clearly, briefly and with precision.

"I must say I admire you," said Stratton. "In your place I should never have been able to resist the temptation to take my eight cops and have a whack at the blighters myself."

"I thought it was a perfectly unjustifiable risk to take."

"Safety first, old boy, eh, what?" said Stratton jovially. "I'm jolly glad you didn't. It's not often we get the chance of a scrap. It would have been a dirty trick to keep the whole show to yourself."

Captain Stratton was all for steaming straight up the river and attacking at once, but Alban pointed out to him the inadvisability of such a course. The sound of the approaching launch would warn the rioters. The long grass at the river's edge offered them cover and they had enough guns to make a landing difficult. It seemed useless to expose the attacking force to their fire. It was silly to forget that they had to face a hundred and fifty desperate men and it would be easy to fall into an ambush. Alban expounded his own plan. Stratton listened to it. He nodded now and then. The plan was evidently a good one. It would enable them to take the rioters on the rear, surprise them, and in all probability finish the job without a single casualty. He would have been a fool not to accept it.

"But why didn't you do that yourself?" asked Stratton.

"With eight men and a sergeant?"

Stratton did not answer.

"Anyhow it's not a bad idea and we'll settle on it. It gives us plenty of time, so with your permission, Mrs. Torel, I'll have a bath."

They set out at sunset, Captain Stratton and his twenty Sikhs, Alban with his policemen and the natives he had collected. The night was dark and moonless. Trailing behind them were the dug-outs that Alban had gathered together and into which after a certain distance they proposed to transfer their force. It was important that no sound should give warning of their approach. After they had gone for about three hours by launch they took to the dug-outs and in them silently paddled up stream. They reached the border of the vast estate and landed. Guides led them along a path so narrow that they had to march in single file. It had been long unused and the going was heavy. They had twice to ford a stream. The path led them circuitously to the rear of the coolie lines, but they did not wish to reach them till nearly dawn and presently Stratton gave the order to halt. It was a long cold wait. At last the night seemed to be less dark; you did not see the trunks of the trees, but were vaguely sensible of them against its darkness. Stratton had been sitting with his back to a tree. He gave a whispered order to a sergeant and in a few minutes the column was once more on the march. Suddenly they found themselves on a road. They formed fours. The dawn broke and in the ghostly light the surrounding objects were wanly visible. The column stopped on a whispered order. They had come in sight of the coolie lines. Silence reigned in them. The column crept on again and again halted. Stratton, his eyes shining, gave Alban a smile.

"We've caught the blighters asleep."

He lined up his men. They inserted cartridges in their guns. He stepped forward and raised his hand. The carbines were pointed at the coolie lines.

"Fire."

There was a rattle as the volley of shots rang out. Then suddenly there was a tremendous din and the Chinese poured out, shouting and waving their arms, but in front of them, to Alban's utter bewilderment, bellowing at the top of his voice and shaking his fist at them, was a white man.

"Who the hell's that?" cried Stratton.

A very big, very fat man, in khaki trousers and a singlet, was running towards them as fast as his fat legs would carry him and as he ran shaking both fists at them and yelling:

"*Smerige flikkers! Verlockte ploerten!*"

"My God, it's Van Hasseldt," said Alban.

This was the Dutch manager of the timber camp which was situated on a considerable tributary of the river about twenty miles away.

"What the hell do you think you're doing?" he puffed as he came up to them.

"How the hell did you get here?" asked Stratton in turn.

He saw that the Chinese were scattering in all directions and gave his men instructions to round them up. Then he turned again to Van Hasseldt.

"What's it mean?"

"Mean? Mean?" shouted the Dutchman furiously. "That's what I want to know. You and your damned policemen. What do you mean by coming here at this hour in the morning and firing a damned volley? Target practice? You might have killed me. Idiots!"

"Have a cigarette," said Stratton.

"How did you get here, Van Hasseldt?" asked Alban again, very much at sea. "This is the force they've sent from Port Wallace to quell the riot."

"How did I get here? I walked. How did you think I got here? Riot be damned. I quelled the riot. If that's what you came for you can take your damned policemen home again. A bullet came within a foot of my head."

"I don't understand," said Alban.

"There's nothing to understand," spluttered Van Hasseldt, still fuming. "Some coolies came to my estate and said the chinks had killed Prynne and burned the bally place down, so I took my assistant and my head overseer and a Dutch friend I had staying with me and came over to see what the trouble was."

Captain Stratton opened his eyes wide.

"Did you just stroll in as if it was a picnic?" he asked.

"Well, you don't think after all the years I've been in this country I'm going to let a couple of hundred chinks put the fear of God into me? I found them all scared out of their lives. One of them had the nerve to pull a gun on me and I blew his bloody brains out. And the rest surrendered. I've got the leaders tied up. I was going to send a boat down to you this morning to come up and get them."

Stratton stared at him for a minute and then burst into a shout of laughter. He laughed till the tears ran down his face. The Dutchman looked at him angrily, then began to laugh too; he laughed with the big belly laugh of a very fat man and his coils of fat heaved and shook. Alban watched them sullenly. He was very angry.

"What about Prynne's girl and the kids?" he asked.

"Oh, they got away all right."

It just showed how wise he had been not to let himself be influenced by Anne's hysteria. Of course the children had come to no harm. He never thought they would.

Van Hasseldt and his little party started back for the timber camp, and as soon after as possible Stratton embarked his twenty Sikhs and leaving Alban with his sergeant and his policemen to deal with the situation departed for Port Wallace. Alban gave him a brief report for the Governor. There was much for him to do. It looked as though he would have to stay for a considerable time; but since every house on the estate had been burned to the ground and he was obliged to install himself in the coolie lines he thought it better that Anne should not join him. He sent her a note to that effect. He was glad to be able to reassure her of the safety of poor Prynne's girl. He set to work at once to make his preliminary enquiry. He examined a host of witnesses. But a week later he received an order to go to Port Wallace at once. The launch that brought it was to take him and he was able to see Anne on the way down for no more than an hour. Alban was a trifle vexed.

"I don't know why the Governor can't leave me to get things straight without dragging me off like this. It's extremely inconvenient."

"Oh, well, the Government never bothers very much about the convenience of its subordinates, does it?" smiled Anne.

"It's just red tape. I would offer to take you along, darling, only I shan't stay a minute longer than I need. I want to get my evidence together for the Sessions Court as soon as possible. I think in a country like this it's very important that justice should be prompt."

When the launch came in to Port Wallace one of the harbour police told him that the harbour-master had a chit for him. It was from the Governor's secretary and informed him that His Excellency desired to see him as soon as con-

venient after his arrival. It was ten in the morning. Alban
went to the club, had a bath and shaved, and then in clean
ducks, his hair neatly brushed, he called a rickshaw and told
the boy to take him to the Governor's office. He was at once
shown in to the secretary's room. The secretary shook hands
with him.

"I'll tell H.E. you're here," he said. "Won't you sit
down?"

The secretary left the room and in a little while came back.

"H.E. will see you in a minute. Do you mind if I get on
with my letters?"

Alban smiled. The secretary was not exactly come-hither.
He waited, smoking a cigarette, and amused himself with his
own thoughts. He was making a good job of the preliminary
enquiry. It interested him. Then an orderly came in and told
Alban that the Governor was ready for him. He rose from
his seat and followed him into the Governor's room.

"Good-morning, Torel."

"Good-morning, sir."

The Governor was sitting at a large desk. He nodded to
Alban and motioned to him to take a seat. The Governor
was all grey. His hair was grey, his face, his eyes; he looked
as though the tropical suns had washed the colour out of
him; he had been in the country for thirty years and had
risen one by one through all the ranks of the Service; he
looked tired and depressed. Even his voice was grey. Alban
liked him because he was quiet; he did not think him clever,
but he had an unrivalled knowledge of the country, and his
great experience was a very good substitute for intelligence.
He looked at Alban for a full moment without speaking and
the odd idea came to Alban that he was embarrassed. He
very nearly gave him a lead.

"I saw Van Hasseldt yesterday," said the Governor suddenly.

"Yes, sir?"

"Will you give me your account of the occurrences at the
Alud Estate and of the steps you took to deal with them."

Alban had an orderly mind. He was self-possessed. He
marshalled his facts well and was able to state them with

precision. He chose his words with care and spoke them fluently.

"You had a sergeant and eight policemen. Why did you not immediately go to the scene of the disturbance?"

"I thought the risk was unjustifiable."

A thin smile was outlined on the Governor's grey face.

"If the officers of this government had hesitated to take unjustifiable risks it would never have become a province of the British Empire."

Alban was silent. It was difficult to talk to a man who spoke obvious nonsense.

"I am anxious to hear your reasons for the decision you took."

Alban gave them coolly. He was quite convinced of the rightness of his action. He repeated, but more fully, what he had said in the first place to Anne. The Governor listened attentively.

"Van Hasseldt, with his manager, a Dutch friend of his, and a native overseer, seems to have coped with the situation very efficiently," said the Governor.

"He had a lucky break. That doesn't prevent him from being a damned fool. It was madness to do what he did."

"Do you realise that by leaving a Dutch planter to do what you should have done yourself, you have covered the Government with ridicule?"

"No, sir."

"You've made yourself a laughing-stock in the whole colony."

Alban smiled.

"My back is broad enough to bear the ridicule of persons to whose opinion I am entirely indifferent."

"The utility of a government official depends very largely on his prestige, and I'm afraid his prestige is likely to be inconsiderable when he lies under the stigma of cowardice."

Alban flushed a little.

"I don't quite know what you mean by that, sir."

"I've gone into the matter very carefully. I've seen Captain Stratton, and Oakley, poor Prynne's assistant, and I've seen Van Hasseldt. I've listened to your defence."

"I didn't know that I was defending myself, sir."

"Be so good as not to interrupt me. I think you committed a grave error of judgment. As it turns out the risk was very small, but whatever it was, I think you should have taken it. In such matters promptness and firmness are essential. It is not for me to conjecture what motive led you to send for a force of constabulary and do nothing till they came. I am afraid, however, that I consider that your usefulness in the Service is no longer very great."

Alban looked at him with astonishment.

"But would you have gone under the circumstances?" he asked him.

"I should."

Alban shrugged his shoulders.

"Don't you believe me?" rapped out the Governor.

"Of course I believe you, sir. But perhaps you will allow me to say that if you had been killed the colony would have suffered an irreparable loss."

The Governor drummed on the table with his fingers. He looked out of the window and then looked again at Alban. When he spoke it was not unkindly.

"I think you are unfitted by temperament for this rather rough and tumble life, Torel. If you'll take my advice you'll go home. With your abilities I feel sure that you'll soon find an occupation much better suited to you."

"I'm afraid I don't understand what you mean, sir."

"Oh, come, Torel, you're not stupid. I'm trying to make things easy for you. For your wife's sake as well as for your own I do not wish you to leave the colony with the stigma of being dismissed from the Service for cowardice. I'm giving you the opportunity of resigning."

"Thank you very much, sir. I'm not prepared to avail myself of the opportunity. If I resign I admit that I committed an error and that the charge you make against me is justified. I don't admit it."

"You can please yourself. I have considered the matter very carefully and I have no doubt about it in my mind. I am forced to discharge you from the Service. The necessary papers will reach you in due course. Meanwhile you will return to your post and hand over to the officer appointed to succeed you on his arrival."

"Very good, sir," replied Alban, a twinkle of amusement in his eyes. "When do you desire me to return to my post?"

"At once."

"Have you any objection to my going to the club and having tiffin before I go?"

The Governor looked at him with surprise. His exasperation was mingled with an unwilling admiration.

"Not at all. I'm sorry, Torel, that this unhappy incident should have deprived the Government of a servant whose zeal has always been so apparent and whose tact, intelligence and industry seemed to point him out in the future for very high office."

"Your Excellency does not read Schiller, I suppose. You are probably not acquainted with his celebrated line: *mit der dummheit kämpfen die Götter selbst vergebens.*"

"What does it mean?"

"Roughly, against stupidity the gods themselves battle in vain."

"Good-morning."

With his head in the air, a smile on his lips, Alban left the Governor's office. The Governor was human, and he had the curiosity to ask his secretary later in the day if Alban Torel had really gone to the club.

"Yes, sir. He had tiffin there."

"It must have wanted some nerve."

Alban entered the club jauntily and joined the group of men standing at the bar. He talked to them in the breezy, cordial tone he always used with them. It was designed to put them at their ease. They had been discussing him ever since Stratton had come back to Port Wallace with his story, sneering at him and laughing at him, and all that had resented his superciliousness, and they were the majority, were triumphant because his pride had had a fall. But they were so taken aback at seeing him now, so confused to find him as confident as ever, that it was they who were embarrassed.

One man, though he knew perfectly, asked him what he was doing in Port Wallace.

"Oh, I came about the riot on the Alud Estate. H.E. wanted to see me. He does not see eye to eye with me about it. The silly old ass has fired me. I'm going home as soon as he appoints a D.O. to take over."

There was a moment of awkwardness. One, more kindly disposed than the others, said:

"I'm awfully sorry."

Alban shrugged his shoulders. "My dear fellow, what can you do with a perfect damned fool? The only thing is to let him stew in his own juice."

When the Governor's secretary had told his chief as much of this as he thought discreet, the Governor smiled.

"Courage is a queer thing. I would rather have shot myself than go to the club just then and face all those fellows."

A fortnight later, having sold to the incoming D.O. all the decorations that Anne had taken so much trouble about, with the rest of their things in packing-cases and trunks, they arrived at Port Wallace to await the local steamer that was to take them to Singapore. The padre's wife invited them to stay with her, but Anne refused; she insisted that they should go to the hotel. An hour after their arrival she received a very kind little letter from the Governor's wife asking her to go and have tea with her. She went. She found Mrs. Hannay alone, but in a minute the Governor joined them. He expressed his regret that she was leaving and told her how sorry he was for the cause.

"It's very kind of you to say that," said Anne, smiling gaily, "but you mustn't think I take it to heart. I'm entirely on Alban's side. I think what he did was absolutely right and if you don't mind my saying so I think you've treated him most unjustly."

"Believe me, I hated having to take the step I took."

"Don't let's talk about it," said Anne.

"What are your plans when you get home?" asked Mrs. Hannay.

Anne began to chat brightly. You would have thought she had not a care in the world. She seemed in great spirits at going home. She was jolly and amusing and made little jokes. When she took leave of the Governor and his wife she thanked them for all their kindness. The Governor escorted her to the door.

The next day but one, after dinner, they went on board the clean and comfortable little ship. The padre and his wife saw them off. When they went into their cabin they found a large parcel on Anne's bunk. It was addressed to Alban. He opened it and saw that it was an immense powder-puff.

"Hullo, I wonder who sent us this," he said, with a laugh. "It must be for you, darling."

Anne gave him a quick look. She went pale. The brutes! How could they be so cruel? She forced herself to smile.

"It's enormous, isn't it? I've never seen such a large powder-puff in my life."

But when he had left the cabin and they were out at sea, she threw it passionately overboard.

And now, now that they were back in London and Sondurah was nine thousand miles away, she clenched her hands as she thought of it. Somehow, it seemed the worst thing of all. It was so wantonly unkind to send that absurd object to Alban, Powder-Puff Percy; it showed such a petty spite. Was that their idea of humour? Nothing had hurt her more and even now she felt that it was only by holding on to herself that she could prevent herself from crying. Suddenly she started, for the door opened and Alban came in. She was still sitting in the chair in which he had left her.

"Hullo, why haven't you dressed?" He looked about the room. "You haven't unpacked."

"No."

"Why on earth not?"

"I'm not going to unpack. I'm not going to stay here. I'm leaving you."

"What are you talking about?"

"I've stuck it out till now. I made up my mind I would till we got home. I set my teeth, I've borne more than I thought it possible to bear, but now it's finished. I've done all that could be expected of me. We're back in London now and I can go."

He looked at her in utter bewilderment.

"Are you mad, Anne?"

"Oh, my God, what I've endured! The journey to Singapore, with all the officers knowing, and even the Chinese stewards. And at Singapore, the way people looked at us at the hotel, and the sympathy I had to put up with, the bricks they dropped and their embarrassment when they realised what they'd done. My God, I could have killed them. That interminable journey home. There wasn't a single passenger on the ship who didn't know. The contempt they had for you and the kindness they went out of their way to show me. And you so self-complacent and so pleased with yourself, seeing nothing, feeling nothing. You must have the hide of a rhinoceros. The misery of seeing you so chatty and agreeable. Pariahs, that's what we were. You seemed to ask them to snub you. How can anyone be so shameless?"

She was flaming with passion. Now that at last she need not wear the mask of indifference and pride that she had forced herself to assume she cast aside all reserve and all self-control. The words poured from her trembling lips in a virulent stream.

"My dear, how can you be so absurd?" he said good-naturedly, smiling. "You must be very nervous and high-strung to have got such ideas in your head. Why didn't you tell me? You're like a country bumpkin who comes to London and thinks everyone is staring at him. Nobody bothered about us and if they did what on earth did it matter? You ought to have more sense than to bother about what a lot of fools say. And what do you imagine they were saying?"

"They were saying you'd been fired."

"Well, that was true," he laughed.

"They said you were a coward."

"What of it?"

"Well, you see, that was true too."

He looked at her for a moment reflectively. His lips tightened a little.

"And what makes you think so?" he asked acidly.

"I saw it in your eyes, that day the news came, when you refused to go to the estate and I followed you into the hall when you went to fetch your topi. I begged you to go, I felt that whatever the danger you must take it, and suddenly I saw the fear in your eyes. I nearly fainted with the horror."

"I should have been a fool to risk my life to no purpose. Why should I? Nothing that concerned me was at stake. Courage is the obvious virtue of the stupid. I don't attach any particular importance to it."

"How do you mean that nothing that concerned you was at stake? If that's true then your whole life is a sham. You've given away everything you stood for, everything we both stand for. You've let all of us down. We did set ourselves up on a pinnacle, we did think ourselves better than the rest of them because we loved literature and art and music, we weren't content to live a life of ignoble jealousies and vulgar tittle-tattle, we did cherish the things of the spirit, and we loved beauty. It was our food and drink. They laughed at us and sneered at us. That was inevitable. The ignorant and the common naturally hate and fear those who are interested in things they don't understand. We didn't care. We called them Philistines. We despised them and we had a right to despise them. Our justification was that we were better and nobler and wiser and braver than they were. And you weren't better, you weren't nobler, you weren't braver. When the crisis came you slunk away like a whipped cur with his tail between his legs. You of all people hadn't the right to be a coward. They despise *us* now and they have the right to despise us. Us and all we stood for. Now they can say that art and beauty are all rot; when it comes to a pinch people like us always let you down. They never stopped looking for a chance to turn and rend us and you gave it to them. They can say that they always expected it. It's a triumph for them. I used to be furious because they called you Powder-Puff Percy. Did you know they did?"

"Of course. I thought it very vulgar, but it left me entirely indifferent."

"It's funny that their instinct should have been so right."

"Do you mean to say you've been harbouring this against me all these weeks? I should never have thought you capable of it."

"I couldn't let you down when everyone was against you. I was too proud for that. Whatever happened I swore to myself that I'd stick to you till we got home. It's been torture."

"Don't you love me any more?"

"Love you? I loathe the very sight of you."

"Anne."

"God knows I loved you. For eight years I worshipped the ground you trod on. You were everything to me. I believed in you as some people believe in God. When I saw the fear in your eyes that day, when you told me that you weren't going to risk your life for a kept woman and her half-caste brats, I was shattered. It was as though someone had wrenched my heart out of my body and trampled on it. You killed my love there and then, Alban. You killed it stone dead. Since then when you've kissed me I've had to clench my hands so as not to turn my face away. The mere thought of anything else makes me feel physically sick. I loathe your complacence and your frightful insensitiveness. Perhaps I could have forgiven it if it had been just a moment's weakness and if afterwards you'd been ashamed. I should have been miserable, but I think my love was so great that I should only have felt pity for you. But you're incapable of shame. And now I believe in nothing. You're only a silly, pretentious, vulgar poseur. I would rather be the wife of a second-rate planter so long as he had the common human virtues of a man than the wife of a fake like you."

He did not answer. Gradually his face began to discompose. Those handsome, regular features of his horribly distorted and suddenly he broke out into loud sobs. She gave a little cry.

"Don't, Alban, don't."

"Oh, darling, how can you be so cruel to me? I adore you. I'd give my whole life to please you. I can't live without you."

She put out her arms as though to ward off a blow.

"No, no, Alban, don't try to move me. I can't. I must go. I can't live with you any more. It would be frightful. I can never forget. I must tell you the truth, I have only contempt for you and repulsion."

He sank down at her feet and tried to cling to her knees. With a gasp she sprang up and he buried his head in the empty chair. He cried painfully with sobs that tore his chest. The sound was horrible. The tears streamed from Anne's eyes and, putting her hands to her ears to shut out that dreadful, hysterical sobbing, blindly stumbling she rushed to the loor and ran out.

SEPTEMBER'S BIRD

IRST the King of Siam had two daughters, and he called them Night and Day. Then he had two more, so he changed the names of the first ones and called the four of them after the seasons, Spring and Autumn, Winter and Summer. But in course of time he had three others, and he changed their names again and called all seven by the days of the week. But when his eighth daughter was born he did not know what to do till he suddenly thought of the months of the year. The Queen said there were only twelve and it confused her to have to remember so many new names, but the King had a methodical mind and when he made it up he never could change it if he tried. He changed the names of all his daughters and called them January, February, March (though of course in Siamese), till he came to the youngest who was called August, and the next one was called September.

"That only leaves October, November and December," said the Queen. "And after that we shall have to begin all over again."

"No, we shan't," said the King, "because I think twelve daughters are enough for any man, and after the birth of dear little December I shall be reluctantly compelled to cut off your head."

He cried bitterly when he said this, for he was extremely fond of the Queen. Of course it made the Queen very uneasy, because she knew that it would distress the King very much if he had to cut off her head. And it would not be very nice for her. But it so happened that there was no need for either of them to worry, because September was the last daughter they ever had. The Queen only had sons after that, and they were called by the letters of the alphabet, so there was no cause for anxiety there for a long time, since she had only reached the letter J.

Now the King of Siam's daughters had had their characters permanently embittered by having to change their names in this way, and the older ones, whose names of course had been changed oftener than the others, had their characters more permanently embittered. But September, who had never known what it was to be called anything but September (except of course by her sisters, who because their characters were embittered called her all sorts of names) had a very sweet and charming nature.

The King of Siam had a habit which I think might be usefully imitated in Europe. Instead of receiving presents on his birthday he gave them, and it looks as though he liked it, for he used often to say he was sorry he had only been born on one day and so only had one birthday in the year. But in this way he managed in course of time to give away all his wedding presents, and the loyal addresses which the mayors of the cities in Siam presented him with, and all his old crowns which had gone out of fashion. One year on his birthday, not having anything else handy, he gave each of his daughters a beautiful green parrot in a beautiful golden cage. There were nine of them, and on each cage was written the name of the month which was the name of the princess it belonged to. The nine princesses were very proud of their parrots, and they spent an hour every day (for like their father they were of a methodical turn of mind) in teaching them to talk. Presently all the parrots could say God save the King (in Siamese, which is very difficult), and some of them could say Pretty Polly in no less than seven Oriental languages. But one day when the Princess September went to say good morning to her parrot she found it lying dead at the bottom of its golden cage. She burst into a flood of tears, and nothing that her Maids of Honour could say comforted her. She cried so much that the Maids of Honour, not knowing what to do, told the Queen, and the Queen said it was stuff and nonsense and the child had better go to bed without any supper. The Maids of Honour wanted to go to a party, so they put the Princess September to bed as quickly as they could and left her by herself. And while she lay in her bed, crying still, even though she felt rather hungry, she saw a little bird hop into her room. She took her thumb out of her mouth and sat up. Then the little bird began to sing, and he sang a beautiful song all about the lake in the King's garden, and the willow trees that looked at themselves in the still water, and the goldfish that glided in and out of the branches that were reflected in it. When he had finished the Princess was not crying any more and she quite forgot that she had had no supper.

"That was a very nice song," she said.

The little bird gave her a bow, for artists have naturally good manners, and they like to be appreciated.

"Would you care to have me instead of your parrot?" said the little bird. "It's true that I'm not so pretty to look at, but on the other hand I have a much better voice."

The Princess September clapped her hands with delight, and then the little bird hopped onto the end of her bed and sang her to sleep.

When she awoke next day the little bird was still sitting there, and as she opened her eyes he said, "Good morning." The Maids of Honour brought in her breakfast, and he ate rice out of her hand, and he had his bath in her saucer. He drank out of it, too. The Maids of Honour said they didn't think it was very polite to drink one's bath water, but the Princess September said that was the artistic temperament. When he had finished his breakfast he began to sing again so beautifully that the Maids of Honour were quite surprised, for they had never heard anything like it, and the Princess September was very proud and happy.

"Now I want to show you to my eight sisters," said the Princess.

She stretched out the first finger of her right hand so that it served as a perch, and the little bird flew down and sat on it. Then, followed by her Maids of Honour, she went through the palace and called on each of the princesses in turn, starting with January, for she was mindful of etiquette, and going all the way down to August. And for each of the princesses the little bird sang a different song. But the parrots could only say God save the King and Pretty Polly. At last she shewed the little bird to the King and Queen. They were surprised and delighted.

"I knew I was right to send you to bed without any supper," said the Queen.

"This bird sings much better than the parrots," said the King.

"I should have thought you got quite tired of hearing people say, 'God save the King,' " said the Queen. "I can't think why those girls wanted to teach their parrots to say it too."

"The sentiment is admirable," said the King, "and I never mind how often I hear it. But I do get tired of hearing those parrots say, 'Pretty Polly.' "

"They say it in seven different languages," said the princesses.

"I dare say they do," said the King, "but it reminds me too much of my councillors. They say the same thing in seven different ways, and it never means anything in any way they say it."

The princesses, their characters as I have already said being naturally embittered, were vexed at this, and the parrots looked very glum indeed. But the Princess September ran through all the rooms of the palace, singing like a lark, while the little bird flew round and round her, singing like a nightingale, which indeed it was.

Things went on like this for several days, and then the eight princesses put their heads together. They went to September and sat down in a circle round her, hiding their feet as it is proper for Siamese princesses to do.

"My poor September," they said, "we are so sorry for the death of your beautiful parrot. It must be dreadful for you not to have a pet bird as we have. So we have put all our pocket money together, and we are going to buy you a lovely green and yellow parrot."

"Thank you for nothing," said September. (This was

not very civil of her, but Siamese princesses are sometimes a little short with one another.) "I have a pet bird which sings the most charming songs to me, and I don't know what on earth I should do with a green and yellow parrot."

January sniffed, then February sniffed, then March sniffed; in fact all the princesses sniffed, but in their proper order of precedence. When they had finished September asked them:

"Why do you sniff? Have you all got colds in the head?"

"Well, my dear," they said, "it's absurd to talk of *your* bird when the little fellow flies in and out just as he likes." They looked round the room and raised their eyebrows so high that their foreheads entirely disappeared.

"You'll get dreadful wrinkles," said September.

"Do you mind our asking where your bird is now?" they said.

"He's gone to pay a visit to his father-in-law," said the Princess September.

"And what makes you think he'll come back?" asked the princesses.

"He always does come back," said September.

"Well, my dear," said the eight princesses, "if you'll take our advice you won't run any risks like that. If he comes back, and mind you, if he does you'll be lucky, pop him into the cage and keep him there. That's the only way you can be sure of him."

"But I like to have him fly about the room," said the Princess September.

"Safety first," said her sisters ominously.

They got up and walked out of the room, shaking their heads, and they left September very uneasy. It seemed to her that her little bird was away a long time, and she could not think what he was doing. Something might have happened to him. What with hawks and men with snares you never knew what trouble he might get into. Besides, he might forget her, or he might take a fancy to somebody else, that would be dreadful; oh, she wished he were safely back again, and in the golden cage that stood there empty and ready. For when the Maids of Honour had buried the dead parrot they had left the cage in its old place.

Suddenly September heard a tweet-tweet just behind her ear, and she saw the little bird sitting on her shoulder. He had come in so quietly and alighted so softly that she had not heard him.

"I wondered what on earth had become of you," said the Princess.

"I thought you'd wonder that," said the little bird. "The fact is I very nearly didn't come back to-night at all. My father-in-law was giving a party, and they all wanted me to stay, but I thought you'd be anxious."

Under the circumstances this was a very unfortunate remark for the little bird to make.

September felt her heart go thump, thump against her chest, and she made up her mind to take no more risks. She put up her hand and took hold of the bird. This he was quite used to, she liked feeling his heart go pit-a-pat, so fast, in the hollow of her hand, and I think he liked the soft warmth of her little hand. So the bird suspected nothing, and he was so surprised when she carried him over to the cage, popped him in, and shut the door on him that for a moment he could think of nothing to say. But in a moment or two he hopped up on the ivory perch and said:

"What is the joke?"

"There's no joke," said September, "but some of Mamma's cats are prowling about to-night, and I think you're much safer in there."

"I can't think why the Queen wants to have all those cats," said the little bird, rather crossly.

"Well, you see, they're very special cats," said the Princess, "they have blue eyes and a kink in their tails, and they're a specialty of the Royal Family, if you understand what I mean."

"Perfectly," said the little bird, "but why did you put me in this cage without saying anything about it? I don't think it's the sort of place I like."

"I shouldn't have slept a wink all night if I hadn't known you were safe."

"Well, just for this once I don't mind," said the little bird, "so long as you let me out in the morning."

He ate a very good supper and then began to sing. But in the middle of his song he stopped.

"I don't know what is the matter with me," he said, "but I don't feel like singing to-night."

"Very well," said September, "go to sleep instead."

So he put his head under his wing and in a minute was fast asleep. September went to sleep too. But when the dawn broke she was awakened by the little bird calling her at the top of his voice.

"Wake up, wake up," he said. "Open the door of this cage and let me out. I want to have a good fly while the dew is still on the ground."

"You're much better off where you are," said September. "You have a beautiful golden cage. It was made by the best workman in my papa's kingdom, and my papa was so pleased with it that he cut off his head so that he should never make another."

"Let me out, let me out," said the little bird.

"You'll have three meals a day served by my Maids of Honour; you'll have nothing to worry you from morning till night, and you can sing to your heart's content."

"Let me out, let me out," said the little bird. And he tried to slip through the bars of the cage, but of course he couldn't, and he beat against the door, but of course he couldn't open it. Then the eight princesses came in, and looked at him. They told September she was very wise to take their advice. They said he would soon get used to the cage and in a few days would quite forget that he had ever been free. The little bird said nothing at all while they were there, but as soon as they were gone he began to cry again: "Let me out, let me out."

"Don't be such an old silly," said September. "I've only put you in the cage because I'm so fond of you. *I* know what's good for you much better than you do yourself. Sing me a little song and I'll give you a piece of brown sugar."

But the little bird stood in the corner of his cage, looking out at the blue sky, and never sang a note. He never sang all day.

"What's the good of sulking?" said September. "Why don't you sing and forget your troubles?"

"How can I sing?" answered the bird. "I want to see the trees and the lake and the green rice growing in the fields."

"If that's all you want I'll take you for a walk," said September.

She picked up the cage and went out, and she walked down to the lake round which grew the willow trees, and she stood at the edge of the rice fields that stretched as far as the eye could see.

"I'll take you out every day," she said. "I love you and I only want to make you happy."

"It's not the same thing," said the little bird. "The rice fields and the lake and the willow trees look quite different when you see them through the bars of a cage."

So she brought him home again and gave him his supper. But he wouldn't eat a thing. The Princess was a little anxious at this, and asked her sisters what they thought about it.

"You must be firm," they said.

"But if he won't eat he'll die," she answered.

"That would be very ungrateful of him," they said. "He must know that you're only thinking of his own good. If he's obstinate and dies it'll serve him right, and you'll be well rid of him."

September didn't see how that was going to do *her* very much good, but they were eight to one and all older than she, so she said nothing.

"Perhaps he'll have got used to his cage by to-morrow," she said.

And next day when she awoke she cried out good-morning in a cheerful voice. She got no answer. She jumped out of bed and ran to the cage. She gave a startled cry, for there the little bird lay, at the bottom, on his side, with his eyes closed, and he looked as if he were dead. She opened the door and putting her hand in lifted him out. She gave a sob of relief for she felt that his little heart was beating still.

"Wake up, wake up, little bird," she said.

She began to cry and her tears fell on the little bird. He

opened his eyes and felt that the bars of the cage were no longer round him.

"I cannot sing unless I'm free, and if I cannot sing I die," he said.

The Princess gave a great sob.

"Then take your freedom," she said. "I shut you in a golden cage because I loved you and wanted to have you all to myself. But I never knew it would kill you. Go. Fly away among the trees that are round the lake and fly over the green rice fields. I love you enough to let you be happy in your own way."

She threw open the window and gently placed the little bird on the sill. He shook himself a little.

"Come and go as you will, little bird," she said. "I will never put you in a cage any more."

"I will come because I love you, little princess," said the bird. "And I will sing you the loveliest songs I know. I shall go far away, but I shall always come back, and I shall never forget you." He gave himself another shake. "Good gracious me, how stiff I am," he said.

Then he opened his wings and flew right away into the blue. But the little princess burst into tears, for it is very difficult to put the happiness of someone you love before your own, and with her little bird far out of sight she felt on a sudden very lonely. When her sisters knew what had happened they mocked her and said that the little bird would never return. But he did at last. And he sat on September's shoulder and ate out of her hand and sang her the beautiful songs he had learned while he was flying up and down the fair places of the world. September kept her window open day and night so that the little bird might come into her room whenever he felt inclined, and this was very good for her; so she grew extremely beautiful. And when she was old enough she married the King of Cambodia and was carried all the way to the city in which he lived on a white elephant. But her sisters never slept with their windows open, so they grew extremely ugly as well as disagreeable, and when the time came to marry them off they were given away to the King's councillors with a pound of tea and a Siamese cat.

THE ALIEN CORN

I HAD known the Blands a long time before I discovered that they had any connection with Ferdy Rabenstein. Ferdy must have been nearly fifty when I first knew him, and at the time of which I write he was well over seventy. He had altered little. His hair, coarse but abundant and curly, was white, but he had kept his figure and held himself as gallantly as ever. It was not hard to believe that in youth he had been as beautiful as people said. He had still his fine Semitic profile and the lustrous black eyes that had caused havoc in so many a Gentile breast. He was very tall, lean, with an oval face and a clear skin. He wore his clothes very well, and in evening dress, even now, he was one of the handsomest men I had ever seen. He wore then large black pearls in his shirt front and platinum and sapphire rings on his fingers. Perhaps he was rather flashy, but you felt it was so much in character that it would have ill become him to be anything else.

"After all, I am an Oriental," he said. "I can carry a certain barbaric magnificence."

I have often thought that Ferdy Rabenstein would make an admirable subject for a biography. He was not a great man, but within the limits he set himself he made of his life a work of art. It was a masterpiece in little, like a Persian miniature, and derived its interest from its perfection. Unfortunately the materials are scanty. They would consist of letters that may very well have been destroyed and the recollections of people who are old now and will soon be dead. His memory is extraordinary, but he would never write his memoirs, for he looks upon his past as a source of purely private entertainment; and he is a man of the most perfect discretion. Nor do I know anyone who could do justice to the subject but Max Beerbohm. There is no one else in this hard world of to-day who can look upon the trivial with such tender sympathy and wring such a delicate pathos from futility. I wonder that Max, who must have known Ferdy much better than I, and long before, was never tempted to exercise his exquisite fancy on such a theme. He was born for Max to write about. And who should have illustrated the elegant book that I see in my mind's eye but Aubrey Beardsley? Thus would have been erected a monument of triple brass and the ephemera imprisoned to succeeding ages in the amber's exquisite translucency.

Ferdy's conquests were social and his venue was the great world. He was born in South Africa and did not come to England till he was twenty. For some time he was on the Stock Exchange, but on the death of his father he inherited a considerable fortune, and retiring from business devoted himself to the life of a man about town. At that period English society was still a closed body and it was not easy for a Jew to force its barriers, but to Ferdy they fell like the walls of Jericho. He was handsome, he was rich, he was a sportsman and he was good company. He had a house in Curzon Street, furnished with the most beautiful French furniture, and a French chef, and a brougham. It would be interesting to know the first steps in his wonderful career: they are lost in the dark abysm of time. When I first met him he had been long established as one of the smartest men in London: this was at a very grand house in Norfolk to which I had been asked as a promising young novelist by the hostess who took an interest in letters, but the company was very distinguished and I was overawed. We were sixteen, and I felt shy and alone among these cabinet ministers, great ladies and peers of the realm who talked of people and things of which I knew nothing. They were civil to me, but indifferent, and I was conscious that I was somewhat of a burden to my hostess. Ferdy saved me. He sat with me, walked with me and talked with me. He discovered that I was a writer and we discussed the drama and the novel; he

learnt that I had lived much on the continent and he talked
to me pleasantly of France, Germany and Spain. He seemed
really to seek my society. He gave me the flattering impression that he and I stood apart from the other members of
the company and by our conversation upon affairs of the
spirit made that of the rest of them, the political situation,
the scandal of somebody's divorce and the growing disinclination of pheasants to be killed, seem a little ridiculous.
But if Ferdy had at the bottom of his heart a feeling of ever
so faint a contempt for the hearty British gentry that surrounded us I am sure that it was only to me that he allowed
an inkling of it to appear, and looking back I cannot but
wonder whether it was not after all a suave and very delicate
compliment that he paid me. I think of course that he liked
to exercise his charm, and I daresay the obvious pleasure his
conversation gave me gratified him, but he could have had
no motive for taking so much trouble over an obscure novelist other than his real interest in art and letters. I felt that
he and I at bottom were equally alien in that company, I because I was a writer and he because he was a Jew, but I
envied the ease with which he bore himself. He was completely at home. Everyone called him Ferdy. He seemed to
be always in good spirits. He was never at a loss for a quip,
a jest or a repartee. They liked him in that house because he
made them laugh but never made them uncomfortable by
talking above their heads. He brought a faint savour of
Oriental romance into their lives, but so cleverly that they
only felt more English. You could never be dull when he
was by and with him present you were safe from the fear of
the devastating silences that sometimes overwhelm a British
company. A pause looked inevitable and Ferdy Rabenstein
had broken into a topic that interested everyone. An invaluable asset to any party. He had an inexhaustible fund of
Jewish stories. He was a very good mimic and he assumed
the Yiddish accent and reproduced the Jewish gestures to
perfection; his head sank into his body, his face grew cunning, his voice oily, and he was a rabbi or an old-clothes
merchant or a smart commercial traveller or a fat procuress
in Frankfort. It was as good as a play. Because he was him-

self a Jew and insisted on it you laughed without reserve, but for my own part not without an undercurrent of discomfort. I was not quite sure of a sense of humour that made such cruel fun of his own race. I discovered afterwards that Jewish stories were his speciality, and I seldom met him anywhere without hearing him tell sooner or later the last he had heard.

But the best story he told me on this occasion was not a Jewish one. It struck me so that I have never forgotten it, but for one reason or another I have never had occasion to tell it again. I give it here because it is a curious little incident concerning persons whose names at least will live in the social history of the Victorian Era and I think it would be a pity if it were lost. He told me then that once when quite a young man he was staying in the country in a house where Mrs. Langtry, at that time at the height of her beauty and astounding reputation, was also a guest. It happened to be within driving distance of that in which lived the Duchess of Somerset, who had been Queen of Beauty at the Eglinton Tournament, and knowing her slightly, it occurred to him that it would be interesting to bring the two women together. He suggested it to Mrs. Langtry, who was willing, and forthwith wrote to the Duchess asking if he might bring the celebrated beauty to call on her. It was fitting, he said, that the loveliest woman of this generation (this was in the eighties) should pay her respects to the loveliest woman of the last. "Bring her by all means," answered the Duchess, "but I warn you that it will be a shock to her." They drove over in a carriage and pair, Mrs. Langtry in a close-fitting blue bonnet with long satin strings, which showed the exquisite shape of her head and made her blue eyes even bluer, and were received by a little ugly old hag who looked with irony out of her beady eyes at the radiant beauty who had come to see her. They had tea, they talked and they drove home again. Mrs. Langtry was very silent and when Ferdy looked at her he saw that she was quietly weeping. When they got back to the house she went to her room and would not come down to dinner that night. For the first time she had realized that beauty dies.

Ferdy asked me for my address and a few days after I got back to London invited me to dinner. There were only six of us, an American woman married to an English peer, a Swedish painter, an actress and a well-known critic. We ate very good food and drank excellent wine. The conversation was easy and intelligent. After dinner Ferdy was persuaded to play the piano. He only played Viennese waltzes—I discovered later that they were his speciality—and the light, tuneful and sensual music seemed to accord well with his discreet flamboyance. He played without affectation, with a lilt, and he had a graceful touch. This was the first of a good many dinners I had with him; he would ask me two or three times a year, and as time passed I met him more and more frequently at other people's houses. I rose in the world and perhaps he came down a little. Of late years I had sometimes found him at parties where other Jews were, and I fancied that I read in his shining liquid eyes, resting for a moment on these members of his race, a certain good-natured amusement at the thought of what the world was coming to. There were people who said he was a snob, but I do not think he was; it just happened that in his early days he had never met any but the great. He had a real passion for art, and in his commerce with those that produced it was at his best. With them he had never that faint air of persiflage which when he was with very grand persons made you suspect that he was never quite the dupe of their grandeur. His taste was exquisite and many of his friends were glad to avail themselves of his knowledge. He was one of the first to value old furniture, and he rescued many an exquisite piece from the attics of ancestral mansions and gave it an honourable place in the drawing-room. It amused him to saunter round the auction rooms, and he was always willing to give his advice to great ladies who desired at once to acquire a beautiful thing and make a profitable investment. He was rich and good-natured. He liked to patronize the arts and would take a great deal of trouble to get commissions for some young painter whose talent he admired or an engagement to play at a rich man's house for a violinist who could in no other way get a hearing. But he never let his rich man down. His taste was too good to deceive, and civil though he might be to the mediocre he would not lift a finger to help them. His own musical parties, very small and carefully chosen, were a treat.

He never married.

"I am a man of the world," he said, "and I flatter myself that I have no prejudices, *tous les goûts sont dans la nature,* but I do not think I could bring myself to marry a Gentile. There's no harm in going to the opera in a dinner-jacket, but it just would never occur to me to do so."

"Then why didn't you marry a Jewess?"

(I did not hear this conversation, but the lively and audacious creature who thus tackled him told me of it.)

"Oh, my dear, our women are so prolific. I could not bear the thought of peopling the world with a little Ikey and a little Jacob and a little Rebecca and a little Leah and a little Rachel."

But he had had affairs of note and the glamour of past romance still clung to him. He was in his youth of an amorous complexion. I have met old ladies who told me that he was irresistible, and when in reminiscent mood they talked to me of this woman and that who had completely lost her head over him, I divined that, such was his beauty, they could not find it in their hearts to blame them. It was interesting to hear of great ladies that I had read of in the memoirs of the day or had met as respectable dowagers garrulous over their grandsons at Eton or making a mess of a hand at bridge and bethink myself that they had been consumed with sinful passion for the handsome Jew. Ferdy's most notorious amour was with the Duchess of Hereford, the loveliest, the most gallant and dashing of the beauties of the end of Queen Victoria's reign. It lasted for twenty years. He had doubtless flirtations meanwhile, but their relations were stable and recognized. It was proof of his marvellous tact that when at last they ended he exchanged an aging mistress for a loyal friend. I remember meeting the pair not so very long ago at luncheon. She was an old woman, tall and of a commanding presence, but with a mask of paint on a ravaged face. We were lunching at the Carlton and Ferdy, our host, came a few minutes late. He offered us a cocktail and the Duchess told him we had already had one.

"Ah, I wondered why your eyes were so doubly bright," he said.

The old raddled woman flushed with pleasure.

My youth passed, I grew middle-aged, I wondered how soon I must begin to describe myself as elderly; I wrote books and plays, I travelled, I underwent experiences, I fell in love and out of it; and still I kept meeting Ferdy at parties. War broke out and was waged, millions of men were killed and the face of the world was changed. Ferdy did not like the war. He was too old to take part in it, and his German name was awkward, but he was discreet and took care not to expose himself to humiliation. His old friends were faithful to him, and he lived in a dignified but not too strict seclusion. But then peace came and with courage he set himself to making the best of changed conditions. Society was mixed now, parties were rowdy, but Ferdy fitted himself to the new life. He still told his funny Jewish stories, he still played charmingly the waltzes of Strauss, he still went round auction rooms and told the new rich what they ought to buy. I went to live abroad, but whenever I was in London I saw Ferdy, and now there was something a little uncanny in him. He did not give in. He had never known a day's illness. He seemed never to grow tired. He still dressed beautifully. He was interested in everybody. His mind was alert and people asked him to dinner, not for old times' sake, but because he was worth his salt. He still gave charming little concerts at his house in Curzon Street.

It was when he invited me to one of these that I made the discovery that started the recollections of him I have here set down. We were dining at a house in Hill Street, a large party, and the women having gone upstairs Ferdy and I found ourselves side by side. He told me that Lea Makart was coming to play for him on the following Friday evening and he would be glad if I would come.

"I'm awfully sorry," I said, "but I'm going down to the Blands."

"What Blands?"

"They live in Sussex at a place called Tilby."

"I didn't know you knew them."

He looked at me rather strangely. He smiled. I didn't know what amused him.

"Oh, yes, I've known them for years. It's a very nice house to stay at."

"Adolph is my nephew."

"Sir Adolphus?"

"It suggests one of the bucks of the Regency, doesn't it? But I will not conceal from you that he was named Adolph."

"Everyone I know calls him Freddy."

"I know, and I understand that Miriam, his wife, only answers to the name of Muriel."

"How does he happen to be your nephew?"

"Because Hannah Rabenstein, my sister, married Alphonse Bleikogel, who ended life as Sir Alfred Bland, first baronet and Adolph, their only son, in due course became Sir Adolphus Bland, second baronet."

"Then Freddy Bland's mother, the Lady Bland who lives in Portland Place, is your sister?"

"Yes, my sister Hannah. She was the eldest of the family. She's eighty, but in full possession of her faculties and a remarkable woman."

"I've never met her."

"I think your friends the Blands would just as soon you didn't. She has never lost her German accent."

"Do you never see them?" I asked.

"I haven't spoken to them for twenty years. I am such a Jew and they are so English." He smiled. "I could never remember that their names were Freddy and Muriel. I used to come out with an Adolph or a Miriam at awkward moments. And they didn't like my stories. It was better that we should not meet. When the war broke out and I would not change my name it was the last straw. It was too late. I could never have accustomed my friends to think of me as anything but Ferdy Rabenstein. I was quite content. I was not ambitious to be a Smith, a Brown, or a Robinson."

Though he spoke facetiously, there was in his tone the

faintest possible derision and I felt, hardly felt even, the
sensation was so shadowy, that, as it had often vaguely
seemed to me before, there was in the depth of his impenetrable heart a cynical contempt for the Gentiles he had conquered.

"Then you don't know the two boys?" I said.

"No."

"The eldest is called George, you know. I don't think he's
so clever as Harry, the other one, but he's an engaging
youth. I think you'd like him."

"Where is he now?"

"Well, he's just been sent down from Oxford. I suppose
he's at home. Harry's still at Eton."

"Why don't you bring George to lunch with me?"

"I'll ask him. I should think he'd love to come."

"It has reached my ears that he's been a little troublesome."

"Oh, I don't know. He wouldn't go into the army, which
is what they wanted. They rather fancied the Guards. And
so he went to Oxford instead. He didn't work and he spent
a great deal of money and he painted the town red. It was
all quite normal."

"What was he sent down for?"

"I don't know. Nothing of any consequence."

At that moment our host rose and we went upstairs.
When Ferdy bade me good-night he asked me not to forget
about his great-nephew.

"Ring me up," he said. "Wednesday would suit me. Or
Friday."

Next day I went down to Tilby. It was an Elizabethan
mansion standing in a spacious park, in which roamed fallow deer, and from its windows you had wide views of rolling downs. It seemed to me that as far as the eye could reach
the land belonged to the Blands. His tenants must have
found Sir Adolphus a wonderful landlord, for I never saw
farms kept in such order, the barns and cow-sheds were spick
and span and the pig-sties were a picture; the public-houses
looked like old English water-colours and the cottages he

had built on the estate combined admirably picturesqueness and convenience. It must have cost him a pot of money to run the place on these lines. Fortunately he had it. The park with its grand old trees (and its nine-hole golf course) was tended like a garden, and the wide-stretching gardens were the pride of the neighbourhood. The magnificent house, with its steep roofs and mullioned windows, had been restored by the most celebrated architect in England and furnished by Lady Bland, with taste and knowledge, in a style that perfectly fitted it.

"Of course it's very simple," she said. "Just an English house in the country."

The dining-room was adorned with old English sporting pictures, and the Chippendale chairs were of incredible value. In the drawing-room were portraits by Reynolds and Gainsborough and landscapes by Old Crome and Richard Wilson. Even in my bedroom with its four-post bed were water-colours by Birket Foster. It was very beautiful and a treat to stay there, but though it would have distressed Muriel Bland beyond anything to know it, it missed oddly enough entirely the effect she had sought. It did not give you for a moment the impression of an English house. You had the feeling that every object had been bought with a careful eye to the general scheme. You missed the dull Academy portraits that hung in the dining-room beside a Carlo Dolci that an ancestor had brought back from the grand tour, and the water-colours painted by a great-aunt that cluttered up the drawing-room so engagingly. There was no ugly Victorian sofa that had always been there and that it never occurred to anybody to take away, and no needlework chairs that an unmarried daughter had so painstakingly worked at about the time of the Great Exhibition. There was beauty but no sentiment.

And yet how comfortable it was and how well looked after you were! And what a cordial greeting the Blands gave you! They seemed really to like people. They were generous and kindly. They were never happier than when they were entertaining the county, and though they had not owned the property for more than twenty years they had established themselves firmly in the favour of their neighbours. Except perhaps in their splendour and the competent way in which the estate was run there was nothing to suggest that they had not been settled there for centuries.

Freddy had been at Eton and Oxford. He was now in the early fifties. He was quiet in manner, courtly, very clever, I imagine, but a trifle reserved. He had great elegance, but it was not an English elegance; he had grey hair and a short pointed grey beard, fine dark eyes and an aquiline nose. He was just above middle-height; I don't think you would have taken him for a Jew, but rather for a foreign diplomat of some distinction. He was a man of character, but gave you, strangely enough, notwithstanding the success he had had in life, an impression of faint melancholy. His successes had been financial and political; in the world of sport, for all his perseverance, he had never shone. For many years he had followed hounds, but he was a bad rider and I think it must have been a relief to him when he could persuade himself that middle-age and pressure of business forced him to give up hunting. He had excellent shooting and gave grand parties for it, but he was a poor shot; and despite the course in his park he never succeeded in being more than an indifferent golfer. He knew only too well how much these things meant in England, and his incapacity was a bitter disappointment to him. However, George would make up for it.

George was scratch at golf, and though tennis was not his game he played much better than the average; the Blands had had him taught to shoot as soon as he was old enough to hold a gun, and he was a fine shot; they had put him on a pony when he was two, and Freddy, watching him mount his horse, knew that out hunting when the boy came to a fence he felt exhilaration and not that sickening feeling in the pit of his stomach which, though he had chased the fox with such grim determination, had always made the sport a torture to him. George was so tall and slim, his curly hair, of a palish brown, was so fine, his eyes were so blue, he was the perfect type of the young Englishman. He had the engaging candour of the breed. His nose was straight, though perhaps a trifle fleshy, and his lips were perhaps a little full and sensual, but he had beautiful teeth, and his smooth skin was like ivory. George was the apple of his father's eye. He did not like Harry, his second son, so well. He was rather stocky, broad-shouldered and strong for his age, but his black eyes, shining with cleverness, his coarse dark hair and his big nose revealed his race. Freddy was severe with him, and often impatient, but with George he was all indulgence. Harry would go into the business, he had brains and push, but George was the heir. George would be an English gentleman.

George had offered to motor me down in the roadster his father had given him as a birthday present. He drove very fast and we arrived before the rest of the guests. The Blands were sitting on the lawn and tea was laid out under a magnificent cedar.

"By the way," I said presently, "I saw Ferdy Rabenstein the other day and he wants me to bring George to lunch with him."

I had not mentioned the invitation to George on the way because I thought that if there had been a family coldness I had better address his parents as well.

"Who in God's name is Ferdy Rabenstein?" said George.

How brief is human glory! A generation back such a question would have seemed grotesque.

"He's by way of being your great-uncle," I replied.

A glance had passed from father to mother when I first spoke.

"He's a horrid old man," said Muriel.

"I don't think it's in the least necessary for George to resume relationships that were definitely severed before he was born," said Freddy with decision.

"Anyhow I've delivered the message," said I, feeling somewhat snubbed.

"I don't want to see the old blighter," said George.

The conversation was broken off by the arrival of other guests, and in a little while George went off to play golf with one of his Oxford friends.

It was not till next day that the matter was referred to again. I had played an indifferent round with Freddy Bland in the morning, and several sets of what is known as country-house tennis in the afternoon, and was sitting alone with Muriel on the terrace. In England we have so much bad weather that it is only fair that a beautiful day should be more beautiful than anywhere in the world, and this June evening was perfect. The blue sky was cloudless and the air was balmy; before us stretched green rolling downs, and woods, and in the distance you saw the red roofs of a little village and the grey tower of the village church. It was a day when to be alive was sufficient happiness. Detached lines of poetry hovered vaguely in my memory. Muriel and I had been chatting desultorily.

"I hope you didn't think it rather horrid of us to refuse to let George lunch with Ferdy," she said suddenly. "He's such a fearful snob, isn't he?"

"D'you think so? He's always been very nice to me."

"We haven't been on speaking terms for twenty years. Freddy never forgave him for his behaviour during the war. So unpatriotic, I thought, and one really must draw the line somewhere. You know, he absolutely refused to drop his horrible German name. With Freddy in Parliament and running munitions and all that sort of thing it was quite impossible. I don't know why he should want to see George. He can't mean anything to him."

"He's an old man. George and Harry are his great-nephews. He must leave his money to some one."

"We'd rather not have his money," said Muriel coldly.

Of course I didn't care a row of pins whether George went to lunch with Ferdy Rabenstein, and I was quite willing to let the matter drop, but evidently the Blands had talked it over and Muriel felt that some explanation was due to me.

"Of course you know that Freddy has Jewish blood in him," she said.

She looked at me sharply. Muriel was rather a big blonde woman and she spent a great deal of time trying to keep down the corpulence to which she was predisposed. She had been very pretty when young and even now was a comely person; but her round blue eyes, slightly prominent, her fleshy nose, the shape of her face and the back of her neck, her exuberant manner, betrayed her race. No Englishwoman, however fair-haired, ever looked like that. And yet her observation was designed to make me take it for granted that she was a Gentile. I answered discreetly.

"So many people have nowadays."

"I know. But there's no reason to dwell on it, is there? After all, we're absolutely English; no one could be more English than George, in appearance and manner and everything; I mean, he's such a fine sportsman and all that sort of thing, I can't see any object in his knowing Jews just because they happen to be distant connections of his."

"It's very difficult in England now not to know Jews, isn't it?"

"Oh, I know, in London one does meet a good many, and I think some of them are very nice. They're so artistic. I don't go so far as to say that Freddy and I deliberately avoid them—of course I wouldn't do that—but it just happens that we don't really know any of them very well. And down here, there simply aren't any to know."

I could not but admire the convincing manner in which she spoke. It would not have surprised me to be told that she really believed every word she said.

"You say that Ferdy might leave George his money. Well, I don't believe it's so very much anyway; it was quite a comfortable fortune before the war, but that's nothing nowadays. Besides, we're hoping that George will go in for politics when he's a little older, and I don't think it would do him any good in the constituency to inherit money from a Mr. Rabenstein."

"Is George interested in politics?" I asked, to change the conversation.

"Oh, I do hope so. After all, there's the family constituency waiting for him. It's a safe Conservative seat and one can't expect Freddy to go on with the grind of the House of Commons indefinitely."

Muriel was grand. She talked already of the constituency as though twenty generations of Blands had sat for it. Her remark, however, was my first intimation that Freddy's ambition was not satisfied.

"I suppose Freddy would go to the House of Lords when George was old enough to stand."

"We've done a good deal for the party," said Muriel.

Muriel was a Catholic and she often told you that she had been educated in a convent—"Such sweet women, those nuns. I always said that if I had a daughter I should have sent her to a convent too"—but she liked her servants to be Church of England, and on Sunday evenings we had what was called supper because the fish was cold and there was ice cream, so that they could go to church, and we were waited on by two footmen instead of four. It was still light when we finished, and Freddy and I, smoking our cigars, walked up and down the terrace in the gloaming. I suppose Muriel had told him of her conversation with me, and it may be that his refusal to let George see his great-uncle still troubled him, but being subtler than she he attacked the question more indirectly. He told me that he had been very much worried about George. It had been a great disappointment that he had refused to go into the army.

"I should have thought he'd have loved the life," he said.

"And he would certainly have looked marvellous in his Guards' uniform."

"He would, wouldn't he?" returned Freddy, ingenuously. "I wonder he could resist that."

He had been completely idle at Oxford; although his father had given him a very large allowance, he had got monstrously into debt; and now he had been sent down. But though he spoke so tartly I could see that he was not a little proud of his scapegrace son, he loved him with, oh, such an un-English love, and in his heart it flattered him that George had cut such a dash.

"Why should you worry?" I said. "You don't really care if George has a degree or not."

Freddy chuckled.

"No, I don't suppose I do really. I always think the only important thing about Oxford is that people know you were there, and I daresay that George isn't any wilder than the other young men in his set. It's the future I'm thinking of.

He's so damned idle. He doesn't seem to want to do anything but have a good time."

"He's young, you know."

"He's not interested in politics, and though he's so good at games he's not even very keen on sport. He seems to spend most of his time strumming the piano."

"That's a harmless amusement."

"Oh, yes, I don't mind that, but he can't go on loafing indefinitely. You see, all this will be his one day." Freddy gave a sweeping gesture that seemed to embrace the whole county, but I knew that he did not own it all yet. "I'm very anxious that he should be fit to assume his responsibilities. His mother is very ambitious for him, but I only want him to be an English gentleman."

Freddy gave me a sidelong glance as though he wanted to say something but hesitated in case I thought it ridiculous; but there is one advantage in being a writer, that, since people look upon you as of no account, they will often say things to you that they would not to their equals. He thought he would risk it.

"You know, I've got an idea that nowhere in the world now is the Greek ideal of life so perfectly cultivated as by the English country gentleman living on his estates. I think his life has the beauty of a work of art."

I could not but smile when I reflected that it was impossible for the English country gentleman in these days to do anything of the sort without a packet of money safely invested in American bonds, but I smiled with sympathy. I thought it rather touching that this Jewish financier should cherish so romantic a dream.

"I want him to be a good landlord. I want him to take his part in the affairs of the country. I want him to be a thorough sportsman."

"Poor mutt," I thought, but said: "Well, what are your plans for George now?"

"I think he has a fancy for the diplomatic service. He's suggested going to Germany to learn the language."

"A very good idea, I should have thought."

"For some reason he's got it into his head that he wants to go to Munich."

"A nice place."

Next day I went back to London and shortly after my arrival rang up Ferdy.

"I'm sorry, but George isn't able to come to lunch on Wednesday."

"What about Friday?"

"Friday's no good either." I thought it useless to beat about the bush. "The fact is, his people aren't keen on his lunching with you."

There was a moment's silence. Then:

"I see. Well, will you come on Wednesday anyway?"

"Yes, I'd like to," I answered.

So on Wednesday at half-past one I strolled round to Curzon Street. Ferdy received me with the somewhat elaborate graciousness that he cultivated. He made no reference to the Blands. We sat in the drawing-room and I could not help reflecting what an eye for beautiful objects that family had. The room was more crowded than the fashion of to-day approves and the gold snuff-boxes in vitrines, the French china, appealed to a taste that was not mine; but they were no doubt choice pieces; and the Louis XV suite, with its beautiful *petit point,* must have been worth an enormous lot of money. The pictures on the walls by Lancret, Pater and Watteau did not greatly interest me, but I recognized their intrinsic excellence. It was a proper setting for this aged man of the world. It fitted his period. Suddenly the door opened and George was announced. Ferdy saw my surprise and gave me a little smile of triumph.

"I'm very glad you were able to come after all," he said as he shook George's hand.

I saw him in a glance take in his great-nephew whom he saw to-day for the first time. George was very elegantly dressed. He wore a short black coat, striped trousers and the grey double-breasted waistcoat which at that time was the mode. You could only wear it with elegance if you were tall and thin and your belly was slightly concave. I felt sure that Ferdy knew exactly who George's tailor was and what haberdasher he went to, and approved of them. George, so smart and trim, wearing his clothes so beautifully, certainly looked very handsome. We went down to luncheon. Ferdy had the social graces at his fingers' ends and he put the boy at his ease, but I saw that he was carefully appraising him; then, I do not know why, he began to tell some of his Jewish stories. He told them with gusto and with his wonderful mimicry. I saw George flush, and though he laughed at them, I could see that it was with embarrassment. I wondered what on earth had induced Ferdy to be so tactless. But he was watching George and he told story after story. It looked as though he would never stop. I wondered if for some reason I could not grasp he was taking a malicious pleasure in the boy's obvious discomfiture. At last we went upstairs, and to make things easier I asked Ferdy to play the piano. He played us three or four little waltzes. He had lost none of his exquisite lightness nor his sense of their lilting rhythm. Then he turned to George.

"Do you play?" he asked him.

"A little."

"Won't you play something?"

"I'm afraid I only play classical music. I don't think it would interest you."

Ferdy smiled slightly, but did not insist. I said it was time for me to go and George accompanied me.

"What a filthy old Jew," he said as soon as we were in the street. "I hated those stories of his."

"They're his great stunt. He always tells them."

"Would you if you were a Jew?"

I shrugged my shoulders.

"How is it you came to lunch after all?" I asked George.

He chuckled. He was a light-hearted creature, with a sense of humour, and he shook off the slight irritation his great-uncle had caused him.

"He went to see Granny. You don't know Granny, do you?"

"No."

"She treats Daddy like a kid in Etons. Granny said I was to go to lunch with great-uncle Ferdy, and what Granny says goes."

"I see."

A week or two later George went to Munich to learn German. I happened then to go on a journey, and it was not till the following spring that I was again in London. Soon after my arrival I found myself sitting next to Muriel Bland at dinner. I asked after George.

"He's still in Germany," she said.

"I see in the papers that you're going to have a great beano at Tilby for his coming of age."

"We're going to entertain the tenants and they're making George a presentation."

She was less exuberant than usual, but I did not pay much attention to the fact. She led a strenuous life and it might be that she was tired. I knew she liked to talk of her son, so I continued.

"I suppose George has been having a grand time in Germany," I said.

She did not answer for a moment and I gave her a glance. I was surprised to see that her eyes were filled with tears.

"I'm afraid George has gone mad," she said.

"What *do* you mean?"

"We've been so frightfully worried. Freddy's so angry, he won't even discuss it. I don't know what we're going to do."

Of course it immediately occurred to me that George, who, I supposed, like most young Englishmen sent to learn the language, had been put with a German family, had fallen in love with the daughter of the house and wanted to marry her. I had a pretty strong suspicion that the Blands were intent on his making a very grand marriage.

"Why, what's happened?" I asked.

"He wants to become a pianist."

"A what?"

"A professional pianist."

"What on earth put that idea in his head?"

"Heaven knows. We didn't know anything about it. We thought he was working for his exam. I went out to see him. I thought I'd like to know that he was getting on all right. Oh, my dear. He looks like nothing on earth. And he used to be so smart; I could have cried. He told me he wasn't going in for the exam and had never had any intention of doing so; he'd only suggested the diplomatic service so that we'd let him go to Germany and he'd be able to study music."

"But has he any talent?"

"Oh, that's neither here nor there. Even if he had the genius of Paderewski we couldn't have George traipsing around the country playing at concerts. No one can deny that I'm very artistic, and so is Freddy—we love music and we've always known a lot of artists—but George will have a very great position; it's out of the question. We've set our hearts on his going into Parliament. He'll be very rich one day. There's nothing he can't aspire to."

"Did you point all that out to him?"

"Of course I did. He laughed at me. I told him he'd break his father's heart. He said his father could always fall back on Harry. Of course I'm devoted to Harry, and he's as clever as a monkey, but it was always understood that he was to go into the business; even though I am his mother I can see that he hasn't got the advantages that George has. Do you know what he said to me? He said that if his father would settle five pounds a week on him he would resign everything in Harry's favour and Harry could be his father's heir and succeed to the baronetcy and everything. It's too ridiculous. He said that if the Crown Prince of Roumania could abdicate a throne he didn't see why he couldn't abdicate a baronetcy. But you can't do that. Nothing can prevent him from being third baronet and, if Freddy should be granted a peerage, from succeeding to it at Freddy's death. Do you know, he even wants to drop the name of Bland and take some horrible German name."

I could not help asking what.

"Bleikogel or something like that," she answered.

That was a name I recognized. I remembered Ferdy telling me that Hannah Rabenstein had married Alphonse

Bleikogel, who became eventually Sir Alfred Bland, first baronet. It was all very strange. I wondered what had happened to the charming and so typically English boy whom I had seen only a few months before.

"Of course when I came home and told Freddy he was furious. I've never seen him so angry. He foamed at the mouth. He wired to George to come back immediately, and George wired back to say he couldn't on account of his work."

"Is he working?"

"From morning till night. That's the maddening part of it. He never did a stroke of work in his life. Freddy used to say he was born idle."

"H'm."

"Then Freddy wired to say that if he didn't come he'd stop his allowance, and George wired back: 'Stop it.' That put the lid on. You don't know what Freddy can be when his back is up."

I knew that Freddy had inherited a large fortune, but I knew also that he had immensely increased it, and I could well imagine that behind the courteous and amiable Squire of Tilby there was a ruthless man of affairs. He had been used to having his own way, and I could believe that when crossed he would be hard and cruel.

"We'd been making George a very handsome allowance, but you know how frightfully extravagant he was. We didn't think he'd be able to hold out long, and in point of fact within a month he wrote to Ferdy and asked him to lend him a hundred pounds. Ferdy went to my mother-in-law——she's his sister, you know——and asked her what it meant. Though they hadn't spoken for twenty years Freddy went to see him and begged him not to send George a penny, and he promised he wouldn't. I don't know how George has been making both ends meet. I'm sure Freddy's right, but I can't help being rather worried. If I hadn't given Freddy my word of honour that I wouldn't send him anything I think I'd have slipped a few notes in a letter in case of accident. I mean, it's awful to think that perhaps he hasn't got enough to eat."

"It'll do him no harm to go short for a bit."

"We were in an awful hole, you know. We'd made all sorts of preparations for his coming of age, and I'd issued hundreds of invitations. Suddenly George said he wouldn't come. I was simply frantic. I wrote and wired. I would have gone over to Germany, only Freddy wouldn't let me. I practically went down on my bended knees to George. I begged him not to put us in such a humiliating position. I mean, it's the sort of thing it's so difficult to explain. Then my mother-in-law stepped in. You don't know her, do you? She's an extraordinary old woman. You'd never think she was Freddy's mother. She was German originally but of very good family."

"Oh?"

"To tell you the truth I'm rather frightened of her. She tackled Freddy and then she wrote to George herself. She said that if he'd come home for his twenty-first birthday she'd pay any debts he had in Munich and we'd all give a patient hearing to anything he had to say. He agreed to that and we're expecting him one day next week. But I'm not looking forward to it I can tell you."

She gave a deep sigh. When we were walking upstairs after dinner Freddy addressed me.

"I see Muriel has been telling you about George. The damned fool! I have no patience with him. Fancy wanting to be a pianist! It's so ungentlemanly."

"He's very young, you know," I said soothingly.

"He's had things too easy for him. I've been much too indulgent. There's never been a thing he wanted that I haven't given him. I'll learn him."

The Blands had a discreet apprehension of the uses of advertisement, and I gathered from the papers that the celebrations at Tilby of George's twenty-first birthday were conducted in accordance with the usage of English county families. There were a dinner party and a ball for the gentry and a collation and a dance in marquees on the lawn for the tenants. Expensive bands were brought down from London. In the illustrated papers were pictures of George, surrounded by his family, being presented with a solid silver tea set by the tenantry. They had subscribed to have his portrait painted, but since his absence from the country had made it impossible for him to sit, the tea service had been substituted. I read in the columns of the gossip writers that his father had given him a hunter, his mother a gramophone that changed its own records, his grandmother the dowager Lady Bland an Encyclopædia Britannica and his great-uncle Ferdinand Rabenstein a Virgin and Child by Pellegrino da Modena. I could not help observing that these gifts were bulky and not readily convertible into cash. From Ferdy's presence at the festivities I concluded that George's unaccountable vagary had effected a reconciliation between uncle and nephew. I was right. Ferdy did not at all like the notion of his great-nephew becoming a professional pianist. At the first hint of danger to its prestige the family drew together and a united front was presented to oppose George's designs. Since I was not there I only know from hearsay what happened when the birthday celebrations were over. Ferdy told me something and so did Muriel, and later George gave me his version. The Blands had very much the impression that when George came home and found himself occupying the centre of the stage, when, surrounded by splendour, he saw for himself once more how much it meant to be the heir of a great estate, he would weaken. They surrounded him with love. They flattered him. They hung on his words. They counted on the goodness of his heart and thought that if they were very kind to him he would not have the courage to cause them pain. They seemed to take it for granted that he had no intention of going back to Germany, and in conversation included him in all their plans. George did not say very much. He seemed to be enjoying himself. He did not open a piano. Things looked as though they were going very well. Peace descended on the troubled house. Then one day at luncheon when they were discussing a garden party to which they had all been asked for one day of the following week, George said pleasantly:

"Don't count on me. I shan't be here."

"Oh, George, why not?" asked his mother.

"I must get back to my work. I'm leaving for Munich on Monday."

There was an awful pause. Everyone looked for something to say, but was afraid of saying the wrong thing, and at last it seemed impossible to break it. Luncheon was finished in silence. Then George went into the garden and the others, old Lady Bland and Ferdy, Muriel and Sir Adolphus, into the morning-room. There was a family council. Muriel wept. Freddy flew into a temper. Presently from the drawing-room they heard the sound of someone playing a nocturne of Chopin. It was George. It was as though, now he had announced his decision, he had gone for comfort, rest and strength to the instrument he loved. Freddy sprang to his feet.

"Stop that noise," he cried. "I won't have him play the piano in my house."

Muriel rang for a servant and gave him a message.

"Will you tell Mr. Bland that her ladyship has a bad headache and would he mind not playing the piano."

Ferdy, the man of the world, was deputed to have a talk with George. He was authorized to make him certain promises if he would give up the idea of becoming a pianist. If he did not wish to go into the diplomatic service his father would not insist, but if he would stand for Parliament he was prepared to pay his election expenses, give him a flat in London and make him an allowance of five thousand a year. I must say it was a handsome offer. I do not know what Ferdy said to the boy. I suppose he painted to him the life that a young man could lead in London on such an income. I am sure he made it very alluring. It availed nothing. All George asked was five pounds a week to be able to continue his studies and to be left alone. He was indifferent to the position that he might some day enjoy. He didn't want to hunt. He didn't want to shoot. He didn't want to be a Member of Parliament. He didn't want to be a millionaire. He didn't want to be a baronet. He didn't want to be a peer. Ferdy left him, defeated and in a state of considerable exasperation.

After dinner that evening there was a battle royal. Freddy was a quick-tempered man, unused to opposition, and he gave George the rough side of his tongue. I gather that it was very rough indeed. The women who sought to restrain his violence were sternly silenced. Perhaps for the first time in his life Freddy would not listen to his mother. George was obstinate and sullen. He had made up his mind and if his father didn't like it he could lump it. Freddy was peremptory. He forbade George to go back to Germany. George answered that he was twenty-one and his own master. He would go where he chose. Freddy swore he would not give him a penny.

"All right, I'll earn money."

"You! You've never done a stroke of work in your life. What do you expect to do to earn money?"

"Sell old clothes," grinned George.

There was a gasp from all of them. Muriel was so taken aback that she said a stupid thing.

"Like a Jew?"

"Well, aren't I a Jew? And aren't you a Jewess and isn't Daddy a Jew? We're all Jews, the whole gang of us, and everyone knows it and what the hell's the good of pretending we're not?"

Then a very dreadful thing happened. Freddy burst suddenly into tears. I'm afraid he didn't behave very much like Sir Adolphus Bland, Bart., M.P., and the good old English gentleman he so much wanted to be, but like an emotional Adolph Bleikogel who loved his son and wept with mortification because the great hopes he had set on him were brought to nothing and the ambition of his life was frustrated. He cried noisily with great loud sobs and pulled his beard and beat his breast and rocked to and fro. Then they all began to cry, old Lady Bland and Muriel, and Ferdy, who sniffed and blew his nose and wiped the tears streaming down his face, and even George cried. Of course it was very painful, but to our rough Anglo-Saxon temperament I am afraid it must seem also a trifle ridiculous. No one tried to console anybody else. They just sobbed and sobbed. It broke up the party.

But it had no result on the situation. George remained obdurate. His father would not speak to him. There were more scenes. Muriel sought to excite his pity; he was deaf to her piteous entreaties, he did not seem to mind if he broke her heart, he did not care two hoots if he killed his father. Ferdy appealed to him as a sportsman and a man of the world. George was flippant and indeed personally offensive. Old Lady Bland with her guttural German accent and strong common sense argued with him, but he would not listen to reason. It was she, however, who at last found a way out. She made George acknowledge that it was no use to throw away all the beautiful things the world laid at his feet unless he had talent. Of course he thought he had, but he might be mistaken. It was not worth while to be a second-rate pianist. His only excuse, his only justification, was genius. If he had genius his family had no right to stand in his way.

"You can't expect me to show genius already," said George. "I shall have to work for years."

"Are you sure you are prepared for that?"

"It's my only wish in the world. I'll work like a dog. I only want to be given my chance."

This was the proposition she made. His father was determined to give him nothing, and obviously they could not let the boy starve. He had mentioned five pounds a week. Well, she was willing to give him that herself. He could go back to Germany and study for two years. At the end of that time he must come back and they would get some competent and disinterested person to hear him play, and if then that person said he showed promise of becoming a first-rate pianist no further obstacles would be placed in his way. He would be given every advantage, help and encouragement. If on the other hand that person decided that his natural gifts were not such as to ensure ultimate success he must promise faithfully to give up all thoughts of making music his profession and in every way accede to his father's wishes. George could hardly believe his ears.

"Do you mean that, Granny?"

"I do."

"But will Daddy agree?"

"I vill see dat he does," she answered.

George seized her in his arms and impetuously kissed her on both cheeks.

"Darling," he cried.

"Ah, but de promise?"

He gave her his solemn word of honour that he would faithfully abide by the terms of the arrangement. Two days later he went back to Germany. Though his father consented unwillingly to his going, and indeed could not help doing so, he would not be reconciled to him and when he left refused to say good-bye to him. I imagine that in no other manner could he have caused himself such pain. I permit myself a trite remark. It is strange that men, inhabitants for so short a while of an alien and inhuman world, should go out of their way to cause themselves so much unhappiness.

George had stipulated that during his two years of study his family should not visit him, so that when Muriel heard some months before he was due to come home that I was passing through Munich on my way to Vienna, whither business called me, it was not unnatural that she should ask me to look him up. She was anxious to have first-hand information about him. She gave me George's address and I wrote ahead, telling him I was spending a day in Munich, and asked him to lunch with me. His answer awaited me at the hotel. He said he worked all day and could not spare the time to lunch with me, but if I would come to his studio about six he would like to show me that and if I had nothing better to do would love to spend the evening with me. So soon after six I went to the address he gave me. He lived on the second floor of a large block of flats and when I came to his door I heard the sound of piano-playing. It stopped when I rang and George opened the door for me. I hardly recognized him. He had grown very fat. His hair was extremely long, it curled all over his head in picturesque confusion; and he had certainly not shaved for three days. He wore a grimy pair of Oxford bags, a tennis shirt and slippers. He was not very clean and his fingernails were rimmed with black. It was a startling change from the spruce, slim youth so elegantly dressed in such beautiful clothes that I had last seen. I could not but think it would be a shock to Ferdy to see him now. The studio was large and bare; on the walls were three or four unframed canvases of a highly cubist nature; there were several armchairs much the worse for wear, and a grand piano. Books were littered about and old newspapers and art magazines. It was dirty and untidy and there was a frousty smell of stale beer and stale smoke.

"Do you live here alone?" I asked.

"Yes, I have a woman who comes in twice a week and cleans up. But I make my own breakfast and lunch."

"Can you cook?"

"Oh, I only have bread and cheese and a bottle of beer for lunch. I dine at a *bier stube*."

It was pleasant to discover that he was very glad to see me. He seemed in great spirits and extremely happy. He asked after his relations and we talked of one thing and another. He had a lesson twice a week and for the rest of the time practised. He told me that he worked ten hours a day.

"That's a change," I said.

He laughed.

"Daddy said I was born tired. I wasn't really lazy. I didn't see the use of working at things that bored me."

I asked him how he was getting on with the piano. He seemed to be satisfied with his progress and I begged him to play to me.

"Oh, not now. I'm all in, I've been at it all day. Let's go out and dine and come back here later and then I'll play. I generally go to the same place; there are several students I know there, and it's rather fun."

Presently we set out. He put on socks and shoes and a very old golf coat, and we walked together through the wide quiet streets. It was a brisk cold day. His step was buoyant. He looked round him with a sigh of delight.

"I love Munich," he said. "It's the only city in the world where there's art in the very air you breathe. After all, art is the only thing that matters, isn't it? I loathe the idea of going home."

"All the same I'm afraid you'll have to."

"I know. I'll go all right, but I'm not going to think about it till the time comes."

"When you do, you might do worse than get a haircut. If

you don't mind my saying so you look almost too artistic to be convincing."

"You English, you're such Philistines," he said.

He took me to a rather large restaurant in a side street, crowded even at that early hour with people dining and furnished heavily in the German medieval style. A table covered with a red cloth, well away from the air, was reserved for George and his friends, and when we went to it four or five youths were at it. There was a Pole studying Oriental languages, a student of philosophy, a painter—I suppose the author of George's cubist pictures—a Swede, and a young man who introduced himself to me, clicking his heels, as Hans Reiting, *dichter,* namely Hans Reiting, poet. Not one of them was more than twenty-two and I felt a trifle out of it. They all addressed George as *du* and I noticed that his German was extremely fluent. I had not spoken it for some time and mine was rusty, so that I could not take much part in the lively conversation. But nevertheless I thoroughly enjoyed myself. They ate sparingly, but drank a good deal of beer. They talked of art and literature and life and ethics and motor-cars and women. They were very revolutionary, and though gay very much in earnest. They were contemptuous of everyone you had ever heard of, and the only point on which they all agreed was that in this topsy-turvy world only the vulgar could hope for success. They argued points of technique with animation, and contradicted one another, and shouted and were obscene. They had a grand time.

At about eleven George and I walked back to his studio. Munich is a city that frolics demurely, and except about the Marienplatz the streets were still and empty. When we got in he took off his coat and said:

"Now I'll play to you."

I sat in one of the dilapidated armchairs, and a broken spring stuck into my behind, but I made myself as comfortable as I could. George played Chopin. I know very little of music, and that is one of the reasons for which I have found this story difficult to write. When I go to a concert at the Queen's Hall and in the intervals read the programme it is all Greek to me. I know nothing of harmony and counterpoint. I shall never forget how humiliated I felt once when, having come to Munich for a Wagner Festival, I went to a wonderful performance of *Tristan und Isolde* and never heard a note of it. The first few bars sent me off and I began to think of what I was writing, my characters leapt into life and I heard their long conversations, I suffered their pains and was a party to their joy; the years swept by and all sorts of things happened to me, the spring brought me its rapture and in the winter I was cold and hungry; and I loved and I hated and I died. I suppose there were intervals in which I walked round and round the garden and probably ate *schinken brödchen* and drank beer, but I have no recollection of them. The only thing I know is that when the curtain for the last time fell I woke with a start. I had had a wonderful time, but I could not help thinking it was very stupid of me to come such a long way and spend so much money if I couldn't pay attention to what I heard and saw.

I knew most of the things George played. They were the familiar pieces of concert programmes. He played with a great deal of dash. Then he played Beethoven's *Appassionata*. I used to play it myself when I played the piano (very badly) in my far distant youth and I still knew every note of it. Of course it is a classic and a great work, it would be foolish to deny it, but I confess that at this time of day it leaves me cold. It is like *Paradise Lost,* splendid, but a trifle stolid. This too George played with vigour. He sweated profusely. At first I could not make out what was the matter with his playing, something did not seem to me quite right, and then it struck me that the two hands did not exactly synchronize, so that there was ever so slight an interval between the bass and the treble; but I repeat, I am ignorant of these things; what disconcerted me might have been merely the effect of his having drunk a good deal of beer that evening, or indeed only my fancy. I said all I could think of to praise him.

"Of course I know I need a lot more work. I'm only a beginner, but I know I can do it. I feel it in my bones. It'll take me ten years, but then I shall be a pianist."

He was tired and came away from the piano. It was after

midnight and I suggested going, but he would not hear of it. He opened a couple of bottles of beer and lit his pipe. He wanted to talk.

"Are you happy here?" I asked him.

"Very," he answered gravely. "I'd like to stay for ever. I've never had such fun in my life. This evening for instance. Wasn't it grand?"

"It was very jolly. But one can't go on leading the student's life. Your friends here will grow older and go away."

"Others'll come. There are always students here and people like that."

"Yes, but you'll grow older too. Is there anything more lamentable than the middle-aged man who tries to go on living the undergraduate's life? The old fellow who wants to be a boy among boys, and tries to persuade himself that they'll accept him as one of themselves—how ridiculous he is. It can't be done."

"I feel so at home here. My poor father wants me to be an English gentleman. It gives me gooseflesh. I'm not a sportsman. I don't care a damn for hunting and shooting and playing cricket. I was only acting."

"You gave a very natural performance."

"It wasn't till I came here that I knew it wasn't real. I loved Eton, and Oxford was a riot, but all the same I knew I didn't belong. I played the part all right, because acting's in my blood, but there was always something in me that wasn't satisfied. The house in Grosvenor Square is a free-hold, and Daddy paid a hundred and eighty thousand pounds for Tilby; I don't know if you understand what I mean, I felt they were just furnished houses we'd taken for the season and one of these days we'd pack up and the real owners would come back."

I listened to him attentively, but I wondered how much he was describing what he had obscurely felt and how much he imagined now in his changed circumstances that he had felt.

"I used to hate hearing Great-uncle Ferdy tell his Jewish stories. I thought it so damned mean. I understand now; it was a safety valve. My God, the strain of being a man about town. It's easier for Daddy, he can play the old English squire at Tilby, but in the city he can be himself. He's all right. I've taken the make-up off and my stage clothes and at last I can be my real self too. What a relief! You know, I don't like English people. I never really know where I am with you. You're so dull and conventional. You never let yourselves go. There's no freedom in you, freedom of the soul, and you're such funks. There's nothing in the world you're so frightened of as doing the wrong thing."

"Don't forget that you're English yourself, George," I murmured.

He laughed.

"I? I'm not English. I haven't got a drop of English blood in me. I'm a Jew and you know it, and a German Jew into the bargain. I don't want to be English. I want to be a Jew. My friends are Jews. You don't know how much more easy I feel with them. I can be myself. We did everything we could to avoid Jews at home; Mummy because she was blonde thought she could get away with it and pretended she was a Gentile. What rot! D'you know, I have a lot of fun wandering about the Jewish parts of Munich and looking at the people. I went to Frankfort once—there are a lot of them there—and I walked about and looked at the frowsy old men with their hooked noses and the fat women with their false hair. I felt such a sympathy for them, I felt I belonged to them, I could have kissed them. When they looked at me I wondered if they knew that I was one of them. I wish to God I knew Yiddish. I'd like to become friends with them, and go into their houses and eat Kosher food and all that sort of thing. I wanted to go to a synagogue, but I was afraid I'd do the wrong thing and be kicked out. I like the smell of the Ghetto and the sense of life, and the mystery and the dust and the squalor and the romance. I shall never get the longing for it out of my head now. That's the real thing. All the rest is only pretence."

"You'll break your father's heart," I said.

"It's his or mine. Why can't he let me go? There's Harry. Harry would love to be squire of Tilby. He'd be an English gentleman all right. You know, Mummy's set her heart on my marrying a Christian. Harry would love to. He'll found the good old English family all right. After all, I ask so little. I only want five pounds a week, and they can keep the title and the park and the Gainsboroughs and the whole bag of tricks."

"Well, the fact remains that you gave your solemn word of honour to go back after two years."

"I'll go back all right," he said sullenly. "Lea Makart has promised to come and hear me play."

"What'll you do if she says you're no good?"

"Shoot myself," he said gaily.

"What nonsense," I answered in the same tone.

"Do *you* feel at home in England?"

"No," I said, "but then I don't feel at home anywhere else."

But he was quite naturally not interested in me.

"I loathe the idea of going back. Now that I know what life has to offer I wouldn't be an English country gentleman for anything in the world. My God, the boredom of it!"

"Money's a very nice thing and I've always understood it's very pleasant to be an English peer."

"Money means nothing to me. I want none of the things it can buy, and I don't happen to be a snob."

It was growing very late and I had to get up early next day. It seemed unnecessary for me to pay too much attention to what George said. It was the sort of nonsense a young man might very well indulge in when thrown suddenly among painters and poets. Art is strong wine and needs a strong head to carry. The divine fire burns most efficiently in those who temper its fury with horse sense. After all, George was not twenty-three yet. Time teaches. And when all was said and done his future was no concern of mine. I bade him good-night and walked back to my hotel. The stars were shining in the indifferent sky. I left Munich in the morning.

I did not tell Muriel on my return to London what George had said to me, or what he looked like, but contented myself with assuring her that he was well and happy, working very hard, and seemed to be leading a virtuous and sober life. Six months later he came home. Muriel asked me to go down to

Tilby for the week-end: Ferdy was bringing Lea Makart to hear George play and he particularly wished me to be there. I accepted. Muriel met me at the station.

"How did you find George?" I asked.

"He's very fat, but he seems in great spirits. I think he's pleased to be back again. He's been very sweet to his father."

"I'm glad of that."

"Oh, my dear, I do hope Lea Makart will say he's no good. It'll be such a relief to all of us."

"I'm afraid it'll be a terrible disappointment to him."

"Life is full of disappointments," said Muriel crisply. "But one learns to put up with them."

I gave her a smile of amusement. We were sitting in a Rolls, and there was a footman as well as a chauffeur on the box. She wore a string of pearls that had probably cost forty thousand pounds. I recollected that in the birthday honours Sir Adolphus Bland had not been one of the three gentlemen on whom the King had been pleased to confer a peerage.

Lea Makart was able to make only a flying visit. She was playing that evening at Brighton and would motor over to Tilby on the Sunday morning for luncheon. She was returning to London the same day because she had a concert in Manchester on the Monday. George was to play in the course of the afternoon.

"He's practising very hard," his mother told me. "That's why he didn't come with me to meet you."

We turned in at the park gates and drove up the imposing avenue of elms that led to the house. I found that there was no party.

I met the dowager Lady Bland for the first time. I had always been curious to see her. I had had in my mind's eye a somewhat sensational picture of an old, old Jewish woman who lived alone in her grand house in Portland Place and, with a finger in every pie, ruled her family with a despotic hand. She did not disappoint me. She was of a commanding presence, rather tall, and stout without being corpulent. Her countenance was markedly Hebraic. She wore a rather heavy moustache and a wig of a peculiarly metallic brown. Her dress was very grand, of black brocade, and she had a row of large diamond stars on her breast and round her neck a chain of diamonds. Diamond rings gleamed on her wrinkled hands. She spoke in a rather loud harsh voice and with a strong German accent. When I was introduced to her she fixed me with shining eyes. She summed me up with despatch and to my fancy at all events made no attempt to conceal from me that the judgment she formed was unfavourable.

"You have known my brother Ferdinand for many years, is it not so?" she said, rolling a guttural *r*. "My brother Ferdinand has always moved in very good society. Where is Sir Adolphus, Muriel? Does he know your guest is arrived? And will you not send for George? If he does not know his pieces by now he will not know them by to-morrow."

Muriel explained that Freddy was finishing a round of golf with his secretary and that she had had George told I was there. Lady Bland looked as though she thought Muriel's replies highly unsatisfactory and turned again to me.

"My daughter tells me you have been in Italy?"

"Yes, I've only just come back."

"It is a beautiful country. How is the king?"

I said I did not know.

"I used to know him when he was a little boy. He was not very strong then. His mother, Queen Margarita, was a great friend of mine. They thought he would never marry. The Duchess of Aosta was very angry when he fell in love with that Princess of Montenegro."

She seemed to belong to some long past period of history, but she was very alert and I imagine that little escaped her beady eyes. Freddy, very spruce in plus fours, presently came in. It was amusing and yet a little touching to see this grey-bearded man, as a rule somewhat domineering, so obviously on his best behaviour with the old lady. He called her Mamma. Then George came in. He was as fat as ever, but he had taken my advice and had his hair cut; he was losing his boyish looks, but he was a powerful and well-set-up young man. It was good to see the pleasure he took in his tea. He ate quantities of sandwiches and great hunks of cake. He had still a boy's appetite. His father watched him with a tender smile, and as I looked at him I could not be surprised at the attachment which they all so obviously felt for him. He had an ingenuousness, a charm and an enthusiasm which were certainly very pleasant. There was about him a generosity of demeanour, a frankness and a natural cordiality which could not but make people take to him. I do not know whether it was owing to a hint from his grandmother or merely of his own good nature, but it was plain that he was going out of his way to be nice to his father; and in his father's soft eyes, in the way he hung upon the boy's words, in his pleased, proud and happy look, you felt how bitterly the estrangement of the last two years had weighed on him. He adored George.

We played golf in the morning, a three-ball match, since Muriel, having to go to Mass, could not join us, and at one Ferdy arrived in Lea Makart's car. We sat down to luncheon. Of course Lea Makart's reputation was well-known to me. She was acknowledged to be the greatest woman pianist in Europe. She was a very old friend of Ferdy's, who with his interest and patronage had greatly helped her at the beginning of her career, and it was he who had arranged for her to come and give her opinion of George's chances. At one time I went as often as I could to hear her play. She had no affectations; she played as a bird sings, without any appearance of effort, very naturally, and the silvery notes dripped from her light fingers in a curiously spontaneous manner, so that it gave you the impression that she was improvising those complicated rhythms. They used to tell me that her technique was wonderful. I could never make up my mind how much the delight her playing gave me was due to her person. In those days she was the most ethereal thing you could imagine, and it was surprising that a creature so sylphlike should be capable of so much power. She was very slight, pale, with enormous eyes and magnificent black hair, and at the piano she had a childlike wistfulness that was most appealing. She was very beautiful in a hardly human way, and when she played, a little smile on her closed lips, she seemed to be remembering things she had heard in another world. Now, however, a woman in the early forties, she was sylphlike no more; she was stout and her face had broadened; she had no longer that lovely remoteness, but the authority of her long succession of triumphs. She was brisk, business-like and somewhat overwhelming. Her vitality lit her with a natural spotlight as his sanctity surrounds the saint with a halo. She was not interested in anything very much but her own affairs, but since she had humour and knew the world she was able to invest them with gaiety. She held the con-versation, but did not absorb it. George talked little. Every now and then she gave him a glance, but did not try to draw him in. I was the only Gentile at the table. All but old Lady Bland spoke perfect English, yet I could not help feeling that they did not speak like English people; I think they rounded their vowels more than we do, they certainly spoke louder, and the words seemed not to fall, but to gush from their lips. I think if I had been in another room where I could hear the tone but not the words of their speech I should have thought it was in a foreign language that they were conversing. The effect was slightly disconcerting.

Lea Makart wished to set out for London at about six, so it was arranged that George should play at four. Whatever the result of the audition, I felt that I, a stranger in the circle which her departure must render exclusively domestic, would be in the way and so, pretexting an early engagement in town next morning, I asked her if she would take me with her in her car.

At a little before four we all wandered into the drawing-room. Old Lady Bland sat on a sofa with Ferdy; Freddy, Muriel and I made ourselves comfortable in armchairs; and Lea Makart sat by herself. She chose instinctively a high-backed Jacobean chair that had somewhat the air of a throne, and in a yellow dress, with her olive skin, she looked very handsome. She had magnificent eyes. She was very much made up and her mouth was scarlet.

George gave no sign of nervousness. He was already seated at the piano when I went in with his father and mother, and he watched us quietly settling ourselves down. He gave me the shadow of a smile. When he saw that we were all at our ease he began to play. He played Chopin. He played two waltzes that were familiar to me, a polonaise and an *étude*. He played with a great deal of *brio*. I wish I knew music well enough to give an exact description of his playing. It had strength and a youthful exuberance, but I felt that he missed what to me is the peculiar charm of Chopin, the tenderness, the nervous melancholy, the wistful gaiety and the slightly faded romance that reminds me always of an early Victorian keepsake. And again I had the vague sensation, so slight that it almost escaped me, that the two hands did not quite synchronize. I looked at Ferdy and saw him give his sister a look of faint surprise. Muriel's eyes were fixed on the pianist, but presently she dropped them and for the rest of the time stared at the floor. His father looked at him too, and his eyes were steadfast, but unless I was much mistaken he went pale and his face betrayed something like dismay. Music was in the blood of all of them, all their lives they had heard the greatest pianists in the world, and they judged with instinctive precision. The only person whose face betrayed no emotion was Lea Makart. She listened very attentively. She was as still as an image in a niche.

At last he stopped and turning round on his seat faced her. He did not speak.

"What is it you want me to tell you?" she asked.

They looked into one another's eyes.

"I want you to tell me whether I have any chance of becoming in time a pianist in the first rank."

"Not in a thousand years."

For a moment there was a dead silence. Freddy's head sank and he looked down at the carpet at his feet. His wife put out her hand and took his. But George continued to look steadily at Lea Makart.

"Ferdy has told me the circumstances," she said at last. "Don't think I'm influenced by them. Nothing of this is very important." She made a great sweeping gesture that took in the magnificent room with the beautiful things it contained and all of us. "If I thought you had in you the makings of an artist I shouldn't hesitate to beseech you to give up everything for art's sake. Art is the only thing that matters. In comparison with art, wealth and rank and power are not worth a row of pins." She gave us a look so sincere that it was void of insolence. "We are the only people who count. We give the world significance. You are only our raw material."

I was not too pleased to be included with the rest under that heading, but that is neither here nor there.

"Of course I can see that you've worked very hard. Don't think it's been wasted. It will always be a pleasure to you to be able to play the piano, and it will enable you to appreciate great playing as no ordinary person can hope to do. Look at your hands. They're not a pianist's hands."

Involuntarily I glanced at George's hands. I had never noticed them before. I was astounded to see how podgy they were and how short and stumpy the fingers.

"Your ear is not quite perfect. I don't think you can ever hope to be more than a very competent amateur. In art the difference between the amateur and the professional is immeasurable."

George did not reply. Except for his pallor no one would have known that he was listening to the blasting of all his hopes. The silence that fell was quite awful. Lea Makart's eyes suddenly filled with tears.

"But don't take my opinion alone," she said. "After all, I'm not infallible. Ask somebody else. You know how good and generous Paderewski is. I'll write to him about you and you can go down and play to him. I'm sure he'll hear you."

George now gave a little smile. He had very good manners and, whatever he was feeling, did not want to make the situation too difficult for others.

"I don't think that's necessary. I am content to accept your verdict. To tell you the truth it's not so very different from my master's in Munich."

He got up from the piano and lit a cigarette. It eased the strain. The others moved a little in their chairs. Lea Makart smiled at George.

"Shall I play to you?" she said.

"Yes, do."

She got up and went to the piano. She took off the rings

with which her fingers were laden. She played Bach. I do not know the names of the pieces, but I recognized the stiff ceremonial of the frenchified little German courts and the sober, thrifty comfort of the burghers, and the dancing on the village green, the green trees that looked like Christmas trees, and the sunlight on the wide German country, and a tender coziness; and in my nostrils there was a warm scent of the soil and I was conscious of a sturdy strength that seemed to have its roots deep in mother earth, and of an elemental power that was timeless and had no home in space. She played exquisitely, with a soft brilliance that made you think of the full moon shining at dusk in the summer sky. With another part of me I watched the others and I saw how intensely they were conscious of the experience. They were rapt. I wished with all my heart that I could get from music the wonderful exaltation that possessed them. She stopped, a smile hovered on her lips, and she put on her rings. George gave a little chuckle.

"That clinches it, I fancy," he said.

The servants brought in tea, and after tea Lea Makart and I bade the company farewell and got into the car. We drove up to London. She talked all the way, if not brilliantly at all events with immense gusto, she told me of her early years in Manchester and of the struggle of her beginnings. She was very interesting. She never even mentioned George; the episode was of no consequence; it was finished and she thought of it no more.

We little knew what was happening at Tilby. When we left, George went out on the terrace and presently his father joined him. Freddy had won the day, but he was not happy. With his more than feminine sensitiveness he felt all that George was feeling, and George's anguish simply broke his heart. He had never loved his son more than then. When he appeared George greeted him with a little smile. Freddy's voice broke. In a sudden and overwhelming emotion he found it in him to surrender the fruits of his victory.

"Look here, old boy," he said, "I can't bear to think that you've had such a disappointment. Would you like to go back to Munich for another year and then see?"

George shook his head.

"No, it wouldn't be any good. I've had my chance. Let's call it a day."

"Try not to take it too hard."

"You see, the only thing in the world I want is to be a pianist. And there's nothing doing. It's a bit thick if you come to think of it."

George, trying so hard to be brave, smiled wanly.

"Would you like to go round the world? You can get one of your Oxford pals to go with you and I'll pay all the expenses. You've been working very hard for a long time."

"Thanks awfully, Daddy, we'll talk about it. I'm just going for a stroll now."

"Shall I come with you?"

"I'd rather go alone."

Then George did a strange thing. He put his arm round his father's neck and kissed him on the lips. He gave a funny little moved laugh and walked away. Freddy went back to the drawing-room. His mother, Ferdy and Muriel were sitting there.

"Freddy, why don't you marry the boy?" said the old lady. "He is twenty-three. It would take his mind off his troubles and when he is married and has a baby he will soon settle down like everybody else."

"Who is he to marry, Mamma?" asked Sir Adolphus, smiling.

"That's not so difficult. Lady Frielinghausen came to see me the other day with her daughter Violet. She is a very nice maiden and she will have money of her own. Lady Frielinghausen gave me to understand that her Sir Jacob would come down very handsome if Violet made a good match."

Muriel flushed.

"I hate Lady Frielinghausen. George is much too young to marry. He can afford to marry anyone he likes."

Old Lady Bland gave her daughter a strange look.

"You are a very foolish girl, Miriam," she said, using the name Muriel had long discarded. "As long as I am here I shall not allow you to commit a foolishness."

She knew as well as if Muriel had said it in so many words

that she wanted George to marry a Gentile, but she knew also that so long as she was alive neither Freddy nor his wife would dare to suggest it.

But George did not go for a walk. Perhaps because the shooting season was about to open he took it into his head to go into the gun-room. He began to clean the gun that his mother had given him on his twentieth birthday. No one had used it since he went to Germany. Suddenly the servants were startled by a report. When they went into the gun-room they found George lying on the floor shot through the heart. Apparently the gun had been loaded and George while playing about with it had accidentally shot himself. One reads of such accidents in the paper often.

THE ROUND DOZEN

I LIKE Elsom. It is a seaside resort in the south of England, not very far from Brighton, and it has something of the late Georgian charm of that agreeable town. But it is neither bustling nor garish. Ten years ago, when I used to go there not infrequently, you might still see here and there an old house, solid and pretentious in no unpleasing fashion (like a decayed gentlewoman of good family whose discreet pride in her ancestry amuses rather than offends you) which was built in the reign of the First Gentleman in Europe and where a courtier of fallen fortunes may well have passed his declining years. The main street had a lackadaisical air and the doctor's motor seemed a trifle out of place. The housewives did their housekeeping in a leisurely manner. They gossiped with the butcher as they watched him cut from his great joint of South Down a piece of the best end of the neck, and they asked amiably after the grocer's wife as he put half a pound of tea and a packet of salt into their string bag. I do not know whether Elsom was ever fashionable: it certainly was not so then; but it was respectable and cheap. Elderly ladies, maiden and widowed, lived there. Indian civilians and retired soldiers: they looked forward with little shudders of dismay to August and September which would bring holiday-makers; but did not disdain to let them their houses and on the proceeds spend a few worldy weeks in a Swiss pension. I never knew Elsom at that hectic time when the lodging-houses were full and young men in blazers sauntered along the front, when Pierrots performed on the beach and in the billiard-room at the Dolphin you heard the click of balls till eleven at night. I only knew it in winter. Then in every house on the sea-front, stucco houses with bow-windows built a hundred years ago, there was a sign to inform you that apartments were to let; and the guests of the Dolphin were waited on by a single waiter and the boots. At ten o'clock the porter came into the smoking-room and looked at you in so marked a manner that you got up and went to bed. Then Elsom was a restful place and the Dolphin a very comfortable inn. It was pleasing to think that the Prince Regent drove over with Mrs. Fitzherbert more than once to drink a dish of tea in its coffee-room. In the hall was a framed letter from Mr. Thackeray ordering a sitting-room and two bedrooms overlooking the sea and giving instructions that a fly should be sent to the station to meet him.

One November, two or three years after the war, having had a bad attack of influenza, I went down to Elsom to regain my strength. I arrived in the afternoon and when I had unpacked my things went for a stroll on the front. The sky was overcast and the calm sea grey and cold. A few seagulls flew close to the shore. Sailing boats, their masts taken down for the winter, were drawn up high on the shingly beach and the bathing huts stood side by side in a long, grey and tattered row. No one was sitting on the benches that the town council had put here and there, but a few people were trudging up and down for exercise. I passed an old colonel with a red nose who stamped along in plus fours followed by a terrier, two elderly women in short skirts and stout shoes and a plain girl in a Tam o' Shanter. I had never seen the front so deserted. The lodging-houses looked like bedraggled old maids waiting for lovers who would never return, and even the friendly Dolphin seemed wan and desolate. My heart sank. Life on a sudden seemed very drab. I returned to the hotel, drew the curtains of my sitting-room, poked the fire and with a book sought to dispel my melancholy. But I was glad enough when it was time to dress for dinner. I went into the coffee-room and found the guests of the hotel already seated. I gave them a casual glance. There was one lady of middle age by herself and there were two elderly gentlemen, golfers probably, with red faces and baldish heads, who ate their food in moody silence. The only other persons in the room were a group of three who sat in the bow-window, and they immediately attracted my surprised attention. The party consisted of an old gentleman and two ladies, one of whom was old and probably his wife, while the other was younger and possibly his daughter. It was the old lady who first excited my interest. She wore a voluminous dress of black silk and a black lace cap; on her wrists were heavy gold bangles and round her neck a substantial gold chain from which hung a large gold locket; at her neck was a large gold brooch. I did not know that anyone still wore jewelry of that sort. Often, passing secondhand jewellers and pawnbrokers, I had lingered for a moment to look at these strangely old-fashioned articles, so solid, costly and hideous, and thought, with a smile in which there was a tinge of sadness, of the women long since dead who had worn them. They suggested the period when the bustle and the flounce were taking the place of the crinoline and the pork-pie hat was ousting the poke-bonnet. The British people liked things solid and good in those days. They went to church on Sunday morning and after church walked in the Park. They gave dinner parties of twelve courses where the master of the house carved the beef and the chickens, and after dinner the ladies who could play favoured the company with Mendelssohn's Songs Without Words and the gentleman with the fine baritone voice sang an old English ballad.

The younger woman had her back turned to me and at first I could see only that she had a slim and youthful figure. She had a great deal of brown hair which seemed to be elaborately arranged. She wore a grey dress. The three of them were chatting in low tones and presently she turned her head so that I saw her profile. It was astonishingly beautiful. The nose was straight and delicate, the line of the cheek exquisitely modelled; I saw then that she wore her hair after the manner of Queen Alexandra. The dinner proceeded to its close and the party got up. The old lady sailed out of the room, looking neither to the right nor to the left, and the young one followed her. Then I saw with a shock that she was old. Her frock was simple enough. The skirt was longer than was at that time worn, and there was something slightly old-fashioned in the cut. I daresay the waist was more clearly indicated than was then usual, but it was a girl's frock. She was tall, like a heroine of Tennyson's, slight, with long legs and a graceful carriage. I had seen the nose before: it was the nose of a Greek goddess; her mouth was beautiful, and her eyes were large and blue. Her skin was of course a little tight on the bones, and there were wrinkles on her forehead and about her eyes, but in youth it must have been lovely. She reminded you of those Roman ladies with features of an exquisite regularity whom Alma-Tadema used to paint, but who, notwithstanding their antique dress, were so stubbornly English. It was a type of cold perfection that one had not seen for five-and-twenty years. Now it is as dead as the epigram. I was like an archæologist who finds some long-buried statue and I was thrilled in so unexpected a manner to hit upon this survival of a past era. For no day is so dead as the day before yesterday.

The gentleman rose to his feet when the two ladies left, and then resumed his chair. A waiter brought him a glass of heavy port. He smelt it, sipped it, and rolled it round his tongue. I observed him. He was a little man, much shorter than his imposing wife, well-covered without being stout, with a fine head of curling grey hair. His face was much wrinkled and it bore a faintly humorous expression. His lips were tight and his chin was square. He was, according to our present notions, somewhat extravagantly dressed. He wore a black velvet jacket, a frilled shirt with a low collar and a large black tie, and very wide evening trousers. It gave you vaguely the effect of costume. Having drunk his port with deliberation, he got up and sauntered out of the room.

When I passed through the hall, curious to know who these singular people were, I glanced at the visitors' book. I saw, written in an angular feminine hand, the writing that was taught to young ladies in modish schools forty years or so ago, the names: Mr. and Mrs. Edwin St. Clair and Miss Porchester. Their address was given as 68, Leinster Square,

Bayswater, London. These must be the names and this the address of the persons who had so much interested me. I asked the manageress who Mr. St. Clair was and she told me that she believed he was something in the City. I went into the billiard-room and knocked the balls about for a little while and then on my way upstairs passed through the lounge. The two red-faced gentlemen were reading the evening paper and the middle-aged lady was dozing over a novel. The party of three sat in a corner. Mrs. St. Clair was knitting, Miss Porchester was busy with embroidery, and Mr. St. Clair was reading aloud in a discreet but resonant tone. As I passed I discovered that he was reading *Bleak House*.

I read and wrote most of the next day, but in the afternoon I went for a walk and on my way home I sat down for a little on one of those convenient benches on the sea-front. It was not quite so cold as the day before and the air was pleasant. For want of anything better to do I watched a figure advancing towards me from a distance. It was a man and as he came nearer I saw that it was rather a shabby little man. He wore a thin black greatcoat and a somewhat battered bowler. He walked with his hands in his pockets and looked cold. He gave me a glance as he passed by, went on a few steps, hesitated, stopped and turned back. When he came up once more to the bench on which I sat he took a hand out of his pocket and touched his hat. I noticed that he wore shabby black gloves, and surmised that he was a widower in straitened circumstances. Or he might have been a mute recovering, like myself, from influenza.

"Excuse me, sir," he said, "but could you oblige me with a match?"

"Certainly."

He sat down beside me and while I put my hand in my pocket for matches he hunted in his for cigarettes. He took out a small packet of Goldflakes and his face fell.

"Dear, dear, how very annoying! I haven't got a cigarette left."

"Let me offer you one," I replied, smiling.

I took out my case and he helped himself.

"Gold?" he asked, giving the case a tap as I closed it. "Gold? That's a thing I never could keep. I've had three. All stolen."

His eyes rested in a melancholy way on his boots, which were sadly in need of repair. He was a wizened little man with a long thin nose and pale blue eyes. His skin was sallow and he was much lined. I could not tell what his age was; he might have been five-and-thirty or he might have been sixty. There was nothing remarkable about him except his insignificance. But though evidently poor he was neat and clean. He was respectable and he clung to respectability. No, I did not think he was a mute, I thought he was a solicitor's clerk who had lately buried his wife and been sent to Elsom by an indulgent employer to get over the first shock of his grief.

"Are you making a long stay, sir?" he asked me.

"Ten days or a fortnight."

"Is this your first visit to Elsom, sir?"

"I have been here before."

"I know it well, sir. I flatter myself there are very few seaside resorts that I have not been to at one time or another. Elsom is hard to beat, sir. You get a very nice class of people here. There's nothing noisy or vulgar about Elsom if you understand what I mean. Elsom has very pleasant recollections for me, sir. I knew Elsom well in bygone days. I was married in St. Martin's Church, sir."

"Really," I said feebly.

"It was a very happy marriage, sir."

"I'm very glad to hear it," I returned.

"Nine months, that one lasted," he said reflectively.

Surely the remark was a trifle singular. I had not looked forward with any enthusiasm to the probability which I so clearly foresaw that he would favour me with an account of his matrimonial experiences, but now I waited if not with eagerness at least with curiosity for a further observation. He made none. He sighed a little. At last I broke the silence.

"There don't seem to be very many people about," I remarked.

"I like it so. I'm not one for crowds. As I was saying just

now I reckon I've spent a good many years at one seaside re-sort after the other, but I never came in the season. It's the winter I like."

"Don't you find it a little melancholy?"

He turned towards me and placed his black-gloved hand for an instant on my arm.

"It is melancholy. And because it's melancholy a little ray of sunshine is very welcome."

The remark seemed to me perfectly idiotic and I did not answer. He withdrew his hand from my arm and got up.

"Well, I mustn't keep you, sir. Pleased to have made your acquaintance."

He took off his dingy hat very politely and strolled away. It was beginning now to grow chilly and I thought I would return to the Dolphin. As I reached its broad steps a landau drove up, drawn by two scraggy horses, and from it stepped Mr. St. Clair. He wore a hat that looked like the unhappy result of a union between a bowler and a top-hat. He gave his hand to his wife and then to his niece. The porter carried in after them rugs and cushions. As Mr. St. Clair paid the driver I heard him tell him to come at the usual time next day, and I understood that the St. Clairs took a drive every afternoon in a landau. It would not have surprised me to learn that none of them had ever been in a motor-car.

The manageress told me that they kept very much to themselves and sought no acquaintance among the other persons staying at the hotel. I rode my imagination on a loose rein. I watched them eat three meals a day. I watched Mr. and Mrs. St. Clair sit at the top of the hotel steps in the morning. He read *The Times* and she knitted. I suppose Mrs. St. Clair had never read a paper in her life, for they never took anything but *The Times* and Mr. St. Clair of course took it with him every day to the City. At about twelve Miss Porchester joined them.

"Have you enjoyed your walk, Eleanor?" asked Mrs. St. Clair.

"It was very nice, Aunt Gertrude," answered Miss Por-chester.

And I understood that just as Mrs. St. Clair took "her

drive" every afternoon Miss Porchester took "her walk" every morning.

"When you have come to the end of your row, my dear," said Mr. St. Clair, with a glance at his wife's knitting, "we might go for a constitutional before luncheon."

"That will be very nice," answered Mrs. St. Clair. She folded up her work and gave it to Miss Porchester. "If you're going upstairs, Eleanor, will you take my work?"

"Certainly, Aunt Gertrude."

"I daresay you're a little tired after your walk, my dear."

"I shall have a little rest before luncheon."

Miss Porchester went into the hotel and Mr. and Mrs. St. Clair walked slowly along the sea-front, side by side, to a certain point, and then walked slowly back.

When I met one of them on the stairs I bowed and received an unsmiling, polite bow in return, and in the morning I ventured upon a good-day, but there the matter ended. It looked as though I should never have a chance to speak to any of them. But presently I thought that Mr. St. Clair gave me now and then a glance, and thinking he had heard my name I imagined, perhaps vainly, that he looked at me with curiosity. And a day or two after that I was sitting in my room when the porter came in with a message.

"Mr. St. Clair presents his compliments and could you oblige him with the loan of Whitaker's Almanack."

I was astonished.

"Why on earth should he think that I have a Whitaker's Almanack?"

"Well, sir, the manageress told him you wrote."

I could not see the connection.

"Tell Mr. St. Clair that I'm very sorry that I haven't got a Whitaker's Almanack, but if I had I would very gladly lend it to him."

Here was my opportunity. I was by now filled with eagerness to know these fantastic persons more closely. Now and then in the heart of Asia I have come upon a lonely tribe living in a little village among an alien population. No one knows how they came there or why they settled in that spot.

They live their own lives, speak their own language, and have no communication with their neighbours. No one knows whether they are the descendants of a band that was left behind when their nation swept in a vast horde across the continent or whether they are the dying remnant of some great people that in that country once held empire. They are a mystery. They have no future and no history. This odd little family seemed to me to have something of the same character. They were of an era that is dead and gone. They reminded me of persons in one of those leisurely, old-fashioned novels that one's father read. They belonged to the eighties and they had not moved since then. How extraordinary it was that they could have lived through the last forty years as though the world stood still! They took me back to my childhood and I recollected people who are long since dead. I wonder if it is only distance that gives me the impression that they were more peculiar than anyone is now. When a person was described then as "quite a character," by heaven, it meant something.

So that evening after dinner I went into the lounge and boldly addressed Mr. St. Clair.

"I'm so sorry I haven't got a Whitaker's Almanack," I said, "but if I have any other book that can be of service to you I shall be delighted to lend it to you."

Mr. St. Clair was obviously startled. The two ladies kept their eyes on their work. There was an embarrassed hush.

"It does not matter at all, but I was given to understand by the manageress that you were a novelist."

I racked my brain. There was evidently some connection between my profession and Whitaker's Almanack that escaped me.

"In days gone by Mr. Trollope used often to dine with us in Leinster Square and I remember him saying that the two most useful books to a novelist were the Bible and Whitaker's Almanack."

"I see that Thackeray once stayed in this hotel," I remarked, anxious not to let the conversation drop.

"I never very much cared for Mr. Thackeray, though he

dined more than once with my wife's father, the late Mr. Sargeant Saunders. He was too cynical for me. My niece has not read *Vanity Fair* to this day."

Miss Porchester blushed slightly at this reference to herself. A waiter brought in the coffee and Mrs. St. Clair turned to her husband.

"Perhaps, my dear, this gentleman would do us the pleasure to have his coffee with us."

Although not directly addressed, I answered promptly.

"Thank you very much."

I sat down.

"Mr. Trollope was always my favourite novelist," said Mr. St. Clair. "He was so essentially a gentleman. I admire Charles Dickens. But Charles Dickens could never draw a gentleman. I am given to understand that young people nowadays find Mr. Trollope a little slow. My niece, Miss Porchester, prefers the novels of Mr. William Black."

"I'm afraid I've never read any," I said.

"Ah, I see that you are like me; you are not up-to-date. My niece once persuaded me to read a novel by a Miss Rhoda Broughton, but I could not manage more than a hundred pages of it."

"I did not say I liked it, Uncle Edwin," said Miss Porchester, defending herself, with another blush. "I told you it was rather fast, but everybody was talking about it."

"I'm quite sure it is not the sort of book your Aunt Gertrude would have wished you to read, Eleanor."

"I remember Miss Broughton telling me once that when she was young people said her books were fast and when she was old they said they were slow, and it was very hard, since she had written exactly the same sort of book for forty years."

"Oh, did you know Miss Broughton?" asked Miss Porchester, addressing me for the first time. "How very interesting! And did you know Ouida?"

"My dear Eleanor, what will you say next! I'm quite sure you've never read anything by Ouida."

"Indeed, I have, Uncle Edwin. I've read *Under Two Flags* and I liked it very much."

"You amaze and shock me. I don't know what girls are coming to nowadays."

"You always said that when I was thirty you gave me complete liberty to read anything I liked."

"There is a difference, my dear Eleanor, between liberty and license," said Mr. St. Clair, smiling a little in order not to make his reproof offensive, but with a certain gravity.

I do not know if in recounting this conversation I have managed to convey the impression it gave me of a charming and old-fashioned air. I could have listened all night to them discussing the depravity of an age that was young in the eighteen-eighties. I would have given a good deal for a glimpse of their large and roomy house in Leinster Square. I should have recognized the suite covered in red brocade that stood stiffly about the drawing-room, each piece in its appointed place; and the cabinets filled with Dresden china would have brought me back my childhood. In the dining-room, where they habitually sat, for the drawing-room was used only for parties, there was a Turkey carpet and a vast mahogany sideboard "groaning" with silver. On the walls were the pictures that had excited the admiration of Mrs. Humphry Ward and her uncle Matthew in the Academy of eighteen-eighty.

Next morning, strolling through a pretty lane at the back of Elsom, I met Miss Porchester, who was taking "her walk." I should have liked to go a little way with her, but felt certain that it would embarrass this maiden of fifty to saunter alone with a man even of my respectable years. She bowed as I passed her, and blushed. Oddly enough, a few yards behind her I came upon the funny shabby little man in black gloves with whom I had spoken for a few minutes on the front. He touched his old bowler hat.

"Excuse me, sir, but could you oblige me with a match?" he said.

"Certainly," I retorted, "but I'm afraid I have no cigarettes on me."

"Allow me to offer you one of mine," he said, taking out the paper case. It was empty. "Dear, dear, I haven't got one either. What a curious coincidence!"

He went on and I had a notion that he a little hastened his steps. I was beginning to have my doubts about him. I hoped he was not going to bother Miss Porchester. For a moment I thought of walking back, but I did not. He was a civil little man and I did not believe he would make a nuisance of himself to a single lady.

I saw him again that very afternoon. I was sitting on the front. He walked towards me with little, halting steps. There was something of a wind and he looked like a dried leaf being driven before it. This time he did not hesitate, but sat down beside me.

"We meet again, sir. The world is a small place. If it will not inconvenience you perhaps you will allow me to rest a few minutes. I am a wee bit tired."

"This is a public bench, and you have just as much right to sit on it as I."

I did not wait for him to ask me for a match, but at once offered him a cigarette.

"How very kind of you, sir! I have to limit myself to so many cigarettes a day, but I enjoy those I smoke. As one grows older the pleasures of life diminish, but my experience is that one enjoys more those that remain."

"That is a very consoling thought."

"Excuse me, sir, but am I right in thinking that you are the well-known author?"

"I am an author," I replied. "But what made you think it?"

"I have seen your portrait in the illustrated papers. I suppose you don't recognize me?"

I looked at him again, a weedy little man in neat but shabby black clothes, with a long nose and watery blue eyes.

"I'm afraid I don't."

"I daresay I've changed," he sighed. "There was a time when my photograph was in every paper in the United Kingdom. Of course, those press photographs never do you justice. I give you my word, sir, that if I hadn't seen my name underneath I should never have guessed that some of them were meant for me."

He was silent for a while. The tide was out, and beyond

the shingle of the beach was a strip of yellow mud. The breakwaters were half buried in it like the backbones of prehistoric beasts.

"It must be a wonderfully interesting thing to be an author, sir. I've often thought I had quite a turn for writing myself. At one time and another I've done a rare lot of reading. I haven't kept up with it much lately. For one thing my eyes are not so good as they used to be. I believe I could write a book if I tried."

"They say anybody can write one," I answered.

"Not a novel, you know. I'm not much of a one for novels; I prefer histories and that like. But memoirs. If anybody was to make it worth my while I wouldn't mind writing my memoirs."

"It's very fashionable just now."

"There are not many people who've had the experiences I've had in one way and another. I did write to one of the Sunday papers about it some little while back, but they never answered my letter."

He gave me a long, appraising look. He had too respectable an air to be about to ask me for half a crown.

"Of course you don't know who I am, sir, do you?"

"I honestly don't."

He seemed to ponder for a moment, then he smoothed down his black gloves on his fingers, looked for a moment at a hole in one of them, and then turned to me not without self-consciousness.

"I am the celebrated Mortimer Ellis," he said.

"Oh?"

I did not know what other ejaculation to make, for to the best of my belief I had never heard the name before. I saw a look of disappointment come over his face, and I was a trifle embarrassed.

"Mortimer Ellis," he repeated. "You're not going to tell me you don't know."

"I'm afraid I must. I'm very often out of England."

I wondered to what he owed his celebrity. I passed over in my mind various possibilities. He could never have been an athlete, which alone in England gives a man real fame, but he might have been a faith-healer or a champion billiard-player. There is of course no one so obscure as a cabinet minister out of office and he might have been the President of the Board of Trade in a defunct administration. But he had none of the look of a politician.

"That's fame for you," he said bitterly. "Why, for weeks I was the most talked-about man in England. Look at me. You must have seen my photograph in the papers. Mortimer Ellis."

"I'm sorry," I said, shaking my head.

He paused a moment to give his disclosure effectiveness.

"I am the well-known bigamist."

Now what are you to reply when a person who is practically a stranger to you informs you that he is a well-known bigamist? I will confess that I have sometimes had the vanity to think that I am not as a rule at a loss for a retort, but here I found myself speechless.

"I've had eleven wives, sir," he went on.

"Most people find one about as much as they can manage."

"Ah, that's want of practice. When you've had eleven there's very little you don't know about women."

"But why did you stop at eleven?"

"There now, I knew you'd say that. The moment I set eyes on you I said to myself, he's got a clever face. You know, sir, that's the thing that always grizzles me. Eleven does seem a funny number, doesn't it? There's something unfinished about it. Now three anyone might have, and seven's all right, they say nine's lucky, and there's nothing wrong with ten. But eleven! That's the one thing I regret. I shouldn't have minded anything if I could have brought it up to the Round Dozen."

He unbuttoned his coat and from an inside pocket produced a bulging and very greasy pocketbook. From this he took a large bundle of newspaper cuttings; they were worn and creased and dirty. But he spread out two or three.

"Now just you look at those photographs. I ask you, are they like me? It's an outrage. Why, you'd think I was a criminal to look at them."

The cuttings were of imposing length. In the opinion of sub-editors Mortimer Ellis had obviously been a news item of value. One was headed, A Much Married Man; another, Heartless Ruffian Brought to Book; a third, Contemptible Scoundrel Meets his Waterloo.

"Not what you would call a good press," I murmured.

"I never pay any attention to what the newspapers say," he answered, with a shrug of his thin shoulders. "I've known too many journalists myself for that. No, it's the judge I blame. He treated me shocking and it did him no good, mind you; he died within the year."

I ran my eyes down the report I held.

"I see he gave you five years."

"Disgraceful, I call it, and see what it says." He pointed to a place with his forefinger. " 'Three of his victims pleaded for mercy to be shown to him.' That shows what they thought of me. And after that he gave me five years. And just look what he called me, a heartless scoundrel—me, the best-hearted man that ever lived—a pest of society and a danger to the public. Said he wished he had the power to give me the cat. I don't so much mind his giving me five years, though you'll never get me to say it wasn't excessive, but I ask you, had he the right to talk to me like that? No, he hadn't, and I'll never forgive him, not if I live to be a hundred."

The bigamist's cheeks flushed and his watery eyes were filled for a moment with fire. It was a sore subject with him.

"May I read them?" I asked him.

"That's what I gave them you for. I want you to read them, sir. And if you can read them without saying that I'm a much wronged man, well, you're not the man I took you for."

As I glanced through one cutting after another I saw why Mortimer Ellis had so wide an acquaintance with the seaside resorts of England. They were his hunting-ground. His method was to go to some place when the season was over and take apartments in one of the empty lodging-houses. Apparently it did not take him long to make acquaintance with some woman or other, widow or spinster, and I noticed that their ages at the time were between thirty-five and fifty.

They stated in the witness-box that they had met him first on the sea-front. He generally proposed marriage to them within a fortnight of this and they were married shortly after. He induced them in one way or another to entrust him with their savings and in a few months, on the pretext that he had to go to London on business, he left them, never to return. Only one had ever seen him again till, obliged to give evidence, they saw him in the dock. They were women of a certain respectability; one was the daughter of a doctor and another of a clergyman; there was a lodging-house keeper, there was the widow of a commercial traveller, and there was a retired dressmaker. For the most part, their fortunes ranged from five hundred to a thousand pounds, but whatever the sum the misguided women were stripped of every penny. Some of them told really pitiful stories of the destitution to which they had been reduced. But they all acknowledged that he had been a good husband to them. Not only had three actually pleaded for mercy to be shown him; but one said in the witness-box that, if he was willing to come, she was ready to take him back. He noticed that I was reading this.

"And she'd have worked for me," he said, "there's no doubt about that. But I said, better let bygones be bygones. No one likes a cut off the best end of the neck better than I do, but I'm not much of a one for cold roast mutton, I will confess."

It was only by an accident that Mortimer Ellis did not marry his twelfth wife and so achieve the Round Dozen which I understand appealed to his love of symmetry. For he was engaged to be married to a Miss Hubbard—"two thousand pounds she had, if she had a penny, in war-loan," he confided to me—and the banns had been read, when one of his former wives saw him, made enquiries, and communicated with the police. He was arrested on the very day before his twelfth wedding.

"She was a bad one, she was," he told me. "She deceived me something cruel."

"How did she do that?"

"Well, I met her at Eastbourne, one December it was, on

the pier, and she told me in course of conversation that she'd been in the millinery business and had retired. She said she'd made a tidy bit of money. She wouldn't say exactly how much it was, but she gave me to understand it was something like fifteen hundred pounds. And when I married her— would you believe it?—she hadn't got three hundred. And that's the one who gave me away. And mind you, I'd never blamed her. Many a man would have cut up rough when he found out he'd been made a fool of. I never showed her that I was disappointed even, I just went away without a word."

"But not without the three hundred pounds, I take it."

"Oh come, sir, you must be reasonable," he returned in an injured tone. "You can't expect three hundred pounds to last for ever, and I'd been married to her four months before she confessed the truth."

"Forgive my asking," I said, "and pray don't think my question suggests a disparaging view of your personal attractions, but—why did they marry you?"

"Because I asked them," he answered, evidently very much surprised at my enquiry.

"But did you never have any refusals?"

"Very seldom. Not more than four or five in the whole course of my career. Of course I didn't propose till I was pretty sure of my ground and I don't say I didn't draw a blank sometimes. You can't expect to click every time, if you know what I mean, and I've often wasted several weeks making up to a woman before I saw there was nothing doing."

I surrendered myself for a time to my reflections. But I noticed presently that a broad smile spread over the mobile features of my friend.

"I understand what you mean," he said. "It's my appearance that puzzles you. You don't know what it is they see in me. That's what comes of reading novels and going to the pictures. You think what women want is the cowboy type, or the romance-of-old-Spain touch, flashing eyes, an olive skin, and a beautiful dancer. You make me laugh."

"I'm glad," I said.

"Are you a married man, sir?"

"I am. But I only have one wife."

"You can't judge by that. You can't generalize from a single instance, if you know what I mean. Now, I ask you, what would you know about dogs if you'd never had anything but one bull-terrier?"

The question was rhetorical and I felt sure did not require an answer. He paused for an effective moment and went on.

"You're wrong, sir. You're quite wrong. They may take a fancy to a good-looking young fellow, but they don't want to marry him. They don't really care about looks."

"Douglas Jerrold, who was as ugly as he was witty, used to say that if he was given ten minutes' start with a woman he could cut out the handsomest man in the room."

"They don't want wit. They don't want a man to be funny; they think he's not serious. They don't want a man who's too handsome; they think he's not serious either. That's what they want, they want a man who's serious. Safety first. And then—attention. I may not be handsome and I may not be amusing, but believe me, I've got what every woman wants. Poise. And the proof is, I've made every one of my wives happy."

"It certainly is much to your credit that three of them pleaded for mercy to be shown to you and that one was willing to take you back."

"You don't know what an anxiety that was to me all the time I was in prison. I thought she'd be waiting for me at the gate when I was released, and I said to the Governor, 'For God's sake, sir, smuggle me out so as no one can see me.'"

He smoothed his gloves again over his hands and his eye once more fell upon the hole in the first finger.

"That's what comes of living in lodgings, sir. How's a man to keep himself neat and tidy without a woman to look after him? I've been married too often to be able to get along without a wife. There are men who don't like being married. I can't understand them. The fact is, you can't do a thing really well unless you've got your heart in it, and I like being a married man. It's no difficulty to me to do the little things that women like and that some men can't be bothered with. As I was saying just now, it's attention a woman wants. I never went out of the house without giving my wife a kiss and I never came in without giving her another. And it was very seldom I came in without bringing her some chocolates or a few flowers. I never grudged the expense."

"After all, it was her money you were spending," I interposed.

"And what if it was? It's not the money that you've paid for a present that signifies, it's the spirit you give it in. That's what counts with women. No, I'm not one to boast, but I will say this for myself, I am a good husband."

I looked desultorily at the reports of the trial which I still held.

"I'll tell you what surprises me," I said. "All these women were very respectable, of a certain age, quiet, decent persons. And yet they married you without any enquiry after the shortest possible acquaintance."

He put his hand impressively on my arm.

"Ah, that's what you don't understand, sir. Women have got a craving to be married. It doesn't matter how young they are or how old they are, if they're short or tall, dark or fair, they've all got one thing in common: they want to be married. And mind you, I married them in church. No woman feels really safe unless she's married in church. You say I'm no beauty. Well, I never thought I was, but if I had one leg and a hump on my back I could find any number of women who'd jump at the chance of marrying me. It's not the man they care about, it's marriage. It's a mania with them. It's a disease. Why, there's hardly one of them who wouldn't have accepted me the second time I saw her only I like to make sure of my ground before I commit myself. When it all came out there was a rare to-do because I'd married eleven times. Eleven times? Why, it's nothing, it's not even a Round Dozen. I could have married thirty times if I'd wanted to. I give you my word, sir, when I consider my opportunities, I'm astounded at my moderation."

"You told me you were very fond of reading history."

"Yes, Warren Hastings said that, didn't he? It struck

me at the time I read it. It seemed to fit me like a glove."

"And you never found these constant courtships a trifle monotonous?"

"Well, sir, I think I've got a logical mind, and it always gave me a rare lot of pleasure to see how the same effects followed on the same causes, if you know what I mean. Now, for instance, with a woman who'd never been married before I always passed myself off as a widower. It worked like a charm. You see, a spinster likes a man who knows a thing or two. But with a widow I always said I was a bachelor: a widow's afraid a man who's been married before knows too much."

I gave him back his cuttings; he folded them up neatly and replaced them in his greasy pocketbook.

"You know, sir, I always think I've been misjudged. Just see what they say about me: a pest of society, unscrupulous villain, contemptible scoundrel. Now just look at me. I ask you, do I look that sort of man? You know me, you're a judge of character, I've told you all about myself; do you think me a bad man?"

"My acquaintance with you is very slight," I answered with what I thought considerable tact.

"I wonder if the judge, I wonder if the jury, I wonder if the public ever thought about my side of the question. The public booed me when I was taken into court and the police had to protect me from their violence. Did any of them think what I'd done for these women?"

"You took their money."

"Of course I took their money. I had to live the same as anybody has to live. But what did I give them in exchange for their money?"

This was another rhetorical question, and though he looked at me as though he expected an answer I held my tongue. Indeed I did not know the answer. His voice was raised and he spoke with emphasis. I could see that he was serious.

"I'll tell you what I gave them in exchange for their money. Romance. Look at this place." He made a wide, circular gesture that embraced the sea and the horizon.

"There are a hundred places in England like this. Look at that sea and that sky; look at these lodging-houses; look at that pier and the front. Doesn't it make your heart sink? It's dead as mutton. It's all very well for you who come down here for a week or two because you're run down. But think of all those women who live here from one year's end to another. They haven't a chance. They hardly know anyone. They've just got enough money to live on and that's all. I wonder if you know how terrible their lives are. Their lives are just like the front, a long, straight, cemented walk that goes on and on from one seaside resort to another. Even in the season there's nothing for them. They're out of it. They might as well be dead. And then I come along. Mind you, I never made advances to a woman who wouldn't have gladly acknowledged to thirty-five. And I give them love. Why, many of them had never known what it was to have a man do them up behind. Many of them had never known what it was to sit on a bench in the dark with a man's arm round their waist. I bring them change and excitement. I give them a new pride in themselves. They were on the shelf and I come along quite quietly and I deliberately take them down. A little ray of sunshine in those drab lives, that's what I was. No wonder they jumped at me, no wonder they wanted me to go back to them. The only one who gave me away was the milliner. She said she was a widow. My private opinion is that she'd never been married at all. You say I did the dirty on them; why, I brought happiness and glamour into eleven lives that never thought they had even a dog's chance of it again. You say I'm a villain and a scoundrel. You're wrong. I'm a philanthropist. Five years, they gave me; they should have given me the medal of the Royal Humane Society."

He took out his empty packet of Goldflakes and looked at it with a melancholy shake of the head. When I handed him my cigarette case he helped himself without a word. I watched the spectacle of a good man struggling with his emotion.

"And what did I get out of it, I ask you?" he continued presently. "Board and lodging and enough to buy cigarettes.

But I never was able to save, and the proof is that now, when I'm not so young as I was, I haven't got half a crown in my pocket." He gave me a sidelong glance. "It's a great come-down for me to find myself in this position. I've always paid my way and I've never asked a friend for a loan in all my life. I was wondering, sir, if you could oblige me with a trifle. It's humiliating to me to have to suggest it, but the fact is, if you could oblige me with a pound it would mean a great deal to me."

Well, I had certainly had a pound's worth of entertainment out of the bigamist and I dived for my pocketbook.

"I shall be very glad," I said.

He looked at the notes I took out.

"I suppose you couldn't make it two, sir?"

"I think I could."

I handed him a couple of pound notes and he gave a little sigh as he took them.

"You don't know what it means to a man who's used to the comforts of home life not to know where to turn for a night's lodging."

"But there is one thing I should like you to tell me," I said. "I shouldn't like you to think me cynical, but I had a notion that women on the whole take the maxim, it is more blessed to give than to receive, as applicable exclusively to our sex. How did you persuade these respectable, and no doubt thrifty, women to entrust you so confidently with all their savings?"

An amused smile spread over his undistinguished features.

"Well, sir, you know what Shakespeare said about ambition o'erleaping itself. That's the explanation. Tell a woman you'll double her capital in six months if she'll give it you to handle and she won't be able to give you the money quick enough. Greed, that's what it is. Just greed."

It was a sharp sensation, stimulating to the appetite (like hot sauce with ice cream) to go from this diverting ruffian to the respectability, all lavender bags and crinolines, of the St. Clairs and Miss Porchester. I spent every evening with them now. No sooner had the ladies left him than Mr. St.

Clair sent his compliments to my table and asked me to drink a glass of port with him. When we had finished it we went into the lounge and drank coffee. Mr. St. Clair enjoyed his glass of old brandy. The hour I thus spent with them was so exquisitely boring that it had for me a singular fascination. They were told by the manageress that I had written plays.

"We used often to go to the theatre when Sir Henry Irving was at the Lyceum," said Mr. St. Clair. "I once had the pleasure of meeting him. I was taken to supper at the Garrick Club by Sir Everard Millais and I was introduced to Mr. Irving as he then was."

"Tell him what he said to you, Edwin," said Mrs. St. Clair.

Mr. St. Clair struck a dramatic attitude and gave not at all a bad imitation of Henry Irving.

" 'You have the actor's face, Mr. St. Clair,' he said to me. 'If you ever think of going on the stage, come to me and I will give you a part.' " Mr. St. Clair resumed his natural manner. "It was enough to turn a young man's head."

"But it didn't turn yours," I said.

"I will not deny that if I had been otherwise situated I might have allowed myself to be tempted. But I had my family to think of. It would have broken my father's heart if I had not gone into the business."

"What is that?" I asked.

"I am a tea-merchant, sir. My firm is the oldest in the City of London. I have spent forty years of my life in combating to the best of my ability the desire of my fellow-countrymen to drink Ceylon tea instead of the China tea which was universally drunk in my youth."

I thought it charmingly characteristic of him to spend a lifetime in persuading the public to buy something they didn't want rather than something they did.

"But in his younger days my husband did a lot of amateur acting and he was thought very clever," said Mrs. St. Clair.

"Shakespeare, you know, and sometimes *The School for Scandal*. I would never consent to act trash. But that is a thing of the past. I had a gift. Perhaps it was a pity to waste it, but it's too late now. When we have a dinner-party I

sometimes let the ladies persuade me to recite the great solil-
oquies of Hamlet. But that is all I do."

Oh! Oh! Oh! I thought with shuddering fascination of
those dinner-parties and wondered whether I should ever be
asked to one of them. Mrs. St. Clair gave me a little smile,
half shocked, half prim.

"My husband was very bohemian as a young man," she
said.

"I sowed my wild oats. I knew quite a lot of painters and
writers, Wilkie Collins, for instance, and even men who
wrote for the papers. Watts painted a portrait of my wife,
and I bought a picture of Millais. I knew a number of the
pre-Raphaelites."

"Have you a Rossetti?" I asked.

"No. I admired Rossetti's talent, but I could not approve
of his private life. I would never buy a picture by an artist
whom I should not care to ask to dinner at my house."

My brain was reeling when Miss Porchester, looking at
her watch, said: "Are you not going to read to us to-night,
Uncle Edwin?"

I withdrew.

It was while I was drinking a glass of port with Mr. St.
Clair one evening that he told me the sad story of Miss
Porchester. She was engaged to be married to a nephew of
Mrs. St. Clair, a barrister, when it was discovered that he
had had an intrigue with the daughter of his laundress.

"It was a terrible thing," said Mr. St. Clair. "A terrible
thing. But of course my niece took the only possible course.
She returned him his ring, his letters and his photographs,
and said that she could never marry him. She implored him
to marry the young person he had wronged and said she
would be a sister to her. It broke her heart. She has never
cared for anyone since."

"And did he marry the young person?"

Mr. St. Clair shook his head and sighed.

"No, we were greatly mistaken in him. It has been a sore
grief to my dear wife to think that a nephew of hers should
behave in such a dishonourable manner. Some time later we
heard that he was engaged to a young lady in a very good

position with ten thousand pounds of her own. I considered
it my duty to write to her father and put the facts before
him. He answered my letter in a most insolent fashion. He
said he would much rather his son-in-law had a mistress before marriage than after."

"What happened then?"

"They were married and now my wife's nephew is one of
His Majesty's Judges of the High Court, and his wife is
My Lady. But we've never consented to receive them. When
my wife's nephew was knighted Eleanor suggested that we
should ask them to dinner, but my wife said that he should
never darken our doors and I upheld her."

"And the laundress's daughter?"

"She married in her own class of life and has a public-
house at Canterbury. My niece, who has a little money of
her own, did everything for her and is godmother to her
eldest child."

Poor Miss Porchester. She had sacrificed herself on the
altar of Victorian morality, and I am afraid the consciousness that she had behaved beautifully was the only benefit
she had got from it.

"Miss Porchester is a woman of striking appearance," I
said. "When she was younger she must have been perfectly
lovely. I wonder she never married somebody else."

"Miss Porchester was considered a great beauty. Alma-
Tadema admired her so much that he asked her to sit as a
model for one of his pictures, but of course we couldn't very
well allow that." Mr. St. Clair's tone conveyed that the suggestion had deeply outraged his sense of decency. "No, Miss
Porchester never cared for anyone but her cousin. She never
speaks of him and it is now thirty years since they parted, but
I am convinced that she loves him still. She is a true woman,
my dear sir, one life, one love, and though perhaps I regret
that she has been deprived of the joys of marriage and
motherhood I am bound to admire her fidelity."

But the heart of woman is incalculable, and rash is the
man who thinks she will remain in one stay. Rash, Uncle
Edwin. You have known Eleanor for many years, for when,

her mother having fallen into a decline and died, you brought the orphan to your comfortable and even luxurious house in Leinster Square, she was but a child; but what, when it comes down to brass tacks, Uncle Edwin, do you really know of Eleanor?

It was but two days after Mr. St. Clair had confided to me the touching story which explained why Miss Porchester had remained a spinster that, coming back to the hotel in the afternoon after a round of golf, the manageress came up to me in an agitated manner.

"Mr. St. Clair's compliments and will you go up to number twenty-seven the moment you come in."

"Certainly. But why?"

"Oh, there's a rare upset. They'll tell you."

I knocked at the door. I heard a "come in, come in," which reminded me that Mr. St. Clair had played Shakespearean parts in probably the most refined amateur dramatic company in London. I entered and found Mrs. St. Clair lying on the sofa with a handkerchief soaked in eau-de-Cologne on her brow and a bottle of smelling salts in her hand. Mr. St. Clair was standing in front of the fire in such a manner as to prevent anyone else in the room from obtaining any benefit from it.

"I must apologize for asking you to come up in this unceremonious fashion, but we are in great distress, and we thought you might be able to throw some light on what has happened."

His perturbation was obvious.

"What *has* happened?"

"Our niece, Miss Porchester, has eloped. This morning she sent in a message to my wife that she had one of her sick headaches. When she has one of her sick headaches she likes to be left absolutely alone, and it wasn't till this afternoon that my wife went to see if there was anything she could do for her. The room was empty. Her trunk was packed. Her dressing-case with silver fittings was gone. And on the pillow was a letter telling us of her rash act."

"I'm very sorry," I said. "I don't know exactly what I can do."

"We were under the impression that you were the only gentleman at Elsom with whom she had any acquaintance."

His meaning flashed across me.

"I haven't eloped with her," I said. "I happen to be a married man."

"I see you haven't eloped with her. At the first moment we thought perhaps . . . but if it isn't you, who is it?"

"I'm sure I don't know."

"Show him the letter, Edwin," said Mrs. St. Clair from the sofa.

"Don't move, Gertrude. It will bring on your lumbago."

Miss Porchester had "her" sick headaches and Mrs. St. Clair had "her" lumbago. What had Mr. St. Clair? I was willing to bet a fiver that Mr. St. Clair had "his" gout. He gave me the letter and I read it with an air of decent commiseration.

Dearest Uncle Edwin and Aunt Gertrude:

When you receive this I shall be far away. I am going to be married this morning to a gentleman who is very dear to me. I know I am doing wrong in running away like this, but I was afraid you would endeavour to set obstacles in the way of my marriage, and since nothing would induce me to change my mind I thought it would save us all much unhappiness if I did it without telling you anything about it. My fiancé is a very retiring man, owing to his long residence in tropical countries not in the best of health, and he thought it much better that we should be married quite privately. When you know how radiantly happy I am I hope you will forgive me. Please send my box to the luggage office at Victoria Station.

Your loving niece,
Eleanor.

"I will never forgive her," said Mr. St. Clair as I returned him the letter. "She shall never darken my doors again. Gertrude, I forbid you ever to mention Eleanor's name in my hearing."

Mrs. St. Clair began to sob quietly.

"Aren't you rather hard?" I said. "Is there any reason why Miss Porchester shouldn't marry?"

"At her age?" he answered angrily. "It's ridiculous. We

shall be the laughing-stock of everyone in Leinster Square. Do you know how old she is? She's fifty-one."

"Fifty-four," said Mrs. St. Clair through her sobs.

"She's been the apple of my eye. She's been like a daughter to us. She's been an old maid for years. I think it's positively improper for her to think of marriage."

"She was always a girl to us, Edwin," pleaded Mrs. St. Clair.

"And who is this man she's married? It's the deception that rankles. She must have been carrying on with him under our very noses. She does not even tell us his name. I fear the very worst."

Suddenly I had an inspiration. That morning after breakfast I had gone out to buy myself some cigarettes and at the tobacconist's I ran across Mortimer Ellis. I had not seen him for some days.

"You're looking very spruce," I said.

His boots had been repaired and were neatly blacked, his hat was brushed, he was wearing a clean collar and new gloves. I thought he had laid out my two pounds to advantage.

"I have to go to London this morning on business," he said.

I nodded and left the shop.

I remembered that a fortnight before, walking in the country, I had met Miss Porchester and, a few yards behind, Mortimer Ellis. Was it possible that they had been walking together and he had fallen back as they caught sight of me? By heaven, I saw it all.

"I think you said that Miss Porchester had money of her own," I said.

"A trifle. She has three thousand pounds."

Now I was certain. I looked at them blankly. Suddenly Mrs. St. Clair, with a cry, sprang to her feet.

"Edwin, Edwin, supposing he doesn't marry her?"

Mr. St. Clair at this put his hand to his head and in a state of collapse sank into a chair.

"The disgrace would kill me," he groaned.

"Don't be alarmed," I said. "He'll marry her all right. He always does. He'll marry her in church."

They paid no attention to what I said. I suppose they thought I'd suddenly taken leave of my senses. I was quite sure now. Mortimer Ellis had achieved his ambition after all. Miss Porchester completed the Round Dozen.

THE VESSEL OF WRATH

THERE are few books in the world that contain more meat than the Sailing Directions published by the Hydrographic Department by order of the Lords Commissioners of the Admiralty. They are handsome volumes, bound (very flimsily) in cloth of different colours, and the most expensive of them is cheap. For four shillings you can buy the Yangste Kiang Pilot, "containing a description of, and sailing directions for, the Yangste Kiang from the Wusung River to the highest navigable point, including the Han Kiang, the Kialing Kiang, and the Min Kiang"; and for three shillings you can get Part III of the Eastern Archipelago Pilot, "comprising the N.E. end of Celebes, Molucca and Gilolo passages, Banda and Arafura Seas, and North, West, and South-West coasts of New Guinea." But it is not very safe to do so if you are a creature of settled habits that you have no wish to disturb or if you have an occupation that holds you fast to one place. These business-like books take you upon enchanted journeys of the spirit; and their matter-of-fact style, the admirable order, the concision with which the material is set before you, the stern sense of the practical that informs every line, cannot dim the poetry that, like the spice-laden breeze that assails your senses with a more than material languor when you approach some of those magic islands of the Eastern seas, blows, with so sweet a fragrance through the printed pages. They tell you the anchorages and the landing places, what supplies you can get at each spot, and where you can get water; they tell you the lights and buoys, tides, winds and weather that you will find there. They give you brief information about the population and the trade. And it is strange when you think how sedately it is all set down, with no words wasted, that so much else is given you besides. What? Well, mystery and beauty, romance and the glamour of the unknown. It is no common book that offers you casually turning its pages such a paragraph as this: "Supplies. A few jungle fowl are preserved, the island is also the resort of vast numbers of sea birds. Turtle are found in the lagoon, as well as quantities of various fish, including grey mullet, shark, and dog-fish; the seine cannot be used with any effect; but there is a fish which may be taken on a rod. A small store of tinned provisions and spirits is kept in a hut for the relief of shipwrecked persons. Good water may be obtained from a well near the landing place." Can the imagination want more material than this to go on a journey through time and space?

In the volume from which I have copied this passage, the compilers with the same restraint have described the Alas Islands. They are composed of a group or chain of islands, "for the most part low and wooded, extending about 75 miles east and west, and 40 miles north and south." The information about them, you are told, is very slight; there are channels between the different groups, and several vessels have passed through them, but the passages have not been thoroughly explored, and the positions of many of the dangers not yet determined; it is therefore advisable to avoid them. The population of the group is estimated at about 8000, of whom 200 are Chinese and 400 Mohammedans. The rest are heathen. The principal island is called Baru, it is surrounded by a reef, and here lives a Dutch Controleur. His white house with its red roof on the top of a little hill is the most prominent object that the vessels of the Royal Netherlands Steam Packet Company see when every other month on their way up to Macassar and every four weeks on their way down to Merauke in Dutch New Guinea they touch at the island.

At a certain moment of the world's history the Controleur was Mynheer Evert Gruyter and he ruled the people who inhabited the Alas Islands with firmness tempered by a keen sense of the ridiculous. He had thought it a very good joke to be placed at the age of twenty-seven in a position of such consequence and at thirty he was still amused by it. There was no cable communication between his islands and Batavia, and the mail arrived after so long a delay that even if he asked advice, by the time he received it, it was useless, and so he equably did what he thought best and trusted to his good fortune to keep out of trouble with the authorities. He was very short, not more than five feet four in height, and extremely fat; he was of a florid complexion. For coolness' sake he kept his head shaved and his face was hairless. It was round and red. His eyebrows were so fair that you hardly saw them; and he had little twinkling blue eyes. He knew that he had no dignity, but for the sake of his position made up for it by dressing very dapperly. He never went to his office, nor sat in court, nor walked abroad but in spotless white. His stengah-shifter, with its bright brass buttons, fitted him very tightly and displayed the shocking fact that, young though he was, he had a round and protruding belly. His good-humoured face shone with sweat and he constantly fanned himself with a palm-leaf fan.

But in his house Mr. Gruyter preferred to wear nothing but a sarong and then with his white podgy little body he looked like a fat funny boy of sixteen. He was an early riser and his breakfast was always ready for him at six. It never varied. It consisted of a slice of papaia, three cold fried eggs, Edam cheese, sliced thin, and a cup of black coffee. When he had eaten it, he smoked a large Dutch cigar, read the papers if he had not read them through and through already, and then dressed to go down to his office.

One morning while he was thus occupied his head boy came into his bedroom and told him that Tuan Jones wanted to know if he could see him. Mr. Gruyter was standing in front of a looking-glass. He had his trousers on and was admiring his smooth chest. He arched his back in order to throw it out and throw in his belly and with a good deal of satisfaction gave his breast three or four resounding slaps. It was a manly chest. When the boy brought the message he looked at his own eyes in the mirror and exchanged a slightly ironic smile with them. He asked himself what the devil his visitor could want. Evert Gruyter spoke English, Dutch and Malay with equal facility, but he thought in Dutch. He liked to do this. It seemed to him a pleasantly ribald language.

"Ask the Tuan to wait and say I shall come directly." He put on his tunic, over his naked body, buttoned it up, and strutted into the sitting-room. The Rev. Owen Jones got up.

"Good-morning, Mr. Jones," said the Controleur. "Have you come in to have a peg with me before I start my day's work?"

Mr. Jones did not smile.

"I've come to see you upon a very distressing matter, Mr. Gruyter," he answered.

The Controleur was not disconcerted by his visitor's gravity nor depressed by his words. His little blue eyes beamed amiably.

"Sit down, my dear fellow, and have a cigar."

Mr. Gruyter knew quite well that the Rev. Owen Jones neither drank nor smoked, but it tickled something prankish in his nature to offer him a drink and a smoke whenever they met. Mr. Jones shook his head.

Mr. Jones was in charge of the Baptist Mission on the Alas Islands. His headquarters were at Baru, the largest of them, with the greatest population, but he had meeting-houses under the care of native helpers in several other islands of the group. He was a tall, thin melancholy man, with a long face, sallow and drawn, of about forty. His brown hair was already white on the temples and it receded from the forehead. This gave him a look of somewhat vacuous intellectuality. Mr. Gruyter both disliked and respected him. He disliked him because he was narrow-minded and dogmatic. Himself a cheerful pagan who liked the good things of the flesh and was determined to get as many of them as his circumstances permitted, he had no patience with a man who disapproved of them all. He thought the customs of the country suited its inhabitants and had no patience with the missionary's energetic efforts to destroy a way of life that for centuries had worked very well. He respected him because he was honest, zealous and good. Mr. Jones, an Australian of Welsh descent, was the only qualified doctor in the group and it was a comfort to know that if you fell ill you need not rely only on a Chinese practitioner, and none knew better than the Controleur how useful to all Mr. Jones's skill had been and with what charity he had given it. On the occasion of an epidemic of influenza the missionary had done the work of ten men and no storm short of a typhoon could prevent him from crossing to one island or another if his help was needed.

He lived with his sister in a little white house about half a mile from the village and when the Controleur had arrived, came on board to meet him and begged him to stay till he could get his own house in order. The Controleur had accepted and soon saw for himself with what simplicity the couple lived. It was more than he could stand. Tea at three sparse meals a day and when he lit his cigar Mr. Jones politely but firmly asked him to be good enough not to smoke since both his sister and he strongly disapproved of it. In twenty-four hours Mr. Gruyter moved into his own house. He fled, with panic in his heart, as though from a plague-stricken city. The Controleur was fond of a joke and he liked to laugh; to be with a man who took your nonsense in deadly earnest and never even smiled at your best story was more than flesh and blood could stand. The Rev. Owen Jones was a worthy man, but as a companion he was impossible. His sister was worse. Neither had a sense of humour, but whereas the missionary was of a melancholy turn, doing his duty so conscientiously, with the obvious conviction that everything in the world was hopeless, Miss Jones was resolutely cheerful. She grimly looked on the bright side of things. With the ferocity of an avenging angel she sought out the good in her fellow men. Miss Jones taught in the mission school and helped her brother in his medical work. When he did operations she gave the anæsthetic and was matron, dresser and nurse of the tiny hospital which on his own initiative Mr. Jones had added to the mission. But the Controleur was an obstinate little fellow and he never lost his capacity of extracting amusement from the Rev. Owen's dour struggle with the infirmities of human nature, and Miss Jones's ruthless optimism. He had to get his fun where he could. The

Dutch boats came in three times in two months for a few hours and then he could have a good old crack with the captain and chief engineer, and once in a blue moon a pearling lugger came in from Thursday Island or Port Darwin and for two or three days he had a grand time. They were rough fellows, the pearlers, for the most part, but they were full of guts, and they had plenty of liquor on board, and good stories to tell, and the Controleur had them up to his house and gave them a fine dinner and the party was only counted a success if they were all too drunk to get back on the lugger again that night. But besides the missionary the only white man who lived on Baru was Ginger Ted, and he, of course, was a disgrace to civilisation. There was not a single thing to be said in his favour. He cast discredit on the white race. All the same, but for Ginger Ted the Controleur sometimes thought he would find life on the island of Baru almost more than he could bear.

Oddly enough it was on account of this scamp that Mr. Jones, when he should have been instructing the pagan young in the mysteries of the Baptist faith, was paying Mr. Gruyter this early visit.

"Sit down, Mr. Jones," said the Controleur. "What can I do for you?"

"Well, I've come to see you about the man they call Ginger Ted. What are you going to do now?"

"Why, what's happened?"

"Haven't you heard? I thought the sergeant would have told you."

"I don't encourage the members of my staff to come to my private house unless the matter is urgent," said the Controleur rather grandly. "I am unlike you, Mr. Jones, I only work in order to have leisure and I like to enjoy my leisure without disturbance."

But Mr. Jones did not care much for small talk and he was not interested in general reflections.

"There was a disgraceful row in one of the Chinese shops last night. Ginger Ted wrecked the place and half killed a Chinaman."

"Drunk again, I suppose," said the Controleur placidly.

"Naturally. When is he anything else? They sent for the police and he assaulted the sergeant. They had to have six men to get him to the gaol."

"He's a hefty fellow," said the Controleur.

"I suppose you'll send him to Macassar."

Evert Gruyter returned the missionary's outraged look with a merry twinkle. He was no fool and he knew already what Mr. Jones was up to. It gave him considerable amusement to tease him a little.

"Fortunately my powers are wide enough to enable me to deal with the situation myself," he answered.

"You have power to deport anyone you like, Mr. Gruyter, and I'm sure it would save a lot of trouble if you got rid of the man altogether."

"I have the power of course, but I am sure you would be the last person to wish me to use it arbitrarily."

"Mr. Gruyter, the man's presence here is a public scandal. He's never sober from morning till night; it's notorious that he has relations with one native woman after another."

"That is an interesting point, Mr. Jones. I had always heard that alcoholic excess, though it stimulated sexual desire, prevented its gratification. What you tell me about Ginger Ted does not seem to bear out this theory."

The missionary flushed a dull red.

"These are physiological matters which at the moment I have no wish to go into," he said, frigidly. "The behaviour of this man does incalculable damage to the prestige of the white race, and his example seriously hampers the efforts that are made in other quarters to induce the people of these islands to lead a less vicious life. He's an out and out bad lot."

"Pardon my asking, but have you made any attempts to reform him?"

"When he first drifted here I did my best to get in touch with him. He repelled all my advances. When there was that first trouble I went to him and talked to him straight from the shoulder. He swore at me."

"No one has a greater appreciation than I of the excellent work that you and other missionaries do on these islands, but are you sure that you always exercise your calling with all the tact possible?"

The Controleur was rather pleased with this phrase. It was extremely courteous and yet contained a reproof that he thought worth administering. The missionary looked at him gravely. His sad brown eyes were full of sincerity.

"Did Jesus exercise tact when he took a whip and drove the money-changers from the Temple? No, Mr. Gruyter. Tact is the subterfuge the lax avail themselves of to avoid doing their duty."

Mr. Jones's remark made the Controleur feel suddenly that he wanted a bottle of beer. The missionary leaned forward earnestly.

"Mr. Gruyter, you know this man's transgressions just as well as I do. It's unnecessary for me to remind you of them. There are no excuses for him. Now he really has over-stepped the limit. You'll never have a better chance than this. I beg you to use the power you have and turn him out once for all."

The Controleur's eyes twinkled more brightly than ever. He was having a lot of fun. He reflected that human beings were much more amusing when you did not feel called upon in dealing with them to allot praise or blame.

"But Mr. Jones, do I understand you right? Are you asking me to give you an assurance to deport this man before I've heard the evidence against him and listened to his defence?"

"I don't know what his defence can be."

The Controleur rose from his chair and really he managed to get quite a little dignity into his five feet four inches.

"I am here to administer justice according to the laws of the Dutch Government. Permit me to tell you that I am exceedingly surprised that you should attempt to influence me in my judicial functions."

The missionary was a trifle flustered. It had never occurred to him that this little whipper-snapper of a boy, ten years younger than himself, would dream of adopting such an attitude. He opened his mouth to explain and apologise, but the Controleur raised a podgy little hand.

"It is time for me to go to my office, Mr. Jones. I wish you good-morning."

The missionary, taken aback, bowed and without another word walked out of the room. He would have been surprised to see what the Controleur did when his back was turned. A broad grin broke on his lips and he put his thumb to his nose and cocked a snook at the Rev. Owen Jones.

A few minutes later he went down to his office. His head clerk, who was a Dutch half-caste, gave him his version of the previous night's row. It agreed pretty well with Mr. Jones's. The Court was sitting that day.

"Will you take Ginger Ted first, sir?" asked the clerk.

"I see no reason to do that. There are two or three cases held over from the last sitting. I will take him in his proper order."

"I thought perhaps as he was a white man you would like to see him privately, sir."

"The majesty of the law knows no difference between white and coloured, my friend," said Mr. Gruyter, somewhat pompously.

The Court was a big square room with wooden benches on which, crowded together, sat natives of all kinds, Polynesians, Bugis, Chinese, Malays, and they all rose when a door was opened and a sergeant announced the arrival of the Controleur. He entered with his clerk and took his place on a little dais at a table of varnished pitch pine. Behind him was a large engraving of Queen Wilhelmina. He despatched half a dozen cases and then Ginger Ted was brought in. He stood in the dock, handcuffed, with a warder on either side of him. The Controleur looked at him with a grave face, but he could not keep the amusement out of his eyes.

Ginger Ted was suffering from a hangover. He swayed a little as he stood and his eyes were vacant. He was a man still young, thirty perhaps, of somewhat over the middle height, rather fat, with a bloated red face and a shock of curly red hair. He had not come out of the tussle unscathed. He had a black eye and his mouth was cut and swollen. He wore khaki shorts, very dirty and ragged, and his singlet had been almost torn off his back. A great rent showed the thick mat of red hair with which his chest was covered, but showed also the astonishing whiteness of his skin. The Controleur looked at the charge sheet. He called the evidence. When he had heard it, when he had seen the Chinaman whose head Ginger Ted had broken with a bottle, when he had heard the agitated story of the sergeant who had been knocked flat when he tried to arrest him, when he had listened to the tale of the havoc wrought by Ginger Ted who in his drunken fury had smashed everything he could lay hands on, he turned and addressed the accused in English.

"Well, Ginger, what have you got to say for yourself?"

"I was blind. I don't remember a thing about it. If they say I half killed 'im I suppose I did. I'll pay the damage if they'll give me time."

"You will, Ginger," said the Controleur, "but it's me who'll give you time."

He looked at Ginger Ted for a minute in silence. He was an unappetising object. A man who had gone completely to pieces. He was horrible. It made you shudder to look at him and if Mr. Jones had not been so officious, at that moment the Controleur would certainly have ordered him to be deported.

"You've been a trouble ever since you came to the islands, Ginger. You're a disgrace. You're incorrigibly idle. You've been picked up in the street dead drunk time and time again. You've kicked up row after row. You're hopeless. I told you the last time you were brought here that if you were arrested again I should deal with you severely. You've gone the limit this time and you're for it. I sentence you to six months' hard labour."

"Me?"

"You."

"By God, I'll kill you when I come out."

He burst into a string of oaths both filthy and blasphemous. Mr. Gruyter listened scornfully. You can swear much better in Dutch than in English and there was nothing that Ginger Ted said that he could not have effectively capped.

"Be quiet," he ordered. "You make me tired."

The Controleur repeated his sentence in Malay and the prisoner was led struggling away.

Mr. Gruyter sat down to tiffin in high good humour. It was astonishing how amusing life could be if you exercised a little ingenuity. There were people in Amsterdam, and even in Batavia and Surabaya, who looked upon his island home as a place of exile. They little knew how agreeable it was and what fun he could extract from unpromising material. They asked him whether he did not miss the club and the races and the cinema, the dances that were held once a week at the Casino and the society of Dutch ladies. Not at all. He liked comfort. The substantial furniture of the room in which he sat had a satisfying solidity. He liked reading French novels of a frivolous nature and he appreciated the sensation of reading one after the other without the uneasiness occasioned by the thought that he was wasting his time. It seemed to him a great luxury to waste time. When his young man's fancy turned to thoughts of love his head boy brought to the house a little dark-skinned bright-eyed creature in a sarong. He took care to form no connection of a permanent nature. He thought that change kept the heart young. He enjoyed freedom and was not weighed down by a sense of responsibility. He did not mind the heat. It made a sluice over with cold water half a dozen times a day a pleasure that had almost an æsthetic quality. He played the piano. He wrote letters to his friends in Holland. He felt no need for the conversation of intellectual persons. He liked a good laugh, but he could get that out of a fool just as well as out of a professor of philosophy. He had a notion that he was a very wise little man.

Like all good Dutchmen in the Far East he began his lunch with a small glass of Hollands gin. It has a musty acrid flavour, and the taste for it must be acquired, but Mr. Gruyter preferred it to any cocktail. When he drank it he felt besides that he was upholding the traditions of his race. Then he had *rystafel*. He had it every day. He heaped a soup-plate high with rice, and then, his three boys waiting on him, helped himself to the curry that one handed him, to the fried egg that another brought, and to the condiment pre-

sented by the third. Then each one brought another dish, of
bacon, or bananas, or pickled fish, and presently his plate
was piled high in a huge pyramid. He stirred it all together
and began to eat. He ate slowly and with relish. He drank
a bottle of beer.

He did not think while he was eating. His attention was
applied to the mass in front of him and he consumed it with
a happy concentration. It never palled on him. And when he
had emptied the great plate it was a compensation to think
that next day he would have *rystafel* again. He grew tired
of it as little as the rest of us grow tired of bread. He finished
his beer and lit his cigar. The boy brought him a cup of
coffee. He leaned back in his chair then and allowed himself
the luxury of reflection.

It tickled him to have sentenced Ginger Ted to the richly
deserved punishment of six months' hard labour, and he
smiled when he thought of him working on the roads with
the other prisoners. It would have been silly to deport from
the island the one man with whom he could occasionally have
a heart-to-heart talk, and besides, the satisfaction it would
have given the missionary would have been bad for that
gentleman's character. Ginger Ted was a scamp and a scally-
wag, but the Controleur had a kindly feeling for him. They
had drunk many a bottle of beer in one another's company
and when the pearl fishers from Port Darwin came in and
they all made a night of it, they had got gloriously tight together. The Controleur liked the reckless way in which
Ginger Ted squandered the priceless treasure of life.

Ginger Ted had wandered in one day on the ship that was
going up from Merauke to Macassar. The captain did not
know how he had found his way there, but he had travelled
steerage with the natives, and he stopped off at the Alas
Islands because he liked the look of them. Mr. Gruyter had
a suspicion that their attraction consisted perhaps in their
being under the Dutch flag and so out of British jurisdiction.
But his papers were in order, so there was no reason why he
should not stay. He said that he was buying pearl-shell for
an Australian firm, but it soon appeared that his commercial
undertakings were not serious. Drink, indeed, took up so

much of his time that he had little left over for other pursuits. He was in receipt of two pounds a week, paid monthly, which came regularly to him from England. The Controleur guessed that this sum was paid only so long as he kept well away from the persons who sent it. It was anyway too small to permit him any liberty of movement. Ginger Ted was reticent. The Controleur discovered that he was an Englishman, this he learnt from his passport, which described him as Edward Wilson, and that he had been in Australia. But why he had left England and what he had done in Australia he had no notion. Nor could he ever quite tell to what class Ginger Ted belonged. When you saw him in a filthy singlet and a pair of ragged trousers, a battered topi on his head, with the pearl fishers and heard his conversation, coarse, obscene and illiterate, you thought he must be a sailor before the mast who had deserted his ship, or a labourer, but when you saw his handwriting you were surprised to find that it was that of a man not without at least some education, and on occasion when you got him alone, if he had had a few drinks but was not yet drunk, he would talk of matters that neither a sailor nor a labourer would have been likely to know anything about. The Controleur had a certain sensitiveness and he realised that Ginger Ted did not speak to him as an inferior to a superior but as an equal. Most of his remittance was mortgaged before he received it, and the Chinamen to whom he owed money were standing at his elbow when the monthly letter was delivered to him, but with what was left he proceeded to get drunk. It was then that he made trouble, for when drunk he grew violent and was then likely to commit acts that brought him into the hands of the police. Hitherto Mr. Gruyter had contented himself with keeping him in gaol till he was sober and giving him a talking to. When he was out of money he cadged what drink he could from anyone who would give it him. Rum, brandy, arak, it was all the same to him. Two or three times Mr. Gruyter had got him work on plantations run by Chinese in one or other of the islands, but he could not stick to it, and in a few weeks was back again at Baru on the beach. It was a miracle how he kept body and soul together. He had, of course, a way with him. He picked up the various dialects spoken on the islands, and knew how to make the natives laugh. They despised him, but they respected his physical strength, and they liked his company. He was as a result never at a loss for a meal or a mat to sleep on. The strange thing was, and it was this that chiefly outraged the Rev. Owen Jones, that he could do anything he liked with a woman. The Controleur could not imagine what it was they saw in him. He was casual with them and rather brutal. He took what they gave him, but seemed incapable of gratitude. He used them for his pleasure and then flung them indifferently away. Once or twice this had got him into trouble, and Mr. Gruyter had had to sentence an angry father for sticking a knife in Ginger Ted's back one night, and a Chinese woman had sought to poison herself by swallowing opium because he had deserted her. Once Mr. Jones came to the Controleur in a great state because the beachcomber had seduced one of his converts. The Controleur agreed that it was very deplorable, but could only advise Mr. Jones to keep a sharp eye on these young persons. The Controleur liked it less when he discovered that a girl whom he fancied a good deal himself and had been seeing for several weeks had all the time been according her favours also to Ginger Ted. When he thought of this particular incident he smiled again at the thought of Ginger Ted doing six months' hard labour. It is seldom in this life that in the process of doing your bounden duty you can get back on a fellow who has played you a dirty trick.

A few days later Mr. Gruyter was taking a walk, partly for exercise and partly to see that some job he wanted done was being duly proceeded with, when he passed a gang of prisoners working under the charge of a warder. Among them he saw Ginger Ted. He wore the prison sarong, a dingy tunic called in Malay a baju, and his own battered topi. They were repairing the road, and Ginger Ted was wielding a heavy pick. The way was narrow and the Controleur saw that he must pass within a foot of him. He remembered his threats. He knew that Ginger Ted was a man of violent passion and the language he had used in the dock made it plain that he had not seen what a good joke it was of the Controleur's to sentence him to six months' hard labour. If Ginger Ted suddenly attacked him with the pick, nothing on God's earth could save him. It was true that the warder would immediately shoot him down, but meanwhile the Controleur's head would be bashed in. It was with a funny little feeling in the pit of his stomach that Mr. Gruyter walked through the gang of prisoners. They were working in pairs a few feet from one another. He set his mind on neither hastening his pace nor slackening it. As he passed Ginger Ted, the man swung his pick into the ground and looked up at the Controleur and as he caught his eye winked. The Controleur checked the smile that rose to his lips and with official dignity strode on. But that wink, so lusciously full of sardonic humour, filled him with satisfaction. If he had been the Caliph of Bagdad instead of a junior official in the Dutch Civil Service, he would forthwith have released Ginger Ted, sent slaves to bathe and perfume him, and having clothed him in a golden robe entertained him to a sumptuous repast.

Ginger Ted was an exemplary prisoner and in a month or two the Controleur, having occasion to send a gang to do some work on one of the outlying islands, included him in it. There was no gaol there, so the ten fellows he sent, under the charge of a warder, were billeted on the natives and after their day's work lived like free men. The job was sufficient to take up the rest of Ginger Ted's sentence. The Controleur saw him before he left.

"Look here, Ginger," he said to him, "here's ten guilder for you so that you can buy yourself tobacco when you're gone."

"Couldn't you make it a bit more? There's eight pounds a month coming in regularly."

"I think that's enough. I'll keep the letters that come for you, and when you get back you'll have a tidy sum. You'll have enough to take you anywhere you want to go."

"I'm very comfortable here," said Ginger Ted.

"Well, the day you come back, clean yourself up and come over to my house. We'll have a bottle of beer together."

"That'll be fine. I guess I'll be ready for a good crack then."

Now chance steps in. The island to which Ginger Ted had been sent was called Maputiti, and like all the rest of them it was rocky, heavily wooded and surrounded by a reef. There was a village among coconuts on the sea-shore opposite the opening of the reef and another village on a brackish lake in the middle of the island. Of this some of the inhabitants had been converted to Christianity. Communication with Baru was effected by a launch that touched at the various islands at irregular intervals. It carried passengers and produce. But the villagers were seafaring folk, and if they had to communicate urgently with Baru, manned a prahu and sailed the fifty miles or so that separated them from it. It happened that when Ginger Ted's sentence had but another fortnight to run the Christian headman of the village on the lake was taken suddenly ill. The native remedies availed him nothing and he writhed in agony. Messengers were sent to Baru imploring the missionary's help; but as ill luck would have it Mr. Jones was suffering at the moment from an attack of malaria. He was in bed and unable to move. He talked the matter over with his sister.

"It sounds like acute appendicitis," he told her.

"You can't go, Owen," she said.

"I can't let the man die."

Mr. Jones had a temperature of a hundred and four. His head was aching like mad. He had been delirious all night. His eyes were shining strangely and his sister felt that he was holding on to his wits by a sheer effort of will.

"You couldn't operate in the state you're in."

"No, I couldn't. Then Hassan must go."

Hassan was the dispenser.

"You couldn't trust Hassan. He'd never dare to do an operation on his own responsibility. And they'd never let him. I'll go. Hassan can stay here and look after you."

"You can't remove an appendix?"

"Why not? I've seen you do it. I've done lots of minor operations."

Mr. Jones felt he didn't quite understand what she was saying.

"Is the launch in?"

"No, it's gone to one of the islands. But I can go in the prahu the men came in."

"You? I wasn't thinking of you. You can't go."

"I'm going, Owen."

"Going where?" he said.

She saw that his mind was wandering already. She put her hand soothingly on his dry forehead. She gave him a dose of medicine. He muttered something and she realised that he did not know where he was. Of course she was anxious about him, but she knew that his illness was not dangerous, and she could leave him safely to the mission boy who was helping her nurse him and to the native dispenser. She slipped out of the room. She put her toilet things, a night-dress, and a change of clothes into a bag. A little chest with surgical instruments, bandages and antiseptic dressings was kept always ready. She gave them to the two natives who had come over from Maputiti, and telling the dispenser what she was going to do gave him instructions to inform her brother when he was able to listen. Above all he was not to be anxious about her. She put on her topi and sallied forth. The mission was about half a mile from the village. She walked quickly. At the end of the jetty the prahu was waiting. Six men manned it. She took her place in the stern and they set off with a rapid stroke. Within the reef the sea was calm, but when they crossed the bar they came upon a long swell. But this was not the first journey of the sort Miss Jones had taken and she was confident in the seaworthiness of the boat she was in. It was noon and the sun beat down from a sultry sky. The only thing that harassed her was that they could not arrive before dark, and if she found it necessary to operate at once she could count only on the light of hurricane lamps.

Miss Jones was a woman of hard on forty. Nothing in her appearance would have prepared you for such determination as she had just shown. She had an odd drooping gracefulness, which suggested that she might be swayed by every breeze; it was almost an affectation; and it made the strength of character which you soon discovered in her seem positively monstrous. She was flat-chested, tall and extremely thin. She had a long sallow face and she was much afflicted with prickly heat. Her lank brown hair was drawn back straight from her forehead. She had rather small eyes, grey in colour, and because they were somewhat too close they gave her face a shrewish look. Her nose was long and thin and a trifle red. She suffered a good deal from indigestion. But this infirmity availed nothing against her ruthless determination to look upon the bright side of things. Firmly persuaded that the world was evil and men unspeakably vicious, she extracted any little piece of decency she could find in them with the modest pride with which a conjurer extracts a rabbit from a hat. She was quick, resourceful and competent. When she arrived on the island she saw that there was not a moment to lose if she was to save the headman's life. Under the greatest difficulties, showing a native how to give the anæsthetic, she operated, and for the next three days nursed the patient with anxious assiduity. Everything went very well and she realised that her brother could not have made a better job of it. She waited long enough to take out the stitches and then prepared to go home. She could flatter herself that she had not wasted her time. She had given medical attention to such as needed it, she had strengthened the small Christian community in its faith, admonished such as were lax and cast the good seed in places where it might be hoped under divine providence to take root.

The launch, coming from one of the other islands, put in somewhat late in the afternoon, but it was full moon and they expected to reach Baru before midnight. They brought her things down to the wharf and the people who were seeing her off stood about repeating their thanks. Quite a little crowd collected. The launch was loaded with sacks of copra, but Miss Jones was used to its strong smell and it did not incommode her. She made herself as comfortable a place to sit in as she could, and waiting for the launch to start, chatted with her grateful flock. She was the only passenger. Suddenly a group of natives emerged from the trees that embowered the little village on the lagoon and she saw that among them was a white man. He wore a prison sarong and a baju. He had long red hair. She at once recognised Ginger

THE VESSEL OF WRATH

Ted. A policeman was with him. They shook hands and Ginger Ted shook hands with the villagers who accompanied him. They bore bundles of fruit and a jar which Miss Jones guessed contained native spirit, and these they put in the launch. She discovered to her surprise that Ginger Ted was coming with her. His term was up and instructions had arrived that he was to be returned to Baru in the launch. He gave her a glance, but did not nod—indeed Miss Jones turned away her head—and stepped in. The mechanic started his engine and in a moment they were jug-jugging through the channel in the lagoon. Ginger Ted clambered on to a pile of sacks and lit a cigarette.

Miss Jones ignored him. Of course she knew him very well. Her heart sank when she thought that he was going to be once more in Baru, creating a scandal and drinking, a peril to the women and a thorn in the flesh of all decent people. She knew the steps her brother had taken to have him deported and she had no patience with the Controleur, who would not see a duty that stared him so plainly in the face. When they had crossed the bar and were in the open sea Ginger Ted took the stopper out of the jar of arak and putting his mouth to it took a long pull. Then he handed the jar to the two mechanics who formed the crew. One was a middle-aged man and the other a youth.

"I do not wish you to drink anything while we are on the journey," said Miss Jones sternly to the elder one.

He smiled at her and drank.

"A little arak can do no one any harm," he answered. He passed the jar to his companion, who drank also.

"If you drink again I shall complain to the Controleur," said Miss Jones.

The elder man said something she could not understand, but which she suspected was very rude, and passed the jar back to Ginger Ted. They went along for an hour or more. The sea was like glass and the sun set radiantly. It set behind one of the islands and for a few minutes changed it into a mystic city of the skies. Miss Jones turned round to watch it and her heart was filled with gratitude for the beauty of the world.

"And only man is vile," she quoted to herself.

They went due east. In the distance was a little island which she knew they passed close by. It was uninhabited. A rocky islet thickly grown with virgin forest. The boatman lit his lamps. The night fell and immediately the sky was thick with stars. The moon had not yet risen. Suddenly there was a slight jar and the launch began to vibrate strangely. The engine rattled. The head mechanic, calling to his mate to take the helm, crept under the housing. They seemed to be going more slowly. The engine stopped. She asked the youth what was the matter, but he did not know. Ginger Ted got down from the top of the copra sacks and slipped under the housing. When he reappeared she would have liked to ask him what had happened, but her dignity prevented her. She sat still and occupied herself with her thoughts. There was a long swell and the launch rolled slightly. The mechanic emerged once more into view and started the engine. Though it rattled like mad they began to move. The launch vibrated from stem to stern. They went very slowly. Evidently something was amiss, but Miss Jones was exasperated rather than alarmed. The launch was supposed to do six knots, but now it was just crawling along; at that rate they would not get into Baru till long, long after midnight. The mechanic, still busy under the housing, shouted out something to the man at the helm. They spoke in Bugi, of which Miss Jones knew very little. But after a while she noticed that they had changed their course and seemed to be heading for the little uninhabited island a good deal to the lee of which they should have passed.

"Where are we going?" she asked the helmsman with sudden misgiving.

He pointed to the islet. She got up and went to the housing and called to the man to come out.

"You're not going there? Why? What's the matter?"

"I can't get to Baru," he said.

"But you must. I insist. I order you to go to Baru."

The man shrugged his shoulders. He turned his back on her and slipped once more under the housing. Then Ginger Ted addressed her.

"One of the blades of the propeller has broken off. He thinks he can get as far as that island. We shall have to stay the night there and he'll put on a new propeller in the morning when the tide's out."

"I can't spend the night on an uninhabited island with three men," she cried.

"A lot of women would jump at it."

"I insist on going to Baru. Whatever happens we must get there to-night."

"Don't get excited, old girl. We've got to beach the boat to put a new propeller on, and we shall be all right on the island."

"How dare you speak to me like that! I think you're very insolent."

"You'll be O.K. We've got plenty of grub and we'll have a snack when we land. You have a drop of arak and you'll feel like a house on fire."

"You're an impertinent man. If you don't go to Baru I'll have you all put in prison."

"We're not going to Baru. We can't. We're going to that island and if you don't like it you can get out and swim."

"Oh, you'll pay for this."

"Shut up, you old cow," said Ginger Ted.

Miss Jones gave a gasp of anger. But she controlled herself. Even out there, in the middle of the ocean, she had too much dignity to bandy words with that vile wretch. The launch, the engine rattling horribly, crawled on. It was pitch dark now, and she could no longer see the island they were making for. Miss Jones, deeply incensed, sat with lips tight shut and a frown on her brow; she was not used to being crossed. Then the moon rose and she could see the bulk of Ginger Ted sprawling on the top of the piled sacks of copra. The glimmer of his cigarette was strangely sinister. Now the island was vaguely outlined against the sky. They reached it and the boatman ran the launch on to the beach. Suddenly Miss Jones gave a gasp. The truth had dawned on her and her anger changed to fear. Her heart beat violently. She shook in every limb. She felt dreadfully faint. She saw it all. Was the broken propeller a put-up job or was it an accident? She could not be certain; anyhow, she knew that Ginger Ted would seize the opportunity. Ginger Ted would rape her. She knew his character. He was mad about women. That was what he had done, practically, to the girl at the mission, such a good little thing she was and an excellent sempstress; they would have prosecuted him for that and he would have been sentenced to years of imprisonment only very unfortunately the innocent child had gone back to him several times and indeed had only complained of his ill usage when he left her for somebody else. They had gone to the Controleur about it, but he had refused to take any steps, saying in that coarse way of his that even if what the girl said was true, it didn't look very much as though it had been an altogether unpleasant experience. Ginger Ted was a scoundrel. And she was a white woman. What chance was there that he would spare her? None. She knew men. But she must pull herself together. She must keep her wits about her. She must have courage. She was determined to sell her virtue dearly, and if he killed her—well, she would rather die than yield. And if she died she would rest in the arms of Jesus. For a moment a great light blinded her eyes and she saw the mansions of her Heavenly Father. They were a grand and sumptuous mixture of a picture palace and a railway station. The mechanics and Ginger Ted jumped out of the launch and, waist deep in water, gathered round the broken propeller. She took advantage of their preoccupation to get her case of surgical instruments out of the box. She took out the four scalpels it contained and secreted them in her clothing. If Ginger Ted touched her she would not hesitate to plunge a scalpel in his heart.

"Now then, miss, you'd better get out," said Ginger Ted. "You'll be better off on the beach than in the boat."

She thought so too. At least there she would have freedom of action. Without a word she clambered over the copra sacks. He offered her his hand.

"I don't want your help," she said coldly.

"You can go to hell," he answered.

It was a little difficult to get out of the boat without showing her legs, but by the exercise of considerable ingenuity she managed it.

"Damned lucky we've got something to eat. We'll make a fire and then you'd better have a snack and a nip of arak."

"I want nothing. I only want to be left alone."

"It won't hurt me if you go hungry."

She did not answer. She walked, with head erect, along the beach. She held the largest scalpel in her closed fist. The moon allowed her to see where she was going. She looked for a place to hide. The thick forest came down to the very edge of the beach; but, afraid of its darkness (after all, she was but a woman), she dared not plunge into its depth. She did not know what animals lurked there or what dangerous snakes. Besides, her instinct told her that it was better to keep those three bad men in sight; then if they came towards her she would be prepared. Presently she found a little hollow. She looked round. They seemed to be occupied with their own affairs and they could not see her. She slipped in. There was a rock between them and her so that she was hidden from them and yet could watch them. She saw them go to and from the boat carrying things. She saw them build a fire. It lit them luridly and she saw them sit around it and eat, and she saw the jar of arak passed from one to the other. They were all going to get drunk. What would happen to her then? It might be that she could cope with Ginger Ted, though his strength terrified her, but against three she would be powerless. A mad idea came to her to go to Ginger Ted and fall on her knees before him and beg him to spare her. He must have some spark of decent feeling in him and she had always been so convinced that there was good even in the worst of men. He must have had a mother. Perhaps he had a sister. Ah, but how could you appeal to a man blinded with lust and drunk with arak? She began to feel terribly weak. She was afraid she was going to cry. That would never do. She needed all her self-control. She bit her lip. She watched them, like a tiger watching his prey; no, not like that, like a lamb watching three hungry wolves. She saw them put more wood on the fire and

Ginger Ted, in his sarong, silhouetted by the flames. Perhaps after he had had his will of her he would pass her on to the others. How could she go back to her brother when such a thing had happened to her? Of course he would be sympathetic, but would he ever feel quite the same to her again? It would break his heart. And perhaps he would think that she ought to have resisted more. For his sake perhaps it would be better if she said nothing about it, naturally the men would say nothing. It would mean twenty years in prison for them. But then supposing she had a baby. Miss Jones instinctively clenched her hands with horror and nearly cut herself with the scalpel. Of course it would only infuriate them if she resisted.

"What shall I do?" she cried. "What have I done to deserve this?"

She flung herself down on her knees and prayed to God to save her. She prayed long and earnestly. She reminded God that she was a virgin and just mentioned, in case it had slipped the divine memory, how much St. Paul had valued that excellent state. And then she peeped round the rock again. The three men appeared to be smoking and the fire was dying down. Now was the time that Ginger Ted's lewd thoughts might be expected to turn to the woman who was at his mercy. She smothered a cry, for suddenly he got up and walked in her direction. She felt all her muscles grow taut, and though her heart was beating furiously she clenched the scalpel firmly in her hand. But it was for another purpose that Ginger Ted had got up. Miss Jones blushed and looked away. He strolled slowly back to the others and sitting down again raised the jar of arak to his lips. Miss Jones, crouching behind the rock, watched with straining eyes. The conversation round the fire grew less and presently she divined, rather than saw, that the two natives wrapped themselves in blankets and composed themselves to slumber. She understood. This was the moment Ginger Ted had been waiting for. When they were fast asleep he would get up cautiously and without a sound, in order not to wake the others, creep stealthily towards her. Was it that he was unwilling to share her with them or did he know that his deed was so dastardly that he did not wish them to know of it? After all, he was a white man and she was a white woman. He could not have sunk so low as to allow her to suffer the violence of natives. But his plan, which was so obvious to her, had given her an idea; when she saw him coming she would scream, she would scream so loudly that it would wake the two mechanics. She remembered now that the elder, though he had only one eye, had a kind face. But Ginger Ted did not move. She was feeling terribly tired. She began to fear that she would not have the strength now to resist him. She had gone through too much. She closed her eyes for a minute.

When she opened them it was broad daylight. She must have fallen asleep and, so shattered was she by emotion, have slept till long after dawn. It gave her quite a turn. She sought to rise, but something caught in her legs. She looked and found that she was covered with two empty copra sacks. Someone had come in the night and put them over her. Ginger Ted. She gave a little scream. The horrible thought flashed through her mind that he had outraged her in her sleep. No. It was impossible. And yet he had had her at his mercy. Defenceless. And he had spared her. She blushed furiously. She raised herself to her feet, feeling a little stiff, and arranged her disordered dress. The scalpel had fallen from her hand and she picked it up. She took the two copra sacks and emerged from her hiding-place. She walked towards the boat. It was floating in the shallow water of the lagoon.

"Come on, Miss Jones," said Ginger Ted. "We've finished. I was just going to wake you up."

She could not look at him, but she felt herself as red as a turkey cock.

"Have a banana?" he said.

Without a word she took it. She was very hungry, and ate it with relish.

"Step on this rock and you'll be able to get in without wetting your feet."

Miss Jones felt as though she could sink into the ground with shame, but she did as he told her. He took hold of her arm—good heavens, his hand was like an iron vice, never,

never could she have struggled with him—and helped her into the launch. The mechanic started the engine and they slid out of the lagoon. In three hours they were at Baru.

That evening, having been officially released, Ginger Ted went to the Controleur's house. He wore no longer the prison uniform, but the ragged singlet and the khaki shorts in which he had been arrested. He had had his hair cut and it fitted his head now like a little curly red cap. He was thinner. He had lost his bloated flabbiness and looked younger and better. Mr. Gruyter, a friendly grin on his round face, shook hands with him and asked him to sit down. The boy brought two bottles of beer.

"I'm glad to see you hadn't forgotten my invitation, Ginger," said the Controleur.

"Not likely. I've been looking forward to this for six months."

"Here's luck, Ginger Ted."

"Same to you, Controleur."

They emptied their glasses and the Controleur clapped his hands. The boy brought two more bottles.

"Well, you don't bear me any malice for the sentence I gave you, I hope."

"No bloody fear. I was mad for a minute, but I got over it. I didn't have half a bad time, you know. Nice lot of girls on that island, Controleur. You ought to give 'em a look over one of these days."

"You're a bad lot, Ginger."

"Terrible."

"Good beer, isn't it?"

"Fine."

"Let's have some more."

Ginger Ted's remittance had been arriving every month and the Controleur now had fifty pounds for him. When the damage he had done to the Chinaman's shop was paid for there would still be over thirty.

"That's quite a lot of money, Ginger. You ought to do something useful with it."

"I mean to," answered Ginger. "Spend it."

The Controleur sighed.

"Well, that's what money's for, I guess."

The Controleur gave his guest the news. Not much had happened during the last six months. Time on the Alas Islands did not matter very much and the rest of the world did not matter at all.

"Any wars anywhere?" asked Ginger Ted.

"No. Not that I've noticed. Harry Jervis found a pretty big pearl. He says he's going to ask a thousand quid for it."

"I hope he gets it."

"And Charlie McCormack's married."

"He always was a bit soft."

Suddenly the boy appeared and said Mr. Jones wished to know if he might come in. Before the Controleur could give an answer Mr. Jones walked in.

"I won't detain you long," he said. "I've been trying to get hold of this good man all day and when I heard he was here I thought you wouldn't mind my coming."

"How is Miss Jones?" asked the Controleur politely. "None the worse for her night in the open, I trust."

"She's naturally a bit shaken. She had a temperature and I've insisted on her going to bed, but I don't think it's serious."

The two men had got up on the missionary's entrance, and now the missionary went up to Ginger Ted and held out his hand.

"I want to thank you. You did a great and noble thing. My sister is right, one should always look for the good in their fellow men; I am afraid I misjudged you in the past: I beg your pardon."

He spoke very solemnly. Ginger Ted looked at him with amazement. He had not been able to prevent the missionary taking his hand. He still held it.

"What the hell are you talking about?"

"You had my sister at your mercy and you spared her. I thought you were all evil and I am ashamed. She was defenceless. She was in your power. You had pity on her. I thank you from the bottom of my heart. Neither my sister nor I will ever forget. God bless and guard you always."

Mr. Jones's voice shook a little and he turned his head

away. He released Ginger Ted's hand and strode quickly to the door. Ginger Ted watched him with a blank face.

"What the blazes does he mean?" he asked.

The Controleur laughed. He tried to control himself, but the more he did the more he laughed. He shook and you saw the folds of his fat belly ripple under the sarong. He leaned back in his long chair and rolled from side to side. He did not laugh only with his face, he laughed with his whole body, and even the muscles of his podgy legs shook with mirth. He held his aching ribs. Ginger Ted looked at him frowning, and because he did not understand what the joke was he grew angry. He seized one of the empty beer bottles by the neck.

"If you don't stop laughing, I'll break your bloody head open," he said.

The Controleur mopped his face. He swallowed a mouthful of beer. He sighed and groaned because his sides were hurting him.

"He's thanking you for having respected the virtue of Miss Jones," he spluttered at last.

"Me?" cried Ginger Ted.

The thought took quite a long time to travel through his head, but when at last he got it he flew into a violent rage. There flowed from his mouth such a stream of blasphemous obscenities as would have startled a marine.

"That old cow," he finished. "What does he take me for?"

"You have the reputation of being rather hot stuff with the girls, Ginger," giggled the little Controleur.

"I wouldn't touch her with the fag end of a bargepole. It never entered my head. The nerve. I'll wring his blasted neck. Look here, give me my money, I'm going to get drunk."

"I don't blame you," said the Controleur.

"That old cow," repeated Ginger Ted. "That old cow."

He was shocked and outraged. The suggestion really shattered his sense of decency.

The Controleur had the money at hand and having got Ginger Ted to sign the necessary papers gave it to him.

"Go and get drunk, Ginger Ted," he said, "but I warn

you, if you get into mischief it'll be twelve months next time."

"I shan't get into mischief," said Ginger Ted sombrely. He was suffering from a sense of injury. "It's an insult," he shouted at the Controleur. "That's what it is, it's a bloody insult."

He lurched out of the house, and as he went he muttered to himself: "dirty swine, dirty swine." Ginger Ted remained drunk for a week. Mr. Jones went to see the Controleur again.

"I'm very sorry to hear that poor fellow has taken up his evil course again," he said. "My sister and I are dreadfully disappointed. I'm afraid it wasn't very wise to give him so much money at once."

"It was his own money. I had no right to keep it back."

"Not a legal right, perhaps, but surely a moral right."

He told the Controleur the story of that fearful night on the island. With her feminine instinct, Miss Jones had realised that the man, inflamed with lust, was determined to take advantage of her, and, resolved to defend herself to the last, had armed herself with a scalpel. He told the Controleur how she had prayed and wept and how she had hidden herself. Her agony was indescribable, and she knew that she could never have survived the shame. She rocked to and fro and every moment she thought he was coming. And there was no help anywhere and at last she had fallen asleep; she was tired out, poor thing, she had undergone more than any human being could stand, and then when she awoke she found that he had covered her with copra sacks. He had found her asleep, and surely it was her innocence, her very helplessness that had moved him, he hadn't the heart to touch her; he covered her gently with two copra sacks and crept silently away.

"It shows you that deep down in him there is something sterling. My sister feels it's our duty to save him. We must do something for him."

"Well, in your place I wouldn't try till he's got through all his money," said the Controleur, "and then if he's not in gaol you can do what you like."

But Ginger Ted didn't want to be saved. About a fortnight after his release from prison he was sitting on a stool outside a Chinaman's shop looking vacantly down the street when he saw Miss Jones coming along. He stared at her for a minute and once more amazement seized him. He muttered to himself and there can be little doubt that his mutterings were disrespectful. But then he noticed that Miss Jones had seen him and he quickly turned his head away; he was conscious, notwithstanding, that she was looking at him. She was walking briskly, but she sensibly diminished her pace as she approached him. He thought she was going to stop and speak to him. He got up quickly and went into the shop. He did not venture to come out for at least five minutes. Half an hour later Mr. Jones himself came along and he went straight up to Ginger Ted with outstretched hand.

"How do you do, Mr. Edward? My sister told me I should find you here."

Ginger Ted gave him a surly look and did not take the proffered hand. He made no answer.

"We'd be so very glad if you'd come to dinner with us next Sunday. My sister's a capital cook and she'll make you a real Australian dinner."

"Go to hell," said Ginger Ted.

"That's not very gracious," said the missionary, but with a little laugh to show that he was not affronted. "You go and see the Controleur from time to time, why shouldn't you come and see us? It's pleasant to talk to white people now and then. Won't you let bygones be bygones? I can assure you of a very cordial welcome."

"I haven't got clothes fit to go out in," said Ginger Ted sulkily.

"Oh, never mind about that. Come as you are."

"I won't."

"Why not? You must have a reason."

Ginger Ted was a blunt man. He had no hesitation in saying what we should all like to when we receive unwelcome invitations.

"I don't want to."

"I'm sorry. My sister will be very disappointed."

Mr. Jones, determined to show that he was not in the

least offended, gave him a breezy nod and walked on. Forty-eight hours later there mysteriously arrived at the house in which Ginger Ted lodged a parcel containing a suit of ducks, a tennis shirt, a pair of socks and some shoes. He was un-accustomed to receiving presents and next time he saw the Controleur asked him if it was he who had sent the things.

"Not on your life," replied the Controleur. "I'm per-fectly indifferent to the state of your wardrobe."

"Well, then, who the hell can have?"

"Search me."

It was necessary from time to time for Miss Jones to see Mr. Gruyter on business and shortly after this she came to see him one morning in his office. She was a capable woman and though she generally wanted him to do something he had no mind to, she did not waste his time. He was a little surprised then to discover that she had come on a very trivial errand. When he told her that he could not take cognizance of the matter in question, she did not as was her habit try to convince him, but accepted his refusal as definite. She got up to go and then as though it were an afterthought said:

"Oh, Mr. Gruyter, my brother is very anxious that we should have the man they call Ginger Ted to supper with us and I've written him a little note inviting him for the day after to-morrow. I think he's rather shy, and I wonder if you'd come with him."

"That's very kind of you."

"My brother feels that we ought to do something for the poor fellow."

"A woman's influence and all that sort of thing," said the Controleur demurely.

"Will you persuade him to come? I'm sure he will if you make a point of it, and when he knows the way he'll come again. It seems such a pity to let a young man like that go to pieces altogether."

The Controleur looked up at her. She was several inches taller than he. He thought her very unattractive. She re-minded him strangely of wet linen hung on a clothes-line to dry. His eyes twinkled, but he kept a straight face.

"I'll do my best," he said.

"How old is he?" she asked.

"According to his passport he's thirty-one."

"And what is his real name?"

"Wilson."

"Edward Wilson," she said softly.

"It's astonishing that after the life he's led he should be so strong," murmured the Controleur. "He has the strength of an ox."

"Those red-headed men sometimes are very powerful," said Miss Jones, but spoke as though she were choking.

"Quite so," said the Controleur.

Then for no obvious reason Miss Jones blushed. She hurriedly said good-bye to the Controleur and left his office.

"*Godverdomme!*" said the Controleur.

He knew now who had sent Ginger Ted the new clothes.

He met him during the course of the day and asked him whether he had heard from Miss Jones. Ginger Ted took a crumpled ball of paper out of his pocket and gave it to him. It was the invitation. It ran as follows:

Dear Mr. Wilson,—

My brother and I would be so very glad if you would come and have supper with us next Thursday at 7.30. The Controleur has kindly promised to come. We have some new records from Australia which I am sure you will like. I am afraid I was not very nice to you last time we met, but I did not know you so well then, and I am big enough to admit it when I have committed an error. I hope you will forgive me and let me be your friend.

> *Yours sincerely,*
> *Martha Jones.*

The Controleur noticed that she addressed him as Mr. Wilson and referred to his own promise to go, so that when she told him she had already invited Ginger Ted she had a little anticipated the truth.

"What are you going to do?"

"I'm not going, if that's what you mean. Damned nerve."

"You must answer the letter."

"Well, I won't."

"Now look here, Ginger, you put on those new clothes and you come as a favour to me. I've got to go, and damn it all, you can't leave me in the lurch. It won't hurt you just once."

Ginger Ted looked at the Controleur suspiciously, but his face was serious and his manner sincere; he could not guess that within him the Dutchman bubbled with laughter.

"What the devil do they want me for?"

"I don't know. The pleasure of your society, I suppose."

"Will there be any booze?"

"No, but come up to my house at seven, and we'll have a tiddly before we go."

"Oh, all right," said Ginger Ted sulkily.

The Controleur rubbed his little fat hands with joy. He was expecting a great deal of amusement from the party. But when Thursday came and seven o'clock Ginger Ted was dead drunk and Mr. Gruyter had to go alone. He told the missionary and his sister the plain truth. Mr. Jones shook his head.

"I'm afraid it's no good, Martha, the man's hopeless."

For a moment Miss Jones was silent and the Controleur saw two tears trickle down her long thin nose. She bit her lip.

"No one is hopeless. Everyone has some good in him. I shall pray for him every night. It would be wicked to doubt the power of God."

Perhaps Miss Jones was right in this, but the divine providence took a very funny way of effecting its ends. Ginger Ted began to drink more heavily than ever. He was so troublesome that even Mr. Gruyter lost patience with him. He made up his mind that he could not have the fellow on the islands any more and resolved to deport him on the next boat that touched at Baru. Then a man died under mysterious circumstances after having been for a trip to one of the islands and the Controleur learnt that there had been several deaths on the same island. He sent the Chinese who was the official doctor of the group to look into the matter, and very soon received intelligence that the deaths were due to cholera. Two more took place at Baru and the certainty was forced upon him that there was an epidemic.

The Controleur cursed freely. He cursed in Dutch, he

cursed in English and he cursed in Malay. Then he drank a bottle of beer and smoked a cigar. After that he took thought. He knew the Chinese doctor would be useless. He was a nervous little man from Java and the natives would refuse to obey his orders. The Controleur was efficient and knew pretty well what must be done, but he could not do everything single-handed. He did not like Mr. Jones, but just then he was thankful that he was at hand, and he sent for him at once. In ten minutes Mr. Jones was in the office. He was accompanied by his sister.

"You know what I want to see you about, Mr. Jones," he said abruptly.

"Yes. I've been expecting a message from you. That is why my sister has come with me. We are ready to put all our resources at your disposal. I need not tell you that my sister is as competent as a man."

"I know. I shall be very glad of her assistance."

They set to without further delay to discuss the steps that must be taken. Hospital huts would have to be erected and quarantine stations. The inhabitants of the various villages on the islands must be forced to take proper precautions. In a good many cases the infected villages drew their water from the same well as the uninfected, and in each case this difficulty would have to be dealt with according to circumstances. It was necessary to send round people to give orders and make sure that they were carried out. Negligence must be ruthlessly punished. The worst of it was that the natives would not obey other natives, and orders given by native policemen, themselves unconvinced of their efficacy, would certainly be disregarded. It was advisable for Mr. Jones to stay at Baru where the population was largest and his medical attention most wanted; and what with the official duties that forced him to keep in touch with his headquarters, it was impossible for Mr. Gruyter to visit all the other islands himself. Miss Jones must go; but the natives of some of the outlying islands were wild and treacherous; the Controleur had had a good deal of trouble with them. He did not like the idea of exposing her to danger.

"I'm not afraid," she said.

"I daresay. But if you have your throat cut I shall get into trouble, and besides, we're so short-handed I don't want to risk losing your help."

"Then let Mr. Wilson come with me. He knows the natives better than anyone and can speak all their dialects."

"Ginger Ted?" The Controleur stared at her. "He's just getting over an attack of D.T.'s."

"I know," she answered.

"You know a great deal, Miss Jones."

Even though the moment was so serious Mr. Gruyter could not but smile. He gave her a sharp look, but she met it coolly.

"There's nothing like responsibility for bringing out what there is in a man, and I think something like this may be the making of him."

"Do you think it would be wise to trust yourself for days at a time to a man of such infamous character?" said the missionary.

"I put my trust in God," she answered gravely.

"Do you think he'd be any use?" asked the Controleur. "You know what he is."

"I'm convinced of it." Then she blushed. "After all, no one knows better than I that he's capable of self-control."

The Controleur bit his lip.

"Let's send for him."

He gave a message to the sergeant and in a few minutes Ginger Ted stood before them. He looked ill. He had evidently been much shaken by his recent attack and his nerves were all to pieces. He was in rags and he had not shaved for a week. No one could have looked more disreputable.

"Look here, Ginger," said the Controleur, "it's about this cholera business. We've got to force the natives to take precautions and we want you to help us."

"Why the hell should I?"

"No reason at all. Except philanthropy."

"Nothing doing, Controleur. I'm not a philanthropist."

"That settles that. That was all. You can go."

But as Ginger Ted turned to the door Miss Jones stopped him.

"It was my suggestion, Mr. Wilson. You see, they want me to go to Labobo and Sakunchi, and the natives there are so funny I was afraid to go alone. I thought if you came I should be safer."

He gave her a look of extreme distaste.

"What do you suppose I care if they cut your throat?"

Miss Jones looked at him and her eyes filled with tears. She began to cry. He stood and watched her stupidly.

"There's no reason why you should." She pulled herself together and dried her eyes. "I'm being silly. I shall be all right. I'll go alone."

"It's damned foolishness for a woman to go to Labobo." She gave him a little smile.

"I daresay it is, but you see, it's my job and I can't help myself. I'm sorry if I offended you by asking you. You must forget about it. I daresay it wasn't quite fair to ask you to take such a risk."

For quite a minute Ginger Ted stood and looked at her. He shifted from one foot to the other. His surly face seemed to grow black.

"Oh, hell, have it your own way," he said at last. "I'll come with you. When d'you want to start?"

They set out next day, with drugs and disinfectants, in the government launch. Mr. Gruyter as soon as he had put the necessary work in order was to start off in a prahu in the other direction. For four months the epidemic raged. Though everything possible was done to localise it one island after another was attacked. The Controleur was busy from morning to night. He had no sooner got back to Baru from one or other of the islands to do what was necessary there than he had to set off again. He distributed food and medicine. He cheered the terrified people. He supervised everything. He worked like a dog. He saw nothing of Ginger Ted, but he heard from Mr. Jones that the experiment was working out beyond all hopes. The scamp was behaving himself. He had a way with the natives; and by cajolery, firmness and on occasion the use of his fist, managed to make them take the steps necessary for their own safety. Miss Jones could congratulate herself on the success of the scheme. But the

Controleur was too tired to be amused. When the epidemic had run its course he rejoiced because out of a population of eight thousand only six hundred had died.

Finally he was able to give the district a clean bill of health.

One evening he was sitting in his sarong on the verandah of his house and he read a French novel with the happy consciousness that once more he could take things easy. His head boy came in and told him that Ginger Ted wished to see him. He got up from his chair and shouted to him to come in. Company was just what he wanted. It had crossed the Controleur's mind that it would be pleasant to get drunk that night, but it is dull to get drunk alone, and he had regretfully put the thought aside. And heaven had sent Ginger Ted in the nick of time. By God, they would make a night of it. After four months they deserved a bit of fun. Ginger Ted entered. He was wearing a clean suit of white ducks. He was shaved. He looked another man.

"Why, Ginger, you look as if you'd been spending a month at a health resort instead of nursing a pack of natives dying of cholera. And look at your clothes. Have you just stepped out of a band-box?"

Ginger Ted smiled rather sheepishly. The head boy brought two bottles of beer and poured them out.

"Help yourself, Ginger," said the Controleur as he took his glass.

"I don't think I'll have any, thank you."

The Controleur put down his glass and looked at Ginger Ted with amazement.

"Why, what's the matter? Aren't you thirsty?"

"I don't mind having a cup of tea."

"A cup of what?"

"I'm on the wagon. Martha and I are going to be married."

"Ginger!"

The Controleur's eyes popped out of his head. He scratched his shaven pate.

"You can't marry Miss Jones," he said. "No one could marry Miss Jones."

"Well, I'm going to. That's what I've come to see you about. Owen's going to marry us in chapel, but we want to be married by Dutch law as well."

"A joke's a joke, Ginger. What's the idea?"

"She wanted it. She fell for me that night we spent on the island when the propeller broke. She's not a bad old girl when you get to know her. It's her last chance, if you understand what I mean, and I'd like to do something to oblige her. And she wants someone to take care of her, there's no doubt about that."

"Ginger, Ginger, before you can say knife she'll make you into a damned missionary."

"I don't know that I'd mind that so much if we had a little mission of our own. She says I'm a bloody marvel with the natives. She says I can do more with a native in five minutes than Owen can do in a year. She says she's never known anyone with the magnetism I have. It seems a pity to waste a gift like that."

The Controleur looked at him without speaking and slowly nodded his head three or four times. She'd nobbled him all right.

"I've converted seventeen already," said Ginger Ted.

"You? I didn't know you believed in Christianity."

"Well, I don't know that I did exactly, but when I talked to 'em and they just came into the fold like a lot of blasted sheep, well, it gave me quite a turn. Blimey, I said, I daresay there's something in it after all."

"You should have raped her, Ginger. I wouldn't have been hard on you. I wouldn't have given you more than three years and three years is soon over."

"Look here, Controleur, don't you ever let on that the thought never entered my head. Women are touchy, you know, and she'd be as sore as hell if she knew that."

"I guessed she'd got her eye on you, but I never thought it would come to this." The Controleur in an agitated manner walked up and down the verandah. "Listen to me, old boy," he said after an interval of reflection, "we've had some grand times together and a friend's a friend. I'll tell you what I'll do, I'll lend you the launch and you can go and hide on one of the islands till the next ship comes along and then I'll get 'em to slow down and take you on board. You've only got one chance now and that's to cut and run."

Ginger Ted shook his head.

"It's no good, Controleur, I know you mean well, but I'm going to marry the blasted woman, and that's that. You don't know the joy of bringing all them bleeding sinners to repentance, and Christ, that girl can make a treacle pudding. I haven't eaten a better one since I was a kid."

The Controleur was very much disturbed. The drunken scamp was his only companion on the islands and he did not want to lose him. He discovered that he had even a certain affection for him. Next day he went to see the missionary.

"What's this I hear about your sister marrying Ginger Ted?" he asked him. "It's the most extraordinary thing I've ever heard in my life."

"It's true nevertheless."

"You must do something about it. It's madness."

"My sister is of full age and entitled to do as she pleases."

"But you don't mean to tell me you approve of it. You know Ginger Ted. He's a bum and there are no two ways about it. Have you told her the risk she's running? I mean, bringing sinners to repentance and all that sort of thing's all right, but there are limits. And does the leopard ever change his spots?"

Then for the first time in his life the Controleur saw a twinkle in the missionary's eye.

"My sister is a very determined woman, Mr. Gruyter," he replied. "From that night they spent on the island he never had a chance."

The Controleur gasped. He was as surprised as the prophet when the Lord opened the mouth of the ass, and she said unto Balaam, "What have I done unto thee, that thou hast smitten me these three times?" Perhaps Mr. Jones was human after all.

"*Allejesus!*" muttered the Controleur.

Before anything more could be said Miss Jones swept into the room. She was radiant. She looked ten years younger. Her cheeks were flushed and her nose was hardly red at all.

"Have you come to congratulate me, Mr. Gruyter?" she cried, and her manner was sprightly and girlish. "You see, I was right after all. Everyone has some good in them. You don't know how splendid Edward has been all through this terrible time. He's a hero. He's a saint. Even I was surprised."

"I hope you'll be very happy, Miss Jones."

"I know I shall. Oh, it would be wicked of me to doubt it. For it is the Lord who has brought us together."

"Do you think so?"

"I know it. Don't you see? Except for the cholera Edward would never have found himself. Except for the cholera we should never have learnt to know one another. I have never seen the hand of God more plainly manifest."

The Controleur could not but think that it was rather a clumsy device to bring those two together that necessitated the death of six hundred innocent persons, but not being well versed in the ways of omnipotence he made no remark.

"You'll never guess where we're going for our honeymoon," said Miss Jones, perhaps a trifle archly.

"Java?"

"No, if you'll lend us the launch, we're going to that island where we were marooned. It has very tender recollections for both of us. It was there that I first guessed how fine and good Edward was. It's there I want him to have his reward."

The Controleur caught his breath. He left quickly, for he thought that unless he had a bottle of beer at once he would have a fit. He was never so shocked in his life.

CHRISTMAS HOLIDAY

WITH a journey before him, Charley Mason's mother was anxious that he should make a good breakfast, but he was too excited to eat. It was Christmas Eve and he was going to Paris. They had got through the mass of work that quarter-day brought with it, and his father, having no need to go to the office, drove him to Victoria. When they were stopped for several minutes by a traffic block in Grosvenor Gardens Charley, afraid that he would miss the train, went white with anxiety. His father chuckled.

"You've got the best part of half an hour."

But it was a relief to arrive.

"Well, good-bye, old boy," his father said, "have a good time and don't get into more mischief than you can help."

The steamer backed into the harbour and the sight of the gray, tall, dingy houses of Calais filled him with elation. It was a raw day and the wind blew bitter. He strode along the platform as though he walked on air. The Golden Arrow, powerful, rich and impressive, which stood there waiting for him, was no ordinary train, but a symbol of romance. While the light lasted he looked out of the window and he laughed in his heart as he recognized the pictures he had seen in galleries; sand dunes, with patches of grass gray under the leaden sky, cramped villages of poor persons' houses with slate roofs, and then a broad, sad landscape of ploughed fields and sparse bare trees; but the day seemed in a hurry to be gone from the cheerless scene and in a short while, when he looked out, he could see only his own reflection and behind it the polished mahogany of the Pullman. He wished he had come by air. That was what he'd wanted to do, but his mother had put her foot down; she'd persuaded his father that in the middle of winter it was a silly risk to take, and his father, usually so reasonable, had made it a condition of his going on the jaunt that he should take the train.

Of course Charley had been to Paris before, half a dozen times at least, but this was the first time that he had ever gone alone. It was a special treat that his father was giving him for a special reason: he had completed a year's work in his father's office and had passed the necessary examinations to enable him to follow usefully his chosen calling. For as long as Charley could remember, his father and mother, his sister Patsy and he had spent Christmas at Godalming with their cousins the Terry-Masons; and to explain why Leslie Mason, after talking over the matter with his wife, had one evening, a smile on his kindly face, asked his son whether instead of coming with them as usual he would like to spend a few days in Paris by himself, it is necessary to go back a little. It is necessary indeed to go back to the middle of the nineteenth century, when an industrious and intelligent man called Sibert Mason, who had been head gardener at a grand place in Sussex and had married the cook, bought with his savings and hers a few acres north of London and set up as a market gardener. Though he was then forty and his wife not far from it they had eight children. He prospered, and with the money he made, bought little bits of land in what was still open country. The city expanded and his market garden acquired value as a building site; with money borrowed from the bank he put up a row of villas and in a short while let them all on lease. It would be tedious to go into the details of his progress, and it is enough to say that when he died, at the age of eighty-four, the few acres he had bought to grow vegetables for Covent Garden, and the properties he had continued to acquire whenever opportunity presented, were covered with bricks and mortar. Sibert Mason took care that his children should receive the education that had been denied him. They moved up in the social scale. He made the Mason Estate, as he had somewhat grandly named it, into a private company and at his death each child received a certain number of shares as an inheritance. The Mason Estate was well managed and though it could not compare in importance with the Westminster or the Portman Estate, for its situation was modest and it had long ceased to have any value as a residential quarter, shops, warehouses, factories, slums, long rows of dingy houses in two storeys, made it sufficiently profitable to enable its proprietors, through no merit and little exertion of their own, to live like the gentlemen and ladies they were now become. Indeed, the head of the family, the only surviving child of old Sibert's eldest son, a brother having been killed in the war and a sister by a fall in the hunting-field, was a very rich man. He was a member of parliament and at the time of King George the Fifth's Jubilee had been created a baronet. He had tacked his wife's name on to his own and was now known as Sir Wilfred Terry-Mason. The family had hopes that his staunch allegiance to the Tory party and the fact that he had a safe seat would result in his being raised to the peerage.

Leslie Mason, youngest of Sibert's many grandchildren, had been sent to a public school and to Cambridge. His share in the Estate brought him in two thousand pounds a year, but to this was added another thousand which he received as secretary of the company. Once a year there was a meeting attended by such members of the family as were in England, for of the third generation some were serving their country in distant parts of the Empire, and some were gentlemen of leisure who were often abroad, and with Sir Wilfred in the chair, he presented the highly satisfactory statement which the chartered accountants had prepared.

Leslie Mason was a man of varied interests. At this time he was in the early fifties, tall, with a good figure, and with his blue eyes, fine gray hair worn rather long, and high colour, of an agreeable aspect. He looked more like a soldier or a colonial governor home on leave than a house agent and you would never have guessed that his grandfather was a gardener and his grandmother a cook. He was a good golfer, for which pastime he had ample leisure, and a good shot. But Leslie Mason was more than a sportsman; he was keenly interested in the arts. The rest of the family had no such foibles and they looked upon Leslie's predilections with an amused tolerance, but when, for some reason or other, one of them wanted to buy a piece of furniture or a picture, his advice was sought and taken. It was natural enough that he should know what he was talking about, for he had married a painter's daughter. John Peron, his wife's father, was a member of the Royal Academy and for a long time, between the eighties and the end of the century, had made a good income by painting pictures of young women in eighteenth-century costume dallying with young men similarly dight. He painted them in gardens of old world flowers, in leafy bowers and in parlours furnished correctly with the chairs and tables of the period. But now when his pictures turned up at Christie's they were sold for thirty shillings or two pounds. Venetia Mason had inherited quite a number when her father died, but they had long stood in a box-room, covered with dust, their faces to the wall; for at this time of day even filial affection could not persuade her that they were anything but dreadful. The Leslie Masons were not in the least ashamed of the fact that his grandmother had been a cook, indeed with their friends they were apt to make a facetious point of it, but it embarrassed them to speak of John Peron. Some of the Mason relations still had on their walls examples of his work; they were a mortification to Venetia.

"I see you've still got father's picture there," she said. "Don't you think it dates rather? Why don't you put it in one of the spare rooms?"

"My father-in-law was a very charming old man," said Leslie, "with beautiful manners, but I'm afraid he wasn't a very good painter."

"Well, my governor gave a tidy sum for it. It would be absurd to put a picture that cost three hundred pounds in a spare bedroom, but if you feel like that about it, I'll tell you what I'll do, I'll sell it you for a hundred and fifty."

For though in the course of three generations they had become ladies and gentlemen, the Masons had not lost their business acumen.

The Leslie Masons had gone a long way in artistic appreciation since their marriage and on the walls of the handsome new house they now inhabited in Porchester Close were pictures by Wilson Steer and Augustus John, Duncan Grant and Vanessa Bell. There was an Utrillo and a Vuillard, both bought while these masters were of moderate price, and there was a Derain, a Marquet and a Chirico. You could not enter their house, somewhat sparsely furnished, without knowing at once that they were in the movement. They seldom missed a private view and when they went to Paris made a point of going to Rosenberg's and the dealers in the Rue de Seine to have a look at what there was to be seen; they really liked pictures and if they did not buy any before the cultured opinion of the day had agreed on their merits this was due partly to a modest lack of confidence in their own judgement and partly to a fear that they might be making a bad bargain. After all, John Peron's pictures had been praised by the best critics and he had sold them for several hundred pounds apiece, and now what did they fetch? Two or three. It made you careful. But it was not only in painting that they were interested. They loved music; they went to Symphony Concerts throughout the winter; they had their favourite conductors and allowed no social engagements to prevent them from attending their performances. They went to hear the *Ring* once a year. To listen to music was a genuine delight to both of them. They had good taste and discrimination. They were regular first-nighters and they belonged to the societies that produce plays which are supposed to be above the comprehension of plain people. They read promptly the books that were talked about. They did this not only because they liked it, but because they felt it right to keep abreast of the times. They were honestly interested in art and it would be unjust even to hint a sneer because their taste lacked boldness and their appreciation originality. It may be that they were conventional in their judgements, but their conventionality was that of the highest culture of their day. They were incapable of making a discovery, but were quick to appreciate the discoveries of others. Though left to themselves they might never have seen anything very much to admire in Cézanne, no sooner was it borne in upon them that he was a great artist than in all sincerity they recognized the fact for themselves. They took no pride in their taste and there was no trace of snobbishness in their attitude.

"We're just very ordinary members of the public," said Venetia.

"Those objects of contempt to the artist, the people who know what they like," added Leslie.

It was a happy accident that they liked Debussy better than Arthur Sullivan and Virginia Woolf better than John Galsworthy.

This preoccupation with art left them little time for social life; they sought neither the great nor the distinguished, and their friends were very nice people who were well-to-do without being rich, and who took a judicious interest in the things of the mind. They did not much care for dinner parties and neither gave them often nor went to them more than civility required; but they were fond of entertaining their friends to supper on Sunday evenings when they could drop in dressed any way they liked and eat kedgeree and sausages and mash. There was good music and tolerable bridge. The conversation was intelligent. These parties were as pleasantly unpretentious as the Leslie Masons themselves, and though all the guests had their own cars and few of them less than five thousand a year, they flattered themselves that the atmosphere was quite bohemian.

But Leslie Mason was never happier than when, with no concert or first night to go to, he could spend the evening in the bosom of his family. He was fortunate in it. His wife had been pretty and now, a middle-aged woman, was still comely. She was nearly as tall as he, with blue eyes and soft brown hair only just streaked with gray. She was inclined to be stout, but her height enabled her to carry with dignity a corpulence which a strict attention to diet prevented from becoming uncomfortable. She had a broad brow, an open countenance and a diffident smile. Though she got her clothes in Paris, not from one of the fashionable dressmakers, but from a little woman "round the corner", she never succeeded in looking anything but thoroughly English. She naturalized whatever she wore, and though she occasionally went to the extravagance of getting a hat at Reboux she had no sooner

put it on her head than it looked as if it had come from the
Army and Navy Stores. She always looked exactly what she
was, an honest woman of the middle class in easy circumstances. She had loved her husband when she married him
and she loved him still. With the community of interests that
existed between them it was no wonder that they should live
in harmony. They had agreed at the beginning of their married life that she knew more about painting than he and that
he knew more about music than she, so that in these matters
each bowed to the superior judgement of the other. When it
came to Picasso's later work, for instance, Leslie said:

"Well, I don't mind confessing it took me some time before I learnt to like it, but Venetia never had a moment's
doubt; with her flair she cottoned on to it like a flash of
lightning."

And Mrs. Mason admitted that she'd had to listen to
Sibelius' Second three or four times before she really understood what Leslie meant when he said that in its way it was
as good as Beethoven.

"But of course he's got a real understanding of music.
Compared with him I'm almost a low-brow."

Leslie and Venetia Mason were not only fortunate in one
another, but also in their children. They had two, which they
thought the perfect number, since an only child might be
spoiled, and three or four meant a great expense, so that they
couldn't have lived as comfortably as they liked to, nor provided for them in such a way as to assure their future. They
had taken their parental duties seriously. Instead of putting
silly, childish pictures on the nursery walls they had decorated them with reproductions of pictures by Van Gogh,
Gauguin and Marie Laurencin, so that from their earliest
years their children's taste should be formed, and they had
chosen the records for the nursery gramophone with equal
care, with the result that before either of them could ride
a bicycle they were familiar with Mozart and Haydn,
Beethoven and Wagner. As soon as they were old enough
they began to learn to play the piano, with very good teach-
ers, and Charley especially showed great aptitude. Both
children were ardent concert-goers. They would scramble in

to a Sunday concert, where they followed the music with a score, or wait for hours to get a seat in the gallery at Covent Garden; for their parents, thinking that it proved a real enthusiasm if they had to listen to music in some discomfort, considered it unnecessary to buy expensive seats for them. The Leslie Masons did not very much care for Old Masters and seldom went to the National Gallery except when a new purchase was making a stir in the papers, but it had seemed to them only right to make their children acquainted with the great paintings of the past, and as soon as they were old enough took them regularly to the National Gallery, but they soon realized that if they wanted to give them a treat they must take them to the Tate, and it was with gratification that they found that what really excited them was the most modern.

"It makes one think a bit," said Leslie to his wife, a smile of pride shining in his kindly eyes, "to see two young things like that taking to Matisse like a duck takes to water."

She gave him a look that was partly amused and partly rueful.

"They think I'm dreadfully old-fashioned because I still like Monet. They say it's pure chocolate-box."

"Well, we trained their taste. We mustn't grouse if they go ahead and leave us behind."

Venetia Mason gave a sweet and affectionate laugh.

"Bless their hearts, I don't grudge it them if they think me hopelessly out of date. I shall go on liking Monet and Manet and Degas whatever they say."

But it was not only to the artistic education of their offspring that the Leslie Masons had given thought. They were anxious that there should be nothing namby-pamby about them and they saw to it that they should acquire proficiency in games. They both rode well and Charley was not half a bad shot. Patsy, who was just eighteen, was studying at the Royal Academy of Music. She was to come out in May and they were giving a ball for her at Claridge's. Lady Terry-Mason was to present her at Court. Patsy was so pretty, with her blue eyes and fair hair, with her slim figure, her attractive smile and her gaiety, she would be snapped up all too soon. Leslie wanted her to marry a rising young barrister with political ambitions. For such a one, with the money she'd eventually inherit from the Mason Estate, with her culture, she'd make an admirable wife. But that would be the end of the united, cosy and happy family life which was so enjoyable. There would be no more of those pleasant, domestic evenings when they dined, the four of them, in the well-appointed dining-room with its Steer over the Chippendale sideboard, the table shining with Waterford glass and Georgian silver, waited on by well-trained maids in neat uniforms; simple English food perfectly cooked; and after dinner with its lively talk about art, literature and the drama, a glass of port, and then a little music in the drawing-room and a game of bridge. Venetia was afraid it was very selfish of her, but she couldn't help feeling glad that it would be some years at least before Charley could afford to marry too.

Charley was born during the war, he was twenty-three now, and when Leslie had been demobbed and gone down to Godalming to stay with the head of the family, already a member of parliament, but then only a knight, Sir Wilfred had suggested that he should be put down for Eton. Leslie would not hear of it. It was not the financial sacrifice he minded, but he had too much good sense to send his boy to a school where he would get extravagant tastes and acquire ideas unfitted to the station in life he would ultimately occupy.

"I went to Rugby myself and I don't believe I can do better than send him there too."

"I think you're making a mistake, Leslie. I've sent my boys to Eton. Thank God, I'm not a snob, but I'm not a fool either, and there's no denying it, it's a social asset."

"I daresay it is, but my position is very different from yours. You're a very rich man, Wilfred, and if things go well, you ought to end up in the House of Lords. I think it's quite right that you should give your sons the sort of start that'll enable them to take their proper place in society, but though officially I'm secretary of the Mason Estate and that sounds very respectable, when you come down to brass tacks I'm only a house agent, and I don't want to bring up my son to be a grand gentleman, I want him to be a house agent after me."

When Leslie spoke thus he was using an innocent diplomacy. By the terms of old Sibert's will and the accidents that have been already narrated, Sir Wilfred now possessed three-eighths of the Mason Estate, and it brought him in an income which was already large, and which, with leases falling in, the increasing value of the property, and good management, would certainly grow much larger. He was a clever, energetic man, and his position and his wealth gave him an influence with the rest of the family which none of its members questioned, but which it did not displease him to have acknowledged.

"You don't mean to say you'd be satisfied to let your boy take on your job?"

"It was good enough for me. Why shouldn't it be good enough for him? One doesn't know what the world's coming to and it may be that when he's grown up he'll be damned glad to step into a cushy billet at a thousand a year. But of course you're the boss."

Sir Wilfred made a gesture that seemed modestly to deprecate this description of himself.

"I'm a shareholder like the rest of you, but as far as I'm concerned, if you want it, he shall have it. Of course it's a long time ahead and I may be dead by then."

"We're a long-lived family and you'll live as long as old Sibert. Anyhow, there'll be no harm in letting the rest of them know that it's an understood thing that my boy should have my job when I'm through with it."

In order to enlarge their children's minds the Leslie Masons spent the holidays abroad, in winter at places where they ski and in summer at seaside resorts in the South of France; and once or twice with the same praiseworthy intention they made excursions to Italy and Holland. When Charley left school his father decided that before going to Cambridge he should spend six months at Tours to learn French. But the result of his sojourn in that agreeable town was unexpected and might very well have been disastrous, for when he came back he announced that he did not want to go to Cambridge, but to Paris, and that he wished to be a painter. His parents were dumbfounded. They loved art, they often said it was the most important thing in their lives; indeed Leslie, not averse at times from philosophical reflection, was inclined to think that it was art only that redeemed human existence from meaninglessness, and he had the greatest respect for the persons who produced it; but he had never envisaged the possibility that any member of his family, let alone his own son, should adopt a career that was uncertain, to some extent irregular, and in most cases far from lucrative. Nor could Venetia forget the fate that had befallen her father. It would be unjust to say that the Leslie Masons were put out because their son had taken their preoccupation with art more seriously than they intended; their preoccupation couldn't have been more serious, but it was from the patron's point of view; though no two people could have been more bohemian, they did have the Mason Estate behind them, and that, as anyone could see, must make a difference. Their reaction to Charley's declaration was quite definite, but they were aware that it would be difficult to put it in a way that wouldn't make their attitude look a trifle insincere.

"I can't think what put the idea into his head," said Leslie, talking it over with his wife.

"Heredity, I suppose. After all, my father was an artist."

"A painter, darling. He was a great gentleman and a wonderful raconteur, but no one in his senses could call him an artist."

Venetia flushed and Leslie saw that he had hurt her feelings. He hastened to make up for it.

"If he's inherited a feeling for art it's much more likely to be from my grandmother. I know old Sibert used to say you didn't know what tripe and onions were until you tasted hers. When she gave up being a cook to become a wife of a market gardener a great artist was lost to the world."

Venetia chuckled and forgave him.

They knew one another too well to have need to discuss their quandary. Their children loved them and looked up to them; they were agreed that it would be a thousand pities by a false step to shake Charley's belief in his parents' wisdom and integrity. The young are intolerant and when you talk common sense to them are only too apt to think you are an old humbug.

"I don't think it would be wise to put one's foot down too decidedly," said Venetia. "Opposition might only make him obstinate."

"The situation's delicate. I don't deny that for a moment."

What made it more awkward was that Charley had brought back several canvases from Tours and when he had shown them they had expressed themselves in terms which it was difficult now to withdraw. They had praised as fond parents rather than as connoisseurs.

"You might take Charley up to the box-room one morning and let him have a look at your father's pictures. Don't make a point of it, you know, but let it seem accidental; and then when I get an opportunity I'll have a talk with him."

The opportunity came. Leslie was in the sitting-room they had arranged for the children so that they might have a place of their own. The reproductions of Gauguin and Van Gogh that had been in their nursery adorned the walls. Charley was painting a bunch of mixed flowers in a green vase.

"I think we'd better have those pictures you brought back from France framed and put up instead of these reproductions. Let's have another look at them."

There was one of three apples on a blue-and-white plate.

"I think it's damned good," said Leslie. "I've seen hundreds of pictures of three apples on a blue-and-white plate and it's well up to the average." He chuckled. "Poor old Cézanne, I wonder what he'd say if he knew how many thousands of times people had painted that picture of his."

There was another still life which represented a bottle of red wine, a packet of French tobacco in a blue wrapper, a pair of white gloves, a folded newspaper and a violin. These objects were resting on a table covered with a cloth in green and white squares.

"Very good. Very promising."

"D'you really think so, daddy?"

"I do indeed. It's not very original, you know, it's the sort of picture that every dealer has a dozen of in his storeroom, but you've never had a lesson in your life and it's a very creditable piece of work. You've evidently inherited some of your grandfather's talent. You have seen his pictures, haven't you?"

"I hadn't for years. Mummy wanted to find something in the box-room and she showed them to me. They're awful."

"I suppose they are. But they weren't thought so in his own day. They were highly praised and they were bought. Remember that a lot of stuff that we admire now will be thought just as awful in fifty years' time. That's the worst of art; there's no room for the second-rate."

"One can't tell what one'll be till one tries."

"Of course not, and if you want to take up painting professionally your mother and I are the last people who'd stand in your way. You know how much art means to us."

"There's nothing I want to do in the world more than paint."

"With the share of the Mason Estate that'll come to you eventually you'll always have enough to live on in a modest way, and there've been several amateurs who've made quite a nice little reputation for themselves."

"Oh, but I don't want to be an amateur."

"It's not so easy to be anything else with a thousand to fifteen hundred a year behind you. I don't mind telling you it'll be a bit of a disappointment to me. I was keeping this job as secretary to the Estate warm for you, but I daresay some of the cousins will jump at it. I should have thought myself it was better to be a competent business man than a mediocre painter, but that's neither here nor there. The great thing is that you should be happy and we can only hope that you'll turn out a better artist than your grandfather."

There was a pause. Leslie looked at his son with kindly eyes.

"There's only one thing I'm going to ask you to do. My grandfather started life as a gardener and his wife was a cook. I only just remember him, but I have a notion that he

was a pretty rough diamond. They say it takes three generations to make a gentleman, and at all events I don't eat peas
with a knife. You're a member of the fourth. You may think
it's just snobbishness on my part, but I don't much like the
idea of you sinking in the social scale. I'd like you to go to
Cambridge and take your degree, and after that if you want
to go to Paris and study painting you shall go with my blessing."

That seemed a very generous offer to Charley and he
accepted it with gratitude. He enjoyed himself very much
at Cambridge. He did not find much opportunity to paint,
but he got into a set interested in the drama and in his first
year wrote a couple of one-act plays. They were acted at
the A.D.C. and the Leslie Masons went to Cambridge to see
them. Then he made the acquaintance of a don who was a
distinguished musician. Charley played the piano better than
most undergraduates, and he and the don played duets together. He studied harmony and counterpoint. After consideration he decided that he would rather be a musician
than a painter. His father with great good humour consented
to this, but when Charley had taken his degree, he carried
him off to Norway for a fortnight's fishing. Two or three
days before they were due to return Venetia Mason received
a telegram from Leslie containing the one word Eureka.
Notwithstanding their culture neither of them knew what
it meant, but its significance was perfectly clear to the re-
cipient and that is the primary use of language. She gave a
sigh of relief. In September Charley went for four months
into the firm of accountants employed by the Mason Estate
to learn something of book-keeping and at the New Year
joined his father in Lincoln's Inn Fields. It was to reward
the application he had shown during his first year in business
that his father was now sending him, with twenty-five pounds
in his pocket, to have a lark in Paris. And a great lark
Charley was determined to have.

ii

THEY were nearly there. The attendants were collecting the luggage and piling it up inside the door so that it could be conveniently handed down to the porters. Women put a last dab of lipstick on their mouths and were helped into their furs. Men struggled into their great-coats and put on their hats. The propinquity in which these persons had sat for a few hours, the pleasant warmth of the Pullman, had made a corporate unity of them, separated as occupants of a coach with its own number from the occupants of other coaches; but now they fell asunder, and each one, or each group of two or three, regained the discreet individuality which for a while had been merged in that of all the others. In the smoke-laden air, rank with stale tobacco, strong scent, the odour of human bodies and the frowst of steam-heating, they acquired on a sudden an air of mystery. Strangers once more, they looked at one another with preoccupied, unseeing eyes. Each one felt in himself a vague hostility to his neighbour. Some were already queuing up in the passage so that they might get out quickly. The heat of the Pullman had coated the windows with vapour and Charley wiped them a bit clean with his hand to look out. He could see nothing.

The train ran into the station. Charley gave his bag to a porter and with long steps walked up the platform; he was expecting his friend Simon Fenimore to meet him. He was disappointed not to see him at once; but there was a great mob at the barrier and he supposed that he was waiting there. He scanned eagerly the eager faces; he passed through; persons struggled through the crowd to seize a new arrival's hand; women kissed one another; he could not see his friend. He was so convinced he must be there that he lingered for a little, but he was intimidated by his porter's obvious impatience and presently followed him out to the courtyard. He felt vaguely let down. The porter got him a taxi and Charley gave the driver the name of the hotel where Simon had taken a room for him. When the

Leslie Masons went to Paris they always stayed at an hotel in the Rue St. Honoré. It was exclusively patronized by English and Americans, but after twenty years they still cherished the delusion that it was a discovery of their own, essentially French, and when they saw American luggage on a landing or went up in the lift with persons who could be nothing but English, they never ceased to be surprised.

"I wonder how on earth *they* happen to be here," they said.

For their own part they had always been careful never to speak about it to their friends; when they had hit upon a little bit of old France they weren't going to risk its being spoilt. Though the director and the porter talked English fluently they always spoke to them in their own halting French, convinced that this was the only language they knew. But the mere fact that he had so often been to this hotel with his family was a sufficient reason for Charley not to stay there when he was going to Paris by himself. He was bent on adventure, and a respectable family hotel, where, according to his parents, nobody went but the French provincial nobility, was hardly the right place for the glorious, wild and romantic experiences with which his imagination for the last month had been distracting his mind. So he had written to Simon asking him to get him a room somewhere in the Latin Quarter; he wasn't particular about sanitary conveniences and didn't mind how grubby it was so long as it had the right atmosphere; and Simon in due course had written back to tell him that he had engaged a room at a hotel near the Gare Montparnasse. It was in a quiet street just off the Rue de Rennes and conveniently near the Rue Campagne Première where he himself lived.

Charley quickly got over his disappointment that Simon had not come to meet him, he was sure either to be at the hotel or to have telephoned to say that he would be round immediately, and driving through the crowded streets that lead from the Gare du Nord to the Seine his spirits rose. It was wonderful to arrive in Paris by night. A drizzling rain was falling and it gave the streets an exciting mystery. The shops were brightly lit. The pavements were multitu-

dinous with umbrellas and the water dripping on them
glistened dimly under the street lamps. Charley remembered
one of Renoir's pictures. Sometimes a gust of wind made
women crouch under their umbrellas and their skirts swirled
round their legs. His taxi drove furiously to his prudent English idea and he gasped whenever with a screeching of brakes
it pulled up suddenly to avoid a collision. The red lights
held them up at a crossing and in both directions a great
stream of persons surged over like a panic-stricken mob flying before a police charge. To Charley's excited gaze they
seemed quite different from an English crowd, more alert,
more eager; when by chance his eyes fell on a girl walking
by herself, a sempstress or a typist going home after the
day's work, it delighted him to fancy that she was hurrying
to meet her lover; and when he saw a pair walking arm in
arm under an umbrella, a young man with a beard, in a
broad-brimmed hat, and a girl with a fur round her neck,
walking as though it were such bliss to be together they did
not mind the rain and were unconscious of the jostling
throng, he thrilled with a poignant and sympathetic joy. At
one corner owing to a block his taxi was side by side with a
handsome limousine. There sat in it a woman in a sable coat,
with painted cheeks and painted lips, and a profile of incredible distinction. She might have been the Duchesse de
Guermantes driving back after a tea party to her house in
the Boulevard St. Germain. It was wonderful to be twenty-
three and in Paris on one's own.

"By God, what a time I'm going to have."

The hotel was grander than he had expected. Its façade,
with its architectural embellishments, suggested the flamboyant taste of the late Baron Haussmann. He found that a
room had been engaged for him, but Simon had left neither
letter nor message. He was taken upstairs not as he had
anticipated by a slovenly boots in a dirty apron, with a sinister look on his ill-shaven face, but by an affable director
who spoke perfect English and wore a morning coat. The
room was furnished with hygienic severity, and there were
two beds in it, but the director assured him that he would
only charge him for the use of one. He showed Charley

with pride the communicating bath-room. Left to himself Charley looked about him. He had expected a little room with heavy curtains of dull rep, a wooden bed with a huge eiderdown and an old mahogany wardrobe with a large mirror; he had expected to find used hairpins on the dressing-table and in the drawer of the table de nuit half a lipstick and a broken comb in which a few dyed hairs were still entangled. That was the idea his romantic fancy had formed of a student's room in the Latin Quarter. A bath-room! That was the last thing he had bargained for. This room might have been a room in one of the cheaper hotels in Switzerland to which he had sometimes been with his parents. It was clean, threadbare and sordid. Not even Charley's ardent imagination could invest it with mystery. He unpacked his bag disconsolately. He had a bath. He thought it rather casual of Simon, even if he could not be bothered to meet him, not to have left a message. If he made no sign of life he would have to dine by himself. His father and mother and Patsy would have got down to Godalming by now; there was going to be a jolly party, Sir Wilfred's two sons and their wives and two nieces of Lady Terry-Mason's. There would be music, games and dancing. He half wished now that he hadn't jumped at his father's offer to spend the holiday in Paris. It suddenly occurred to him that Simon had perhaps had to go off somewhere for his paper and in the hurry of an unexpected departure had forgotten to let him know. His heart sank.

Simon Fenimore was Charley's oldest friend and indeed it was to spend a few days with him that he had been so eager to come to Paris. They had been at a private school together and together at Rugby; they had been at Cambridge together too, but Simon had left without taking a degree, at the end of his second year in fact, because he had come to the conclusion that he was wasting time; and it was Charley's father who had got him on to the London newspaper for which for the last year he had been one of the Paris correspondents. Simon was alone in the world. His father was in the Indian Forest Department and while Simon was still a young child had divorced his mother for promiscuous adultery. She had left India and Simon, by order of the court in his father's custody, was sent to England and put into a clergyman's family till he was old enough to go to school. His mother vanished into obscurity. He had no notion whether she was alive or dead. His father died of cirrhosis of the liver when Simon was twelve and he had but a vague recollection of a thin, slightly-built man with a sallow, lined face and a tight-lipped mouth. He left only just enough money to educate his son. The Leslie Masons had been touched by the poor boy's loneliness and had made a point of asking him to spend a good part of his holidays with them. As a boy he was thin and weedy, with a pale face in which his black eyes looked enormous, a great quantity of straight dark hair which was always in need of a brush, and a large, sensual mouth. He was talkative, forward for his age, a great reader, and clever. He had none of the diffidence which was in Charley such an engaging trait. Venetia Mason, though from a sense of duty she tried hard, could not like him. She could not understand why Charley had taken a fancy to someone who was in every way so unlike him. She thought Simon pert and conceited. He was insensible to kindness and took everything that was done for him as a matter of course. She had a suspicion that he had no very high opinion either of her or of Leslie. Sometimes when Leslie was talking with his usual good sense and intelligence about something interesting Simon would look at him with a glimmer of irony in those great black eyes of his and his sensual lips pursed in a sarcastic pucker. You would have thought Leslie was being prosy and a trifle stupid. Now and then when they were spending one of their pleasant quiet evenings together, chatting of one thing and another, he would go into a brown study; he would sit staring into vacancy, as though his thoughts were miles away, and perhaps, after a while, take up a book and start reading as though he were by himself. It gave you the impression that their conversation wasn't worth listening to. It wasn't even polite. But Venetia Mason chid herself.

"Poor lamb, he's never had a chance to learn manners. I *will* be nice to him. I *will* like him."

Her eyes rested on Charley, so good-looking, with his slim body, ("it's awful the way he grows out of his clothes, the sleeves of his dinner-jacket are too short for him already,") his curling brown hair, his blue eyes, with long lashes, and his clear skin. Though perhaps he hadn't Simon's showy brilliance, he was good, and he was artistic to his fingers' ends. But who could tell what he might have become if she had run away from Leslie and Leslie had taken to drink, and if instead of enjoying a cultured atmosphere and the influence of a nice home he had had, like Simon, to fend for himself? Poor Simon! Next day she went out and bought him half a dozen ties. He seemed pleased.

"I say, that's jolly decent of you. I've never had more than two ties at one time in my life."

Venetia was so moved by the spontaneous generosity of her pretty gesture that she was seized with a sudden wave of sympathy.

"You poor lonely boy," she cried, "it's so dreadful for you to have no parents."

"Well, as my mother was a whore, and my father a drunk, I daresay I don't miss much."

He was seventeen when he said this.

It was no good, Venetia simply couldn't like him. He was harsh, cynical and unscrupulous. It exasperated her to see how much Charley admired him; Charley thought him brilliant and anticipated a great career for him. Even Leslie was impressed by the extent of his reading and the clearness with which even as a boy he expressed himself. At school he was already an ardent socialist and at Cambridge he became a communist. Leslie listened to his wild theories with good-humoured tolerance. To him it was all talk, and talk, he had an instinctive feeling, was just talk; it didn't touch the essential business of life.

"And if he does become a well-known journalist or gets into the House, there'll be no harm in having a friend in the enemy's camp."

Leslie's ideas were liberal, so liberal that he didn't mind admitting the Socialists had several notions that no reasonable man could object to; theoretically he was all in favour of the nationalization of the coal-mines, and he didn't see why the state shouldn't run the public services as well as private companies; but he didn't think they should go too far. Ground rents, for instance, that was a matter that was really no concern of the state; and slum property; in a great city you had to have slums, in point of fact the lower classes preferred them to model dwelling-houses, not that the Mason Estate hadn't done what it could in this direction, but you couldn't expect a landlord to let people live in his houses for nothing, and it was only fair that he should get a decent return on his capital.

Simon Fenimore had decided that he wanted to be a foreign correspondent for some years so that he could gain a knowledge of Continental politics which would enable him when he entered the House of Commons to be an expert on a subject of which most Labour members were necessarily ignorant; but when Leslie took him to see the proprietor of the newspaper who was prepared to give a brilliant young man his chance, he warned him that the proprietor was a very rich man, and that he could not expect to create a favourable impression if he delivered himself of revolutionary sentiments. Simon, however, made a very good impression on the magnate by the modesty of his demeanour, his air of energy and his easy conversation.

"He was as good as gold," Leslie told his wife afterwards. "He's got his head screwed on his shoulders all right, that young fellow. It's what I always told you, talk doesn't amount to anything really. When it comes down to getting a job with a living wage attached to it, like every sensible man he's prepared to put his theories in his pocket."

Venetia agreed with him. It was quite possible, their own experience proved it, to have a real love for beauty and at the same time to realize the importance of material things. Look at Lorenzo de' Medici; he'd been a successful banker and an artist to his finger-tips. She thought it very good of Leslie to have taken so much trouble to do a service for someone who was incapable of gratitude. Anyhow the job he had got him would take Simon to Vienna and thus remove Charley from an influence which she had always regarded with misgiving. It was that wild talk of his that had put it into the boy's head that he wanted to be an artist. It was all very well for Simon, he hadn't a penny in the world and no connections; but Charley had a snug berth to go into. There were enough artists in the world. Her consolation had been that Charley had so much candour of soul and a disposition of such sweetness that no evil communications could corrupt his good manners.

At this moment Charley was dressing himself and wondering, forlorn, how he should spend the evening. When he had got his trousers on he rang up the office of Simon's newspaper, and it was Simon himself who answered.

"Simon."

"Hulloa, have you turned up? Where are you?"

Simon seemed so casual that Charley was taken aback.

"At the hotel."

"Oh, are you? Doing anything to-night?"

"No."

"We'd better dine together, shall we? I'll stroll around and fetch you."

He rang off. Charley was dashed. He had expected Simon to be as eager to see him as he was to see Simon, but from Simon's words and from his manner you would have thought that they were casual acquaintances and that it was a matter of indifference to him if they met or not. Of course it was two years since they'd seen one another and in that time Simon might have changed out of all recognition. Charley had a sudden fear that his visit to Paris was going to be a failure and he awaited Simon's arrival with a nervousness that annoyed him. But when at last he walked into the room there was in his appearance at least little alteration. He was now twenty-three and he was still the lanky fellow, though only of average height, that he had always been. He was shabbily dressed in a brown jacket and gray flannel trousers and wore neither hat nor great coat. His long face was thinner and paler than ever and his black eyes seemed larger. They were never still. Hard, shining, inquisitive, suspicious, they seemed to indicate the quality of the brain behind. His mouth was large and ironical, and he had small irregular teeth that somewhat reminded you of one of the smaller beasts of prey. With his pointed chin and prominent cheek-bones he was not good-looking, but his expression was so high-strung, there was in it so strange a disquiet, that you could hardly have passed him in the street without taking notice of him. At fleeting moments his face had a sort of tortured beauty, not a beauty of feature but the beauty of a restless, striving spirit. A disturbing thing about him was that there was no gaiety in his smile, it was a sardonic grimace, and when he laughed his face was contorted as though he were suffering from an agony of pain. His voice was high-pitched; it did not seem to be quite under his control, and when he grew excited often rose to shrillness.

Charley, restraining his natural impulse to run to the door and wring his hand with the eager friendliness of his happy nature, received him coolly. When there was a knock he called "Come in," and went on filing his nails. Simon did not offer to shake hands. He nodded as though they had met already in the course of the day.

"Hulloa!" he said. "Room all right?"

"Oh, yes. The hotel's a bit grander than I expected."

"It's convenient and you can bring anyone in you like. I'm starving. Shall we go along and eat?"

"O.K."

"Let's go to the Coupole."

They sat down opposite one another at a table upstairs and ordered their dinner. Simon gave Charley an appraising look.

"I see you haven't lost your looks, Charley," he said with his wry smile.

"Luckily they're not my fortune."

Charley was feeling a trifle shy. The separation had for the moment at all events destroyed the old intimacy there had so long been between them. Charley was a good listener, he had indeed been trained to be so from early childhood, and he was never unwilling to sit silent while Simon poured out his ideas with eloquent confusion. Charley had always disinterestedly admired him; he was convinced he was a genius so that it seemed quite natural to play second fiddle to him. He had an affection for Simon because he was alone in the world and nobody much liked him, whereas he himself had a happy home and was in easy circumstances; and it gave him a sense of comfort that Simon, who cared for so few people, cared for him. Simon was often bitter and sarcastic, but with him he could also be strangely gentle. In one of his rare moments of expansion he had told him that he was the only person in the world that he gave a damn for. But now Charley felt with malaise that there was a barrier between them. Simon's restless eyes darted from his face to his hands, paused for an instant on his new suit and then glanced rapidly at his collar and tie; he felt that Simon was not surrendering himself as he had to him alone in the old days, but was holding back, critical and aloof; he seemed to be taking stock of him as if he were a stranger and he were making up his mind what sort of a person this was. It made Charley uncomfortable and he was sore at heart.

"How d'you like being a business man?" asked Simon.

Charley faintly coloured. After all the talks they had had in the past he was prepared for Simon to treat him with derision because he had in the end fallen in with his father's wishes, but he was too honest to conceal the truth.

"I like it much better than I expected. I find the work very interesting and it's not hard. I have plenty of time to myself."

"I think you've shown a lot of sense," Simon answered, to his surprise. "What did you want to be a painter or a pianist for? There's a great deal too much art in the world. Art's a lot of damned rot anyway."

"Oh, Simon!"

"Are you still taken in by the artistic pretensions of your excellent parents? You must grow up, Charley. Art! It's an amusing diversion for the idle rich. Our world, the world we live in, has no time for such nonsense."

"I should have thought . . ."

"I know what you would have thought; you would have thought it gave a beauty, a meaning to existence; you would have thought it was a solace to the weary and heavy-laden and an inspiration to a nobler and fuller life. Balls! We may want art again in the future, but it won't be your art, it'll be the art of the people."

"Oh, Lord!"

"The people want dope and it may be that art is the best form in which we can give it them. But they're not ready for it yet. At present it's another form they want."

"What is that?"

"Words."

It was extraordinary, the sardonic vigour he put into the monosyllable. But he smiled, and though his lips grimaced Charley saw in his eyes for a moment that same look of good-humoured affection that he had been accustomed to see in them.

"No, my boy," he continued, "you have a good time, go to your office every day and enjoy yourself. It can't last very long now and you may just as well get all the fun out of it that you can."

"What d'you mean by that?"

"Never mind. We'll talk about it some other time. Tell me, what have you come to Paris for?"

"Well, chiefly to see you."

Simon flushed darkly. You would have thought that a word of kindness, and when Charley spoke you could never doubt that it was from the heart, horribly embarrassed him.

"And besides that?"

"I want to see some pictures, and if there's anything good in the theatre I'd like to go. And I want to have a bit of a lark generally."

"I suppose you mean by that that you want to have a woman."

"I don't get much opportunity in London, you know."

"Later on I'll take you to the Sérail."

"What's that?"

"You'll see. It's not bad fun."

They began to talk of Simon's experiences in Vienna, but he was reticent about them.

"It took me some time to find my feet. You see, I'd never been out of England before. I learnt German. I read a great deal. I thought. I met a lot of people who interested me."

"And since then, in Paris?"

"I've been doing more or less the same thing; I've been putting my ideas in order. I'm young. I've got plenty of time. When I'm through with Paris I shall go to Rome, Berlin or Moscow. If I can't get a job with the paper, I shall get some other job; I can always teach English and earn enough to keep body and soul together. I wasn't born in the purple and I can do without things. In Vienna, as an exercise in self-denial, I lived for a month on bread and milk. It wasn't even a hardship. I've trained myself now to do with one meal a day."

"D'you mean to say this is your first meal to-day?"

"I had a cup of coffee when I got up and a glass of milk at one."

"But what's the object of it? You're adequately paid in your job, aren't you?"

"I get a living wage. Certainly enough to have three meals a day. Who can achieve mastery over others unless he first achieves mastery over himself?"

Charley grinned. He was beginning to feel more at his ease.

"That sounds like a tag out of a dictionary of quotations."

"It may be," Simon replied indifferently. "Je prends mon bien où je le trouve. A proverb distils the wisdom of the ages and only a fool is scornful of the commonplace. You don't suppose I intend to be a foreign correspondent for a London paper or a teacher of English all my life. These are my Wanderjahre. I'm going to spend them in acquiring the education I never got at the stupid school we both went to or in that suburban cemetery they call the University of Cambridge. But it's not only knowledge of men and books that I want to acquire; that's only an instrument; I want to acquire something much harder to come by and more important: an unconquerable will. I want to mould myself as the Jesuit novice is moulded by the iron discipline of the Order. I think I've always known myself; there's nothing that teaches you what you are, like being alone in the world, a stranger everywhere, and living all your life with people to whom you mean nothing. But my knowledge was instinctive. In these two years I've been abroad I've learnt to know myself as I know the fifth proposition of Euclid. I know my strength and my weakness and I'm ready to spend the next five or six years cultivating my strength and ridding myself of my weakness. I'm going to take myself as a trainer takes an athlete to make a champion of him. I've got a good brain. There's no one in the world who can see to the end of his nose with such perspicacity as I can, and believe me, in the world we live in that's a great force. I can talk. You have to persuade men to action not by reasoning, but by rhetoric. The general idiocy of mankind is such that they can be swayed by words, and however mortifying, for the present you have to accept the fact as you accept it in the cinema that a film to be a success must have a happy ending. Already I can do pretty well all I like with words; before I'm through I shall be able to do anything."

Simon took a long draught of the white wine they were drinking and sitting back in his chair began to laugh. His face writhed into a grimace of intolerable suffering.

"I must tell you an incident that happened a few months ago here. They were having a meeting of the British Legion or something like that, I forget what for, war graves or something; my chief was going to speak, but he had a cold in the head and he sent me instead. You know what our paper is, bloody patriotic as long as it helps our circulation, all the dirt we can get, and a high moral tone. My chief's the right man in the right place. He hasn't had an idea in his head for twenty years. He never opens his mouth without saying the obvious and when he tells a dirty story it's so stale that it doesn't even stink any more. But he's as shrewd as they make 'em. He knows what the proprietor wants and he gives it to him. Well, I made the speech he would have made. Platitudes dripped from my mouth. I made the welkin ring with claptrap. I gave them jokes so hoary that even a judge would have been ashamed to make them. They roared with laughter. I gave them pathos so shaming that you would have thought they would vomit. The tears rolled down their cheeks. I beat the big drum of patriotism like a Salvation Lass sublimating her repressed sex. They cheered me to the echo. It was the speech of the evening. When it was all over the big-wigs wrung my hand still overwhelmed with emotion. I got them all right. And d'you know, I didn't say a single word that I didn't know was contemptible balderdash. Words, words, words! Poor old Hamlet."

"It was a damned unscrupulous thing to do," said Charley. "After all, I daresay they were just a lot of ordinary, decent fellows who were only wanting to do what they thought was the right thing, and what's more they were probably prepared to put their hands in their pockets to prove the sincerity of their convictions."

"You would think that. In point of fact more money was raised for whatever the damned cause was than had ever been raised before at one of their meetings and the organizers told my chief it was entirely due to my brilliant speech."

Charley in his candour was distressed. This was not the Simon he had known so long. Formerly, however wild his theories were, however provocatively expressed, there was a sort of nobility in them. He was disinterested. His indignation was directed against oppression and cruelty. Injustice roused him to fury. But Simon did not notice the effect he had on Charley or if he did was indifferent to it. He was absorbed in himself.

"But brain isn't enough and eloquence, even if it's necessary, is after all a despicable gift. Kerensky had them both and what did they avail him? The important thing is character. It's my character I've got to mould. I'm sure one can do anything with oneself if one tries. It's only a matter of will. I've got to train myself so that I'm indifferent to insult, neglect and ridicule. I've got to acquire a spiritual aloofness so complete that if they put me in prison I shall feel myself as free as a bird in the air. I've got to make myself so strong that when I make mistakes I am unshaken, but profit by them to act rightly. I've got to make myself so hard that not only can I resist the temptation to be pitiful, but I don't even feel pity. I've got to wring out of my heart the possibility of love."

"Why?"

"I can't afford to let my judgement be clouded by any feel-

ing that I might have for a human being. You are the only
person I've ever cared for in the world, Charley. I shan't
rest till I know in my bones that if it were necessary to put
you against a wall and shoot you with my own hands I could
do it without a moment's hesitation and without a moment's
regret."

Simon's eyes had a dark opaqueness which reminded you
of an old mirror, in a deserted house, from which the quick-
silver was worn away, so that when you looked in it you
saw, not yourself, but a sombre depth in which seemed to
lurk the reflections of long past events and passions long
since dead and yet in some terrifying way tremulous still with
a borrowed and mysterious life.

"Did you wonder why I didn't come to the station to meet
you?"

"It would have been nice if you had. I supposed you
couldn't get away."

"I knew you'd be disappointed. It's our busy time at the
office, we have to be on tap then to telephone to London the
news that's come through in the course of the day, but it's
Christmas Eve, the paper doesn't come out to-morrow and
I could have got away easily. I didn't come because I wanted
to so much. Ever since I got your letter saying you were
coming over I've been sick with the desire to see you. When
the train was due and I knew you'd be wandering up the
platform looking for me and rather lost in that struggling
crowd, I took a book and began to read. I sat there, forcing
myself to attend to it, and refusing to let myself listen for
the telephone that I expected every moment to ring. And
when it did and I knew it was you, my joy was so intense
that I was enraged with myself. I almost didn't answer. For
more than two years now I've been striving to rid myself
of the feeling I have for you. Shall I tell you why I wanted
you to come over? One idealizes people when they're away,
it's true that absence makes the heart grow fonder, and when
one sees them again one's often surprised that one saw anything in them at all. I thought that if there were anything
left in me of the old feeling I had for you the few days
you're spending here now would be enough to kill it."

"I'm afraid you'll think me very stupid," said Charley, with his engaging smile, "but I can't for the life of me see why you want to."

"I do think you're very stupid."

"Well, taking that for granted, what is the reason?"

Simon frowned a little and his restless eyes darted here and there like a hare trying to escape a pursuer.

"You're the only person who ever cared for me."

"That's not true. My father and mother have always been very fond of you."

"Don't talk such nonsense. Your father was as indifferent to me as he is to art, but it gave him a warm, comfortable feeling of benevolence to be kind to the orphan penniless boy whom he could patronize and impress. Your mother thought me unscrupulous and self-seeking. She hated the influence she thought I had over you and she was affronted because she saw that I thought your father an old humbug, the worst sort of humbug, the one who humbugs himself; the only satisfaction I ever gave her was that she couldn't look at me without thinking how nice it was that you were so very different from me."

"You're not very flattering to my poor parents," said Charley, mildly.

Simon took no notice of the interruption.

"We clicked at once. What that old bore Goethe would have called elective affinity. You gave me what I'd never had. I, who'd never been a boy, could be a boy with you. I could forget myself in you. I bullied you and ragged you and mocked you and neglected you, but all the time I worshipped you. I felt wonderfully at home with you. With you I could be just myself. You were so unassuming, so easily pleased, so gay and so good-natured, merely to be with you rested my tortured nerves and released me for a moment from that driving force that urged me on and on. But I don't want rest and I don't want release. My will falters when I look at your sweet and diffident smile. I can't afford to be soft, I can't afford to be tender. When I look into those blue eyes of yours, so friendly, so confiding in human nature,

I waver, and I daren't waver. You're my enemy and I hate you."

Charley had flushed uncomfortably at some of the things that Simon had said to him, but now he chuckled good-humouredly.

"Oh, Simon, what stuff and nonsense you talk."

Simon paid no attention. He fixed Charley with his glittering, passionate eyes as though he sought to bore into the depths of his being.

"Is there anything there?" he said, as though speaking to himself. "Or is it merely an accident of expression that gives the illusion of some quality of the soul?" And then to Charley: "I've often asked myself what it was that I saw in you. It wasn't your good looks, though I daresay they had something to do with it; it wasn't your intelligence, which is adequate without being remarkable; it wasn't your guileless nature or your good temper. What is it in you that makes people take to you at first sight? You've won half your battle before ever you take the field. Charm? What is charm? It's one of the words we all know the meaning of, but we can none of us define. But I know if I had that gift of yours, with my brain and my determination there's no obstacle in the world I couldn't surmount. You've got vitality and that's part of charm. But I have just as much vitality as you; I can do with four hours' sleep for days on end and I can work for sixteen hours a day without getting tired. When people first meet me they're antagonistic, I have to conquer them by sheer brain-power, I have to play on their weaknesses, I have to make myself useful to them, I have to flatter them. When I came to Paris my chief thought me the most disagreeable young man and the most conceited he'd ever met. Of course he's a fool. How can a man be conceited when he knows his defects as well as I know mine? Now he eats out of my hand. But I've had to work like a dog to achieve what you can do with a flicker of your long eyelashes. Charm is essential. In the last two years I've got to know a good many prominent politicians and they've all got it. Some more and some less. But they can't all have it by nature. That shows it can be acquired. It means nothing, but it arouses the devotion of their followers so that they'll do blindly all they're bidden and be satisfied with the reward of a kind word. I've examined them at work. They can turn it on like water from a tap. The quick, friendly smile; the hand that's so ready to clasp yours. The warmth in the voice that seems to promise favours, the show of interest that leads you to think your concerns are your leader's chief preoccupation, the intimate manner which tells you nothing, but deludes you into thinking you are in your master's confidence. The clichés, the hundred varieties of dear old boy that are so flattering on influential lips. The ease and naturalness, the perfect acting that imitates nature, and the sensitiveness that discerns a fool's vanity and takes care never to affront it. I can learn all that, it only means a little more effort and a little more self-control. Sometimes of course they overdo it, the pros, their charm becomes so mechanical that it ceases to work; people see through it, and feeling they've been duped are resentful." He gave Charley another of his piercing glances. "Your charm is natural, that's why it's so devastating. Isn't it absurd that a tiny wrinkle should make life so easy for you?"

"What on earth do you mean?"

"One of the reasons why I wanted you to come over was to see exactly in what your charm consisted. As far as I can tell it depends on some peculiar muscular formation of your lower orbit. I believe it to be due to a little crease under your eyes when you smile."

It embarrassed Charley to be thus anatomized, and to divert the conversation from himself, he asked:

"But all this effort of yours, what is it going to lead you to?"

"Who can tell? Let's go and have our coffee at the Dôme."

"All right. I'll get hold of a waiter."

"I'm going to stand you your dinner. It's the first meal that we've had together that I've ever paid for."

When he took out of his pocket some notes to settle up with he found with them a couple of cards.

"Oh, look, I've got a ticket for you for the Midnight Mass

at St. Eustache. It's supposed to be the best church music in Paris and I thought you'd like to go."

"Oh, Simon, how nice of you. I should love to. You'll come with me, won't you?"

"I'll see how I feel when the time comes. Anyhow take the tickets."

Charley put them in his pocket. They walked to the Dôme. The rain had stopped, but the pavement was still wet and when the light of a shop window or a street lamp fell upon it, palely glistened. A lot of people were wandering to and fro. They came out of the shadow of the leafless trees as though from the wings of a theatre, passed across the light and then were lost again in another patch of night. Cringing but persistent, the Algerian peddlers, their eyes alert for a possible buyer, passed with a bundle of Eastern rugs and cheap furs over their arms. Coarse-faced boys, a fez on their heads, carried baskets of monkey-nuts and monotonously repeated their raucous cry: cacaouettes, cacaouettes. At a corner stood two negroes, their dark faces pinched with cold, as though time had stopped and they waited because there was nothing in the world to do but wait. The two friends reached the Dôme. The terrace where in summer the customers sat in the open was glassed in. Every table was engaged, but as they came in a couple got up and they took the empty places. It was none too warm, and Simon wore no coat.

"Won't you be cold?" Charley asked him. "Wouldn't you prefer to sit inside?"

"No, I've taught myself not to mind cold."

"What happens when you catch one?"

"I ignore it."

Charley had often heard of the Dôme, but had never been there, and he looked with eager curiosity at the people who sat all round them. There were young men in turtle-neck sweaters, some of them with short beards, and girls bareheaded, in raincoats; he supposed they were painters and writers, and it gave him a little thrill to look at them.

"English or American," said Simon, with a scornful shrug of the shoulders. "Wasters and rotters most of them, pathetically dressing up for a role in a play that has long ceased to be acted."

Over there was a group of tall, fair-haired youths who looked like Scandinavians, and at another table a swarthy, gesticulating, loquacious band of Levantines. But the greater number were quiet French people, respectably dressed, shop-keepers from the neighbourhood who came to the Dôme because it was convenient, with a sprinkling of provincials who, like Charley, still thought it the resort of artists and students.

"Poor brutes, they haven't got the money to lead the Latin Quarter life any more. They live on the edge of star-vation and work like galley-slaves. I suppose you've read the *Vie de Bohême?* Rodolphe now wears a neat blue suit that he's bought off the nail and puts his trousers under his mat-tress every night to keep them in shape. He counts every penny he spends and takes care to do nothing to compromise his future. Mimi and Musette are hard-working girls, trade unionists, who spend their spare evenings attending party meetings, and even if they lose their virtue, keep their heads."

"Don't you live with a girl?"

"No."

"Why not? I should have thought it would be very pleasant. In the year you've been in Paris you must have had plenty of chances of picking someone up."

"Yes, I've had one or two. Strange when you come to think of it. D'you know what my place consists of? A studio and a kitchen. No bath. The concierge is supposed to come and clean up every day, but she has varicose veins and hates climbing the stairs. That's all I have to offer and yet there've been three girls who wanted to come and share my squalor with me. One was English, she's got a job here in the Inter-national Communist Bureau, another was a Norwegian, she's working at the Sorbonne, and one was French—you'd have thought she had more sense; she was a dressmaker and out of work. I picked her up one evening when I was going out to dinner, she told me she hadn't had a meal all day and I stood her one. It was a Saturday night and she stayed till Monday. She wanted to stay on, but I told her to get out and she went. The Norwegian was rather a nuisance. She wanted to darn my socks and cook for me and scrub the floor. When I told her there was nothing doing she took to waiting for me at street corners, walking beside me in the street and telling me that if I didn't relent she'd kill herself. She taught me a lesson that I've taken to heart. I had to be rather firm with her in the end."

"What d'you mean by that?"

"Well, one day I told her that I was sick of her pestering. I told her that next time she addressed me in the street I'd knock her down. She was rather stupid and she didn't know I meant it. Next day when I came out of my house, it was about twelve and I was just going to the office, she was standing on the other side of the street. She came up to me, with that hang-dog look of hers, and began to speak. I didn't let her get more than two or three words out, I hit her on the chin and she went down like a ninepin."

Simon's eyes twinkled with amusement.

"What happened then?"

"I don't know. I suppose she got up again. I walked on and didn't look round to see. Anyhow she took the hint and that's the last I saw of her."

The story made Charley very uncomfortable and at the same time made him want to laugh. But he was ashamed of this and remained silent.

"The comic one was the English communist. My dear, she was the daughter of a dean. She'd been to Oxford and she'd taken her degree in economics. She was terribly genteel, oh, a perfect lady, but she looked upon promiscuous fornication as a sacred duty. Every time she went to bed with a comrade she felt she was helping the Cause. We were to be good pals, fight the good fight together, shoulder to shoulder, and all that sort of thing. The dean gave her an allowance and we were to pool our resources, make my studio a Centre, have the comrades in to afternoon tea and discuss the burning questions of the day. I just told her a few home truths and that finished her."

He lit his pipe again, smiling to himself quietly, with that painful smile of his, as though he were enjoying a joke that hurt him. Charley had several things to say, but did not know how to put them so that they should not sound affected and so arouse Simon's irony.

"But is it your wish to cut human relations out of your life altogether?" he asked, uncertainly.

"Altogether. I've got to be free. I daren't let another person get a hold over me. That's why I turned out the little sempstress. She was the most dangerous of the lot. She was gentle and affectionate. She had the meekness of the poor who have never dreamt that life can be other than hard. I could never have loved her, but I knew that her gratitude, her adoration, her desire to please, her innocent cheerfulness, were dangerous. I could see that she might easily become a habit of which I couldn't break myself. Nothing in the world is so insidious as a woman's flattery; our need for it is so enormous that we become her slave. I must be as impervious to flattery as I am indifferent to abuse. There's nothing that binds one to a woman like the benefits one confers on her. She would have owed me everything, that girl, I should never have been able to escape from her."

"But, Simon, you have human passions like the rest of us. You're twenty-three."

"And my sexual desires are urgent? Less urgent than you imagine. When you work from twelve to sixteen hours a day and sleep on an average six, when you content yourself with one meal a day, much as it may surprise you, your desires are much attenuated. Paris is singularly well arranged for the satisfaction of the sexual instinct at moderate expense and with the least possible waste of time, and when I find that my appetite is interfering with my work I have a woman just as when I'm constipated I take a purge."

Charley's clear blue eyes twinkled with amusement and a charming smile parting his lips displayed his strong white teeth.

"Aren't you missing a lot of fun? You know, one's young for such a little while."

"I may be. I know one can do nothing in the world unless one's single-minded. Chesterfield said the last word about sexual congress: the pleasure is momentary, the position is ridiculous, and the expense is damnable. It may be an instinct that one can't suppress, but the man's a pitiful fool who allows it to divert him from his chosen path. I'm not afraid of it any more. In a few more years I shall be entirely free from its temptation."

"Are you sure you can prevent yourself from falling in love one of these days? Such things do happen, you know, even to the most prudent men."

Simon gave him a strange, one might even have thought a hostile, look.

"I should tear it out of my heart as I'd wrench out of my mouth a rotten tooth."

"That's easier said than done."

"I know. Nothing that's worth doing is done easily, but that's one of the odd things about man, if his self-preservation is concerned, if he has to do something on which his being depends, he can find in himself the strength to do it."

Charley was silent. If anyone else had spoken to him as Simon had done that evening he would have thought it a pose adopted to impress. Charley had heard during his three years at Cambridge enough extravagant talk to be able, with his common sense and quiet humour, to attach no more importance to it than it deserved. But he knew that Simon never talked for effect. He was too contemptuous of his fellows' opinion to extort their admiration by taking up an attitude in which he did not believe. He was fearless and sincere. When he said that he thought this and that, you could be certain that he did, and when he said he had done that and the other you need not hesitate to believe that he had. But just as the manner of life that Simon had described seemed to Charley morbid and unnatural, so the ideas he expressed with a fluency that showed they were well considered seemed to him outrageous and horrible. He noticed that Simon had avoided saying what was the end for which he was thus so sternly disciplining himself; but at Cambridge he had been violently communist and it was natural to suppose that he was training himself to play his part in the revolution they had then, all of them, anticipated in the near future. Charley, much more concerned with the arts, had listened with interest, but without feeling that the matter was any particular affair of his, to the heated arguments he heard in Simon's rooms. If he had been obliged to state his views on a subject to which he had never given much thought, he would have agreed with his father: whatever might happen on the Continent there was no danger of communism in England; the hash they'd made in Russia showed it was impracticable; there always had been rich and poor in the world and there always would be; the English working man was too shrewd to let himself be led away by a lot of irresponsible agitators; and after all he didn't have a bad time.

Simon went on. He was eager to deliver himself of thoughts that he had bottled up for many months and he had been used to impart them to Charley for as long as he could remember. Though he reflected upon them with the intensity which was one of his great gifts, he found that they gained in clearness and force when he had this perfect listener to put them to.

"An awful lot of hokum is talked about love, you know. An importance is ascribed to it that is entirely at variance with fact. People talk as though it were self-evidently the greatest of human values. Nothing is less self-evident. Until Plato dressed his sentimental sensuality in a captivating literary form the ancient world laid no more stress on it than was sensible; the healthy realism of the Muslims has never looked upon it as anything but a physical need; it was Christianity, buttressing its emotional claims with neo-Platonism, that made it into the end and aim, the reason, the justification of life. But Christianity was the religion of slaves. It offered the weary and the heavy-laden heaven to compensate them in the future for their misery in this world and the opiate of love to enable them to bear it in the present. And like every drug it enervated and destroyed those who became subject to it. For two thousand years it's suffocated us. It's weakened our wills and lessened our courage. In this modern world we live in we know that almost everything is more important to us than love, we knew that only the soft and the stupid allow it to affect their actions, and yet we pay it a foolish lip-service. In books, on the stage, in the pulpit, on the platform the same old sentimental rubbish is talked that was used to hoodwink the slaves of Alexandria."

"But, Simon, the slave population of the ancient world was just the proletariat of to-day."

Simon's lips trembled with a smile and the look he fixed on Charley made him feel that he had said a silly thing.

"I know," said Simon quietly.

For a while his restless eyes were still, but though he looked at Charley his gaze seemed fixed on something in the far distance. Charley did not know of what he thought, but he was conscious of a faint malaise.

"It may be that the habit of two thousand years has made love a human necessity and in that case it must be taken into account. But if dope must be administered the best person to do so is surely not a dope-fiend. If love can be put to some useful purpose it can only be by someone who is himself immune to it."

"You don't seem to want to tell me what end you expect to attain by denying yourself everything that makes life pleasant. I wonder if any end can be worth it."

"What have you been doing with yourself for the last year, Charley?"

The sudden question seemed inconsequent, but he answered it with his usual modest frankness.

"Nothing very much, I'm afraid. I've been going to the office pretty well every day; I've spent a certain amount of time on the Estate getting to know the properties and all that sort of thing: I've played golf with father. He likes to get in a round two or three days a week. And I've kept up with my piano-playing. I've been to a good many concerts. I've seen most of the picture shows. I've been to the opera a bit and seen a certain number of plays."

"You've had a thoroughly good time?"

"Not bad. I've enjoyed myself."

"And what d'you expect to do next year?"

"More or less the same, I should think."

"And the year after, and the year after that?"

"I suppose in a few years I shall get married and then my father will retire and hand over his job to me. It brings in a thousand a year, not so bad in these days, and of course eventually I shall get my half of my father's share in the Mason Estate."

"And then you'll lead the sort of life your father has led before you?"

"Unless the Labour party confiscate the Mason Estate. Then of course I shall be in the cart. But until then I'm quite prepared to do my little job and have as much fun as I can on the income I've got."

"And when you die will it have mattered a damn whether you ever lived or not?"

For a moment the unexpected question disconcerted Charley and he flushed.

"I don't suppose it will."

"Are you satisfied with that?"

"To tell you the truth I've never thought about it. But if you ask me point-blank, I think I should be a fool if I weren't. I could never have become a great artist. I talked it over with father that summer after I came down when we went fishing in Norway. He put it awfully nicely. Poor old dear, he was very anxious not to hurt my feelings, but I couldn't help admitting that what he said was true. I've got a natural facility for doing things, I can paint a bit and write a bit and play a bit, perhaps I might have had a chance if I'd only been able to do one thing; but it was only a facility. Father was quite right when he said that wasn't enough, and I think he was right too when he said it was better to be a pretty good business man than a second-rate artist. After all, it's a bit of luck for me that old Sibert Mason married the cook and started growing vegetables on a bit of land that the growth of London turned into a valuable property. Don't you think it's enough if I do my duty in that state of life in which providence or chance, if you like, has placed me?"

Simon gave him a smile more indulgent than any that had tortured his features that evening.

"I daresay, Charley. But not for me. I would sooner be

smashed into a mangled pulp by a bus when we cross the street than look forward to a life like yours."

Charley looked at him calmly.

"You see, Simon, I have a happy nature and you haven't."

Simon chuckled.

"We must see if we can't change that. Let's stroll along. I'll take you to the Sérail."

iii

THE front door, a discreet door in a house of respectable appearance, was opened for them by a negro in Turkish dress and as they entered a narrow ill-lit passage a woman came out of an ante-room. She took them in with a quick, cool glance, but then recognizing Simon, immediately assumed an air of geniality. They shook hands warmly.

"This is Mademoiselle Ernestine," he said to Charley and then to her: "My friend has arrived from London this evening. He wishes to see life."

"You've brought him to the right place."

She gave Charley an appraising look. Charley saw a woman who might have been in the later thirties, good-looking in a cold, hard way, with a straight nose, thin painted lips and a firm chin; she was neatly dressed in a dark suit of somewhat masculine cut. She wore a collar and tie and as a pin the crest of a famous English regiment.

"He's good-looking," she said. "These ladies will be pleased to see him."

"Where is Madame to-night?"

"She's gone home to spend the holidays with her family. I am in charge."

"We'll go in, shall we?"

"You know your way."

The two young men passed along the passage and opening a door found themselves in a vast room garishly decorated in the pinchbeck style of a Turkish bath. There were settees round the walls and in front of them little tables and chairs. A fair sprinkling of people were sitting about, mostly in day clothes, but a few in dinner-jackets; men in twos and threes; and at one table a mixed party, the women in evening frocks, who had evidently come to see one of the sights of Paris. Waiters in Turkish dress stood about and attended to orders. On a platform was an orchestra consisting of a pianist, a fiddler and a man who played the saxophone. Two benches facing one another jutted out on to the dance floor and on these sat ten or twelve young women. They wore Turkish slippers, but with high heels, baggy trousers of some shimmering material that reached to their ankles, and small turbans on their heads. The upper part of their bodies was naked. Other girls similarly dressed were seated with men who were standing a drink. Simon and Charley sat down and ordered a bottle of champagne. The band started up. Three or four men rose to their feet and going over to the benches chose partners to dance with. The rest of the girls listlessly danced together. They talked in a desultory way to one another and threw inquisitive glances at the men who were sitting at the various tables. It was apparent that the party of sight-seers, with the smart women from a different world, excited their curiosity. On the face of it, except that the girls were half naked, there was nothing to distinguish the place from any night club but the fact that there was room to dance in comfort. Charley noticed that at a table near theirs two men with dispatch-cases, from which in the course of conversation they extracted papers, were talking business as unconcernedly as if they were in a café. Presently one of the men from the group of sight-seers went and spoke to two girls who were dancing together, whereupon they stopped and went up to the table from which he had come; one of the women, beautifully dressed in black, with a string of emeralds round her neck, got up and began dancing with one of the two girls. The other went back to the bench and sat down. The sous-maîtresse, the woman in the coat and skirt, came up to Simon and Charley.

"Well, does your friend see any of these ladies who takes his fancy?"

"Sit down with us a minute and have a drink. He's having a look round. The night's young yet."

She sat down and when Simon called the waiter ordered an orangeade.

"I'm sorry he's come here for the first time on such a quiet night. You see, on Christmas Eve a lot of people have to stay at home. But it'll get more lively presently. A crowd of English have come over to Paris for the holidays. I saw in the paper that they're running the Golden Arrow in three sections. They're a great nation, the English; they have money."

Charley, feeling rather shy, was silent, and she asked Simon if he understood French.

"Of course he does. He spent six months in Touraine to learn it."

"What a beautiful district! Last summer when I took my holiday I motored all through the Châteaux country. Angèle comes from Tours. Perhaps your friend would like to dance with her." She turned to Charley. "You do dance, don't you?"

"Yes, I like it."

"She's very well educated and she comes from an excellent family. I went to see them when I was in Tours and they thanked me for all that I had done for their daughter. They were persons of the greatest respectability. You mustn't think that we take anyone here. Madame is very particular. We have our name and we value it. All these ladies here come from families who are highly esteemed in their own town. That is why they like to work in Paris. Naturally they don't want to cause embarrassment to their relations. Life is hard and one has to earn one's living as best one can. Of course I don't pretend that they belong to the aristocracy, but the aristocracy in France is thoroughly corrupt, and for my part I set much greater value on the good French bourgeois stock. That is the backbone of the country."

Mademoiselle Ernestine gave you the impression of a sensible woman of sound principle. You could not but feel that her views on the social questions of the day would be well worth listening to. She patted Simon's hand and again speaking to Charley said:

"It always gives me pleasure to see Monsieur Simon. He's a good friend of the house. He doesn't come very often, but when he does he behaves like a gentleman. He is never drunk like some of your compatriots and one can talk to him of interesting subjects. We are always glad to see journalists here. Sometimes I think the life we lead is a little narrow and it does one good to talk to someone who is in the centre of things. It takes one out of one's rut. He's sympathetic."

In those surroundings, as though he felt himself strangely at home, Simon was easy and genial. If he was acting it was a very good performance that he was giving. You would have thought that he felt some queer affinity between himself and the sous-maîtresse of the brothel.

"Once he took me to a répétition générale at the Français. All Paris was there. Academicians, ministers, generals. I was dazzled."

"And I may add that not one of the women looked more distinguished than you. It did my reputation a lot of good to be seen with you."

"You should have seen the faces of some of the big-wigs who come here, when they saw me in the foyer walking on the arm of Monsieur Simon."

Charley knew that to go to a great social function with such a companion was the kind of joke that appealed to Simon's sardonic humour. They talked a little more and then Simon said:

"Listen, my dear, I think we ought to do our young friend proud as it's the first time he's been here. What about introducing him to the Princess? Don't you think he'd like her?"

Mademoiselle Ernestine's strong features relaxed into a smile and she gave Charley an amused glance.

"It's an idea. It would at least be an experience that he hasn't had before. She has a pretty figure."

"Let's have her along and stand her a drink."

Mademoiselle Ernestine called a waiter.

"Tell the Princess Olga to come here." Then to Charley: "She's Russian. Of course since the revolution we have been swamped with Russians, we're fed to the teeth with them and their Slav temperament; for a time the clients were amused by it, but they're tired of them now. And then they're not serious. They're noisy and quarrelsome. The truth is, they're barbarians, and they don't know how to behave. But Princess Olga is different. She has principles. You can see that she's been well brought up. She has something, there's no denying it."

While she was speaking Charley saw the waiter go up to a girl who was sitting on one of the benches and speak to her. His eyes had been wandering and he had noticed her before. She sat strangely still, and you would have thought that she was unconscious of her surroundings. She got up now, gave a glance in their direction, and walked slowly towards them. There was a singular nonchalance in her gait. When she came up she gave Simon a slight smile and they shook hands.

"I saw you come in just now," she said, as she sat down.

Simon asked her if she would drink a glass of champagne.

"I don't mind."

"This is a friend of mine who wants to know you."

"I'm flattered." She turned an unsmiling glance on Charley. She looked at him for a time that seemed to him embarrassingly long, but her eyes held neither welcome nor invitation; their perfect indifference was almost nettling. "He's handsome." Charley smiled shyly and then the faintest suspicion of a smile trembled on her lips. "He looks good-natured."

Her turban, her baggy trousers were of gauze, pale blue and thickly sprinkled with little silver stars. She was not very tall; her face was heavily made up, her cheeks extravagantly rouged, her lips scarlet and her eyelids blue; eyebrows and eyelashes were black with mascara. She was certainly not beautiful, she was only prettyish, with rather high cheekbones, a fleshy little nose and eyes not set deep in their sockets, not prominent either, but on a level as it were with her face, like windows set flush with a wall. They were large and blue, and their blue, emphasized both by the colour of her turban and by the mascara, was like a flame. She had a neat, trim, slight figure, and the skin of her body, pale amber in hue, had a look of silky softness. Her breasts were small and round, virginal, and the well-shaped nipples were rosy.

"Why don't you ask the Princess to dance with you, Charley?" said Simon.

"Will you?" said he.

She gave the very faintest shrug of one shoulder and without a word rose to her feet. At the same time Mademoiselle Ernestine, saying she had affairs to attend to, left them. It was a new and thrilling experience for Charley to dance with a girl with nothing on above the waist. It made him rather breathless to put his hand on her naked body and to feel her bare breasts against him. The hand which he held in his was small and soft. But he was a well-brought-up young man, with good manners, and feeling it was only decent to make polite conversation, talked in the same way as he would have to any girl at a dance in London whom he did not know. She answered civilly enough, but he had a notion that she was not giving much heed to what he said. Her eyes wandered vaguely about the room, but there was no indication that they found there anything to excite her interest. When he clasped her a little more closely to him she accepted the more intimate hold without any sign that she noticed it. She acquiesced. The band stopped playing and they returned to their table. Simon was sitting there alone.

"Well, does she dance well?" he asked.

"Not very."

Suddenly she laughed. It was the first sign of animation she had given and her laugh was frank and gay.

"I'm sorry," she said, speaking English, "I wasn't attending. I can dance better than that and next time I will."

Charley flushed.

"I didn't know you spoke English. I wouldn't have said that."

"But it was quite true. And you dance so well, you deserve a partner who can dance too."

Hitherto they had spoken French. Charley's was not very accurate, but it was fluent enough, and his accent was good. She spoke it very well, but with the sing-song Russian intonation which gives the language an alien monotony. Her English was not bad.

"The Princess was educated in England," said Simon.

"I went there when I was two and stayed till I was fourteen. I haven't spoken it much since then and I've forgotten."

"Where did you live?"

"In London. In Ladbroke Grove. In Charlotte Street. Wherever it was cheap."

"I'm going to leave you young things now," said Simon. "I'll see you to-morrow, Charley."

"Aren't you going to the Mass?"

"No."

He left them with a casual nod.

"Have you known Monsieur Simon long?" asked the Princess.

"He's my oldest friend."

"Do you like him?"

"Of course."

"He's very different from you. I should have thought he was the last person you would have taken to."

"He's brilliantly clever. He's been a very good friend to me."

She opened her mouth to speak, but then seemed to think better of it, and kept silent. The music began to play once more.

"Will you dance with me again?" she asked. "I want to show you that I *can* dance when I want to."

Perhaps it was because Simon had left them and she felt less constraint, perhaps it was something in Charley's manner, maybe his confusion when he had realized that she spoke English, that had made her take notice of him, there was a difference in her attitude. It had now a kindliness which was unexpected and attractive. While they danced she talked with something approaching gaiety. She went back to her childhood and spoke with a sort of grim humour of the squalor in which she and her parents had lived in cheap London lodgings. And now, taking the trouble to follow Charley's steps, she danced very well. They sat down again and

Charley glanced at his watch; it was getting on towards midnight. He was in a quandary. He had often heard them speak at home of the church music at St. Eustache, and the opportunity of hearing Mass there on Christmas Eve was one that he could not miss. The thrill of arriving in Paris, his talk with Simon, the new experience of the Sérail and the champagne he had drunk, had combined to fill him with a singular exaltation and he had an urgent desire to hear music; it was as strong as his physical desire for the girl he had been dancing with. It seemed silly to go at this particular juncture and for such a purpose; but there it was, he wanted to, and after all nobody need know.

"Look," he said, with an engaging smile, "I've got a date. I must go away now, but I shall be back in an hour. I shall still find you here, shan't I?"

"I'm here all night."

"But you won't get fixed up with anybody else?"

"Why have you got to go away?"

He smiled a trifle shyly.

"I'm afraid it sounds absurd, but my friend has given me a couple of tickets for the Mass at St. Eustache, and I may never have another opportunity of hearing it."

"Who are you going with?"

"Nobody."

"Will you take me?"

"You? But how could you get away?"

"I can arrange that with Mademoiselle. Give me a couple of hundred francs and I'll fix it."

He gave her a doubtful glance. With her naked body, her powder-blue turban and trousers, her painted face, she did not look the sort of person to go to church with. She saw his glance and laughed.

"I'd give anything in the world to go. Do, do. I can change in ten minutes. It would give me so much pleasure."

"All right."

He gave her the money and telling him to wait for her in the entrance, she hurried away. He paid for the wine and after ten minutes, counted on his watch, went out.

As he stepped into the passage a girl came up to him.

"I haven't kept you waiting, you see. I've explained to Mademoiselle. Anyway she thinks Russians are mad."

Until she spoke he had not recognized her. She wore a brown coat and skirt and a felt hat. She had taken off her make-up, even the red on her lips, and her eyes under the thin fair line of her shaven eyebrows looked neither so large nor so blue. In her brown clothes, neat but cheap, she looked nondescript. She might have been a workgirl such as you see pouring along side streets from the back door of a department store at the luncheon hour. She was hardly even pretty, but she looked very young; and there was something humble in her bearing that gave Charley a pang.

"Do you like music, Princess?" he asked, when they got into a taxi.

He did not quite know what to call her. Even though she was a prostitute, he felt it would be rude, with her rank, on so short an acquaintance to call her Olga, and if she had been reduced to so humiliating a position by the stress of circumstances it behoved him all the more to treat her with respect.

"I'm not a princess, you know, and my name isn't Olga. They call me that at the Sérail because it flatters the clients to think they are going to bed with a princess and they call me Olga because it's the only Russian name they know besides Sasha. My father was a professor of economics at the University at Leningrad and my mother was the daughter of a customs official."

"What is your name then?"

"Lydia."

They arrived just as the Mass was beginning. There were crowds of people and no chance of getting a seat. It was bitterly cold and Charley asked her if she would like his coat. She shook her head without answering. The aisles were lit by naked electric globes and they threw harsh beams on the vaulting, the columns and the dark throng of worshippers. The choir was brilliantly lit. They found a place by a column where, protected by its shadow, they could feel themselves isolated. There was an orchestra on a raised platform. At the altar were priests in splendid vestments. The music seemed to Charley somewhat florid, and he listened to it with a faint sense of disappointment. It did not move him as he had expected it would and the soloists, with their metallic, operatic voices, left him cold. He had a feeling that he was listening to a performance rather than attending a religious ceremony, and it excited in him no sensation of reverence. But for all that he was glad to have come. The darkness into which the light from the electric globes cut like a bright knife, making the Gothic lines grimmer; the soft brilliance of the altar, with its multitude of candles, with the priests performing actions whose meaning was unknown to him; the silent crowd that seemed not to participate but to wait anxiously like a crowd at a station barrier waiting for the gate to open; the stench of wet clothes and the aromatic perfume of incense; the bitter cold that lowered like a threatening unseen presence; it was not a religious emotion that he got from all this, but the sense of a mystery that had its roots far back in the origins of the human race. His nerves were taut, and when on a sudden the choir to the full accompaniment of the orchestra burst with a great shout into the Adeste Fideles he was seized with an exultation over he knew not what. Then a boy sang a canticle; the thin, silvery voice rose in the silence and the notes trickled, with a curious little hesitation at first, as though the singer were not quite sure of himself, trickled like water crystal-clear trickling over the white stones of a brook; and then, the singer gathering assurance, the sounds were caught up, as though by great dark hands, and borne into the intricate curves of the arches and up to the night of the vaulted roof. Suddenly Charley was conscious that the girl by his side, Lydia, was crying. It gave him a bit of a turn, but with his polite English reticence he pretended not to notice; he thought that the dark church and the pure sound of the boy's voice had filled her with a sudden sense of shame. He was an imaginative youth and he had read many novels. He could guess, he fancied, what she was feeling and he was seized with a great pity for her. He found it curious, however, that she should be so moved by music that was not of the best quality. But now she began to be shaken by heavy sobs and he could pretend no longer that he did not know she was in trouble. He put out a hand and took hers, thinking to offer her thus the comfort of his sympathy, but she snatched away her hand almost roughly. He began to be embarrassed. She was now crying so violently that the bystanders could not but notice it. She was making an exhibition of herself and he went hot with shame.

"Would you like to go out?" he whispered.

She shook her head angrily. Her sobbing grew more and more convulsive and suddenly she sank down on her knees and, burying her face in her hands, gave herself up to uncontrolled weeping. She was heaped up on herself strangely, like a bundle of cast-off clothes, and except for the quivering shoulders you would have thought her in a dead faint. She lay crouched at the foot of the tall pillar, and Charley, miserably self-conscious, stood in front of her trying to protect her from view. He saw a number of persons cast curious glances at her and then at him. It made him angry to think what they must suppose. The musicians were hushed, the choir was mute, and the silence had a thrilling quality of awe. Communicants, serried row upon row, pressed up to the altar steps to take in their mouths the Sacred Host that the priest offered them. Charley's delicacy prevented him from looking at Lydia and he kept his eyes fixed on the bright-lit chancel. But when she raised herself a little he was conscious of her movement. She turned to the pillar and putting her arm against it hid her face in the crook of her elbow. The passion of her weeping had exhausted her, but the way in which she now sprawled, leaning against the hard stone, her bent legs on the stone paving, expressed such a hopelessness of woe that it was even more intolerable than to see her crushed and bowed on the floor like a person thrown into an unnatural attitude by a violent death.

The service reached its close. The organ joined with the orchestra for the voluntary, and an increasing stream of people, anxious to get to their cars or to find taxis, streamed to the doors. Then it was finished, and a great throng swept down the length of the church. Charley waited till they were alone in the place they had chosen and the last thick wedge of people seemed to be pressing to the doors. He put his hand on her shoulder.

"Come. We must go now."

He put his arm round her and lifted her to her feet. Inert, she let him do what he liked. She held her eyes averted. Linking her arm in his he led her down the aisle and waited again a little till all but a dozen people had gone out.

"Would you like to walk a few steps?"

"No, I'm so tired. Let's get into a taxi."

But they had to walk a little after all, for they could not immediately find one. When they came to a street lamp she stopped and taking a mirror from her bag looked at herself. Her eyes were swollen. She took out a puff and dabbed it over her face.

"There's not much to be done," he said, with a kindly smile. "We'd better go and have a drink somewhere. You can't go back to the Sérail like that."

"When I cry my eyes always swell. It'll take hours to go down."

Just then a taxi passed and Charley hailed it.

"Where shall we go?"

"I don't care. The Select. Boulevard Montparnasse."

He gave the address and they drove across the river. When they arrived he hesitated, for the place she had chosen seemed crowded, but she stepped out of the taxi and he followed her. Notwithstanding the cold a lot of people were sitting on the terrace. They found a table within.

"I'll go into the ladies' room and wash my eyes."

In a few minutes she returned and sat down by his side. She had pulled down her hat as far as she could to hide her swollen lids and had powdered herself, but she had put on no rouge and her face was white. She was quite calm. She said nothing about the passion of weeping that had overcome her and you might have thought she took it as a natural thing that needed no excuse.

"I'm very hungry," she said. "You must be hungry, too."

Charley was ravenous and while he waited for her had wondered whether in the circumstances it would seem very gross if he ordered himself bacon and eggs. Her remark relieved his mind. It appeared that bacon and eggs were just what she fancied. He wanted to order a bottle of champagne, thinking she needed the stimulant, but she would not let him.

"Why should you waste your money? Let's have some beer."

They ate their simple meal with appetite. They talked little. Charley, with his good manners, tried to make polite conversation, but she did not encourage him and presently they fell into silence. When they had finished and had had coffee, he asked Lydia what she would like to do.

"I should like to sit here. I'm fond of this place. It's cosy and intimate. I like to look at the people who come here."

"All right, we'll sit here."

It was not exactly how he had proposed to pass his first night in Paris. He wished he hadn't been such a fool as to take her to the Midnight Mass. He had not the heart to be unkind to her. But perhaps there was some intonation in his reply that struck her, for she turned a little to look him in the face. She gave him once more the smile he had already seen two or three times on her. It was a queer sort of smile. It hardly moved the lips; it held no gaiety, but was not devoid of kindliness; there was more irony in it than amusement and it was rare and unwilling, patient and disillusioned.

"This can't be very amusing for you. Why don't you go back to the Sérail and leave me here?"

"No, I won't do that."

"I don't mind being alone, you know. I sometimes come here by myself and sit for hours. You've come to Paris to enjoy yourself. You'd be a fool not to."

"If it doesn't bore you I'd like to sit here with you."

"Why?" She gave him on a sudden a disdainful glance. "Do you look upon yourself as being noble and self-sacrificing? Or are you sorry for me or only curious?"

Charley could not imagine why she seemed angry with him or why she said these wounding things.

"Why should I feel sorry for you? Or curious?"

He meant her to understand that she was not the first prostitute he had met in his life and he was not likely to be impressed with a life-story which was probably sordid and in all likelihood untrue. Lydia stared at him with an expression which to him looked like incredulous surprise.

"What did your friend Simon tell you about me?"

"Nothing."

"Why do you redden when you say that?"

"I didn't know I reddened," he smiled.

In fact Simon had told him that she was not a bad romp, and would give him his money's worth, but that was not the sort of thing he felt inclined to tell her just then. With her pale face and swollen eyelids, in that poor brown dress and the black felt hat, there was nothing to remind one of the creature, in her blue Turkish trousers, with a naked body, who had had a curious, exotic attractiveness. It was another person altogether, quiet, respectable, demure, with whom Charley could as little think of going to bed as with one of the junior mistresses at Patsy's old school. Lydia relapsed into silence. She seemed to be sunk in reverie. When at last she spoke it was as though she were continuing her train of thought rather than addressing him.

"If I cried just now in church it wasn't for the reason that you thought. I've cried enough for that, heaven knows, but just then it was for something different. I felt so lonely. All those people, they have a country, and in that country, homes; to-morrow they'll spend Christmas Day together, father and mother and children; some of them, like you, went only to hear the music, and some have no faith, but just then, all of them, they were joined together by a common feeling; that ceremony, which they've known all their lives, and whose meaning is in their blood, every word spoken, every action of the priests, is familiar to them, and even if they don't believe with their minds, the awe, the mystery, is in their bones and they believe with their hearts; it is part of the recollections of their childhood, the gardens they played in, the countryside, the streets of the towns. It binds them together, it makes them one, and some deep instinct tells them that they belong to one another. But I am a stranger. I have no country, I have no home, I have no language. I belong nowhere. I am outcast."

She gave a mournful little chuckle.

"I'm a Russian and all I know of Russia is what I've read. I yearn for the broad fields of golden corn and the forests of silver beech that I've read of in books and though I try and try, I can't see them with my mind's eye. I know Moscow from what I've seen of it at the cinema. I sometimes rack my brain to picture to myself a Russian village, the straggling village of log houses with their thatched roofs that you read about in Chekov, and it's no good, I know that what I see isn't that at all. I'm a Russian and I speak my native language worse than I speak English and French. When I read Tolstoi and Dostoievsky it is easier for me to read them in a translation. I'm just as much a foreigner to my own people as I am to the English and French. You who've got a home and a country, people who love you, people whose ways are your ways, whom you understand without knowing them— how can you tell what it is to belong nowhere?"

"But have you no relations at all?"

"Not one. My father was a socialist, but he was a quiet, peaceable man absorbed in his studies, and he took no active part in politics. He welcomed the revolution and thought it was the opening of a new era for Russia. He accepted the Bolsheviks. He only asked to be allowed to go on with his work at the university. But they turned him out and one day he got news that he was going to be arrested. We escaped through Finland, my father, my mother and me. I was two. We lived in England for twelve years. How, I don't know. Sometimes my father got a little work to do, sometimes people helped us, but my father was homesick. Except when he was a student in Berlin he'd never been out of Russia before; he couldn't accustom himself to English life, and at last he felt he had to go back. My mother implored him not to. He couldn't help himself, he had to go, the desire was too strong for him; he got into touch with people at the Russian embassy in London, he said he was prepared to do any work the Bolsheviks gave him; he had a good reputation in Russia, his books had been widely praised, and he was an authority on his subject. They promised him everything and he sailed. When the ship docked he was taken off by the agents of the Cheka. We heard that he'd been taken to a cell on the fourth floor of the prison and thrown out of the window. They said he'd committed suicide."

She sighed a little and lit another cigarette. She had been smoking incessantly since they finished supper.

"He was a mild gentle creature. He never did anyone harm. My mother told me that all the years they'd been married he'd never said a harsh word to her. Because he'd made his peace with the Bolsheviks the people who'd helped us before wouldn't help us any more. My mother thought we'd be better off in Paris. She had friends there. They got her work addressing letters. I was apprenticed to a dressmaker. My mother died because there wasn't enough to eat for both of us and she denied herself so that I shouldn't go hungry. I found a job with a dressmaker who gave me half the usual wages because I was Russian. If those friends of my mother's, Alexey and Evgenia, hadn't given me a bed to sleep in I should have starved too. Alexey played the violin in an orchestra at a Russian restaurant and Evgenia ran the ladies' cloak-room. They had three children and the six of us lived in two rooms. Alexey was a lawyer by profession, he'd been one of my father's pupils at the university."

"But you have them still?"

"Yes, I have them still. They're very poor now. You see, everyone's sick of the Russians, they're sick of Russian restaurants and Russian orchestras. Alexey hasn't had a job for four years. He's grown bitter and quarrelsome and he drinks. One of the girls has been taken charge of by an aunt who lives at Nice, and another has gone into service, the son has become a gigolo and he does the night clubs at Montmartre; he's often here, I don't know why he isn't here this evening, perhaps he's clicked. His father curses him and beats him when he's drunk, but the hundred francs he brings home when he's found a friend helps to keep things going. I live there still."

"Do you?" said Charley in surprise.

"I must live somewhere. I don't go to the Sérail till night and when trade is slack I often get back by four or five. But it's terribly far away."

For a while they sat in silence.

"What did you mean when you said just now you hadn't been crying for the reason I thought?" asked Charley at length.

She gave him once more a curious, suspicious look.

"Do you really mean that you don't know who I am? I thought that was why your friend Simon sent for me."

"He told me nothing except—except that you'd give me a good time."

"I'm the wife of Robert Berger. That is why, although I'm a Russian, they took me at the Sérail. It gives the clients a kick."

"I'm afraid you'll think me very stupid, but I honestly don't know what you're talking about."

She gave a short, hard laugh.

"Such is fame. A day's journey and the name that's on every lip means nothing. Robert Berger murdered an English bookmaker called Teddie Jordan. He was condemned to fifteen years' penal servitude. He's at St. Laurent in French Guiana."

She spoke in such a matter-of-fact way that Charlie could hardly believe his ears. He was startled, horrified and thrilled.

"And you really didn't know?"

"I give you my word I didn't. Now you speak of it I remember reading about the case in the English papers. It created rather a sensation because the—the victim was English, but I'd forgotten the name of the—of your husband."

"It created a sensation in France, too. The trial lasted three days. People fought to get to it. The papers gave it the whole of their front page. No one talked of anything else. Oh, it was a sensation all right. That was when I first saw your friend Simon, at least that's when he first saw me, he was reporting the case for his paper and I was in court. It was an exciting trial, it gave the journalists plenty of opportunity. You must get him to tell you about it. He's proud of the articles he wrote. They were so clever, bits of them got translated and were put in the French papers. It did him a lot of good."

Charley did not know what to say. He was angry with

Simon; he recognized his puckish humour in putting him in the situation in which he now found himself.

"It must have been awful for you," he said lamely.

She turned a little and looked into his eyes. He, whose life had been set in pleasant places, had never before seen on a face a look of such hideous despair. It hardly looked like a human face, but like one of those Japanese masks which an artist has fashioned to portray a certain emotion. He shivered. Lydia till now, for Charley's sake, had been talking mostly in English, breaking into French now and then when she found it too difficult to say what she wanted in the unfamiliar language, but now she went on in French. The singsong of her Russian accent gave it a strange plaintiveness, but at the same time lent a sense of unreality to what she said. It gave you the impression of a person talking in a dream.

"I'd only been married six months. I was going to have a baby. Perhaps it was that that saved his neck. That and his youth. He was only twenty-two. The baby was born dead. I'd suffered too much. You see, I loved him. He was my first love and my last love. When he was sentenced they wanted me to divorce him, transportation is a sufficient reason in French law; they told me that the wives of convicts always divorced and they were angry with me when I wouldn't. The lawyer who defended him was very kind to me. He said that I'd done everything I could, and that I'd had a bad time, but I'd stood by him to the end and now I ought to think of myself, I was young and must remake my life, I was making it even more difficult if I stayed tied to a convict. He was impatient with me when I said that I loved Robert and Robert was the only thing in the world that mattered to me, and that whatever he did I'd love him, and that if ever I could go out to him, and he wanted me, I'd go and gladly. At last he shrugged his shoulders and said there was nothing to be done with us Russians, but if ever I changed my mind and wanted a divorce I was to come to him and he'd help me. And Evgenia and Alexey, poor drunken, worthless Alexey, they gave me no peace. They said Robert was a scoundrel, they said he was wicked, they said it was disgraceful that I should love him. As if one could stop loving because it's disgraceful to love! It's so easy to call a man a scoundrel. What does it mean? He murdered and he suffered for his crime. None of them knew him as I knew him. You see, he loved me. They didn't know how tender he was, how charming, how gay, how boyish. They said he came near killing me as he killed Teddie Jordan; they didn't see that it only made me love him more."

It was almost impossible for Charley, knowing nothing of the circumstances, to get anything coherent out of what she was saying.

"Why should he have killed you?" he asked.

"When he came home—after he'd killed Jordan, it was very late and I'd gone to bed, but his mother was waiting up for him. We lived with her. He was in high spirits, but when she looked at him she knew he'd done something terrible. You see, for weeks she'd been expecting it and she'd been frantic with anxiety.

" 'Where have you been all this time?' she asked him.

" 'I? Nowhere,' he said. 'Round with the boys.' He chuckled and gently patted her cheek. 'It's so easy to kill a man, mother,' he said. 'It's quite ridiculous, it's so easy.'

"Then she knew what he'd done and she burst out crying.

" 'Your poor wife,' she said. 'Oh, how desperately unhappy you're going to make her.'

"He looked down and sighed.

" 'Perhaps it would be better if I killed her too,' he said.

" 'Robert!' she cried.

"He shook his head.

" 'Don't be afraid, I shouldn't have the courage,' he said. 'And yet, if I did it in her sleep, she'd know nothing.'

" 'My God, why did you do it?' she cried.

"Suddenly he laughed. He had a wonderfully gay, infectious laugh. You couldn't hear it without feeling happy.

" 'Don't be so silly, mother, I was only joking,' he said. 'I've done nothing. Go to bed and to sleep.'

"She knew he was lying. But that's all he would say. At last she went to her room. It was a tiny house, in Neuilly, but it had a bit of garden and there was a little pavilion at the end of it. When we married she gave us the house and moved in there so that she could be with her son and yet not on the top of us. Robert came up to our room and he waked me with a kiss on my lips. His eyes were shining. He had blue eyes, not so blue as yours, gray rather, but they were large and very brilliant. There was almost always a smile in them. They were wonderfully alert."

But Lydia had gradually slowed down the pace of her speech as she came to these sentences. It was as though a thought had struck her and she was turning it over in her mind while she talked. She looked at Charley with a curious expression.

"There *is* something in your eyes that reminds me of him, and your face is the same shape as his. He wasn't so tall as you and he hadn't got your English complexion. He was very good-looking." She was silent for a moment. "What a malicious fool that Simon of yours is."

"What do you mean by that?"

"Nothing."

She leant forward, with her elbows on the table, her face in her hands, and went on, in a rather monotonous voice, as though she were reciting under hypnosis something that was passing before her vacant eyes.

"I smiled when I woke.

" 'How late you are,' I said. 'Be quick and come to bed.'

" 'I can't sleep now,' he said. 'I'm too excited. I'm hungry. Are there any eggs in the kitchen?'

"I was wide awake by then. You can't think how charming he looked sitting on the side of the bed in his new gray suit. He was always well-dressed and he wore his clothes wonderfully well. His hair was very beautiful, dark brown and waving, and he wore it long, brushed back on his head.

" 'I'll put on a dressing-gown and we'll go and see,' I said.

"We went into the kitchen and I found eggs and onions. I fried the onions and scrambled them with the eggs. I made some toast. Sometimes when we went to the theatre or had been to a concert we used to make ourselves something to eat when we got home. He loved scrambled eggs and onions, and I cooked them just in the way he liked. We used to love those modest suppers that we had by ourselves in the kitchen. He went into the cellar and brought out a bottle of champagne. I knew his mother would be cross, it was the last of half a dozen bottles that Robert had had given him by one of his racing friends, but he said he felt like champagne just then and he opened the bottle. He ate the eggs greedily and he emptied his glass at a gulp. He was in tearing spirits. When we first got into the kitchen I'd noticed that though his eyes were shining so brightly his face was pale, and if I hadn't known that nothing was more unlikely I should have thought he'd been drinking, but now the colour came back to his cheeks. I thought he'd been just tired and hungry. He'd been out all day, tearing about, I was sure, and it might be that he hadn't had a bite to eat. Although we'd only been parted a few hours he was almost crazy with joy at being with me again. He couldn't stop kissing me and while I was scrambling the eggs I had to push him away because he wanted to hug me and I was afraid he'd spoil the cooking. But I couldn't help laughing. We sat side by side at the kitchen table as close as we could get. He called me every sweet, endearing name he could think of, he couldn't keep his hands off me, you would have thought we'd only been married a week instead of six months. When we'd finished I wanted to wash everything up so that when his mother came in for breakfast she shouldn't find a mess, but he wouldn't let me. He wanted to get to bed quickly.

"He was like a man possessed of a god. I never thought it was possible for a man to love a woman as he loved me that night. I never knew a woman was capable of such adoration as I was filled with. He was insatiable. It seemed impossible to slake his passion. No woman ever had such a wonderful lover as I had that night. And he was my husband. Mine! Mine! I worshipped him. If he'd let me I would have kissed his feet. When at last he fell asleep exhausted, the dawn was already peeping through a chink in the curtains. But I couldn't sleep. I looked at his face as the light grew stronger; it was the unlined face of a boy. He slept, holding me in his arms, and there was a tiny smile of happiness on his lips. At last I fell asleep too.

"He was still sleeping when I woke and I got out of bed very quietly so as not to disturb him. I went into the kitchen to make his coffee for him. We were very poor. Robert had worked in a broker's office, but he'd had a quarrel with his employer and had walked out on him, and since then he hadn't found anything regular to do. He was crazy about racing and sometimes he made a bit that way, though his mother hated it, and occasionally he earned a little money by selling second-hand cars on commission, but all we really had to depend on was his mother's pension, she was the widow of an army doctor, and the little money she had besides. We didn't keep a servant and my mother-in-law and I did the housework. I found her in the kitchen, peeling potatoes for lunch.

" 'How is Robert?' she asked me.

" 'He's still asleep. I wish you could see him. With his hair all tousled he looks as if he was sixteen.'

"The coffee was on the hob and the milk was warm. I put it on to boil and had a cup, then I crept upstairs to get Robert's clothes. He was a dressy fellow and I'd learnt how to press them. I wanted to have them all ready for him and neatly laid out on a chair when he woke. I brought them down into the kitchen and gave them a brush and then I put an iron on to heat. When I put the trousers on the kitchen table I noticed there were stains on one of the legs.

" 'What on earth is that?' I cried. 'Robert *has* got his trousers in a mess.'

"Madame Berger got up from her chair so quickly that she upset the potatoes. She snatched up the trousers and looked at them. She began to tremble.

" 'I wonder what it is,' I said. 'Robert will be furious. His new suit.'

"I saw she was upset, but you know, the French are funny in some ways, they don't take things like that as casually as we Russians do. I don't know how many hundred francs Robert had paid for the suit, and if it was ruined she wouldn't sleep for a week thinking of all the money that had been wasted.

" 'It'll clean,' I said.

" 'Take Robert up his coffee,' she said sharply. 'It's after eleven and quite time he woke. Leave me the trousers. I know what to do with them.'

"I poured him out a cup and was just going upstairs with it when we heard Robert clattering down in his slippers. He nodded to his mother and asked for the paper.

" 'Drink your coffee while it's hot,' I said to him.

"He paid no attention to me. He opened the paper and turned to the latest news.

" 'There's nothing,' said his mother.

"I didn't know what she meant. He cast his eyes down the columns and then took a long drink of coffee. He was unusually silent. I took his coat and began to give it a brush.

" 'You made your trousers in an awful mess last night,' I said. 'You'll have to wear your blue suit to-day.'

"Madame Berger had put them over the back of a chair. She took them to him and showed him the stains. He looked at them for a minute while she watched him in silence. You would have thought he couldn't take his eyes off them. I couldn't understand their silence. It was strange. I thought they were taking a trivial accident in an absurdly tragic way. But of course the French have thrift in their bones.

" 'We've got some petrol in the house,' I said. 'We can get the stains out with that. Or they can go to the cleaner's.'

"They didn't answer. Robert, frowning, looked down. His mother turned the trousers round, I suppose to look if there were stains on the back, and then, I think, felt that there was something in the pockets.

" 'What have you got here?'

"He sprang to his feet.

" 'Leave it alone. I won't have you look in my pockets.'

"He tried to snatch the trousers from her, but before he could do so she had slipped her hand into the hip-pocket and taken out a bundle of bank-notes. He stopped dead when he saw she had them. She let the trousers drop to the ground and with a groan put her hand to her breast as though she'd been stabbed. I saw then that they were both of them as pale as death. A sudden thought seized me; Robert had often said to me that he was sure his mother had a little hoard hidden away somewhere in the house. We'd been terribly short of money lately. Robert was crazy to go down to the Riviera; I'd never been there and he'd been saying for weeks that if we could only get a bit of cash we'd go down and have a honeymoon at last. You see, at the time we married, he was working at that broker's and couldn't get away. The thought flashed through my mind that he'd found his mother's hoard. I blushed to the roots of my hair at the idea that he'd stolen it and yet I wasn't surprised. I hadn't lived with him for six months without knowing that he'd think it rather a lark. I saw that they were thousand-franc notes that she held in her hand. Afterwards I knew there were seven of them. She looked at him as though her eyes would start out of her head.

" 'When did you get them, Robert?' she asked.

"He gave a laugh, but I saw he was nervous.

" 'I made a lucky bet yesterday,' he answered.

" 'Oh, Robert,' I cried, 'you promised your mother you'd never play the horses again.'

" 'This was a certainty,' he said, 'I couldn't resist. We shall be able to go down to the Riviera, my sweet. You take them and keep them or they'll just slip through my fingers.'

" 'No, no, she mustn't have them,' cried Madame Berger. She gave Robert a look of real horror, so that I was astounded, then she turned to me. 'Go and do your room. I won't have the rooms left unmade all day long.'

"I saw she wanted to get rid of me and I thought I'd be better out of the way if they were going to quarrel. The position of a daughter-in-law is delicate. His mother worshipped Robert, but he was extravagant and it worried her to death. Now and then she made a scene. Sometimes they'd shut themselves up in her pavilion at the end of the garden and I'd hear their voices raised in violent discussions. He would come away sulky and irritable and when I saw her I knew she'd been crying. I went upstairs. When I came down again they stopped talking at once and Madame Berger told me to go out and buy some eggs for lunch. Generally Robert went out about noon and didn't come back till night, often very late, but that day he stayed in. He read and played the piano. I asked him what had passed between him and his mother, but he wouldn't tell me, he told me to mind my own business. I think neither of them spoke more than a dozen sentences all day. I thought it would never end. When we went to bed I snuggled up to Robert and put my arms round his neck, for of course I knew he was worried and I wanted to console him, but he pushed me away.

" 'For God's sake leave me alone,' he said. 'I'm in no mood for love-making to-night. I've got other things to think about.'

"I was bitterly wounded, but I didn't speak. I moved away from him. He knew he'd hurt me, for in a little while he put out his hand and lightly touched my face.

" 'Go to sleep, my sweet,' he said. 'Don't be upset because I'm in a bad humour to-day. I drank too much yesterday. I shall be all right to-morrow.'

" 'Was it your mother's money?' I whispered.

"He didn't answer at once.

" 'Yes,' he said at last.

" 'Oh, Robert, how could you?' I cried.

"He paused again before he said anything. I was wretched. I think I began to cry.

" 'If anyone should ask you anything you never saw me with the money. You never knew that I had any.'

" 'How can you think I'd betray you?' I cried.

" 'And the trousers. Maman couldn't get the stains out. She's thrown them away.'

"I suddenly remembered that I'd smelt something burning that afternoon while Robert was playing and I was sitting with him. I got up to see what it was.

" 'Stay here,' he said.

" 'But something's burning in the kitchen,' I said.

" 'Maman's probably burning old rags. She's in a dirty temper to-day, she'll bite your head off if you go and inter-fere with her.'

"I knew now that it wasn't old rags she was burning; she hadn't thrown the trousers away, she'd burnt them. I began to be horribly frightened, but I didn't say anything. He took my hand.

" 'If anyone should ask you about them,' he said, 'you must say that I got them so dirty cleaning a car that they had to be given away. My mother gave them to a tramp the day before yesterday. Will you swear to that?'

" 'Yes,' I said, but I could hardly speak.

"Then he said a terrifying thing.

" 'It may be that my head depends on it.'

"I was too stunned, I was too horrified, to say anything. My head began to ache so that I thought it would burst. I don't think I closed my eyes all night. Robert slept fitfully. He was restless even in his sleep and turned from side to side. We went downstairs early, but my mother-in-law was already in the kitchen. As a rule she was very decently dressed and when she went out she looked quite smart. She was a doctor's widow and the daughter of a staff officer; she had a feeling about her position and she would let no one know to what economies she was reduced to make the show she did when she went to pay visits on old army friends. Then, with her waved hair and her manicured hands, with rouge on her cheeks, she didn't look more than forty; but now, her hair tousled, without any make-up, in a dressing-gown, she looked like an old procuress who'd retired to live on her savings. She didn't say good morning to Robert. Without a word she handed him the paper. I watched him while he read it and I saw his expression change. He felt my eyes upon him and looked up. He smiled.

" 'Well, little one,' he said gaily, 'what about this coffee? Are you going to stand there all the morning looking at your lord and master or are you going to wait on him?'

"I knew there was something in the paper that would tell me what I had to know. Robert finished his breakfast and went upstairs to dress. When he came down again, ready to go out, I had a shock, for he was wearing the light gray suit that he had worn two days before, and the trousers that went with it. But then of course I remembered that he'd had a second pair made when he ordered the suit. There had been a lot of discussion about it. Madame Berger had grumbled at the expense, but he had insisted that he couldn't hope to get a job unless he was decently dressed and at last she gave in as she always did, but she insisted that he should have a second pair of trousers, she said it was always the trousers that grew shabby first and it would be an economy in the end if he had two pairs. Robert went out and said he wouldn't be in to lunch. My mother-in-law went out soon afterwards to do her marketing and the moment I was alone I seized the paper. I saw that an English bookmaker, called Teddie Jordan, had been found dead in his flat. He had been stabbed in the back. I had often heard Robert speak of him. I knew it was he who had killed him. I had such a sudden pain in my heart that I thought I should die. I was terrified. I don't know how long I sat there. I couldn't move. At last I heard a key in the door and I knew it was Madame Berger coming in again. I put the paper back where she'd left it and went on with my work."

Lydia gave a deep sigh. They had not got to the restaurant till one or after and it was two by the time they finished supper. When they came in the tables were full and there was a dense crowd at the bar. Lydia had been talking a long time and little by little people had been going. The crowd round the bar thinned out. There were only two persons sitting at it now and only one table besides theirs was occupied. The waiters were getting restive.

"I think we ought to be going," said Charley. "I'm sure they want to be rid of us."

At that moment the people at the other table got up to go. The woman who brought their coats from the cloak-room brought Charley's too and put it on the table beside him. He called for the bill.

"I suppose there's some place we could go to now?"

"We could go to Montmartre. Graaf's is open all night. I'm terribly tired."

"Well, if you like I'll drive you home."

"To Alexey and Evgenia's? I can't go there to-night. He'll be drunk. He'll spend the whole night abusing Evgenia for bringing up the children to be what they are and weeping over his own sorrows. I won't go to the Sérail. We'd better go to Graaf's. At least it's warm there."

She seemed so woebegone, and really so exhausted, that

Charley with hesitation made a proposal. He remembered that Simon had told him that he could take anyone into the hotel.

"Look here, I've got two beds in my room. Why don't you come back with me there?"

She gave him a suspicious look, but he shook his head smiling.

"Just to sleep, I mean," he added. "You know, I've had a journey to-day and what with the excitement and one thing and another I'm pretty well all in."

"All right."

There was no cab to be found when they got out into the street, but it was only a little way to the hotel and they walked. A sleepy night watchman opened the door for them and took them upstairs in the lift. Lydia took off her hat. She had a broad, white brow. He had not seen her hair before. It was short, curling round the neck, and pale brown. She kicked off her shoes and slipped out of her dress. When Charley came back from the bathroom, having got into his pyjamas, she was not only in bed but asleep. He got into his own bed and put out the light. They had not exchanged a word since they left the restaurant.

Thus did Charley spend his first night in Paris.

iv

IT WAS late when he woke. For a moment he had no notion where he was. Then he saw Lydia. They had not drawn the curtains and a gray light filtered through the shutters. The room with its pitchpine furniture looked squalid. She lay on her back in the twin bed with her eyes open, staring up at the dingy ceiling. Charley glanced at his watch. He felt shy of the strange woman in the next bed.

"It's nearly twelve," he said. "We'd better just have a cup of coffee and then I'll take you to lunch somewhere if you like."

She looked at him with grave, but not unkindly, eyes.

"I've been watching you sleep. You were sleeping as peace-

fully, as profoundly, as a child. You had such a look of innocence on your face, it was shattering."

"My face badly needs a shave," said he.

He telephoned down to the office for coffee and it was
brought by a stout, middle-aged maid, who gave Lydia a
glance, but whose expression heavily conveyed nothing.
Charley smoked a pipe and Lydia one cigarette after another. They talked little. Charley did not know how to deal
with the singular situation in which he found himself and
Lydia seemed lost in thoughts unconcerned with him. Presently he went into the bathroom to shave and bath. When
he came back he found Lydia sitting in an armchair at the
window in his dressing-gown. The window looked into the
courtyard and all there was to see was the windows, storey
above storey, of the rooms opposite. On the gray Christmas
morning it looked incredibly cheerless. She turned to him.

"Couldn't we lunch here instead of going out?"

"Downstairs, d'you mean? If you like. I don't know what
the food's like."

"The food doesn't matter. No, up here, in the room. It's
so wonderful to shut out the world for a few hours. Rest,
peace, silence, solitude. You would think they were luxuries
that only the very rich can afford, and yet they cost nothing.
Strange that they should be so hard to come by."

"If you like I'll order you lunch here and I'll go out."

Her eyes lingered on him and there was a slightly ironic
smile in them.

"I don't mind you. I think probably you're very sweet and
nice. I'd rather you stayed; there's something cosy about you
that I find comforting."

Charley was not a youth who thought very much about
himself, but at that moment he could not help a slight sense
of irritation because really she seemed to be using him with
more unconcern than was reasonable. But he had naturally
good manners and did not betray his feeling. Besides, the
situation was odd, and though it was not to find himself in
such a one that he had come to Paris, it could not be denied
that the experience was interesting. He looked round the
room. The beds were unmade; Lydia's hat, her coat and

skirt, her shoes and stockings were lying about, mostly on the floor; his own clothes were piled up untidily on a chair.

"The place looks terribly frowsy," he said. "D'you think it would be very nice to lunch in all this mess?"

"What does it matter?" she answered, with the first laugh he had heard from her. "But if it upsets your prim English sense of decorum, I'll make the beds, or the maid can while I'm having a bath."

She went into the bathroom and Charley telephoned for a waiter. He ordered some eggs, some meat, cheese and fruit, and a bottle of wine. Then he got hold of the maid. Though the room was heated there was a fireplace and he thought a fire would be cheerful. While the maid was getting the logs he dressed himself, and then, when she got busy setting things to rights, he sat down and looked at the grim courtyard. He thought disconsolately of the jolly party at the Terry-Masons'. They would be having a glass of sherry now before sitting down to their Christmas dinner of turkey and plum pudding, and they would be all very gay, pleased with their Christmas presents, noisy and jolly. After a while Lydia came back. She had no make-up on her face, but she had combed her hair neatly, the swelling of her eyelids had gone down, and she looked young and pretty; but her prettiness was not the sort that excites carnal desires and Charley, though naturally susceptible, saw her come in without a flutter of his pulse.

"Oh, you've dressed," she said. "Then I can keep on your dressing-gown, can't I? Let me have your slippers. I shall float about in them, but it doesn't matter."

The dressing-gown had been a birthday present from his mother, and it was of blue patterned silk; it was much too long for her, but she arranged herself in it so that it was not unbecoming. She was glad to see the fire and sat down in the chair he had drawn up for her. She smoked a cigarette. What seemed to him strange was that she took the situation as though there were nothing strange in it. She was as casual in her behaviour as though she had known him all her life; if anything more was needed to banish any ideas he might have cherished about her, nothing could have been more efficacious than the impression he so clearly got from her that she had put out of her mind for good and all the possibility of his wanting to go to bed with her. He was surprised to see with what good appetite she ate. He had a notion after what she had told him the night before that she was too distraught to eat but sparingly, and it was a shock to his romantic sensibility to see that she ate as much as he did and with obvious satisfaction.

They were drinking their coffee when the telephone rang. It was Simon.

"Charley? Would you like to come round and have a talk?"

"I'm afraid I can't just now."

"Why not?" Simon asked sharply.

It was characteristic of him to think that everyone should be ready to drop whatever he was doing if he wanted him. However little something mattered to him, if he had a whim for it and he was crossed, it immediately assumed consequence.

"Lydia's here."

"Who the devil's Lydia?"

Charley hesitated an instant.

"Well, Princess Olga."

There was a pause and then Simon burst into a harsh laugh.

"Congratulations, old boy. I knew you'd click. Well, when you have a moment to spare for an old friend, let me know."

He rang off. When Charley turned back to Lydia she was staring into the fire. Her impassive face gave no sign that she had heard the conversation. Charley pushed back the little table at which they had lunched and made himself as comfortable as he could in a shallow armchair. Lydia leaned over and put another log on the fire. There was a sort of intimacy in the action that did not displease Charley. She was settling herself down as a small dog turns round two or three times on a cushion and, having made a suitable hollow, curls up in it. They stayed in all the afternoon. The joyless light of the winter day gradually failed and they sat by the light of the wood-fire. In the rooms on the opposite side of the court lights were turned on here and there, and the pale, uncurtained windows had a false strange look like lighted windows in the stage-set of a street. But they were not more unreal than the position in which he found himself seemed to Charley, sitting in that sordid bedroom, by the fitful blazing of the log fire, while that woman whom he did not know told him her terrible story. It seemed not to occur to her that he might be unwilling to listen. So far as he could tell she had no inkling that he might have anything else to do, nor that in baring her heart to him, in telling him her anguish, she was putting a burden on him that a stranger had no right to exact. Was it that she wanted his sympathy? He wasn't even sure of that. She knew nothing about him and wanted to know nothing. He was only a convenience, and but for his sense of humour, he would have found her indifference exasperating. Towards evening she fell silent, and presently by her quiet breathing Charley knew she had fallen asleep. He got up from his chair, for he had sat in it so long that his limbs ached, and went to the window, on tiptoe so as not to wake her, and sitting down on a stool looked out into the court-yard. Now and again he saw someone pass behind the lighted windows; he saw an elderly woman watering a flower-pot; he saw a man in his shirt-sleeves lying on his bed reading; he wondered who and what these people were. They looked like ordinary middle-class persons in modest circumstances, for after all the hotel was cheap and the quarter dowdy; but seen like that, through the windows, as though in a peep-show, they looked strangely unreal. Who could tell what people were really and what grim passions, what crimes, their commonplace aspect concealed? In some of the rooms the curtains were drawn and only a chink of light between them showed that there was anyone there. Some of the windows were black; they were not empty, for the hotel was full, but their occupants were out. On what mysterious errands? Charley's nerves were shaken and he had a sudden feeling of horror for all those unknown persons whose lives were so strange to him; below the smooth surface he seemed to sense something confused, dark, monstrous and terrible.

He pondered, his brow knit in concentration, the long,

unhappy story to which he had listened all the afternoon. Lydia had gone back and forth, now telling him of her struggle to live when she was working for a pittance at a dressmaker's and after that some incident of her poverty-stricken childhood in London; then more of those agonizing days that followed the murder, the terror of the arrest and the anguish of the trial. He had read detective stories, he had read the papers, he knew that crimes were committed, he knew that people lived in penury, but he had known it all, as it were from the outside; it gave him a strange, a frightening sensation to find himself thrown into personal contact with someone to whom horrible things had actually happened. He remembered suddenly, he did not know why, a picture of Manet's of somebody's execution—was it Maximilian's?—by a shooting squad. He had always thought it a striking picture. Now it came to him as a shock to realize that it portrayed an incident that had occurred. The Emperor had in fact stood in that place, and as the soldiers levelled their rifles, it must have seemed incredible to him that he should stand there and in a moment cease to live.

And now that he knew Lydia, now that he had listened to her last night and that day, now that he had eaten with her, and danced with her, now that for so many hours they had lived together in such close proximity, it seemed unbelievable that such things should have befallen her.

If ever anything looked like pure chance it was that Lydia and Robert Berger met at all. Through the friends she lived with, who worked in a Russian restaurant, Lydia sometimes got a ticket for a concert, and when she couldn't and there was something she very much wanted to hear, she scraped together out of her weekly earnings enough to buy herself standing-room. This was her only extravagance and to go to a concert her only recreation. It was chiefly Russian music she liked. Listening to that she felt that somehow she was getting to the heart of the country she had never seen, but which drew her with a yearning that must ever remain unsatisfied. She knew nothing of Russia but what she had heard from the lips of her father and mother, from the conversation between Evgenia and Alexey when they talked of old

times, and from the novels she had read. It was when she
was listening to the music of Rimsky-Korsakov and Gla-
zounov, to the racy and mordant compositions of Stravinsky,
that the impressions she had thus gained gathered form and
substance. Those wild melodies, those halting rhythms, in
which there was something so alien from Europe, took her
out of herself and her sordid existence and overwhelmed her
with such a passion of love that happy, releasing tears flowed
down her cheeks. But because nothing of what she saw with
the mind's eye had she seen with a bodily eye, because it was
a product of hearsay and a fevered imagination, she saw it
in a strangely distorted fashion; she saw the Kremlin, with
its gilt and star-sprinkled domes, the Red Square and the
Kitai Gorod, as though they were the setting of a fairy tale;
for her Prince Andrey and the charming Natasha still went
their errands in the busy streets of Moscow, Dmitri Karamazov, after a wild night with the gipsies, still met the
sweet Alyosha on the Mostbaretsk Bridge, the merchant
Rogozhin dashed past in his sled with Nastasya Filippovna
by his side, and the wan characters of Chekov's stories
drifted hither and yon at the breath of circumstance like
dead leaves before the wind; the Summer Garden and the
Nevsky Prospekt were magic names, and Anna Karenina
still drove in her carriage, Vronsky elegant in his new uniform climbed the stairs of the great houses on the Fontanka
Canal, and the misbegotten Raskolnikov walked the Liteiny.
In the passion and nostalgia of that music, with Turgeniev
at the back of her mind, she saw the spacious, dilapidated
country houses where they talked through the scented night,
and the marshes, pale in the windless dawn, where they shot
the wild duck; with Gorki, the wretched villages where they
drank furiously, loved brutally and killed; the turbid flow of
the Volga, the interminable steppes of the Caucasus, and the
enchanting garish Crimea. Filled with longing, filled with regret for a life that had passed for ever, homesick for a home
she had never known, a stranger in a hostile world, she felt
at that moment one with the great, mysterious country. Even
though she spoke its language haltingly, she was Russian,
and she loved her native land; at such moments she felt that

there was where after all she belonged and she understood how it was that her father, despite the warnings, was obliged, even at the risk of death, to return to it.

It was at a concert, one where all the music was Russian, that she found herself standing next to a young man who, she noticed, now and then looked at her curiously. Once she happened to turn her eyes on him and was struck by the passionate absorption with which he seemed to be listening; his hands were clasped and his mouth slightly open as though he were out of breath. He was rapt in ecstasy. He had clean-cut features and looked well-bred. Lydia gave him but a passing glance and once more returned to the music and the crowding dreams it awoke in her. She too was carried away and she was hardly aware that a little sob broke from her lips. She was startled when she felt a small, soft hand take hers and give it a slight pressure. She quickly drew her hand away. The piece was the last before the interval and when it ended the young man turned to her. He had lovely eyes, gray under bushy eyebrows, and they were peculiarly gentle.

"You're crying, Mademoiselle."

She had thought he might be Russian like herself, but his accent was purely French. She understood that that quick pressure of her hand was one of instinctive sympathy, and was touched by it.

"Not because I am unhappy," she answered, with a faint smile.

He smiled back and his smile was charming.

"I know. This Russian music, it's strangely thrilling and yet it tears one's heart to pieces."

"But you're French. What can it mean to you?"

"Yes. I'm French. I don't know what it means to me. It's the only music I want to listen to. It is power and passion, blood and destruction. It makes every nerve in my body tingle." He gave a little laugh at himself. "Sometimes when I listen to it I feel there is nothing that man is capable of that I cannot do."

She did not answer. It was singular that the same music could say such different things to different people. To her the music they had just heard spoke of the tragedy of human destiny, the futility of striving against fate, and the joy, the peace of humility and resignation.

"Are you coming to next week's concert?" he asked then. "That's to be all Russian too."

"I don't think so."

"Why not?"

He was very young, he could be no older than herself, and there was an ingenuousness in him that made it impossible for her to answer too stiffly a question which in a stranger was indiscreet. There was something in his manner that made her sure he was not trying to pick her up. She smiled.

"I'm not a millionaire. They're rare now, you know, the Russians who are."

"I know some of the people who are running these concerts. I have a pass that admits two. If you like to meet me next Sunday in the doorway, you can come in on it."

"I don't think I could quite do that."

"Do you think it would be compromising?" he smiled. "The crowd would surely be a sufficient chaperon."

"I work in a dressmaker's shop. It would be hard to compromise me. I don't know that I can put myself under an obligation to a total stranger."

"I am sure you are a very well-brought-up young lady, but you should not have unreasonable prejudices."

She did not want to argue the point.

"Well, we'll see. In any case I thank you for the suggestion."

They talked of other things till the conductor once more raised his baton. At the end of the concert he turned to say good-bye to her.

"Till next Sunday then?" he said.

"We'll see. Don't wait for me."

They lost one another in the crowd that thronged towards the exits. During the next week she thought from time to time of the good-looking young man with the large gray eyes. She thought of him with pleasure. She had not arrived at her age without having had to resist now and then the advances of men. Both Alexey and his son the gigolo had made a pass at her, but she had not found it difficult to deal with them. A smart box on the ear had made the lachrymose drunkard understand that there was nothing doing, and the boy she had kept quiet by a judicious mingling of ridicule and plain speech. Often enough men had tried to pick her up in the street, but she was always too tired and often too hungry to be tempted by their advances; it caused her a grim amusement to reflect that the offer of a square meal would have tempted her much more than the offer of a loving heart. She had felt, with her woman's instinct, that the young man of the concert was not quite like that. Doubtless, like any other youth of his age, he would not miss an opportunity for a bit of fun if he could get it, but it was not for the sake of that that he had offered to take her to the concert on Sunday. She had no intention of going, but she was touched that he had asked her. There was something very nice about him, something ingenuous and frank. She felt that she could trust him. She looked at the programme. They were giving the Symphonie Pathétique, she didn't much care about that, Tchaikovsky was too Europeanized for her taste, but they were giving also the *Sacre du Printemps* and Borodin's string quartet. She wondered whether the young man had really meant what he said. It might very well be that his invitation had been issued on the spur of the moment and in half an hour completely forgotten. When Sunday came she had half a mind to go and see, she did very much want to hear the concert, and she had not a penny more in her pocket than she needed for her Metro and her lunches during the week, she had had to give everything else to Evgenia to provide the household with food; if he was not there no harm would have been done, and if he was and really had a pass for two, well, it would cost him nothing and committed her to nothing.

Finally an impulse took her to the Salle Pleyel and there he was, where he had said he would be, waiting for her. His eyes lit up and he shook her warmly by the hand as though they were old friends.

"I'm so glad you've come," he said. "I've been waiting for twenty minutes. I was so afraid I'd miss you."

She blushed and smiled. They went into the concert room and she found he had seats in the fifth row.

"Did you get these given you?" she asked with surprise.

"No, I bought them. I thought it would be nice to be comfortable."

"What folly! I'm so used to standing."

But she was flattered by his generosity and when presently he took her hand did not withdraw it. She felt that if it gave him pleasure to hold it, it did her no harm, and she owed him that. During the interval he told her his name, Robert Berger, and she told him hers. He added that he lived with his mother at Neuilly and that he worked in a broker's office. He talked in an educated way, with a boyish enthusiasm that made her laugh, and there was an animation about him that Lydia could not but feel attractive. His shining eyes, the mobility of his face, suggested an ardent nature. To sit next to him was like sitting in front of a fire; his youth glowed with a physical warmth. When the concert was over they walked along the Champs-Élysées together and then he asked her if she would like some tea. He would not let her refuse. It was a luxury Lydia had never known to sit in a smart tea-shop among well-dressed people, and the appetizing smell of cakes, the heady smell of women's perfume, the warmth, the comfortable chairs, the noisy talk, went to her head. They sat there for an hour. Lydia told him about herself, what her father had been and what had happened to him, how she lived now and how she earned her living; he listened as eagerly as he talked. His gray eyes were tender with sympathy. When it was time for her to go he asked her whether she would come to a cinema one evening. She shook her head.

"Why not?"

"You are a rich young man, and . . ."

"Oh, no, I'm not. Far from it. My mother has little more than her pension and I have only the little I make."

"Then you shouldn't have tea at expensive tea-rooms. Anyhow I am a poor working girl. Thank you for all your kindness to me, but I am not a fool; you have been sweet to me, I don't think it would be very nice of me to accept more of your kindness when I can make no return for it."

"But I don't want a return. I like you. I like to be with

you. Last Sunday, when you were crying, you looked so touching, it broke my heart. You're alone in the world, and I—I'm alone too in my way. I was hoping we could be friends."

She looked at him coolly for a moment. They were the same age, but of course really she was years older than he; his mien was so candid she had no doubt that he believed what he said, but she was wise enough to know that he was talking nonsense.

"Let me be quite frank with you," she said. "I know I'm not a raving beauty, but after all I'm young and there are people who think me prettyish, people who like the Russian type, it's asking too much of me to believe that you are seeking my society just for the pleasure of my conversation. I've never been to bed with a man. I don't think it would be very honest of me if I let you go on wasting your time and your money on me when I have no intention of going to bed with you."

"That is frank enough in all conscience," he smiled, oh, so charmingly, "but you see, I knew that. I haven't lived in Paris all my life without learning something. I know instinctively whether a girl is ready for a little fun or if she isn't. I saw at once that you were good. If I held your hand at the concert it was because you were feeling the music as deeply as I was, and the touch of your hand—I hardly know how to explain it—I felt that your emotion flowed into me and gave mine a richer intensity. Anyhow there was in my feeling nothing of desire."

"And yet we were feeling very different things," she said thoughtfully. "Once I looked at your face and I was startled by its expression. It was cruel and ruthless. It was not like a human face any more, it was a mask of triumphant malice. It frightened me."

He laughed gaily and his laugh was so young, so musical and care-free, the look of his eyes so tenderly frank, it was impossible to believe that for a moment under the influence of that emotional music his features had borne an expression of such cold ferocity.

"What fancies you have! You don't think I am a white-slaver, like at the cinema, and that I am trying to get you into my clutches and shall then ship you out to Buenos Aires?"

"No," she smiled, "I don't think that."

"How can it hurt you to come to the pictures with me? You've made the position quite clear and I accept it."

She laughed now. It was absurd to make so much fuss. She had little enough amusement in her life, and if he liked to give her a treat and was content merely to sit beside her and to talk, she would be a fool to forgo it. After all, she was nothing. She need answer for her actions to nobody. She could take care of herself and she had given him full warning.

"Oh, very well," she said.

They went to the pictures several times and after the show Robert accompanied Lydia to whichever was the nearest station for her to get a train home. During the little walk he took her arm and for a part of the performance he held her hand, once or twice when they parted he kissed her lightly on both cheeks, but these were the only familiarities he permitted himself. He was good company. He had a chaffing, ironic way of talking about things that pleased her. He did not pretend to have read very much, he had no time, he said, and life was more entertaining than books, but he was not stupid and he could speak intelligently of such books as he had read. It interested Lydia to discover that he had a peculiar admiration for André Gide. He was an enthusiastic tennis-player and he told her that at one time he had been encouraged to take it seriously; people of importance in the game, thinking he had the making of a champion, had interested themselves in him. But nothing came of it.

"One needs more money and more time to get into the first rank than I could dispose of," he said.

Lydia had a notion that he was in love with her, but she would not allow herself to be certain of it, for she could not but fear that her own feelings made her no safe judge of his. He occupied her thoughts more and more. He was the first friend of her own age that she had ever had. She owed him happy hours at the concerts he took her to on Sunday afternoons, and happy evenings at the cinema. He gave her life an interest and excitement it had never had before. For him she took pains to dress more prettily. She had never been in the habit of making up, but on the fourth or fifth time she met him she rouged her cheeks a little and made up her eyes.

"What have you done to yourself?" he said, when they got into the light. "Why have you been putting all that stuff on your face?"

She laughed and blushed under her rouge.

"I wanted to be a little more of a credit to you. I couldn't bear that people should think you were with a little kitchen-maid who'd just come up to Paris from her native province."

"But almost the first thing I liked in you was that you were so natural. One gets so tired of all these painted faces. I don't know why, I found it touching that you had nothing on your pale cheeks, nothing on your lips, nothing on your eyebrows. It was refreshing, like a little wood that you come into after you've been walking in the glare of the road. Having no make-up on gives you a look of candour and one feels it is a true expression of the uprightness of your soul."

Her heart began to beat almost painfully, but it was that curious sort of pain which is more blissful than pleasure.

"Well, if you don't like it, I'll not do it again. After all, I only did it for your sake."

She looked with an inattentive mind at the picture he had brought her to see. She had mistrusted the tenderness in his musical voice, the smiling softness of his eyes, but after this it was almost impossible not to believe that he loved her. She had been exercising all the self-control she possessed to prevent herself from falling in love with him. She had kept on saying to herself that it was only a passing fancy on his part and that it would be madness if she let her feelings run away with her. She was determined not to become his mistress. She had seen too much of that sort of thing among the Russians, the daughters of refugees who had so much difficulty in making any sort of a living; often enough, because they were bored, because they were sick of grinding poverty, they entered upon an affair, but it never lasted; they seemed to have no capacity for holding a man, at least not the Frenchmen whom they generally fell for; their lovers grew tired of them, or impatient, and chucked them; then they were even worse off than they had been before, and often nothing remained but the brothel. But what else was there that she could hope for? She knew very well he had no thought of marriage. The possibility of such a thing would never have crossed his head. She knew French ideas. His mother would not consent to his marrying a Russian sewing-woman, which was all she was really, without a penny to bless herself with. Marriage in France was a serious thing; the position of the respective families must be on a par and the bride had to bring a dowry conformable with the bridegroom's situation. It was true that her father had been a professor of some small distinction at the university, but in Russia, before the revolution, and since then Paris swarmed with princes and counts and guardsmen who were driving taxis or doing manual labour. Everyone looked upon the Russians as shiftless and undependable. People were sick of them. Lydia's mother, whose grandfather had been a serf, was herself hardly more than a peasant, and the professor had married her in accordance with his liberal principles; but she was a pious woman and Lydia had been brought up with strict principles. It was in vain that she reasoned with herself; it was true that the world was different now and one must move with the times: she could not help it, she had an instinctive horror of becoming a man's mistress. And yet. And yet. What else was there to look forward to? Wasn't she a fool to miss the opportunity that presented itself? She knew that her prettiness was only the prettiness of youth, in a few years she would be drab and plain; perhaps she would never have another chance. Why shouldn't she let herself go? Only a little relaxation of her self-control and she would love him madly, it would be a relief not to keep that constant rein on her feelings, and he loved her, yes, he loved her, she knew it, the fire of his passion was so hot it made her gasp, in the eagerness of his mobile face she read his fierce desire to possess her; it would be heavenly to be loved by someone she loved to desperation, and if it didn't last, and of course it couldn't, she would have had the ecstasy of it, she would have the recollection, and wouldn't that be worth all the anguish, the bitter anguish she must suffer when he left her? When all was said and done, if it was intolerable there was always the Seine or the gas oven.

But the curious, the inexplicable, thing was that he didn't seem to want her to be his mistress. He used her with a consideration that was full of respect. He could not have behaved differently if she had been a young girl in the circle of his family acquaintance whose situation and fortune made it reasonable to suppose that their friendship would eventuate in a marriage satisfactory to all parties. She could not understand it. She knew that the notion was absurd, but in her bones she had a queer inkling that he wished to marry her. She was touched and flattered. If it was true he was one in a thousand, but she almost hoped it wasn't, for she couldn't bear that he should suffer the pain that such a wish must necessarily bring him; whatever crazy ideas he harboured, there was his mother in the background, the sensible, practical, middle-class Frenchwoman, who would never let him jeopardize his future and to whom he was devoted as only a Frenchman can be to his mother.

But one evening, after the cinema, when they were walking to the Metro station he said to her:

"There's no concert next Sunday. Will you come and have tea at home? I've talked about you so much to my mother that she'd like to make your acquaintance."

Lydia's heart stood still. She realized the situation at once. Madame Berger was getting anxious about this friendship that her son had formed, and she wanted to see her, the better to put an end to it.

"My poor Robert, I don't think your mother would like me at all. I think it's much wiser we shouldn't meet."

"You're quite wrong. She has a great sympathy for you. The poor woman loves me, you know, I'm all she has in the world, and it makes her happy to think that I've made friends with a young girl who is well brought up and respectable."

Lydia smiled. How little he knew women if he imagined that a loving mother could feel kindly towards a girl that her son had casually picked up at a concert! But he pressed her so strongly to accept the invitation, which he said he issued on his mother's behalf, that at last she did. She thought indeed that it would only make Madame Berger look upon her with increased suspicion if she refused to meet her. They arranged that he should pick her up at the Porte St. Denis at four on the following Sunday and take her to his mother's. He drove up in a car.

"What luxury!" said Lydia, as she stepped in.

"It's not mine, you know. I borrowed it from a friend."

Lydia was nervous of the ordeal before her and not even Robert's affectionate friendliness sufficed to give her confidence.

They drove to Neuilly.

"We'll leave the car here," said Robert, drawing up to the kerb in a quiet street. "I don't want to leave it outside our house. It wouldn't do for the neighbours to think I had a car and of course I can't explain that it's only lent."

They walked a little.

"Here we are."

It was a tiny detached villa, rather shabby from want of paint and smaller than, from the way Robert had talked, she expected. He took her into the drawing-room. It was a small room crowded with furniture and ornaments, with oil pictures in gold frames on the walls, and opened by an archway on to the dining-room in which the table was set for tea. Madame Berger put down the novel she was reading and came forward to greet her guest. Lydia had pictured her as a rather stout, short woman in widow's weeds, with a mild face and the homely, respectable air of a person who has given up all thought of earthly vanity; she was not at all like that; she was thin, and in her high-heeled shoes as tall as Robert; she was smartly dressed in black flowered silk and she wore a string of false pearls round her neck; her hair, permanently waved, was very dark brown and though she must have been hard on fifty there was not a white streak in it. Her sallow skin was somewhat heavily powdered. She had fine eyes, Robert's delicate, straight nose, and the same thin lips, but in her, age had given them a certain hard-

ness. She was in her way and for her time of life a good-looking woman, and she evidently took pains over her appearance, but there was in her expression nothing of the charm
that made Robert so attractive. Her eyes, so bright and
dark, were cool and watchful. Lydia felt the sharp, scrutiniz-
ing look with which Madame Berger took her in from head
to foot as she entered the room, but it was immediately
superseded by a cordial and welcoming smile. She thanked
Lydia effusively for coming so long a distance to see her.

"You must understand how much I wanted to see a young
girl of whom my son has talked to me so much. I was prepared for a disagreeable surprise. I have, to tell you the
truth, no great confidence in my son's judgement. It is a relief to me to see that you are as nice as he told me you were."

All this she said with a good deal of facial expression, with
smiles and little nods of the head, flatteringly, in the manner of a hostess accustomed to society trying to set a stranger
at her ease. Lydia, watchful too, answered with becoming
diffidence. Madame Berger gave an emphatic, slightly forced
laugh and made an enthusiastic little gesture.

"But you are charming. I'm not surprised that this son of
mine should neglect his old mother for your sake."

Tea was brought in by a stolid-looking young maid whom
Madame Berger, while continuing her gesticulative, com-
plimentary remarks, watched with sharp, anxious eyes, so
that Lydia guessed that a tea-party was an unusual event in
the house and the hostess was not quite sure that the servant
knew how to set about things. They went into the dining-
room and sat down. There was a small grand piano in it.

"It takes up room," said Madame Berger, "but my son
is passionately devoted to music. He plays for hours at a
time. He tells me that you are a musician of the first class."

"He exaggerates. I'm very fond of it, but very ignorant."

"You are too modest, mademoiselle."

There was a dish of little cakes from the confectioner's
and a dish of sandwiches. Under each plate was a doyley
and on each a tiny napkin. Madame Berger had evidently
taken pains to do things in a modish way. With a smile in
her cold eyes she asked Lydia how she would like her tea.

"You Russians always take lemon, I know, and I got a lemon for you specially. Will you begin with a sandwich?"

The tea tasted of straw.

"I know you Russians smoke all through your meals. Please do not stand on any ceremony with me. Robert, where are the cigarettes?"

Madame Berger pressed sandwiches on Lydia, she pressed cakes; she was one of those hostesses who look upon it as a mark of hospitality to make their guests eat however unwilling they may be. She talked without ceasing, well, in a high-pitched, metallic voice, smiling a great deal, and her politeness was effusive. She asked Lydia a great many questions, which had a casual air so that on the face of it they looked like the civil inquiries a woman of the world would put out of sympathy for a friendless girl, but Lydia realized that they were cleverly designed to find out everything she could about her. Lydia's heart sank; this was not the sort of woman who for love of her son would allow him to do an imprudent thing; but the certainty of this gave her back her own assurance. It was obvious that she had nothing to lose; she certainly had nothing to hide; and she answered the questions with frankness. She told Madame Berger, as she had already told Robert, about her father and mother, and what her life had been in London and how she had lived since her mother's death. It even amused her to see behind Madame Berger's warm sympathy, through her shocked commiserating answers, the shrewdness that weighed every word she heard and drew conclusions upon it. After two or three unavailing attempts to go, which Madame Berger would not hear of, Lydia managed to tear herself away from so much friendliness. Robert was to see her home. Madame Berger seized both her hands when she said good-bye to her and her fine dark eyes glittered with cordiality.

"You are delicious," she said. "You know your way now, you must come and see me often, often; you will be always sure of a hearty welcome."

When they were walking along to the car Robert took her arm with an affectionate gesture which seemed to ask for protection rather than to offer it and which charmed her.

"Well, my dear one, it went off very well. My mother liked you. You made a conquest of her at once. She'll adore you."

Lydia laughed.

"Don't be so silly. She detested me."

"No, no, you're wrong. I promise you. I know her, I saw at once that she took to you."

Lydia shrugged her shoulders, but did not answer. When they parted they arranged to go to the cinema on the following Tuesday. She agreed to his plan, but she was pretty sure that his mother would put a stop to it. He knew her address now.

"If anything should happen to prevent you, you'll send me a petit bleu?"

"Nothing will happen to prevent me," he said fondly.

She was very sad that evening. If she could have got by herself she would have cried. But perhaps it was just as well that she couldn't; it was no good making oneself bad blood. It had been a foolish dream. She would get over her unhappiness; after all, she was used to it. It would have been much worse if he had been her lover and thrown her over.

Monday passed, Tuesday came; but no petit bleu. She was certain that it would be there when she got back from work. Nothing. She had an hour before she need think of getting ready, and she passed it waiting with sickening anxiety for the bell to ring; she dressed with the feeling that she was foolish to take the trouble, for the message would arrive before she was finished. She wondered if it were possible that he would let her go to the cinema and not turn up. It would be heartless, it would be cruel, but she knew that he was under his mother's thumb, she suspected he was weak, and it might be that to let her go to a meeting-place and not come himself would seem to him the best way, brutal though it was, to show her that he was done with her. No sooner had this notion occurred to her than she was sure of it and she nearly decided not to go. Nevertheless she went. After all, if he could be so beastly it would prove that she was well rid of him.

But he was there all right and when he saw her walking

along he came towards her with the springy gait which marked his eager vitality. On his face shone his sweet smile. His spirits seemed even higher than usual.

"I'm not in the mood for the pictures this evening," he said. "Let us have a drink at Fouquet's and then go for a drive. I've got a car just round the corner."

"If you like."

It was fine and dry, though cold, and the stars in the frosty night seemed to laugh with a good-natured malice at the gaudy lights of the Champs-Élysées. They had a glass of beer, Robert meanwhile talking nineteen to the dozen, and then they walked up the Avenue George V to where he had parked his car. Lydia was puzzled. He talked quite naturally, but she had no notion what were his powers of dissimulation, and she could not help asking herself whether he proposed the drive in order to break unhappy news to her. He was an emotional creature, sometimes, she had discovered, even a trifle theatrical, (but that amused rather than offended her), and she wondered whether he was setting the stage for an affecting scene of renunciation.

"This isn't the same car that you had on Sunday," she said, when they came to it.

"No. It belongs to a friend who wants to sell. I said I wanted to show it to a possible purchaser."

They drove to the Arc de Triomphe and then along the Avenue Foch till they came to the Bois. It was dark there except when they met the head-lights of a car coming towards them, and deserted except for a car parked here and there in which one surmised a couple was engaged in amorous conversation. Presently Robert drew up at the kerb.

"Shall we stop here and smoke a cigarette?" he said. "You're not cold?"

"No."

It was a solitary spot and in other circumstances Lydia might have felt a trifle nervous. But she thought she knew Robert well enough to know that he was incapable of taking advantage of the situation. He had too nice a nature. Moreover she had an intuition that he had something on his mind, and was curious to know what it was. He lit her cigarette and his and for a moment kept silent. She realized that he was embarrassed and did not know how to begin. Her heart began to beat anxiously.

"I've got something to say to you, my dear," he said at last.

"Yes?"

"Mon Dieu, I hardly know how to put it. I'm not often nervous, but at the moment I have a curious sensation that is quite new to me."

Lydia's heart sank, but she had no intention of showing that she was suffering.

"If one has something awkward to say," she answered lightly, "it's better to say it quite plainly, you know. One doesn't do much good by beating about the bush."

"I'll take you at your word. Will you marry me?"

"Me?"

It was the last thing she had expected him to say.

"I love you passionately. I think I fell in love with you at first sight, when we stood side by side at that concert, and the tears poured down your pale cheeks."

"But your mother?"

"My mother is delighted. She's waiting now. I said that if you consented I would take you to her. She wants to embrace you. She's happy at the thought that I'm settling down with someone she entirely approves of, and the idea is that after we've all had a good cry together we should crack a bottle of champagne."

"Last Sunday when you took me to see your mother, had you told her that you wished to marry me?"

"But of course. She very naturally wanted to see what you were like. She's not stupid, my mother; she made up her mind at once."

"I had an idea she didn't like me."

"You were wrong."

They smiled into one another's eyes, and she raised her face to his. For the first time he kissed her on the lips.

"There's no doubt," he said, "that a right-hand drive is much more convenient for kissing a girl than a left-hand."

"You fool," she laughed.

"Then you do care for me a little?"

"I've worshipped you ever since I first saw you."

"But with the reserve of a well-brought-up young woman who will not give free rein to her emotions until she's quite sure it's prudent?" he answered, tenderly chaffing her.

But she answered seriously:

"I've suffered so much in my short life, I didn't want to expose myself to a suffering perhaps greater than I could bear."

"I adore you."

She had never known such happiness; indeed, she could hardly bring herself to believe it: at that moment her heart overflowed with gratitude to life. She would have liked to sit there, nestling in his arms, for ever; at that moment she would have liked to die. But she bestirred herself.

"Let us go to your mother," she said.

She felt on a sudden warm with love for that woman who but just knew her, and yet, contrary to all expectation, because her son loved her, because with her sharp eyes she had seen that she deeply loved her son, had consented, even gladly, to their marriage. Lydia did not think there could be another woman in France who was capable of such a sacrifice.

They drove off. Robert parked the car in a street parallel to the one in which he lived. When they reached the little house he opened the front door with his latch-key and excitedly preceded Lydia into the sitting-room.

"O.K., mother."

Lydia immediately followed him in and Madame Berger, in the same black dress of flowered silk as she had worn on Sunday, came forward and took her in her arms.

"My dear child," she cried. "I'm so happy."

Lydia burst into tears. Madame Berger kissed her tenderly.

"There, there, there! You mustn't cry. I give you my son with all my heart. I know you'll make him a good wife. Come, sit down. Robert will open a bottle of champagne."

Lydia composed herself and dried her eyes.

"You are too good to me, Madame. I don't know what I've done to deserve so much kindness."

Madame Berger took her hand and gently patted it.

"You have fallen in love with my son and he has fallen in love with you."

Robert had gone out of the room. Lydia felt that she must at once state the facts as they were.

"But, Madame, I don't feel sure that you realize the circumstances. The little money that my father was able to get out of Russia went years ago. I have nothing but what I earn. Nothing, absolutely nothing. And only two dresses besides the one I'm wearing."

"But, my dear child, what does that matter? Oh, I don't deny it, I should have been pleased if you had been able to bring Robert a reasonable dot, but money isn't everything. Love is more important. And nowadays what is money worth? I flatter myself that I am a good judge of character and it didn't take me long to discover that you have a sweet and honest nature. I saw that you had been well brought up and I judged that you had good principles. After all that is what one wants in a wife, and you know, I know my Robert, he would never have been happy with a little French bourgeoise. He has a romantic disposition and it says something to him that you are Russian. And it isn't as if you were nobody; it is after all something one need not be ashamed of to be the daughter of a professor."

Robert came in with glasses and a bottle of champagne. They sat talking late into the night. Madame Berger had her plan cut and dried and they could do nothing but accept it; Lydia and Robert should live in the house while she would make herself comfortable in the little pavilion at the back of the garden. They would have their meals in common, but otherwise she would keep to her own quarters. She was decided that the young couple must be left to themselves and not exposed to interference from her.

"I don't want you to look upon me as a mother-in-law," she told Lydia. "I want to be the mother to you that you've lost, but I also want to be your friend."

She was anxious that the marriage should take place without delay. Lydia had a League of Nations passport and a Carte de Séjour; her papers were in order; so they had only to wait the time needed for notification to be made at the Mairie. Since Robert was Catholic and Lydia Orthodox, they decided, notwithstanding Madame Berger's reluctance, to waive a religious ceremony that neither of them cared about. Lydia was too excited and too confused to sleep that night.

The marriage took place very quietly. The only persons present were Madame Berger and an old friend of the family, Colonel Legrand, an army doctor who had been a brother officer of Robert's father; Evgenia and Alexey and their children. It took place on a Friday and since Robert had to go to work on the Monday morning their honeymoon was brief. Robert drove Lydia to Dieppe in a car that he had been lent and drove her back on Sunday night.

Lydia did not know that the car, like the cars in which he had on other occasions driven her, was not lent, but stolen; that was why he had always parked them a street or two from that in which he lived; she did not know that Robert had a few months before been sentenced to two years' imprisonment with sursis, that is, with a suspended sentence because it was his first conviction; she did not know that he had since been tried on a charge of smuggling drugs and had escaped conviction by the skin of his teeth; she did not know that Madame Berger had welcomed the marriage because she thought it would settle Robert and that it was indeed the only chance he had of leading an honest life.

v

CHARLEY had no idea how long he had been sitting at the window, absent-mindedly gazing out into the dark court, when he was called back from the perplexed welter of his thoughts by the sound of Lydia's voice.

"I believe I've been asleep," she said.

"You certainly have."

He turned on the light, which he had not done before for

fear of waking her. The fire was almost out and he put on another log.

"I feel so refreshed. I slept without dreaming."

"D'you have bad dreams?"

"Fearful."

"If you'll dress we might go out to dinner."

There was an ironic, but not unkindly, quality in the smile she gave him.

"I don't suppose this is the way you usually spend Christmas Day."

"I'm bound to say it isn't," he answered, with a cheerful grin.

She went into the bathroom and he heard her having a bath. She came back still wearing his dressing-gown.

"Now if you'll go in and wash, I'll dress."

Charley left her. He accepted it as quite natural that though she had slept all night in the next bed to his she should not care to dress in his presence.

Lydia took him to a restaurant she knew in the Avenue du Maine where she said the food was good. Though a trifle self-consciously old-world, with its panelled walls, chintz curtains and pewter plates, it was a friendly little place, and there was no one there but two middle-aged women in collars and ties and three young Indians who ate in moody silence. You had a feeling that, lonely and friendless, they dined there that evening because they had no place to go.

Lydia and Charley sat in a corner where their conversation could not be overheard. Lydia ate with hearty appetite. When he offered her a second helping of one of the dishes they had ordered she pushed forward her plate.

"My mother-in-law used to complain of my appetite. She used to say that I ate as though I had never had enough in my life. Which was true, of course."

It gave Charley a turn. It was a queer sensation to sit down to dinner with someone who year in and year out had never had quite enough to eat. And another thing: it disturbed his preconceived ideas to discover that one could undergo all the misery she had undergone and yet eat voraciously. It made her tragedy a little grotesque; she was not a romantic figure, but just a quite ordinary young woman, and that somehow made all that had happened to her more horrible.

"Did you get on well with your mother-in-law?" he asked.

"Yes. Reasonably. She wasn't a bad woman. She was hard, scheming, practical and avaricious. She was a good housekeeper and she liked everything in the house to be just so. I used to infuriate her with my Russian sloppiness, but she had a great control over her temper and never allowed an irritable word to escape her. After Robert, her great passion was for respectability. She was proud of her father having been a staff officer and her husband a colonel in the Medical Service. They were both officers in the Legion of Honour. Her husband had lost a leg in the war. She was very proud of their distinguished record, and she had a keen sense of the social importance their position gave her. I suppose you'd say she was a snob, but in such a pretty way that it didn't offend you, it only made you laugh. She had notions of morality that foreigners often think are unusual in France. For instance, she had no patience with women who were unfaithful to their husbands, but she looked upon it as natural enough that men should deceive their wives. She would never have dreamt of accepting an invitation unless she had the power to return it. Once she'd made a bargain she'd stick to it even though it turned out to be a bad one. Though she counted every penny she spent she was scrupulously honest, honest by principle and honest from loyalty to her family. She had a deep sense of justice. She knew she'd acted dishonourably in letting me marry Robert in the dark, and should at least have given me the chance of deciding whether, knowing all, I would marry him or not—and of course I would never have hesitated; but she didn't know that, and she thought that I should have good cause to blame her when I found out and all she could answer was that where Robert was concerned she was prepared to sacrifice anyone else; and because of that she forced herself to be tolerant of a great deal in me that she didn't like. She put all her determination, all her self-control, all her tact, into the effort of making the marriage a success. She felt it was the only chance that Robert had of reforming and her love was so great that she was prepared to lose him to me. She was even prepared to lose her influence over him, and that I think is what a woman values, whether it's a son or a husband or a lover or anything, even more than his love for her. She said that she wouldn't interfere with us and she never did. Except in the kitchen, later on when we gave up the maid, and at meal times, we hardly saw her. When she wasn't out she spent the whole time in her little pavilion at the end of the garden and when, thinking she was lonely, we asked her to come and sit with us, she refused on the excuse that she had work to do, letters to write, or a book she wanted to finish. She was a woman whom it was difficult to love, but impossible not to respect."

"What has happened to her now?" asked Charley.

"The cost of the trial ruined her. Most of her small fortune had already gone to keep Robert out of prison and the rest went on lawyers. She had to sell the house which was the mainstay of her pride in her position as an officer's widow and she had to mortgage her pension. She was always a good cook, she's gone as general servant in the apartment of an American who has a studio at Auteuil."

"D'you ever see her?"

"No. Why should I? We have nothing in common. Her interest in me ceased when I could be no further use in keeping Robert straight."

Lydia went on to tell him about her married life. It was a pleasure for her to have a house of her own and heaven not to have to go to work every morning. She soon discovered that there was no money to waste, but compared with what she had been used to, the circumstances in which she now lived were affluent. And at least she had security. Robert was sweet to her, he was easy to live with, inclined to let her wait on him, but she loved him so much that this was a delight to her, gay with an impudent, happy-go-lucky cynicism that made her laugh, and brim-full of vitality. He was generous to a fault considering how poor they were. He gave her a gold wrist-watch and a vanity case that must have cost at least a couple of thousand francs and a bag in crocodile skin. She was surprised to find a tram ticket in one of the pockets, and when she asked Robert how it got there, he laughed. He said he had bought the bag off a girl who had had a bad day at the races. Her lover had only just given it her and it was such a bargain that he had not been able to resist buying it. Now and then he took her to the theatre and then they went to Montmartre to dance. When she wanted to know how he had the money for such extravagance he answered gaily that with the world full of fools it would be absurd if a clever man couldn't get on to a good thing now and again. But these excursions they kept secret from Madame Berger. Lydia would have thought it impossible to love Robert more than when she married him, but every day increased her passion. He was not only a charming lover, but also a delightful companion.

About four months after their marriage Robert lost his job. This created a disturbance in the household that she failed to understand, for his salary had been negligible; but he and his mother shut themselves up in the pavilion for a long time, and when Lydia saw her mother-in-law next it was obvious that she had been crying. Her face was haggard and she gave Lydia a look of sullen exasperation as though she blamed her. Lydia could not make it out. Then the old doctor, the friend of the family, Colonel Legrand, came and the three of them were again closeted in Madame Berger's room. For two or three days Robert was silent and for the first time since she had known him somewhat irritable; when she asked him what was the matter he told her sharply not to bother. Then, thinking perhaps that he must offer some explanation, he said the whole trouble was that his mother was so avaricious. Lydia knew that though she was sparing, she was never so where her son was concerned, for him nothing was too good; but seeing that Robert was in a highly nervous state, she felt it better to say nothing. For two or three days Madame Berger looked dreadfully worried, but then, whatever the difficulty was, it was settled; she dismissed, however, the maid to keep whom had been almost a matter of principle, for so long as she had a servant Madame Berger could look upon herself as a lady. But now she told Lydia that it was a useless waste; the two of them could easily run the little house between them, and doing the marketing herself she could be sure of not being robbed; and besides, with nothing to do really, she would enjoy cooking. Lydia was only too willing to do the housework.

Life went on pretty much as it had before. Robert quickly regained his good humour and was as gay, loving and delightful as he had ever been. He got up late in the morning and went out to hunt for a job, and often he did not come back till late in the night. Madame Berger always had a good meal for Robert, but when the two women were alone they ate sparingly; a bowl of thin soup, a salad and a bit of cheese. It was plain that Madame Berger was harassed. More than once Lydia came into the kitchen and found her standing there, doing nothing, with her face distraught, as though an intolerable anxiety possessed her, but on Lydia's approach she chased the expression away and busied herself with the work upon which she was engaged. She still kept up appearances, and on the "days" of old friends dressed herself in her best, faintly rouged her cheeks, and sallied forth, very upright and a pattern of middle-class respectability, to pay her visit. After a short while, though he was still without a job, Robert seemed to have no less spending-money than he had before. He told Lydia that he had managed to sell one or two secondhand cars on commission; and then that he had got in with some racing men at a bar he went to and got tips from them. Lydia did not know why a suspicion insinuated itself into her unwilling mind that something was going on that was not above board. On one occasion an incident occurred which troubled her. One Sunday Robert told his mother that a man who, he hoped, was going to give him a job had asked him to bring Lydia to lunch at his house near Chartres and he was going to drive her down; but when they had started, picking up the car two streets off the one in which they lived, he told Lydia that this was an invention. He had had a bit of luck at the races on the previous Thursday and was taking her to lunch at Jouy. He had told his mother this story because she would look upon it as an unjustified extravagance to go and spend money at a restaurant. It was a warm and beautiful day. Luncheon was served in the garden and the place was crowded. They found two seats at a table that was already occupied by a party of four. This party were finishing their meal and left while they were but half through theirs.

"Oh, look," said Robert, "one of those ladies has left her bag behind."

He took it and, to Lydia's surprise, opened it. She saw there was money inside. He looked quickly right and left and then gave her a sharp, cunning, malicious glance. Her heart stood still. She had a conviction that he was just about to take the money out and put it in his pocket. She gasped with horror. But at that moment one of the men who had been at the table came back and saw Robert with the bag in his hands.

"What are you doing with that bag?" he asked.

Robert gave him his frank and charming smile.

"It was left behind. I was looking to see if I could find out to whom it belonged."

The man looked at him with stern, suspicious eyes.

"You had only to give it to the proprietor."

"And do you think you would ever have got it back?" Robert answered blandly, returning him the bag.

Without a word the man took it and went away.

"Women are criminally careless with their bags," said Robert.

Lydia gave a sigh of relief. Her suspicion was absurd. After all, with people all around, no one could have the effrontery to steal money out of a bag; the risk was too great. But she knew every expression of Robert's face and, unbelievable as it was, she was certain that he had intended to take it. He would have looked upon it as a capital joke.

She had resolutely put the occurrence out of her mind, but on that dreadful morning when she read in the paper that the English bookmaker, Teddie Jordan, had been murdered it returned to her. She remembered the look in Robert's eyes. She had known then, in a horrible flash of insight, that he was capable of anything. She knew now what the stain was on his trousers. Blood! And she knew where those thousand-franc notes had come from. She knew also why, when he had lost his job, Robert had worn that sullen look, why his mother had been distracted and why Colonel Legrand, the doctor, had been closeted with mother and son for hours of agitated colloquy. Because Robert had stolen money. And if Madame Berger had sent away the maid and since then had skimped and saved it was because she had had to pay a sum she could ill afford to save him from prosecution. Lydia read once more the account of the crime. Teddie Jordan lived alone in a ground-floor flat which the concierge kept clean for him. He had his meals out, but the concierge brought him his coffee every morning at nine. It was thus she had found him. He was lying on the floor, in his shirt-sleeves, a knife wound in his back, near the gramophone, with a broken record under him so that it looked as if he had been stabbed while changing it. His empty pocket-book was on the chimney-piece. There was a half-finished whiskey and soda on a table by the side of an armchair and another glass, unused, on a tray with the bottle of whiskey, a syphon and an uncut cake. It was obvious that he had been expecting a visitor, but the visitor had refused to drink. Death had taken place some hours before. The reporter had apparently conducted a small investigation of his own, but how much fact there was in what he narrated and how much fiction, it was hard to say. He had questioned the concierge, and from her learnt that so far as she knew no women ever came to the apartment, but a certain number of men, chiefly young, and from this she had drawn her own conclusions. Teddie Jordan was a good tenant, gave no trouble, and when in funds, was gener-ous. The knife had been thrust into his back with such violence that, according to the reporter, the police were con-vinced that the murderer must have been a man of powerful physique. There were no signs of disorder in the room, which indicated that Jordan had been attacked suddenly and had had no chance to defend himself. The knife was not found, but stains on the window curtain showed that it had been wiped on it. The reporter went on to say that, though the police had looked with care, they had discovered no finger-prints; from this he concluded that the murderer had either wiped them away or worn gloves. In the first case it showed great coolness and in the second premeditation.

The reporter had then gone on to Jojo's Bar. This was a small bar in a back street behind the Boulevard de la Madeleine, frequented by jockeys, bookmakers and betting men. You could get simple fare, bacon and eggs, sausages and chops, and it was here that Jordan regularly had his meals. It was here too that he did much of his business. The reporter learnt that Jordan was popular among the bar's frequenters. He had his ups and downs, but when he had had a good day was open-handed. He was always ready to stand anyone a drink and was hail-fellow-well-met with everyone. All the same he had the reputation of being a pretty wily customer. Sometimes he was up against it and then would run up a fairly heavy bill, but in the end he always paid up. The reporter mentioned the concierge's suspicions to Jojo, the proprietor of the bar, but was assured by him that there was no foundation for them. He ended his graphic story by saying that the police were actively engaged in making inquiries and expected to make an arrest within twenty-four hours.

Lydia was terrified. She did not doubt for a moment that Robert was guilty of the crime; she was as sure of that as if she had seen him commit it.

"How could he? How could he?" she cried.

But she was startled at the sound of her own voice. Even though the kitchen was empty she must not let her thoughts find expression. Her first, her only feeling was that he must be saved from the terrible danger that faced him. Whatever he had done, she loved him; nothing he could do would ever make her love him less. When it occurred to her that they might take him from her she could have screamed with anguish. Even at that moment she was intoxicated by the thought of his soft lips on hers and the feel of his slim body, still a boy's body, in her arms. They said the knife-thrust had shown great violence, and they were looking for a big, powerful man. Robert was strong and wiry, but he was neither big nor powerful. And then there was what the concierge suspected. The police would hunt in the night-clubs and the cafés, in Montmartre and the Rue de Lappe, which the homosexuals frequented. Robert never went to such places and no one knew better than she how far he was from any abnormal inclination. It was true that he went a good deal to Jojo's Bar, but so did many others; he went to get tips from the jockeys and better odds from the bookmakers than he was likely to get at the tote. It was all above board. There was no reason why suspicion should ever fall on him. The trousers had been destroyed, and who would ever think that Madame Berger, with her thrift, had persuaded Robert to buy a second pair? If the police discovered that Robert knew Jordan (and Jordan knew masses of people) and made an examination of the house (it was unlikely, but it might be that they would make enquiries of everyone with whom the bookmaker was known to have been friendly) they would find nothing. Except that little packet of thousand-franc notes. At the thought of them Lydia was panic-stricken. It would be easy to ascertain that they had been in straitened circumstances. Robert and she had always thought that his mother had a little hoard hidden away somewhere in her pavilion, but that doubtless had gone at the time Robert lost his job; if suspicion once fell on him it was inevitable that the police should discover what the trouble had been; and how then could she explain that she had several thousand francs? Lydia did not know how many notes there had been in the packet. Perhaps eight or ten. It was a substantial sum to poor people. It was a sum that Madame Berger, even though she knew how Robert had got the notes, would never have the courage to part with. She would trust in her own cunning to hide them where no one would think of looking. Lydia knew it would be useless to talk to her. No argument would move her in such a case. The only thing was to get at them herself and burn them. She would never have a moment's peace till then. Then the police might come and no incriminating evidence could be discovered. With frenzied anxiety she set her mind to think where Madame Berger would have been most likely to put them. She did not often go into the pavilion, for Madame Berger did the room herself, but she had in her mind's eye a pretty clear picture of it, and in her thought now she examined minutely every piece of furniture and every likely place of concealment. She determined to take the first opportunity to make a search.

The opportunity presented itself sooner than she could have foreseen. That very afternoon, after the meagre lunch which the two women had eaten in silence, Lydia was sitting in the parlour, sewing. She could not read, but she had to do something to calm the frightful disquietude that gnawed at her heartstrings. She heard Madame Berger come into the house and supposed she was going into the kitchen, but the door was opened.

"If Robert comes back tell him I shall be in soon after five."

To Lydia's profound astonishment she saw that her mother-in-law was dressed in all her best. She wore her black dress of flowered silk and a black satin toque and she had a silver fox round her neck.

"Are you going out?" Lydia cried.

"Yes, it's the last day of la générale. She would think it very ill-mannered of me if I did not put in an appearance. Both she and the general had a great affection for my poor husband."

Lydia understood. She saw that in view of what might happen Madame Berger was determined that on that day of all others she must behave as she naturally would. To omit a social duty might be ascribed to fear that her son was implicated in the murder of the bookmaker. To fulfil it, on the other hand, was proof that the possibility had never entered her head. She was a woman of indomitable courage. Beside her, Lydia could only feel herself weak and womanish.

As soon as she was gone Lydia bolted the front door so that no one could come in without ringing and crossed the tiny garden. She gave it a cursory glance; there was a patch of weedy grass surrounded by a gravel walk, and in the middle of the grass a bed in which chrysanthemums had been planted to flower in the autumn. She had a conviction that her mother-in-law was more likely to have hidden the notes in her own apartment than there. The pavilion consisted of one largish room with a closet adjoining which Madame

Berger had made into her dressing-room. The larger room was furnished with a highly carved bedroom suite in mahogany, a sofa, an armchair and a rosewood desk. On the walls were enlarged photographs of herself and her deceased husband, a photograph of his grave, under which hung his medals and his Legion of Honour, and photographs of Robert at various ages. Lydia considered where a woman of that sort would naturally hide something. She had doubtless a place that she always used, since for years she had had to keep her money where Robert could not find it. She was too cunning to choose such an obvious hiding-place as the bed, a secret drawer in the writing-desk, or the slits in the armchair and the sofa. There was no fireplace in the room, but a gas stove with an iron pipe. Lydia looked at it. She saw no possibility of concealing anything there; besides, in winter it was used, and Lydia thought her mother-in-law the sort of woman who, having found a safe place, would stick to it. She stared about her with perplexity. Because she could think of nothing better to do she unmade the bed and took the pillow out of its slip. She looked at it carefully and felt it over. The mattress was covered with a material so hard that she felt sure Madame Berger could not have cut one of the seams and re-sewn it. If she had used the same hiding-place for a long period it must be one that she could get at conveniently and such that, if she wanted to take money out, she could quickly efface all trace of her action. For form's sake Lydia looked through the chest of drawers and the writing-desk. Nothing was locked and everything was carefully arranged. She looked into the wardrobe. Her mind had been working busily all the time. She had heard innumerable stories of how the Russians hid things, money and jewels, so that they might save them from the Bolsheviks. She had heard stories of extreme ingenuity that had been of no avail and of others in which by some miracle discovery had been averted. She remembered one of a woman who had been searched in the train between Moscow and Leningrad. She had been stripped to the skin, but she had sewn a diamond necklace in the hem of her fur-coat, and though it had been carefully examined the diamonds were overlooked. Madame

Berger had a fur-coat too, an old astrakhan that she had had for years, and this was in the wardrobe. Lydia took it out and made a thorough search, but she could neither see nor feel anything. There was no sign of recent stitching. She replaced it and one by one took out the three or four dresses that Madame Berger possessed. There was no possibility that the notes could have been sewn up in any of them. Her heart sank. She was afraid that her mother-in-law had hidden the notes so well that she would never find them. A new idea occurred to her. People said that the best way to hide something was in a place so conspicuous that no one would think of looking there. A work-basket, for instance, like the one Madame Berger had on a little table beside the armchair. Somewhat despondently, with a look at her watch, for time was passing and she could not afford to stay too long, she turned the things in it over. There was a stocking that Madame Berger had been mending, scissors, needles, various odds and ends, and reels of cotton and silk. There was a half-finished tippet in black wool that Madame Berger was making to put over her shoulders when she came from the pavilion to the house. Among the reels of black and white cotton Lydia was surprised to find one of yellow thread. She wondered what her mother-in-law used that for. Her heart gave a great leap as her eyes fell on the curtains. The only light in the room came from the glass door, and one pair hung there; another pair served as a portière for the door that led to the dressing-room. Madame Berger was very proud of them, they had belonged to her father the colonel and she remembered them from her childhood. They were very rich and heavy, with a fringed and festooned pelmet, and they were of yellow damask. Lydia went up first to those at the window and turned back the lining. They had been made for a higher room than that in which they now were, and since Madame Berger had not had the heart to cut them, had been turned up at the bottom. Lydia examined the deep hem; it had been sewn by a professional sempstress and the thread was faded. Then she looked at the curtains on each side of the door. She gave a deep sigh. At the corner nearest to the front wall, and so in darkness, there was a little piece about four inches long which the clean thread showed to have been recently stitched. Lydia got the scissors out of the work-basket and quickly cut; she slipped her hand through the opening and pulled out the notes. She put them in her dress and then it did not take her more than a few minutes to get a needle and the yellow thread and sew up the seam so that no one could tell it had been touched. She looked round the room to see that no trace of her interference remained. She went back to the house, upstairs into the bathroom, and tore the notes into little pieces; she threw them into the pan of the closet and pulled the plug. Then she went downstairs again, drew back the bolt on the front door, and sat down once more to her sewing. Her heart was beating so madly that she could hardly endure it; but she was infinitely relieved. Now the police could come and they would find nothing.

Presently Madame Berger returned. She came into the drawing-room and sank down on a sofa. The effort she had made had taken it out of her and she was all in. Her face sagged and she looked an old woman. Lydia gave her a glance, but said nothing. In a few minutes, with a sigh of weariness, she raised herself to her feet and went to her room. When she came back she had taken off her smart clothes and wore felt slippers and a shabby black dress. Notwithstanding the marcelled hair, the paint on her lips and the rouge on her face, she looked like an old charwoman.

"I'll see about preparing dinner," she said.

"Shall I come and help you?" asked Lydia.

"No, I prefer to be alone."

Lydia went on working. The silence in the little house was sinister. It was so intense that the sound after a while of Robert inserting his latch-key in the lock had all the effect of a frightening noise. Lydia clenched her hands to prevent herself from crying out. He gave his little whistle as he entered the house, and Lydia, gathering herself together, went out into the passage. He had two or three papers in his hand.

"I've brought you the evening papers," he cried gaily. "They're full of the murder."

He went into the kitchen where he knew his mother would be and threw the papers on the table. Lydia followed him in. Without a word Madame Berger took one of them and began to read it. There were big headlines. It was front-page news.

"I've been to Jojo's Bar. They can talk of nothing else. Jordan was one of their regular clients and everybody knew him. I talked to him myself on the night he was murdered. He'd not done so badly on the day's racing and he was standing everybody drinks."

His conversation was so easy and natural, you would have thought he had not a care in the world. His eyes glittered and there was a slight flush on the cheeks that were usually rather pasty. He was excited, but showed no sign of nervousness. Trying to make her tone as unconcerned as his, Lydia asked him:

"Have they any idea who the murderer was?"

"They suspect it was a sailor. The concierge says she saw Jordan come in with one about a week ago. But of course it may just as well have been someone disguised as a sailor. They're rounding up the frequenters of the notorious bars in Montmartre. From the condition of the skin round the wound it appears that the blow was struck with great force. They're looking for a husky, big man of powerful physique. Of course there are one or two boxers who have a funny reputation."

Madame Berger put down the paper without remark.

"Dinner will be ready in a few minutes," she said. "Is the cloth laid, Lydia?"

"I'll go and lay it."

When Robert was there they took the two principal meals of the day in the dining-room, even though it gave more work. But Madame Berger said:

"We can't live like savages. Robert has been well brought up and he's accustomed to having things done properly."

Robert went upstairs to change his coat and put on his slippers. Madame Berger could not bear him to sit about the house in his best clothes. Lydia set about laying the table. Suddenly a thought occurred to her, and it was such a violent shock that she staggered and to support herself had to put her hand on the back of a chair. It was two nights before that Teddie Jordan had been murdered, and it was two nights before that Robert had awakened her, made her cook supper for him, and then hurried her to bed. He had come to her arms straight from committing the horrible crime; and his passion, his insatiable desire, the frenzy of his lust had their source in the blood of a human being.

"And if I conceived that night?"

Robert clattered downstairs in his slippers.

"I'm ready, mummy," he cried.

"I'm coming."

He entered the dining-room and sat down in his usual place. He took his napkin out of the ring and stretched over to take a piece of bread from the platter on which Lydia had put it.

"Is the old woman giving us a decent dinner tonight? I've got a beautiful appetite. I had nothing but a sandwich at Jojo's for lunch."

Madame Berger brought in the bowl of soup and taking her seat at the head of the table ladled out a couple of spoonfuls for the three of them. Robert was in high spirits. He talked gaily. But the two women hardly answered. They finished the soup.

"What's coming next?" he asked.

"Cottage pie."

"Not one of my favourite dishes."

"Be thankful you have anything to eat at all," his mother answered sharply.

He shrugged his shoulders and gave Lydia a gay wink. Madame Berger went into the kitchen to fetch the cottage pie.

"The old woman doesn't seem in a very good humour to-night. What's she been doing with herself?"

"It was the générale's last day of the season. She went there."

"The old bore! That's enough to put anyone out of temper."

Madame Berger brought in the dish and served it. Robert helped himself to some wine and water. He went on talking of one thing and another, in his usual ironical and rather amusing way, but at last he could ignore no longer the taciturnity of his companions.

"But what is the matter with you both to-night?" he interrupted himself angrily. "You sit there as glum as two mutes at a funeral."

His mother, forcing herself to eat, had been sitting with her eyes glued to her plate, but now she raised them and, silently, looked him full in the face.

"Well, what is it?" he cried flippantly.

She did not answer, but continued to stare at him. Lydia gave her a glance. In those dark eyes, as full of expression as Robert's, she read reproach, fear, anger, but also an unhappiness so poignant that it was intolerable. Robert could not withstand the intensity of that anguished gaze and dropped his eyes. They finished the meal in silence. Robert lit a cigarette and gave one to Lydia. She went into the kitchen to fetch the coffee. They drank it in silence.

There was a ring at the door. Madame Berger gave a little cry. They all sat still as though they were paralysed. The ring was repeated.

"Who is that?" whispered Madame Berger.

"I'll go and see," said Robert. Then, with a hard look on his face: "Pull yourself together, mother. There's nothing to get upset about."

He went to the front door. They heard strange voices, but he had closed the parlour door after him and they could not distinguish what was said. In a minute or two he came back. Two men followed him into the room.

"Will you both go into the kitchen," he said. "These gentlemen wish to talk to me."

"What do they want?"

"That is precisely what they are going to tell me," Robert answered coolly.

The two women got up and went out. Lydia stole a glance at him. He seemed perfectly self-possessed. It was impossible not to guess that the two strangers were detectives. Madame

Berger left the kitchen door open, hoping she would be able to hear what was being said, but across the passage, through a closed door, the words spoken were inaudible. The conversation went on for the best part of an hour, then the door was opened.

"Lydia, go and fetch me my coat and my shoes," cried Robert. "These gentlemen want me to accompany them."

He spoke in his light, gay voice, as though his assurance were unperturbed, but Lydia's heart sank. She went upstairs to do his bidding. Madame Berger said never a word. Robert changed his coat and put on his shoes.

"I shall be back in an hour or two," he said. "But don't wait up for me."

"Where are you going?" asked his mother.

"They want me to go to the Commissariat. The Commissaire de Police thinks I may be able to throw some light on the murder of poor Teddie Jordan."

"What has it got to do with you?"

"Only that, like many others, I knew him."

Robert left the house with the two detectives.

"You'd better clear the table and help me to wash up," said Madame Berger.

They washed up and put everything in its place. Then they sat on each side of the kitchen table to wait. They did not speak. They avoided one another's eyes. They sat for an interminable time. The only sound that broke the ominous silence was the striking of the cuckoo clock in the passage. When it struck three Madame Berger got up.

"He won't come back to-night. We'd better go to bed."

"I couldn't sleep. I'd rather wait here."

"What is the good of that? It's only wasting the electric light. You've got something to make you sleep, haven't you? Take a couple of tablets."

With a sigh Lydia rose to her feet. Madame Berger gave her a frowning glance and burst out angrily:

"Don't look as if the world was coming to an end. You've got no reason to pull a face like that. Robert's done nothing that can get him into trouble. I don't know what you suspect."

Lydia did not answer, but she gave her a look so charged with pain that Madame Berger dropped her eyes.

"Go to bed! Go to bed!" she cried angrily.

Lydia left her and went upstairs. She lay awake all night waiting for Robert, but he did not come. When in the morning she came down, Madame Berger had already been out to get the papers. The Jordan murder was still front-page news, but there was no mention of an arrest; the Commissaire was continuing his investigations. As soon as she had drunk her coffee Madame Berger went out. It was eleven before she came back. Lydia's heart sank when she saw her drawn face.

"Well?"

"They won't tell me anything. I got hold of the lawyer and he's gone to the Commissariat."

They were finishing a miserable luncheon when there was a ring at the front door. Lydia opened it and found Colonel Legrand and a man she had not seen before. Behind them were two other men, whom she at once recognized as the police officers who had come the night before, and a grim-faced woman. Colonel Legrand asked for Madame Berger. Her anxiety had brought her to the kitchen door, and seeing her, the man who was with him pushed past Lydia.

"Are you Madame Léontine Berger?"

"I am."

"I am Monsieur Lukas, Commissaire de Police. I have an order to search this house." He produced a document. "Colonel Legrand has been designated by your son, Robert Berger, to attend the search on his behalf."

"Why do you want to search my house?"

"I trust that you will not attempt to prevent me from fulfilling my duty."

She gave the Commissaire an angry, scornful look.

"If you have an order I have no power to prevent you."

Accompanied by the Colonel and the two detectives the Commissaire went upstairs, while the woman who had come with them remained in the kitchen with Madame Berger and Lydia. There were two rooms on the upper floor, a fairly large one which Robert and his wife used, and a smaller one in which he had slept as a bachelor. There was besides only a bathroom with a geyser. They spent nearly two hours there and when they came down the Commissaire had in his hand Lydia's vanity-case.

"Where did you get this?" he asked.

"My husband gave it me."

"Where did he get it?"

"He bought it off a woman who was down and out."

The Commissaire gave her a searching look. His eyes fell on the wrist-watch she was wearing and he pointed to it.

"Did your husband also give you that?"

"Yes."

He made no further observation. He put the vanity-case down and rejoined his companions who had gone into the double room which was part dining-room and part parlour. But in a minute or two Lydia heard the front door slam and looking out of the window saw one of the police officers go to the gate and drive off in the car that was standing at the kerb. She looked at the pretty vanity-case with sudden misgiving. Presently, so that a search might be made of the kitchen, Lydia and Madame Berger were invited to go into the parlour. Everything there was in disorder. It was plain that the search had been thorough. The curtains had been taken down and they lay on the floor. Madame Berger winced when her eyes fell on them, and she opened her mouth to speak, but by an effort of will kept silence. But when, after some time in the kitchen, the men crossed the tiny patch of garden to the pavilion, she could not prevent herself from going to the window and looking at them. Lydia saw that she was trembling and was afraid the woman who was with them would see it too. But she was idly looking at a motor paper. Lydia went up to the window and took her mother-in-law's hand. She dared not even whisper that there was no danger. When Madame Berger saw the yellow brocade curtains being taken down she clutched Lydia's hand violently, and all Lydia could do was by an answering pressure to attempt to show her that she need not fear. The men remained in the room nearly as long as they had remained upstairs.

While they were there the officer who had gone away returned. After a little he went out again and fetched two shovels from the waiting car. The two underlings, with Colonel Legrand watching, proceeded to dig up the flower bed. The Commissaire came into the sitting-room.

"Have you any objection to letting this lady search you?" he asked.

"None."

"None."

He turned to Lydia.

"Then perhaps Madame would go to her room with this person."

When Lydia went upstairs she saw why they had been so long. It looked as though the room had been ransacked by burglars. On the bed were Robert's clothes and she guessed that they had been subjected to very careful scrutiny. The ordeal over, the Commissaire asked Lydia questions about her husband's wardrobe. They were not difficult to answer, for it was not extensive: two pairs of tennis trousers, two suits besides the one he had on, a dinner-jacket and plus-fours; and she had no reason not to reply truthfully. It was past seven o'clock when the search was at last concluded. But the Commissaire had not yet done. He took up Lydia's vanity-case which she had brought in from the kitchen and which was lying on a table.

"I am going to take this away with me and also your watch, Madame, if you will kindly give it me."

"Why?"

"I have reason to suspect that they are stolen goods."

Lydia stared at him in dismay. But Colonel Legrand stepped forward.

"You have no right to take them. Your warrant to search the house does not permit you to remove a single thing from it."

The Commissaire smiled blandly.

"You are quite right, Monsieur, but my colleague has, on my instructions, secured the necessary authority."

He made a slight gesture, whereupon the man who had gone away in the car—on an errand which was now patent

—produced from his pocket a document which he handed to him. The Commissaire passed it on to Colonel Legrand. He read it and turned to Lydia.

"You must do as Monsieur le Commissaire desires."

She took the watch off her wrist. The Commissaire put it with the vanity-case in his pocket.

"If my suspicions prove to be unfounded the objects will of course be returned to you."

When at last they all left and Lydia had bolted the door behind them, Madame Berger hurried across the garden. Lydia followed her. Madame Berger gave a cry of consternation when she saw the condition in which the room was.

"The brutes!"

She rushed to the curtains. They were lying on the floor. She gave a piercing scream when she saw that the seams had been ripped up. She flopped on to the ground and turned on Lydia a face contorted with horror.

"Don't be afraid," said Lydia. "They didn't find the notes. I found them and destroyed them. I knew you'd never have the courage."

She gave her hand to Madame Berger and helped her to her feet. Madame Berger stared at her. They had never spoken of the subject that for forty-eight hours had obsessed their tortured thoughts. But now the time for silence was passed. Madame Berger seized Lydia's arm with a cruel grip and in a harsh, intense voice said:

"I swear to you by all the love I bear him that Robert didn't murder the Englishman."

"Why do you say that when you know as certainly as I do that he did?"

"Are you going to turn against him?"

"Does it look like it? Why do you suppose I destroyed those notes? You must have been mad to think they wouldn't find them. Could you think a trained detective would miss such an obvious hiding-place?"

Madame Berger released her hold of Lydia's arm. Her expression changed and a sob burst from her throat. Suddenly she stretched out her arms, took Lydia in them, and pressed her to her breast.

"Oh, my poor child, what trouble, what unhappiness I've brought upon you."

It was the first time Lydia had ever seen Madame Berger betray emotion. It was the first time she had ever known her show an uncalculated, disinterested affection. Hard, painful sobs rent her breast and she clung desperately to Lydia. Lydia was deeply moved. It was horrible to see that self-controlled woman, with her pride and her iron will, break down.

"I ought never to have let him marry you," she wailed. "It was a crime. It was unfair to you. It seemed his only chance. Never, never, never should I have allowed it."

"But I loved him."

"I know. But will you ever forgive him? Will you ever forgive me? I'm his mother, it doesn't matter to me, but you're different; how can your love survive this?"

Lydia snatched herself away and seized Madame Berger by the shoulders. She almost shook her.

"Listen to me. I don't love for a month or a year. I love for always. He's the only man I've loved. He's the only man I shall ever love. Whatever he's done, whatever the future has in store, I love him. Nothing can make me love him less. I adore him."

Next day the evening papers announced that Robert Berger had been arrested for the murder of Teddie Jordan.

A few weeks later Lydia knew that she was with child and she realized with horror that she had received the fertilizing seed on the very night of the brutal murder.

Silence fell between Lydia and Charley. They had long since finished their dinner and the other diners had gone. Charley, listening without a word, absorbed as he had never been in his life, to Lydia's story, had, all the same, been conscious that the restaurant was empty and that the waitresses were anxious for them to go, and once or twice he had been on the point of suggesting to Lydia that they should move. But it was difficult, for she spoke as if in a trance, and though often her eyes met his he had an uncanny sensation that she did not see him. But then a party of Americans came in, six of them, three men and three girls, and asked if it was too late to have dinner. The patronne, foreseeing a lucrative order, since they were all very lively, assured them that her husband was the cook and if they didn't mind waiting, would cook them whatever they wished. They ordered champagne cocktails. They were out to enjoy themselves and their gaiety filled the little restaurant with laughter. But Lydia's tragic story seemed to encompass the table at which she and Charley sat with a mysterious and sinister atmosphere which the high spirits of that happy crowd could not penetrate; and they sat in their corner, alone, as though they were surrounded by an invisible wall.

"And do you love him still?" asked Charley at last.

"With all my heart."

She spoke with such a passionate sincerity that it was impossible not to believe her. It was strange, and Charley could not prevent the slight shiver of dismay that passed through him. She did not seem to belong to quite the same human species as he did. That violence of feeling was rather terrifying, and it made him a little uncomfortable to be with her. He might have felt like that if he had been talking quite casually to someone for an hour or two and then suddenly discovered it was a ghost. But there was one thing that troubled him. It had been on his mind for the last twenty-four hours, but not wishing her to think him censorious, he had not spoken of it.

"In that case I can't help wondering how you can bear to be in a place like the Sérail. Couldn't you have found some other means of earning your living?"

"I tried to. I'm a good needle-woman, I was apprenticed to a dress-maker. You'd have thought I could have got work in that business; when they found out who I was no one would have me. It meant that or starvation."

There seemed nothing more to say, and Charley was silent. She planted her elbows on the red-and-white checkered table-cloth and rested her face on her hands. Charley was sitting opposite to her and she gazed into his eyes with a long reflective look that seemed to bore into the depths of his being.

"I didn't mind as much as you might have thought I would." She hesitated for an instant. "I wanted to atone."

Charley stared at her uncomprehendingly. Her words, spoken hardly above a whisper, gave him a shock. He had a sensation that he had never had before; it seemed to him that a veil that painted the world in pleasant, familiar colours had been suddenly rent and he looked into a convulsed and writhing darkness.

"What in God's name do you mean?"

"Though I love Robert with all my heart, with all my soul, I know that he sinned. I felt that the only way I could serve Robert now was by submitting to a degradation that was the most horrible I could think of. At first I thought I would go to one of those brothels where soldiers go, and workmen, and the riffraff of a great city, but I feared I should feel pity for those poor people whose hurried, rare visits to such places afford the only pleasure of their cruel lives. The Sérail is frequented by the rich, the idle, the vicious. There was no chance there that I should feel anything but hatred and contempt for the beasts who bought my body. There my humiliation is like a festering wound that nothing can heal. The brutal indecency of the clothes I have to wear is a shame that no habit can dull. I welcome the suffering. I welcome the contempt these men have for the instrument of their lust. I welcome their brutality. I'm in hell as Robert is in hell and my suffering joins with his, and it may be that my suffering makes it more easy for him to bear his."

"But he's suffering because he committed a crime. You suffered enough for no fault of yours. Why should you expose yourself to suffering unnecessarily?"

"Sin must be paid for by suffering. How can you with your cold English nature know what the love is that is all my life? I am his and he is mine. I should be as vile as his crime was if I hesitated to share his suffering. I know that my suffering as well as his is necessary to expiate his sin."

Charley hesitated. He had no particular religious feelings. He had been brought up to believe in God, but not to think of him. To do that would be—well, not exactly bad form, but rather priggish. It was difficult for him now to say what he had in mind, but he found himself in a situation where it seemed almost natural to say the most unnatural things.

"Your husband committed a crime and was punished for it. I daresay that's all right. But you can't think that a—a merciful God demands atonement from you for somebody else's misdeeds."

"God? What has God to do with it? Do you suppose I can look at the misery in which the vast majority of the people live in the world and believe in God? Do you suppose I believe in God who let the Bolsheviks kill my poor, simple father? Do you know what I think? I think God has been dead for millions upon millions of years. I think when he took infinity and set in motion the process that has resulted in the universe, he died, and for ages and ages men have sought and worshipped a being who ceased to exist in the act of making existence possible for them."

"But if you don't believe in God I can't see the point of what you're doing. I could understand it if you believed in a cruel God who exacted an eye for an eye and a tooth for a tooth. Atonement, the sort of atonement you want to make, is meaningless if there's no God."

"You would have thought so, wouldn't you? There's no logic in it. There's no sense. And yet, deep down in my heart, no, much more than that, in every fibre of my body, I know that I must atone for Robert's sin. I know that that is the only way he can gain release from the evil that racks him. I don't ask you to think I'm reasonable. I only ask you to understand that I can't help myself. I believe that somehow—how I don't know—my humiliation, my degradation, my bitter, ceaseless pain, will wash his soul clean, and even if we never see one another again he will be restored to me.'

Charley sighed. It was all strange to him, strange, morbid and disturbing. He did not know what to make of it. He felt more than ever ill-at-ease with that alien woman with her crazy fancies; and yet she looked ordinary enough, a prettyish little thing, not very well dressed; a typist or a girl in the post-office. Just then, at the Terry-Masons', they would probably have started dancing; they would be wearing the paper caps they'd got out of the crackers at dinner. Some of the chaps would be a bit tight, but hang it all, on Christmas Day no one could mind. There'd have been a lot of kissing under the mistletoe, a lot of fun, a lot of ragging, a lot of laughter; they were all having a grand time. It seemed very far away, but thank God, it was there, normal, decent, sane and real; this was a nightmare. A nightmare? He wondered if there was anything in what she said, this woman with her tragic history and her miserable life, that God had died when he created the wide world; and was he lying dead on some vast mountain range on a dead star or was he absorbed into the universe he had caused to be? It was rather funny, if you came to think of it, Lady Terry-Mason rounding up all the house party to go to church on Christmas morning. And his own father backing her up.

"I don't pretend I'm much of a church-goer myself, but I think one ought to go on Christmas Day. I mean, I think it sets a good example."

That's what he would say.

"Don't look so serious," said Lydia. "Let's go."

They walked along the forbidding, sordid street that leads from the Avenue du Maine to the Place de Rennes, and there Lydia suggested that they should go to the news reel for an hour. It was the last performance of the day. Then they had a glass of beer and went back to the hotel. Lydia took off her hat and the fur she wore round her neck. She looked at Charley thoughtfully.

"If you want to come to bed with me you can, you know," she said in just the same tone as she might have used if she had asked him if he would like to go to the Rotonde or the Dôme.

Charley caught his breath. All his nerves revolted from the idea. After what she had told him he could not have touched her. His mouth for a moment went grim with anger; he really was not going to have her mortify her flesh at his expense. But his native politeness prevented him from uttering the words that were on the tip of his tongue.

"Oh, I don't think so, thank you."

"Why not? I'm there for that and that's what you came to Paris for, isn't it? Isn't that why all you English come to Paris?"

"I don't know. Anyhow I didn't."

"What else did you come for?"

"Well, partly to see some pictures."

She shrugged her shoulders.

"It's just as you like."

She went into the bathroom. Charley was a trifle piqued that she accepted his refusal with so much unconcern. He thought at least she might have given him credit for his delicacy. Because perhaps she owed him something, at least board and lodging for twenty-four hours, he might well have looked upon it as a right to take what she offered; it wouldn't have been unbecoming if she had thanked him for his disinterestedness. He was inclined to sulk. He undressed, and when she came in from the bathroom, in his dressing-gown, he went in to wash his teeth. She was in bed when he returned.

"Will it bother you if I read a little before I go to sleep?" he asked.

"No. I'll turn my back to the light."

He had brought a Blake with him. He began to read. Presently from Lydia's quiet breathing in the next bed he knew she was asleep. He read on for a little and switched off the light.

Thus did Charley Mason spend Christmas Day in Paris.

vi

THEY did not wake till so late next morning that by the time they had had their coffee, read the papers (like a domestic couple who had been married for years), bathed and dressed, it was nearly one.

"We might go along and have a cocktail at the Dôme and then lunch," he said. "Where would you like to go?"

"There's a very good restaurant on the boulevard in the other direction from the Coupole. Only it's rather expensive."

"Well, that doesn't matter."

"Are you sure?" She looked at him doubtfully. "I don't want you to spend more than you can afford. You've been very sweet to me. I'm afraid I've taken advantage of your kindness."

"Oh, rot!" he answered, flushing.

"You don't know what it's meant to me, these two days. Such a rest. Last night's the first night for months that I've slept without waking and without dreams. I feel so refreshed. I feel quite different."

She did indeed look much better this morning. Her skin was clearer and her eyes brighter. She held her head more alertly.

"It's been a wonderful little holiday you've given me. It's helped me so much. But I mustn't be a burden to you."

"You haven't been."

She smiled with gentle irony.

"You've been very well brought up, my dear. It's nice of you to say that, and I'm so unused to having people say nice things to me that it makes me want to cry. But after all you've come to Paris to have a good time; you know now you're not likely to have it with me. You're young and you must enjoy your youth. It lasts so short a while. Give me lunch to-day if you like and this afternoon I'll go back to Alexey's."

"And to-night to the Sérail?"

"I suppose so."

She sighed, but she checked the sigh and with a little gay shrug of the shoulders gave him a bright smile. Frowning slightly in his uncertainty Charley looked at her with pained eyes. He felt awkward and big, and his radiant health, his sense of well-being, the high spirits that bubbled inside him, seemed to himself in an odd way an offence. He was like a rich man vulgarly displaying his wealth to a poor relation. She looked very frail, a slim little thing in a shabby brown dress, and after that good night so much younger that she seemed almost a child. How could you help being sorry for her? And when you thought of her tragic story, when you thought—oh, unwillingly, for it was ghastly and senseless, yet troubling so that it haunted you—of that crazy idea of hers of atoning for her husband's crime by her own degradation, your heart-strings were wrung. You felt that you didn't matter at all, and if your holiday in Paris, to which you'd looked forward with such excitement, was a wash-out —well, you just had to put up with it. It didn't seem to Charley that it was he who was uttering the halting words he spoke, but a power within him that acted independently of his will. When he heard them issue from his lips he didn't even then know why he said them.

"I don't have to get back to the office till Monday morning and I'm staying till Sunday. If you care to stay on here till then, I don't see why you shouldn't."

Her face lit up so that you might have thought a haphazard ray of the winter sun had strayed into the room.

"Do you mean that?"

"Otherwise I wouldn't have suggested it."

It looked as though her legs suddenly gave way, for she sank on to a chair.

"Oh, it would be such a blessing. It would be such a rest. It would give me new courage. But I can't, I can't."

"Why not? On account of the Sérail?"

"Oh, no, not that. I could send them a wire to say I had influenza. It's not fair to you."

"That's my business, isn't it?"

It seemed a bit grim to Charley that he should have to persuade her to do what it was quite plain she was only too anxious to do, and what he would just as soon she didn't. But he didn't see how else he could act now. She gave him a searching look.

"Why should you do this? You don't want me, do you?" He shook his head. "What can it matter to you if I live or die, what can it matter to you if I'm happy or not? You've not known me forty-eight hours yet. Friendship? I'm a stranger to you. Pity? What has one got to do with pity at your age?"

"I wish you wouldn't ask me embarrassing questions," he grinned.

"I suppose it's just natural goodness of heart. They always say the English are kind to animals. I remember one of our landladies who used to steal our tea took in a mangy mongrel because it was homeless."

"If you weren't so small I'd give you a smack on the face for that," he retorted cheerfully. "Is it a go?"

"Let's go out and have lunch. I'm hungry."

During luncheon they spoke of indifferent things, but when they had finished and Charley, having paid the bill, was waiting for his change, she said to him:

"Did you really mean it when you said I could stay with you till you went away?"

"Definitely."

"You don't know what a boon it would be to me. I can't tell you how I long to take you at your word."

"Then why don't you?"

"It won't be much fun for you."

"No, it won't," he answered frankly, but with a charming smile. "But it'll be interesting."

She laughed.

"Then I'll go back to Alexey's and get a few things. At least a toothbrush and some clean stockings."

They separated at the station and Lydia took the Metro. Charley thought that he would see if Simon was in. After asking his way two or three times he found the Rue Campagne Première. The house in which Simon lived was tall and dingy, and the wood of the shutters showed gray under the crumbling paint. When Charley put in his head at the concierge's loge he was almost knocked down by the stink of fug, food and human body that assailed his nostrils. A little old woman in voluminous skirts, with her head wrapped in a dirty red muffler, told him in rasping, angry tones, as though she violently resented his intrusion, where exactly Simon lived, and when Charley asked if he was in bade him go and see. Charley, following her directions, went through the dirty courtyard and up a narrow staircase smelling of stale urine. Simon lived on the second floor and in answer to Charley's ring opened the door.

"H'm. I wondered what had become of you."

"Am I disturbing you?"

"No. Come in. You'd better keep on your coat. It's not very warm in here."

That was true. It was icy. It was a studio, with a large north light, and there was a stove in it, but Simon, who had apparently been working, for the table in the middle was littered with papers, had forgotten to keep it up and the fire was almost out. Simon drew a shabby armchair up to the stove and asked Charley to sit down.

"I'll put some more coke on. It'll soon get warmer. I don't feel the cold myself."

Charley found that the armchair, having a broken spring, was none too comfortable. The walls of the studio were a cold slate-gray, and they too looked as though they hadn't been painted for years. Their only ornament was large maps tacked up with drawing-pins. There was a narrow iron bed which hadn't been made.

"The concierge hasn't been up to-day yet," said Simon, following Charley's glance.

There was nothing else in the studio but the large dining-table, bought second-hand, which Simon wrote at, some shelves with books in them, a desk-chair such as they use in offices, two or three kitchen chairs piled up with books, and a strip of worn carpet by the bed. It was cheerless and the cold winter light coming in through the north window added its moroseness to the squalid scene. A third-class waiting-room at a wayside station could not have seemed more un-friendly.

Simon drew a chair up to the stove and lit a pipe. With his quick wits he guessed the impression his surroundings were making on Charley and smiled grimly.

"It's not very luxurious, is it? But then I don't want lux-ury." Charley was silent and Simon gave him a coolly dis-dainful look. "It's not even comfortable, but then I don't want comfort. No one should be dependent on it. It's a trap that's caught many a man who you would have thought had more sense."

Charley was not without a streak of malice and he was not inclined to let Simon put it over on him.

"You look cold and peaked and hungry, old boy. What

about taking a taxi to the Ritz Bar and having some scrambled eggs and bacon in warmth and comfortable armchairs?"

"Go to hell. What have you done with Olga?"

"Her name's Lydia. She's gone home to get a toothbrush. She's staying with me at the hotel till I go back to London."

"The devil she is. Going some, aren't you?" The two young men stared at one another for a moment. Simon leant forward. "You haven't fallen for her, have you?"

"Why did you bring us together?"

"I thought it would be rather a joke. I thought it would be a new experience for you to go to bed with the wife of a notorious murderer. And to tell you the truth, I thought she might fall for you. I should laugh like a hyena if she has. After all, you're rather the same type as Berger, but a damned sight better-looking."

Charley suddenly remembered a remark that Lydia had made when they were having supper together after the Midnight Mass. He had not understood what she meant at the time, but now he did.

"It may surprise you to learn that she tumbled to that. I'm afraid you won't be able to laugh like a hyena."

"Have you been together ever since I left you with her on Christmas Eve?"

"Yes."

"It seems to agree with you. You look all right. A bit pale, perhaps."

Charley tried not to look self-conscious. He would not for the world have had Simon know that his relations with Lydia had been entirely platonic. It would only have aroused his derisive laughter. He would have looked upon Charley's behaviour as despicably sentimental.

"I don't think it was a very good joke to get me off with her without letting me know what I was in for," said Charley.

Simon gave him a tortured smile.

"It appealed to my sense of humour. It'll be something to tell your parents when you go home. Anyhow you've got nothing to grouse about. It's all panned out very well. Olga knows her job and will give you a damned good time in that way, and she's no fool; she's read a lot and she can talk much more intelligently than most women. It'll be a liberal education, my boy. D'you think she's as much in love with her husband as ever she was?"

"I think so."

"Curious, human nature is, isn't it? He was an awful rotter, you know. I suppose you know why she's at the Sérail? She wants to make enough money to pay for his escape; then she'll join him in Brazil."

Charley was disconcerted. He had believed her when she told him that she was there because she wanted to atone for Robert's sin, and even though the notion had seemed to him extravagant there was something about it that had strangely moved him. It was a shock to think that she might have lied to him. If what Simon said were true she had just been making a fool of him.

"I covered the trial for our paper, you know," Simon went on. "It caused rather a sensation in England because the fellow that Berger killed was an Englishman, and they gave it a lot of space. It was a snip for me; I'd never been to a murder trial in France before and I was pretty keen to see one. I've been to the Old Bailey, and I was curious to compare their methods with ours. I wrote a very full account of it; I've got it here; I'll give it you to read if you like."

"Yes, I would."

"The murder created a great stir in France. You see, Robert Berger wasn't an apache or anything like that. He was by way of being a gent. His people were very decent. He was well-educated and he spoke English quite passably. One of the papers called him the Gentleman Gangster and it caught on; it took the public fancy and made him quite a celebrity. He was good-looking too, in his way, and young, only twenty-two, and that helped. The women all went crazy over him. God, the crush there was to get into the trial! It was a real thrill when he came into the court-room. He was brought in between two warders for the press photographers to have a go at him before the judges came in. I never saw anyone so cool. He was quite nicely dressed and he knew how to wear his clothes. He was freshly shaved and his hair was very neat. He had a fine head of dark brown hair. He smiled at the photographers and turned this way and that, as they asked him to, so that they could all get a good view of him. He looked like any young chap with plenty of money that you might see at the Ritz Bar having a drink with a girl. It tickled me to think that he was such a rogue. He was a born criminal. Of course his people weren't rich, but they weren't starving, and I don't suppose he ever really wanted for a hundred francs. I wrote a rather pretty article about him for one of the weekly papers, and the French press printed extracts from it. It did me a bit of good over here. I took the line that he engaged in crime as a form of sport. See the idea? It worked up quite amusingly. He'd been almost a first-class tennis-player and there was some talk of training him for championship play, but oddly enough, though he played a grand game in ordinary matches, he had a good serve and was quick at the net, when it came to tournaments he always fell down. Something went wrong then. He hadn't got power of resistance, determination or whatever it is, that the great tennis-player has got to have. An interesting psychological point, I thought. Anyhow his career as a tennis-player came to an end because money began to be missed from the changing-room when he was about, and though it was never actually proved that he'd taken it everyone concerned was pretty well convinced that he was the culprit."

Simon relit his pipe.

"One thing that peculiarly struck me in Robert Berger was his combination of nerve, self-possession and charm. Of course charm is an invaluable quality, but it doesn't often go with nerve and self-possession. Charming people are generally weak and irresolute, charm is the weapon nature gives them to cope with their disadvantages; I would never set much trust in anyone who had it."

Charley gave his friend a slightly amused glance; he knew that Simon was belittling a quality he did not think he possessed in order to assure himself that it was of no great consequence beside those he was convinced he had. But he did not interrupt.

"Robert Berger was neither weak nor irresolute. He very

nearly got away with his murder. It was a damned smart bit of work on the part of the police that they got him. There was nothing sensational or spectacular in the way they went about the job; they were just thorough and patient. Perhaps accident helped them a little, but they were clever enough to take advantage of it. People must always be prepared to do that, you know, and they seldom are."

An absent look came into Simon's eyes, and once more Charley was aware that he was thinking of himself.

"What Lydia didn't tell me was how the police first came to suspect him," said Charley.

"When first they questioned him they hadn't the ghost of an idea that he had anything to do with the murder. They were looking for a much bigger man."

"What sort of a chap was Jordan?"

"I never ran across him. He was a bad hat, but he was all right in his way. Everybody liked him. He was always ready to stand you a drink, and if you were down and out he never minded putting his hand in his pocket. He was a little fellow, he'd been a jockey, but he'd got warned off in England, and it turned out later that he'd done nine months at Wormwood Scrubs for false pretences. He was thirty-six. He'd been in Paris ten years. The police had an idea that he was mixed up in the drug traffic, but they'd never been able to get the goods on him."

"But how did the police come to question Berger at all?"

"He was one of the frequenters of Jojo's Bar. That's where Jordan used to have his meals. It's rather a shady place patronized by bookmakers and jockeys, touts, runners and the sort of people with the reputation that we journalists describe as unsavoury, and naturally the police interviewed as many of them as they could get hold of. You see, Jordan had a date with someone that night, that was shown by the fact that there were a couple of glasses on the tray and a cake, and they thought he might have dropped a hint about whom he was going to meet. They had a pretty shrewd suspicion that he was queer, and it was just possible one of the chaps at Jojo's had seen him about with someone. Berger had been rather pally with Jordan, and Jojo, the owner of the bar, told the police he'd seen him touch the bookie for money several times. Berger had been tried on a charge of smuggling heroin into France from Belgium, and the two men who were up with him went to jug, but he got off somehow. The police knew he was as guilty as hell, and if Jordan had been mixed up with dope and had met his death in connection with that, they thought Berger might very well know who was responsible. He was a bad lot. He'd been convicted on another charge, stealing motor-cars, and got a suspended sentence of two years."

"Yes, I know that," said Charley.

"His system was as simple as it was ingenious. He used to wait till he saw someone drive up to one of the big stores, the Printemps or the Bon Marché, in a Citroën, and go in, leaving it at the kerb. Then he'd walk up, as bold as brass, as though he'd just come out of the store, jump in and drive off."

"But didn't they lock the cars?"

"Seldom. And he had some Citroën keys. He always stuck to the one make. He'd use the car for two or three days and then leave it somewhere, and when he wanted another, he'd start again. He stole dozens. He never tried to sell them, he just borrowed them when he wanted one for a particular purpose. That was what gave me the idea for my article. He pinched them for the fun of the thing, for the pleasure of exercising his audacious cleverness. He had another ingenious dodge that came out at the trial. He'd hang around in his car about the bus stops just at the time the shops closed, and when he saw a woman waiting for a bus he'd stop and ask her if she'd like a lift. I suppose he was a pretty good judge of character and knew the sort of woman who'd be likely to accept a ride from a good-looking young man. Well, the woman got in and he'd drive off in the direction she wanted to go, and when they came to a more or less deserted street he stalled the car. He pretended he couldn't get it to start and he would ask the woman to get out, lift the hood and tickle the carburettor while he pressed the self-starter. The woman did so, leaving her bag and her parcels in the car, and just as she was going to get in again, when the engine was running, he'd shoot off and be out of sight before she realized what he was up to. Of course a good many women went and complained to the police, but they'd only seen him in the dark, and all they could say was that he was a good-looking, gentlemanly young man in a Citroën, with a pleasant voice, and all the police could do was to tell them that it was very unwise to accept lifts from good-looking, gentlemanly young men. He was never caught. At the trial it came out that he must often have done very well out of these transactions.

"Anyhow a couple of police officers went to see him. He didn't deny that he'd been at Jojo's Bar on the evening of the murder and had been with Jordan, but he said he'd left about ten o'clock and hadn't seen him after that. After some conversation they invited him to accompany them to the Commissariat. The Commissaire de Police who was in charge of the preliminary proceedings had no notion, mind you, that Berger was the murderer. He thought it was a toss-up whether Jordan had been killed by some tough that he'd brought to his flat or by a member of the drug-ring whom he might have double-crossed. If the latter, he thought he could wheedle, jockey, bully or frighten Berger into giving some indication that would enable the police to catch the man they were after.

"I managed to get an interview with the Commissaire. He was a chap called Lukas. He was not at all the sort of type you'd expect to find in a job like that. He was a big, fat, hearty fellow, with red cheeks, a heavy moustache and great shining black eyes. He was a jolly soul and you'd have bet a packet that there was nothing he enjoyed more than a good dinner and a bottle of wine. He came from the Midi and he had an accent that you could cut with a knife. He had a fat, jovial laugh. He was a friendly, back-slapping, good-natured man to all appearances and you felt inclined to confide in him. In point of fact he'd had wonderful success in getting confessions out of suspects. He had great physical endurance and was capable of conducting an examination for sixteen hours at a stretch. There's no third degree in France of the American sort, no knocking about, I mean, or tooth-drilling or anything like that, to extort a confession; they just bring a man into the room and make him stand, they don't let him smoke and they don't give him anything to eat, they just ask him questions; they go on and on, they smoke, and when they're hungry they have a meal brought in to them; they go on all night, because they know that at night a man's powers of resistance are at their lowest; and if he's guilty he has to be very strong-minded if by morning for the sake of a cup of coffee and a cigarette he won't confess. The Commissaire got nothing out of Berger. He admitted that at one time he'd been friendly with the heroin smugglers, but he asserted his innocence of the charge on which he'd been tried and acquitted. He said he'd done stupid things in his youth, but he'd had his lesson; after all, he'd only borrowed cars for two or three days to take girls out, it wasn't a very serious crime, and now that he was married he was going straight. As far as the drug traffickers were concerned he'd had nothing to do with them since his trial and he had had no idea that Teddie Jordan was mixed up with them. He was very frank. He told the Commissaire that he was very much in love with his wife, and his great fear was that she would discover his past. For her sake as well as for his own and his mother's, he was determined to lead in future a decent and honourable life. The fat, jolly man went on asking questions, but in a friendly, sympathetic way so that you felt, I think, that he couldn't wish you any harm. He applauded Berger's good resolutions, he congratulated him on marrying a penniless girl for love, he hoped they would have children which were not only an ornament to a home, but a comfort to their parents. But he had Berger's dossier; he knew that in the heroin case, though the jury had refused to convict, he was undoubtedly guilty, and from enquiries he had made that day, that he had been discharged from the broker's firm and had only escaped prosecution because his mother had made restitution of the money he had embezzled. It was a lie that since his marriage he had been leading an honest life. He asked him about his financial circumstances. Berger confessed that they were difficult, but his mother had a little and soon he was bound to get a job and then they would be all right. And pocket money? Now and then he made a bit racing and he introduced clients to bookmakers, that was how he'd become friendly with Jordan, and got a commission. Sometimes he just went without.

" 'En effet,' said the Commissaire, 'the day before he was killed you said you were penniless and you borrowed fifty francs from Jordan.'

" 'He was good to me. Poor chap. I shall miss him.'

"The Commissaire was looking at Berger with his friendly, twinkling eyes, and it occurred to him that the young man was not ill-favoured. Was it possible? But no, that was nonsense. He had a notion that Berger was lying when he said he had given up all relations with the drug traffickers. After all, he was hard up and there was good money to be made there; Berger went about among the sort of people who were addicted to dope. The Commissaire had an impression, though he had no notion on what he founded it, that Berger, if he didn't know for certain who'd committed the murder, had his suspicions: of course he wouldn't tell, but if they found heroin hidden away in the house at Neuilly they might be able to force him to. The Commissaire was a shrewd judge of character and he was pretty sure that Berger would give a friend away to save his own skin. He made up his mind that he would hold Berger and have the house searched before he had any chance of disposing of anything that was there. With the same idea in his mind he asked him about his movements on the night of the murder. Berger stated that he had come in from Neuilly rather late and had walked to Jojo's Bar; he had found a lot of men there who had come in after the races. He got two or three drinks stood him, and Jordan, who'd had a good day, said he'd pay for his dinner. After he'd eaten he hung about for a bit, but it was very smoky and it made his head ache, so he went for a stroll on the boulevard. Then about eleven he went back to the bar and stayed there till it was time to catch the last Metro back to Neuilly.

" 'You were away just long enough to kill the Englishman

in point of fact,' said the Commissaire in a joking sort of way.

"Berger burst out laughing.

" 'You're not going to accuse me of that?' he said.

" 'No, not that,' laughed the other.

" 'Believe me, Jordan's death is a loss to me. The fifty francs he lent me the day before he was murdered wasn't the first I'd had from him. I don't say it was very scrupulous, but when he'd had a few drinks it wasn't hard to get money out of him.'

" 'Still, he'd made a lot that day, and though he wasn't drunk when he left the bar, he was in a happy mood. You might have thought it worth while to make sure of a few thousand francs at one go rather than get it in fifties from time to time.'

"The Commissaire said this more to tease than because he thought there was anything in it. And he didn't think it a bad thing to let Berger suppose he was a possible object of suspicion. It would certainly not make him less disinclined to tell the culprit's name if he had an inkling of it. Berger took out the money in his pocket and put it on the table. It amounted to less than ten francs.

" 'If I'd robbed poor Jordan of his money you don't suppose I'd only have that in my pocket now.'

" 'My dear boy, I suppose nothing. I only pointed out that you had the time to kill Jordan and that money would have been useful to you.'

"Berger gave him his frank and disarming smile.

" 'Both those things, I admit,' he said.

" 'I will be perfectly open with you,' said the other. 'I don't think you murdered Jordan, but I'm fairly certain that if you don't know who did, you have at least a suspicion.'

"Berger denied this, and though the Commissaire pressed him, persisted in his denial. It was late by now and the Commissaire thought it would be better to resume the conversation next day, he thought also that a night in the cells would give Berger an opportunity to consider his position. Berger, who had been arrested twice before, knew that it was useless to protest.

"You know that the dope traffickers are up to every sort of trick to conceal their dope. They hide it in hollow walking-sticks, in the heels of shoes, in the lining of old clothes, in mattresses and pillows, in the frames of bedsteads, in every imaginable place, but the police know all their dodges, and you can bet your boots that if there'd been anything in the house at Neuilly they'd have found it. They found nothing. But when the Commissaire had been going through Lydia's bedroom he'd come across a vanity-case, and it struck him that it was an expensive one for a woman of that modest class to have. She had a watch on that looked as if it had cost quite a lot of money. She said that her husband had given her both the watch and the vanity-case, and it occurred to the Commissaire that it might be interesting to find out how he had got the money to buy them. On getting back to his office he had inquiries made and in a very short while learnt that several women had reported that they had had bags stolen by a young man who had offered them lifts in a Citroën. One woman had left a description of a vanity-case which she had thus lost and it corresponded with that which the Commissaire had found in Lydia's possession; another stated that there had been in her bag a gold watch from such and such a maker. The same maker's name was on Lydia's. It was plain that the mysterious young man whom the police had never been able to lay their hands on was Robert Berger. That didn't seem to bring the solution of the Jordan murder any nearer, but it gave the Commissaire an additional weapon to induce Berger to spill the beans. He had him brought into his room and asked him to explain how he had come by the vanity-case and the watch. Berger said he'd bought one of them from a tart who wanted money and the other from a man he'd met in a bar. He could give the name of neither. They were casual persons whom he'd got into conversation with and had neither seen before nor since. The Commissaire then formally arrested him on a charge of theft, and telling him that he would be confronted next morning with the two women to whom he was convinced the articles belonged, tried to persuade him to save trouble by making a confession. But Berger stuck

to his story and refused to answer any more questions till
he had the assistance of a lawyer, which by French law,
now that he was arrested, he was entitled to have at an examination. The Commissaire could do nothing but acquiesce,
and that finished the proceedings for the night.

"On the following morning the two women in question
came to the Commissariat and immediately they were shown
the objects recognized them. Berger was brought in and
one of them at once identified him as the obliging young man
who had given her a lift. The other was doubtful; it was
night when she had accepted his offer to drive her home and
she had not seen his face very well, but she thought she
would recognize his voice. Berger was told to read out a
couple of sentences from a paper and he had not read half a
dozen words before the woman cried out that she was
certain it was the same man. I may tell you that Berger had
a peculiarly soft and caressing voice. The women were dismissed and Berger taken back to the cell. The vanity-case
and the watch were on the table before him and the Commissaire looked at them idly. Suddenly his expression grew
more intent."

Charley interrupted.

"Simon, how could you know that? You're romancing."

Simon laughed.

"I'm dramatizing a little. I'm telling you what I said in
my first article. I had to make as good a story out of it as I
could, you know."

"Go on then."

"Well, he sent for one of his men, and asked him if Berger
had on a wrist-watch when he was arrested, and if he had,
to bring it. Remember, all this came out at the trial afterwards. The cop got Berger's watch. It was an imitation gold
thing, in a metal that I think's called aureum, and it had
a round face. The press had given a lot of details about
Jordan's murder; they'd said, for instance, that the knife
with which the blow had been inflicted hadn't been found,
and, incidentally, it never was; and they'd said that the police hadn't discovered any finger-prints. You'd have expected
to find some either on the leather note-case in which Jordan

had kept his money or on the door handle; and of course they deduced from that that the murderer had worn gloves. But what they didn't say, because the police had taken care to keep it dark, was that when they had gone through Jordan's room with a fine comb they had found fragments of a broken watch-glass. It couldn't have belonged to Jordan's watch, and it needn't necessarily have belonged to the murderer's, but there was just a chance that somehow or other, in his nervousness or haste, by an accidental knock against a piece of furniture, the murderer had broken the glass of his watch. It wasn't a thing he would be likely to notice at such a moment. Not all the pieces had been found, but enough to show that the watch they had belonged to was small and oblong. The Commissaire had the pieces in an envelope, carefully wrapped up in tissue-paper, and he now laid them out before him. They would have exactly fitted Lydia's watch. It might be only a coincidence; there were in use thousands of watches of just that size and shape. Lydia's had a glass. But the Commissaire pondered. He turned over in his mind various possibilities. They seemed so far-fetched that he shrugged his shoulders. Of course during the period, three-quarters of an hour at least, that Berger claimed he'd been strolling along the boulevard, he would have had plenty of time to get to Jordan's apartment, a ten minutes' walk from Jojo's Bar, commit the murder, wash his hands, tidy himself up, and walk back again; but why should he have been wearing his wife's watch? He had one of his own. His own, of course, might have been out of order. The Commissaire nodded his head thoughtfully."

Charley giggled.

"Really, Simon."

"Shut up. He gave instructions that plain-clothes men should go to every watchmaker's within a radius of two miles round the house in Neuilly where the Bergers lived. They were to ask if within the last week any watchmaker had repaired a watch in imitation gold or had put a glass in a small lady's-watch with an oblong face. Within a few hours one of the men came back and said that a watchmaker, not more than a quarter of a mile from the Bergers' house, said that he had repaired a watch corresponding to the description and it had been called for, and at the same time the customer had brought another watch to have a glass put in. He had done it on the spot and she had come in for it half an hour later. He couldn't remember what the customer looked like, but he thought she had a Russian accent. The two watches were taken for the watchmaker to look at and he claimed that they were those he had repaired. The Commissaire beamed as he might have beamed if he had a great plate of bouillabaisse set before him in the Old Port at Marseilles. He knew he'd got his man."

"What was the explanation?" asked Charley.

"Simple as A B C. Berger had broken his watch and borrowed the one he'd given to Lydia. She hardly ever went out and didn't need it. You must remember that in those days she was a quiet, modest, rather shy girl with few friends of her own, and I should say somewhat lethargic. At the trial two men swore that they'd noticed Berger wearing it. Jojo, who was a police informer, knew that Berger was a crook and wondered how he had got it. In a casual way he mentioned to Berger that he had a new watch on and Berger told him it was his wife's. Lydia went to the watchmaker's to get her husband's watch the morning after the murder, and very naturally, since she was there, had a new glass put in her own. It never occurred to her to mention it and Berger never knew that he had broken it."

"But you don't mean to say that he was convicted on that?"

"No. But it was enough to justify the Commissaire charging him with the murder. He thought, quite rightly as it turned out, that new evidence would be forthcoming. All through his interrogations Berger conducted himself with amazing adroitness and self-possession. He admitted everything that could be proved and no longer attempted to deny that it was he who had robbed all those women of their handbags, he admitted that even after his conviction he had gone on pinching cars whenever he wanted one; he said the ease with which it could be done was too much for him and the risk appealed to his adventurousness; but he denied absolutely that he'd had anything to do with the murder. He claimed that the fact of the pieces of glass fitting Lydia's watch proved nothing, and she swore black and blue that she'd broken the glass herself. The juge d'instruction in whose charge the case was of course eventually placed was puzzled because no trace could be found of the money Berger must have stolen, and actually it never was found. Another odd thing was that there was no trace of blood on the clothes that Berger was wearing on that particular night. The knife wasn't found either. It was proved that Berger had one, in the circles he moved in that was usual enough, but he swore that he'd lost it a month before. I told you that the detectives' work was pretty good. There'd been no finger-prints on the stolen cars nor on the stolen handbags, which when he'd emptied he'd apparently just thrown into the street and some of which had eventually got into the hands of the police, so it was pretty obvious that he had worn gloves. They found a pair of leather gauntlets among his things, but it was unlikely that he would have kept them on when he went to see Jordan, and from the place in which the body was found, which suggested that Jordan had been changing a record when he was struck, it was plain that Berger hadn't murdered him the moment Jordan let him into the room. Besides, they were too large to go in his pocket and if he had had them at the bar someone would have noticed them. Of course Berger's photo had been published in all the papers, and in their difficulty the police got the press to help them. They asked anyone who could remember having sold about such-and-such a date a pair of gloves, probably gray, to a young man in a gray suit, to come forward. The papers made rather a thing about it; they put his photo in again with the caption: 'Did you sell him the gloves he wore to kill Teddie Jordan?'

"You know, a thing that has always struck me is people's fiendish eagerness to give anyone away. They pretend it's public spirit, I don't believe a word of it, I don't believe it's even, as a rule anyway, the desire for notoriety; I believe it's just due to the baseness of human nature that gets a kick out of injuring others. You know, of course, that in

England the Treasury and the King's Proctor are supposed to have a wonderful system of espionage to detect income-tax evasions, and collusion and so forth in divorce cases. Well, there's not a word of truth in it. They depend entirely on anonymous letters. There are a whole mass of people who can't wait if they have the chance of doing down some-one who's trying to get away with anything."

"It's a grim thought," said Charley, but added cheerfully: "I can only hope you're exaggerating."

"Well, anyhow, a woman from the glove department at the Trois Quartiers came forward and said she remembered selling a young man a pair of gray suède gloves on the day of the murder. She was a woman of about forty and she'd liked the look of him. He was particularly anxious that they should match his gray suit and he wanted them rather large so that he shouldn't have any difficulty in slipping into them. Berger was paraded with a dozen other young men and she picked him out at once, but, as his lawyer pointed out, that was easy since she had only just seen his picture in the paper. Then they got hold of one of Berger's crooked friends who said he'd met him on the night of the murder, not walking towards the boulevard, but in a direction that would have taken him to Jordan's apartment. He'd shaken hands with him and had noticed that he was wearing gloves. But that particular witness was a thorough scamp. He had a foul record, and Berger's counsel at the trial attacked him violently. Berger denied that he had seen him on that partic-ular evening and his counsel tried to persuade the jury that it was a cooked-up story that the man had invented in order to ingratiate himself with the police. The damning thing was the trousers. There'd been a lot of stuff in the papers about Berger's smart clothes, the well-dressed gangster and all that sort of thing; you'd have thought, to read it, that he got his suits in Savile Row and his haberdashery at Charvet's. The prosecution was anxious to prove that he was in desperate need of money and they went round to all the shops that supplied things both to him and for the house-hold to find out if there had been any pressure put to settle unpaid accounts. But it appeared that everything bought for the house was paid for on the nail and there were no outstanding debts. So far as clothes were concerned Berger, it turned out, had bought nothing since he lost his job but one gray suit. The detective who was interviewing the tailor asked when this had been paid for and the tailor turned up his books. He was an advertising tailor in a large way of business who made clothes to measure at a lowish price. It was then discovered that Berger had ordered an extra pair of trousers with the suit. The police had a list of every article in his wardrobe, and this pair of trousers didn't figure on it. They at once saw the importance of the fact and they made up their minds to keep it dark till the trial.

"It was a thrilling moment, believe me, when the prosecution introduced the subject. There could be no doubt that Berger had had two pairs of trousers to his new gray suit and that one of the pairs was missing. When he was asked about it he never even attempted to explain. He didn't seem flummoxed. He said he didn't know they were missing. He pointed out that he had had no opportunity of going over his wardrobe for some months, having been in prison awaiting trial, and when he was asked how he could possibly account for their disappearance suggested flippantly that perhaps one of the police officers who had searched the house was in need of a pair of new trousers and had sneaked them. But Madame Berger had her explanation pat, and I'm bound to say I thought it a very ingenious one. She said that Lydia had been ironing the trousers, as she always did after Robert had worn them, and the iron was too hot and she had burnt them. He was fussy about his clothes and it had been something of a struggle to find the money to pay for the suit, they knew he would be angry with his wife, and Madame Berger, wishing to spare her his reproaches and seeing how scared she was, proposed that they shouldn't tell him; she would get rid of the trousers and Robert perhaps would never notice that they had disappeared. Asked what she had done with them she said that a tramp had come to the door, asking for money, and she had given him the trousers instead. The size of the burn was gone into. She claimed that it made the trousers unwearable, and when the public prosecutor pointed out that invisible mending would have repaired the damage, she answered that it would have cost more than the trousers were worth. Then he suggested that in their impoverished circumstances Berger might well have worn them in the house; it would surely have been better to risk his displeasure than to throw away a garment which might still be useful. Madame Berger said she never thought of that, she gave them to the tramp on an impulse, to get rid of them. The prosecutor put it to her that she had to get rid of them because they were blood-stained and that she hadn't given them to a tramp who had so conveniently presented himself, but had herself destroyed them. She hotly denied this. Then where was the tramp? He would read of the incident in the papers and knowing that a man's life was at stake would surely present himself. She turned to the press, throwing out her arms with a dramatic gesture.

" 'Let all these gentlemen,' she cried, 'spread it far and wide. Let them beseech him to come forward and save my son.'

"She was magnificent on the witness stand. The public prosecutor subjected her to a merciless examination; she fought like a fury. He took her through young Berger's life and she admitted all his misdeeds, from the episode at the tennis club to his thefts from the broker who after his conviction had, out of charity, given him another chance. She took all the blame of them on herself. A French witness is allowed much greater latitude than is allowed to a witness in an English criminal trial, and with bitter self-reproach she confessed that his errors were due to the indulgence with which she had brought him up. He was an only child and she had spoilt him. Her husband had lost a leg in the war, while attending to the wounded under fire, and his ill health had made it necessary for her to give him unremitting attention to the detriment of her maternal duties. His untimely end had left the wretched boy without guidance. She appealed to the emotions of the jury by dwelling on the grief that had afflicted them both when death robbed their little family of its head. Then her son had been her only consolation. She described him as high-spirited, headstrong, easily led by bad companions, but deeply affectionate and, whatever else he was guilty of, incapable of murdering a man who had never shown him anything but kindness.

"But somehow she didn't create a favourable impression. She insisted on her own unimpeachable respectability in a way that grated on you. Even though she was defending the son she adored she missed no opportunity to remind the Court that she was the daughter of a staff officer. She was smartly dressed, in black, perhaps too smartly, she gave you the impression of a woman who was trying to live above her station; and she had a calculating expression on her hard, decided features; you couldn't believe that she'd have given a crust of bread, much less a pair of trousers, even though damaged, to a beggar."

"And Lydia?"

"Lydia was rather pathetic. She was very much in the family way. Her face was swollen with tears and her voice hardly rose above a whisper, so that you could only just hear what she said. No one believed her story that she had broken the glass of the watch herself, but the prosecutor wasn't hard on her as he'd been on her mother-in-law; she was too obviously the innocent victim of a cruel fate. Madame Berger and Robert had used her unmercifully for their own ends. The Court took it as natural enough that she should do everything in her power to save her husband. It was even rather touching when she told how kind and sweet he had always been to her. It was quite clear that she was madly in love with him. The look she gave him when she came on to the witness stand was very moving. Out of all that crowd of witnesses, policemen and detectives, jailors, bar-loungers, informers, crooks, mental experts—they called a couple of experts who had made a psychological examination of Berger and a pretty picture they painted of his character—out of all that crowd, I say, she was the only one who appeared to have any human feeling.

"They'd got Maître Lemoine, one of the best criminal lawyers at the French bar, to defend Berger; he was a very tall, thin man, with a long sallow face, immense black eyes and very black thick hair. He had the most eloquent hands

I've ever seen. He was a striking figure in his black gown, with the white of his lawyer's bands under his chin. He had a deep, powerful voice. He reminded you, I hardly know why, of one of those mysterious figures in a Longhi picture. He was an actor as well as an orator. By a look he could express his opinion of a man's character and by a pause the improbability of his statements. I wish you could have seen the skill with which he treated the hostile witnesses, the suavity with which he inveigled them into contradicting themselves, the scorn with which he exposed their baseness, the ridicule with which he treated their pretensions. He could be winningly persuasive and brutally harsh. When the mental experts deposed that on repeated examinations of Berger in prison they had formed the opinion that he was vain, arrogant and mendacious, ruthless, devoid of moral sense, unscrupulous and insensible to remorse, he reasoned with them as though he were a trained psychologist. It was a delight to watch the working of his subtle brain. He spoke generally in an easy, conversational tone, but enriched by his lovely voice and with a beautiful choice of words; you felt that everything he said could have gone straight down in a book without alteration; but when he came to his final speech and used all the resources at his disposal the effect was stupendous. He insisted on the flimsiness of the evidence; he poured contempt on the credibility of the disreputable witnesses; he drew red herrings across the path; he contended that the prosecution hadn't made out a case upon which it was possible to convict. Now he was chatty and seemed to talk to the jury as man to man, now he worked up to a flight of impassioned pleading and his voice grew and grew in volume till it rang through the court-room like the pealing of thunder. Then a pause so dramatic that you felt your skin go all goosy. His peroration was magnificent. He told the jury that they must do their duty and decide according to their conscience, but he besought them to put out of their minds all the prejudice occasioned by the young man's admitted crimes, and his voice low and tremulous with emotion—by God! it was effective—he reminded them that the man the public prosecutor asked them to sentence to death was the son of a widow, herself the daughter of a soldier who had deserved well of his country, and the son of an officer who had given his life in its defence; he reminded them that he was recently married, and had married for love, and his young wife now bore in her womb the fruits of their union. Could they let this innocent child be brought into the world with the stigma that his father was a con victed murderer? Claptrap? Of course it was claptrap, but if you'd been there and heard those thrilling, grave accents you wouldn't have thought so. Gosh! how people cried. I nearly did myself, only I saw the tears coursing down Berger's cheeks and him wiping his eyes with a handkerchief, and that seemed to me so comic that I kept my head. But it was a fine effort, and not all the huissiers in the world could have prevented the applause that burst from the crowd when he sat down.

"The prosecuting counsel was a stout, rubicund fellow of thirty-five, I should say, or forty, who looked like a North Country farmer. He oozed self-satisfaction. You felt that for him the case was a wonderful chance to make a splash and so further his career. He was verbose and confused, so that, if the presiding judge hadn't come to his help now and then, the jury would hardly have known what he was getting at. He was cheaply melodramatic. On one occasion he turned to Berger who had just made some remark aside to one of the warders who sat in the dock with him, and said:

" 'You may smile now, but you won't smile when, with your arms pinioned behind your back, you walk in the cold gray light of dawn and see the guillotine rear its horror before your eyes. No smile then will break on your lips, but your limbs will shake with terror, and remorse for your monstrous crime wring your heart.'

"Berger gave the warder an amused look, but so contemptuous of what the public prosecutor had said, that if he hadn't been eaten up with vanity he couldn't have failed to be disconcerted. It was grand to see the way Lemoine treated him. He paid him extravagant compliments, but charged with such corrosive irony that, for all his conceit, the public prosecutor couldn't help seeing he was made a fool of. Lemoine was so malicious, but with such perfect courtesy and with such a condescending urbanity, that you could see in the eyes of the presiding judge a twinkle of appreciation. I very much doubt if the prosecuting counsel advanced his career by his conduct of this case.

"The three judges sat in a row on the bench. They were rather impressive in their scarlet robes and black squarish caps. Two were middle-aged men and never opened their mouths. The presiding judge was a little old man, with the wrinkled face of a monkey, and a tired, flat voice, but he was very observant; he listened attentively, and when he spoke it was without severity, but with a passionless calm that was rather frightening. He had the exquisite reasonableness of a man who has no illusions about human nature, but having long since learnt that man is capable of any vileness accepts the fact as just as much a matter of course as that he has two arms and two legs. When the jury went out to consider their verdict we journalists scattered to have a chat, a drink or a cup of coffee. We all hoped they wouldn't be too long, because it was getting late and we wanted to get our stuff in. We had no doubt that they'd find Berger guilty. One of the odd circumstances I've noticed in the murder trials I've attended is how unlike the impression is you get about things in court to that which you get by reading about them in the paper. When you read the evidence you think that after all it's rather slight, and if you'd been on the jury you'd have given the accused the benefit of the doubt. But what you've left out of account is the general atmosphere, the feeling that you get; it puts an entirely different colour on the evidence. After about an hour we were told that the jury had arrived at a decision and we trooped in again. Berger was brought up from the cells and we all stood up as the three judges trailed in one after the other. The lights had been lit and it was rather sinister in that crowded court. There was a tremor of apprehension. Have you ever been to the Old Bailey?"

"No, in point of fact, I haven't," said Charley.

"I go often when I'm in London. It's a good place to learn about human nature. There's a difference in feeling between that and a French court that made a most peculiar impression on me. I don't pretend to understand it. At the Old Bailey you feel that a prisoner is confronted with the majesty of the law. It's something impersonal that he has to deal with, Justice in the abstract. An idea, in fact. It's awful in the literal sense of the word. But in that French court, during the two days I spent there, I was beset by a very different feeling, I didn't get the impression that it was permeated by a grandiose abstraction, I felt that the apparatus of law was an arrangement by which a bourgeois society protected its safety, its property, its privileges from the evil-doer who threatened them. I don't mean the trial wasn't fair or the verdict unjustified, what I mean is that you got the sensation of a society that was outraged because it feared, rather than of a principle that must be upheld. The prisoner was up against men who wanted to safeguard themselves rather than, as with us, up against an idea that must prevail though the heavens fall. It was terrifying rather than awful. The verdict was guilty of murder with extenuating circumstances."

"What were the extenuating circumstances?"

"There were none, but French juries don't like to sentence a man to death, and by French law when there are extenuating circumstances capital punishment can't be inflicted. Berger got off with fifteen years' penal servitude."

Simon looked at his watch and got up.

"I must be going. I'll give you the stuff I wrote about the trial and you can read it at your leisure. And look, here's the article I wrote on crime as a form of sport. I showed it to your girl friend, but I don't think she liked it very much; anyhow, she returned it without a word of comment. As an exercise in sardonic humour it's not so dusty."

vii

SINCE he had no wish to read Simon's articles in Lydia's presence, Charley, on parting from his friend, went to the Dôme, ordered himself a cup of coffee, and settled himself down to their perusal. He was glad to read a connected account of the murder and the trial, for Lydia's various narratives had left him somewhat confused. She had told him this and that, not in the order in which it had occurred, but as her emotion dictated. Simon's three long articles were coherent, and though there were particulars which Charley had learnt from Lydia and of which he was ignorant, he had succeeded in constructing a graphic story which it was easy to follow. He wrote almost as he spoke, in a fluent journalistic style, but he had managed very effectively to present the background against which the events he described had been enacted. You got a sinister impression of a world, sordid, tumultuous, in which these gangsters, dope traffickers, bookies and race-course touts lived their dark and hazardous lives. Dregs of the population of a great city, living on their wits, suspicious of one another, ready to betray their best friend if it could be of advantage to themselves, open-handed, sociable, gaily cynical, even good-humoured, they seemed to enjoy that existence, with all its dangers and vicissitudes, which kept you up to the mark and made you feel that you really were living. Each man's hand was against his neighbour's, but the alertness which this forced upon you was exhilarating. It was a world in which a man would shoot another for a trifle, but was just as ready to take flowers and fruit, bought at no small sacrifice, to a third who was sick in hospital. The atmosphere with which Simon had not unskilfully encompassed his story filled Charley with a strange unease. The world he knew, the peaceful happy world of the surface, was like a pretty lake in which were reflected the dappled clouds and the willows that grew on its bank, where care-free boys paddled their canoes and the girls with them trailed their fingers in the soft water. It was terrifying to think that below, just below, dangerous weeds waved tentacles to ensnare you and all manner of strange, horrible things, poisonous snakes, fish with murderous jaws, waged an unceasing and hidden warfare. From a word here, a word there, Charley got the impression that Simon had peered fascinated into those secret depths, and he asked himself whether it was merely curiosity, or some horrible attraction, that led him to observe those crooks and blackguards with a cynical indulgence.

In this world Robert Berger had found himself wonderfully at home. Of a higher class and better educated than most of its inhabitants, he had enjoyed a certain prestige. His charm, his easy manner and his social position attacted his associates, but at the same time put them on their guard against him. They knew he was a crook, but curiously enough, because he was a garçon de bonne famille, a youth of respectable parentage, took it somewhat amiss that he should be. He worked chiefly alone, without confederates, and kept his own counsel. They had a notion that he despised them, but they were impressed when he had been to a concert and talked enthusiastically and, for all they could tell, with knowledge of the performance. They did not realize that he felt himself wonderfully at ease in their company. In his mother's house, with his mother's friends, he felt lonely and oppressed; he was irritated by the inactivity of the respectable life. After his conviction on the charge of stealing a motor car he had said to Jojo in one of his rare moments of confidence:

"Now I needn't pretend any more. I wish my father were alive, he would have turned me out of the house and then I should be free to lead the only life I like. Evidently I can't leave my mother. I'm all she has."

"Crime doesn't pay," said Jojo.

"You seem to make a pretty good thing out of it," Robert laughed. "But it's not the money, it's the excitement and the power. It's like diving from a great height. The water looks terribly far away, but you make the plunge, and when you rise to the surface, gosh! you feel pleased with yourself."

Charley put the newspaper cuttings back in his pocket, and, his brow slightly frowning with the effort, tried to piece together what he now knew of Robert Berger in order to get some definite impression of the sort of man he really was. It was all very well to say he was a worthless scamp of whom society was well rid; that was true of course, but it was too simple and too sweeping a judgement to be satisfactory; the idea dawned in Charley's mind that perhaps men were more complicated than he had imagined, and if you just said that a man was this or that you couldn't get very far. There was Robert's passion for music, especially Russian music, which, so unfortunately for her, had brought Lydia and him together. Charley was very fond of music. He knew the delight it gave him, the pleasure, partly sensual, partly intellectual, when intoxicated by the loveliness that assailed his ears, he remained yet keenly appreciative of the subtlety with which the composer had worked out his idea. Looking into himself, as perhaps he had never looked before, to find out what exactly it was he felt when he listened to one of the greater symphonies, it seemed to him that it was a complex of emotions, excitement and at the same time peace, love for others and a desire to do something for them, a wish to be good and a delight in goodness, a pleasant languor and a funny detachment as though he were floating above the world and whatever happened there didn't very much matter; and perhaps if you had to combine all those feelings into one and give it a name, the name you'd give it was happiness. But what was it that Robert Berger got when he listened to music? Nothing like that, that was obvious. Or was it unjust to dismiss such emotions as music gave *him* as vile and worthless? Might it not be rather that in music he found release from the devil that possessed him, that devil which was stronger than himself so that he neither could be delivered, nor even wanted to be delivered, from the urge that drove him to crime because it was the expression of his warped nature, because by throwing himself into antagonism with the forces of law and order he realized his personality— might it not be that in music he found peace from that impelling force and for a while, resting in heavenly acquiescence, saw as though through a rift in the clouds a vision of love and goodness?

Charley knew what it was to be in love. He knew that it made you feel friendly to all men, he knew that you wanted to do everything in the world for the girl you loved, he knew that you couldn't bear the thought of hurting her and he knew that you couldn't help wondering what she saw in you, because of course she was wonderful, definitely, and if you were honest with yourself you were bound to confess that you couldn't hold a candle to her. And Charley supposed that if he felt like that everyone else must feel like that and therefore Robert Berger had too. There was no doubt that he loved Lydia with passion, but if love filled him with a sense of—Charley jibbed at the word that came to his mind, it made him almost blush with embarrassment to think of it—well, with a sense of holiness, it was strange that he could commit sordid and horrible crimes. There must be two men in him. Charley was perplexed, which can hardly be considered strange, for he was but twenty-three, and older, wiser men have failed to understand how a scoundrel can love as purely and disinterestedly as a saint. And was it possible for Lydia to love her husband even now with an all-forgiving devotion if he were entirely worthless?

"Human nature wants a bit of understanding," he muttered to himself.

Without knowing it, he had said a mouthful.

But when he came to consider the love that consumed Lydia, a love that was the cause of her every action, the inspiration of her every thought, so that it was like a symphonic accompaniment that gave depth and significance to the melodic line which was her life from day to day, he could only draw back in an almost horrified awe as he might have drawn back, terrified but fascinated, at the sight of a forest on fire or a river in flood. This was something with which his experience could not cope. By the side of this he knew that his own little love affairs had been but trivial flirtations and the emotion which had from time to time brought charm and gaiety into his somewhat humdrum life no more than a boy's sentimentality. It was incomprehensible that in the body of that commonplace, drab little woman there should be room for a passion of such intensity. It was not only what she said that made you realize it, you felt it, intuitively as it were, in the aloofness which, for all the intimacy with which she treated you, kept you at a distance; you saw it in the depths of her transparent eyes, in the scorn of her lips when she didn't know you were looking at her, and you heard it in the undertones of her sing-song voice.

It was not like any of the civilized feelings that Charley was familiar with, there was something wild and brutal in it, and notwithstanding her high-heeled shoes, her silk stockings, and her coat and skirt, Lydia did not seem a woman of to-day, but a savage with elemental instincts who still harboured in the darkest recesses of her soul the ape-like creature from which the human being is descended.

"By God! what have I let myself in for?" said Charley.

He turned to Simon's article. Simon had evidently taken pains over it for the style was more elegant than that of his reports of the trial. It was an exercise in irony written with detachment, but beneath the detachment you felt the troubled curiosity with which he had considered the character of this man who was restrained neither by scruple nor by the fear of consequences. It was a clever little essay, but so callous that you could not read it without discomfort. Trying to make the most of his ingenious theme, Simon had forgotten that human beings, with feelings, were concerned; and if you smiled, for it was not lacking in a bitter wit, it was with malaise. It appeared that Simon had somehow gained admittance to the little house at Neuilly, and in order to give an impression of the environment in which Berger had lived, he described with acid humour the tasteless, stuffy and pretentious room into which he had been ushered. It was furnished with two drawing-room suites, one Louis Quinze and the other Empire. The Louis Quinze suite was in carved wood, gilt and covered in blue silk with little pink flowers on it; the Empire suite was upholstered in light yellow satin. In the middle of the room was an elaborately-carved gilt table with a marble top. Both suites had evidently come from one of those shops in the Boulevard St. Antoine that manufacture period furniture wholesale, and had been then bought at auction when their first owners had wanted to get rid of them. With two sofas and all those chairs it was impossible to move without precaution and there was nowhere you could sit in comfort. On the walls were large oil paintings in heavy gold frames, which, it was obvious, had been bought at sale-rooms because they were going for nothing.

The prosecution had reconstructed the story of the murder with plausibility. It was evident that Jordan had taken a fancy to Robert Berger. The meals he had stood him, the winners he had given him and the money he had lent him, proved that. At last Berger had consented to come to his apartment, and so that their leaving the bar together should not attract attention they had arranged for one to go some minutes after the other. They met according to plan, and since the concierge was certain she had admitted that night no one who asked for Jordan, it was plain that they had entered the house together. Jordan lived on the ground floor. Berger, still wearing his smart new gloves, sat down and smoked a cigarette while Jordan busied himself getting the whiskey and soda and bringing in the cake from his tiny kitchen. He was the sort of man who always sat in his shirt-sleeves at home, and he took off his coat. He put on a record. It was a cheap, old-fashioned gramophone, without an automatic change, and it was while Jordan was putting on a new record that Berger, coming up behind him as though to see what it was, had stabbed him in the back. To claim, as the defence did, that he had not the strength to give a blow of such violence as the post-mortem indicated, was absurd. He was very wiry. Persons who had known him in his tennis days testified that he had been known for the power of his forehand drive. If he had never got into the first rank it was not due to an inadequate physique, but to some psychological failing that defeated his will to win.

Simon accepted the view of the prosecution. He thought they had got the facts pretty accurately, and that the reason they gave for Jordan's asking the young man to come to his apartment was correct, but he was convinced they were wrong in supposing that Berger had murdered him for the money he knew he had made during the day. For one thing, the purchase of the gloves showed that he had decided upon the deed before he knew that Jordan would be in possession that night of an unusually large sum. Though the money had never been found Simon was persuaded that he had taken it, but that was by the way; it was there for the taking and he was glad enough to get it, but to do so was not the

motive of the murder. The police claimed that he had stolen
between fifty and sixty cars; he had never even attempted to
sell one of them; he abandoned them sometimes after a few
hours, at the most after a few days. He purloined them for
the convenience of having one when he needed it, but much
more to exercise his daring and resource. His robberies from
women, by means of the simple trick he had devised,
brought him little profit; they were practical jokes that
appealed to his sense of humour. To carry them out required
the charm which he loved to exert. It made him giggle to
think of those women left speechless and gaping in an empty
street while he sped on. The thing was, in short, a form of
sport, and each time he had successfully brought it off he was
filled with the self-satisfaction that he might have felt when
by a clever lob or by a drop shot he won a point off an
opponent at tennis. It gave him confidence. And it was the
risk, the coolness that was needed, the power to make a quick
decision if it looked as though discovery were inevitable,
much more than the large profits, that had induced him to
engage in the business of smuggling dope into France. It
was like rock-climbing; you had to be sure of foot, you had
to keep your head; your life depended on your nerve, your
strength, your instinct; but when you had surmounted every
difficulty and achieved your aim, how wonderful after that
terrific strain was the feeling of deliverance and how intoxicating the sense of victory! Certainly for a man of his slender
means he had got a good deal of money out of the broker
who had employed him; but it had come in driblets and he
had spent it on taking Lydia to night clubs and for excursions in the country, or with his friends at Jojo's Bar.
Every penny had gone by the time he was caught; and it
was only a chance that he was; the method he had conceived
for robbing his employer was so adroit that he might very
well have got away with it indefinitely. Here again it looked
as though it were much more for the fun of the thing, than
for profit, that he had committed a crime. He told his
lawyer quite frankly that the broker was so confident of his
own cleverness, he could not resist making a fool of him.

But by now, Simon went on, pursuing his idea, Robert

Berger had exhausted the amusement he was capable of getting out of the smaller varieties of evil-doing. During one of the periods he spent in jail awaiting trial he had made friends with an old lag, and had listened to his stories with fascinated interest. The man was a cat burglar who specialized in jewellery and he made an exciting tale of some of his exploits. First there was the marking down of the prey, then the patient watching to discover her habits, the examination of the premises; you had to find out not only where the jewels were kept and how to get into the house, but also what were the chances of making a quick get-away if necessary; and after you had made sure of everything there was the long waiting for the suitable opportunity. Often months elapsed between the time when you made up your mind to go after the stuff and the time when at last you had a whack at it. That was what choked Berger off; he had the nerve, the agility and the presence of mind that were needed, but he would never have had the patience for the complicated business that must precede the burglary.

Simon likened Robert Berger to a man who has shot partridge and pheasant for years, and having ceased to find diversion in the exercise of his skill, craves for a sport in which there is an element of danger and so turns his mind to big game. No one could say when Berger began to be obsessed with the idea of murder, but it might be supposed that it took possession of him gradually. Like an artist heavy with the work demanding expression in his soul, who knows that he will not find peace till he has delivered himself of the burden, Berger felt that by killing he would fulfil himself. After that, having expressed his personality to its utmost, he would be at rest and then could settle down with Lydia to a life of humdrum respectability. His instincts would have been satisfied. He knew that it was a monstrous crime, he knew that he risked his neck, but it was the monstrousness of it that tempted him and the risk that made it worth the attempt.

Here Charley put the article down. He thought that Simon was really going too far. He could just fancy himself committing murder in a moment of ungovernable rage, but

by no effort of imagination could he conceive of anyone doing such a thing—doing it not even for money, but for sport
as Simon put it—because he was driven to it by an urge to
destroy and so assert his own being. Did Simon really believe
there was anything in his theory, or was it merely that he
thought it would make an effective article? Charley, though
with a slight frown on his handsome face, went on reading.

Perhaps, Simon continued, Robert Berger would have
been satisfied merely to toy with the idea if circumstances
had not offered him the predestined victim. He may often,
when drinking with one of his boon companions, have considered the feasibility of killing him and put the notion aside
because the difficulties were too great or detection too certain. But when chance threw him in contact with Teddie
Jordan he must have felt that here was the very man he had
been looking for. He was a foreigner, with a large acquaintance, but no close friends, who lived alone in a blind alley.
He was a crook; he was connected with the dope traffic;
if he were found dead one day the police might well suppose
that his murder was the result of a gangsters' quarrel. If
they knew nothing of his sexual habits, they would be sure
to find out about them after his death and likely enough
to assume that he had been killed by some rough who wanted
more money than he was prepared to give. Among the vast
number of bullies, blackmailers, dope-peddlers and bad hats
who might have done him in, the police would not know
where to look, and in any case he was an undesirable alien
and they would think he was just as well out of the way. They
would make enquiries and if results were not soon obtained
quietly shelve the case. Berger saw that Jordan had taken
a fancy to him and he played him like an angler playing a
trout. He made dates which he broke. He made half-
promises which he did not keep. If Jordan, thinking he was
being made a fool of, threatened to break away, he exercised his charm to induce him to have patience. Jordan
thought it was he who pursued and the other who fled. Berger laughed in his sleeve. He tracked him as a hunter day
after day tracks a shy and suspicious beast in the jungle,
waiting for his opportunity, with the knowledge that, for all

its instinctive caution, the brute will at last be delivered into his hands. And because Berger had no feeling of animosity for Jordan, neither liking him nor disliking him, he was able to devote himself without hindrance to the pleasure of the chase. When at length the deed was done and the little bookmaker lay dead at his feet, he felt neither fear nor remorse, but only a thrill so intense that he was transported.

Charley finished the essay. He shuddered. He did not know whether it was Robert Berger's brutal treachery and callousness that more horrified him or the cool relish with which Simon described the workings of the murderer's depraved and tortuous mind. It was true that this description was the work of his own invention, but what fearful instinct was it in him that found delight in peering into such vile depths? Simon leaned over to look into Berger's soul, as one might lean over the edge of a fearful precipice, and you had the impression that what he saw filled him with envy. Charley did not know how he had got the impression (because there was nothing in those careful periods or in that half-flippant irony actually to suggest it) that while he wrote he asked himself whether there was in him, Simon Fenimore, the courage and the daring to do a deed so shocking, cruel and futile. Charley sighed.

"I've know Simon for nearly fifteen years. I thought I knew him inside out. I'm beginning to think I don't know the first thing about him."

But he smiled happily. There were his father and his mother and Patsy. They would be leaving the Terry-Masons next day, tired after those strenuous days of fun and laughter, but glad to get back to their bright, artistic and comfortable house.

"Thank God, they're decent, ordinary people. You know where you are with them."

He suddenly felt a wave of affection for them sweep over him.

But it was growing late; Lydia would be getting back and he did not want to keep her waiting, she would be lonely, poor thing, by herself in that sordid room; he stuffed the essay into his pocket with the other cuttings and walked back to the hotel. He need not have fashed himself. Lydia was not there. He took Mansfield Park, which with Blake's Poems was the only book he had brought with him, and began to read. It was a delight to move in the company of those well-mannered persons who after the lapse of more than a hundred years seemed as much alive as anyone you met to-day. There was a gracious ease in the ordered course of their lives, and the perturbations from which they suffered were not so serious as to distress you. It was true that Cinderella was an awful little prig and Prince Charming a monstrous pedant; it was true that you could not but wish that instead of setting her prim heart on such an owl she had accepted the proposals of the engaging and witty villain; but you accepted with indulgence Jane Austen's determination to reward good sense and punish levity. Nothing could lessen the delight of her gentle irony and caustic humour. It took Charley's mind off that story of depravity and crime in which he seemed to have got so strangely involved. He was removed from the dingy, cheerless room and in fancy saw himself sitting on a lawn, under a great cedar, on a pleasant summer evening; and from the fields beyond the garden came the scent of hay. But he began to feel hungry and looked at his watch. It was half-past eight. Lydia had not returned. Perhaps she had no intention of doing so? It wouldn't be very nice of her to leave him like that, without a word of explanation or farewell, and the possibility made him rather angry, but then he shrugged his shoulders.

"If she doesn't want to come back, let her stay away."

He didn't see why he should wait any longer, so he went out to dinner, leaving word at the porter's desk where he was going so that if she came she could join him. Charley wasn't quite sure if it amused, flattered or irritated him, that the staff should treat him with a sort of confidential familiarity as though they got a vicarious satisfaction out of the affair which, naturally enough, they were convinced he was having. The porter was smilingly benevolent and the young woman at the cashier's desk excited and curious. Charley chuckled at the thought of their shocked surprise if they had known

how innocent were his relations with Lydia. He came back
from his solitary dinner and she was not yet there. He went
up to his room and went on reading, but now he had to make
a certain effort to attend. If she didn't come back by twelve
he made up his mind to give her up and go out on the loose.
It was absurd to spend the best part of a week in Paris and
not have a bit of fun. But soon after eleven she opened the
door and entered, carrying a small and very shabby suitcase.

"Oh, I'm tired," she said. "I've brought a few things with
me. I'll just have a wash and then we'll go out to dinner."

"Haven't you dined? I have."

"Have you?"

She seemed surprised.

"It's past eleven."

She laughed.

"How English you are! Must you always dine at the same
hour?"

"I was hungry," he answered rather stiffly.

It seemed to him that she really might express some regret
for having kept him waiting so long. It was plain, however,
that nothing was farther from her thoughts.

"Oh, well, it doesn't matter, I don't want any dinner.
What a day I've had! Alexey was drunk; he had a row with
Paul this morning, because he didn't come home last night,
and Paul knocked him down. Evgenia was crying, and she
kept on saying: 'God has punished us for our sins. I have lived
to see my son strike his father. What is going to happen to
us all?' Alexey was crying too. 'It is the end of everything,'
he said. 'Children no longer respect their parents. Oh, Russia, Russia!'"

Charley felt inclined to giggle, but he saw that Lydia was
taking the scene in all seriousness.

"And did you cry too?"

"Naturally," she answered, with a certain coldness.

She had changed her dress and now wore one of black
silk. It was plain enough but well cut. It suited her. It made
her clear skin more delicate and deepened the colour of her
blue eyes. She wore a black hat, rather saucy in shape, with a
feather in it, and much more becoming than the old black

felt. The smarter clothes had had an effect on her; she wore them more elegantly and carried herself with a graceful assurance. She no longer looked like a shop-girl, but like a young woman of some distinction, and prettier than Charley had ever seen her, but she gave you less than ever the impression that there was anything doing, as the phrase goes; if she had given before the effect of a respectable work-girl who knew how to take care of herself, she gave now that of a modish young woman perfectly capable of putting a too enterprising young man in his place.

"You've got a different frock on," said Charley, who was already beginning to get over his ill humour.

"Yes, it's the only nice one I've got. I thought it was too humiliating for you to have to be seen with such a little drab as I was looking. After all, the least a handsome young man in beautiful clothes can ask is that when he goes into a restaurant with a woman people shouldn't say: how can he go about with a slut who looks as though she were wearing the cast-off clothes of a maid of all work? I must at least try to be a credit to you."

Charley laughed. There was really something rather likeable about her.

"Well, we'd better go out and get you something to eat. I'll sit with you. If I know anything about your appetite you could eat a horse."

They started off in high spirits. He drank a whiskey and soda and smoked his pipe while Lydia ate a dozen oysters, a beefsteak and some fried potatoes. She told him at greater length of her visit to her Russian friends. She was greatly concerned at their situation. There was no money except the little the children earned. One of these days Paul would get sick of doing his share and would disappear into that equivocal night life of Paris, to end up, if he was lucky, when he had lost his youth and looks, as a waiter in a disreputable hotel. Alexey was growing more and more of a soak and even if by chance he got a job would never be able to hold it. Evgenia had no longer the courage to withstand the difficulties that beset her; she had lost heart. There was no hope for any of them.

"You see, it's twenty years since they left Russia. For a long time they thought there'd be a change there and they'd go back, but now they know there's no chance. It's been hard on people like that, the revolution; they've got nothing to do now, they and all their generation, but to die."

But it occurred to Lydia that Charley could not be much interested in people whom he had not even seen. She could not know that while she was talking to him about her friends he was telling himself uneasily that, if he guessed aright what was in Simon's mind, it was just such a fate that he was preparing for him, for his father, mother and sister, and for their friends. Lydia changed the subject.

"And what have you been doing with yourself this afternoon? Did you go and see any pictures?"

"No. I went to see Simon."

Lydia was looking at him with an expression of indulgent interest, but when he answered her question, she frowned.

"I don't like your friend Simon," she said. "What is it that you see in him?"

"I've known him since I was a kid. We were at school together and at Cambridge. He's been my friend always. Why don't you like him?"

"He's cold, calculating and inhuman."

"I think you're wrong there. No one knows better than I do that he's capable of great affection. He's a lonely creature. I think he hankers for a love that he can never arouse."

Lydia's eyes shone with mockery, but, as ever, there was in it a rueful note.

"You're very sentimental. How can anyone expect to arouse love who isn't prepared to give himself? In spite of all the years you've known him I wonder if you know him as well as I do. He comes a lot to the Sérail; he doesn't often go up with a girl and then not from desire, but from curiosity. Madame makes him welcome, partly because he's a journalist and she likes to keep in with the press, and partly because he sometimes brings foreigners who drink a lot of champagne. He likes to talk to us and it never enters his head that we find him repulsive."

"Remember that if he knew that he wouldn't be offended. He'd only be curious to know why. He has no vanity."

Lydia went on as though Charley had said nothing.

"He hardly looks upon us as human beings, he despises us and yet he seeks our company. He's at ease with us. I think he feels that our degradation is so great, he can be himself, whereas in the outside world he must always wear a mask. He's strangely insensitive. He thinks he can permit himself anything with us and he asks us questions that put us to shame and never sees how bitterly he wounds us."

Charley was silent. He knew well enough how Simon, with his insatiable curiosity, could cause people profound embarrassment and was only surprised and scornful when he found that they resented his enquiries. He was willing enough to display the nakedness of his soul and it never occurred to him that the reserves of others could be due, not to stupidity as he thought, but to modesty. Lydia continued:

"Yet he's capable of doing things that you'd never expect of him. One of our girls was suddenly taken ill. The doctor said she must be operated on at once, and Simon took her to a nursing home himself so that she shouldn't have to go to the hospital, and paid for the operation; and when she got better he paid her expenses to go away to a convalescent home. And he'd never even slept with her."

"I'm not surprised. He attaches no importance to money. Anyhow it shows you that he's capable of a disinterested action."

"Or do you think he wanted to examine in himself what the emotion of goodness exactly was?"

Charley laughed.

"It's obvious that you haven't got much use for poor Simon."

"He's talked to me a great deal. He wanted to find out all I could tell him about the Russian Revolution, and he wanted me to take him to see Alexey and Evgenia so that he could ask them. You know he reported Robert's trial. He tried to make me tell him all sorts of things that he wanted to know. He went to bed with me because he thought he could get me to tell him more. He wrote an article about it.

All that pain, all that horror and disgrace, were no more to him than an occasion to string clever, flippant words together; and he gave it me to read to see how I would take it. I shall never forgive him that. Never."

Charley sighed. He knew that Simon, with his amazing insensitiveness to other people's feelings, had shown her that cruel essay with no intention of hurting, but from a perfectly honest desire to see how she reacted to it and to discover how far her intimate knowledge would confirm his fanciful theory.

"He's a strange creature," said Charley. "I daresay he has a lot of traits which one would rather he hadn't, but he has great qualities. There's one thing at all events that you can say about him: if he doesn't spare others, he doesn't spare himself. After not seeing him for two years, and he's changed a lot in that time, I can't help finding his personality rather impressive."

"Frightening, I should have said."

Charley moved uneasily on his plush seat, for that also, somewhat to his dismay, was what he had found it.

"He lives an extraordinary life, you know. He works sixteen hours a day. The squalor and discomfort of his surroundings are indescribable. He's trained himself to eat only one meal a day."

"What is the object of that?"

"He wants to strengthen and deepen his character. He wants to make himself independent of circumstances. He wants to prepare himself for the role he expects one day to be called upon to play."

"And has he told you what that role is?"

"Not precisely."

"Have you ever heard of Dzerjinsky?"

"No."

"Simon has talked to me about him a great deal. Alexey was a lawyer in the old days, a clever one with liberal principles, and he defended Dzerjinsky at one of his trials. That didn't prevent Dzerjinsky from having Alexey arrested as a counter-revolutionary and sending him for three years to Alexandrovsk. That was one of the reasons why Simon wanted me so much to take him to see Alexey. And when I wouldn't, because I couldn't bear that he should see to what depths that poor, broken-down man had sunk, he charged me with questions to put to him."

"But who was Dzerjinsky?" asked Charley.

"He was the head of the Cheka. He was the real master of Russia. He had an unlimited power over the life and death of the whole population. He was monstrously cruel; he imprisoned, tortured and killed thousands upon thousands of people. At first I thought it strange that Simon should be so interested in that abominable man, he seemed to be fascinated by him, and then I guessed the reason. That is the role he means to play when the revolution he's working for takes place. He knows that the man who is master of the police is master of the country."

Charley's eyes twinkled.

"You make my flesh creep, dear. But you know, England isn't like Russia; I think Simon will have to wait a hell of a long time before he's dictator of England."

But this was a matter upon which Lydia could brook no flippancy. She gave him a dark look.

"He's prepared to wait. Didn't Lenin wait? Do you still think the English are made of different clay from other men? Do you think the proletariat, which is growing increasingly conscious of its power, is going to leave the class you belong to indefinitely in possession of its privileges? Do you think that a war, whether it results in your defeat or your victory, is going to result in anything but a great social upheaval?"

Charley was not interested in politics. Though, like his father, of liberal views, with mildly socialistic tendencies so long as they were not carried beyond the limits of prudence, by which, though he didn't know it, he meant so long as they didn't interfere with his comfort and his income, he was quite prepared to leave the affairs of the country to those whose business it was to deal with them; but he could not let these provocative questions of Lydia's go without an answer.

"You talk as though we did nothing for the working classes. You don't seem to know that in the last fifty years their condition has changed out of all recognition. They work fewer hours than they did and get higher wages for what they do. They have better houses to live in. Why, on our own estate we're doing away with slums as quickly as it's economically possible. We've given them old age pensions and we provide them with enough to live on when they're out of work. They get free schooling, free hospitals, and now we're beginning to give them holidays with pay. I really don't think the British working man has much to complain of."

"You must remember that the views of a benefactor and the views of a beneficiary on the value of a benefaction are apt to differ. Do you really expect the working man to be grateful to you for the advantages he's extracted from you at the point of a pistol? Do you think he doesn't know that he owes the favours you've conferred on him to your fear rather than to your generosity?"

Charley was not going to let himself be drawn into a political discussion if he could help it, but there was one more thing he couldn't refrain from saying.

"I shouldn't have thought that the condition in which you and your Russian friends now find yourselves would lead you to believe that mob-rule was a great success."

"That is the bitterest part of our tragedy. However much we may deny it, we know in our hearts that whatever has happened to us, we've deserved it."

Lydia said this with a tragic intensity that somewhat disconcerted Charley. She was a difficult woman; she could take nothing lightly. She was the sort of woman who couldn't even ask you to pass the salt without giving you the impression that it was no laughing matter. Charley sighed; he supposed he must make allowances, for she had had a rotten deal, poor thing; but was the future really so black?

"Tell me about Dzerjinsky," he said, stumbling a little over the pronunciation of the difficult name.

"I can only tell you what Alexey has told me. He says the most remarkable thing about him was the power of his eyes; he had a curious gift, he was able to fix them upon you for an immensely long time, and the glassy stare of them, with their dilated pupils, was simply terrifying. He was extremely thin, he'd contracted tuberculosis in prison, and he was tall; not bad-looking, with good features. He was absolutely single-minded, that was the secret of his power, he had a cold, arid temperament; I don't suppose he'd ever given himself up with a whole heart to a moment's pleasure. The only thing he cared about was his work; he worked day and night. At the height of his career he lived in one small room with nothing in it but a desk and an old screen, and behind the screen a narrow iron bed. They say that in the year of famine, when they brought him decent food instead of horseflesh, he sent it away, demanding the same rations as were given to the other workers in the Cheka. He lived for the Cheka and nothing else. There was no humanity in him, neither pity nor love, only fanaticism and hatred. He was terrible and implacable."

Charley shuddered a little. He could not but see why Lydia had told him about the terrorist, and in truth it was startling to note how close the resemblance was between the sinister man she had described and the man he had so surprisingly discovered that Simon was become. There was the same asceticism, the same indifference to the pleasant things of life, the same power of work, and perhaps the same ruthlessness. Charley smiled his good-natured smile.

"I daresay Simon has his faults like the rest of us. One has to be tolerant with him because he hasn't had a very happy or a very easy life. I think perhaps he craves for affection, and there's something that people find repellent in his personality which prevents him from getting it. He's frightfully sensitive and things which wouldn't affect ordinary people wound him to the quick. But at heart I think he's kind and generous."

"You're deceived in him. You think he has your own good nature and unselfish consideration. I tell you, he's dangerous. Dzerjinsky was the narrow idealist who for the sake of his ideal could bring destruction upon his country without a qualm. Simon isn't even that. He has no heart, no conscience, no scruple, and if the occasion arises he will sacrifice you who are his dearest friend without hesitation and without remorse."

viii

THEY woke next day at what was for them an early hour. They had breakfast in bed, each with his tray, and after breakfast, while Charley, smoking his pipe read the *Mail*, Lydia, a cigarette between her lips, did her hands. You would have thought, to see them, each engaged on his respective occupation, that they were a young married couple whose first passion had dwindled into an easy friendship. Lydia painted her nails and spread out her fingers on the sheet to let them dry. She gave Charley a mischievous glance.

"Would you like to go to the Louvre this morning? You came to Paris to see pictures, didn't you?"

"I suppose I did."

"Well, let's get up then and go."

When the maid who brought them their coffee drew the curtains the day that filtered into the room from the courtyard had looked as gray and bleak as on the mornings that had gone before; and they were surprised, on stepping into the street, to see that the weather had suddenly changed. It was cold still, but the sun was bright and the clouds, high up in the heavens, were white and shining. The air had a frosty bite that made your blood tingle.

"Let's walk," said Lydia.

In that gay, quivering light the Rue de Rennes lost its dinginess, and the gray, shabby houses no longer wore the down-at-heel, despondent air they usually do, but had a mellow friendliness as though, like old women in reduced circumstances, they felt less forlorn now that the unexpected sunshine smiled on them as familiarly as on the grand new buildings on the other side of the river. When they crossed the Place St. Germain-des-Prés and there was a confusion of buses and trams, recklessly-speeding taxis, lorries and private cars, Lydia took Charley's arm; and like lovers, or a grocer and his wife taking a walk of a Sunday afternoon, they sauntered arm in arm, stopping now and then to look into the window of a picture-dealer, down the narrow Rue de Seine. Then they came on to the quay. Here the Paris day burst upon them in all its winter beauty and Charley gave a little exclamation of delight.

"You like this?" smiled Lydia.

"It's a picture by Raffaelli." He remembered a line in a poem that he had read at Tours: "Le vierge, le vivace et le bel aujourd'hui."

The air had a sparkle so that you felt you could take it up in your hands and let it run through your fingers like the water of a fountain. To Charley's eyes, accustomed to the misty distances and soft haze of London, it seemed amazingly transparent. It outlined the buildings, the bridge, the parapet by the side of the river, with an elegant distinctness, but the lines, as though drawn by a sensitive hand, were tender and gracious. Tender too was the colour, the colour of sky and cloud, the colour of stone; they were the colours of the eighteenth-century pastelists; and the leafless trees, their slim branches a faint mauve against the blue, repeated with exquisite variety a pattern of delicate intricacy. Because he had seen pictures of just that scene Charley was able to take it in, without any sense of surprise, but with a loving, understanding recognition; its beauty did not shatter him by its strangeness, nor perplex him by its unexpectedness, but filled him with a sense of familiar joy such as a countryman might feel when after an absence of years he sees once more the dear, straggling street of his native village.

"Isn't it lovely to be alive?" he cried.

"It's lovely to be as young and enthusiastic as you are,' said Lydia, giving his arm a little squeeze, and if she choked down a sob he did not notice it.

Charley knew the Louvre well, for every time his parents spent a few days in Paris (to let Venetia get her clothes from the little dressmaker who was just as good as those expensive places in the Rue Royale and the Rue Cambon) they made a point of taking their children there. Leslie Mason made no bones at confessing that he preferred new pictures to old.

"But after all, it's part of a gentleman's education to have done the great galleries of Europe, and when people talk about Rembrandt and Titian and so on, you look a bit of a fool if you can't put your word in. And I don't mind telling you that you couldn't have a better guide than your mother. She's very artistic, and she knows what's what, and she won't waste your time over a lot of tripe."

"I don't claim that your grandfather was a great artist," said Mrs. Mason, with the modest self-assurance of someone who is without conceit aware that he knows his subject, "but he knew what was good. All I know about art he taught me."

"Of course you had a flair," said her husband.

Mrs. Mason considered this for a moment.

"Yes, I suppose you're right, Leslie. I had a flair."

What made it easier to do the Louvre with expedition and spiritual profit was that in those days they had not rearranged it, and the Salon Carré contained most of the pictures which Mrs. Mason thought worthy of her children's attention. When they entered that room they walked straight to Leonardo's Gioconda.

"I always think one ought to look at that first," she said. "It puts you in the right mood for the Louvre."

The four of them stood in front of the picture and with reverence gazed at the insipid smile of that prim and sex-starved young woman. After a decent interval for meditation Mrs. Mason turned to her husband and her two children. There were tears in her eyes.

"Words fail me to express what that picture always makes me feel," she said, with a sigh. "Leonardo was a Great Artist. I think everybody's bound to acknowledge that."

"I don't mind admitting that I'm a bit of a philistine when it comes to old masters," said Leslie, "but that's got a je ne sais quoi that gets you, there's no denying that. Can you remember that bit of Pater's, Venetia? He hit the nail on the head and no mistake."

"You mean the bit that begins: 'Hers is the head upon which all the ends of the world are come.' I used to know it by heart years ago; I'm afraid I've forgotten it now."

"That's a pity."

"Well, my memory isn't what it was. Let's go and look at the Raphael now, shall we?"

But it was impossible to avoid seeing the two vast canvases of Paolo Veronese that faced one another on opposite walls.

"It's worth while giving them a glance," she said. "Your grandfather had a very high opinion of them. Of course Veronese was neither subtle nor profound. He had no soul. But he certainly had a gift of composition, and you must remember that there's no one now who could arrange so great a number of figures in a harmonious, and yet natural, design. You must admire them if for no other reason because of their vitality and for the sheer physical vigour Veronese must have had to paint such enormous pictures. But I think there's more in them than that. They do give you an impression of the abundant, multicoloured life of the period and of the pleasure-loving, pagan spirit which was characteristic of patrician Venice in the heyday of its glory."

"I've often tried to count the number of figures in the Marriage of Cana," said Leslie Mason, "but every time I make it different."

The four of them began to count, but none of the results they reached agreed. Presently they strolled into the Grande Galerie.

"Now here is L'Homme au Gant," said Mrs. Mason. "I'm not sorry you looked at the Veroneses first, because they do bring out very clearly the peculiar merit of Titian. You remember what I said about Veronese having no soul; well, you've only got to look at L'Homme au Gant to see that soul is just what Titian had."

"He was a remarkable old buffer," said Leslie Mason. "He lived to the age of ninety-nine and then it needed the plague to kill him."

Mrs. Mason smiled slightly.

"I have no hesitation," she continued, "in saying that I consider this one of the finest portraits that's ever been painted. Of course one can't compare it with a portrait by Cézanne or even by Manet."

"We mustn't forget to show them the Manet, Venetia."

"No, we won't do that. We'll come to that presently. But what I mean to say is that you must accept the idiom of the time at which it was painted, and bearing that in mind I don't think anyone can deny that it's a masterpiece. Of course just as a piece of painting it's beyond praise, but it's got a distinction and an imaginative quality which are very unique. Don't you think so, Leslie?"

"Definitely."

"When I was a girl I used to spend hours looking at it. It's a picture that makes you dream. Personally I think it's a finer portrait than Velasquez's Pope, the one in Rome, you know, just because it's more suggestive. Velasquez was a very great painter, I admit that, and he had an enormous influence on Manet, but what I miss in him is exactly what Titian had—Soul."

Leslie Mason looked at his watch.

"We mustn't waste too much time here, Venetia," he said, "or we shall be late for lunch."

"All right. We'll just go and look at the Ingres and the Manet."

They walked on, glancing right and left at the pictures that lined the walls, but there was nothing that Mrs. Mason thought worth lingering over.

"It's no good burdening their minds with a lot of impressions that'll only confuse them," she told her husband. "It's much better that they should concentrate on what's really important."

"Definitely," he answered.

They entered the Salle des États, but at the threshold Mrs. Mason stopped.

"We won't bother about the Poussins to-day," she said. "You have to come to the Louvre to see them, and there's no doubt that he was a Great Artist. But he was more of a painter's painter than a layman's, and I think you're a little young to appreciate him. One day when you're both of you a bit older we'll come and have a good go at him. I mean you have to be rather sophisticated to thoroughly understand him. The room that we're coming to now is nineteenth century. But I don't think we need bother about Delacroix either. He was a painter's painter too, and I wouldn't expect you to see in him what I do; you must take my word for it that he was a very considerable artist. He was no mean colourist and he had a strong romantic feeling. And you certainly needn't trouble your heads with the Barbizon School. In my young days they were very much admired, but that was before we understood the Impressionists even, and of course we hadn't so much as heard of Cézanne or Matisse; they don't amount to anything and they can be safely ignored. I want you to look first at the Odalisque of Ingres and then at the Olympia of Manet. They're wonderfully placed, opposite one another, so that you can look at both of them at the same time, compare them and draw your own conclusions."

Having said this Mrs. Mason advanced into the room with her husband by her side, while Charley and Patsy followed together a step or two behind. On reaching the exact spot where she thought the two pictures which she particularly wanted her offspring to admire could be seen to best advantage, she stopped with the triumphant air with which a conjurer extracts a rabbit from a hat and cried:

"There!"

They stood in a row for some minutes and Mrs. Mason gazed at the two nudes with rapture. Then she turned to the children.

"Now let's go and examine them close at hand."

They stood in front of the Odalisque.

"It's no good, Venetia," said Leslie. "You may say I'm a philistine, but I don't like the colour. The pink of that body is just the pink of that face cream you used to put on at night till I made you stop it."

"You needn't reveal the secrets of the alcove to these innocent children," said Venetia with a prim and at the same time roguish smile. "But I would never claim for a moment that Ingres was a great colourist; all the same I do think that blue is a very sweet colour and I've often thought I'd like an evening dress just like it. D'you think it would be too young, Patsy?"

"No, darling. Not a bit."

"But that's neither here nor there. Ingres was probably the greatest draughtsman who ever lived. I don't know how anyone can look at those firm and lovely lines and not feel he's in the presence of one of the great manifestations of the human spirit. I remember my father telling me that once he came here with one of his fellow-students from Julien's who'd never seen it, and when his eyes fell on it he was so overcome with its beauty of line that he actually fainted."

"I think it's much more likely that it was long past the hour at which reasonable people have lunch and that he fainted with hunger."

"Isn't your father awful?" smiled Mrs. Mason. "Well, let's just have five minutes more for the Olympia, Leslie, and then I'm ready to go."

They marched up to Manet's great picture.

"When you come to a masterpiece like this," said Mrs. Mason, "you can do nothing but keep your mouth shut and admire. The rest, as Hamlet said, is silence. No one, not even Renoir, not even El Greco, has ever painted flesh like that. Look at that right breast. It's a miracle of loveliness. One is simply left gasping. Even my poor father, who couldn't bear the moderns, was forced to admit that the painting of that breast was pretty good. Pretty good? I ask you. Now I suppose you see a black line all round the figure. You do, Charley, don't you?"

Charley acknowledged that he did.

"And you, Patsy?"

"Yes."

"Well, I don't," she cried triumphantly. "I used to see it, I know it's there, but I give you my word, I don't see it any more."

After that they went to lunch.

Through his long-standing acquaintance with the famous gallery and the useful information he had acquired from his mother, Charley, with Lydia by his side, entered the Salon Carré now with something of the confidence of a good tennis-player stepping on to the court. He was eager to show Lydia his favourite pictures and ready to explain to her exactly what was admirable in them. It was, however, something of a surprise to discover that the room had been re-

arranged and the Gioconda, to which he would naturally
have taken her first, was nowhere to be seen. They spent but
ten minutes there. When Charley went with his parents it
took them an hour to do that room and even then, his mother
said, they hadn't exhausted its treasures. But L'Homme au
Gant was in its old place and he gently led her up to it. They
looked at it for a while.

"Stunning, isn't it?" he said then, giving her arm an affectionate pressure.

"Yes, it's all right. What business is it of yours?"

Charley turned his head sharply. No one had ever asked
him a question like that about a picture before.

"What on earth d'you mean? It's one of the great portraits of the world. Titian, you know."

"I daresay. But what's it got to do with you?"

Charley didn't quite know what to say.

"Well, it's a very fine picture and it's beautifully painted.
Of course it doesn't tell a story if that's what you mean."

"No, I don't," she smiled.

"I don't suppose it's got anything to do with me really."

"Then why should you bother about it?"

Lydia moved on and Charley followed her. She gave other
pictures an indifferent glance. Charley was troubled by what
she had said and he puzzled his brains to discover what could
be at the back of her mind. She gave him an amused smile.

"Come," she said. "I'll show you some pictures."

She took his arm and they walked on. Suddenly he caught
sight of the Gioconda.

"There she is," he cried. "I must stop and have a good
look at that. I make a point of it when I come to the
Louvre."

"Why?"

"Hang it all, it's Leonardo's most celebrated picture. It's
one of the most important pictures in the world."

"Important to you?"

Charley was beginning to find her a trifle irritating; he
couldn't make out what she was getting at; but he was a
good-humoured youth, and he wasn't going to lose his
temper.

"A picture may be important even if it isn't very important to me."

"But it's only you who count. So far as you're concerned the only meaning a picture has is the meaning it has for you."

"That seems an awfully conceited way of looking at it."

"Does that picture say anything to you really?"

"Of course it does. It says all sorts of things, but I don't suppose I could put them any better than Pater did. He wrote a piece about it that's in all the anthologies."

But even as he spoke he recognized that his answer was lame. He was beginning to have a vague inkling of what Lydia meant, and then the uneasy feeling came to him that there was something in art that he'd never been told about. But he fortunately remembered what his mother had said about Manet's Olympia.

"In point of fact I don't know why you should say anything about a picture at all. You either like it or you don't."

"And you really like that one?" she asked in a tone of mild interrogation.

"Very much."

"Why?"

He thought for a moment.

"Well, you see, I've known it practically all my life."

"That's why you like your friend Simon, isn't it?" she smiled.

He felt it was an unfair retort.

"All right. You take me and show me the pictures you like."

The position was reversed. It was not he, as he had expected, who was leading the way and with such information as would add interest to the respective canvases, sympathetically drawing her attention to the great masterpieces he had always cared for; but it was she who was conducting him. Very well. He was quite ready to put himself in her hands and see what it was all about.

"Of course," he said to himself, "she's Russian. One has to make allowances for that."

They trudged past acres of canvas, through one room after another, for Lydia had some difficulty in finding her

way; but finally she stopped him in front of a small picture
that you might easily have missed if you had not been looking for it.

"Chardin," he said. "Yes, I've seen that before."

"But have you ever looked at it?"

"Oh, yes. Chardin wasn't half a bad painter in his way.
My mother thinks a lot of him. I've always rather liked his
still lifes myself."

"Is that all it means to you? It breaks my heart."

"That?" cried Charley with astonishment. "A loaf of
bread and a flagon of wine? Of course it's very well painted."

"Yes, you're right; it's very well painted; it's painted with
pity and love. It's not only a loaf of bread and a flagon of
wine; it's the bread of life and the blood of Christ, but not
held back from those who starve and thirst for them and
doled out by priests on stated occasions; it's the daily fare
of suffering men and women. It's so humble, so natural, so
friendly; it's the bread and wine of the poor who ask no
more than that they should be left in peace, allowed to work
and eat their simple food in freedom. It's the cry of the
despised and rejected. It tells you that whatever their sins
men at heart are good. That loaf of bread and that flagon
of wine are symbols of the joys and sorrows of the meek and
lowly. They ask for your mercy and your affection; they tell
you that they're of the same flesh and blood as you. They tell
you that life is short and hard and the grave is cold and
lonely. It's not only a loaf of bread and a flagon of wine; it's
the mystery of man's lot on earth, his craving for a little
friendship and a little love, the humility of his resignation
when he sees that even they must be denied him."

Lydia's voice was tremulous and now the tears flowed
from her eyes. She brushed them away impatiently.

"And isn't it wonderful that with those simple objects,
with his painter's exquisite sensibility, moved by the charity
in his heart, that funny, dear old man should have made
something so beautiful that it breaks you? It was as though,
unconsciously perhaps, hardly knowing what he was doing,
he wanted to show you that if you only have enough love, if
you only have enough sympathy, out of pain and distress and

unkindness, out of all the evil of the world, you can create beauty."

She was silent and for long stood looking at the little picture. Charley looked at it too, but with perplexity. It was a very good picture; he hadn't really given it more than a glance before, and he was glad Lydia had drawn his attention to it; in some odd way it was rather moving; but of course he could never have seen in it all she saw. Strange, unstable woman! It was rather embarrassing that she should cry in a public gallery; they did put you in an awkward position, these Russians; but who would have thought a picture could affect anyone like that? He remembered his mother's story of how a student friend of his grandfather's had fainted when he first saw the Odalisque of Ingres; but that was away back in the nineteenth century, they were very romantic and emotional in those days. Lydia turned to him with a sunny smile on her lips. It disconcerted him to see with what suddenness she could go from tears to laughter.

"Shall we go now?" she said.

"But don't you want to see any more pictures?"

"Why? I've seen one. I feel happy and peaceful. What could I get if I saw another?"

"Oh, all right."

It seemed a very odd way of doing a picture gallery. After all, they hadn't looked at the Watteaus or the Fragonards. His mother was bound to ask him if he'd seen the Embarkation for Cythera. Someone had told her they'd cleaned it and she'd want to know how the colours had come out.

They did a little shopping and then lunched at a restaurant on the quay on the other side of the river and Lydia as usual ate with a very good appetite. She liked the crowd that surrounded them and the traffic that passed noisily in the roadway. She was in a good humour. It was as though the violent emotion from which she had suffered had rinsed her spirit clean, and she talked of trivial things with a pleasant cheerfulness. But Charley was thoughtful. He did not find it so easy to dismiss the disquietude that affected him. She did not usually notice his moods, but the trouble of his mind was so clearly reflected on his face that at last she could not but be struck by it.

"Why are you so silent?" she asked him, with a kindly, sympathetic smile.

"I was thinking. You see, I've been interested in art all my life. My parents are very artistic, I mean some people might even say they were rather highbrow, and they were always keen on my sister and me having a real appreciation of art; and I think we have. It rather worries me to think that with all the pains I've taken, and the advantages I've had, I don't seem really to know so much about it as you do."

"But I know nothing about art," she laughed.

"But you do seem to feel about it very strongly, and I suppose art is really a matter of feeling. It's not as though I didn't like pictures. I get an enormous kick out of them."

"You mustn't be worried. It's very natural that you should look at pictures differently from me. You're young and healthy, happy and prosperous. You're not stupid. They're a pleasure to you among a lot of other pleasures. It gives you a feeling of warmth and satisfaction to look at them. To walk through a gallery is a very agreeable way of passing an idle hour. What more can you want? But you see, I've always been poor, often hungry, and sometimes terribly lonely. They've been riches to me, food and drink and company. When I was working and my employer had nagged me to distraction I used to slip into the Louvre at the luncheon hour and her scolding didn't matter any more. And when my mother died and I had nobody left, it comforted me. During those long months when Robert was in prison before the trial and I was pregnant, I think I should have gone mad and killed myself if it hadn't been that I could go there, where nobody knew me and nobody stared at me, and be alone with my friends. It was rest and peace. It gave me courage. It wasn't so much the great well-known masterpieces that helped me, it was the smaller, shyer pictures that no one noticed, and I felt they were pleased that I looked at them. I felt that nothing really mattered so very much, because everything passed. Patience! Patience! That's what I learnt there. And I felt that above all the horror and misery and cruelty of the world, there was something that helped you to bear it, something that was greater and more important than all that, the spirit of man and the beauty he created. Is it really strange that that little picture I showed you this morning should mean so much to me?"

To make the most of the fine weather they walked up the busy Boulevard St. Michel and when they got to the top turned into the gardens of the Luxembourg. They sat down and, talking little, idly watched the nurses, no longer, alas, wearing the long satin streamers of a generation ago, trundling prams, the old ladies in black who walked with sober gait in charge of little children, and the elderly gentlemen, with thick scarves up to their noses, who paced up and down immersed in thought; with friendly hearts they looked at the long-legged boys and girls who ran about playing games, and when a pair of young students passed wondered what it was they so earnestly discussed. It seemed not a public park, but a private garden for the people on the left bank, and the scene had a moving intimacy. But the chilly rays of the waning sun gave it withal a certain melancholy, for within the iron grille that separated it from the bustle of the great city, the garden had a singular air of unreality, and you had a feeling that those old people who trod the gravel paths, those children whose cries made a cheerful hubbub, were ghosts taking phantom walks or playing phantom games, who at dusk would dissolve, like the smoke of a cigarette, into the oncoming darkness. It was growing very cold, and Charley and Lydia wandered back, silent friendly companions, to the hotel.

When they got to their room Lydia took out of her suitcase a thin sheaf of piano pieces.

"I brought some of the things Robert used to play. I play so badly and we haven't got a piano at Alexey's. D'you think you could play them?"

Charley looked at the music. It was Russian. Some of the pieces were familiar to him.

"I think so," he said.

"There's a piano downstairs and there'll be nobody in the salon now. Let's go down."

The piano badly wanted tuning. It was an upright. The keyboard was yellow with age and because it was seldom played on the notes were stiff. There was a long music stool and Lydia sat down by Charley's side. He put on the rack a piece by Scriabin that he knew and after a few resounding chords to try the instrument began to play. Lydia followed the score and turned the pages for him. Charley had had as good masters as could be found in London, and he had worked hard. He had played at concerts at school and afterwards at Cambridge, so that he had acquired confidence. He had a light, pleasant touch. He enjoyed playing.

"There," he said when he came to the end of the piece.

He was not displeased with himself. He knew that he had played it according to the composer's intention and with the clear, neat straightforwardness that he liked in piano-playing.

"Play something else," said Lydia.

She chose a piece. It was an arrangement for the piano of folk songs and folk dances by a composer of whom Charley had never heard. It startled him to see the name of Robert Berger written in a firm, bold hand on the cover. Lydia stared at it in silence and then turned the page. He looked at the music he was about to play and wondered what Lydia was thinking now. She must have sat by Robert's side just as she was sitting by his. Why did she want to torture herself by making him play those pieces that must recall to her bitter memories of her short happiness and the misery that followed it?

"Well, begin."

He played well at sight and the music was not difficult. He thought he acquitted himself of his task without discredit. Having struck the last chord he waited for a word of praise.

"You played it very nicely," said Lydia, "but where does Russia come in?"

"What exactly d'you mean by that?" he asked, somewhat affronted.

"You play it as if it was about a Sunday afternoon in London with people in their best clothes walking around those great empty squares and wishing it was time for tea. But that's not what it is at all. It's the old, old song of peasants who lament the shortness and the hardness of their life, it's the wide fields of golden corn and the labour of gathering in the harvest, it's the great forest of beech-trees, and the nostalgia of the workers for an age when peace and plenty reigned on the earth, and it's the wild dance that for a brief period brings them forgetfulness of their lot."

"Well, you play it better."

"I can't play," she answered, but she edged him along the bench and took his seat.

He listened. She played badly, but for all that got something out of the music that he hadn't seen in it. She managed, though at a price, to bring out the tumult of its emotion and the bitterness of its melancholy; and she infused the dance rhythms with a barbaric vitality that stirred the blood. But Charley was put out.

"I must confess I don't see why you should think you get the Russian atmosphere better by playing false notes and keeping your foot firmly on the loud pedal," he said, acidly, when she finished.

She burst out laughing and flinging both her arms round his neck kissed him on the cheeks.

"You are a sweet," she cried.

"It's very nice of you to say so," he answered coldly, disengaging himself.

"Have I offended you?"

"Not at all."

She shook her head and smiled at him with soft tenderness.

"You play very well and your technique is excellent, but it's no good thinking you can play Russian music; you can't. Play me some Schumann. I'm sure you can."

"No, I'm not going to play any more."

"If you're angry with me, why don't you hit me?"

Charley couldn't help chuckling.

"You fool. It never occurred to me. Besides, I'm not angry."

"You're so big and strong and handsome, I forget that

you're only a young boy." She sighed. "And you're so unprepared for life. Sometimes when I look at you I get such a pang."

"Now don't get all Russian and emotional."

"Be nice to me and play some Schumann."

When Lydia liked she could be very persuasive. With a diffident smile Charley resumed his seat. Schumann, in point of fact, was the composer he liked best and he knew a great deal by heart. He played to her for an hour, and whenever he wanted to stop she urged him to go on. The young woman at the cashier's desk was curious to see who was playing the piano and peeped in. When she went back to her counter she murmured to the porter with an arch and meaning smile:

"The turtle doves are having a good time."

When at last Charley stopped, Lydia gave a little sigh of contentment.

"I knew that was the music to suit you. It's like you, healthy and comfortable and wholesome. There's fresh air in it and sunshine and the delicious scent of pine-trees. It's done me good to listen to it and it's done me good to be with you. Your mother must love you very much."

"Oh, come off it."

"Why are you so good to me? I'm tiresome, dull and exasperating. You don't even like me very much, do you?"

Charley considered this for a moment.

"Well, I don't very much, to tell you the truth."

She laughed.

"Then why do you bother about me? Why don't you just turn me out into the street?"

"I can't imagine."

"Shall I tell you? Goodness. Just pure, simple, stupid goodness."

"Go to hell."

They dined in the Quarter. It had not escaped Charley's notice that Lydia took no interest in him as an individual. She accepted him as you might accept a person with whom you find yourself on a ship for a few days and so forced to a certain intimacy, but it does not matter to you where he came from and what sort of a man he is; he emerged from non-existence when he stepped on board and will return to it when, on reaching port, you part company with him. Charley was modest enough not to be piqued by this, for he could not but realize that her own troubles and perplexities were so great that they must absorb her attention; and he was not a little surprised now when she led him to talk about himself. He told her of his artistic inclinations and of the wish he had so long harboured to be an artist, and she approved his common sense which in the end had persuaded him to prefer the assured life of a business man. He had never seen her more cheerful and more human. Knowing English domestic life only through Dickens, Thackeray and H. G. Wells, she was curious to hear how existence was pursued in those prosperous, sober houses in Bayswater that she knew but from their outside. She asked him about his home and his family. These were subjects on which he was always glad to talk. He spoke of his father and mother with a faintly mocking irony which Lydia saw well enough he assumed only to conceal the loving admiration with which he regarded them. Without knowing it he drew a very pleasant picture of an affectionate, happy family who lived unpretentiously in circumstances of moderate affluence at peace with themselves and the world and undisturbed by any fear that anything might happen to affect their security. The life he described lacked neither grace nor dignity; it was healthy and normal, and through its intellectual interests not entirely material; the persons who led it were simple and honest, neither ambitious nor envious, prepared to do their duty by the state and by their neighbours according to their lights; and there was in them neither harm nor malice. If Lydia saw how much of their good nature, their kindliness, their not unpleasing self-complacency depended on the long-established and well-ordered prosperity of the country that had given them birth; if she had an inkling that, like children building castles on the sea sand, they might at any moment be swept away by a tidal wave, she allowed no sign of it to appear on her face.

"How lucky you English are," she said.

But Charley was a trifle surprised at the impression his

own words made on him. In the course of his recital he had for the first time seen himself from the standpoint of an observer. Until now, like an actor who says his lines, but never having seen the play from the front, has but a vague idea of what it is all about, he had played his part without asking himself whether it had any meaning. It would be too much to say that it made him uneasy, it slightly perplexed him, to realize that while they were all, his father, his mother, his sister, himself, busy from morning till night, so that the days were not long enough for what they wanted to do; yet when you came to look upon the life they led from one year's end to another it gave you an uncomfortable feeling that they, none of them, did anything at all. It was like one of those comedies where the sets are good and the clothes pretty, where the dialogue is clever and the acting competent, so that you pass an agreeable evening, but a week later cannot remember a thing about it.

When they had finished dinner they took a taxi to a cinema on the other side of the river. It was a film of the Marx brothers and they rocked with laughter at the extravagant humour of the marvellous clowns; but they laughed not only at Groucho's wise-cracks and at Harpo's comic quandaries, they laughed at one another's laughter. The picture finished at midnight, but Charley was too excited to go quietly to bed and he asked Lydia if she would come with him to some place where they could dance.

"Where would you like to go?" asked Lydia. "Montmartre?"

"Wherever you like as long as it's gay." And then, remembering his parents' constant, but seldom achieved, desire when they came to Paris: "Where there aren't a lot of English people."

Lydia gave him the slightly mischievous smile that he had seen on her lips once or twice before. It surprised him, but at the same time was sympathetic to him. It surprised him because it went so strangely with what he thought he knew of her character; and it was sympathetic to him because it suggested that, for all her tragic history, there was in her a vein of high spirits and of a rather pleasing, teasing malice.

"I'll take you somewhere. It won't be gay, but it may be interesting. There's a Russian woman who sings there."

They drove a long way, and when they stopped Charley saw that they were on the quay. The twin towers of Notre-Dame were distinct against the frosty, starry night. They walked a few steps up a dark street and then went through a narrow door; they descended a flight of stairs and Charley, to his astonishment, found himself in a large cellar with stone walls; from these jutted out wooden tables large enough to accommodate ten or twelve persons, and there were wooden benches on each side of them. The heat was stifling and the air gray with smoke. In the space left by the tables a dense throng was dancing to a melancholy tune. A slatternly waiter in shirt-sleeves found them two places and took their order. People sitting here and there looked at them curiously and whispered to one another; and indeed Charley in his well-cut English blue serge, Lydia in her black silk and her smart hat with the feather in it, contrasted violently with the rest of the company. The men wore neither collars nor ties, and they danced with their caps on, the end of a cigarette stuck to their lips. The women were bareheaded and extravagantly painted.

"They look pretty tough," said Charley.

"They are. Most of them have been in jug and those that haven't should be. If there's a row and they start throwing glasses or pulling knives, just stand against the wall and don't move."

"I don't think they much like the look of us," said Charley. "We seem to be attracting a good deal of attention."

"They think we're sight-seers and that always puts their backs up. But it'll be all right. I know the patron."

When the waiter brought the two beers they had ordered Lydia asked him to get the landlord along. In a moment he came, a big fellow with the naked look of a fat priest, and immediately recognized Lydia. He gave Charley a shrewd, suspicious stare, but when Lydia introduced him as a friend of hers, shook hands with him warmly and said he was glad to see him. He sat down and for a few minutes talked with Lydia in an undertone. Charley noticed that their neigh-

bours watched the scene and he caught one man giving another a wink. They were evidently satisfied that it was all
right. The dance came to an end and the other occupants
of the table at which they sat came back. They gave the
strangers hostile looks, but the patron explained that they
were friends, whereupon one of the party, a sinister-looking
chap, with the scar of a razor wound on his face, insisted on
offering them a glass of wine. Soon they were all talking
merrily together. They were plainly eager to make the young
Englishman at home, and a man sitting by his side explained
to him that though the company looked a bit rough they
were all good fellows with their hearts in the right place.
He was a little drunk. Charley, having got over his first
uneasiness, began to enjoy himself.

Presently the saxophone player got up and advanced his
chair. The Russian singer of whom Lydia had spoken came
forward with a guitar in her hand and sat down. There was
a burst of applause.

"C'est La Marishka," said Charley's drunken friend,
"there's no one like her. She was the mistress of one of the
commissars, but Stalin had him shot and if she hadn't managed to get out of Russia he'd have shot her too."

A woman on the other side of the table overheard him.

"What nonsense you're telling him, Loulou," she cried.
"La Marishka was the mistress of a grand duke before the
revolution, everyone knows that, and she had diamonds
worth millions, but the Bolsheviks took everything from her.
She escaped disguised as a peasant."

La Marishka was a woman of forty, haggard and sombre,
with gaunt, masculine features, a brown skin, and enormous,
blazing eyes under black, heavy, arching brows. In a raucous
voice, at the top of her lungs, she sang a wild, joyless song,
and though Charley could not understand the Russian words
a cold feeling ran down his spine. She was loudly applauded.
Then she sang a sentimental ballad in French, the lament of
a girl for her lover who was to be executed next morning,
which roused her audience to frenzy. She finished, for the
time being, with another Russian song, lively this time, and
her face lost its tragic cast; it took on a look of rude and

brutal gaiety, and her voice, deep and harsh, acquired a rollicking quality; your blood was stirred and you could not but exult, but at the same time you were moved, for below the bacchanalian merriment was the desolation of futile tears. Charley looked at Lydia and caught her mocking glance. He smiled good-naturedly. That grim woman got something out of the music which he was conscious now was beyond his reach. Another burst of applause greeted the end of the number, but La Marishka, as though she did not hear it, without a sign of acknowledgement, rose from her chair and came over to Lydia. The two women began to talk in Russian. Lydia turned to Charley.

"She'll have a glass of champagne if you'll offer it to her."

"Of course."

He signalled to a waiter and ordered a bottle; then, with a glance at the half-dozen people sitting at the table, changed his order.

"Two bottles and some glasses. Perhaps these gentlemen and ladies will allow me to offer them a glass too."

There was a murmur of polite acceptance. The wine was brought and Charley filled a number of glasses and passed them down the table. There was a great deal of health drinking and clinking of glasses together.

"Vive l'Entente Cordiale."

"À nos alliés."

They all got very friendly and merry. Charley was having a grand time. But he had come to dance; and when the orchestra began once more to play he pulled Lydia to her feet. The floor was soon crowded and he noticed that a lot of curious eyes were fixed upon her; he guessed that it had spread through the company who she was; it made her to those bullies and their women, somewhat to Charley's embarrassment, an object of interest, but she did not seem even to be aware that anyone looked at her.

Presently the patron touched her on the shoulder.

"I have a word to say to you," he muttered.

Lydia released herself from Charley's arms and going to one side with the fat landlord listened to what he said. Charley could see that she was startled. He was evidently trying to point someone out to her, for Charley saw her craning her neck; but with the thick mass of dancers in the way she could see nothing, and in a moment she followed the patron to the other end of the long cellar. She seemed to have forgotten Charley. Somewhat piqued, he went back to his table. Two couples were sitting there comfortably enjoying his champagne, and they greeted him heartily. They were all very familiar now and they asked him what he had done with his little friend. He told them what had happened. One of the men was a short thick-set fellow with a red face and a magnificent moustache. His shirt open at the neck showed his hairy chest, and his arms, for he had taken off his coat in that stifling heat and turned up his shirt-sleeves, were profusely tattooed. He was with a girl who might have been twenty years younger than he. She had very sleek black hair, parted in the middle, with a bun on her neck, a face dead-white with powder, scarlet lips and eyes heavy with mascara. The man nudged her with his elbow.

"Now then, why don't you dance with the Englishman? You've drunk his bubbly, haven't you?"

"I don't mind," she said.

She danced clingingly. She smelt strongly of scent, but not so strongly as to disguise the fact that she had eaten at dinner a dish highly flavoured with garlic. She smiled alluringly at Charley.

"He must be rotten with vice, this pretty little Englishman," she gurgled, with a squirm of a lithe body in her black, but dusty, velvet gown.

"Why do you say that?" he smiled.

"To be with the wife of Berger, what's that if it isn't vice?"

"She's my sister," said Charley gaily.

She thought this such a good joke that when the band stopped and they went back to the table she repeated it to the assembled company. They all thought it very funny, and the thick-set man with the hairy chest slapped him on the back.

"Farceur, va!"

Charley was not displeased to be looked upon as a humorist. It was nice to be a success. He realized that as the lover of a notorious murderer's wife he was something of a personage there. They urged him to come again.

"But come alone next time," said the girl he had just danced with.

"We'll find you a girl. What d'you want to get mixed up with one of the Russians for? The wine of the country, that's what you want."

Charley ordered another bottle of champagne. He was far from tight, but he was merry. He was seeing life with a vengeance. When Lydia came back he was talking and laughing with his new friends as if he had known them all his life. He danced the next dance with her. He noticed that she was not keeping step with him and he gave her a little shake.

"You're not attending."

She laughed.

"I'm sorry. I'm tired. Let's go."

"Has something happened to upset you?"

"No. It's getting very late and the heat's awful."

Having warmly shaken hands with their new friends, they left and got into a taxi. Lydia sank back exhausted. He was feeling happy and affectionate and he took her hand and held it. They drove in silence.

They went to bed, and in a few minutes Charley became aware from her regular breathing that Lydia had fallen asleep. But he was too excited to sleep. The evening had amused him and he was keenly alert. He thought it all over for a while and chuckled at the grand story he would make of it when he got home. He turned on the light to read. But he could not give his attention to the poems of Blake just then. Disordered notions flitted across his mind. He switched off the light and presently fell into a light doze, but in a little while awoke. He was tingling with desire. He heard the quiet breathing of the sleeping woman in the bed by his side and a peculiar sensation stirred his heart. Except on that first evening at the Sérail no feeling for Lydia had touched him except pity and kindliness. Sexually she did not in the least attract him. After seeing her for several days all day long he did not even think her pretty; he did not like the squareness of her face, her high cheek-bones, and the way her pale eyes were set flat in their orbits; sometimes, indeed, he thought her really plain. Notwith-standing the life she had adopted—for what strange, un-natural reason—she gave him a sense of such deadly re-spectability that it choked him off. And then her indifference to sexual congress was chilling. She looked with contempt and loathing on the men who for money sought their pleas-ure of her. The passionate love she bore for Robert gave her an aloofness from all human affections that killed desire. But besides all that Charley didn't think he liked her very much for herself; she was sometimes sullen, almost always indifferent; she took whatever he did for her as her right; it was all very well to say that she asked for nothing, it would have been graceful if she had shown, not gratitude, but a glimmering recognition of the fact that he was trying to do his best for her. Charley had an uneasy fear that she was making a mug of him; if what Simon said was true and she was making money at the brothel in order to help Robert to escape, she was nothing but a callous liar; he flushed hotly when it occurred to him that she was laughing behind his back at his simplicity. No, he didn't admire her, and the more he thought of her the less he thought he liked her. And yet at that moment he was so breathless with desire of her that he felt he would choke. He thought of her not as he saw her every day, rather drab, like a teacher at a Sunday school, but as he had first seen her in those baggy Turkish trousers and the blue turban spangled with little stars, her cheeks painted and her lashes black with mascara; he thought of her slender waist, her clear, soft, honey-coloured skin, and her small firm breasts with their rosy nipples. He tossed on his bed. His desire now was uncon-trollable. It was anguish. After all, it wasn't fair; he was young and strong and normal; why shouldn't he have a bit of fun when he had the chance? She was there for that, she'd said so herself. What did it matter if she thought him a dirty swine? He'd done pretty well by her, he deserved something in return. The faint sound of her quiet breathing was strangely exciting and it quickened his own. He thought of the feel of her soft lips when he pressed his mouth to hers and the feel of her little breasts when he took them in his hands; he thought of the feel of her lissom body in his arms and the feel of his long legs lying against hers. He put on the light, thinking it might wake her, and got out of bed. He leaned over her. She lay on her back, her hands crossed over her breast like a stone figure on a tomb; tears were running out of her closed eyes and her mouth was distorted with grief. She was crying in her sleep. She looked like a child, lying there, and her face had a child's look of hopeless misery, for a child does not know that sorrow, like all other things, will pass. Charley gave a gasp. The unhappiness of that sleeping woman was intolerable to see, and all his passion, all his desire, were extinguished by the pity that overcame him. She had been gay during the day, easy to talk to and companionable, and it had seemed to him that she was free, at least for a while, from the pain that, he was conscious, lurked always in the depths of her being; but in sleep it had returned to her and he knew only too well what unhappy dreams distraught her. He gave a deep sigh.

But he felt more disinclined for sleep than ever, and he could not bear the thought of getting into bed again. He turned the shade down so that the light should not disturb Lydia, and going to the table filled his pipe and lit it. He drew the heavy curtain that was over the window and sitting down looked out into the court. It was in darkness but for one lighted window, and this had a sinister look. He wondered whether someone lay ill in that room or, simply sleepless like himself, brooded over the perplexity of life. Or perhaps some man had brought a woman in, and their lust appeased, they lay contented in one another's arms. Charley smoked. He felt dull and flat. He did not think of anything in particular. At last he went back to bed and fell asleep.

ix

CHARLEY was awakened by the maid bringing in the morning coffee. For a moment he forgot the events of the previous night.

"Oh, I was sleeping so soundly," he said, rubbing his eyes.

"I'm sorry, but it's half-past ten and I have an engagement at eleven-thirty."

"It doesn't matter. It's my last day in Paris and it would be silly to waste it in sleep."

The maid had brought the two breakfasts on one tray and Lydia told her to give it to Charley. She put on a dressing-gown and sat down at the end of his bed, leaning against the foot. She poured out a cup of coffee, cut a roll in two and buttered it for him.

"I've been watching you sleep," she said. "It's nice; you sleep like an animal or a child, so deep, so quiet, it rests one just to look at you."

Then he remembered.

"I'm afraid you didn't have a very good night."

"Oh, yes, I did. I slept like a top. I was tired out, you know. That's one of the things I'm most grateful to you for, I've had such wonderful nights. I dream terribly. But since I've been here I haven't dreamt once; I've slept quite peacefully. And I who thought I should never sleep like that again."

He knew that she had been dreaming that night and he knew what her dreams were about. She had forgotten them. He forebore to look at her. It gave him a grim, horrible, and rather uncanny sensation to think that a vivid, lacerating life could go on when one was sunk in unconsciousness, a life so real that it could cause tears to stream down the face and twist the mouth in woe, and yet when the sleeper woke left no recollection behind. An uncomfortable thought crossed his mind. He could not quite make it explicit, but had he been able to, he would perhaps have asked himself:

"Who are we really? What do we know about ourselves? And that other life of ours, is that less real than this one?"

It was all very strange and complicated. It looked as though nothing were quite so simple as it seemed; it looked as though the people we thought we knew best carried secrets that they didn't even know themselves. Charley had a sudden inkling that human beings were infinitely mysterious. The fact was that you knew nothing about anybody.

"What's this engagement you've got?" he asked, more for the sake of saying something than because he wanted to know.

Lydia lit a cigarette before she answered.

"Marcel, the fat man who runs the place we were at last night, introduced me to two men there and I've made an appointment to meet them at the Palette this morning. We couldn't talk in all that crowd."

"Oh!"

He was too discreet to ask who they were.

"Marcel's in touch with Cayenne and St. Laurent. He often gets news. That's why I wanted to go there. They landed at St. Nazaire last week."

"Who? The two men? Are they escaped convicts?"

"No. They've served their sentence. They got their passage paid by the Salvation Army. They knew Robert." She hesitated a moment. "If you want to, you can come with me. They've got no money. They'd be grateful if you gave them a little."

"All right. Yes, I'd like to come."

"They seem very decent fellows. One of them doesn't look more than thirty now. Marcel told me he was a cook and he was sent out for killing another man in the kitchen of the restaurant where he worked. I don't know what the other had done. You'd better go and have your bath." She went over to the dressing-table and looked at herself in the glass. "Funny, I wonder why my eyelids are swollen. To look at me you'd think I'd been crying, and you know I haven't, don't you?"

"Perhaps it was that smoky atmosphere last night. By George! you could have cut it with a knife."

"I'll ring down for some ice. They'll be all right after we've been out in the air for five minutes."

The Palette was empty when they got there. Late break-fasters had had their coffee and gone, and it was too early for anyone to have come in for an apéritif before luncheon. They sat in a corner, near the window, so that they could look out into the street. They waited for several minutes.

"There they are," said Lydia.

Charley looked out and saw two men walking past. They glanced in, hesitated a moment and strolled on, then came back; Lydia gave them a smile, but they took no notice of her; they stood still, looking up and down the street, and then doubtfully at the café. It looked as though they couldn't make up their minds to enter. Their manner was timid and furtive. They said a few words to one another and the younger of the two gave a hasty anxious glance behind him. The other seemed on a sudden to force himself to a de-cision and walked towards the door. His friend followed quickly. Lydia gave them a wave and a smile when they came in. They still took no notice. They looked round stealthily, as though to assure themselves that they were safe, and then, the first with averted eyes, the other fixing the ground, came up. Lydia shook hands with them and introduced Charley. They evidently had expected her to be alone and his presence disconcerted them. They gave him a look of suspicion. Lydia explained that he was an Englishman, a friend who was spending a few days in Paris. Charley, a smile on his lips which he sought to make cordial, stretched out his hand; they took it, one after the other, and gave it a limp pressure. They seemed to have nothing to say. Lydia bade them sit down and asked them what they would have.

"A cup of coffee."

"You'll have something to eat?"

The elder one gave the other a faint smile.

"A cake, if there is one. The boy has a sweet tooth, and over there, from where we come, there wasn't much in that line."

The man who spoke was a little under the middle height. He might have been forty. The other was two or three inches taller and perhaps ten years younger. Both were very thin. They both wore collars and ties and thick suits, one of a gray-and-white check and the other dark green, but the suits were ill-cut and sat loosely on them. They did not look at ease in them. The elder one, sturdy though short, had a well-knit figure; his sallow, colourless face was much lined. He had an air of determination. The other's face was as sallow and colourless, but his skin, drawn tightly over the bones, was smooth and unlined; he looked very ill. There was another trait they shared; the eyes of both seemed preternaturally large, and when they turned them on you they did not appear to look at you, but beyond, with a demented stare, as though they were gazing at something that filled them with horror. It was very painful. At first they were shy, and since Charley was shy too, though he tried to show his friendliness by offering them cigarettes, while Lydia, seeming to find no need for words, contented herself with looking at them, they sat in silence. But she looked at them with such tender concern that the silence was not embarrassing. The waiter brought them coffee and a dish of cakes. The elder man toyed with one of them, but the other ate greedily, and as he ate he gave his friend now and then little touching looks of surprised delight.

"The first thing we did when we got out by ourselves in Paris was to go to a confectioner's, and the boy ate six chocolate éclairs one after the other. But he paid for it."

"Yes," said the other seriously. "When we got out into the street I was sick. You see, my stomach wasn't used to it. But it was worth it."

"Did you eat very badly over there?"

The elder man shrugged his shoulders.

"Beef three hundred and sixty-five days of the year. One doesn't notice it after a time. And then, if you behave yourself you get cheese and a little wine. And it's better to behave yourself. Of course it's worse when you've done your sentence and you're freed. When you're in prison you get board and lodging, but when you're free you have to shift for yourself."

"My friend doesn't know," said Lydia. "Explain to him. They don't have the same system in England."

"It's like this. You're sentenced to a term of imprisonment, eight, ten, fifteen, twenty years, and when you've done it you're a libéré. You have to stay in the colony the same number of years that you were sentenced to. It's hard to get work. The libérés have a bad name and people won't employ them. It's true that you can get a plot of land and cultivate it, but it's not everyone who can do that. After being in prison for years, taking orders from the warders and half the time doing nothing, you've lost your initiative; and then there's malaria and hook-worm; you've lost your energy. Most of them get work only when a ship comes in to harbour and they can earn a little by unloading the cargo. There's nothing much for the libéré but to sleep in the market, drink rafia when he gets the chance, and starve. I was lucky. You see, I'm an electrician by trade, and a good one; I know my job as well as anyone, so they needed me. I didn't do so badly."

"How long was your sentence?" asked Lydia.

"Only eight years."

"And what did you do?"

He slightly shrugged his shoulders and gave Lydia a deprecating smile.

"Folly of youth. One's young, one gets into bad company, one drinks too much and then one day something happens and one has to pay for it all one's life. I was twenty-four when I went out and I'm forty now. I've spent my best years in that hell."

"He could have got away before," said the other, "but he wouldn't."

"You mean you could have escaped?" said Lydia.

Charley gave her a quick, searching glance but her face told him nothing.

"Escape? No, that's a mug's game. One can always escape, but there are few who get away. Where can you go? Into the bush? Fever, wild animals, starvation, and the natives who'll take you for the sake of the reward. A good many try it. You see, they get so fed up with the monotony, the food, the orders, the sight of all the rest of the prisoners, they think anything's better, but they can't stick it out; if they don't die of illness or starvation, they're captured or give themselves up; and then it's two years' solitary confinement, or more, and you have to be a hefty chap if that doesn't break you. It was easier in the old days when the Dutch were building their railway, you could get across the river and they'd put you to work on it, but now they've finished the railway and they don't want labour any more. They catch you and send you back. But even that had its risks. There was a customs official who used to promise to take you over the river for a certain sum, he had a regular tariff, you'd arrange to meet him at a place in the jungle at night, and when you kept the appointment he just shot you dead and emptied your pockets. They say he did away with more than thirty fellows before he was caught. Some of them get away by sea. Half a dozen club together and get a libéré to buy a rickety boat for them. It's a hard journey, without a compass or anything, and one never knows when a storm will spring up; it's more by luck than good management if they get anywhere. And where can they go? They won't have them in Venezuela any longer and if they land there they're just put in prison and sent back. If they land in Trinidad the authorities keep them for a week, stock them up with provisions, even give them a boat if theirs isn't seaworthy, and then send them off, out into the sea with no place to go to. No, it's silly to try to escape."

"But men do," said Lydia. "There was that doctor, what was his name? They say he's practising somewhere in South America and doing well."

"Yes, if you've got money you can get away sometimes, not if you're on the islands, but if you're at Cayenne or St. Laurent. You can get the skipper of a Brazilian schooner to pick you up at sea, and if he's honest he'll land you somewhere down the coast and you're pretty safe. If he isn't, he takes your money and chucks you overboard. But he'll want twelve thousand francs now, and that means double because the libéré who gets the money in for you takes half as his commission. And then you can't land in Brazil without a penny in your pocket. You've got to have at least thirty thousand francs, and who's got that?"

Lydia asked a question and once more Charley gave her an enquiring look.

"But how can you be sure that the libéré will hand over the money that's sent him?" she said.

"You can't. Sometimes he doesn't, but then he ends with a knife in his back, and he knows very well the authorities aren't going to bother very much if a damned libéré is found dead one morning."

"Your friend said just now you could have got away sooner, but didn't. What did he mean by that?"

The little man gave his shoulders a deprecating shrug.

"I made myself useful. The commandant was a decent chap and he knew I was a good worker and honest. They soon found out they could leave me in a house by myself when they wanted a job done and I wouldn't touch a thing. He got me permission to go back to France when I still had two more years to go of my time as a libéré." He gave his friend a touching smile. "But I didn't like to leave that young scamp. I knew that without me to look after him he'd get into trouble."

"It's true," said the other. "I owe everything to him."

"He was only a kid when he came out. He had the next bed to mine. He put up a pretty good show in the daytime, but at night he'd cry for his mother. I felt sorry for him. I don't know how it happened, I got an affection for him; he was lost among all those men, poor little chap, and I had to look after him. Some of them were inclined to be nasty to him, one Algerian was always bothering, but I settled his hash and after that they left the boy in peace."

"How did you do that?"

The little man gave a grin so cheerful and roguish that it made him look on a sudden ten years younger.

"Well, you know, in that life a man can only make himself respected if he knows how to use his knife. I ripped him up the belly."

Charley gave a gasp. The man made the statement so naturally that one could hardly believe one had heard right.

"You see, one's shut up in the dormitory from nine till five and the warders don't come in. To tell you the truth, it would be as much as their lives were worth. If in the morning a man's found with a hole in his gizzard, the authorities ask no questions so as they won't be told no lies. So you see, I felt a kind of responsibility for the boy. I had to teach him everything. I've got a good brain and I soon discovered that out there if you want to make it easy for yourself the only thing is to do what you're told and give no trouble. It's not justice that reigns on the earth, it's force, and they've got the force, the authorities; one of these days perhaps we shall have it, we the working-men, and then we shall get a bit of our own back on the bourgeois, but till then we've got to obey. That's what I taught him, and I taught him my job too, and now he's almost as good an electrician as I am."

"The only thing now is to find work," said the other. "Work together."

"We've gone through so much together we can't be parted now. You see, he's all I've got. I've got no mother, no wife, no kids. I had, but my mother's dead, and I lost my wife and my kids when I had my trouble. Women are bitches. It's hard for a chap to live without any affection in his life."

"And I, who have I got? It's for life, us two."

There was something very affecting in the friendship that bound those two hapless men together. It gave Charley a sense of exaltation that somewhat embarrassed him; he would have liked to tell them that he thought it brave and beautiful, but he knew he could never bring himself to say anything so unusual. But Lydia had none of his shyness.

"I don't think there are many men who would have stayed in that hell for two long years when they could get away, for the sake of a friend."

The man chuckled.

"You see, over there time is just the opposite of money; there a little money is a great deal and a lot of time is nothing very much. While six sous is a sum that you hoard as if it was a fortune, two years is a period that's hardly worth talking about."

Lydia sighed deeply. It was plain of what she was thinking.

"Berger isn't there for so long, is he?"

"Fifteen years."

There was a silence. One could see that Lydia was making a great effort to control her emotion, but when she spoke there was a break in her voice.

"Did you see him?"

"Yes. I talked to him. We were in hospital together. I went in to have my appendix out, I didn't want to get back to France and have trouble with it here. He'd been working on the road they're making from St. Laurent to Cayenne and he got a bad go of malaria."

"I didn't know. I've had one letter from him, but he said nothing about it."

"Out there everyone has malaria sooner or later. It's not worth making a song and dance about. He's lucky to have got it so soon. The chief medical officer took a fancy to him, he's an educated man, Berger, and there aren't many of them. They were going to apply to get him transferred to the hospital service when he recovered. He'll be all right there."

"Marcel told me last night that he'd given you a message for me."

"Yes, he gave me an address." He took a bundle of papers out of his pocket and gave Lydia a scrap on which something was written. "If you can send any money, send it there. But remember that he'll only get half what you send."

Lydia took the bit of paper, looked at it, and put it in her bag.

"Anything else?"

"Yes. He said you weren't to worry. He said it wasn't so bad as it might be, and he was finding his feet and he'd make out all right. And that's true, you know. He's no fool. He won't make many mistakes. He's a chap who'll make the best of a bad job. You'll see, he'll be happy enough."

"How can he be happy?"

"It's funny what one can get used to. He's a bit of a wag, isn't he? He used to make us laugh at some of the things he said. He's a rare one for seeing the funny side of things, there's no mistake about that."

Lydia was very pale. She looked down in silence. The elder man turned to his friend.

"What was that funny thing I told you he'd said about that cove in the hospital who cut his blasted throat?"

"Oh, I remember. Now what was it? It's clean gone out of my mind, but I know it made me laugh my head off."

A long silence fell. There seemed nothing more to say. Lydia was pensive; and the two men sat limp on their chairs, their eyes vacant, like the mechanical dolls they sell on the Boulevard Montparnasse which gyrate, rocking, round and round and then on a sudden stop dead. Lydia sighed.

"I think that's about all," she said. "Thank you for coming. I hope you'll get the job you're looking for."

"The Salvation Army are doing what they can for us. I expect something will turn up."

Charley fished his note-case out of his pocket.

"I don't suppose you're very flush. I'd like to give you something to help you along till you find work."

"It would be useful," the man smiled pleasantly. "The Army doesn't do much but give one board and lodging."

Charley handed them five hundred francs.

"Give it to the kid to take care of. He's got the saving disposition of the peasant he is, he sweats blood when he has to spend money, and he can make five francs go farther than any old woman in the world."

They went out of the café, the four of them, and shook hands. During the hour they had spent together the two men had lost their shyness, but when they got out into the street it seized them again. They seemed to shrink as though they desired to make themselves as inconspicuous as possible, and looked furtively to right and left as if afraid that someone would pounce upon them. They walked off side by side, with bent heads, and after another quick glance backward slunk round the nearest corner.

"I suppose it's only prejudice on my part," said Charley, "but I'm bound to say that I didn't feel very much at my ease in that company."

Lydia made no reply. They walked along the boulevard in silence; they lunched in silence. Lydia was immersed in thought the nature of which he could guess and he felt that any attempt on his part at small talk would be unwelcome. Besides, he had thoughts of his own to occupy him. The conversation they had had with the two convicts, the questions Lydia asked, had revived the suspicion which Simon had sown in his mind and which, though he had tried to put it aside, had since then lurked in his consciousness like the musty smell of a long closed room which no opening of windows can quite dispel. It worried him, not so much because he minded being made a fool of, as because he did not want to think that Lydia was a liar and a hypocrite.

"I'm going along to see Simon," he said when they had finished luncheon. "I came over largely to see him and I've hardly had a glimpse of him. I ought at least to go and say good-bye."

"Yes, I suppose you ought."

He also wanted to return to Simon the newspaper cuttings and the article which he had lent him. He had them in his pocket.

"If you want to spend the afternoon with your Russian friends, I'll drive you there first if you like."

"No, I'll go back to the hotel."

"I don't suppose I shall be back till late. You know what Simon is when he gets talking. Won't you be bored by yourself?"

"I'm not used to so much consideration," she smiled. "No, I shan't be bored. It's not often I have the chance to be alone. To sit in a room by oneself and to know that no one can come in—why, I can't imagine a greater luxury."

They parted and Charley walked to Simon's. He knew that at that hour he stood a good chance of finding him in. Simon opened the door on his ring. He was in pyjamas and a dressing-gown.

"Hulloa! I thought you might breeze along. I didn't have to go out this morning, so I didn't dress!"

He hadn't shaved and he looked as though he hadn't washed either. His long straight hair was in disorder. By the bleak light that came through the north window his restless, angry eyes looked coal-black in his white thin face and there were dark shadows beneath them.

"Sit down," he continued. "I've got a good fire to-day and the studio's warm."

It was, but it was as forlorn, cheerless and unswept as before.

"Is the love affair still going strong?"

"I've just left Lydia."

"You're going back to London to-morrow, aren't you? Don't let her sting you too much. There's no reason why you should help to get her rotten husband out of jug."

Charley took the cuttings from his pocket.

"By your article I judged that you had a certain amount of sympathy for him."

"Sympathy, no. I found him interesting just because he was such an unmitigated, cold-blooded, unscrupulous cad. I admired his nerve. In other circumstances he might have been a useful instrument. In a revolution a man like that who'll stick at nothing, who has courage and no scruples, may be invaluable."

"I shouldn't have thought a very reliable instrument."

"Wasn't it Danton who said that in a revolution it's the scum of society, the rogues and criminals, who rise to the surface? It's natural. They're needed for certain work and when they've served their purpose they can be disposed of."

"You seem to have it all cut and dried, old boy," said Charley, with a cheerful grin.

Simon impatiently shrugged his bony shoulders.

"I've studied the French Revolution and the Commune. The Russians did too and they learnt a lot from them, but we've got the advantage now that we can profit by the lessons we've learnt from subsequent events. They made a bad mess of things in Hungary, but they made a pretty good job of it in Russia and they didn't do so badly either in Italy or in Germany. If we've got any sense we ought to be able to emulate their success, but avoid their mistakes. Bela Kun's revolution failed because people were hungry. The rise of the proletariat has made it comparatively simple to make a revolution, but the proletariat must be fed. Organization is needed to see that means of transport are adequate and food supplies abundant. That incidentally is why power, which the proletariat thought to seize by making the revolution, must always elude their grasp and fall into the hands of a small body of intelligent leaders. The people are incapable of governing themselves. The proletariat are slaves and slaves need masters.".

"You would hardly describe yourself any longer as a good democrat, I take it," said Charley with a twinkle in his blue eyes.

Simon impatiently dismissed the ironical remark.

"Democracy is moonshine. It's an unrealizable ideal which the propagandist dangles before the masses as you dangle a carrot before a donkey. Those great watchwords of the nineteenth century, liberty, equality, fraternity, are pure hokum. Liberty? The mass of men don't need liberty and don't know what to do with it when they've got it. Their duty and their pleasure is to serve; thus they attain the security which is their deepest want. It's been decided long ago that the only liberty worth anything is the liberty to do right, and right is decided by might. Right is an idea occasioned by public opinion and prescribed by law, but public opinion is created by those who have the power to enforce their point of view, and the only sanction of law is the might behind it. Fraternity? What do you mean by fraternity?"

Charley considered the question for a moment.

"Well, I don't know. I suppose it's a feeling that we're all members of one great family and we're here on earth for so short a time, it's better to make the best of one another."

"Anything else?"

"Well, only that life is a difficult job, and it probably makes it easier for everybody if we're kind and decent to one another. Men have plenty of faults, but there's a lot of good in them. The more you know people the nicer you find they are. That rather suggests that if you give them a chance they'll meet you half way."

"Tosh, my dear boy, tosh. You're a sentimental fool. In the first place it's not true that people improve as you know them better: they don't. That's why one should only have acquaintances and never make friends. An acquaintance shows you only the best of himself, he's considerate and polite, he conceals his defects behind a mask of social convention; but grow so intimate with him that he throws the mask aside, get to know him so well that he doesn't trouble any longer to pretend; then you'll discover a being of such meanness, of such a trivial nature, of such weakness, of such corruption, that you'd be aghast if you didn't realize that that was his nature and it was just as stupid to condemn him as to condemn the wolf because he ravens or the cobra because he strikes. For the essence of man is egoism. Egoism is at once his strength and his weakness. Oh, I've got to know men pretty well during the two years I've spent in the newspaper world. Vain, petty, unscrupulous, avaricious, double-faced and abject, they'll betray one another, not even for their own advantage, but from sheer malice. There's no trick they won't descend to in order to queer a rival's pitch; there's no humiliation they won't accept to obtain a title or an order; and not only politicians; lawyers, doctors, merchants, artists, men of letters. And their craving for publicity; they'll cringe and flatter a twopenny-halfpenny journalist to get a good press. Rich men will hesitate at no shabby dodge to make a few pounds that they have no use for. Honesty, political honesty, commercial honesty—the only thing that counts with them is what they can get away with; the only thing that restrains them is fear. For they're craven. And the protestations they make, the high-flown humbug that falls from their lips, the shameless lies they tell themselves. Oh, believe me, you can't do the work I've been doing since I left Cambridge and preserve many illusions about human nature. Men are vile. Cowards and hypocrites. I loathe them."

Charley looked down. He was a little shy about saying what he wanted to. It sounded rather silly.

"Haven't you any pity for them?"

"Pity? Pity is womanish. Pity is what the beggar entreats of you because he hasn't the guts, the industry and the brains to make a decent living. Pity is the flattery the failure craves so that he may preserve his self-esteem. Pity is the cheap blackmail that the prosperous pay to the down-and-out so that they may enjoy their own prosperity with a better conscience."

Simon drew his dressing-gown angrily round his thin body. Charley recognized it as an old one of his which he had been going to throw away when Simon asked if he could have it; he had laughed and said he would give him a new one, but Simon, saying it was quite good enough for him, had insisted on having it. Charley wondered uncomfortably if he resented the trifling gift. Simon went on:

"Equality? Equality is the greatest nonsense that's ever muddled the intelligence of the human race. As if men were equal or could be equal! They talk of equality of opportunity. Why should men have that when they can't take advantage of it? Men are born unequal; different in character, in vitality, in brain; and no equality of opportunity can offset that. The vast majority are densely stupid. Credulous, shallow, feckless, why should they be given equality of opportunity with those who have character, intelligence, industry and force? And it's that natural inequality of man that knocks the bottom out of democracy. What a stupid farce it is to govern a country by the counting of millions of empty heads! In the first place they don't know what's good for them and in the second, they haven't the capacity to get the good they want. What does democracy come down to? The persuasive power of slogans invented by wily, self-seeking politicians. A democracy is ruled by words, and the orator seldom has brains, and if he has, he hasn't time to use them, since all his energy has to be given to cajoling the fools on whose votes he depends. Democracy has had a hundred years' trial: theoretically it was always absurd, and now we know that practically it's a wash-out."

"Notwithstanding which you propose, if you can, to get into parliament. You're a very dishonest fellow, my poor Simon."

"In an old-fashioned country like England, which cherishes its established institutions, it would be impossible to gain sufficient power to carry out one's plans except from within those institutions. I don't suppose anyone could gain support in the country and gather round himself an adequate band of followers to effect a coup d'état unless he were a prominent member of one of the great parties in the House of Commons. And since an upheaval can only be effected by means of the people it would have to be the Labour party. Even when the conditions are ripe for revolution the possessing classes still retain enough of their privileges to make it worth their while to make the best of a bad job."

"What conditions have you in mind? Defeat in war and economic distress?"

"Exactly. Even then the possessing classes only suffer relatively. They put down their cars or close their country houses, thus adding to unemployment, but not greatly inconveniencing themselves. But the people starve. Then they will listen to you when you tell them they have nothing to lose but their chains, and when you dangle before them the bait of other people's property the greed, the envy, which they've had to repress because they had no means of gratifying them, are let loose. With liberty and equality as your watchwords you can lead them to the attack. The history of the last five-and-twenty years shows that they're bound to win. The possessing classes are enervated by their possessions, they're humanitarian and sentimental, they have neither the will nor the courage to defend themselves; their counsels are divided, and when their only chance is in immediate and ruthless action they waste their time in recrimination. But the mob, which is the instrument of the revolutionary leaders, is a thing not of reason but of instinct, it is amenable to hypnotic suggestion and you can rouse it to frenzy by catchwords; it is an entity, and so is indifferent to the death in its ranks of such as fall; it knows neither pity nor mercy. It rejoices in destruction because in destruction it becomes conscious of its own power."

"I suppose you wouldn't deny that that entails the killing of thousands of inoffensive people and the destruction of institutions that have taken hundreds of years to build up."

"There's bound to be destruction in a revolution and there's bound to be killing. Engels said years ago that the possessing classes must be expected to resist suppression by every means in their power. It's a fight to the death. Democracy has attached an absurd importance to human life. Morally man is worthless and it's no loss to suppress him. Biologically he's of no consequence; there's no more reason why it should shock you to kill a man than to swat a fly."

"I begin to see why you were interested in Robert Berger."

"I was interested in him because he killed, not for any sordid motive, not for money, nor jealousy, but to prove himself and affirm his power."

"Of course it remains to be proved that communism is practicable."

"Communism? Who talked of communism? Everyone knows now that communism is a wash-out. It was the dream of impractical idealists who knew nothing of the realities of life. Communism is the lure you offer to the working classes to rouse them to revolt just as the cry of liberty and equality is the slogan with which you fire them to dare. Throughout the history of the world there have always been exploiters and exploited. There always will be. And it's right that it should be so because the great mass of men are made by nature to be slaves; they are unfit to control themselves, and for their own good need masters."

"That's rather a startling assertion."

"It's not mine, old boy," Simon answered ironically. "It's Plato's, but the history of the world since he made it has amply demonstrated its truth. What has been the result of the revolutions we've seen in our own lifetime? The people haven't lost their masters, they've only changed them, and nowhere has authority beeen wielded with a more iron hand than under communism."

"Then the people are duped?"

"Of course. Why not? They're fools, and they deserve to be. What does it matter? Their gain is substantial. They're not asked to think for themselves any more; they're told what to do, and so long as they're obedient they have the security they've always hankered after. The dictators of our own day have made mistakes and we can learn by their errors. They've forgotten Machiavelli's dictum that you can enslave the people politically if you leave their private lives free. I should give the people the illusion of liberty by allowing them as much personal freedom as is compatible with the safety of the state. I would socialize industry as widely as the idosyncrasy of the human animal permits and so give men the illusion of equality. And since they would all be brothers under one yoke they would even have the illusion of fraternity. Remember that a dictator can do all sorts of things for the benefit of the people that democracy is prevented from doing because it has to consider vested interests, jealousies and personal ambitions, and so he has an unparalleled opportunity to alleviate the lot of the masses. I went to a great communist meeting the other day and on banner after banner I read the words Peace, Work and Well-Being. Could any claims be more natural? And yet here man is after a hundred years of democracy still making them. A dictator can satisfy them by a stroke of the pen."

"But by your own admission the people only change their master; they're still exploited; what makes you think that they'll put up with it?"

"Because they'll damned well have to. Under present conditions a dictator with planes to drop bombs and armoured cars to fire machine guns can quell any revolt. The possessing classes could do the same, and no revolution would succeed, but the event has shown that they haven't the nerve; they kill a hundred men, a thousand even, but then they get scared, they want to compromise, they offer to make concessions, but it's too late then for concession or compromise and they're swept away. But the people will accept their master because they know that he is better and wiser than they are."

"Why should he be better and wiser?"

"Because he's stronger. Because he has the power, what he says is right *is* right and what he says is good *is* good."

"It's as simple as A B C but even less convincing," said Charley with some flippancy.

Simon gave him an angry scowl.

"You'd find it convincing enough if not only your bread and butter but your life depended on it."

"And who, pray, is to choose the master?"

"Nobody. He's the ineluctable product of circumstances."

"That's a bit of a mouthful, isn't it?"

"He rises to the top because he has the instinct to lead. He has the will to power. He has audacity and enthusiasm, ability, industry and energy. He fears nothing because to him danger is the salt of life."

"No one could say that you hadn't a good conceit of yourself, Simon," smiled Charley.

"Why do you say that?"

"Well, I suppose you imagine yourself to possess the qualities you've just enumerated."

"What makes you suppose it? I know myself as well as any man can know himself. I know my capacities, but I also know my limitations. A dictator must have a mystic appeal so that he excites his followers to a religious frenzy. He must have a magnetism which makes it a privilege for them to lay down their lives for him. In him they must feel that they more greatly live. I have nothing in me of that. I repel rather than attract. I could make people fear me, I could never make them love me. You remember what Lincoln said: 'You can fool some of the people all the time, and all the people some of the time, but you can't fool all the people all the time.' But that's just what a dictator must do; he must fool all the people all the time and there's only one way he can do that, he must also fool himself. None of the dictators has a lucid, logical brain; he has drive, force, magnetism, charm, but if you examine his words closely you'll see that his intelligence is mediocre; he can act because he acts on instinct, but when he begins to think he gets muddled. I have too good a brain and too little charm to be a dictator. Besides, it's better that the dictator brought to power by the proletariat should be a member of it. The working classes will find it more easy to identify themselves with him and thus will give him more willingly their obedience and devotion. The technique of revolution has been perfected. Given the right conditions it's easy for a resolute body of men to seize power; the difficulty is to hold it. The Russian revolution in the clearest possible way, the Italian and the German revolutions in a lesser degree, have shown that there's only

one means by which it can be done. Terror. The working
man who becomes head of a state is exposed to temptations
that only a very strong character can resist. He must be
almost superhuman if his head isn't turned by adulation and
if his resolution isn't enfeebled by unaccustomed luxury.
The working man is naturally sentimental; he's kind-hearted
and so accessible to pity; when he's got what he wants he
sits back and lets things slide; he forgives his enemies and
is surprised when they stick a knife in him as soon as his
back is turned. He needs at his elbow someone who by his
birth, education, training and character, is indifferent to
the trappings of greatness and immune to the debilitating
influence of success."

Simon for some time had been walking up and down the
studio, but now he came to an abrupt halt before his friend.
With his white unshaven face and dishevelled hair, in the
dressing-gown huddled round his emaciated limbs, he presented a grotesque appearance. But in a past that is not so
distant other young men as pale, as thin, as unkempt as he,
in shabby suits or in a student's blouse, had walked about
their sordid rooms and told of dreams seemingly as unrealizable; and yet time and opportunity had strangely
made their dreams come true, and, fighting their way to
power through blood, they held in their hands the life of
millions.

"Have you ever heard of Dzerjinsky?"

Charley gave him a startled look. That was the name
Lydia had mentioned.

"Yes, oddly enough I have."

"He was a gentleman. His family had been landowners
in Poland since the seventeenth century. He was a cultivated,
well-read man. Lenin and the Old Guard made the revolution, but without Dzerjinsky it would have been crushed
within a year. He saw that it could only be saved by terror.
He applied for the post that gave him control of the police
and organized the Cheka. He made it into an instrument of
repression that acted with the precision of a perfect machine.
He let neither love nor hate interfere with his duty. His industry was prodigious. He would work all night examining

the suspects himself, and they say he acquired so keen an insight into the hearts of men that it was impossible for them to conceal their secrets from him. He invented the system of hostages which was one of the most effective systems the revolution ever discovered to preserve order. He signed hundreds, nay, thousands of death warrants with his own hand. He lived with spartan simplicity. His strength was that he wanted nothing-for himself. His only aim was to serve the revolution. And he made himself the most powerful man in Russia. It was Lenin the people acclaimed and worshipped, but it was Dzerjinsky who ruled them."

"And is that the part you wish to play if ever revolution comes to England?"

"I should be well fitted for it."

Charley gave him his boyish, good-natured smile.

"It's just possible that I'd be doing the country a service if I strangled you here and now. I could, you know."

"I daresay. But you'd be afraid of the consequences."

"I don't think I should be found out. No one saw me come in. Only Lydia knows I was going to see you and she wouldn't give me away."

"I wasn't thinking of those consequences. I was thinking of your conscience. You're not tough-fibred enough for that, Charley, old boy. You're soft."

"I daresay you're right."

Charley did not speak for a while.

"You say Dzerjinsky wanted nothing for himself," he said then, "but you want power."

"Only as a means."

"What to do?"

Simon stared at him fixedly and there was a light in his eyes that seemed to Charley almost crazy.

"To fulfil myself. To satisfy my creative instinct. To exercise the capacities that nature has endowed me with."

Charley found nothing to say. He looked at his watch and got up.

"I must go now."

"I don't want to see you again, Charley."

"Well, you won't. I'm off to-morrow."

"I mean, ever."

Charley was taken aback. He looked into Simon's eyes. They were dark and grim.

"Oh? Why?"

"I'm through with you."

"For good?"

"For good and all."

"Don't you think that's rather a pity? I haven't been a bad friend to you, Simon."

Simon was silent for a space no longer than it takes for an over-ripe fruit to fall from the tree to the ground.

"You're the only friend I've ever had."

There was a break in his voice and his distress was so plain that Charley, moved, with both hands outstretched, stepped forward impulsively.

"Oh, Simon, why d'you make yourself so unhappy?"

A flame of rage leapt into Simon's tortured eyes and clenching his fist he hit Charley as hard as he could on the chin. The blow was so unexpected that he staggered and then, his feet slipping on the uncarpeted floor, fell headlong; he was on his feet in a flash and, furious with anger, sprang forward to give Simon the hiding he had often, when driven beyond endurance, given him before. Simon stood quite still, his hands behind his back, as though ready and willing to take the chastisement that was coming to him without an effort to defend himself, and on his face was an expression of so much suffering, of such consternation, that Charley's wrath was melted. He stopped. His chin was hurting him, but he gave a good-natured, chuckling laugh.

"You are an ass, Simon," he said. "You might have hurt me."

"For God's sake, get out. Go back to that bloody whore. I'm fed to the teeth with you. Go, go."

"All right, old man, I'm going. But I want to give you a little presy that I brought you for your birthday on the seventh."

He took out of his pocket one of those watches, covered in leather, which you open by pulling out the two sides, and which are wound by opening.

"There's a ring on it so you can hang it on your key-chain."

He put it down on the table. Simon would not look at it. Charley, his eyes twinkling with amusement, gave him a glance. He waited for him to say something, but he did not speak. Charley went to the door, opened it and walked out.

It was night, but the Boulevard Montparnasse was brightly lit. With the New Year imminent there was a holi-day feeling in the air. The street was crowded and the cafés were chock-a-block. Everybody was taking it easy. But Char-ley was depressed. He had a feeling of mortification, as one might have if one had gone to a party, expecting to enjoy oneself, and because one had been stupid and tactless, had come away conscious that one had left behind a bad im-pression. It was a comfort to get back to the sordid bed-room at the hotel. Lydia was sitting by the log fire sewing, and the air was thick with the many cigarettes she had smoked. The scene had a pleasant domesticity. It reminded one of an interior of Vuillard's, with its intimate, cosy charm, but painted by Utrillo so that it had at the same time a touching squalor. Lydia greeted him with her quiet, friendly smile.

"How was your friend Simon?"

"Mad as a hatter."

Lighting his pipe, he sat down on the floor in front of the fire, with his back against the seat of her chair. Her near-ness gave him a sense of comfort. He was glad that she did not speak. He was troubled by all the horrible things Simon had said to him. He could not get out of his head the picture of that thin creature, his pale face scrubby with a two days' beard, underfed and overworked, walking up and down in his old dressing-gown and with a cold-blooded, ruthless malignance delivering himself of his fantastic ideas. But breaking in upon this, as it were, was the recollection of the little boy with the big dark eyes who seemed to yearn for affection and yet repelled it, the little boy with whom he went to the circus during the Christmas holidays and who got so wildly excited at the unaccustomed treat, with whom he bicycled or went for long walks in the country, who was at times so gay and amusing, with whom it was jolly to talk and laugh and rag and play the fool. It seemed incredible that that little boy should have turned into that young man, and so heart-rending that he could have wept.

"I wonder what'll happen to Simon in the end?" he muttered.

Hardly knowing that he had spoken aloud, he almost thought Lydia had read his thoughts when she answered:

"I don't know the English. If he were Russian I'd say he'll either become a dangerous agitator or he'll commit suicide."

Charley chuckled.

"Oh well, we English have a wonderful capacity for making our wild oats into a nourishing diet. It's equally on the cards that he'll end up as the editor of *The Times*."

He got up and seated himself in the armchair which was the only fairly comfortable seat in the room. He looked reflectively at Lydia busily plying her needle. There was something he wanted to say to her, but the thought of it made him nervous, and yet he was leaving next day and this might well be his last opportunity. The suspicion that Simon had sown in his candid heart rankled. If she had been making a fool of him, he would sooner know; then when they parted he could shrug his shoulders and with a good conscience forget her. He decided to settle the matter there and then, but being shy of making her right out the offer he had in mind, he approached it in a round-about way.

"Have I ever told you about my Great-Aunt Martha?" he started lightly.

"No."

"She was my great-grandfather's eldest child. She was a grim-featured spinster with more wrinkles on her sallow face than I've ever seen on a human being. She was very small and thin, with tight lips, and she never looked anything but acidly disapproving. She used to terrify me when I was a kid. She had an enormous admiration for Queen Alexandra and to the end of her days wore her hair, only it was a wig, as the Queen wore hers. She always dressed in black, with very full long skirts and a pinched-in waist, and the collar of her bodice came up to her ears. She wore a heavy gold chain round her neck, with a large gold cross dangling from it, and gold bangles on her wrists. She was appallingly genteel. She continued to live in the grand house old Sibert Mason built for himself when he began to get on in the world and she never changed a thing. To go there was like stepping back into the eighteen-seventies. She died only a few years ago at a great age and left me five hundred pounds."

"That was nice."

"I should have rather liked to blue it, but my father persuaded me to save it. He said I should be damned thankful to have a little nest egg like that when I came to marry and wanted to furnish a flat. But I don't see any prospect of my marrying for years yet and I don't really want the money. Would you like me to give you two hundred of it?"

Lydia, going on with her work, had listened amiably, though without more than polite interest, to a story that could mean nothing very much to her, but now, jabbing her needle in the material she was sewing, she looked up.

"What on earth for?"

"I thought it might be useful to you."

"I don't understand. What have I done that you should wish to give me two hundred pounds?"

Charley hesitated. She was gazing at him with those blue, large, but rather flat eyes of hers, and there was in them an extreme attention as though she were trying to see into the depths of his soul. He turned his head away.

"You could do a good deal to help Robert."

A faint smile broke on her lips. She understood.

"Has your friend Simon been telling you that I was at the Sérail to earn enough money to enable Robert to escape?"

"Why should you think that?"

She gave a little scornful laugh.

"You're very naïve, my poor friend. It's what they all suppose. Do you think I would trouble to undeceive them and do you think they would understand if I told them the truth? I don't want your money; I have no use for it." Her voice grew tender. "It's sweet of you to offer it. You're a dear creature, but such a kid. Do you know that what you're suggesting is a crime which might easily land you in prison?"

"Oh well."

"You didn't believe what I told you the other day?"

"I'm beginning to think it's very hard to know what to believe in this world. After all, I was nothing to you, there was no reason for you to tell me the truth if you didn't want to. And those men this morning and the address they gave you to send money to. You can't be surprised if I put two and two together."

"I'm glad if I can send Robert money so that he can buy himself cigarettes and a little food. But what I told you was true. I don't want him to escape. He sinned and he must suffer."

"I can't bear the thought of your going back to that horrible place. I know you a little now; it's awful to think of you of all people leading that life."

"But I told you; I must atone; I must do for him what he hasn't the strength to do for himself."

"But it's crazy. It's so morbid. It's senseless. I might understand, though even then I'd think it outrageously wrong-headed, if you believed in a cruel god who exacted vengeance and who was prepared to take your suffering, well, in part-payment for the wrong Robert had done, but you told me you don't believe in God."

"You can't argue with feeling. Of course it's unreasonable, but reason has nothing to do with it. I don't believe in the god of the Christians who gave his son in order to save mankind. That's a myth. But why should it have arisen if it didn't express some deep-seated intuition in men? I don't know what I believe, because it's instinctive, and how can you describe an instinct with words? I have an instinct that the power that rules us, human beings, animals and things, is a dark and cruel power and that everything has to be paid for, a power that demands an eye for an eye and a tooth for a tooth, and that though we may writhe and squirm we have to submit, for the power is ourselves."

Charley made a vague gesture of discouragement. He felt as if he were trying to talk with someone whose language he could not understand.

"How long are you going on at the Sérail?"

"I don't know. Until I have done my share. Until the time

comes when I feel in my bones that Robert is liberated not from his prison, but from his sin. At one time I used to address envelopes. There are hundreds and hundreds of them and you think you'll never get them all done, you scribble and scribble interminably, and for a long time there seem to be as many to do as there ever were, and then suddenly, when you least expect it, you find you've done the last one. It's such a curious sensation."

"And then, will you go out to join Robert?"

"If he wants me."

"Of course he'll want you," said Charley.

She gave him a look of infinite sadness.

"I don't know."

"How can you doubt it? He loves you. After all, think what your love must mean to him."

"You heard what those men said to-day. He's gay, he's got a soft billet, he's making the best of things. He was bound to. That's what he's like. He loved me, yes, I know, but I know also that he's incapable of loving for very long. I couldn't have held him indefinitely even if nothing had happened. I knew that always. And when the time comes for me to go, what hope have I that anything will be left of the love he once bore me?"

"But how, if you think that, can you still do what you're doing?"

"It's stupid, isn't it? He's cruel and selfish, unscrupulous and wicked. I don't care. I don't respect him, I don't trust him, but I love him; I love him with my body, with my thoughts, with my feelings, with everything that's me." She changed her tone to one of light raillery. "And now that I've told you that, you must see that I'm a very disreputable woman who is quite unworthy of your interest or sympathy."

Charley considered for a moment.

"Well, I don't mind telling you that I'm rather out of my depth. But for all the hell he's enduring I'm not sure if I wouldn't rather be in his shoes than yours."

"Why?"

"Well, to tell you the truth, because I can't imagine any-

thing more heart-rending than to love with all your soul
someone that you know is worthless."

Lydia gave him a thoughtful, rather surprised look, but
did not answer.

x

CHARLEY'S TRAIN left at midday. Somewhat to his surprise
Lydia told him that she would like to come and see him off.
They breakfasted late and packed their bags. Before going
downstairs to pay his bill Charley counted his money. He
had plenty left.

"Will you do me a favour?" he asked.

"What is it?"

"Will you let me give you something to keep in case of
emergency?"

"I don't want your money," she smiled. "If you like you
can give me a thousand francs for Evgenia. It'll be a god-
send to her."

"All right."

They drove first to the Rue du Chateau d'Eau, where
she lived, and there she left her bag with the concierge. Then
they drove to the Gare du Nord. Lydia walked along the
platform with him and he bought a number of English
papers. He found his seat in the Pullman. Lydia, coming in
with him, looked about her.

"D'you know, this is the first time I've ever been inside a
first-class carriage in my life," she said.

It gave Charley quite a turn. He had a sudden realization
of a life completely devoid not only of the luxuries of the
rich, but even of the comforts of the well-to-do. It caused
him a sharp pang of discomfort to think of the sordid existence that had always been, and always would be, hers.

"Oh well, in England I generally go third," he said
apologetically, "but my father says that on the Continent one
ought to travel like a gentleman."

"It makes a good impression on the natives."

Charley laughed and flushed.

"You have a peculiar gift for making me feel a fool."

They walked up and down the platform, trying as people do on such occasions to think of something to say, but able to think of nothing that seemed worth saying. Charley wondered if it passed through her mind that in all probability they would never see one another again in all their lives. It was odd to think that for five days they had been almost inseparable and in an hour it would be as though they had never met. But the train was about to start. He put out his hand to say good-bye to her. She crossed her arms over her breast in a way she had which had always seemed to him strangely moving; she had had her arms so crossed when she wept in her sleep; and raised her face to his. To his amazement he saw that she was crying. He put his arms round her and for the first time kissed her on the mouth. She disengaged herself and, turning away from him, quickly hurried down the platform. Charley got into his compartment. He was singularly troubled. But a substantial luncheon, with half a bottle of indifferent Chablis, did something to restore his equanimity; and then he lit his pipe and began to read *The Times*. It soothed him. There was something solid in the feel of the substantial fabric on which it was printed that seemed to him grandly English. He looked at the picture papers. He was of a resilient temper. By the time they reached Calais he was in tearing spirits. Once on board he had a small Scotch and pacing the deck watched with satisfaction the waves that Britannia traditionally rules. It was grand to see the white cliffs of Dover. He gave a sigh of relief when he stepped on the stubborn English soil. He felt as though he had been away for ages. It was a treat to hear the voices of the English porters, and he laughed at the threatening uncouthness of the English customs officials who treated you as though you were a confirmed criminal. In another two hours he would be home again. That's what his father always said:

"There's only one thing I like better than getting out of England, and that's getting back to it."

Already the events of his stay in Paris seemed a trifle dim.

It was like a nightmare which left you shaken when with a start you awoke from it, but as the day wore on faded in your recollection, so that after a while you remembered nothing but that you had had a bad dream. He wondered if anyone would come to meet him; it would be nice to see a friendly face on the platform. When he got out of the Pullman at Victoria almost the first person he saw was his mother. She threw her arms round his neck and kissed him as though he had been gone for months.

"I told your father that as he'd seen you off I was going to meet you. Patsy wanted to come too, but I wouldn't let her. I wanted to have you all to myself for a few minutes."

Oh, how good it was to be enveloped in that safe affection!

"You are an old fool, mummy. It's idiotic of you to risk catching your death of cold on a draughty platform on a bitter night like this."

They walked, arm in arm and happy, to the car. They drove to Portchester Close. Leslie Mason heard the front door open and came out into the hall, and then Patsy tore down the stairs and flung herself into Charley's arms.

"Come into my study and have a tiddly. The whiskey's there. You must be perished with the cold."

Charley fished out of his great-coat pocket the two bottles of scent he had brought for his mother and Patsy. Lydia had chosen them.

"I smuggled 'em," he said triumphantly.

"Now those two women will stink like a brothel," said Leslie Mason, beaming.

"I've brought you a tie from Charvet, daddy."

"Is it loud?"

"Very."

"Good."

They were all so pleased with one another that they burst out laughing. Leslie Mason poured out the whiskey and insisted that his wife should have some to prevent her from catching cold.

"Have you had any adventures, Charley?" asked Patsy.

"None."

"Liar."

"Well, you must tell us all about everything later," said Mrs. Mason. "Now you'd better go and have a nice hot bath and dress for dinner."

"It's all ready for you," said Patsy. "I've put in half a bottle of bath salts."

They treated him as though he had just come back from the North Pole after a journey of incredible hardship. It warmed the cockles of his heart.

"Is it good to be home again?" asked his mother, her eyes tender with love.

"Grand."

But when Leslie, partly dressed, went into his wife's room to have a chat with her while she did her face, she turned to him with a somewhat anxious look.

"He's looking awfully pale, Leslie," she said.

"A bit washed out. I noticed that myself."

"His face is so drawn. It struck me the moment he got out of the Pullman, but I couldn't see very well till we got here. And he's as white as a ghost."

"He'll be all right in a day or two. I expect he's been racketing about a bit. By the look of him I suspect he's helped quite a number of pretty ladies to provide for their respectable old age."

Mrs. Mason was sitting at her dressing-table, in a Chinese jacket trimmed with white fur, carefully doing her eye-brows, but now, the pencil in her hand, she suddenly turned round.

"What *do* you mean, Leslie? You don't mean to say you think he's been having a lot of horrid foreign women."

"Come off it, Venetia. What d'you suppose he went to Paris for?"

"To see the pictures and Simon, and well, go to the Français. He's only a boy."

"Don't be so silly, Venetia. He's twenty-three. You don't suppose he's a virgin, do you?"

"I do think men are disgusting."

Her voice broke, and Leslie, seeing she was really upset, put his hand kindly on her shoulder.

"Darling, you wouldn't like your only son to be a eunuch, would you now?"

Mrs. Mason didn't quite know whether she wanted to laugh or cry.

"I don't suppose I would really," she giggled.

It was with a sense of peculiar satisfaction that Charley, half an hour later, in his second-best dinner-jacket, seated himself with his father in a velvet coat, his mother in a tea-gown of mauve silk and Patsy maidenly in rose chiffon, at the Chippendale table. The Georgian silver, the shaded candles, the lace doyleys which Mrs. Mason had bought in Florence, the cut glass—it was all pretty, but above all it was familiar. The pictures on the walls, each with its own strip-lighting, were meritorious; and the two maids, in their neat brown uniforms, added a nice touch. You had a feeling of security, and the world outside was comfortably distant. The good, plain food was designed to satisfy a healthy appetite without being fattening. In the hearth an electric fire very satisfactorily imitated burning logs. Leslie Mason looked at the menu.

"I see we've killed the fatted calf for the prodigal son," he said, with an arch look at his wife.

"Did you have any good food in Paris, Charley?" asked Mrs. Mason.

"All right. I didn't go to any of the smart restaurants, you know. We used to have our meals at little places in the Quarter."

"Oh. Who's we?"

Charley hesitated an instant and flushed.

"I dined with Simon, you know."

This was a fact. His answer neatly concealed the truth without actually telling a lie. Mrs. Mason was aware that her husband was giving her a meaning look, but she paid no attention to it; she continued to gaze on her son with tenderly affectionate eyes, and he was much too ingenuous to suspect that they were groping deep into his soul to discover whatever secrets he might be hiding there.

"And did you see any pictures?" she asked kindly.

"I went to the Louvre. I was rather taken with the Chardins."

"Were you?" said Leslie Mason. "I can't say he's ever

appealed to me very much. I always thought him on the dull side." His eyes twinkled with the jest that had occurred to him. "Between you and me and the gatepost I prefer Charvet to Chardin. At least he is modern."

"Your father's impossible," Mrs. Mason smiled indulgently. "Chardin was a very conscientious artist, one of the minor masters of the eighteenth century, but of course he wasn't Great."

In point of fact, however, they were much more anxious to tell him about their doings than to listen to his. The party at Cousin Wilfred's had been a riot, and they had come back so exhausted that they'd all gone to bed immediately after dinner on the night of their return. That showed you how they'd enjoyed themselves.

"Patsy had a proposal of marriage," said Leslie Mason.

"Thrilling, wasn't it?" cried Patsy. "Unfortunately the poor boy was only sixteen, so I told him that, bad woman as I was, I hadn't sunk so low as to snatch a baby from his cradle, and I gave him a chaste kiss on the brow and told him I would be a sister to him."

Patsy rattled on. Charley, smiling, listened to her, and Mrs. Mason took the opportunity to look at him closely. He was really very good-looking and his pallor suited him. It gave her an odd little feeling in her heart to think how much those women in Paris must have liked him; she supposed he'd gone to one of those horrible houses; what a success he must have had, so young and fresh and charming, after the fat, bald, beastly old men they were used to! She wondered what sort of girl he had been attracted by, she so hoped she was young and pretty, they said men were attracted by the same type as their mother belonged to. She was sure he'd be an enchanting lover; she couldn't help feeling proud of him; after all, he was her son and she'd carried him in her womb. The dear; and he looked so white and tired. Mrs. Mason had strange thoughts, thoughts that she wouldn't have had anybody know for anything in the world; she was sad, and a little envious, yes, envious of the girls he had slept with, but at the same time proud, oh, so proud, because he was strong and handsome and virile.

Leslie interrupted Patsy's nonsense and her own thoughts. "Shall we tell him the great secret, Venetia?"

"Of course."

"But mind, Charley, keep it under your hat. Cousin Wilfred's worked it. There's an ex-Indian governor that the party want to find a safe seat for, so Wilfred's giving up his and in recognition he's to get a peerage. What d'you think of that?"

"It's grand."

"Of course he pretends it means nothing to him, but he's as pleased as Punch really. And you know, it's nice for all of us. I mean, having a peer in the family adds to one's prestige. Well, it gives one a sort of position. And when you think how we started . . ."

"That'll do, Leslie," said Mrs. Mason, with a glance at the servants. "We needn't go into that." And when they left the room immediately afterwards, she added: "Your father's got a mania for telling everyone about his origins. I really think the time has now arrived when we can let bygones be bygones. It's not so bad when we're with people of our own class, they think it's rather chic to have a grandfather who was a gardener and a grandmother who was a cook, but there's no need to tell the servants. It only makes them think you're no better than they are."

"I'm not ashamed of it. After all the greatest families in England started just as humbly as we did. And we've worked the oracle in less than a century."

Mrs. Mason and Patsy got up from the table and Charley was left with his father to drink a glass of port. Leslie Mason told him of the discussions they had had about the title Cousin Wilfred should assume. It wasn't so easy as you might think to find a name which didn't belong to somebody else, which had some kind of connection with you, and which sounded well.

"I suppose we'd better join the ladies," he said, when he had exhausted the subject. "I expect your mother will want a rubber before we go to bed."

But as they were at the door and about to go out, he put his hand on his son's shoulder.

"You look a bit washed out, old boy. I expect you've been going the pace a bit in Paris. Well, you're young and that's to be expected." He suddenly felt a trifle embarrassed. "Anyhow, that's no business of mine, and I think there are things a father and son needn't go into. But accidents will happen in the best regulated families, and well, what I want to say is, if you find you've got anything the matter with you, don't hesitate but go and see a doctor right away. Old Sinnery brought you into the world and so you needn't be shy of him. He's discretion itself and he'll put you right in no time; the bill will be paid and no questions asked. That's all I wanted to tell you; now let's go and join your poor mother."

Charley had blushed scarlet when he understood what his father was talking about. He felt he ought to say something, but could think of nothing to say.

When they came into the drawing-room Patsy was playing a waltz of Chopin's and after she had finished his mother asked Charley to play something.

"I suppose you haven't played since you left?"

"One afternoon I played a little on the hotel piano, but it was a very poor one."

He sat down and played again that piece of Scriabin's that Lydia thought he played so badly, and as he began he had a sudden recollection of that stuffy, smoky cellar to which she had taken him, of those roughs he had made such friends with, and of the Russian woman, gaunt and gipsy-skinned, with her enormous eyes, who had sung those wild, barbaric songs with such a tragic abandon. Through the notes he struck he seemed to hear her raucous, harsh and yet deeply moving voice. Leslie Mason had a sensitive ear.

"You play that thing differently from the way you used," he said when Charley got up from the piano.

"I don't think so. Do I?"

"Yes, the feeling's quite different. You get a sort of tremor in it that's rather effective."

"I like the old way better, Charley. You made it sound rather morbid," said Mrs. Mason.

They sat down to bridge.

"This is like old times," said Leslie. "We've missed our family bridge since you've been away."

Leslie Mason had a theory that the way a man played bridge was an indication of his character, and since he looked upon himself as a dashing, open-handed, free-and-easy fellow, he consistently overcalled his hand and recklessly doubled. He looked upon a finesse as un-English. Mrs. Mason on the other hand played strictly according to the rules of Culbertson and laboriously counted up the pips before she ventured on a call. She never took a risk. Patsy was the only member of the family who by some freak of nature had a card sense. She was a bold, clever player and seemed to know by intuition how the cards were placed. She made no secret of her disdain for the respective methods of play of her parents. She was domineering at the card table. The game proceeded in just the same way as on how many evenings it had done. Leslie, after overcalling, was doubled by his daughter, redoubled, and with triumph went down fourteen hundred; Mrs. Mason, with her hand full of picture cards, refused to listen to her partner's insistent demand for a slam; Charley was careless.

"Why didn't you return me a diamond, you fool?" cried Patsy.

"Why should I return you a diamond?"

"Didn't you see me play a nine and then a six?"

"No, I didn't."

"Gosh, that I should be condemned to play all my life with people who don't know the ace of spades from a cow's tail."

"It only made the difference of a trick."

"A trick? A trick? A trick can make all the difference in the world."

None of them paid any attention to Patsy's indignation. They only laughed and she, giving them up as a bad job, laughed with them. Leslie carefully added up the scores and entered them in a book. They only played for a penny a hundred, but they pretended to play for a pound, because it looked better and was more thrilling. Sometimes Leslie would have marked up against him in the book sums like fifteen hundred pounds and would say with seeming seriousness that if things went on like that he'd have to put down the car and go to his office by bus.

The clock struck twelve and they bade one another goodnight. Charley went to his warm and comfortable room and began to undress, but suddenly he felt very tired and sank into an armchair. He thought he would have one more pipe before he went to bed. The evening that had just gone by was like innumerable others that he had passed, and none had ever seemed to him more cosy and more intimate; it was all charmingly familiar, in every particular it was exactly as he would have wished it to be; nothing could be, as it were, more stable and substantial; and yet, he could not for the life of him tell why, he had all the time been fretted by an insinuating notion that it was nothing but make-believe. It was like a pleasant parlour-game that grown-ups played to amuse children. And that nightmare from which he thought he had happily awakened—at this hour Lydia, her eyelids stained and her nipples painted, in her blue Turkish trousers and her blue turban, would be dancing at the Sérail or, naked, lying mortified and cruelly exulting in her mortification, in the arms of a man she abhorred; at this hour Simon, his work at the office finished, would be walking about the emptying streets of the Left Bank, turning over in his morbid and tortured mind his monstrous schemes; at this hour Alexey and Evgenia, whom Charley had never seen but whom through Lydia he seemed to know so well that he was sure he would have recognized them if he met them in the street; Alexey, drunk, would be inveighing with maudlin tears against the depravity of his son, and Evgenia, sewing, sewing for dear life, would cry softly because life was so bitter; at this hour the two released convicts, with those staring eyes of theirs that seemed to be set in a gaze of horror at what they had seen, would be sitting, each with his glass of beer, in the smoky, dim cellar and there hidden amid the crowd feel themselves for a moment safe from the ever-present fear that someone watched them; and at this hour Robert Berger, over there, far away on the coast of South America, in the pink-and-white stripes of the prison garb, with the ugly straw hat on his shaven head, walking from the hospital on some errand, would cast his eyes across the wide expanse of sea and, weighing the chances of escape, think for a moment of Lydia with tolerant affection—and that nightmare from which he thought he had happily awakened had a fearful reality which rendered all else illusory. It was absurd, it was irrational, but that, all that, seemed to have a force, a dark significance, which made the life he shared with those three, his father, his mother, his sister, who were so near his heart, and the larger, decent yet humdrum life of the environment in which some blind chance had comfortably ensconced him, of no more moment than a shadow play. Patsy had asked him if he had had adventures in Paris and he had truthfully answered no. It was a fact that he had done nothing; his father thought he had had a devil of a time and was afraid he had contracted a venereal disease, and he hadn't even had a woman; only one thing had happened to him, it was rather curious when you came to think of it, and he didn't just then quite know what to do about it: the bottom had fallen out of his world.

EL GRECO
An Essay

PAINTERS, not unnaturally, since so much nonsense has been written on the subject, have always resented writers expressing their opinions on pictures. They have insisted, often with great vehemence, that only the painter can speak of painting with authority, and that the man of letters, looking at a picture from his literary point of view, can know nothing of its specific value. His part is to admire in silence and if he has the money, buy. This seems to me a narrow way of thinking. Doubtless they are right when they claim that only painters should discuss technique, but technique is not the whole of painting. You might as well say that only a dramatist can appreciate a play. The drama also has its technique, though it is not so abstruse as some of its professors like to pretend, but it is the business only of the dramatist. To understand the technique of an art may be a diversion, it may even give the layman the feeling, agreeable to some people, of being in the know (like addressing the head-waiter of a fashionable restaurant by his first name), but it is not essential to appreciation. It may greatly interfere with it. We know that painters are often very bad judges of pictures, for their interest in technique absorbs them so that they cannot recognise merits, unconnected with it, that may give a picture value. For technique is only the method by which the artist achieves his aim. It is no more than the knowledge that has gradually been acquired of the best ways to attain the specific excellencies of which a medium is capable. It cannot touch the heart nor excite the mind. An inadequate technique will not prevent the artist from doing this. I do not think people are sufficiently conscious of the great difference there is between the attitude of the artist towards the work he creates and the attitude of the beholder. The connection between them is slight. For the moment I will leave on one side the position of the artist and consider the work of art in relation with the beholder.

But first I should like to deal with the meaning of a word. To the term artist is now attached a judgement of value, and (though painters are not so squeamish) most of us who practise an art are as shy of calling ourselves artists as we are of calling ourselves gentlemen. In this sense the term is the sport of fashion. A painter may be at one period considered an artist and at another a charlatan. What makes it more confusing is that it does not always correspond with preëminence. I suppose few people would deny that Addison was a greater artist than Charles Dickens, but few could doubt which was the greater writer. The word craftsman has unfortunate associations, nor does it indicate the act of creation, which is the essence of the matter; and the word creator is intolerably pretentious. I do not know any word that will do but artist; I must use it, but I mean by it only someone who is engaged in the arts. He may be a good artist or a bad one.

I have long since abjured the heresy prevalent in my youth of art for art's sake. Oscar Wilde popularized it in England and Oscar Wilde learnt it from Whistler. It gave art an esoteric quality that flattered the artist and it was accepted by the cultured public with the humility that characterises them. The cultured public have always taken a masochistic pleasure in the contempt that artists have shown them and, browbeaten and intimidated, have comforted themselves with a feeling of superiority over the common herd. It was believed that the object of a work of art was to arouse the æsthetic emotion and when you had felt that you had got all it had to give you. But what is an emotion that results in nothing? To experience the æsthetic emotion is pleasurable and all pleasure is good; but it is pleasurable also to drink a glass of beer and no one has ever been able to show that, taken simply as pleasure, one surpasses the other. Attempts have been made by moralists to prove that spiritual pleasures are keener and more lasting than sensual pleasures; they carry no conviction. No pleasure endures and to please it must be taken in small doses and at not too frequent intervals. It would be no less tedious to hear Beethoven's Fifth Symphony every day than it would be to eat caviare. And until age has blunted the sensibilities the general experience is surely that the pleasures of sense are more vivid than the pleasures of the spirit. We have all known omnivorous readers who read for the delight of it; they absorb books as the machines in Chicago absorb hogs, but no sausages come out of them at the other end; and we have all known the people who moon their days away in picture galleries in imbecile contemplation; they are no better than opium smokers, worse if anything, for the opium smoker at all events is not self-complacent. The value of emotion lies in its effects. Santa Teresa insisted on this over and over again: the ecstasy of union with the Godhead was precious only if it resulted in greater capacity for works. The æsthetic emotion, however delightful and however subtle, has worth only if it leads to action.

The work of art, whether the artist intended it or not, and for my part I think he seldom does, proffers a communication. This has nothing to do with the artist. From his standpoint it may only be a by-product of his activity: so the esculent swallows build nests to rear their young and are unaware that for their aphrodisiac qualities they will go to make soup for the enfeebled but amative Chinese. This communication is made in two voices. For the work of art is a diversion, an escape from the bitterness of life and a solace in the world's inevitable cruelty, a rest from its turmoil and a relief from labour. This is much, and if a work of art has only this communication to make it justifies itself. But great works speak with another voice too; they enrich the soul so that it is capable of a nobler and more fruitful activity. Their effects are worthy deeds. But should you ask me what these are I must confess that I should find it hard to reply. Provisionally at all events I should be willing enough to accept the maxim of Fray Luis de Leon: "The beauty of life," he says, "is nothing but this, that each should act in conformity with his nature and his business."

Notwithstanding this long preamble I do not wish to say much of El Greco's pictures. Nothing is so tedious as a description of the greens, yellows and blues that are in a picture; you cannot visualise them even with a photograph before you and the narrator's enthusiasm does not matter to you a row of pins. It is enough to say that El Greco's cool, silvery colours are lovely. When the art critics begin to talk of upper triangles and lower triangles, as they do with the Burial of Count Orgaz, or of inner and outer ellipses in the San Maurizio, I sigh. Do they really think that an artist bothers his head with such things? You look at a picture as a whole, that is one of the advantages the plastic arts have over the descriptive, and it is as a whole that it must affect you. The study of its parts is merely amusement. An emotion analysed is no longer an emotion. I do not suppose the painter creates a work of art differently from any other artist. The artist works by instinct combined with knowledge and his knowledge he acquires partly from his predecessors and partly from his own errors. I have had the greatest admiration for El Greco and if now my admiration is a trifle qualified that is perhaps because I have got out of him all that I am capable of getting. For my own part I find that when a work of art has given me a powerful emotion I cannot recapture it any more than I can eat a dinner I have already eaten. In this I am very unlike a cow. One gets tired of everything. But what remains is the personality behind the work of art; that to some minds is the great interest in the artist's work; and that, so complex is man, is an interest that endures when you know his work by heart.

It is with the personality then of the Greek that I am concerned. There is only one word that I know to describe it and that is one we are told to eschew. The late, but excellent, Fowler tells us that there is no excuse for the use of the word intriguing. He asks plaintively why we should not say interesting or perplexing, but really they do not mean quite the same thing, and if ever the word is justified it is here. To me it suggests an ambiguity, a puzzle that invites you to solve it and a secret that demands all your subtlety to discover it. It is all very well to tell us that it is formed from the word intrigue; the adjective has by now acquired a meaning of its own. I would say boldly then that no great artist is more intriguing than El Greco. I have wondered whether from the little that is known of his life, from some acquaintance with the circumstances in which he lived and from his strange and beautiful paintings, it was possible to get a coherent idea of the person he was. This indeed was essential if I was in my pages to draw the portrait of a living man. I thought also that I might thus explain, at least to my own satisfaction, something of the mysteriousness of his pictures.

Of his life very little is known and that little is unexpected. Until recently he was thought to have been born about 1545, or even later, for there is a letter, dated 1570, from Julio Clovio recommending him to the attention of Cardinal Farnese in which he is described as a youth; but lately an erudite Spaniard, Don Francisco San Roman, has proved that he was born in 1541. It seems strange that Julio Clovio should have called him a youth when he was hard on thirty; at that time, and indeed much later, that age was looked upon as the flower of manhood and youth already passed; but it agrees well enough with the statement made by Jusepe Martinez that he died at an advanced age. It is known that he died in 1614. The explanation may be that Julio Clovio thought thus to excite the sympathy of a possible patron and it may be that, being himself seventy-three, he looked upon a man of thirty as no more than a boy. In his letter he describes him further as a pupil of Titian, and this is at first sight surprising, since the works by which we chiefly know him show the influence of Tintoretto rather than of Titian. But it appears that El Greco's early pictures owe much to him, and the wily Julio Clovio may well have thought it more useful to describe the young man as the pupil of the better known master. He was born in Crete. Of his boyhood nothing is known, but it is supposed that he learnt to paint in the monastery schools in which the manufacture of icons had long been a flourishing industry. He went to Venice, but at what age is uncertain, and after a lengthy sojourn there settled down in Rome. Here he seems to have passed five or six years, and sometime between 1575 and 1577, being then about thirty-five, he went to Spain. He stayed there for the rest of his life. The common view is that in Toledo he recognised his spiritual home. It is held that he acquired his magic colour from the grey walls of that city built upon a rock and from the austere tones of the surrounding country; in his encounter with the Spanish character it is held that he developed an originality that his early works had given small hint of, and in his contact with the passionate Spanish faith achieved the mystical exaltation that inspires his great religious pictures. He has been seen as a man of an austere temper, indifferent to the things of the earth, who went his lonely ascetic way intent only on expressing his rapt vision; and those later pictures of his with their fantastic distortions seemed the final effort to represent a spiritual experience.

This is plausible, romantic enough to please the fancy, and coherent. But it is only credible if you leave out everything that is known of El Greco and that can be seen in his pictures that does not fit in with it. Those cool colours of his were there before ever he went to Spain: it may be that they were the colours he learnt in the Cretan monastery in which he had been taught to paint icons, or it may be that he discovered them in his own sensibility. There is no reason to believe that they would have been different if he had never left Italy. It is singular to find in the portrait of Julio Clovio, painted before his journey to Spain, a landscape with the same tortured sky that he painted so often in his later pictures. It is a sky that in point of fact you do not see in Toledo nearly so often as you do in Venice and indeed you will find it in several of Tintoretto's pictures in the Scuola di San Rocco. In the Madonna del Orto you will find the heavy grey clouds, with their abrupt outlines, looking as though they were cut out of tufa, that are so characteristic of El Greco.

There is no knowing why he went to Spain. It may be of course that he went because he hoped to get work. Artists were being engaged to decorate the Escorial and a painter who could find little to do at home might well think it worth his while to try his luck abroad. So English actors who cannot get a job in London go to New York and often achieve a success that their own country denied them. A certain Mancini, a contemporary, states that he left Rome because the painters and patrons of the arts resented a remark he had made about Michael Angelo's Last Judgement. The Pope, considering certain figures indecent, desired to have them painted over, whereupon El Greco said that if he would destroy the whole work he would do another, "not a whit worse than Michael Angelo's as a work of art, which would be both chaste and decorous in addition." Painters must have changed very much since then if they took so much to heart a fellow painter's criticism of a dead painter, and patrons of the arts had much to learn if they attached great importance to what one artist said of another. I can see nothing in El Greco's character to persuade me that any indignation a flout of his might arouse would have driven him from a place he did not want to leave. In a dispute between El Greco and the chapter of Toledo over his picture El Espolio, when asked during the legal proceedings that took place why he had come to Spain, he refused to answer. Considering that he was a foreigner, living among people who did not like foreigners, and at loggerheads with the Church, which few were inclined to affront, it seems strange that he should have declined to give his reason without good cause. It looks very much as though he had something to hide. When you read the novels and biographies of the day it occurs to you how often a journey was occasioned by the tragic outcome of a quarrel. Swords were drawn quickly, often on trivial grounds, and if you were unlucky enough to kill your antagonist it was usual to go while the going was good. I have wondered whether research in the police records of Rome, if such still exist, would not reward the industrious investigator with the explanation why El Greco went to Spain and stayed there. At the same trial he stated that he did not understand Spanish very well. This does not seem to have been questioned. He had then been in Toledo for three or four years. El Greco had provided himself with a sleeping dictionary; which our empire-builders recommend as the best way to acquire the speech of the country they inhabit and so make themselves more competent to bear the white man's burden. He took a mistress, Doña Jeronima de las Cubas, and in 1578, it is supposed, had a son by her. Levantines are quick at learning languages. El Greco's indifference to acquiring Spanish does not look as though he were very much interested in the country which was to be his home for the rest of his life. He never lost his pride in his Greek birth. As is well known he signed his pictures with his full name in Greek characters and added the fact that he was a Cretan. A list of the books in his possession at his death has been found. There were about two hundred of them. Of these only seventeen were in Spanish; but unfortunately their titles are not given. The rest were in Italian or Greek. It is hard to resist the conclusion that his curiosity about Spanish literature was not intense.

Toledo, when El Greco settled there, was no longer the capital of Spain, but it was still the centre of much artistic and literary activity. Churches were being built that had to be decorated. Ecclesiastics lived splendidly. Poets and dramatists made lengthy sojourns. The painter might very well have known Lope de Vega and Cervantes; he certainly knew Gongora, the obscure, irascible and conceptist poet. Plays were given by professional actors and by aristocratic amateurs, and every possible occasion was seized upon, the birth of a royal prince, the signing of a peace, for splendid festivities. An attractive picture of the life of the place is given in the Cigarrales de Toledo to which I have already referred. It is a dull book, it must be confessed, and the euphuistic style in which it is written is tedious. The time of day is told you with such witty conceits that to discover what it is you need not only some acquaintance with astronomy but also with mythology. When you are told that a curtain is indebted to the labours of architectural worms it is easy to guess that it is made of silk, but you have to think a moment before you discover that when the author informs you that snow, transformed into wax by the parturition of the republican but tiny birds, was burning, he means that the candles were lit. To our modern taste it seems a roundabout way of saying that you threw a letter into the fire unopened to state that only the flames were given leave to unseal it. But for all that you get an impression of leisured, courtly, well-bred persons who took delight in beautiful things. They passed the summer mornings in the pleasures of the chase and fishing (the fish biting with avidity because the bait was offered them by such fair hands) ; the afternoons in peaceful games, tilting and racing; and the nights in dancing, delectable argument and ingenious devising.

The reader may think that this picture does not correspond very well with what I have said before about the poverty that so constantly oppressed the Spaniards of the Golden Age. Let him go to the Mall on the evening of a Court and look at the long line of cars driving up in which sit dowagers in their diamonds and débutantes in grand new dresses. They tell me that the scene within the Palace is gorgeous beyond description. Then let him stroll along to the Admiralty Arch. He will find a coffee-stall where the hungry are given for nothing a cup of tea and a bite to eat. There he will see a string of men a quarter of a mile long, patiently waiting, one hour, two hours, for the stall to open. He will admit that there is nothing contradictory in what I have said and indeed that it is just what you would expect.

It has been supposed that El Greco lived in the cultured society of the city, consorting with grave ecclesiastics and eminent lawyers; but the only evidence I know of this is that he painted portraits of such personages. He was a man of education and of a pleasant discourse. Among his Greek books, besides classics such as Homer, Euripides, Plutarch and Lucian were the works of certain of the Fathers, St. John Chrysostom, St. Justin, St. Basil; and it is probable that he could converse suitably with the reverend gentlemen who were his principal patrons. Among his Italian books were Petrarch, Ariosto, and Bernardo Tasso. In his life, which was described as singular and extravagant, there is nothing to suggest the ascetic. He dwelt in a large house with a display that was thought ostentatious, and he had musicians

come from Venice to play to him while he was at dinner.
Nothing of this is surprising, for it is an error to suppose
that the artist lives in a garret from choice. Philosophers
may content themselves with plain living, but painters, writers and musicians are occupied with the things of sense and
whenever they have been able, have lived with splendour.
They have liked grand houses, with as many servants to wait
upon them as they could pay for, and they have seldom hesitated to run into debt to provide themselves with fine clothes.
El Greco had a keen eye on the profits of his trade He made
a great deal of money. Of the few documents concerning him
that have come down to us several have to do with his quarrels over payment with the patrons who had commissioned
him to paint a picture. When the authorities taxed him upon
the profits of his work at Illescas he fought them and got a
judgement in his favour. So far as I can understand the argument his contention was that what he sold was not canvas
and paint, but the art with which he had arranged the paint,
and this was not dutiable. Like many another artist before
and after him, he was a shrewd business man. He kept in his
studio sketches of his pictures so that when the patron came
along for an altarpiece he could order what he wanted, a St.
Francis or a Magdalen, an Assumption of the Virgin or
Christ bearing the Cross: they were all there, you paid your
money and you took your choice. He repeated pictures as
often as he was required to. There are two or three versions
at least of most of his paintings and of St. Francis in Meditation there are, it appears, over twenty.

There is a peculiar thing about the process of artistic creation which I should not have thought was any different in a
painter and a writer. When a writer has been occupied with
a subject and has done what he could with it, he is so sick of
it that he takes no more interest in it at all. He is like a snake
that has sloughed its skin. The subject that has absorbed him
ceases to be a part of him; the emotion that filled him when
he was working at it is dead and he cannot by any effort of
will recapture it. When a writer must take up a theme out of
which he has got all he could, making a play out of a novel, to
take an example, the labour is mechanical. He cannot expect

to have any inspiration. It is a task he performs by exercise of the knowledge he has acquired. I cannot understand how El Greco could have painted the same pictures over and over again if he was really filled with the religious emotion people find in them. I should have thought he could only do this if the subject was of no consequence to him.

The authorities have dealt with this matter in a very simple way. They have divided El Greco's pictures into good, indifferent, and bad. They claim that he painted the good ones by himself, the indifferent with the help of his assistants, who painted the bad ones all by themselves. It seems to me a little too simple. He must have been a very wonderful artist indeed if he never painted a bad picture. It is strange that Tristan, the best of his pupils, when he worked on his own, painted no pictures so good as the worst of those that are with any probability ascribed to his master. Of course El Greco had assistants who prepared the canvas, squared up the design, and presumably did some underpainting; but the contracts that various religious bodies made with him go into such particular detail, they are so careful to state what they want, you cannot persuade yourself that they would have accepted work which they were not reasonably sure was from his own hand. Indeed when there was a possibility that through death or other hindrance he could not finish a certain work a clause was inserted in the contract that it should be finished by his son Jorge Manuel or by some other specified person. I think some explanation must be sought for the fact that no painter of genius so often repeated his pictures as did El Greco.

Now let us look at the portraits he painted of himself. There is one in the Burial of Count Orgaz and another in the St. Maurizio in the Escorial. It is not certain that they are his portraits, it is only a tradition that they are, but they are evidently portraits of the same man and it is likely that the tradition is true. Accepting them then, on the great authority of Don Manuel Cossio, as authentic I think one may safely say that El Greco may not have looked like this, but this is what he thought he looked like. It is a thin, intelligent face, fresh-coloured, a rather long face; the beard, of a palish, reddish brown, is well trimmed; the hair is dark; the forehead is high and noble; the eyes, somewhat close-set, are cool, observant and reflective. You have the impression of a man who gave a good deal of thought to his appearance. You would have said from the look of him that this was a composed, intelligently curious man, but one capable neither of great passion nor of deep emotion. In neither of these pictures is there in the expression any of the seriousness which one would have thought the occasion demanded. This person seems to preserve a strangely ironic detachment; it would never occur to you that he was a mystic; you might have taken him for a sardonic humorist.

Often the portraits that an artist paints will tell you as much about himself as about his sitters, and I have wondered whether El Greco's would not offer some clue to what I sought. Now when you look at a collection of El Greco's portraits, in the Prado for instance, the first thing that strikes you is their distinction. They have a well-bred elegance. They have gravity and decorum. But it would be absurd to say that they are profound. They seem indeed to be painted in the most perfunctory fashion. The colour is cool and subdued, but no effort is made to use the mass in an effective manner; the bony structure is barely indicated; the heads have no backs to them and the bodies no weight. You get the impression that the Greek was not interested in the people he painted. These men were the contemporaries of the conquistadores and of the saints; they are as empty of character as lord mayors. When you compare these portraits with those of Zurbaran, so actual, so strongly individualized, they cease to exist. More than once certainly El Greco painted a magnificent portrait, but only when some eccentricity in the sitter's appearance gave him the obvious opportunity. Now in fiction it is easy to make a striking character of a person with marked characteristics; the difficulty is to make a man live when he is more or less like everybody else. Any competent novelist could create the father in the Brothers Karamazov; he needed to be more than that who created the old servant in Un Cœur Simple. I should have thought it was the same in portrait painting. More insight and more imagination were needed, I should have thought, to paint the Man with the Glove than the Grand Inquisitor. It looks as though El Greco regarded his sitters with a singular detachment. Is it possible that this mystic took no interest in the human soul? Though infinitely well-born these people look terribly stupid. They were. The history of Spain during the Golden Age is a history of the abysmal ineptitude of which the human race is capable. A Greek, subtle and quick-witted, a man of culture, it may well be that he was impatient of these fine gentlemen's stupidity.

Years ago I went to Crete, not hoping to find any trace of El Greco, but curious to see the island that had given him birth. From the sea it offers a jagged aspect. It seems to consist of ridge upon ridge of rough, barren and stony hills. Their sharp outlines silhouetted against the sky have an austere and unapproachable beauty. Yet when you go into the interior you find that these hills, tawny, arid and sparsely covered with coarse herbage, separate into pleasing valleys. Here flourish great plantations of ancient olives and in more favourable places vines. Ash-trees and cypresses grow along the streams and oleanders luxuriate at their brim. But when you come away it is not so much the memory of the smiling valleys and the shallow rippling streams that you take with you, but rather of the desolate, wild and tawny hills. When the Greek looked at the gaunt mountain ranges of Castile it must have seemed to him that he was very close to the landscape he had known in childhood.

Candia, outside the main street untidy and bedraggled, is a town of narrow tortuous streets, with low houses that offer a blank wall to the view; and the unpaved road, all holes, is dusty in dry weather and a morass in wet. You might think yourself back in the sixteenth century. By the side of the grand new Greek church is a little old one, very low, dark, and heavy with stale incense. Its reredos is richly carved and gilt and on the walls hang large icons that you can scarcely see. In the sacristy are others. Some of them are very old and one or two are fine. In several a foreign influence is manifest. In them the Byzantine feeling is swamped, but not entirely destroyed, by the easy splendour and the courtly formality of Venetian art. It is not unreasonable to suppose that it was the exciting charm of this new style that impelled the young painter to make his way to Venice.

No one knows how long the Cretan lived in Italy, ten, twelve or fifteen years; but they were the impressionable years of his youth and we know the sort of circumstances he was thrown in. Venice had lost much of its political power and the population was declining, but it was the playground of Europe and life, splendid still, was led by the rich with pomp. Manners were easy, scruples were few. The Bride of the Adriatic resisted as well as she could the efforts of the Papacy to reform her morals and to purify her faith. Thought was free and the intelligent were elegantly sceptical. Rome, alarmed by the Reformation, was making some effort to set her house in order, but there is no evidence that the individual was much inconvenienced by the fervour that reigned in high places. Artists have ever proved hostile to the limitations that puritanism has sought to impose on their private behaviour. From the little that is known of El Greco it seems likely that he would have remained an indifferent spectator of a spiritual movement that his foreign birth made of no great moment to him. Since he died fortified by the rites of the Catholic Church he was presumably received into it, but when you look at his coolly sceptical face you cannot but wonder whether it meant as much to him as those have thought who see in his pictures the most fervent expression of the passion of the Counter-reformation.

Everyone knows how Philip II commissioned El Greco to paint a picture of St. Maurice and his companions for one of the altars of the Escorial and when it was delivered liked it so little that he would not let it be placed in the church but banished it to a cellar. It hangs now in the Sala Capitular and is the greatest glory of the Escorial. In the eyes of the cultured not one of the actions of his long reign has redounded more to the discredit of Philip II. I think he has been harshly treated. He was a sufficiently enlightened patron of the arts to buy the pictures of Titian and to ask Paul Veronese to come to Spain to decorate the stupendous building on which he lavished such vast treasure. He was a

deeply and sincerely religious man. He shared the common
(and not unreasonable) opinion of his time that saints should
be painted in such a manner that one did not lose the desire
to pray before them, nay, that they should engender devotion, "since the chief effect and the end of painting them
must be this." El Greco's picture is of superb vivacity, its
colouring is so brilliant and original that the neighbouring
pictures look dull beside it; but Philip knew a religious picture when he saw one. In the San Maurizio the three chief
figures wear what I suppose are leather jerkins, but they are
in effect nudes; their muscles are drawn as in a studio study
and even the navels are shown. The angels that fly about
the clouds or in easy attitudes rest upon them, playing
musical instruments and singing, seem to take part in a
divertisement like those prepared by great nobles to honour
a royal guest. The figures in the background, the Theban
legion, might be stripped for the Olympian games rather
than to attest their faith by martyrdom. It would not be
strange if Philip was shocked by the frivolity with which
El Greco had treated the scene. The attitude of those various personages is a triumph of elegance. Never did El Greco
more obviously paint gestures for their beauty rather than
their significance. It is a picture that gives enjoyment; it does
not excite devotion.

I cannot but ask myself why El Greco, who could draw so
beautifully when he wanted to, should, apart from his deliberate distortions, at times have drawn so carelessly. Why
does he put a Virgin's eye half way down her face or make
it pop out of her head as though, poor thing, she had
exophthalmic goitre? Why does he sometimes give his saints
the look of ducks dying of fright in a thunderstorm? The
Virgin in the Crucifixion in the Prado is grotesque; that face
would not be out of keeping in a satyric painting by Goya.
(But how lovely is the colour, the green tunic worn by St.
John, the exquisite tone of the body hanging on the cross, so
tender and ethereal, and the richness of that tempestuous
sky!) I am tempted to ask myself whether when he painted
a religious picture he did not give way sometimes to a sardonic humour. It is difficult to see more than a conventional

devotion in those single figures of Franciscan saints which as we know he painted wholesale. The St. Antony in the Prado is composed so perfunctorily that it does not even make sense. In one hand the saint delicately holds a madonna lily, while with the other he supports a heavy open book in which is a small brown object that he seems to study in pitch-black night; for the background is that stormy sky which El Greco used with amazing pertinacity. And beautiful as I find the Resurrection in the Prado, with the slender, soaring, movingly painted figure; exciting as I find the sweep of those others with their arms raised in such expressive gesture; I am not conscious of any depth of religious feeling. Nor is there any that I can see in the Baptism of Christ. It is a lovely picture, with colour of an intoxicating beauty; those elongated forms, nude but for their loin-cloths, of the Saviour and the Baptist, have an exquisite sophisticated grace; but I feel there no fervour of belief nor rapture of ecstasy. It is disconcerting in that fine picture of Christ bearing the Cross to see the elegance with which the Saviour clasps it. Indeed it is on the hands that El Greco has concentrated the interest. The face, with the eyes showing a great deal of white under the pupil, which was the Cretan's simple way of expressing religious emotion, is the face of a comic actor. Ernest Thesiger might have sat for it. The right hand rests on the cross with the third and fourth fingers together, an old trick of the painter's to get away from the awkwardness of those five odd digits; while the left, again with the third and fourth fingers together, has the little one slightly crooked as ladies of easy virtue to show their refinement crook their little fingers when they drink a glass of champagne.

Not far from the San Maurizio in the Sala Capitular of the Escorial is a picture that portrays religious emotion in a very different manner. It is a Deposition from the Cross, and it is by Van der Weyden. Here the emotion is sincere and natural. The expressions are real. The painter felt what he painted and expressed what he felt. You are moved because he was moved himself. It is an awful moment that is represented and there is a sense of despair in the droop of those figures that makes you feel that here is the most terrifying moment in the world's history. The men are stricken with grief, but gravely masters of it; Mary has swooned and there is another woman, Mary Magdalen, I suppose, whose clumsy, broken attitude gives you a tragic impression of hopelessness. All these people feel as they would feel and act as they would act. It is a beautiful picture, a terrible scene, and one to bring home to a rude and brutal people the horror of the event represented. Its sincerity is shattering. You cannot look at it and again believe in El Greco's religious sense.

I do not doubt that he was one of the greatest painters that ever lived. I think the Burial of Count Orgaz is one of the greatest pictures in the world. It has a sweep, a freshness and a vitality that are amazing. It fills you with stupefaction. El Greco was a master of gesture. You would never think that an outflung arm, a raised hand, a foot on tip-toe or an extended leg, could have such a miraculous grace. He had indeed a wonderful sense of the beautiful though limited gestures permitted to the hand. The general effect of a large number of his pictures together, as you may see them in the room in the Prado, is thrilling; it is not only that distinguished, cool yet not cold, colour that moves you, but something in the pictures themselves, apart also from their subjects, their form and architecture. It is something troubling, sinister and enigmatic; I can only suppose it is the personality of the painter. It is like looking into the darkness of a lake in the mountains. You feel vaguely scared. You wonder whether there is anything there at the bottom, a secret that it would be good for you to know, or whether it is an aimless depth that has no purpose. For depth in itself has no greater significance than breadth. The lake may look bottomless only because it is muddy, and if you take a header into it you can easily crack your skull. In literature, I know, the obscure is very often taken for the profound. Here, however, time plays an odd trick; it dissipates obscurity as a breeze dissipates fog, and then are discovered, not the great truths we hoped for, but painted trifles. Thus time has made most of Mallarmé's poems quite clear and we see that all that labyrinthine imagery hid from the vulgar nothing more abstruse than the poetic commonplaces of the day. All that remains to delight us is a number of pellucid and beautiful phrases.

It gives you a curious sensation to go from the room in which the El Grecos are hung into the Velasquez room next door. It is like coming into the warm light of common day. You cannot but feel that Velasquez is somewhat superficial, but he is superficial on the grand scale. He had an equable, sunny temperament and his pictures are delightfully gay. He had that alegria which is the Andalusian's most cherished and characteristic grace. He does not in his portraits suggest a criticism of his sitters. He takes them at their face value. He was the greatest of court-painters. His charm was combined with a genial heartlessness. His dwarfs and fools are painted with amusement. So might Shakespeare have drawn them. He had no feeling for the horror of their deformity or the misery of their lot. His cheerful temper enabled him to look upon these loathsome abortions with the good humour of one who knew that the Almighty had created them to be the playthings of princes. I suppose no one can deny his miraculous skill in painting, the silvery lustre of his blacks and the richness of his sober tones. He could paint the dress of an infanta in such a manner as to take one's breath away. But even as one admires one is filled with a slight sense of uneasiness and one asks oneself whether this wonderful skill is worth while. It reminds one of a writer who says things with exquisite sobriety, but says nothing of any great consequence. But how skilfully these figures are placed on the canvas to make a pattern pleasing to the eye! In the full length of Philip IV with his gun and in the companion picture of the Cardinal-Infante pure representation seems to achieve perfect beauty. There is nothing to be said. You can only stand and gape.

When you go back to the El Greco room you enter a troubled world. Here is a wild intensity that seems to seek utterance for no emotion that can be made clear by symbols. It is a vague and tormenting sensation that seems to oppress him, like that anxiety, common at times to us all, I suppose, to which no cause can be assigned; you do not know whether it is of the body or the spirit. It was not a man of equable and sunny temper who painted these pictures, but a man of uncertain humour perplexed by fantastic longings; it was a man striving with pain for an expression that he sought in the abyss of his soul as though it were a memory hovering just below consciousness that it exasperated him to be unable to recall. But if he was a mystic his mysticism must surely be sought in another sphere than the religious. Pacheco, who saw him in his old age, says of El Greco that he was a great philosopher, very witty in his speech, personal, profound, with an original answer to everything. We know that he was luxurious and improvident; indeed he died insolvent; the portraits he painted of himself suggest scepticism and irony; and one's own sensibility persuades one that he was very lonely. Even in Rome he had a high conceit of himself and later on his arrogance was overweening. In the action over his remuneration for the Burial of Count Orgaz he finished his pleadings with the words: "As true as it is that the payment is inferior to the value of my sublime work, my name will pass to posterity, which will recompense my work and glorify the author as one of the greatest geniuses of Spanish painting." He was a Levantine and the Levantines are apt to express themselves with grandiloquence. No writer can have gone to Alexandria or Beyrout without being visited by some young author who tells him in bad but fluent French that he has written a novel vastly better than anything that Balzac, Anatole France or—Zola ever wrote. It is a bombastic use of words that does not preclude a real and often touching modesty. But humility is the very substance of the soil on which religious mysticism grows and it would be absurd to say that El Greco had it. There is a story which, if true, shows that he was something of an actor and the art of bluff was not unfamiliar to him. The story runs as follows: Tristan, his pupil, had painted for a stipulated price a picture for the Jeronimite monks of the convent of Sisla, but when the picture was finished the monks (doubtless with justice) thought it was not worth it and wanted to pay less. The matter was submitted to the arbitration of El Greco. He looked at the picture and then, flying into a passion, began to beat Tristan with his stick. The monks interposed. "Tristan is but young," they said, "and does not understand that he is asking too much." "Too much!" cried El Greco. "It is a sublime and beautiful work and I am beating him for daring to ask two hundred ducats for a picture that is worth five hundred, and if you don't pay the money at once I'm going to take it myself." The monks paid.

Taking it all in all you have the impression of a man who possessed most of the traits that we generally hold to be typical of the Levantine, and if you combined these ingeniously I do not think it would be impossible to construct an image coherent enough to be credible. The various particulars fit like the pieces of a jig-saw puzzle. The flaw lies in the fact that there is nothing in the sort of man you have thus created to account for the pictures he painted. One must look further.

Not long ago I came across the suggestion, made in a ribald spirit, that El Greco was homosexual. I have thought it worth considering. So far as an artist's work is concerned there is as a rule little interest in knowing about his sexual life, upon which indeed an exaggerated stress is generally laid. There is a notion that men who have in any way greatly distinguished themselves should in this respect be different from their fellows, and when the student discovers that they have had love affairs he is apt to think the fact strangely significant. For all the to-do that has been made over the amours of Shelley and Byron I cannot but doubt whether they were very different from those of other young men of their class. Many a smart young broker in the City of London would have looked upon them with supercilious amusement as extremely meagre. But when it comes to an abnormality the case is different. I have suggested that talent consists in an individual way of seeing the world combined with a natural aptitude for creation and that genius is talent with a greater capacity and a universal sympathy. Now it cannot be denied that the homosexual has a narrower outlook on the world than the normal man. In certain respects the natural responses of the species are denied to him. Some at least of the broad and typical human emotions he can never experience. However subtly he sees life he cannot see it whole. If it were not for the perplexing sonnets I should say that the homosexual can never reach the supreme heights of genius. I cannot now help asking myself whether what I see in El Greco's work of tortured fantasy and sinister strangeness is not due to such a sexual abnormality as this. I hasten to add that this can be nothing but surmise, as is all else I have said of him. Besides his pictures, the letter of Julio Clovio, certain legal documents, his death certificate and the list of his effects there is no material for any direct knowledge of him. Whatever does not proceed from this, however confidently it is stated, can be no more than plausible.

When you survey possibilities it must be admitted that there is in this one a good deal that saves it from being wildly improbable. El Greco spent his childhood and youth in places where he can have conceived no instinctive aversion to that idiosyncrasy. I should say that a distinctive trait of the homosexual is a lack of deep seriousness over certain things that normal men take seriously. This ranges from an inane flippancy to a sardonic humour. He has a wilfulness that attaches importance to things that most men find trivial and on the other hand regards cynically the subjects which the common opinion of mankind has held essential to its spiritual welfare. He has a lively sense of beauty, but is apt to see beauty especially in decoration. He loves luxury and attaches peculiar value to elegance. He is emotional, but fantastic. He is vain, loquacious, witty and theatrical. With his keen insight and quick sensibility he can pierce the depths, but in his innate frivolity he fetches up from them not a priceless jewel but a tinsel ornament. He has small power of invention, but a wonderful gift for delightful embroidery. He has vitality, brilliance, but seldom strength. He stands on the bank, aloof and ironical, and watches the river of life flow on. He is persuaded that opinion is no more than prejudice. In short he has many of the characteristics that surprise us in El Greco. It may be that in this abnormality lies the explanation why his pictures fail of that ultimate greatness which is release. They thrill; they do not give you peace. They excite; but do not satisfy. We know that whatever imagination El Greco had he did not apply it to the composition of his pictures. The learned have traced the patterns of some of them to the Byzantine icons with which he may be presumed to have been familiar in his early youth and of others to pictures he had seen in Italy. It is curious that in the full flush of his early manhood, when fancy is generally exuberant, he should have been content so often to take his designs from the woodcuts, engravings and etchings that were at that time current articles of commerce in Italy. When he had to invent something out of his head he was not remarkable. The Burial of Count Orgaz betrays its Byzantine inspiration. A dozen artists in Italy could have arranged it on a more satisfactory plan. It is only the miraculous painting that prevents that row of heads, cutting the picture into two parts, from being disconcerting. And when he had to represent the martyrdom of St. Maurice he shirked it and painted a group of young men who might be discussing the handicapping for the school sports. There is in Toledo a San Bernardino, with a tiny head, a courtly little pointed beard and an immensely long body against a gloomy sky, which is quite charming; but in the same way as the twisted pillars of a plateresque patio are charming. It is a delicious picture for a great lady's oratory. But it could hardly arouse devotion. It is perfectly frivolous. I think no religious painter ever expressed emotion so perfunctorily as El Greco. This would not be strange if he were entirely devoid of it.

A little while ago, confessing a former error, I made a distinction between the artist's work from his creative standpoint and its communication, which is what the layman is concerned with. I think a good deal of criticism is rendered less illuminating than it should be because critics often do not clearly distinguish between the two. They step from one to the other without realising that they are doing so. There need be no relation between them. The artist is not justified in claiming to be judged from the standpoint of his intention. That is important to him, and to anyone who cares to study his personality, but it is of no importance to the observer. The artist is driven to produce by an instinct within him that impels him to express his personality. He does not try to do this; it is an inevitable accident that he does so. He is in all probability not very much interested in his personality. (I am not speaking of the journeyman who busies himself with the arts to earn an honest living or the spent worker who continues to do so from habit.) The artist can no more help creating than water can help running down hill. It is a release from the burden on his soul. It is a spiritual exercise which is infinitely pleasurable, and it is accompanied by a sense of power that is in itself delightful. When production fulfills it he enjoys a heavenly sense of liberation. For one delicious moment he rests in a state of equilibrium. What the painter paints or the writer writes is an experience of himself and the theorists of art for art's sake were right when they claimed that it had no moral value. Nor need this experience and its expression, whatever its importance for the person who feels it, have any value for anybody else. That must depend on the interest for the world of the personality that has thus been forced to exteriorise itself.

I think there are two ways in which El Greco sought deliverance. One was in decoration. To my mind he was singularly indifferent to his subjects. They were given him and like all artists he worked out his own intentions within the limitations imposed upon him by the circumstances of his time. That is why he could paint the same picture over and over again. These saints, Francis or Antony, meant no more to him than did their abstract designs to the early cubists. To him they were merely excuses for his decorative inventions. And that is why he was so much more interested in the hand than in the head. The hand has a possibility of lovely gesture that is denied to the head. No one has painted hands more exquisitely. But in many of the pictures they are placed with such an affected grace that, considering the episode represented, you are shocked by the unseemliness. El Greco was ready to sacrifice truth of gesture to beauty of attitude. His reaction was, in short, baroque.

The reader must pardon me if I indulge now in a short disquisition on baroque. I do this not only because I think the subject in itself interesting, but because I seem to discern in that form of art and the circumstances that brought it about much that corresponds with the art of the present day and the conditions in which we are now living. I suppose everyone is agreed that massivity and movement are the essentials of baroque. It used decoration, not to complete a composition, but for its own sake; and its wonderful discovery was that movement was decorative. The spectacular nature of architecture has caused the learned to study baroque particularly in that art. This has made it a little more difficult to discover its distinctive features. The decorative element is not so noticeable in a building because the architect has made it for a certain use and this use conditions his treatment. But when you look more closely you cannot but see how much these great artists were concerned with it. They aimed at unity, whereas the Renaissance architects were content to make a harmonious composition of self-subsisting parts; and unity of effect is the first demand of decoration. We hesitate when we are told that the baroque architects sought to represent movement and our inclination is to think that they were aiming at something foreign to the spirit of their art and therefore necessarily bad. The play they made with light and shade seems like a device to deceive the eye into accepting what is contrary to nature. It takes a little while to recognise that mass is but an instant in the unending curve of movement. It is not my business here to point out the various uses they made of the expedients at their command and the triumphant success with which they achieved their ends. But the sway of baroque was by no means confined to architecture; it affected the painters and sculptors too, the writers, and I should imagine the musicians. Indeed I suspect that it gave their art for the first time the possibility of reaching the cloud-capped heights which Beethoven and Wagner attained. But of music I know nothing. I went to Cambridge to ask a great authority whether there was anything in my surmise, but thinking perhaps that it was no affair of mine he would not tell me.

Baroque is often considered to be the characteristic expression of the Counter-reformation. It seems unlikely that it was created by it. The Counter-reformation built new churches and restored old ones. The artists who worked in

them were baroque artists. They were sentimental, violent
and theatrical as was the religion of the period, but not
necessarily on account of it. Religion was declamatory; it
exaggerated the manifestations of its piety in reaction from
the pagan scepticism of the Renaissance and in challenge to
the Lutheran strenuousness. It suited very well the new style
the artists were now making use of; the extravagant emotions they were asked to express gave them an opportunity to
use movement for purely decorative purposes and movement
they could only represent by mass. I should have said that the
Counter-reformation, so far as it was not dictated by fear,
corresponded to a feeling that was in the air and it was this
feeling that created the universal tendency towards the
baroque.

It is interesting to consider why this absorption in decoration, which to my mind is the essence of the style, should just
at this time have made itself felt. Some writers have ascribed
it to a normal reaction from the preceding period. The
Renaissance was over and people were tired of the works it
had produced. That was very natural, for man desires change
and he wearies even of perfection. Beauty is a full stop and
when you have reached it you can do nothing but start another sentence. The inspiration that the discovery of the
antique had brought was exhausted. But boredom with one
style cannot give rise to another; a new style arises from a
new state of the spirit.

The Renaissance cultivated measure and repose. It cherished the golden mean. Its strength was tranquil. Art not
only occupied an important part in men's lives, but the artists
felt themselves in conformity with the life about them. They
were citizens of the state as well as artists. Sin was original
sin and the individual did not feel himself answerable for it.
Man was free, if not always in fact, in imagination. And
freedom was the most cherished of his ideals.

But the attempt to think again the thoughts and live once
more the life enshrined in the literatures of Greece and
Rome failed. Liberty died. Half of Italy was in the hands of
Spain and the rest in the power of petty tyrants. The In-
quisition, fostered by the Spanish kings as an instrument of

state, acquired a new power in Italy. Incidents here and there in the picaresque novels prove the terror it inspired. Catholicism was restored by force. The Church claimed control over all the activities of the human mind, its philosophy, its science and its art. A strange disquiet oppressed the spirits of men. It seemed as though in their long struggle with intellect they had grown exhausted. Believers, notwithstanding, were uneasy, and they drowned their hesitations in a sea of declamation. They were intolerant because they were afraid. Man was deprived of his inalienable right of self-realisation and freedom was lost to him it seemed for ever.

Freedom is man's greatest good. When you rob the artist of this you force him back upon himself. When he can no longer deal with the great issues of life that in happier times occupy the souls of men, his instinct of creation, which nevertheless demands expression, can but turn to decoration. When men are wretched they look into their hearts and some inexplicable instinct leads them to ascribe their misery to their own shortcomings. Their minds turn to another world and they look for solace to their vexed spirits in the eternal. Sin was no longer original sin; it was personal, and a rigid reckoning would be demanded of the sinner. Decoration with its vague meanings can very well express the desire for the unearthly, the vague fear and the sense of guilt that haunted the souls of men to whom the healthy and inspiring activity of free men was denied. The Renaissance, essentially objective, copied and idealised nature; but baroque used nature as a vehicle to display its own morbid sensibility. It was subjective. And the most direct expression of the subjective is decoration. It is worth while to consider for a moment how the writers reacted to the conditions in which they found themselves. They turned away from matter and busied themselves with form. They sought brilliant and exquisite conceits, no matter how frivolous, and put them in the manner most calculated to surprise. They cultivated rhetoric, the play upon words, flowers of speech, archaisms and such-like toys. They wanted to show their cleverness rather than to discover their hearts. All artists have in them something of the child. They like to play and if they lack serious and great convictions are very likely to squander their faculties on spiritual kickshaws. They do not try to make bread without leaven; they try to make bread with nothing but leaven. Michael Angelo, resuming in himself the restlessness and dissatisfaction of the age, tried by vastness, by violence, to express the passion of his tortured heart, and so became in the plastic arts the father of baroque. His contemporaries and successors felt the significance of what he had invented. Realising quickly the immense decorative value of mass and movement they began with growing assurance to make them the principles of their activity. But because they lacked his spiritual power their works seldom achieved his complete sincerity; and decoration, which had been grave and sincere because it corresponded to a deep instinct in the artist's nature, degenerated with time to the frivolous ornament of rococo.

Now let me return to El Greco. There was in him to my mind a temper that exactly suited the spirit that he found prevalent to some extent in Venice, and at its height in Rome. So he became the greatest of baroque painters. Looking at the whole series of his pictures I seem to see his interest in decoration for decoration's sake grow in intensity. His contemporaries thought that he painted in an increasingly fantastic manner because he went mad. I do not believe it. More recently it has been suggested that he suffered from astigmatism and it has been said that if you put on the right glasses his vertiginous figures would assume normal proportions. I do not believe it. Their immense elongation, which, I may remind the reader, he will find also in many of Tintoretto's pictures, seems to me a natural development of treating the human form as decoration. Because El Greco was aiming at this and nothing else I think he grew more and more indifferent to fact. This, I think, explains also his cock-eyed virgins. If the body, with its mass, is treated as a unit of expression the face becomes of no importance. It is not strange that the moderns should have set such great store by El Greco. If he were alive to-day I imagine he would paint pictures as abstract as the later work of Bracque, Picasso and Fernand Léger. And it may be that the interest in formal design of the present day is due to the same causes as produced baroque art in the sixteenth century. Now too we are spiritually at sixes and sevens. Afraid of the sublime, we take refuge in the multiplication table.

For now the world is sullen and jealous as was the world of the Counter-reformation. The great issues that occupied the Victorians, which seemed to offer the spirit boundless horizons, have played us false. We mock at those who maunder of truth, goodness and beauty. We are afraid of greatness. And we too have lost the inestimable blessing of freedom. Liberty throughout the world is dying or dead. Like the Jesuit novice who lost his personality to find it again in the Company we are asked to surrender our own to find it again in the State. Nobody dares tackle great subjects and the heresy has become orthodox that subject is of no consequence. Only the pretty, the ingenious, the amusing are cultivated. Artists have not yet learnt how to deal with what really matters to our world and so are driven to devote themselves to decoration. They make technical devices the end and aim of their endeavour. They have cast off the shackles of tradition, but use their independence to stand on their heads and, like Hippokleides, kick their legs in the air. Modern critics are wrong when they blame writers for writing about themselves. When art is no more than a side issue they have nothing else to write about.

But of course there is more in El Greco than the fantastic patterns he devised, his grace and distinction, the elegance of his gestures and his dramatic intensity, seldom falling into theatricalism, with which as I take it he satisfied the sardonic, ironic, sumptuous, sinister side of his nature. When you see many of a painter's pictures together you find in them often a certain monotony. An artist can only give you himself and he is unfortunately always very like himself. The startling thing about El Greco is that, such is his vitality, he can under the most unlikely conditions give you an impression of variety. Take for instance that collection of the Apostles which is in what is now called la casa del Greco. They are three-quarter lengths, canvases of the same size, and the personages are not happily individualised; but the vigour with which they are painted makes them lively and different. You feel in them the stubborn idiosyncrasy of their creator, in wonderful possession of his faculties, who, regardless of what people thought, was getting marvellous satisfaction out of their exercise. Then there is his colour. This, I think, was the second of the two methods by which he strove to release his spirit from its burden; and it is his colour that makes him so wonderful an artist. A painter thinks with his brushes. Such thoughts as he has that can be put into words are for the most part commonplace. Why artists are often incomprehensible to other people is that they express their profoundest feelings in a language of their own. I think El Greco put the most serious emotion of his strange, perhaps inexplicable personality into the colours that he set down on canvas. However he acquired his palette, he gave it an intensity, a significance, which were his own. Colour was his complete and unique experience. They are not so far wrong who see in him a mystic, though I cannot help thinking that to look upon him as a religious mystic is superficial. If mysticism is that state that renders you conscious of depths of truth unknown to the intellect, revealing like "glimpses of forgotten dreams" a greater significance in life and union with some larger reality, then I think you can hardly fail to find it in El Greco's painting. I seem to see as great a mystic rapture in the painting of the right side of the body of Christ in the Crucifixion in the Louvre as in any of the experiences of Santa Teresa.